compound - pure sub - resolved into 2 pure subs

elem - is pure sub which cannot be resolved

molec - small part of a pure sub contain a few atoms

ionic - compound which carries electrical charge

Boyle - $V = K/P$ temp

Charle - $V = KT$ press

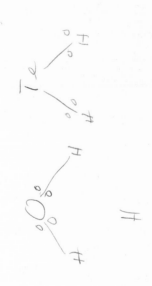

EN

Te S Se Te → decrease

CHEMICAL

PRINCIPLES

WILLIAM L. MASTERTON

ASSOCIATE PROFESSOR OF CHEMISTRY
UNIVERSITY OF CONNECTICUT, STORRS, CONNECTICUT

EMIL J. SLOWINSKI

CHAIRMAN, DEPARTMENT OF CHEMISTRY
MACALESTER COLLEGE, ST. PAUL, MINNESOTA

W. B. SAUNDERS COMPANY

PHILADELPHIA AND LONDON

W. B. Saunders Company: West Washington Square, Philadelphia, Pa. 19105

12 Dyott Street, London, W.C.1.

Reprinted August, 1966

Chemical Principles

To The Students

PREFACE

The author of a textbook in general chemistry must expect to be asked the embarrassing question as to why he chose to write it in the first place. It might seem that one would have to be either extremely naïve or extremely presumptuous to suppose that he could make an original contribution in this area. We confess that many of our ideas for a fresh approach to general chemistry did not work out in quite the way we planned. Our students and colleagues, who have been exposed to a preliminary edition of this text for the past two years, have been kind enough to point this out to us.

Nevertheless, experience has convinced us that we were justified in departing from the traditional approach in one important area: the presentation of descriptive inorganic chemistry. Generations of students have been exposed to an extensive series of lectures, organized around the periodic table, in which substances with entirely different chemical properties, such as ammonia and nitric acid, are discussed simultaneously. The results of this approach are all too evident when a student on a final examination paper writes a balanced equation to "prove" that the reaction of ammonia with water gives anhydrous nitric acid with hydrogen gas as a by-product.

We have chosen to organize descriptive chemistry around the types of reactions in which substances participate rather than the elements they contain. Following this approach, precipitation reactions are discussed in Chapter 16, acid-base reactions in Chapters 17 and 18, complex-ion formation in Chapter 19, and redox reactions in Chapters 20–22. The applications of each type of reaction to problems in preparative inorganic chemistry, analytical chemistry, and selected industrial processes are pointed out. Chapter 18, for example, deals with acid-base reactions in quantitative analysis (Section 18.2), the preparation of salts and volatile acids (Section 18.3), group separations in qualitative analysis (Section 18.4), and the Solvay Process (Section 18.5).

The first four chapters of the text place heavy emphasis on chemistry as a quantitative, experimental science. It is anticipated that many of the experiments described, dealing with the measurement of physical properties, the determination of atomic weights, chemical analysis, and stoichiometry, will be carried out by the students in the laboratory. The amount of lecture time devoted to these chapters will, of course, depend upon the students' background. It has been our experience that, with well-prepared students, much of this material can be covered by assigning problems to be discussed in recitation or laboratory.

Chapter 5 introduces the student, at an elementary level, to the principles of chemical thermodynamics. This topic is further discussed in chapters dealing with chemical equilibrium (Chapter 14) and the spontaneity of oxidation-reduction reactions (Chapter 21). We are under no illusion that, in the limited time available in a beginning course, a student is likely to acquire a thorough understanding of thermodynamics. It seems important, however, to expose him to a discipline which addresses itself directly to a basic theme of any course in chemistry, the prediction of the spontaneity of chemical reactions and the extent to which they occur. To accomplish this purpose, we have departed from the traditional treatment of thermodynamics by introducing the concept of free energy at an early stage and applying it immediately to predict whether reactions will take place at specified temperatures and pressures.

The physical behavior of gases (Chapter 6) is discussed in terms of the Ideal Gas Law. Experience with the so-called "factor method" of working gas-law problems has convinced us of its shortcomings. In any problem of interest to chemistry, such as the experimental determination of molecular weights, the calculations are greatly simplified by using the Ideal Gas Law. A consideration of condensed phases is postponed to Chapters 12 (liquids and solids) and 13 (solutions). At that point, sufficient material on chemical bonding has been presented to enable the student to relate the properties of liquids, solids, and solutions to interatomic and intermolecular forces.

We feel that the student, at a very early stage in his study of chemistry, should start thinking in terms of the particle structure of substances. For this reason, a brief discussion of the structure of atoms, ions, and molecules is included in Chapter 2. A much more extensive treatment of electronic structure is presented in Chapter 8, followed by ionic bonding (Chapter 9) and covalent bonding (Chapter 10). In Chapter 11, which deals with particle structure and bonding in elementary substances, sections on defect crystals and metallic bonding are included. Additional material on chemical bonding is presented in Chapter 19 in connection with the coordination compounds of the transition metals. The bonding in these compounds is described first in terms of the valence-bond approach and then by the crystal field theory.

The quantitative aspects of chemical equilibrium are stressed throughout the chapters dealing with reactions in the gas phase and in water solution (Chapters 15–22). In particular, the spontaneity of redox reactions (Chapter 21) is interpreted in terms of equilibrium constants for these reactions, as derived from standard electrode potentials. The equally important topic of reaction rate, introduced in Chapter 14, is discussed in connection with gas phase reactions (Chapter 15), ligand exchange in coordination compounds (Chapter 19), radioactive decay (Chapter 23), and substitution reactions in organic chemistry (Chapter 24).

Methods of balancing redox reactions have been relegated to one of the latter chapters of the book (Chapter 20). This material can, of course, be introduced earlier if desired. It is our feeling that this is one area which is far too heavily emphasized in many beginning chemistry courses. We commonly find students who, given the formulas of products and reactants, can balance the most complicated equation, yet are unable to say what happens when the simplest kind of reaction is carried out.

One of our objectives in writing this text was to restrict the material to what could be readily covered in a typical year course. To do this, we have left out certain topics traditionally covered in the elementary course and have gone less deeply into others than we might have wished. Many instructors will wish to supplement this text with one or more of the paperbacks available in selected areas of general chemistry. Three which we can recommend to the student who wishes to expand his knowledge of chemistry are:

Murmann, R. Kent, *Inorganic Complex Compounds*, Reinhold Publishing Corp., New York, N.Y., 1964.

Sebra, Donald K., *Electronic Structure and Chemical Bonding*, Blaisdell Publishing Co., New York, N.Y., 1964.

Nash, L. K., *Elements of Chemical Thermodynamics*, Addison-Wesley Publishing Co., Inc., Reading, Mass., 1962.

We would like to express our appreciation to Professor William Stratton, who read the manuscript and made many helpful suggestions concerning the organization of material; to Professor Charles E. Waring, whose frank and penetrating criticisms of the preliminary edition have contributed, we trust, to a clearer presentation; and to Mr. Benjamin Lofquist of the W. B. Saunders Co. for the encouragement and support he has given us.

Storrs, Connecticut   William L. Masterton
St. Paul, Minnesota   Emil J. Slowinski

CONTENTS

1

SOME BASIC CONCEPTS

1.1 WHAT CHEMISTRY IS

Although you may not, as yet, have undertaken any study of chemistry at all, the effects of chemistry on your lives are indeed profound. Much of the material required for your daily living has been developed and created, often during your lifetime, by chemists. Application of chemical principles to the development of new substances and the improvement of existing ones has resulted in modern antibiotic medicines, synthetic textile fibers, plastics of many kinds, artificial rubber, better gasoline, and many other important products. Entire industries have resulted from the development of these materials, giving employment to many thousands of workers, skilled and unskilled. Some of the most highly trained people in the world are engaged in chemical research, striving to discover new and better substances for the improvement of our living conditions. Chemistry is now an important and expanding factor in both the scientific and economic areas of our society and in all likelihood will so continue for many years.

Chemistry, like many sciences, is a science of substances, those materials of which the earth and the universe are composed. Specifically, the science of chemistry deals with the properties and structures of substances, and their creation from and interaction with other substances. Since chemistry is a very broad subject, the boundaries which separate it from physics, geology, pharmacy, engineering, and the biological sciences are often indefinite. We find that the fields overlap extensively and that knowledge gained in one area is often applicable to another. Many of you will, therefore, be studying chemistry mainly because of its importance in other fields in which you have a specific interest.

Within chemistry itself there are several areas of study, which may be classified according to the types of matter of primary interest in that area. Thus we have *organic* chemistry, to deal with the many substances containing carbon, *inorganic* chemistry, whose province includes all other substances, and *nuclear* chemistry, in which we study the chemical behavior of radioactive substances. There are also areas in which the division is based on the purpose of the work in that area. Here we find *analytical* chemistry, which encompasses both qualitative and quantitative methods for investigating the composition of matter, and *physical* chemistry, which deals with the determination of the properties and structure of matter and the laws and theories of chemistry.

1

In this, a general course, we shall endeavor to introduce the principles that underlie all chemistry and to present applications of these principles so that we can obtain a clear understanding of chemical reactions. In discussing principles, we shall often use mathematical relations both to state the principles and to calculate certain quantities. It is most important that you become familiar with these relations (there are many of them) and learn to use them intelligently. Some of these relations are beautiful in their simplicity; others may tax your knowledge of mathematics to its limit. The fact that these relations exist makes chemistry an exact science, a science that really began when men first recognized the possibility of expressing chemical observations in mathematical terms. Work in this course will include the study of many fundamental mathematical chemical relations.

1.2   MAKING MEASUREMENTS

To discuss intelligently the principles of chemistry, one must have available systems of measurement which will allow quantitative descriptions of the properties and behavior of matter. Some very useful measuring instruments are in common use. Among the most important of these are the **rule** (or meter stick), the **balance**, and the **thermometer.** Prior to any scientific studies, we may recognize the practical importance of each of these devices, but our ideas are probably nebulous, and sometimes incorrect, as to exactly what they do for us. Let us assume, for the present, that we are unfamiliar with any of these instruments and also that we have performed an experiment that we wish to describe in an article in a scientific journal. We shall attempt to devise means for reporting the observations and, in so doing, shall see why each of the instruments is necessary and how it accomplishes its purpose. As we shall see, the lines of reasoning which lead to the development of these devices are not always as simple as one might expect.

The assumed experiment is a very simple one. We have taken a certain volume of water and to it added a certain amount of a solid crystalline substance called potassium nitrate. When the mixture was stirred, the potassium nitrate dissolved, and the temperature of the solution fell by a certain amount. We wish to report our experimental procedure and observations as exactly as possible, to state how much water was used, how much potassium nitrate, and how much the temperature dropped, so that another person could perform the experiment and check our results.

The Rule

We must, first of all, report what volume of water was used. One possible way would be to state in the article that we would send a container of the proper size to anyone interested in repeating the work. This could certainly insure exact duplication of the volume used, but this method could present difficulties, particularly financial, if a thousand people claimed to be interested.

Another approach would be to include in the article a line whose length was equal to that of the edge of a cube having the volume of our container. In this way our skill, that of the publisher, and that of the reader could combine to produce the correct volume. This second method, though cumbersome, has some advantages over that given first. The line of a given length could serve essentially as a standard of length, and on the basis of it, the reader, using the laws of geometry, could in principle reproduce any given length, area, or volume.

The latter method is, as a matter of fact, very similar to that now used throughout the world. An arbitrary standard reference length has been adopted by international agreement, and copies of it have been made to the extent that each of us has undoubtedly seen a copy of a copy of a copy. The standard length is called the **meter** (m.). Probably all of you have seen a meter stick. The meter is part of the metric system of measurement, which is used by scientists everywhere. In the United States the common standard of length is the foot, defined as equal to 12 inches, and is part of the English system. The relation between the two systems is of necessity fixed, and one meter is just about equal to 39.37 inches (Figure 1.1).

[handwritten: 1 m = 39.37 in]

A rule which measures centimeters

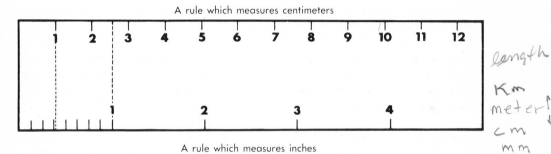

[handwritten right margin: length / Km / meter / cm / mm]

A rule which measures inches

1 inch* = 2.54 centimeters   1 centimeter* = 0.394 inches

FIGURE 1.1 The rule.

The metric system has a great advantage over the English system when extensive computation is involved. It is a decimal system, in that all units are related to the basic one by some power of ten. The common units of length smaller than the meter are the **centimeter** (cm.), which is equal to **one hundredth of a meter,** and the **millimeter** (mm.), which is **one thousandth of a meter.** Very small lengths are often expressed in **Ångstroms; one Ångstrom** (Å) is equal to 10^{-8} **centimeter.** A larger unit of length is the **kilometer** (km.), which is **one thousand meters.** In the metric system, conversion from one unit of length to another is very simply accomplished. For instance, using the foregoing relations, one can easily see that

$$0.065 \text{ kilometer (km.)} = 65 \text{ meters (m.)}$$
$$= 6500 \text{ centimeters (cm.)}$$
$$= 65000 \text{ millimeters (mm.)}$$

[handwritten: important]

The analogous conversion from miles to yards to feet to inches would not be nearly so easy to do and would, in general, involve the use of decimal fractions. The metric system is the common system in use in most countries; conservatism coupled with a

---

* In equations of this kind, 1 inch may be taken to mean *exactly* 1 inch, and 1 centimeter to be *exactly* 1 centimeter. In a similar way, in equations relating dimensions in the *same* system, such as

1 foot = 12 inches

both numbers may be taken to be exact. *Exactly* 1 foot equals *exactly* 12 inches. (See Appendix 1 for a discussion of significant figures.)

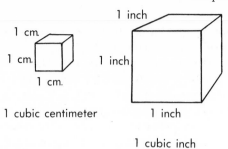

1 cubic centimeter   1 cubic inch

FIGURE 1.2 Some relationships between metric and English volume units: 1 liter = 1000 milliliters = 1000 cubic centimeters (very nearly) = 61.025 cubic inches = 1.0567 quarts.

1 liter = 1000 milliliters = 1000 cubic centimeters (very nearly)

= 61.025 cubic inches   1.0567 quarts

certain amount of human stubbornness has kept the English system in existence in the United States and the British Commonwealth.

Once standard lengths have been established, areas and volumes can also be measured. In the metric system the unit of area is the **square centimeter** (sq. cm. or cm.^{2}) which is the amount of surface in a **square, one centimeter on an edge.** In the English system the unit of area is the square inch or the square foot. One square inch is equal to just about 6.45 square centimeters. Chemists ordinarily do not make many measurements of areas, but areas do enter in an important way when one considers pressures.

Volume units in the metric system are also very simply related to those of length. **A cube one centimeter on an edge** has a volume equal to **one cubic centimeter** (cc. or cm.^{3}) and this is the basic volume unit. When speaking of liquids, we often wish to consider a larger volume unit called the **liter** (l.), which contains very close to **one thousand cubic centimeters.** The **milliliter** (ml.) is equal to **one thousandth of a liter,** and for our purposes we can consider the milliliter and the cubic centimeter to have the same volume (see page 7). In the English system, 1.0567 quarts is about equal to 1 liter (Figure 1.2).

In our laboratories we have containers of very accurate volumes, copies made by manufacturers from standards. We could, using these volumetric devices, measure out 250 ml. of water for the experiment referred to previously and report this in our article, with confidence that others could very readily obtain very close to the same volume.

By means of the rule, man is able to measure and record length, area, and volume with a high degree of accuracy and precision. Measurements of length have in some instances been reported to nine significant figures. The standard international meter is equal to 1650763.73 times the wavelength of the orange krypton-86 spectral line in air under certain standard conditions of temperature and pressure.

The Balance

The problem of reporting the amount of potassium nitrate used in the experiment is somewhat more difficult than was the case with the volume of the water. We could, of course, report the volume of solid used in the metric volume units which are available. However, in the case of a solid, crystal size could make a considerable difference in the amount of material required to fill a given container. A fine powder would leave much less unfilled air space in a vessel than would large chunks of solid. It thus seems desirable to measure amounts of this sort of material in another way. Analogous situations arise frequently. For example, when someone asks us how big our small brother is, we never answer, "His volume now is about 17 quarts." There are several other very important reasons for developing a method for measuring amounts of matter in a way completely independent of volume, and these will be encountered later in our work.

The **amount of matter** in, or the **mass** of, a substance is a more complex notion than is its volume. Sir Isaac Newton, in about 1686, made some very significant statements regarding the masses of objects. His observations were not restricted to the measurement of mass, and cannot all be treated here. However, we can apply his laws and thus find a successful method for measuring the mass of an object.

To measure mass a mechanical device, called a balance, is used. Such a device might be constructed in several ways, but the most common one is illustrated in Figure 1.3. The left- and right-hand sides of the balance are made as nearly identical as possible, and with no material on either pan the balance will come to rest with both pans at an equal height. If our sample of potassium nitrate is placed on the left pan, that pan will go down, since the pull of gravity on the sample will upset the balance in that direction. If now, however, we add some pieces of metal to the right-hand pan, we can cause that pan ultimately to lower, and, if we are careful enough,

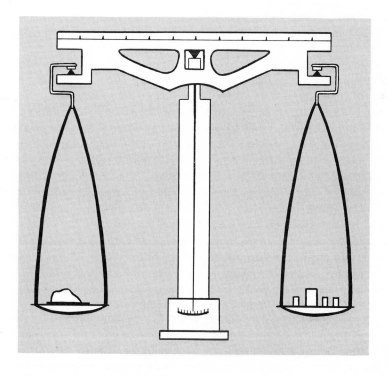

FIGURE 1.3 Schematic diagram of the balance.

with the proper choice of metal pieces we can bring the system to balance again.

The operation of balancing the system under load is, as you probably know, called *weighing* the sample, and we say that, at balance, the weight of the sample and the weight of the metal pieces are the same. Now, exactly what is this property called the weight? Certainly the metal and the sample are not identical in their appearance, reactivity, or volume. The balance, by its very nature, allows the relation of only one property common to the two pieces of matter; that property is the force by which each is attracted to the earth. At balance, the force attracting the sample to the earth is equal to the force attracting the metal pieces to the earth. This statement is entirely equivalent to saying that, at balance, the weight of the sample is equal to the weight of the metal pieces. The definition of weight is embodied in the two sentences.

Newton's Law states that, under the conditions obtaining in the balance, the weight of the sample and its mass are proportional to each other through the same proportionality constant that relates the weight of the metal pieces to their mass. Mathematically, the foregoing statement can be expressed as

$$\text{weight of sample} = k \times \text{mass of sample}$$
$$\text{weight of metal} = k \times \text{mass of metal}$$

Dividing the two equations, one by the other, we obtain

$$\frac{\text{weight of sample}}{\text{weight of metal}} = \frac{\text{mass of sample}}{\text{mass of metal}}$$

Since, at balance,

$$\text{weight of sample} = \text{weight of metal}$$

it is true that, at balance,

$$\text{mass of sample} = \text{mass of metal}$$

At balance, then, not only are the weights of the sample and metal pieces equal, but also their masses are equal. That is, the balance detects **equality of weight and equality of mass.**

Strictly speaking, in chemistry we are more interested in mass than in weight. The mass of an object is an inherent property of the object, and is a measure of the amount of material in the object. By its very nature, the weight of an object does not remain constant over the surface of the earth, since it depends on the gravitational pull, which varies with altitude and with latitude. The weight of an object, then, depends on where you weigh it. The mass of an object is presumably a constant throughout the universe. For this reason we record amounts of matter in terms of mass and set up standards on the basis of mass.

The standard unit of **mass** is the **gram**. One **gram** (g.) is very nearly equal to the **mass** of **one cubic centimeter of water** under certain specified conditions of temperature and pressure (see page 7). Thus the standard of mass is ultimately related to the standard of length in the metric system. Such a relation makes it very easy to estimate the mass of a given volume of water. For example, we can say that 250 ml. or 250 cc. of water will have a mass of just about 250 g. The English and metric systems of mass are related by the fact that a pound has a mass of 453.6 grams, so a liter of water (1000 g.) has a mass of about 2.2 lb.

Analogous to those used for expressing lengths, there are units for masses larger and smaller than the gram. **One thousand grams** is called a **kilogram** (kg.) and

one thousandth of a gram is called a **milligram** (mg.). Again, we can very easily convert these units:

0.032965 kilogram (kg.) = 32.965 grams (g.) = 32965 milligrams (mg.)

In working with masses, lengths, and volumes, we usually choose a unit such that, if possible, the number lies between 1 and 1000. In the example given, the mass would probably be reported in grams. The relationships among metric units are summarized in Table 1.1.

TABLE 1.1 RELATIONSHIPS AMONG METRIC UNITS

Length	1 kilometer = 1000 meters
	1 meter = 100 centimeters
	1 centimeter = 10 millimeters = 10^8 Angstroms*
Area	1 square meter = 10^4 square centimeters
	1 square centimeter = 100 square millimeters
Volume	1 liter = 1000 milliliters = 1000 cubic centimeters
Mass	1 kilogram = 1000 grams
	1 gram = 1000 milligrams

Standard masses, excellent copies of the international standard, are available in laboratories throughout the world. These standard masses are made of inert metal like platinum or stainless steel. The measurement of mass is almost invariably made on a balance similar to the one just described. With such balances, masses of up to 100 g. can be measured to about six significant figures. In our experiment we could measure out 32.50 g. of potassium nitrate and report this value with confidence.

Originally, the gram was thought to be exactly equal to the mass of one cubic centimeter of water at 760 mm. Hg pressure and 4°C, the temperature at which the density of water is maximum. It was later found that the standard gram had a mass equal to that of 1.000027 cubic centimeters of water under the given conditions. The liter is defined as being equal to the volume of one kilogram of water under these conditions, so we find that one liter of water equals 1000.027 cubic centimeters. The discrepancy is very small, and for our purposes we may take one milliliter to be equal to one cubic centimeter, and the mass of one cubic centimeter of water to be one gram.

In discussing masses, chemists have unfortunately fallen into habits of loose usage. They might say, for instance, "The weight of the sample was 6.459 grams." Since the gram is not a unit of weight, the statement is simply not correct as it stands. The following statements are correct, and give the true meaning of the above statement:

The mass of the sample was 6.459 g.
The sample has a weight equal to that of 6.459 g.
The sample weighs 6.459 g.

Since mass and weight of substances are always proportional to each other, and since our work in chemistry usually involves only relative masses and weights, no numerical errors arise when the words *mass* and *weight* are used interchangeably as they often are by chemists. In order to be consistent with common chemical usage, we shall sometimes use *weight* where *mass* is the proper word; to do otherwise would mean either

---

* Exponential notation is discussed in Appendix 1.

to create a new terminology for this text or to have, occasionally, some very awkward statements. The student should remember that chemistry is not the word of God; it was made by men, and men, though they strive mightily and do many wondrous things, are inherently imperfect.

The Thermometer

In the experiment with the potassium nitrate, we noted that the temperature dropped. When we speak informally of temperature and temperature change, we have confidence that our words are understood. Yet many of us, when asked what temperature is and what is done to measure it, would be at a loss for words. The concepts from which temperature arises are not obvious, and their development is somewhat more abstract than was the case with either the rule or the balance.

A discussion of temperature is perhaps best begun by noting our natural sensitivity to things called hot or cold. We say that hot things have a higher **temperature** than do cold ones, and create the word temperature to describe these sensations.

Now, let us suppose we have a block of copper which we decide, by touching it once, is hot, and a block of steel, which is cold. If we place the two blocks in contact with each other we notice that the copper block becomes cooler and the steel block warmer. We say that heat is flowing from the copper to the steel. Indeed, heat is defined by an experiment of this sort; *heat is that which flows spontaneously from a body at a higher temperature to one at lower temperature when they are placed in contact with each other.*

Our definition of heat may seem rather poor, since it does not endow heat with any sort of tangible nature. Early scientists considered heat to be a sort of fluid, which flowed from hot bodies to cold, and that bodies containing a large amount of the fluid, which was called caloric, were hot. It was never possible to demonstrate experimentally the existence of caloric, and the idea was ultimately dropped.

During the period in which the copper block is cooling we can say that its temperature falls, but find, of course, that touching it allows for only a very qualitative description of the change that is occurring. It is desirable to have available some method for following the temperature change in an objective manner, with the variability of the human sense of touch eliminated entirely if possible.

One approach to the problem would be to use an instrument to measure some property of the metal as its temperature changes. For instance, we might measure the length of the copper block during the process. If we use a very precise type of rule, called a micrometer, we find that the length of the copper block decreases as it cools. The dimensions of the block are, then, a function of its temperature. This experiment makes it apparent that temperature can be related in a quantitative way to the properties, in this case length and volume, of the material under examination.

After the two metal blocks have been in contact for some time, the micrometer indicates that the length of the copper block is no longer changing, and our rather less sensitive sense of touch confirms the associated fact that its temperature is no longer changing. Under such conditions, we say that the two blocks have come to thermal equilibrium and that their *temperatures* are *equal.*

So far we have not been able to assign any numerical values to our temperatures, although it is clear that temperature and physical properties are related. To obtain a numerical temperature scale we resort to a third object, designed in such a way that it is very sensitive to temperature changes; this object is called a **thermometer.**

A typical thermometer is constructed to take advantage of the fact that the volume of a substance and its temperature are dependent on each other. In such a thermometer a liquid is usually the measuring material, and although many liquids would be satisfactory, mercury is most commonly used. The mercury is enclosed in a glass container which consists of a bulb attached to a fine capillary tube. If the container is filled with mercury to some point in the capillary, the mercury level changes very noticeably for a small temperature change.

Such a thermometer could be used in the experiment with the two metal blocks. We could mark the mercury levels when the thermometer was in contact with each of the blocks in turn and also the level when the system reached thermal equilibrium. In the latter case we would find that the mercury level was the same, independent of the block with which it was in contact (Figure 1.4).

We could use this thermometer to report our observations on the temperature of the solution of potassium nitrate in water, but detailed dimensions would have to be included in our article so that another experimenter could construct a thermometer exactly like ours. As with the measurement of volume, it is readily apparent that some standard system of temperature measurement, which would allow temperatures to be expressed as numbers, would be very helpful. This, of course, has been accomplished and can be understood quite simply.

A thermometer like that we have described is placed in a container in which there is a mixture of pure water and cracked ice. In such a mixture we note that the mercury remains at a constant level so long as both ice and water are present in the container. On the basis of this observation we say that the temperature of the mixture of ice and water is constant. This level of the mercury is marked and arbitrarily assigned a value of temperature equal to zero degrees (0°).

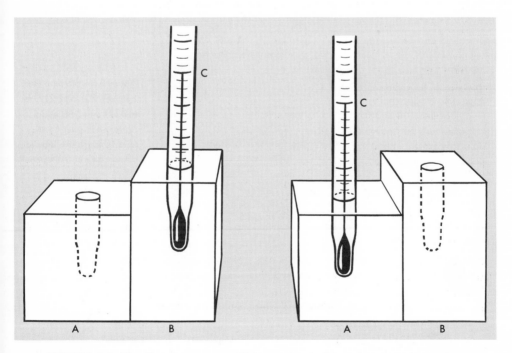

FIGURE 1.4 Equality of temperature. If the mercury in C is at the same height when C is in contact with A as when C is in contact with B, then temperature of A = temperature of B.

The thermometer is then placed in a container in which water is boiling at standard atmospheric pressure (760 mm. Hg), and again it is found that the mercury level remains constant so long as both water and steam are present in the container. We arbitrarily assign to this level a value of temperature equal to 100°. The mercury level at 100° is higher than the level at 0° by a certain distance on the capillary. We measure this distance and divide it into 100 equal parts. Each division is marked on the capillary. Using the same size of division, we can engrave lines above 100° and below 0°.

If the thermometer is placed in a liquid of unknown temperature and the mercury level comes to rest 45 divisions above the zero line, we say that the temperature of the liquid is 45°. If the level comes to rest 130 divisions above the zero level we say that the temperature of the liquid is 130°. In this way any temperature within the range of the thermometer can be measured.

Since the scale of temperature we have set up is not the only one used by scientists, we must always indicate the temperature scale used to express a specified temperature. The scale we have described is called the **centigrade** scale (or **Celsius** scale) since the boiling point of water was taken to be 100° and the freezing point of water to be 0°. In the examples given, the temperatures would properly be reported as 45° centigrade and 130° centigrade or, more commonly, 45°C and 130°C.

The common temperature scale in use in the United States is the Fahrenheit scale. On this scale 32° corresponds to the freezing point of water and 212° to the temperature of its normal boiling point. The centigrade and Fahrenheit scales are related by a simple algebraic expression which can be derived easily (Figure 1.5).

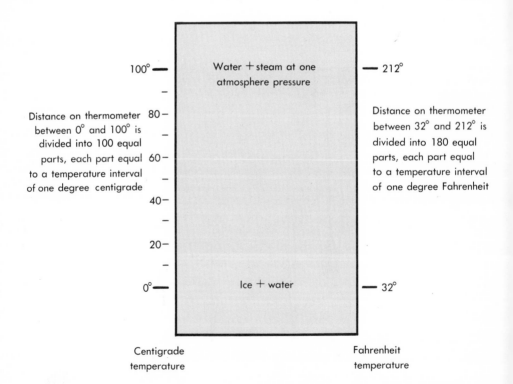

FIGURE 1.5 The centigrade and Fahrenheit temperature scales.

In this book we shall usually use the centigrade scale. However, when discussing the behavior of gases, we shall find that still another scale, called the absolute or Kelvin scale, is employed.

The absolute temperature scale is useful in theoretical chemistry since on that scale the physical properties of pure substances are most simply expressed in mathematical terms. The absolute temperature ($°A$), sometimes called the Kelvin temperature ($°K$), is found to be equal to the centigrade temperature, $°C$, plus 273. That is,

$$°A \text{ (or } °K) = °C + 273 \qquad (1.1)$$

The absolute temperature of water at its normal boiling point, 100°C, is, by equation 1.1, equal to 373°A or 373°K. Similarly, the melting point of oxygen, −218°C, is 55°K. In Chapter 6, in which the properties of gases are discussed, the origin and significance of the absolute temperature scale will be considered.

The mercury-in-glass thermometer (constructed and calibrated essentially as we describe here) is the one most widely used by the scientific community, and for most purposes it is satisfactory. In our experiment with the potassium nitrate, we could measure the temperatures with such a thermometer and report meaningfully that the temperature dropped from 23°C to 5°C.

Thus, using the rule, the balance, and the thermometer as measuring devices, one can report that when 32.50 g. of potassium nitrate is dissolved in 250 ml. of water, if the initial temperature of the substances is 23°C, the final temperature of the resulting solution is 5°C.

In setting up a scale of temperature as we have done, there are some disadvantages which are not at once apparent. Although mercury is ordinarily used in thermometers, other liquids, among them ethyl alcohol and pentane, are sometimes employed. We find that, although thermometers made with different liquids agree with one another at 0°C and 100°C, at intermediate temperatures they may disagree by appreciable amounts. Obviously then, a scale of temperature should be set up in such a way that it is independent of the properties of any one substance. In our work with gases we shall present the results of efforts made in that direction.

Another difficulty that arises in connection with liquid-in-glass thermometers is that their range is limited. At some low temperature the liquid will freeze, and at high temperatures it will tend to boil; both situations make for unsatisfactory performance in a thermometer.

For the measurement of extremely low or high temperatures, other properties of substances can be used. At temperatures above about 600°C all substances emit visible light, which becomes more intense and changes in color from red to nearly white as the temperature goes up to about 2000°C. By visually comparing the emitted light with that given off by a standard substance, usually a filament of tungsten, in a device called an optical pyrometer, one can measure high temperatures fairly accurately over a very wide range. High-temperature studies can also be made using the electrical resistance of an inert, high-melting metal wire (platinum is often employed) as the temperature-dependent property. Another type of thermometer involves the use of a thermocouple; in this device the property measured is the electrical potential between junctions of dissimilar metals at two temperatures. For each of the two latter approaches, satisfactory temperature scales can be set up by methods analogous to those we have described.

A third disadvantage of liquid-in-glass thermometers is mechanical; that is, the accuracy of the thermometer is limited by the manufacturer's ability to attain uniformity of the bore in the capillary used. The problem is much more difficult than reproducing masses or volumes accurately, and we find that discrepancies of 1°C between presumably identical mercury-in-glass thermometers are not at all uncommon.

The Manometer and the Measurement of Pressure

By recording the volume, the mass, and the temperature of a sample, we can in most cases describe its state very satisfactorily. However, particularly when we deal with gases, there is another property which is very useful in specifying the state of a system, and that is the pressure. When a gas is confined in a container it will exert a force on the container wall; this force puts the container under a stress and, if sufficiently large, can expand or rupture the container. The **pressure** of a gas is defined as the **force per unit area** of container wall. Since the unit of force in the metric system is the **dyne,** the unit of pressure is the **dyne per square centimeter.**

The measurement of pressure can be accomplished very easily with a device called a **manometer** (Figure 1.6). A manometer consists of a glass U-tube partially filled with mercury. One side of the U-tube is connected to the container in which the pressure is to be measured, and the other side is connected to a region of known pressure. The gas in the container will exert a force on the mercury column and will tend to make it go down. This force will be opposed by that created by the gas over the other surface. The difference, as measured on a rule, between the two mercury levels at equilibrium is directly proportional to the difference between the gas pressure and the known pressure. Gas pressures are often reported in **millimeters of mercury** (mm Hg), rather than in dynes per square centimeter, since it is experimentally more convenient. In Figure 1.6, since pressures in a fluid are equal at equal

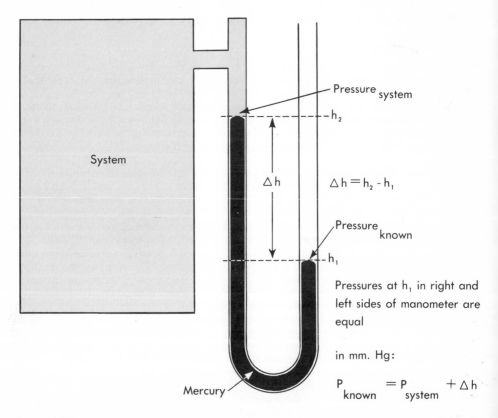

FIGURE 1.6 The manometer and the measurement of pressure. Pressures at h_1 in right and left sides of manometer are equal. All pressures are in millimeters of mercury.

heights, we can say that, at level h_1,

$$\text{pressure}_{\text{known}} = \text{pressure}_{\text{system}} + \text{pressure due to } \Delta h \text{ mm. Hg}$$

If we agree to measure pressure in terms of the height of a column of mercury equivalent in force per unit area to that pressure, then ($\text{pressure}_{\text{known}}$) will be determined in mm. Hg, and

$$\text{pressure}_{\text{system}} = \text{pressure}_{\text{known}} - \Delta h \quad \text{(all in mm. Hg)}$$

The known pressure is usually either that of the atmosphere or that of a vacuum. In the former case it is found with a barometer, a device described in Chapter 6, and in the latter case it is zero. It is possible, given the properties of mercury at the temperature of the manometer, to find the pressure in dynes/sq. cm., but this is not usually done.

A larger pressure unit is the standard atmosphere (atm.); this is the pressure exerted by a column of mercury 76.0 cm. (760 mm.) high at 0°C. This pressure is on the average, equal to that of the atmosphere at sea level, and in the English system equals about 14.7 lb./sq. in. We will discuss the pressure of gases further in Chapter 6.

The manometer, like many instruments, depends on the rule, the balance, and the thermometer to some extent for its operation. Though it is perhaps not as basic as these three, it is still an extremely important and useful tool.

The Mathematics of Dimensions

In chemical problems we are often required to convert from one given dimensional unit to another. This can be accomplished by means of the so-called **conversion factor method,** which is at once powerful, general, and easy to learn. The conversion factor method for dimensions is illustrated in the examples that follow and can readily be extended to include chemical problems, when they arise in later chapters. (In these examples we shall follow the rules governing significant figures which are discussed in Appendix 1.)

Example 1.1.　How many meters are there in 45 centimeters?

Solution.　To solve this problem we must know the conversion factor for centimeters to meters. In the previous discussion we noted that

$$1 \text{ meter (m.)} = 100 \text{ centimeters (cm.)}$$

This equation can also be expressed as

$$\frac{1 \text{ m.}}{100 \text{ cm.}} = 1$$

This is the conversion factor form for the given relation.

If we multiply 45 cm. by 1 we do not change its magnitude, but, by using a conversion factor equal to 1 as a multiplier, we can change its dimensions. This is done as follows:

$$45 \text{ centimeters} \times \frac{1 \text{ meter}}{100 \text{ centimeters}} = \frac{45 \text{ meters}}{100} = 0.45 \text{ meter}$$

By this step a length given in centimeters is converted into meters. The conversion factor was written in such a way that centimeters appeared as a dimension in both numerator and denominator of the product; thus they cancel out and were eliminated from the expression. This example illustrates the use of the conversion factor method in the simplest case.

Example 1.2. How many feet are there in 458 cm.?

Solution. To convert 458 cm. into feet one must proceed as in Example 1.1, but now, instead of one conversion factor, several are necessary. Using the relations given previously, we have

$$12 \text{ inches} = 1 \text{ foot} \quad \text{or, equivalently,} \quad \frac{12 \text{ in.}}{1 \text{ ft.}} = 1$$

$$1 \text{ m.} = 39.37 \text{ in.} \quad \text{or} \quad \frac{1 \text{ m.}}{39.37 \text{ in.}} = 1$$

Multiplying 458 cm. by the appropriate conversion factors,

$$458 \text{ cm.} \times \frac{1 \text{ meter}}{100 \text{ cm.}} \times \frac{39.37 \text{ inches}}{1 \text{ meter}} \times \frac{1 \text{ foot}}{12 \text{ inches}} = \frac{458 \times 39.37 \text{ feet}}{100 \times 12} = 15.0 \text{ feet}$$

In this problem, although several conversion factors were used, all dimensions except the one desired canceled out. Note that we inverted some of the factors in order to make the dimensions cancel properly. This, of course, does not change the value of the factors, which remain unity.

Example 1.3. One milliliter of mercury weighs 13.6 g. What is the mass in pounds of 1.500 l. of mercury?

Solution. In this problem two kinds of dimension, mass and volume, must be dealt with. We are asked to convert liters of mercury to their equivalent in pounds of mercury. Given that

$$1 \text{ liter} = 1000 \text{ milliliters} \quad \text{or} \quad \frac{1 \text{ l.}}{1000 \text{ ml.}} = 1$$

$$1 \text{ pound} = 453.6 \text{ grams} \quad \text{or} \quad \frac{1 \text{ lb.}}{453.6 \text{ g.}} = 1$$

$$1 \text{ ml. mercury} \simeq 13.6 \text{ g.} \quad \text{or} \quad \frac{1 \text{ ml. Hg}}{13.6 \text{ g.}} \simeq 1$$

(Hg is the chemical symbol for mercury.)

Setting up the conversion factors as before:

$$1.500 \text{ l. Hg} \times \frac{1000 \text{ ml.}}{1 \text{ l.}} \times \frac{13.6 \text{ g.}}{1 \text{ ml. Hg}} \times \frac{1 \text{ lb.}}{453.6 \text{ g.}} \simeq \frac{1.500 \times 1000 \times 13.6 \text{ lb. Hg}}{453.6}$$

$$\simeq 45.0 \text{ lb.}$$

In this problem we made use of the symbol $\simeq$, which is to be read as "is equivalent to." In cases in which the kinds of dimension are changed, the quantities involved are equivalent in some respect, rather than identical, to other quantities. We shall find the symbol very useful in treating chemical systems in later chapters.

    In any problem that involves conversion from one dimension to a related one, the approach is analogous to that used in these examples. First, determine what the quantity to be converted is; this is usually, but not always, obvious. Second, write the pertinent equations and conversion factors. Third, multiply the original quantity by the product of the conversion factors, chosen in such a way that all dimensions, except the one that is to appear in the final answer, occur in both the numerator and denominator of the product and, hence, cancel algebraically.

    The calculations to be made in solving the type of problems we have presented are most readily carried out on a slide rule. Ordinary slide-rule precision is satisfactory for most of the calculations that must be made to solve mathematical problems in general chemistry.

1.3 MATTER AND CHEMISTRY

The matter of which the earth is composed is, even to the casual observer, extremely variable and complex. When we look through a microscope at a leaf, a stone, or a drop of blood, it is apparent that each of these materials is composed of many substances. Matter like this, consisting of regions of different compositions, is said to be **heterogeneous,** in contrast with matter having constant composition throughout, which is called **homogeneous** A scientist who wishes to study the laws of chemistry cannot work directly with ordinary matter, since it is far too complex. Rather, matter must be sought which initially appears to be relatively simple in composition; homogeneous samples would therefore usually be preferred to heterogeneous. Given such a sample a chemist can attempt, using methods we shall presently describe, to resolve it into its components. When a chemist is able to obtain samples of matter which contain one pure substance, and only then, he can hope to study intelligently the laws that govern the science of chemistry.

heter - composed of many sub.

homo - composed of const sub. throughout

The Resolution of Matter into Pure Substances

The procedures used to separate matter into its components are not obvious. They depend upon our experimental observations about the behavior of matter when it is carried through certain changes in its condition or state which do not result in altering the kinds of substances present in the matter. Such changes in state are called **physical** changes. They must be distinguished from changes in which the substances present in the matter are converted to other substances; these are called **chemical** changes.

Matter can be made to undergo many physical changes. Two very simple but important examples are the melting of a solid and the boiling of a liquid. Neither of these changes results in changing the kinds of substances present in the system.

By experiment it has been determined that matter which is carried through physical changes in state has an inherent tendency to be resolved into its components. To resolve a sample of matter completely may require many physical changes, properly conceived, but the separation is, in principle, considered possible. As a result of these changes, one ultimately obtains substances which cannot be further resolved by any physical changes. These materials are called **pure substances.**

We shall now show how a resolution can be accomplished in a simple case. Assume we have a sample of sea water, selected as a potentially simple material because it appeared homogeneous when it was collected. The resolution is begun by filtering the sample through a fine-pored paper, called filter paper, to remove any small amount of solid material from the liquid. In most separations of this sort, such obvious contaminants would first be removed.

The filtered sea water is put in a device called a distillation apparatus, consisting of a glass container connected to a cooled tube (Figure 1.7). Heat is applied to the liquid and a thermometer in the container indicates a rapid rise in temperature until the liquid begins to bubble and boil. After boiling begins the temperature rises slowly with time. The vapor which leaves the boiling liquid passes into the cooled tube, where it condenses to a liquid and is collected. After boiling proceeds for some time, solid appears in the boiling liquid. By the time the liquid has all evaporated, a

phys change - state which does not result in altering the kind of sub.

chem. " - sub converted to another sub.

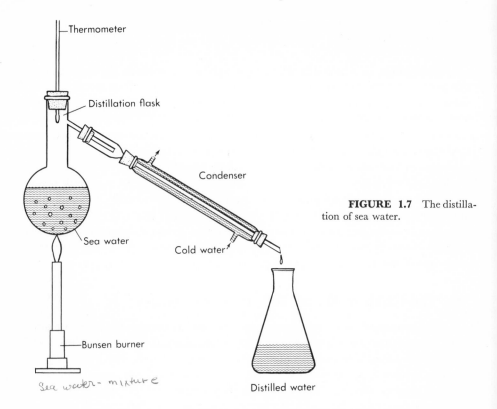

FIGURE 1.7 The distillation of sea water.

considerable solid residue is present in the container, and the temperature is considerably higher than when boiling began.

The fact that the distillation of sea water results in the recovery of both a solid and a liquid means, of course, that sea water is not a pure substance, but a mixture.

We now proceed to attempt to further resolve the liquid obtained during the distillation. We redistill the liquid; this time no solid residue appears, and the temperature of the boiling liquid remains constant until the liquid is all evaporated. Successive distillations occur at the same temperature and no residues are observed. These experiments indicate that, at least as far as physical changes resulting from vaporization and condensation are concerned, the liquid obtained is a pure substance.

However, more evidence is needed to prove conclusively that the liquid is indeed a pure substance. We therefore cool the liquid until it begins to freeze and note that the temperature of the solid-liquid mixture holds constant during the freezing. We remove some of the solid which first appears and compare its boiling and freezing points with those of the bulk liquid; they are found to be identical, indicating that no fractionation occurs on freezing. We carry the liquid through other physical changes, but in each case find that the properties of any fraction of the sample taken during the change are identical with those of any other fraction. Failing to separate this liquid into components by means of any physical changes, we can conclude that it is a pure substance.

Experiments of this type have been performed on many different kinds of matter, and they indicate clearly that there exists a large group of substances, called **pure substances,** which cannot be resolved into components by processes like those described. The substances have definite properties, such as boiling point and freezing point, which differ markedly from those of other pure substances. Pure water, the liquid which was prepared in the example, can freeze at only one temperature under ordinary conditions and, at a given pressure, can boil at only one temperature.

Analogous procedures to those used with the liquid could, in principle, be employed to separate the solid residue obtained from the distillation of sea water into its component pure substances. In this case we would find that the solid contained many pure substances, some present in very small amounts.

Another example of matter which appears to be relatively simple to analyze is the air around us. This material is most easily examined for its components by first cooling it until it condenses to a liquid; this occurs at about −180°C. If we let this liquid boil we find that, at a given pressure, its boiling point increases with time; this implies that air is a mixture and that its resolution by distillation is possible. If we carefully distill the liquid air in a special type of distillation apparatus, taking advantage of the fact that the boiling points of the components of the air differ appreciably, we are able to separate air into its component substances. A typical analysis of air is given in Table 1.2. We find that air consists principally of two substances, nitrogen and oxygen, and several other substances, some in very small amounts. We note that the physical properties of the pure substances which constitute the mixture we call air are different from one another. These differences make possible the resolution of air.

TABLE 1.2   THE COMPOSITION OF DRY AIR

Component	Per Cent by Volume	Boiling Point (°C)	Freezing Point (°C)
Nitrogen	78.03	−195.8	−209.9
Oxygen	20.99	−183.0	−218.4
Argon	0.94	−185.7	−189.2
Carbon dioxide	0.03	sublimes at −78.5	−56.6
Hydrogen	0.01	−252.8	−259.1
Neon	0.0015	−245.9	−248.7
Helium	0.0005	−268.9	−272.2
Krypton	0.00011	−152.9	−156.6
Xenon	0.000009	−107.1	−112

Many physical changes can be used to resolve matter into its components. In addition to distillation, freezing, and fractional distillation, we should mention **fractional crystallization, electrophoresis, thin-layer chromatography, vapor phase chromatography,** and **ion exchange** (Chapter 16). Some of these procedures are about as old as chemistry itself. Some of the more powerful methods, however, such as vapor phase chromatography, have been developed since 1950.

Chromatography

Many years ago it was discovered that pure substances could often be separated by using the differences in their solubilities in a given solvent as the distinguishing property. In a typical experiment a tube, usually of Pyrex glass, which is packed with a finely divided solid, is employed. The solid is often silica gel, small particles of quartz, or another chemically inert substance, which tends to hold, or adsorb, small amounts of other substances on its surface. The sample to be separated is put into solution and poured into the tube, which is called a

chromatography column. The packing adsorbs the sample and holds it at the top of the column.

A better solvent for the sample is then flowed slowly through the column. The different components of the sample, which have somewhat different solubilities in this solvent, are gradually flushed down the column, being continuously dissolved in the solvent and readsorbed on the packing. As the experiment proceeds, the various components become separated into zones, or bands, in the column, and finally pass from the bottom of the column as purified fractions, which may be pure substances. The procedure is called chromatography after the Greek word *chroma*, meaning color, since in some of the earlier experiments the separated bands were identified by their colors.

Column chromatography, which we have described, has the disadvantage that it is relatively slow, both in the experiment and in the preliminary work of selection of suitable solvents and column materials. Thin-layer chromatography, in which the packing is deposited as a thin layer on a flat plate, does not have these drawbacks. In this method the sample is applied, usually from solution, at the bottom of the plate, which is then placed in a tank in which there is a shallow layer of solvent. By capillary action the solvent slowly rises on the coating, flowing through the sample and separating its components into spots, or zones. Detection is by selective staining, or if radioactive tracers are used, by use of a radiation counter. Since the experiment is rapid and easily performed, and requires only a few micrograms (1 microgram $= 10^{-6}$ g.) of sample, it has recently come into very common use by organic and biochemists (Figure 1.8).

In still another variation on the basic experiment, vapors, rather than liquids, are used. A column similar to that in the previously described experiment is employed, and the sample, either in solution or as a vapor, is injected into the top of the column, where it is adsorbed. An inert gas, usually helium, is used as the eluting material, and gradually the components in the sample separate as they continuously vaporize into the helium and readsorb on the packing. Since the experiment is carried out at a temperature at which the sample has an appreciable volatility, and the sample passes down the column as a vapor, the procedure is called vapor chromatography. The resolving power of this method far exceeds that of any other approach yet devised, and, because of the exceedingly sensitive detectors which have been developed, requires only micrograms of sample. Because of the importance of the method to chemical research, many commercial vapor chromatographs have been developed in the few years since this kind of apparatus first became popular (Figure 1.9).

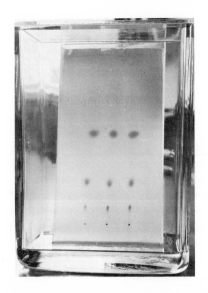

FIGURE 1.8   A thin-layer chromatogram showing the separation of three dyes (butter yellow, Sudan Red G, and indophenol) on activated Silica Gel G with benzene. Plate is shown in developing tank in solvent layer. (Photograph by L. A. Webb, courtesy of Dr. J. M. Bobbitt, University of Connecticut.)

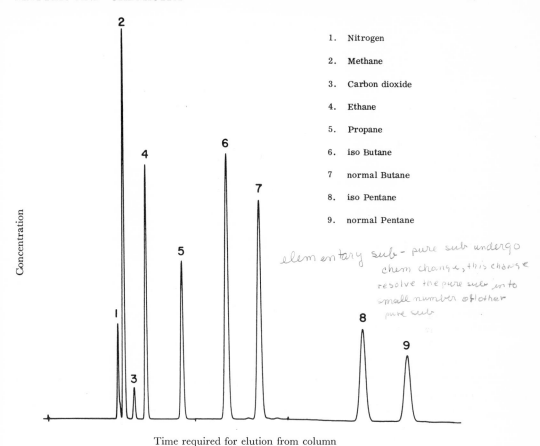

1. Nitrogen
2. Methane
3. Carbon dioxide
4. Ethane
5. Propane
6. iso Butane
7. normal Butane
8. iso Pentane
9. normal Pentane

elementary sub - pure sub undergo chem change, this change resolve the pure sub into small number of other pure sub

Time required for elution from column

FIGURE 1.9 Vapor-gas chromatogram of a natural gas synthetic blend. Analytical conditions:
Instrument: F & M Model 810 research gas chromatograph
Column: 50-ft,. 4 mm. copper; 30 per cent DC-200/350 cstks.; 60/80 Chromosorb P
Temperatures: Injector, 150°C; detector, 150°C; column, 100°C.
Detector: Thermal conductivity (WX filaments)
Sample size: 2 ml.
(Chromatogram courtesy of F & M Scientific Division of Hewlett-Packard, Avondale, Pa.)

Compound Substances and Elementary Substances

We find, then, experimentally that ordinary matter can be resolved into pure substances by subjecting it to one or more physical changes. The number of pure substances which have been isolated and characterized is now in excess of one million.

Although pure substances are stable to physical changes, they are often not stable to more powerful resolving conditions. Examples of such conditions are heating the substance to very high temperatures or subjecting it to electrical or chemical energy. By means of these more stringent and powerful conditions we can cause most pure substances to undergo chemical changes; these changes can often be made to result in the resolution of the pure substance into a relatively small number of other pure substances, called **elementary** substances.

An example of a powerful resolution is the electrolysis of water. A storage battery, such as is used in an automobile, is connected to an apparatus of the type illustrated in Figure 1.10, consisting of a glass container fitted with inert metal

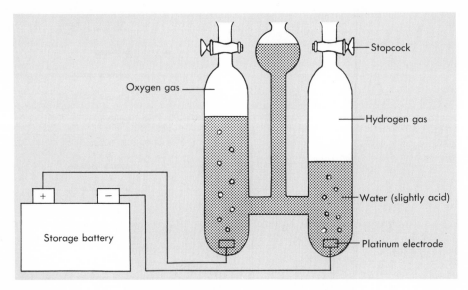

FIGURE 1.10 The electrolysis of water.

electrodes. Water, to which has been added a trace of sulfuric acid to speed up the reaction, is added to the container. As a result of the passage of the electric current two gases are produced, one at each of the electrodes. The gases, which are different pure substances called hydrogen and oxygen, are produced in the decomposition of water by electrical energy. If we mix the two gases in a container and cause a spark to pass, we observe that a violent reaction occurs during which the gases recombine to produce water with the evolution of energy.

In the electrolysis experiment the pure substance, water, is decomposed into the pure substances, hydrogen and oxygen. No further resolution of hydrogen and oxygen is found to be possible by any physical or chemical means. Hydrogen and oxygen are therefore examples of pure substances of the kind we call **elementary;** water is a pure substance of the kind we call **compound.**

A compound substance, often called a compound, is a pure substance which can be resolved into two or more pure substances. An elementary substance is a pure substance which cannot be so resolved.

Since hydrogen and oxygen cannot be resolved by any means analogous to those used to decompose water, we make an important assumption regarding the ultimate nature of those two gases. The assumption is that the matter which constitutes hydrogen is of only one kind; we say that the elementary substance hydrogen contains only the **element** hydrogen. Similarly, the elementary substance oxygen contains only the element oxygen. Water is a compound substance containing the elements hydrogen and oxygen.

The use of high temperatures for the decomposition of compound substances into elementary substances is rather common. Some of the compounds of oxygen with metals break down to yield the elementary substances at fairly low temperatures. Silver oxide, a brown solid at room temperature, decomposes to the elementary substances, silver (solid) and oxygen (gas), at about 200°C.

The decomposition of a great many compound substances has been accomplished. From such decompositions only 103 elementary substances have so far been obtained.

We say, therefore, that there are 103 known elements. It follows that all the pure substances are composed in their entirety from one or more of the 103 elements. These elements constitute all matter, and, because this is true, are at the very heart of chemistry.

The Discovery of the Elements

Elements were discovered in ancient times and continue to be discovered even today. Some of the elementary substances are readily isolated, and ancient peoples probably noted their presence either free in nature or in the remains of fires. Among the elements known since antiquity are gold, silver, copper, iron, lead, tin, mercury, sulfur, and carbon.

During the alchemical period, prior to 1700, a few more elements were found. Among them were arsenic, antimony, bismuth, phosphorus, and zinc. The alchemist, working purely empirically, could not do more than obtain a few more of the easily resolved elements.

About 1770, with the explanation of combustion and the discovery of oxygen, nitrogen, and hydrogen by Lavoisier and Priestley, chemistry began as a science. In about 1800 the atomic theory, as proposed by Dalton, gave recognition to the existence of elements. Between 1770 and 1830 about 35 elements were discovered, twice as many as in all the preceding centuries. It is obvious that a few men, working on the basis of correct principles, can do far more than many who rely almost exclusively on chance.

A rather remarkable fact is that, although chemistry developed tremendously during the nineteenth century, 14 of the 103 elements have been discovered since about 1935. The reason for this is not that the early chemists were rather lackadaisical in their search for new elements, but lies in a completely unexpected area. The elements found since 1935 actually do not exist in nature, but were synthesized by chemists and physicists from known elements. These new elements are all unstable and spontaneously decompose to other elements, in some cases very quickly. Both the synthesis and decomposition of these elements involve far more energy than is observed in any physical or chemical changes, and so we do not consider such reactions to invalidate our criterion for the existence of the elementary substances.

Chemical Symbols of the Elements

In dealing with the physical and chemical behavior of the elementary and compound substances one can, as we have done in this section, describe experimental observations with words. Although this is always possible, chemists make extensive use of a brief and informative shorthand notation to accomplish the same purposes.

Basic to the system are the symbols for the elements. As you know, each element has a name, which in many cases was given to it by its discoverer. Thus we have the elements cobalt, boron, polonium, and gold. In addition each element is represented by a symbol. The symbol consists of one or two letters, taken frequently, but not always, from the first two letters in the name of the element. For the just mentioned elements, the symbols are Co, B, Po, and Au. Some symbols derive from the Latin name of the element or one of its compounds (see list in Table 1.3). The names and symbols of the elements are an important part of the language of chemistry and should be learned thoroughly. A table giving the names of the elements and the symbols which have been assigned them is inside the front cover of this book.

The chemical symbols for the elements find their most important use in expressions called chemical formulas, which serve to indicate both the nature and relative amounts of the elements present in pure substances. Since chemical formulas are based on the atomic theory, further discussion of them will be postponed until that theory has been presented.

TABLE 1.3 ELEMENTS WHOSE SYMBOLS
ARE DERIVED FROM LATIN NAMES

Element	Latin Name	Symbol
Antimony	Stibium	Sb
Copper	Cuprum	Cu
Gold	Aurum	Au
Iron	Ferrum	Fe
Lead	Plumbum	Pb
Mercury	Hydrargyrum	Hg
Potassium	Kalium	K
Silver	Argentum	Ag
Sodium	Natrium	Na
Tin	Stannum	Sn

1.4 THE PHYSICAL PROPERTIES OF PURE SUBSTANCES

The pure substances can be separated from one another because of the differences in their physical properties. The behavior of a mixture undergoing a physical change is different from that of a pure substance. The temperature of the boiling point of sea water was seen to increase with time, whereas that of pure water is constant. Similarly, the temperature of a freezing mixture in general decreases as freezing proceeds, while that of a freezing pure substance remains constant until all the liquid is frozen.

The boiling point and the freezing point of a pure substance are, then, constant (under a given pressure) and serve to characterize the pure substance. Such properties as the boiling and freezing points are called **physical properties.** There are many physical properties one can determine. Among the more important are the density and specific heat (which are discussed in succeeding sections), and the following:

Refractive index—a measure of the degree to which a light ray is bent on entering the substance.

Heat of vaporization—the amount of heat required to vaporize (boil off) a given amount of a liquid.

Heat of fusion—the amount of heat required to melt a given amount of the solid.

Infrared absorption spectrum—a measure of the extent to which different wavelengths ("colors") in infrared light are absorbed by the substance.

The physical properties of the pure substances are so specific that they are the means of identification of those substances. There is only one pure substance which has the physical properties of water, and hence if one has an unknown pure substance with those properties, that substance *is* water. Much chemical research involves the identification of pure substances, and it is largely through their physical properties that their identity with known substances or their characterization as new substances is accomplished.

Density

We previously discussed methods by which we can measure the volume and mass of a given material. Neither of these quantities by itself is characteristic of the substance constituting the material. We could measure out 1, or 25, or 96 ml. of water, gasoline, or lighter fluid. Or we could measure 5, 16, or 4500 g. of water, gasoline, or lighter fluid. However, if we should measure out 16 ml. of water, the mass of that water would also be fixed by the measuring process; that is, we cannot arbitrarily choose *both* the mass *and* the volume of a substance in a sample. One or the other may be chosen, but the second will thereby be determined. We say, then, that the mass and the volume of a substance are related to each other in a definite way. If we double the volume of a sample we double its mass, and if we measure out a volume one tenth that of an original volume, the mass is also one tenth that of the original. Mathematically, we say that the mass of a sample is proportional to its volume, or that the mass is a linear function of the volume. In an equation, for a given amount of a substance

$$\text{mass} = d \times \text{volume} \quad \text{or} \quad m = dV$$

in which d is the proportionality constant.

The proportionality constant d is called the **density** and is one of the physical properties of a pure substance. Its physical significance is readily seen if the foregoing equation is solved for the density. We see that

$$d = m/V \qquad (1.2)$$

That is, the **density** of a substance is equal to its **mass** divided by its **volume.** It is seen to be the **mass per unit volume** of substance.

The density is a property of a substance which is not dependent on the amount being considered. Such properties are called **intensive** and are useful in characterizing pure substances. The mass and volume, both of which depend on the amount of material, are called **extensive** properties, and taken separately, are not characteristic of any substance (Table 1.4). Intensive properties, like the density, often relate to a specific volume or mass of substance, although this is not necessarily the case (for example, boiling point and freezing point).

TABLE 1.4 INTENSIVE AND EXTENSIVE PROPERTIES

Intensive Property	Extensive Property
Temperature	Mass
Density	Volume
Pressure	Weight
Color	Cost
Refractive index	Heat released on combustion

The density of a pure substance is one of its most important properties; like other physical properties it can aid in the identification of the substance, but it is also useful in another way. The mathematical relation among mass, density, and volume permits the calculation of any one of these quantities if the other two are known. For example, if the density and volume of a sample are known, its mass can be calculated. An understanding of and ability to perform this kind of calculation are essential. Some typical methods of solution are applied to the illustrative problems below.

Example 1.4.   The density of iron is given as 7.86 g./cm.^{3}. Calculate the mass of 156 cm.^{3} of iron.

Solution.   From the defining equation for the density we have

$$\text{mass}_{Fe} = d_{Fe} V_{Fe} \quad \text{(Fe is the chemical symbol for iron.)}$$

If we substitute numerical values into the equation, we obtain

$$\text{mass}_{Fe} = \frac{7.86 \text{ g.}}{\text{cm.}^3} \times 156 \text{ cm.}^3 = 1.23 \times 10^3 \text{ g.}$$

Example 1.5.   Aluminum has a density of 2.71 g./cm.^{3}. How many pounds would 3.00 cu. ft. of aluminum weigh?

Solution.   In problems involving density calculations it is often necessary to use the conversion-factor method to obtain the proper dimensions. We can, if we wish, consider the density itself to be a conversion factor that allows converting units of mass to units of volume or vice versa. We are given the following relations:

$$1 \text{ ft.} = 12 \text{ in.} \qquad \text{or} \qquad \frac{1 \text{ ft.}}{12 \text{ in.}} = 1$$

$$1 \text{ in.} = 2.54 \text{ cm.} \qquad \text{or} \qquad \frac{1 \text{ in.}}{2.54 \text{ cm.}} = 1$$

$$1 \text{ lb.} = 454 \text{ g.} \qquad \text{or} \qquad \frac{1 \text{ lb.}}{454 \text{ g.}} = 1$$

$$1 \text{ cm.}^3 \text{ Al} \simeq 2.71 \text{ g.} \qquad \text{or} \qquad \frac{1 \text{ cm}^3 \text{ Al}}{2.71 \text{ g.}} \simeq 1$$

We now write the conversion equation, using the proper factors:

$$3.00 \text{ ft.}^3 \text{Al} \times \left(\frac{12 \text{ in.}}{1 \text{ ft.}}\right)^3 \times \left(\frac{2.54 \text{ cm.}}{1 \text{ in.}}\right)^3 \times \frac{2.71 \text{ g.}}{1 \text{ cm.}^3 \text{ Al}} \times \frac{1 \text{ lb.}}{454 \text{ g.}} \simeq 507 \text{ lb.}$$

To measure the density of a substance we need merely to find the mass and the volume of a given sample. If the substance is a liquid, the procedure is very straightforward. A small container of a precisely known volume (about 5 ml.) is weighed empty and then filled with the liquid. The mass of the liquid is obtained by difference; the density is obtained by dividing this mass by the volume of the container. The container, which is called a pycnometer, can be calibrated with a liquid of known density.

The density of a solid crystalline material is not so easily determined as that of a liquid. One approach is to weigh a sample of crystals and add them to a container of known mass and volume. The container is then filled with a nonsolvent liquid of known density and weighed. From these measurements the volume of the crystals can be found and their density calculated (Figure 1.11).

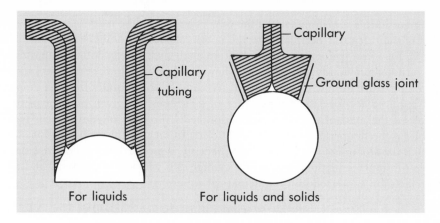

FIGURE 1.11 Pycnometers for measuring densities.

It is also possible to measure density by using Archimedes' Principle, that a body immersed in a liquid is buoyed up by a force equal to the weight of the liquid it displaces. A body will float if it can displace its own weight of liquid, and will float at a higher level in a liquid of greater density. In the hydrometer, often used to measure the density of the liquid in an automobile storage battery, a float is calibrated to read density directly as a function of floating level.

Archimedes' Principle is also used in a laboratory instrument, called the Westphal balance, in which density is measured by comparing the buoyant force of a liquid on a standard plummet with the force exerted on the plummet by a reference liquid, usually water. The principle can be applied to the measurement of the densities of solids in an almost obvious way. One finds, by trial and error, a liquid in which the unknown solid will remain suspended, neither sinking nor floating. Under such conditions the densities of the solid and liquid are equal and so can be found by measuring the density of the liquid.

The dimensions of density are important and must be recorded with the value. Ordinarily density of liquids or solids is given in grams per milliliter (g./ml.), but by using the appropriate conversion factors one can easily express the density in pounds per cubic foot (lb./ft.³) or any other convenient set of units.

The density of a liquid or solid is only slightly influenced by changes in temperature or pressure. At 25°C the density of water is 0.997 g./ml.; at 100°C it is 0.958 g./ml. These values reflect the general rule that density decreases as temperature rises. As you would expect, the densities of liquids and solids increase slightly with increasing pressure. At 25°C the density of water increases from 0.997 to 0.998 g./ml. as the pressure increases to 20 atm. Since these effects are small, we can usually consider the densities of liquids and solids to be constant and independent of temperature and pressure. Gas densities, in contrast, are strongly influenced by both temperature and pressure, and we shall postpone their discussion until Chapter 6.

Specific Heat

In the discussion of the thermometer and a scale of temperature, we introduced the word heat and defined heat as that which passes from a hot to a cold body when the two are placed in contact with each other. We did not then attempt to indicate how quantitative measurements of the flow of heat could be made since the development of that idea was peripheral to the notion of the thermometer. Amount of heat flow is, however, quite important, and we shall look briefly into the matter now.

As noted previously, whenever heat flows into a solid, liquid, or gaseous substance, the temperature of that substance rises. We find experimentally that the amount of heat required to raise the temperature of a substance a given number of degrees doubles if the mass of the substance is doubled. Also, the amount of heat required doubles if the temperature change is doubled. In view of these observations we can say that the amount of heat, or the heat effect, Q, is proportional to both the mass (m) of the substance and the temperature change ΔT which it is made to undergo. If these facts are expressed in a mathematical equation

$$\text{heat effect} = C \times \text{mass} \times \text{temperature change} \quad \text{or} \quad \boxed{Q = C\,m\,\Delta T}$$

in which C is the proportionality constant. The constant C in the equation is called the **specific heat** of the substance. It is one of the physical properties of a pure substance. The physical significance of the specific heat can perhaps be more readily grasped by solving the equation for C.

$$C = \frac{Q}{m\,\Delta T} \tag{1.3}$$

Clearly, if in a heating process one raises the temperature of unit mass of the substance one degree, the heat effect is numerically equal to the specific heat. If, as is usually the case, the mass is expressed in grams and the temperature change in degrees centigrade, then the **specific heat** of a substance is equal to the **amount of heat** required to raise the **temperature of one gram** of the substance by **one degree centigrade.** The specific heat of a substance, like its density, is only slightly temperature dependent. Over relatively small temperature intervals it can usually be assumed to remain constant.

As with mass and length, a standard unit to express the amount of heat flow is necessary. The reference material is again water; the unit of heat is called the **calorie. One calorie** is the **amount of heat** required to raise the **temperature of one gram of water** from 14.5 to 15.5°C. Heat effects, or amounts, are usually expressed in calories, although, as with mass and length, other units are sometimes used. Knowledge of the specific heats of substances allows us to relate heat flow to mass and temperature change in exactly the same way that information about density allows us to relate the masses and volumes of substances. Some frequently encountered heat problems are illustrated below.

Example 1.6. How many calories are required to raise the temperature of 240 g. of lead from 20.00° to 26.00°C? The specific heat of lead is 0.0306 cal. $\cdot$ g.$^{-1}$ $\cdot$ °C^{-1}.

Solution. By the defining equation for heat flow,

$$\text{heat effect} = \text{specific heat} \times \text{mass} \times \text{temperature change}$$

$$Q = C\,m\,\Delta T = \frac{0.0306 \text{ cal.}}{\text{g. Pb} \times \text{°C}} \times 240 \text{ g. Pb} \times 6.00°C = 44.1 \text{ cal.}$$

Example 1.7. When 1 lb. of coal burns, about 3.5×10^6 calories are liberated. With this amount of heat how many liters of water, H_2O, can be heated from 25°C to the boiling point? You may assume that $C_{H_2O} = 1$ cal. $\cdot$ g.$^{-1}$ $\cdot$ °C^{-1} and that the density of water is 1 g./ml.

Solution. In this problem the heat effect Q is known and is equal to 3.5×10^6 cal. The temperature change ΔT is also known to be equal to $(100 - 25)$°C or 75°C.

Rearranging the governing equation, we have, for the mass

$$m = \frac{Q}{C\Delta T} = \frac{3.5 \times 10^6 \text{ cal.}}{\dfrac{1.0 \text{ cal.}}{\text{g. }°C} \times 75°C} = 4.7 \times 10^4 \text{ g.}$$

We know that 1 liter equals 1000 ml. and that 1 ml. $H_2O \simeq 1$ g. H_2O. Making the conversion from grams of H_2O to liters of H_2O,

$$4.7 \times 10^4 \text{ g. } H_2O \times \frac{1 \text{ ml. } H_2O}{1 \text{ g. } H_2O} \times \frac{1 \text{ liter}}{1000 \text{ ml.}} = 47 \text{ liters } H_2O$$

The measurement of amount of heat flow is accomplished by well established methods in the field of **calorimetry.** The procedures which are used are somewhat more involved than those required to determine other physical properties and will be discussed in Chapter 5 when we treat energy relations.

PROBLEMS

1.1 In what areas of chemistry would you expect the following to fall:
    a. The synthesis of rubber?
    b. The percentage of the elements in the composition of a stainless steel?
    c. Spectroscopy?
    d. Radioactive fallout?
    e. The development of semiconductors?

1.2 What is a measuring rule? Why is the metric system used by scientists instead of the English system?

1.3 What does a balance measure?

1.4 Distinguish between weight and mass.

1.5 When you say "The temperature of the room is 27°C," what do you really mean?

1.6 When you say "The temperature of the air is 89°F," what do you really mean?

1.7 Given the freezing and boiling points of water as 0° and 100° on the centigrade scale and 32° and 212° on the Fahrenheit scale, find the equation allowing you to convert °C to °F.

1.8 If the temperature of some water is 26°C, find its temperature in °F and in °K.

1.9 The temperature of some freezing mercury is −39°F; find its temperature in °C and in °K.

1.10 The pressure in a vessel containing oxygen gas is 624 mm. Hg. What is the pressure in atmospheres?

1.11 A vial weighs 6.2597 g. Express its mass in milligrams and kilograms.

1.12 A solution has a volume of 425 ml. Find its volume in cubic centimeters and in liters.

1.13 The density of some water is 0.997 g./ml. How many pounds would 25 liters of the water weigh?

1.14 There are 5280 ft. in a mile. How many miles per hour is a car going if its speed is 75 km./hr.?

1.15 A sheet of platinum with dimensions of 1.00 in. × 4.00 in. × 0.0200 in. weighs 1.00 oz. Find the density of platinum in g./ml. One pound equals 16 ounces.

1.16 An empty pycnometer having a volume of 5.627 ml. weighs 12.047 g. When filled with a liquid it weighs 16.723 g. What is the density of the liquid in g./ml.? In lb./cu. ft.?

1.17 To the pycnometer in Problem 1.16 is added 3.454 g. of an unknown crystalline solid. A liquid having a density of 1.466 g./ml. is then added to fill the pycnometer. The final mass of the pycnometer plus solid plus liquid is 19.899 g. Find the density of the solid.

1.18 Classify each of the following as being heterogeneous or homogeneous:

a. Gasoline Het	e. Milk Hom
b. Concrete Het	f. Paper Hom
c. Maple syrup Hom	g. Cracked ice Hom
d. Brass Het	h. Cotton Het

1.19 How could you determine whether gasoline is a pure substance or a mixture?

1.20 An unknown gas burns in oxygen to yield water vapor and nitrogen gas. On the basis of this information decide whether the unknown gas can be elementary.

1.21 An unknown solid is melted and distilled at high temperature. The boiling point is constant throughout the distillation. What can be said about the solid on the basis of this information?

1.22 A chemist prepares a pure solid substance which he believes might be an elementary form of a new element. How could he determine whether the solid contains only one element? How would he test to find out if it is a new element?

1.23 When 928 cal. passes into 148 g. of metallic tin, its temperature rises 115°C. What is the specific heat of tin in cal. $\cdot$ g.$^{-1}$ $\cdot$ °C^{-1}?

1.24 How many pounds of coal would have to be burned to raise the temperature of 50 gallons of water from 25°C to the boiling point? (See Example 1.7.)

*1.25 A temperature scale is set up on the basis of the properties of benzene, a common organic liquid. On the benzene scale, 0°B is set at the freezing point of benzene, which occurs at 5°C; 100°B is set at the temperature at which benzene normally boils, which is also 80°C. Find the temperature on the benzene scale, in °B, at which water normally boils.

*1.26 The volume of one gram of water at atmospheric pressure is given by the equation:

$$V = V_0(1 - 4.5 \times 10^{-5} t + 6.7 \times 10^{-6} t^2 - 1.9 \times 10^{-8} t^3)$$

in which V_0 is its volume in ml. at 0°C and t is its temperature in °C. A water-in-glass thermometer is calibrated at 0°C and 100°C. What temperature would it read in a bath which is actually at 50°C? What temperature would it indicate for a sample actually at 5°C? What can be said about using water as a thermometric fluid?

---

* Those problems in this text which require extra effort and ability on the part of the student will be indicated by an asterisk.

2 | ATOMS, MOLECULES, AND IONS

We have discussed some of the tools used by chemists and some of the experimental procedures they employ to obtain and characterize pure substances. In this chapter, we shall consider some of the quantitative experiments which can be performed with elementary and compound substances. We shall be particularly interested in learning how these experiments led to the discovery of the natural laws governing chemical changes and the development of the basic theoretical concepts of chemistry, particularly those pertaining to the atom and its properties.

Scientific laws tell us how natural systems behave. Thus we have the Law of Conservation of Mass (Section 2.2), which tells us that mass can neither be created nor destroyed in a chemical change. Like all natural laws, this one was found by experiment. When sufficient experimental data are available, it is sometimes possible to correlate and explain the data by making certain assumptions concerning the nature of the systems being examined. A group of such assumptions, or postulates, constitutes a theory. A successful theory allows us to predict, on the basis of a few simple postulates, much of the experimental behavior of a system. Using the postulates of the modern atomic theory (Section 2.3), one can make certain predictions concerning the atom ratios in which two elements combine with each other.

Theories simplify our study of chemistry by furnishing general principles by which many related observations can be discussed, correlated, and better understood.

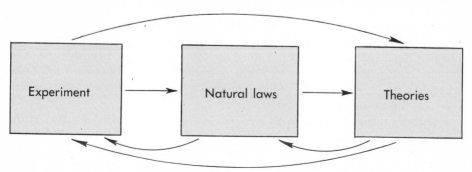

FIGURE 2.1 The scientific method.

Theories often also suggest further experiments which may result in new laws and modification or replacement of the theories themselves. The atomic theory proposed by Dalton 150 years ago raised certain fundamental questions concerning the structure and properties of atoms that still occupy the attention of experimental chemists and theoreticians. The scientific method involves the use of experiment, law, and theory to create and develop knowledge and understanding.

2.1 THE PARTICLE NATURE OF MATTER

Basic to any theory of matter is a conception of its ultimate structure. Does a pure substance contain discrete particles or is it infinitely divisible into smaller and smaller entities? If a pure substance contains particles which determine its properties, then sufficient subdivision of the substance would yield a sample containing only a part of one of the basic particles; this sample would presumably have properties different from those of the bulk material. If, however, a pure substance is completely continuous and contains no particles, then repeated division would never change its inherent properties.

It is difficult to answer this basic question by direct experiment. Measurement of the physical properties of very minute samples is impossible. The smallest sample that can be examined under an optical microscope is about 10^{-4} cm. in diameter; a sample of any pure liquid substance under such a microscope shows no evidence whatsoever of any particles. It follows, then, that if pure substances are composed of discrete particles, they must be very small by ordinary standards.

In spite of the apparent difficulties, the concept that matter is particle in nature turns out to be one of the most basic and fruitful tenets of chemical theory. It is worth-while to look into the steps taken by man which led to this not-so-obvious idea.

The notion that matter ultimately consists of discrete particles is a very old one. About 400 B.C. this idea was put forward in the writings of Democritus, a Greek philosopher, who apparently had been introduced to it by his teacher, a man named Leucippus. The idea was rejected by Plato and Aristotle, and it was not until about 1650 A.D. that it again was suggested, this time by the Italian physicist Gassendi. Sir Isaac Newton (1642–1727) supported Gassendi's arguments with these words:

> ". . . it seems probable to me that God, in the Beginning, formed Matter in solid, massy, hard, impenetrable, movable Particles, of such Sizes and Figures, and with such other Properties, and in such Proportions to Space, as most conduced to the End for which he formed them. . . ."

Until about 1800, the idea that matter is particle in nature was based mainly on the intuition of its adherents, who included, in addition to Newton, the English scientists Boyle and Higgins. It remained for John Dalton, an English chemist and schoolteacher, to place this idea on a firm experimental basis. In about 1808, Dalton proposed a simple explanation of the then known laws of chemistry that came to be known as the **atomic theory.**

Dalton's theory stated that all elements consist of tiny particles called **atoms.** He postulated that all the atoms in a given elementary substance are alike and that compound substances are formed when one or more atoms of one element combine in a definite proportion with one or more atoms of another element. This theory, simple though it was, was very convincing in its ability to explain the experimentally observed laws. The theory was rather quickly accepted by scientists and was directly responsible for much of the great progress in chemistry in the nineteenth century.

As the science of chemistry developed, it became necessary to modify certain of Dalton's ideas concerning the nature and chemical behavior of atoms. Gradually there evolved what we now recognize as modern atomic theory, which must be considered one of the main foundations upon which modern chemistry rests. The rudiments of this theory will be presented later in this chapter (Section 2.3). Before we do so, it may be helpful to review the laws and related experiments upon which Dalton and his successors based their ideas. Certain of these laws are so familiar to us that we take them for granted; all of them can be confirmed by relatively simple experiments which can be performed by students in the elementary chemistry laboratory. For precisely these reasons, it is vitally important that we obtain a thorough understanding of these fundamental laws, their implications, and their limitations.

2.2 QUANTITATIVE LAWS OF CHEMISTRY

The foundation of chemistry, like that of all the other physical sciences, is based upon quantitative measurements. The science of chemistry developed out of the art of alchemy when, late in the eighteenth century, chemists started to study the weight relationships involved in reactions of elements with each other. By the turn of the nineteenth century, these studies had led to the establishment of three of the fundamental laws of chemistry: the Law of Conservation of Mass, the Law of Constant Composition, and the Law of Combining Weights. These laws formed the experimental basis of Dalton's atomic theory. The discovery shortly thereafter of another of the quantitative laws governing the reactions of elements with each other, the Law of Multiple Proportions, supported the validity of the atomic theory.

Conservation of Mass

Before one can hope to develop a quantitative foundation for the study of chemical reactions, it is necessary to establish a relationship between the masses of reactants and products. In order to do this, one must carry out reactions in such a way that all of the reactants and all of the products can be weighed. To illustrate, consider a specific reaction, that between the elementary substances aluminum and oxygen to produce aluminum oxide. If this reaction is carried out in the ordinary way, by heating aluminum in an open vessel, it is virtually impossible to weigh the oxygen gas which enters into the reaction and thereby obtain a quantitative relationship between the total masses of product and reactants. Consider, however, what happens when aluminum and oxygen react in a photographic flash bulb (Figure 2.2). The aluminum oxide produced is trapped within the bulb as a finely divided powder; consequently, its mass can be compared accurately with that of the elements from which it is formed.

Careful weighing of a flash bulb before and after flashing, using the most sensitive analytical balance, reveals no change in mass. In other words, within experimental error, the mass of the aluminum oxide produced by the reaction is exactly equal to that of the reactants, aluminum and oxygen. On the basis of this and a great many

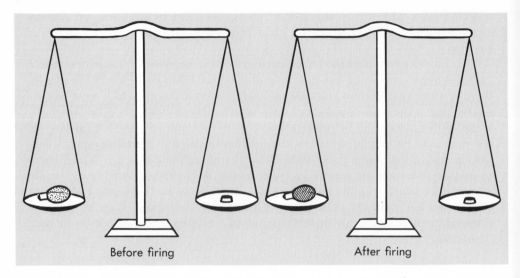

Before firing   After firing

FIGURE 2.2 Flash bulb. In a chemical reaction, mass of reactants = mass of products (Law of Conservation of Mass).

other quantitative experiments of similar design, it is possible to state the Law of Conservation of Mass: **There is no detectable change in mass in an ordinary chemical reaction.** This law was first proposed by the Russian scientist and poet Lomonosov in 1756 and established independently by the French chemist Lavoisier in 1774 on the basis of a series of experiments involving the reaction of tin with oxygen. Near the end of the nineteenth century, Landolt in Germany checked the validity of the Law of Conservation of Mass in several extremely precise experiments. Studying several different reactions, he found no change in mass, at least within one part in ten million.

In stating this law, we have been careful to say that there is no *detectable* change in mass in an *ordinary* chemical reaction. Einstein's equation:

$$E = mc^2$$

which relates energy (E) to mass (m), predicts that in any reaction in which energy is exchanged with the surroundings, the mass of the products will differ from that of the reactants. However, if one inserts the value of 3.0×10^{10} cm./sec. for the proportionality constant "c" (the velocity of light), it is found, upon converting to the proper units, that 1 kcal. of energy is equivalent to only 4.7×10^{-11} g. of mass. The reaction that occurs when a flash bulb is set off evolves in the neighborhood of 100 kcal. of energy. This amount of energy is equivalent to:

$$100 \text{ kcal.} \times \frac{4.7 \times 10^{-11} \text{ g.}}{1 \text{ kcal.}} = 4.7 \times 10^{-9} \text{ g.}$$

In principle, then, the aluminum oxide formed by this reaction would weigh about 0.0000000047 g. less than the aluminum and oxygen from which it is produced. However, the most sensitive analytical balance capable of weighing an object the size of a flash bulb gives results accurate to at best 1.0×10^{-5} or 0.00001 g. Clearly, it is impossible to detect any difference in mass between reactants and products in this or similar chemical reactions. In nuclear transformations, conversions of mass to energy are often large enough to detect experimentally. This "extraordinary" type of reaction will be discussed in a later chapter on nuclear chemistry.

Constant Composition

The Law of Conservation of Mass helps us to determine the mass relations in chemical reactions. If it is found, for example, that 0.529 g. of aluminum burns in an open crucible to form 1.000 g. of aluminum oxide, it follows that $(1.000 - 0.529)$ g. or 0.471 g. of oxygen must have taken part in the reaction. In general, if the masses of all but one of the products and reactants are known, that mass can be calculated by applying the Law of Conservation of Mass.

One important question remained to be answered before chemists could proceed with a systematic study of the weight relationships in chemical reactions; are the results of such reactions reproducible? That is, if in a particular experiment, 0.529 g. of aluminum yields 1.000 g. of aluminum oxide, is it safe to say that a second experiment using the same weight of aluminum will give the same weight of product? If one starts with twice as much aluminum (1.058 g.), will twice as much aluminum oxide (2.000 g.) be formed?

The simplest way to answer these questions is to carry out the indicated experiments. If this is done, the reacting weight ratio of aluminum to aluminum oxide is always found to be 0.529:1.000, i.e.:

$$0.529 \text{ g. aluminum} + 0.471 \text{ g. oxygen} \rightarrow 1.000 \text{ g. aluminum oxide}$$

Similarly, a study of the reaction between lead and sulfur shows that, regardless of how the reaction is carried out, 1.155 g. of lead sulfide is formed for every gram of lead reacting.

$$1.000 \text{ g. lead} + 0.155 \text{ g. sulfur} \rightarrow 1.155 \text{ g. lead sulfide}$$

Looking at these data in a slightly different way, one can say that aluminum oxide always contains certain definite proportions by weight of aluminum and oxygen:

$$\% \text{ aluminum} = \frac{\text{wt. aluminum}}{\text{wt. aluminum oxide}} \times 100 = \frac{0.529 \text{ g.}}{1.000 \text{ g.}} \times 100 = 52.9\% \text{ Al}$$

$$\% \text{ oxygen} = \frac{\text{wt. oxygen}}{\text{wt. aluminum oxide}} \times 100 = \frac{0.471 \text{ g.}}{1.000 \text{ g.}} \times 100 = 47.1\% \text{ O}$$

For lead sulfide:

$$\% \text{ lead} = \frac{\text{wt. lead}}{\text{wt. lead sulfide}} \times 100 = \frac{1.000 \text{ g.}}{1.155 \text{ g.}} \times 100 = 86.6\% \text{ Pb}$$

$$\% \text{ sulfur} = \frac{\text{wt. sulfur}}{\text{wt. lead sulfide}} \times 100 = \frac{0.155 \text{ g.}}{1.155 \text{ g.}} \times 100 = 13.4\% \text{ S}$$

These observations serve to verify one of the most fundamental of chemical relationships, the Law of Constant Composition. **A chemical compound,** regardless of its origin or method of preparation, **always contains the same elements in the same percentages by weight.** This law was first established in 1799 by Joseph Proust, a French chemist working in Madrid, on the basis of very careful analyses of several pure compounds. Prior to Proust's work, many chemists, including Berthollet and his co-workers in Paris, had maintained that the composition of a compound could vary within wide limits depending upon where it was found or how it was prepared. Proust was able to show that the "compounds" Berthollet worked with were actually highly impure mixtures from which one could hardly expect to obtain meaningful analytical data.

Combining Weights

Once the two laws just referred to had been established, it became possible to make a systematic, quantitative study of the weight relationships involved in chemical reactions. The chemists of the late eighteenth and early nineteenth centuries carried out such a study for one particular type of reaction, that in which two elementary substances combine to yield a single, compound substance. In reporting the results of their experiments, they frequently referred to a quantity known as the **gram equivalent weight** of an element, which may be defined as the *weight in grams which reacts exactly with eight grams of oxygen.*

Since the concept of gram equivalent weight proved to be extremely useful in the development of modern atomic theory, it will be instructive to consider some of the methods by which it may be obtained experimentally. The most obvious approach involves the determination of the weight ratio in which an element reacts with oxygen. Consider, for example, the metal magnesium: its gram equivalent weight can be calculated from data obtained by burning a weighed sample of the metal in air, or, better yet, in a stream of pure oxygen (Example 2.1).

Example 2.1.   A sample of magnesium weighing 1.600 g. is burned in oxygen, giving 2.653 g. of oxide. Calculate the gram equivalent weight of magnesium.

Solution.   In order to calculate the weight of magnesium that reacts with 8.000 g. of oxygen, we must find, from the data given, the weight ratio in which the two elements combine. To do this, we first calculate the weight of oxygen that reacted, making use of the Law of Conservation of Mass:

$$\text{weight O reacting} = 2.653 \text{ g.} - 1.600 \text{ g.} = 1.053 \text{ g.}$$

Hence, 1.600 g. of magnesium reacts with, or is chemically equivalent to, 1.053 g. of oxygen:

$$1.600 \text{ g. Mg} \simeq 1.053 \text{ g. O}$$

The weight of magnesium that reacts with 8.000 g. of oxygen must be:

$$8.000 \text{ g. O} \times \frac{1.600 \text{ g. Mg}}{1.053 \text{ g. O}} = 12.16 \text{ g. Mg} \quad \text{(G.E.W. Mg)}$$

Note that in solving this problem, we used the "conversion factor" method; 8.000 g. of oxygen was, in a sense, "converted" to the required weight of magnesium with the aid of the relation: 1.600 g. Mg $\simeq$ 1.053 g. O. This procedure is quite analogous to that used in Chapter 1 to convert from one set of units to another. Throughout this text, the conversion factor method will be used to solve chemical problems. You should keep in mind that this is a way of *solving* problems, not of *analyzing* them. No problem can be solved until you have decided upon the path by which to proceed from what is given to what is asked for.

Magnesium is one of the few elements whose gram equivalent weight can be accurately determined by direct reaction with oxygen. With many less reactive metals, it is more convenient to decompose a weighed sample of the pure metal oxide, often prepared by indirect means, and weigh the metal remaining. One way to do this is to heat the oxide in a stream of hydrogen, forming water as a volatile by-product (Figure 2.3).

By the end of the eighteenth century, gram equivalent weights had been determined for a considerable number of elements. Almost immediately, it became apparent that the concept of gram equivalent weight could be extended beyond reactions involving oxygen. In particular, it was found that the gram equivalent weights of different elements could represent not only the weights reacting with eight grams of

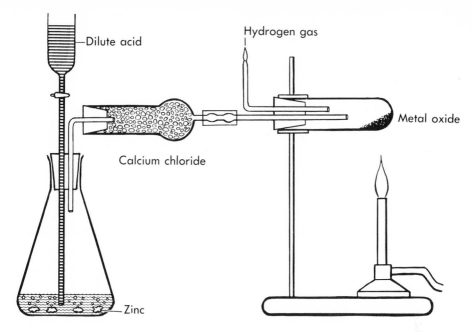

FIGURE 2.3 Reduction of oxides by hydrogen.

oxygen but also the weights that react with a fixed amount of various other elements. Consider, for example, the three metals lithium, calcium, and silver. By analyzing the compounds which these metals form with oxygen, their gram equivalent weights can be established as 6.94 g., 20.0 g., and 108 g. respectively. Now, if one studies the reactions of these metals with chlorine, it turns out that 6.94 g. of lithium, 20.0 g. of calcium, or 108 g. of silver react quantitatively with a certain, fixed amount, 35.5 g., of chlorine. Again, it is found that a constant amount of sulfur, 16.0 g., is required to react exactly with 6.94 g. of lithium or 20.0 g. of calcium or 108 g. of silver. In other words:

6.94 g. Li ≃ 8.00 g. O	or	35.5 g. Cl	or	16.0 g. S
20.0 g. Ca ≃ 8.00 g. O	or	35.5 g. Cl	or	16.0 g. S
108 g. Ag ≃ 8.00 g. O	or	35.5 g. Cl	or	16.0 g. S

From a slightly different point of view, one might say that the quantities represented by 6.94 g. of lithium, 20.0 g. of calcium, or 108 g. of silver are equivalent in "combining power," regardless of whether they react with oxygen, chlorine, or sulfur.

Observations of this type can be correlated in terms of what is known as the Law of Combining Weights. One of the simplest ways to state this law is to say that **when two elements react with each other, one gram equivalent weight of the first element reacts exactly with one gram equivalent weight of the second.** From this standpoint, we can consider 8.00 g. of oxygen, 35.5 g. of chlorine, and 16.0 g. of sulfur to represent the gram equivalent weights of these elements, since they are the weights which react exactly with one gram equivalent weight of lithium (6.94 g.), calcium (20.0 g.), or silver (108 g.).

The Law of Combining Weights not only extends the usefulness of gram equivalent weights; it also simplifies their experimental determination. Instead of finding the weight of an element which combines with eight grams of oxygen, one can determine the weight that combines with 16.0 g. of sulfur, 35.5 g. of chlorine, 108 g. of silver, or in general, one gram equivalent weight of any other element. Moreover, the establishment of the Law of Combining Weights served as a tremendous stimulus to the development of modern chemical theory.

Multiple Proportions

It has been known for over 150 years that many elements form more than one compound with oxygen. Carbon forms two well-known oxides, carbon monoxide and carbon dioxide; many of the heavier metals including copper and tin also form two or more oxides. Indeed, tin and copper form two different sets of compounds with a series of elements including chlorine, bromine, and sulfur. This behavior complicates the experimental determination of gram equivalent weights and somewhat restricts their usefulness. An element which forms more than one compound with other elements such as oxygen, chlorine, and bromine must clearly have more than one gram equivalent weight.

If one analyzes the various compounds formed by copper, a significant fact emerges. Copper compounds fall neatly into two groups. In one series, copper shows a gram equivalent weight of 63.54 g.; in the other, a gram equivalent weight exactly half this, 31.77 g. (Table 2.1).

TABLE 2.1 COMPOUNDS OF COPPER

Series I	Color	% Cu	G.E.W. Cu	Series II	Color	% Cu	G.E.W. Cu
Copper(I) oxide	red	88.82	63.54 g.	Copper(II) oxide	black	79.88	31.77 g.
Copper(I) sulfide	black	79.85	63.54 g.	Copper(II) sulfide	black	66.46	31.77 g.
Copper(I) chloride	white	64.19	63.54 g.	Copper(II) chloride	brown	47.26	31.77 g.
Copper(I) bromide	white	44.29	63.54 g.	Copper(II) bromide	black	28.45	31.77 g.

The behavior of copper is typical of those elements which form more than one series of compounds and hence show more than one gram equivalent weight. **The different gram equivalent weights of an element are always in a simple, whole number ratio** (2:1, 3:2, 5:3, and so forth) **to each other.** This generalization is often referred to as the Law of Multiple Proportions. Another way of stating this law is to say that the different weights of one element which combine with a fixed weight of another element are in a simple, whole-number ratio to each other (Table 2.2).

TABLE 2.2 GRAM EQUIVALENT WEIGHTS

H	1.008 g.	F	19.00 g.	Cl	35.45 g.	C	3.003, 6.006 g.
Li	6.939 g.	Ca	20.04 g.	K	39.10 g.	S	5.344, 8.016, 16.03 g.
O	8.000 g.	Na	22.99 g.	Br	79.91 g.	P	6.195, 10.32 g.
Al	8.994 g.	Ni	29.36 g.	Ag	107.9 g.	Sn	29.67, 59.35 g.
Mg	12.16 g.	Zn	32.69 g.	I	126.9 g.	Cu	31.77, 63.54 g.

2.3 MODERN ATOMIC THEORY

The quantitative laws discussed in Section 2.2 formed the experimental basis for Dalton's atomic theory. This theory was of necessity modified to agree with later experimental discoveries. Three main postulates of the modern atomic theory are given below, with examples illustrating the meaning of each.

1. *An element is composed of extremely small particles called atoms. The atoms of a given element all exhibit identical chemical properties.*

The element oxygen is made up of oxygen atoms, all of which behave chemically in the same way.

2. *Atoms of different elements have different chemical properties. No atom of one element, in the course of an ordinary chemical reaction, disappears or is changed into an atom of another element.*

The chemical behavior of oxygen atoms is different from that of hydrogen atoms or from that of any other kind of atom. When the elementary substances hydrogen and oxygen combine with each other, all of the hydrogen atoms and all of the oxygen atoms that react are present in the water formed and no atoms of any other element are formed in the process.

3. *Compound substances are formed when atoms of more than one element combine. In a given pure compound the relative numbers of atoms of the elements present will be definite and constant. In general, these relative numbers can be expressed as integers or simple fractions.*

In the compound substance water, hydrogen atoms and oxygen atoms are combined with one another. For every oxygen atom present, there are always two hydrogen atoms. Ammonia, a gaseous compound of nitrogen and hydrogen, always contains three hydrogen atoms for every nitrogen atom. If aluminum oxide, a high-melting solid, is decomposed, we always find that three oxygen atoms are recovered for every two aluminum atoms.

Let us now consider how these postulates explain the four quantitative laws discussed in Section 2.2.

1. *Law of Conservation of Mass.* Postulate 2 states that atoms are "conserved" in a reaction. Since there is no change in the numbers or kinds of atoms, it follows that there can be no change in mass.

2. *Law of Constant Composition.* Since, in any pure compound, the relative numbers of atoms of the different elements are fixed and constant (Postulate 3), it follows that the relative weights, or percentages by weight, of these elements must also be constant. Consider, for example, the compound substance water in which there are always two hydrogen atoms for every oxygen atom. The relative weights of hydrogen and oxygen in water must always be:

$$\frac{\text{wt. hydrogen}}{\text{wt. oxygen}} = \frac{2 \times \text{wt. H atom}}{1 \times \text{wt. O atom}}$$

This equation suggests an interesting possibility. For the Law of Constant Composition to apply exactly, it is necessary not only that the atom ratio of hydrogen to oxygen be fixed but also that the relative weights of hydrogen and oxygen atoms be fixed. Now, it happens that there are two different kinds of hydrogen atoms (Section 2.4), one of which is twice as heavy as the other. One can calculate that in a sample of water containing only "light" hydrogen atoms, the percentage of hydrogen should be 11.188; if only "heavy" hydrogen atoms were present, this value would be 20.113. "Ordinary" water analyzes 11.190 per cent hydrogen, reflecting the fact that light hydrogen atoms are by far the more abundant. Repeated fractional distillation of water concentrates the heavy hydrogen atoms in the residue; in this way, it is possible to prepare nearly pure "heavy water" in which the percentage of hydrogen exceeds 20.

The same process occurs to a limited extent in nature. The hydrogen content of water from the Dead Sea is slightly greater than 11.190 per cent; repeated evaporation has enriched the water in heavy hydrogen.

Within the past two decades, a quite different type of deviation from the Law of Constant Composition has been detected. It is now known that in many compounds, particularly metal oxides and sulfides, the atom ratio may vary slightly from a whole-number value. Careful analyses of apparently homogeneous samples of a certain oxide of tungsten give atom ratios of oxygen to tungsten varying from 2.88:1 to 2.92:1 rather than the 3:1 ratio that one might expect. In another case, it has been found that different samples of zinc oxide may contain up to 0.03 per cent of excess zinc atoms above the hypothetical 1:1 ratio. Interestingly enough, zinc oxide was one of the compounds cited by Berthollet in disputing the Law of Constant Composition. The data he gave showed variations of up to 3 per cent in zinc content, approximately 100 times that now accepted.

Compounds of this type are often referred to as "Berthollides" or nonstoichiometric compounds. The deviations from constant composition arise because of defects in the crystal structure. In later chapters, we shall examine the nature of these defects and their effect on certain of the physical and chemical properties of the solids in which they occur.

3. *Law of Multiple Proportions.* When two elements combine to form more than one compound, one would expect from Postulate 3 of the atomic theory that the different atom ratios would be in a simple, whole-number relation to each other. This in turn would require that the weight ratios of the elements in the different compounds show this same simple relation, as predicted by the Law of Multiple Proportions. Suppose, for example, that the elements X and Y form two compounds in which the atom ratios of X to Y are 2:1 and 1:1 respectively. Clearly, the weight of X combined with a fixed weight of Y in the first compound would be twice that in the second.

4. *Law of Combining Weights.* This law can be interpreted in terms of the atomic theory to mean that the relative combining powers of different atoms tend to remain the same in all of the compounds that they form. Consider, for example, two elements, A and B. Suppose that in the oxides of these elements there are respectively 2 atoms of A and 1 atom of B per atom of oxygen. It would then seem reasonable that twice as many atoms of A as of B would be required to combine with a fixed amount of chlorine, sulfur, or any other element. This means that the weights of A and B which react with 8 g. of oxygen should also react with a fixed amount of chlorine, sulfur, and so forth. From this point of view, one can interpret the gram equivalent weight of an element as representing the mass of a number of atoms of fixed combining power. Thus, the atoms in 6.94 g. of lithium would combine with the same number of atoms of oxygen, chlorine, and so on, as would the atoms in 20.0 g. of calcium or 108 g. of silver.

This interpretation of the Law of Combining Weights focuses attention on the relative combining powers of atoms of different elements. The concept of combining power remained rather vague, at least until Frankland in 1852 introduced the idea of valence. In the past century, we have made a great deal of progress toward a better understanding of the ratios in which atoms combine. We shall have more to say on this subject in later chapters, in which we will discuss the forces holding atoms together in pure substances.

2.4 STRUCTURE OF ATOMS

Like any useful scientific theory, the atomic theory raised more questions than it answered. Even before Dalton's ideas had been generally accepted, many philosophers and scientists were speculating as to whether atoms, tiny as they are, might be broken down into still smaller particles. Nearly 100 years were to pass before this question could be answered in the affirmative on the basis of experimental evidence. The pioneer work in this area was done by two English physicists, Sir J. J. Thomson and Lord Rutherford.

Evidence for Subatomic Particles

The first convincing demonstration of the existence of subatomic particles came from experiments involving the conduction of electricity through gases at low pressures. It had been known for some time that when an apparatus of the type shown in Figure 2.4 is partially evacuated and connected to a high-voltage source such as a spark coil, a current flows across the tube. At the same time, streaks of bluish light can be seen, appearing to originate at the negative electrode (cathode). Many of the properties of these so-called **cathode rays** were established in the last two decades of the nineteenth century; among these was their deflection by electrical or magnetic fields. J. J. Thomson, from a careful study of the extent of this deflection, was able to demonstrate in 1897 that the rays consist of a stream of negatively charged particles, called **electrons.** Thomson succeeded in determining the charge-to-mass ratio of these particles and also of the positive **ions** which are formed simultaneously with electrons in the discharge tube. From his data, he concluded that the electron must have a mass several orders of magnitude less than that of the lightest atom and must then be a subatomic particle.

In 1896, one year before Thomson announced the results of his experiments with cathode rays, the phenomenon of natural radioactivity was discovered by Becquerel (Chapter 23). It was soon demonstrated that radioactive elements such as uranium may spontaneously give off three different kinds of radiation: alpha, beta, and gamma rays. At the turn of the twentieth century, Ernest Rutherford showed that β rays, like cathode rays, consist of a stream of electrons. He further demonstrated that α rays were made up of a stream of identical, positively charged ions with masses considerably smaller than that of the uranium atoms from which they were formed.

Composition of Atoms

The experiments of Thomson and Rutherford proved conclusively that atoms, which are neutral to begin with, can, under certain conditions, break down into

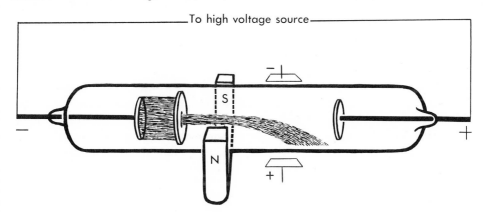

FIGURE 2.4 Cathode ray tube. A cathode ray beam is deflected by magnetic and electric fields in such a way as to indicate that it is negatively charged.

negatively and positively charged particles. At this point, we shall not attempt to describe the long series of experiments which followed, leading eventually to our present ideas of the structure of the atom. Neither shall we attempt to list all of the subatomic particles which have been identified in the past several decades. For the time being, it will be sufficient to consider an atom as being made up of two different kinds of particles:

1. **Electrons,** which are present in all atoms and so are present in all matter. The mass of an electron is only about $\frac{1}{2000}$ of that of the lightest atom, the hydrogen atom; the diameter of an electron is only about $\frac{1}{10000}$ of that of the hydrogen atom. Probably the most important property of an electron is its electric charge. Each electron carries the same amount of charge; the magnitude of the charge, which is negative, is 4.80×10^{-10} e.s.u., or 1.60×10^{-19} coulomb. The electric current is the result of the flow of electrons through a metal. Since a current of one ampere is equal to one coulomb per second being carried through a wire, it is obvious that very large numbers of electrons are on the move when electricity is being used.

There is really some question whether we should call the electron a particle in the ordinary sense. In many experiments the electron does behave as a particle, but sometimes its behavior is more similar in character to that of a light wave. Electrons have a measurable mass, like particles, but they can also exhibit the phenomena of interference and diffraction, as do light waves. This behavior is part of a larger problem which arose about 1925 regarding the relation between light and matter. The problem is not yet definitely solved, but in this book we will find it most useful to consider electrons to be particles.

All atoms contain an integral number of electrons. This number, which may vary from 1 to at least 103, is characteristic of an atom of a particular element. All hydrogen atoms contain one electron; all atoms of the element lawrencium contain 103 electrons. We shall have more to say later about the way in which these electrons are distributed in relation to one another. For the time being, it will be sufficient to point out that electrons are found in the outer regions of atoms, forming a negative charge cloud about the atomic center.

2. A **nucleus,** located at the center of the atom. The nucleus has about the same diameter as an electron and a mass very nearly equal to that of the atom. It carries a positive charge, just equal and opposite to the total negative charge of the electrons in the atom, making the atom an electrically neutral particle.

The charge of the nucleus, like the number of electrons, is characteristic of the atom of a particular element. All hydrogen atoms have nuclei which carry a unit positive charge equal in magnitude to that of the electron; all nuclei of the element lawrencium have a charge of $+103$ on the same scale.

Rather recently, it has been discovered that nuclei of atoms of the same element may differ in mass. For example, two different kinds of hydrogen atoms are found in nature; in one of them the nucleus has a mass just twice that of the other. Carbon atoms are found to have three different masses with relative magnitudes 12, 13, and 14. When an element contains atoms with nuclei having "n" possible masses, we say that the element has **n isotopes.** Thus, carbon has three isotopes; tin, remarkably enough, has 10 isotopes. A few elements, including sodium, fluorine, phosphorus, and gold, have only one stable isotope.

Summarizing, atoms consist of two kinds of tiny particles, electrons and nuclei. The mass of an atom is concentrated in its nucleus, which is the positively charged center about which the light, negatively charged electrons move. The number of electrons or the nuclear charge of a given atom is characteristic of the element to which that atom belongs and may vary from 1 to 103. The nuclei of different atoms vary in mass as well as charge; it is possible for atoms of the same element to have different nuclear masses. Since atoms have diameters about 10,000 times those of electrons and nuclei, it follows that most of the interior of an atom is empty space. The physical and chemical properties of atoms, and of matter, must therefore be the result of electrical, rather than mechanical, interactions of particles.

2.5 ATOMIC MASSES

One of the postulates of the atomic theory states that "An element is composed of extremely small particles called atoms." The question arises as to precisely *how* small (or how large) atoms of different elements are. We should like to know, for example, how much atoms of elements such as sodium and fluorine weigh.

From an experimental standpoint, it turns out to be much simpler to determine relative rather than absolute masses of atoms. That is, it is easier to obtain the ratio of the masses of sodium and fluorine atoms than it is to determine the masses of either of these atoms individually. Fortunately, it turns out that, so far as the development of atomic theory is concerned, we can obtain almost as much information from relative as from absolute atomic masses.

To illustrate the importance of knowing the relative masses of atoms, consider the two elements hydrogen and oxygen. By conventional chemical analysis, we can establish that these two elements, in reacting to form the compound substance water, combine in a weight ratio of $1:8$ (i.e., one part by weight of hydrogen to eight parts by weight of oxygen). To obtain a better understanding of this reaction, we would very much like to know the atom ratio in which these two elements combine. In order to do this, we need only one additional piece of information: the relative masses of hydrogen and oxygen atoms. Suppose, for example, that we were to find that a hydrogen atom were $\frac{1}{8}$ as heavy as an oxygen atom. In that case, a $1:1$ reacting atom ratio would give the observed $1:8$ combining weight ratio. If, on the other hand, a hydrogen atom were only $\frac{1}{16}$ as heavy as an oxygen atom, two hydrogen atoms would have to react with one oxygen atom to give a $1:8$ combining weight ratio. In general, if we know the weight ratio in which two elements combine *and* the relative masses of their atoms, we can immediately calculate the atom ratio in which they combine (cf. Chapter 3).

In the next several pages, we shall consider how one can experimentally determine the relative masses of different atoms. Before doing so, it will be helpful to introduce two new quantities, atomic weight and gram atomic weight.

Meaning of Atomic Weights

Relative weights of different atoms are most often expressed in terms of atomic weights. The **atomic weight of an element is a number which indicates how heavy,** on the average,* **an atom of an element is compared to an atom of another element.** For example, the fact that hydrogen has an atomic weight slightly greater than 1 and oxygen an atomic weight of almost exactly 16 tells us that a hydrogen atom is about $\frac{1}{16}$ as heavy as an oxygen atom. In another case, we conclude that since the atomic weight of sulfur is 32.064, an atom of sulfur must be a little more than

---

* The word "average" is used here because of the existence of isotopes (Section 2.4).

twice as heavy as an oxygen atom. To be exact, a sulfur atom is 32.064/15.9994 = 2.0041 times as heavy as an oxygen atom. In general, for two elements X and Y,

$$\frac{\text{mass of an atom of X}}{\text{mass of an atom of Y}} = \frac{\text{atomic weight of X}}{\text{atomic weight of Y}}$$

When the atomic weight table was being set up in the first half of the nineteenth century, the atomic weight of the lightest element, hydrogen, was generally taken to be 1. It soon became apparent that oxygen would be a more convenient base for atomic weights since it forms stable compounds with many more elements than does hydrogen. The Belgian chemist J. S. Stas, in a series of experiments initiated in 1850, obtained precise values for the atomic weights of several elements relative to that of oxygen, which he took to be exactly 16. It was supposed at the time that these two standards, i.e., H = 1.000, O = 16.000, were equivalent to each other. However, Prof. E. W. Morley of Western Reserve University, in the period from 1882 to 1895, demonstrated by the synthesis and analysis of water that the ratio of the atomic weights of hydrogen and oxygen differed from 1:16 by nearly 1 per cent. Since most atomic weights had been established relative to oxygen, it was agreed in 1905 to take the atomic weight of oxygen to be exactly 16.

In the 1930's, physicists interested in nuclear reactions were faced with the problem of determining the relative masses of elementary particles. Using the mass spectrograph (see p. 45) to determine these quantities, they found it most convenient to use the mass of a particular isotope as the basis for an atomic weight scale. They chose the most common isotope of oxygen as a standard, assigning it an atomic weight of exactly 16. Since naturally occurring oxygen, on which the chemist's scale was based, contains traces of heavier isotopes, the two scales differed slightly from each other. To convert from the chemists' to the physicists' scale of atomic weights, it was necessary to multiply by 1.000275.

As the years passed, the existence of two atomic weight scales differing slightly from each other proved sufficiently annoying to cause scientists to work for the adoption of a single scale acceptable to both physicists and chemists. This was accomplished in 1961 when it was agreed to set up a uniform scale in which the atomic weight 12 was assigned to the most common isotope of carbon. Such a compromise satisfied the physicists' requirement that a single isotope be used as a standard. For chemists, it resulted in a change of only about 0.004 per cent from the old chemical scale. The atomic weight of oxygen, for example, changed from 16.0000 to 15.9994 with the adoption of the new scale. The atomic weights used throughout this text are all based on this so-called "carbon-12" scale.

G. A. W – wt in g containing 16g of O_2

Gram Atomic Weight: Relation to Gram Equivalent Weight

The gram atomic weight of an element is the **weight in grams which contains the same number of atoms as sixteen grams of oxygen** (more exactly, 15.9994 g. of oxygen, or twelve grams of carbon-12). If the atomic weight of an element is known, its gram atomic weight can be written down immediately. To illustrate, consider sulfur: since the atomic weight of this element is 32, a sulfur atom must be $\frac{32}{16}$ as heavy as an oxygen atom. If the number of atoms in sixteen grams of oxygen is represented by N, then the weight of an equal number, N, of sulfur atoms must be:

$$\tfrac{32}{16} \times \text{wt. of N oxygen atoms} = \tfrac{32}{16} \times 16 \text{ g.} = 32 \text{ g.}$$

In other words, the gram atomic weight of an element is numerically equal to its atomic weight. It must be kept in mind, however, that while the atomic weight of an element is dimensionless, its gram atomic weight has the unit of grams. It is often stated, somewhat loosely, that the gram atomic weight is the "atomic weight expressed in grams."

It was discovered over a century ago that the gram atomic weight of an element is almost always an integral multiple of its gram equivalent weight. That is:

$$\text{G.A.W.} = n(\text{G.E.W.}) \quad \text{where} \quad n = 1, 2, 3, \ldots \tag{2.1}$$

Comparison of a table of gram equivalent weights (Table 2.2) with a table of gram atomic weights shows that $n = 1$ for sodium, 2 for magnesium, 3 for aluminum.

The existence of the simple relationship expressed by equation 2.1 is of great importance in the experimental determination of gram atomic weights. Gram equivalent weights can be determined with great accuracy from reacting weight data or from chemical analysis. It is much more difficult to obtain directly gram atomic weights of comparable accuracy. However, if one is able to obtain an approximate value of the gram atomic weight of an element, it can be determined whether n in equation 2.1 is 1, 2, 3 or some other whole number. Knowing the exact value of the gram equivalent weight and the proper value of n, one can use equation 2.1 to obtain an accurate value for the gram atomic weight of the element.

Atomic Weights from Specific Heats

A major portion of chemical research in the nineteenth century was devoted to the determination of atomic weights. The early investigators in this area were faced with the problem of determining the relative masses of particles that are much too small to be counted or weighed individually, even on the most sensitive analytical balance. The approach that they used was to search for methods of selecting macroscopic samples of different elements containing the same number of atoms. The relative weights of these samples should then represent the ratio of the atomic weights of the elements involved.

In 1819, two French chemists, Dulong and Petit, suggested one method by which samples of different elements containing the same number of atoms could be selected. They postulated that the amount of heat required to raise the temperature of a solid element by a given amount, let us say 1°C, should depend only on the *number* of atoms in the sample and not upon the type of atom. Samples which require the same amount of heat to raise their temperature by unit amount should then contain the same number of atoms. Stated another way, since 1 gram atomic weight of every element contains the same number of atoms, a constant amount of heat should be required to raise the temperature of 1 gram atomic weight of any solid element by 1°C.

The hypothesis of Dulong and Petit is consistent with specific heat data for a large number of metallic elements. If one calculates the amount of heat required to raise the temperature of 1 gram equivalent weight of various metals by 1°C, it turns out that this value is approximately 6 calories for a series of elements, including lithium, sodium, and silver; for another group of elements (calcium, nickel, zinc), it is about 3 calories, while for a third group (aluminum, scandium, chromium), it is nearly 2 calories. This curious relationship can be explained if one assumes that a constant amount of heat, approximately 6 calories, is required to raise the temperature of the atoms in 1 gram atomic weight of any solid element by 1°C. This would mean that for the first series of elements, the gram atomic weight would be equal to the gram equivalent weight, for the second series, it would be twice the gram equivalent weight and, for the third group, three times as great. In other words, in equation 2.1, "n" would be 1, 2, and 3 respectively.

TABLE 2.3 HEAT REQUIRED TO RAISE ONE GRAM ATOMIC WEIGHT OF VARIOUS METALS 1°C (20 to 21°C)

Element	G.A.W.	C*	Q*	Element	G.A.W.	C	Q
Na	23.0 g.	0.295	6.79	Cu	63.5 g.	0.0921	5.85
Mg	24.3 g.	0.246	5.98	Zn	65.4 g.	0.0925	6.05
Al	27.0 g.	0.214	5.78	Ga	69.7 g.	0.0789	5.50
Ca	40.0 g.	0.155	6.21	Ag	108 g.	0.0558	6.02
Fe	55.9 g.	0.106	5.93	U	238 g.	0.0281	6.69

* C = Specific heat (cal.·g.$^{-1}$·°C^{-1});   Q = Cal. required to raise T of one gram atomic weight 1°C.

It can be seen from Table 2.3 that Q for many metals deviates from the predicted value of 6 cal. by several per cent. This makes it impossible to calculate accurate values of gram atomic weights from specific heat data alone. However, such data can be used to determine the value of "n" in equation 2.1. The calculations involved in determining the gram atomic weight of an element by this method are illustrated by Example 2.2.

Example 2.2. A certain metal is found to have a specific heat of 0.107 cal.·g.$^{-1}$·°C^{-1}. The oxide of the metal contains 22.55 per cent by weight of oxygen. Calculate the gram atomic weight of the metal.

Solution. We shall first calculate the gram equivalent weight from the weight data given. From the specific heat of the metal, we can then calculate an approximate value for the gram atomic weight. This value should be sufficiently accurate to enable us to determine the number (1, 2, 3, . . .) by which the gram equivalent weight is to be multiplied to obtain the gram atomic weight.

To find the gram equivalent weight, we note that:

100.00 g. metal oxide contains 22.55 g. oxygen and (100.00 − 22.55) g. or 77.45 g. metal

$$77.45 \text{ g. metal} \simeq 22.55 \text{ g. oxygen}$$

$$\text{G.E.W.} = 8.000 \text{ g. O} \times \frac{77.45 \text{ g. metal}}{22.55 \text{ g. O}} = 27.48 \text{ g.}$$

To obtain an approximate value for the gram atomic weight, we must calculate the weight of metal raised 1°C by 6 cal. of heat:

$$1 \text{ g. metal} \simeq 0.107 \text{ cal.}   \text{(for an increase in T of 1°C)}$$

$$\text{wt. of metal raised 1°C by 6 cal.} = 6 \text{ cal.} \times \frac{1 \text{ g. metal}}{0.107 \text{ cal.}} = 56 \text{ g.}$$

Note that 56 g. is approximately twice the gram equivalent weight (27.48 g.); therefore n in the equation G.A.W. = n(G.E.W.) must be 2 and:

$$\text{G.A.W.} = 2(27.48 \text{ g.}) = 54.96 \text{ g.}$$

In the century and a half that has passed since the work of Dulong and Petit, chemists have worked out several other methods of determining the atomic weights of elements. One of these, suggested by Stanislao Cannizzaro in 1858, proved to be particularly useful for determining atomic weights of elements such as carbon, hydrogen, and nitrogen, which form a large number of gaseous compounds. The theory upon which this method is based and the calculations involved are illustrated by Problem 2.23 at the end of this chapter. In 1870, the establishment by Mendeleev of the periodic table (Chapter 7) offered still another method of estimating atomic weights. Both these approaches, like that of Dulong and Petit, led to approximate atomic weights, from which more precise values could be calculated from equation 2.1. Indeed, all chemical methods for determining the relative weights of atoms rely ultimately on the accurate determination of the gram equivalent weights of elements.

Atomic Weights from Mass Spectra

During the past few decades, a new and quite different approach to the determination of atomic weights has been developed, primarily by physicists. This technique makes use of an instrument known as a mass spectrograph, a simple model of which is shown in Figure 2.5. This instrument, which measures the charge to mass ratio of atomic particles, can be used to investigate a wide variety of chemical problems. Before discussing how the mass spectrograph can be applied to atomic weight measurements, let us consider the principle upon which it is based.

To operate a mass spectrograph, a gaseous sample, introduced in very small quantities into the area around the filament (F), is bombarded by a stream of electrons from a cathode ray source. A few of the gas particles are converted into positively charged ions which are then accelerated toward the slits S_1 and S_2. A narrow beam of ions enters the region H′; here a "velocity selector" (a combination of magnetic and electrical fields) allows only ions of a certain velocity to pass on through S_3. These ions pass through a magnetic field (H) which deflects them from their straight line path. The extent of deflection of the ion beam is measured by noting the point at which the ions strike the detector (D). In its simplest form, the detector may be a photographic plate; a black line forms on the plate where a beam of ions strikes it.

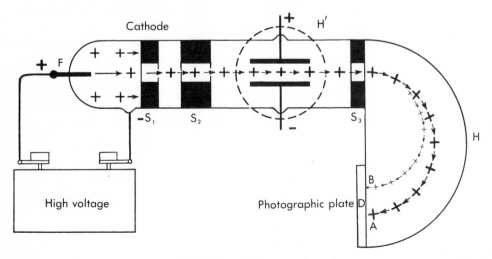

FIGURE 2.5   Mass spectrograph.

The extent to which ions of a given velocity are deflected by a magnetic field depends upon their charge to mass ratio. The greater the charge of an ion, the greater will be its deflection. If a $+1$ ion strikes the detector at A (Figure 2.5), a $+2$ ion of the same mass might appear at B. The deflection of an ion is inversely related to its mass; the lighter an ion is, the more readily it is pulled off its course by the magnetic field. If all the ions emerging from S_3 had the same charge but differed in mass, the heavier ions might arrive at A while the lighter ions were striking the plate at B.

Depending upon the nature of the gas being analyzed in the mass spectrograph, one may observe either a relatively simple or an exceedingly complex pattern of lines on the photographic plate at D. One of the simplest spectra is shown by helium, which consists of individual atoms almost all of which have a mass of 4. Here, the principal species formed is a $+1$ ion. These ions produce a heavy, dark line where they strike the plate at A. A few ions of charge $+2$ may also be formed; these ions would yield a very faint line on the photographic plate at B.

If the gas used is neon rather than helium, the pattern of lines appearing on the plate is more complex. Neon consists of a mixture of three isotopes. About 90 per cent of the neon atoms have a mass of 20; other isotopes of mass 21 and mass 22 are present in smaller amounts. Consequently, in a mass spectrograph, one can detect three different kinds of neon ions differing from each other in mass. The strongest lines are formed by the most abundant isotope of mass 20. Ions of this mass show a greater deflection than those of the same charge formed by the heavier isotopes of masses 21 and 22.

To illustrate how the mass spectrograph can be used to determine atomic weights, let us consider an element, helium, which has a particularly simple mass spectrum. In principle, it is possible, knowing the position at which a helium ion of mass 4 strikes the photographic plate, to calculate the absolute mass of this ion. However, in order to do this, one must know the velocity of the ion beam and the strength of the magnetic field. Neither of these quantities is easy to measure directly with high accuracy.

In practice, mass spectrographic data are ordinarily used to determine relative rather than absolute masses of particles. For example, one might compare the position of the trace formed by a beam of helium ions with that produced by ions of the carbon isotope of mass 12. From the relative positions of helium and carbon-12 ions of known charge, one can readily calculate the relative masses of the corresponding atoms. In this particular case, it turns out that a helium atom of mass 4 is 0.3336 times as heavy as a carbon atom of mass 12.

To calculate the atomic weight of helium from this data, we recall that the scale is set up by taking the atomic weight of the carbon isotope mentioned above to be exactly 12. Therefore, the atomic weight of the helium atom of mass 4 must be:

$$0.3336 \times 12.0000 = 4.003$$

But, since naturally occurring helium contains essentially 100 per cent of this isotope,* the number 4.003 must also represent the atomic weight of the element helium.

---

* Helium does have another stable isotope of mass 3. However, since this isotope constitutes less than one part per million of ordinary helium, its presence does not, to four significant figures, affect the atomic weight of the element.

Quite clearly, the determination, from mass spectrographic data, of the atomic weight of an element such as neon, in which more than one isotope must be considered, is a more complicated problem. Here it is necessary to determine not only the mass but also the relative abundance of each isotope. The latter quantity can be determined quite accurately with a mass spectrograph. In principle, this can be done by measuring the relative intensities of the lines produced by the different isotopes of an element. A more sophisticated model of the mass spectrograph incorporates a current measuring device as a detector; in this case, the total current corresponding to ions of a particular isotope is a measure of the abundance of that isotope.

Once the masses and abundances of the isotopes of a particular element have been determined, its "average" atomic weight is readily calculated (Example 2.3).

Example 2.3. From mass spectrographic data, it can be determined that the element neon consists of three isotopes, whose masses on the carbon-12 scale are 19.99, 20.99, and 21.99. The abundances of these isotopes are respectively 90.92 per cent, 0.25 per cent, and 8.83 per cent. Calculate an accurate value for the atomic weight of neon.

Solution. The atomic weight of any element can be found by adding the contributions of each of the isotopes. In the case of neon, we have:

	mass	×	fraction		
neon-20	19.99	×	0.9092	=	18.17
neon-21	20.99	×	0.0025	=	0.05
neon-22	21.99	×	0.0883	=	1.94
			atomic weight of neon =		20.16

Absolute Masses of Atoms: Avogadro's Number

A knowledge of the atomic weights of elements makes it possible to calculate the relative masses of different atoms. While such quantities are of great value in chemistry, we should like to go one step further and calculate the absolute masses of atoms. In order to do so, the number of atoms in one gram atomic weight of any element must be known. This number, known as Avogadro's number and given the symbol N, may be calculated in various ways; two different methods are illustrated by Problems 2.24 and 2.25 at the end of this chapter.

Avogadro's number has been found to be, to four significant figures, 6.023×10^{23} (i.e., 602,300,000,000,000,000,000,000). This is a number so large as to defy comprehension. Some idea of its magnitude may be gained when one realizes that if the entire population of the world were to be assigned to counting the number of atoms in one gram atomic weight of an element, each person counting one atom per second and working a 48-hour week, the task would require somewhat more than three billion years. From another point of view, the fact that Avogadro's number is so huge means that the atom itself is almost inconceivably small. Individual atoms are far too small to be seen with the most powerful microscope or weighed on the most sensitive analytical balance (Example 2.4). In the head of a common pin, there are more iron atoms than there are people on the earth.

Example 2.4. Calculate:
  a. the mass of a hydrogen atom.
  b. the number of magnesium atoms in a sample weighing 1.0×10^{-6} g. (This is the smallest sample of magnesium that can be weighed on the most sensitive analytical balance.)

Solution.

a. Knowing that one gram atomic weight of hydrogen weighs 1.008 g. and contains 6.023×10^{23} atoms, we have:

$$1.008 \text{ g. H} = 6.023 \times 10^{23} \text{ atoms H}$$

$$\text{mass of 1 atom H} = 1 \text{ atom H} \times \frac{1.008 \text{ g. H}}{6.023 \times 10^{23} \text{ atoms}} = 1.674 \times 10^{-24} \text{ g.}$$

b. 1 G.A.W. Mg = 24.31 g. Mg = 6.023×10^{23} atoms Mg

$$\text{number of atoms Mg} = 1.0 \times 10^{-6} \text{ g.} \times \frac{6.023 \times 10^{23} \text{ atoms}}{24.31 \text{ g.}}$$

$$= 2.5 \times 10^{16} \text{ atoms } (25{,}000{,}000{,}000{,}000{,}000)$$

2.6 ATOMS IN MATTER

So far, we have been discussing the properties of atoms as distinct entities. Actually, individual atoms are rarely encountered in matter. Only in a very few elementary substances, the so-called noble gases (He, Ne, Ar, Kr, Xe, Rn), can we consider individual atoms to be the fundamental building blocks of which the substance is composed. In most elementary substances and all compounds, we find that groups of atoms are combined to form stable aggregates. Such aggregates may range in composition from the very simple to the very complex. They may contain anywhere from two to many billions of atoms of one or more elements. We shall now examine briefly some of the types of aggregates that are found in elementary and compound substances; a more extensive discussion of this topic will be found in Chapters 9 to 11.

Molecules

In a very large and important group of pure substances, the aggregates are small, discrete particles containing only a few atoms. Aggregates, or particles, of this type are called **molecules.** In molecules, the constituent atoms are linked together by strong forces, called chemical bonds. By contrast the forces between molecules are relatively weak. Molecules, therefore, do not usually interact strongly with one another but behave as more or less independent particles.

Carbon dioxide is one example of a molecular substance. The carbon dioxide molecule contains one carbon atom and two oxygen atoms. As shown in Figure 2.6, each of the oxygen atoms is bonded to the carbon atom. Carbon dioxide molecules are discrete particles which, under ordinary conditions, are stable; that is, they do not react chemically with one another or with most other molecules. The properties of carbon dioxide are determined by the properties of its molecules.

There are many other pure substances with which you are familiar that also contain simple molecules. Figure 2.6 shows schematic diagrams of the molecules that would be present in oxygen, water, and ethylene. Oxygen, like several elementary substances, is molecular. Oxygen molecules are diatomic; that is, they contain two atoms linked together by a chemical bond. Water molecules contain one oxygen atom bonded to two hydrogen atoms. The water molecule is bent, whereas the carbon dioxide

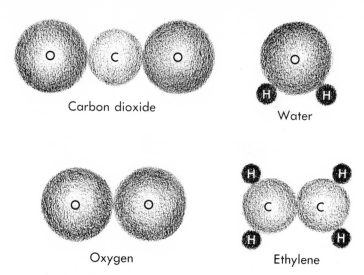

Carbon dioxide

Water

Oxygen

Ethylene

FIGURE 2.6 Schematic diagrams of some simple molecules.

molecule is linear. In ethylene, the gas which is the raw material for the production of polyethylene, the molecule contains two carbon atoms and four hydrogen atoms; each carbon atom is bound to two hydrogen atoms and to the other carbon atom.

Nonmolecular Substances

Although there are a great many substances which are molecular, there are many which are not. Nonmolecular substances, which are nearly all solids under ordinary conditions, contain no small aggregates which can be considered as discrete stable entities. Rather, in a given solid particle all the constituent atomic species are linked together in one giant aggregate whose size is really that of the macroscopic particle. There are, then, literally billions of atomic-size particles all linked together in such a solid particle.

Three general kinds of nonmolecular substances, distinguished on the basis of the constituent species and the kind of bonding between them, will now be considered.

One group of nonmolecular substances contains atoms which are chemically bonded together in what is often called a **macromolecule.** Two familiar macromolecular substances are diamond, a form of elementary carbon, and carborundum (silicon carbide). In a "flawless" diamond, every carbon atom is bonded to four other atoms to give a huge aggregate (Figure 11.2, p. 247). The structure of silicon carbide is similar to that of diamond, except that every other atom is a silicon atom, giving a silicon-to-carbon atom ratio of exactly 1. In neither of these substances can we identify any small discrete molecules, as we could in carbon dioxide or oxygen.

Another group of nonmolecular substances includes all those materials we know as metals. In metals the electrons from the metal atoms are much freer to move about than they are in a substance like diamond. The mobile electrons give metals their characteristic properties (for example, high electrical and thermal conductivity and ductility) and are responsible for the bonding between metal atoms, called **metallic bonding** (cf. Chapter 11, Section 11.5).

In the third group of nonmolecular substances the situation is somewhat different from any we have yet encountered. In these substances, all of which are compounds, the constituent species are not atoms, but rather are small particles which carry electrical charges. These particles may simply be atoms which by means of chemical reaction have gained or lost one or more electrons, or they may be small charged aggregates of atoms. In either case, the particles are designated as **ions.**

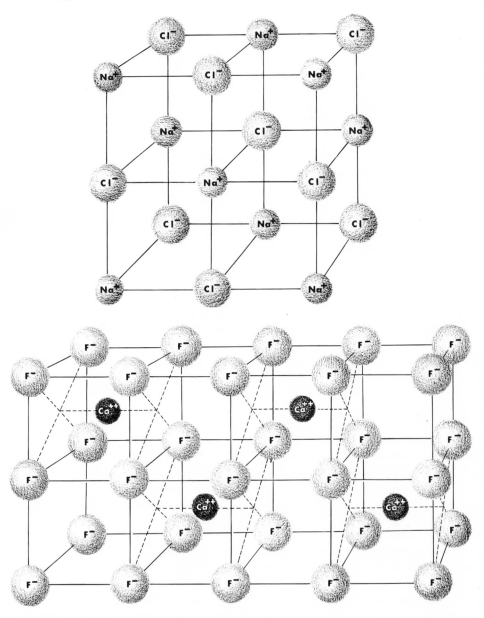

FIGURE 2.7 The structures of two ionic crystals, sodium chloride and calcium fluoride. The upper structure persists throughout a macroscopic sodium chloride crystal; Na^+ and Cl^- ions alternate along lines forming edges of cubes in lattice. In the calcium fluoride crystal, the fluoride ions are in a simple cubic lattice; the calcium ions are at the centers of alternate cubes along each of the three principal axes.

We always find two different kinds of ions in an ionic compound, those with positive charge and those with negative charge. Thus ionic compounds are unique in that they contain two different particles with opposite charges. Any macroscopic sample of an ionic compound will be electrically neutral and so must contain ions carrying equal total amounts of positive and negative charge. The ions in an ionic compound are considered to be bonded together primarily by the electrostatic forces resulting from their electric charges.

Ionic substances are reasonably common and include most of the compounds known as salts. The structure of sodium chloride, common salt, which is a typical ionic substance, is shown in Figure 2.7. In this material the constituent particles are sodium ions (Na^+) and chloride ions (Cl^-). Sodium ions are sodium atoms which have lost one electron and have thereby acquired one unit of positive electric charge, denoted by the $+$ superscript. Chloride ions are chlorine atoms which have gained one electron and thereby its unit of negative charge, denoted by the $-$ superscript. In sodium chloride the ionic charges and the requirement for electroneutrality of the solid salt fix the sodium : chloride ion ratio at exactly 1:1. In the compound calcium fluoride the negative particle is the fluoride ion, F^-. The positive charge is carried by the calcium ion, Ca^{+2}, which is a calcium atom which has lost two electrons. The fact that calcium fluoride is an electrically neutral substance requires that in the solid there be *two* fluoride ions, each carrying a -1 charge, for each calcium ion ($+2$ charge).

2.7 MOLECULAR MASSES

In dealing with substances such as carbon dioxide, oxygen, or ethylene, in which the fundamental building block is the molecule, it is convenient to consider a number known as the molecular weight, which is defined in a manner entirely analogous to atomic weight. The **molecular weight** is a number that tells us how heavy a molecule of a substance is compared to an atom of the most common isotope of carbon, carbon-12. When we learn, for example, that the molecular weight of carbon dioxide is 44, we deduce that a carbon dioxide molecule is $\frac{44}{12}$ as heavy as a carbon-12 atom.

Knowing the composition of a molecule, one can readily calculate the molecular weight of the corresponding substance. For example, once it is established that the oxygen molecule is diatomic, it follows that the molecular weight of oxygen must be exactly twice its atomic weight.

$$2 \times 16.00 = 32.00$$

Again, knowing that the ethylene molecule contains two carbon atoms and four hydrogen atoms, one can calculate the molecular weight of ethylene to be 28.05.

$$2 \times \text{A.W. of C} = 2 \times 12.01 = 24.02$$
$$4 \times \text{A.W. of H} = 4 \times 1.008 = \underline{4.03}$$
$$28.05$$

While this is a very convenient method of calculating molecular weights on paper, it requires that one know the atomic composition of the molecule. Molecular compositions are ordinarily deduced from measured molecular weights. Two different experimental approaches to the determination of molecular weights will be discussed later (Chapters 6 and 13).

In dealing with molecular substances, it is convenient to define a unit of mass known as the **gram molecular weight,** which bears the same relation to molecular weight as does gram atomic weight to atomic weight. We have seen that the gram atomic weight of an element is the weight in grams which contains Avogadro's number of atoms; the gram molecular weight of an elementary or compound substance is the weight in grams which contains Avogadro's number (6.023×10^{23}) of molecules. Thus 16.00 g. of oxygen or 1.008 g. of hydrogen contain 6.023×10^{23} *atoms*; 32.00 g. of oxygen (2 atoms of oxygen per molecule) or 18.02 g. of water (2 atoms of hydrogen, 1 atom of oxygen per molecule) contain 6.023×10^{23} *molecules*.

The gram molecular weight can be obtained directly from the molecular weight, just as the gram atomic weight is obtained from the atomic weight.

Element	A.W.	G.A.W.	Molecular Substance	M.W.	G.M.W.
Oxygen	16.00	16.00 g.	Oxygen	32.00	32.00 g.
Chlorine	35.45	35.45 g.	Water	18.02	18.02 g.
Uranium	238.0	238.0 g.	Ethylene	28.05	28.05 g.

Knowing the gram molecular weight of a substance, we can readily calculate the weight of an individual molecule (Example 2.5).

Example 2.5.   Calculate the mass in grams of a water molecule.

Solution.   We know that the gram molecular weight of water is 18.02 g.; one gram molecular weight of any substance contains 6.023×10^{23} molecules. Therefore:

$$18.02 \text{ g. water} = 6.023 \times 10^{23} \text{ molecules water}$$

$$\text{mass of 1 molecule water} = 1 \text{ molecule} \times \frac{18.02 \text{ g.}}{6.023 \times 10^{23} \text{ molecules}} = 2.992 \times 10^{-23} \text{ g.}$$

(Note the similarity to Example 2.4.)

2.8 SUMMARY

In this chapter, we have presented an outline of the modern atomic *theory* (Section 2.3). This theory offers a rational explanation of certain natural *laws* governing chemical changes, notably the Law of Conservation of Mass, the Law of Constant Proportions, the Law of Combining Weights and the Law of Multiple Proportions (Section 2.2). The atomic theory in turn raises several fundamental questions concerning the physical and chemical properties of atoms. In particular, it leads us to inquire into the structure of atoms (Section 2.4), their masses (Section 2.5), and the manner in which atoms combine with each other to make up elementary and compound substances (Section 2.6).

The atomic theory and the laws from which it is derived are based on experimental observations. In this chapter, we have discussed certain quantitative experiments from which one can obtain information concerning the masses of atoms (determination of atomic weights, Section 2.5) and the weight ratios in which they combine (determination of gram equivalent weights, Section 2.2). In addition, we have described qualitatively the experimental evidence for the existence of subatomic particles (Section 2.4).

In developing the properties of atoms, we have had occasion to refer to three units of mass:

· 1. The gram equivalent weight of an element (the weight that combines with eight grams of oxygen or its equivalent).

2. The gram atomic weight of an element (the weight that contains Avogadro's number of atoms, i.e., the same number of atoms as 16.00 grams of oxygen).

3. The gram molecular weight of a substance (the weight that contains Avogadro's number of molecules).

In addition, we have referred to two *numbers*, atomic weight and molecular weight. For a given substance, these quantities have the same numerical value as the gram atomic or gram molecular weight respectively.

PROBLEMS

2.1   What is an atom? a molecule? an ion?

2.2   In terms of the atomic theory, what constitutes a pure substance? an elementary substance? a compound substance?

2.3   Distinguish between a molecular and an ionic substance; between a molecular and a macromolecular substance.

2.4   Distinguish between gram equivalent weight and gram atomic weight. Which is easier to determine experimentally?

2.5   What does one really mean by the statement, "The atomic weight of aluminum is 26.98"?

2.6   In 1815, an English physician, William Prout, suggested that all atoms are built up of atoms of hydrogen.
   a. Assuming that Prout's hypothesis is correct, list several of its consequences.
   b. For each of the statements listed in (a), describe an experiment which would prove or disprove it.
   c. In light of our present-day concepts of atomic structure, comment on the validity of Prout's hypothesis.

2.7   A student heats a weighed sample of cobalt with sulfur and weighs the cobalt sulfide produced. From his data, he calculates the weight of cobalt which combines with 16.0 g. of sulfur and reports this as the gram equivalent weight. Perhaps without realizing it, he has assumed the validity of certain of the laws discussed in Section 2.2. State precisely how these laws are involved.

2.8   The element chromium forms three different oxides in which the percentages of chromium are respectively 52.0, 68.4, and 76.5. Show how these data illustrate the Law of Multiple Proportions.

2.9   Using the data in Table 2.2, calculate:
   a. the number of grams of chlorine that combines with 10.0 g. of lithium.
   b. the percentage by weight of bromine in silver bromide.
   c. the percentages by weight of tin in the two chlorides of that element.

2.10 When 2.24 g. of a certain metal oxide is reduced with hydrogen, 1.76 g. of metal is formed. What is the gram equivalent weight of the metal?

2.11 If the atomic weight scale had been set up so that the atomic weight of oxygen were 8.00 rather than 16.00,
   a. what would be the atomic weight of calcium?
   b. what would be the gram equivalent weight of calcium?
   c. in equation 2.1, what would be the possible values of n?

2.12 How many atoms of calcium are required to balance 20 atoms of oxygen? 15 atoms of argon? 2×10^4 atoms of neon?

2.13 The specific heat of a certain metal is 0.086 cal.·g.$^{-1}$·°C^{-1}; its gram equivalent weight is 23.24 g. Calculate, to four significant figures, the gram atomic weight of the metal.

2.14 It is found that 1.0 cal. is required to raise the temperature of 10 g. of a certain metal 1°C. Analysis of the chloride of this metal shows it to contain 54.4 per cent chlorine. Calculate the gram atomic weight of the metal.

2.15 Calculate:
   a. the number of grams in 4.12 gram atomic weights of phosphorus.
   b. the number of gram atomic weights in 209 g. of palladium.
   c. the mass of the number of potassium atoms which is just equal to the number of atoms in 8.00 g. of oxygen.

2.16 The element fluorine consists of a single isotope which is found from mass spectrographic data to have a mass 1.583 times that of carbon-12. Calculate the atomic weight of fluorine.

2.17 The element magnesium consists of three isotopes of masses 24.0, 25.0, and 26.0. The percentages of these isotopes are respectively 78.6, 10.1, and 11.3. Calculate the atomic weight of magnesium.

2.18 Given that chlorine consists of two isotopes of masses 34.97 and 36.97 and has an atomic weight of 35.45, calculate the percentages of these two isotopes.

2.19 Calculate:
   a. the mass, in grams, of a carbon-12 atom.
   b. the number of atoms of copper in a piece of copper wire 1.00 mm. in diameter and 1.0 m. long (density Cu = 8.9 g./cc.).
   c. the mass in grams of 2.14×10^{12} molecules of carbon dioxide.

2.20 The gram equivalent weight of antimony in a certain sulfide of that element is 40.6 g.; the gram atomic weight of antimony is 121.8 g. What is the atom ratio of antimony to sulfur in this compound?

2.21 A metal forms two different chlorides. One contains 54.7 per cent chlorine, the other 64.4 per cent chlorine. List some possible values for the atomic weight of this element. How could you determine which of these values is the correct one?

*2.22 When 1.293 g. of a certain metal bromide is treated with chlorine, 1.093 g. of the chloride is formed. What is the gram equivalent weight of the metal?

*2.23 Cannizzaro, in 1858, suggested a method of deducing the atomic weight of an element such as hydrogen, based on the following reasoning:
   It is known from Avogadro's Law (Chapter 6) that in one liter of any gas at 0°C and 1 atm., there is a certain definite number of molecules, x. In at least one of the gaseous compounds of hydrogen, there should be one atom of hydrogen per molecule. Consequently, by studying the weights of hydrogen in one liter of several of its gaseous compounds, it should be possible to deduce the weight of x hydrogen atoms. A similar study applied to a series of gaseous compounds of oxygen should yield the weight of x oxygen atoms.
   Applying Cannizzaro's reasoning to the data given below, obtain the atomic weight of hydrogen.

Hydrogen Compounds	Wt. 1 liter (0°C, 1 atm.)	%H	Oxygen Compounds	Wt. 1 liter (0°C, 1 atm.)	%O
Hydrogen bromide	3.636 g.	1.246	Nitrous oxide	1.975 g.	36.35
Acetylene	1.170 g.	7.743	Oxygen difluoride	2.422 g.	29.63
Ammonia	0.765 g.	17.76	Carbon dioxide	1.975 g.	72.71
Hydrogen sulfide	1.532 g.	5.915	Nitrogen dioxide	2.071 g.	69.55

*2.24 It is found that when a direct electric current is passed through a water solution containing Cu^{+2} ions, the following reaction occurs:

$$Cu^{+2} + 2\,e^- \longrightarrow Cu$$

A total of 1.93×10^5 coulombs is required to produce one gram atomic weight of copper by this reaction. Given that an electron carries a charge of 1.60×10^{-19} coulomb, calculate the number of atoms in one gram atomic weight of copper (Avogadro's number).

*2.25 By a technique known as x-ray diffraction (Chapter 12), it is possible to determine the geometric pattern in which atoms are arranged in a crystal and the distances between atoms. In this way, it has been shown that in a crystal of sodium, 2 atoms effectively occupy the volume of a cube 4.29 Å on an edge. Knowing that the density of sodium is 0.970 g./cc., calculate the number of atoms in one gram atomic weight of sodium (Avogadro's number).

*2.26 You will note that the atomic weight of neon, as calculated from the data in Example 2.3, does not agree exactly with the value given in the table of atomic weights. Suggest possible reasons for this discrepancy. (For a discussion, see an article in the Journal of the American Chemical Society, Vol. 84, p. 4182, 1962.)

*2.27 In Figure 2.7 the crystal structures of sodium chloride and calcium fluoride are indicated. By recognizing that crystals of these substances contain many ions arranged as described in the sketches, show that the $Na^+ : Cl^-$ ion ratio in sodium chloride is $1:1$, and that the $Ca^{+2} : F^-$ ion ratio in calcium fluoride is $1:2$.

3 | CHEMICAL FORMULAS FROM ANALYSIS

3.1 INTRODUCTION

In Chapter 2, we pointed out that if one knows the weight ratio in which two elements combine and the relative masses of their atoms, it is possible to determine the atom ratio in which the elements react. For example, knowing that hydrogen and oxygen react in a $1:8$ (or $2:16$) weight ratio and that a hydrogen atom is $\frac{1}{16}$ as heavy as an oxygen atom, we deduce that in this reaction, in which water is formed, two hydrogen atoms must combine with one atom of oxygen.

In this chapter, we shall develop a general method for determining from experimental data what is known as the simplest or empirical formula of a compound. The simplest formula indicates the simplest, whole-number ratio between the numbers of atoms of the different elements making up the compound. For example, the simplest formula of the compound substance water is H_2O. The subscript 2 written after the symbol H in this formula indicates that in water there are two hydrogen atoms for every oxygen atom (the subscript 1 is omitted). The simplest formula of potassium chlorate, $KClO_3$, tells us that in this compound the elements potassium, chlorine, and oxygen are combined in an atom ratio of $1:1:3$ respectively. Simplest formulas can be written for all compound substances and frequently are of great help to us in distinguishing one such substance from another.

Regardless of how many elements a compound contains or how complicated its structure may be, its simplest formula can be obtained by subjecting it to an experimental technique known as **quantitative analysis,** in which the proportions by weight of the constituent elements are determined. Whenever a new compound is prepared, it is analyzed and, on that basis, assigned a simplest formula. Even if the compound has been prepared before, it is often analyzed to determine its purity. The importance of analysis as a research tool may be inferred from the observation that in a recent (January 20, 1965) issue of the Journal of the American Chemical Society, elementary analyses were reported for some 92 different compounds.

In discussing the application of chemical analysis to the determination of simplest formulas, we shall start with binary compounds, some of which were

56

mentioned in Chapter 2. The methods used to analyze such substances are readily extended to compounds containing three or more elements. The technique used to calculate simplest formulas from analytical data requires only a knowledge of the atomic weights of the elements present and is the same regardless of the number of elements involved.

3.2 FORMULAS OF BINARY COMPOUNDS FROM ANALYSIS

Two different experimental approaches are available for the determination of the proportions by weight of the elements in a binary compound. These are: (1) decomposition of the compound to yield an elementary substance and (2) conversion to another compound of known composition.

Decomposition of the Compound to Yield an Elementary Substance

This method is applicable to the determination of the simplest formulas of many of the binary compounds of the metals. One starts with a weighed sample of the pure compound, decomposes it by one means or another, and weighs the metal residue. The weight of the second element, which may be oxygen, chlorine, sulfur, or some other nonmetal, is ordinarily found by difference (i.e., weight of compound — weight of metal). When the proportions by weight in which the two elements are combined are known, the simplest formula of the compound can be calculated. Example 3.1 illustrates, in some detail, a two-step approach to this calculation which we shall use throughout this chapter to obtain simplest formulas from analytical data.

Example 3.1. A sample of a certain oxide of iron weighing 4.978 g. is heated in a stream of hydrogen until all of the oxygen has been driven off as water vapor. The residue of pure iron weighs 3.602 g. Calculate the simplest formula of the compound.

Solution. From the data, it is clear that 3.602 g. of iron are combined with (4.978 − 3.602) g. = 1.376 g. of oxygen:

$$3.602 \text{ g. Fe} \simeq 1.376 \text{ g. O}$$

To obtain the simplest formula of the compound, we proceed as follows:
1. *Determine the relative numbers of gram atomic weights of iron and oxygen present.*

In 3.602 g. of Fe there are: $3.602 \text{ g. Fe} \times \dfrac{1 \text{ G.A.W. Fe}}{55.85 \text{ g. Fe}} = 0.0645 \text{ G.A.W. Fe}$

In 1.376 g. of O there are: $1.376 \text{ g. O} \times \dfrac{1 \text{ G.A.W. O}}{16.00 \text{ g. O}} = 0.0860 \text{ G.A.W. O}$

In other words, 0.0645 G.A.W. of iron is combined with 0.0860 G.A.W. of oxygen.

$$0.0645 \text{ G.A.W. Fe} \simeq 0.0860 \text{ G.A.W. O}$$

2. *Convert these numbers to their simplest whole-number ratio.* Perhaps the most direct way to do this is to first calculate the number of gram atomic weights of oxygen reacting with one gram atomic weight of iron:

$$1 \text{ G.A.W. Fe} \times \frac{0.0860 \text{ G.A.W. O}}{0.0645 \text{ G.A.W. Fe}} = 1.33 \text{ G.A.W. O}, \quad \text{i.e.,} \quad 1 \text{ G.A.W. Fe} \simeq 1.33 \text{ G.A.W. O}$$

Multiplying by three gives the simplest whole-number ratio:

$$3\text{ G.A.W. Fe} \simeq 4\text{ G.A.W. O}$$

But, since the conversion factor relating the number of gram atomic weights to the number of atoms is the same (1 G.A.W. $= 6.023 \times 10^{23}$ atoms) for all elements, it follows that the ratio of G.A.W.'s must be the same as the atom ratio:

$$3\text{ atoms Fe} \simeq 4\text{ atoms O} \qquad \text{Simplest formula} = Fe_3O_4$$

This type of decomposition may be brought about in any of several ways:

1. With a few compounds, heat alone is sufficient. Silver oxide is an example; heated above 190°C, it breaks down quantitatively to the elements, silver and oxygen. *heat*

2. More commonly, the nonmetallic element in the compound is removed as a volatile by-product by heating with an element such as hydrogen or carbon. Many metal oxides can be decomposed by heating with hydrogen in an apparatus such as that shown in Figure 2.3; the water formed escapes as a vapor through the exit tube. The oxides of lead can be decomposed by heating with carbon, which combines with the oxygen in the compound to form the gas, carbon dioxide. *replacement*

3. Many binary compounds which are not readily decomposed thermally or chemically can be broken down to the elements by applying electrical energy. If a direct electric current is passed through a solution of a copper compound, the copper is deposited quantitatively at one of the electrodes. By measuring the weight of copper produced from a known amount of compound, the percentages by weight of the two elements present can be determined. Many of the soluble salts of the heavier metals including copper, cobalt, nickel, and zinc lend themselves to analysis by this method. We shall return to the subject of electrolytic decomposition in Chapter 20. *Electrolytic*

Conversion to Another Compound of Known Composition

This technique is perhaps more widely used in elemental analysis than any other. It involves carrying out a reaction sequence by means of which the compound whose formula is to be determined is converted to another compound whose formula is known. From the weights of reactants and products, it is possible to determine the simplest formula of the starting compound. The method can be adapted to either ionic or molecular compounds.

Analysis **Ionic Compounds.** The analysis of binary compounds of the metals ordinarily involves their conversion to water-insoluble compounds. To illustrate, let us consider how one might go about determining the simplest formula of the chloride of a metal such as scandium.

If a weighed sample of scandium chloride is dissolved in water and treated with excess silver nitrate solution, a white precipitate of silver chloride is formed. This precipitate is carefully filtered, dried and weighed. Knowing the formula of silver chloride to be AgCl, it is possible to determine the percentage by weight of chlorine in scandium chloride and hence the simplest formula of the latter. Example 3.2 illustrates the calculations involved.

Example 3.2. A sample of scandium chloride weighing 2.159 g. is dissolved in water and treated with Ag^+ to quantitatively precipitate the Cl^- ions as AgCl. The precipitated silver chloride weighs 6.134 g. Calculate the percentage composition and the simplest formula of scandium chloride.

Solution. Let us first calculate the weight of chlorine in the precipitated silver chloride. To do this, we obtain the percentage of chlorine in AgCl and then multiply by the weight of silver chloride formed (6.134 g.).

$$\% \text{ Cl in AgCl} = \frac{\text{A.W. Cl}}{\text{A.W. Ag} + \text{A.W. Cl}} \times 100 = \frac{35.45}{107.87 + 35.45} \times 100 = 24.74\%$$

(1) wt. Cl in 6.134 g. AgCl = .2474 × 6.134 g. = 1.518 g.

This is the weight of chlorine, not only in the precipitated silver chloride but also in the original sample of scandium chloride. The percentage composition of scandium chloride must then be:

(2) $$\% \text{ Cl} = \frac{\text{wt. Cl}}{\text{wt. sample}} \times 100 = \frac{1.518 \text{ g.}}{2.159 \text{ g.}} \times 100 = 70.31\%$$

(3) $$\% \text{ Sc} = 100.00 - 70.31 = 29.69\%$$

To calculate the simplest formula of scandium chloride:

$$29.69 \text{ g. Sc} \simeq 70.31 \text{ g. Cl}$$

$$\text{no. of G.A.W. Sc in 29.69 g.} = 29.69 \text{ g. Sc} \times \frac{1 \text{ G.A.W. Sc}}{44.96 \text{ g. Sc}} = 0.660$$

$$\text{no. of G.A.W. Cl in 70.31 g.} = 70.31 \text{ g. Cl} \times \frac{1 \text{ G.A.W. Cl}}{35.45 \text{ g. Cl}} = 1.98$$

Hence,   0.660 G.A.W. Sc $\simeq$ 1.98 G.A.W. Cl

1 G.A.W. Sc $\simeq$ 3 G.A.W. Cl   Simplest formula = $ScCl_3$

The experimental procedure outlined here can, of course, be applied to the analysis of any soluble metal chloride. It was used by Professor Richards of Harvard to determine the atomic weights of a series of metals; this work won him, in 1914, the first Nobel Prize in chemistry to be awarded to an American.

Precipitation analyses have been worked out for the determination of the elementary composition of a wide variety of soluble metal salts. Bromides can be determined by precipitation as silver bromide, AgBr, which, like silver chloride, is quantitatively insoluble in water. The percentage of barium in salts of that element can be determined by precipitating as barium sulfate, $BaSO_4$. Mercury is often determined as the insoluble sulfide, HgS; tin as the oxide, SnO_2.

Frequently, difficulties arise in separating precipitates in pure form from water solution. Many precipitates tend to take on water which is sometimes very difficult to remove quantitatively. For example, in order to determine aluminum as the insoluble oxide, Al_2O_3, the precipitate must be heated at 1200°C to remove all the water. Another problem encountered in precipitation analyses is the adsorption of foreign ions by the precipitate. If solutions of sodium sulfate and barium chloride are mixed, the barium sulfate precipitate is badly contaminated with sodium chloride. Even though sodium chloride is quite soluble in water, repeated washing of the precipitate fails to remove all of the Na^+ and Cl^- ions, which are embedded within the barium sulfate crystals. These ions can, however, be removed by allowing the precipitate to remain in contact with the solution for several hours at a temperature near 100°C. Under these conditions, the impure crystals first formed dissolve and recrystallize in purer form.

Molecular Compounds. Among the most important types of binary compounds are those containing the two elements hydrogen and carbon. Thousands of such compounds, known collectively as hydrocarbons, have been isolated. Many of them are found in natural gas and petroleum deposits. Gasoline, obtained by the fractional distillation of petroleum, is a complex mixture of a great many hydrocarbons. One of the most important of these is normal hexane, a colorless, water-insoluble liquid that boils at 69°C.

Hexane, like most hydrocarbons, undergoes only one convenient quantitative reaction, that of combustion. If a sample of hexane is burned in excess air or pure oxygen, it reacts to form carbon dioxide, CO_2, and water vapor, H_2O. The percentage of carbon in hexane can be determined by measuring the amount of carbon dioxide formed from a weighed sample. The percentage of hydrogen can then be calculated by difference. (Alternatively, it could be determined directly from the weight of water formed, as in Example 3.5.)

Example 3.3 illustrates the calculations involved in determining the simplest formula of hexane from combustion data.

Example 3.3. A sample of normal hexane weighing 2.650 g. is burned in excess oxygen. The products formed are passed through the absorption train shown in Figure 3.1. The weight of carbon dioxide formed, determined from the increase in weight of the tube in which it is absorbed, is 8.105 g. Calculate the % composition and the simplest formula of hexane.

Solution. We shall follow a procedure analogous to that used in Example 3.2, obtaining first the weight of carbon, then the percentage composition of hexane, and finally the simplest formula.

To obtain the weight of carbon, we have:

$$\% \text{ C in } CO_2 = \frac{\text{A.W. C}}{\text{M.W. } CO_2} \times 100 = \frac{12.01}{44.01} \times 100 = 27.29\%$$

(1) wt. of C in CO_2 = .2729 × 8.105 g. = 2.212 g. = wt. C in hexane sample

To obtain the percentages of carbon and hydrogen in hexane:

(2) $$\% \text{ C in hexane} = \frac{\text{wt. C}}{\text{wt. sample}} \times 100 = \frac{2.212 \text{ g.}}{2.650 \text{ g.}} \times 100 = 83.47\%$$

(3)   % H in hexane = 100.00 − 83.47 = 16.53%

100.00 g. of hexane therefore contain 83.47 g. C and 16.53 g. H.

Since 1 G.A.W. C = 12.01 g. and 1 G.A.W. H = 1.008 g.

$$\text{no. of G.A.W. C} = 83.47 \text{ g. C} \times \frac{1 \text{ G.A.W. C}}{12.01 \text{ g. C}} = 6.95 \text{ G.A.W. C}$$

$$\text{no. of G.A.W. H} = 16.53 \text{ g. H} \times \frac{1 \text{ G.A.W. H}}{1.008 \text{ g. H}} = 16.4 \text{ G.A.W. H}$$

Hence: 6.95 G.A.W. C ≃ 16.4 G.A.W. H

$$1 \text{ G.A.W. C} \simeq \frac{16.4}{6.95} \text{ G.A.W. H} = 2.36 \text{ G.A.W. H}$$

Multiplying by 3 (really as a result of trial and error):

3 G.A.W. C ≃ 7 G.A.W. H   simplest formula = C_3H_7

Note that the ratio of carbon to hydrogen atoms does not appear to be *exactly* 3:7. A person unfamiliar with the limits of accuracy inherent in analyses of this type might be tempted to report a "simplest" formula such as $C_{25}H_{59}$. Actually, one can calculate that a change of as little as 0.2 per cent in the reported weight of carbon dioxide would shift the carbon-to-hydrogen atom ratio to 1:2.33, in agreement with the formula C_3H_7. In practice, one can hardly hope to avoid errors of at least 0.1 per cent in conventional methods of chemical analysis; in many analytical techniques, the inherent error is considerably greater than this. Consequently, one has to exercise a certain amount of discretion in reporting simplest formulas on the basis of elementary analysis.

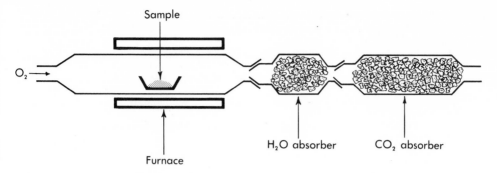

Sample

$O_2 \rightarrow$

H₂O absorber   CO₂ absorber

Furnace

FIGURE 3.1   Schematic diagram of an absorption train for carbon-hydrogen analysis.

Combustion analysis is generally applicable to all types of hydrocarbons. It may also be used to obtain the formulas of such binary carbon compounds as carbon tetrachloride, CCl_4, and carbon disulfide, CS_2.

3.3 COMPOUNDS CONTAINING MORE THAN TWO ELEMENTS

The usual method of analyzing a compound containing more than two elements involves breaking it down into simpler substances whose compositions are known. These substances may be elementary or may be binary compounds. They may be produced from the parent compound by thermal decomposition, precipitation, combustion, or other means. The experimental procedure and calculations involved are illustrated by the following descriptions of the analyses of two compounds, lithium chlorate and ethyl alcohol.

Lithium Chlorate

The analysis of lithium chlorate reveals it to be a ternary compound containing the three elements lithium, chlorine, and oxygen. The percentages by weight of the three elements can be determined by a two-step analytical procedure. A weighed sample of the compound is first heated to approximately 300°C; at this temperature all the oxygen is driven off to leave a solid residue of the binary compound lithium chloride. This residue is analyzed for chlorine by precipitation with silver nitrate (recall Example 3.2). By combining the data from these two experiments, one can calculate the percentages by weight of lithium, chlorine, and oxygen and hence the simplest formula of lithium chlorate.

Example 3.4.   A sample of lithium chlorate weighing 2.500 g. is heated to constant weight at 300°C; the residue weighs 1.170 g. This residue, on precipitation with silver nitrate, yields 3.963 g. of AgCl. Calculate:
  a. The weight percentages of lithium, chlorine, and oxygen in lithium chlorate.
  b. The simplest formula of lithium chlorate.

Solution.
  a. Let us first calculate the weights of the three elements in the 2.500 g. sample. The loss in weight of the sample on heating must represent the weight of oxygen:

$$\text{wt. of oxygen} = 2.500 \text{ g.} - 1.170 \text{ g.} = 1.330 \text{ g. O}$$

To determine the weight of chlorine, we recall from Example 3.2 that the percentage of Cl in AgCl is 24.74. Therefore:

$$\text{wt. of chlorine} = .2474 \times 3.963 \text{ g.} = 0.9804 \text{ g.}$$

The weight of lithium can now be found by difference:

$$\text{wt. lithium} = \text{wt. lithium chlorate} - \text{wt. chlorine} - \text{wt. oxygen}$$

$$= 2.500 \text{ g.} - 1.330 \text{ g.} - 0.980 \text{ g.} = 0.190 \text{ g.}$$

Hence:

$$\% \text{ Li} = \frac{0.190 \text{ g.}}{2.500 \text{ g.}} \times 100 = 7.60\%$$

$$\% \text{ Cl} = \frac{0.9804 \text{ g.}}{2.500 \text{ g.}} \times 100 = 39.22\%$$

$$\% \text{ O} = \frac{1.330 \text{ g.}}{2.500 \text{ g.}} \times 100 = 53.20\%$$

b. In 100 grams of lithium chlorate there are:

$$7.60 \text{ g. Li,} \quad 39.22 \text{ g. Cl,} \quad 53.20 \text{ g. O}$$

We proceed, as usual, to calculate the relative numbers of gram atomic weights:

$$\text{no. of G.A.W. Li} = 7.60 \text{ g. Li} \times \frac{1 \text{ G.A.W. Li}}{6.94 \text{ g. Li}} = 1.10 \text{ G.A.W. Li}$$

$$\text{no. of G.A.W. Cl} = 39.22 \text{ g. Cl} \times \frac{1 \text{ G.A.W. Cl}}{35.45 \text{ g. Cl}} = 1.11 \text{ G.A.W. Cl}$$

$$\text{no. of G.A.W. O} = 53.20 \text{ g. O} \times \frac{1 \text{ G.A.W. O}}{16.00 \text{ g. O}} = 3.33 \text{ G.A.W. O}$$

It is readily seen that the three numbers 1.10, 1.11, and 3.33 are in the ratio 1:1:3. It follows that the simplest formula of lithium chlorate must be $LiClO_3$.

It is found experimentally that lithium chlorate has the properties of an ionic compound. Further investigation shows that $LiClO_3$ is made up of two different kinds of ions, the monatomic Li^+ ion (lithium ion) and the polyatomic ClO_3^- ion (chlorate ion). The chlorate ion, as its formula implies, is a structural unit made up of a chlorine atom joined to three oxygen atoms by strong chemical bonds. The ClO_3^- ion is found in many other compounds including potassium chlorate, $KClO_3$, and magnesium chlorate, $Mg(ClO_3)_2$. Note that the formula of magnesium chlorate is written to emphasize that it contains two ClO_3^- ions for every Mg^{+2} ion.

Ethyl Alcohol

Ethyl alcohol is one of a large number of organic compounds which contain the three elements carbon, hydrogen, and oxygen. These compounds, like the hydrocarbons previously discussed, burn to give carbon dioxide and water. The percentages of carbon and hydrogen can be calculated from the amounts of CO_2 and H_2O produced by combustion of a weighed sample. The percentage of oxygen is then obtained by difference. The calculations involved are illustrated by Example 3.5.

Example 3.5. A sample of ethyl alcohol weighing 2.000 g. is burned to form 3.810 g. of CO_2 and 2.360 g. of H_2O. Calculate the percentages by weight of carbon, hydrogen, and oxygen in ethyl alcohol and the simplest formula of the compound.

Solution. Let us first obtain the weights in grams of the three elements. To do this, we first note that the percentage of carbon in CO_2 is 27.29 (see Example 3.3) and that the percentage of hydrogen in H_2O is 11.19. Consequently:

$$\text{wt. of C} = .2729 \times 3.810 \text{ g.} = 1.040 \text{ g. C}$$
$$\text{wt. of H} = .1119 \times 2.360 \text{ g.} = 0.264 \text{ g. H}$$

The remainder of the 2.000 g. sample of ethyl alcohol must be oxygen:

$$\text{wt. of O} = 2.000 \text{ g.} - (1.040 + 0.264) \text{ g.} = 0.696 \text{ g. O}$$

The percentages of the three elements must then be:

$$\% \text{ C} = \frac{1.040}{2.000} \times 100 = 52.0 \qquad \% \text{ H} = \frac{0.264}{2.000} \times 100 = 13.2 \qquad \% \text{ O} = \frac{0.696}{2.000} \times 100 = 34.8$$

To obtain the simplest formula, we note that in 100 g. of ethyl alcohol, there are:

$$52.0 \text{ g. C} \qquad 13.2 \text{ g. H} \qquad 34.8 \text{ g. O}$$

Converting to gram atomic weights:

$$\text{no. of G.A.W. C} = 52.0 \text{ g. C} \times \frac{1 \text{ G.A.W. C}}{12.01 \text{ g. C}} = 4.33 \text{ G.A.W. C}$$

$$\text{no. of G.A.W. H} = 13.2 \text{ g. H} \times \frac{1 \text{ G.A.W. H}}{1.008 \text{ g. H}} = 13.1 \text{ G.A.W. H}$$

$$\text{no. of G.A.W. O} = 34.8 \text{ g. O} \times \frac{1 \text{ G.A.W. O}}{16.00 \text{ g. O}} = 2.18 \text{ G.A.W. O}$$

To find the simplest whole number ratio, we divide by the smallest of these numbers, 2.18:

$$2 \text{ G.A.W. C} \simeq 6 \text{ G.A.W. H} \simeq 1 \text{ G.A.W. O} \qquad \text{Simplest formula} = C_2H_6O$$

Such important compounds as methyl alcohol (CH_4O), ether ($C_4H_{10}O$), acetone (C_3H_6O), and sugar ($C_{12}H_{22}O_{11}$) may be analyzed in the manner illustrated above for ethyl alcohol. Indeed, the analysis of any organic compound, regardless of how many elements it contains, resembles that of ethyl alcohol. The first step is a carbon-hydrogen determination carried out as described in Example 3.5. Elements such as chlorine, nitrogen, or sulfur are then determined separately. The percentage of oxygen, one of the most difficult elements to analyze for directly, is ordinarily obtained by difference from 100 per cent.

3.4 SCOPE OF QUANTITATIVE ANALYSIS

In the preceding sections of this chapter, we have outlined a few of the analytical procedures which can be applied to the quantitative determination of certain elements. Before leaving this important subject, it may be helpful to indicate some of the other techniques which are available for this purpose.

The methods employed in quantitative analysis can be classified as either chemical or physical, depending upon whether or not the analysis involves carrying out a chemical reaction. The methods that we have discussed so far fall into the first category, involving such reactions as precipitation, combustion, and thermal decomposition. Chemical methods of quantitative analysis are further subdivided into:

Gravimetric methods, by which the amount of reaction product and therefore the percentage by weight of a particular element is obtained by weighing. Examples of such methods include the determination of chlorine by precipitation and weighing as silver chloride and the determination of carbon by combustion and weighing as carbon dioxide.

Volumetric methods, by which the amount of a particular constituent is found by measuring the volume of reagent required to react with it. Several examples of this type of analysis will be discussed later in Chapters 16 and 18.

Physical methods of analysis take advantage of a physical property of a constituent to determine its mass or its concentration in solution. Examples include:

1. The determination of the concentration of a species in solution by measuring the extent to which it absorbs visible light or other radiation. One can determine the concentration of Cu^{+2} ions in water solution by measuring the intensity of the blue color characteristic of solutions of salts containing this ion. The intensity of the color, which is directly proportional to the concentration of Cu^{+2}, is ordinarily determined by comparison with standard solutions of known concentration. This can be done visually, or, more conveniently, with an instrument known as an absorption spectrophotometer, in which the intensity of the light passing through a solution is measured by means of a photoelectric cell.

Absorption spectrophotometry is not limited to the determination of colored species in solution. Almost any inorganic ion or molecule can be converted to a light-absorbing species by treatment with the proper reagent. To cite one example, the Fe^{+3} ion, which is virtually colorless in dilute solution, gives a blood-red color upon addition of SCN^-, with which it reacts to give a species which may be represented most simply as $Fe(SCN)^{+2}$. Within the past two decades, commercial instruments capable of measuring light absorption outside the visible range have been developed. Ultraviolet and infrared spectrophotometry have now become routine analytical techniques. Organic compounds, most of which are colorless, invariably have characteristic absorption spectra in the infrared region. Such spectra are used by organic chemists to identify reaction products and to unravel the structures of molecules of such complex natural products as cholesterol and chlorophyll.

2. The determination of certain elements by measuring the intensity of the light emitted when a sample is heated in a flame. The theory relevant to this type of analysis is mentioned in Chapter 8. At this point, it is sufficient to point out that elements such as sodium and potassium, which are extremely difficult to analyze for by ordinary methods, give off light of a characteristic wavelength when heated to relatively low temperatures. By measuring the intensity of this light, using a device known as a flame photometer, one can analyze for as little as one part of sodium in 100 million with an accuracy of about 1 per cent.

Physical methods of analysis as a general class are particularly well adapted to rapid, small-scale determinations. As the foregoing discussion implies, they are often carried out with the aid of rather complex instruments. The design and commercial availability of such instruments has, within the past decade or so, produced what can only be described as revolutionary advances in the field of analytical chemistry.

3.5 MOLECULAR FORMULAS

Chemical analysis gives only the atom ratio in which elements are combined in a compound; it tells us nothing about the way in which the atoms are grouped. Stated another way, calculations based on analytical data alone give only the simplest formula of a compound. If we wish to go beyond this to arrive at more descriptive formulas, we need additional information concerning the structure of the compound.

For a substance consisting of molecules, it is possible to write a molecular formula which represents the actual number of atoms in the molecule. The molecular formula is often identical with the simplest formula. This is true for water; not only is the atom ratio of hydrogen to oxygen 2:1, but there are two hydrogen atoms and one oxygen atom in a molecule of water. On the other hand, some substances have molecular formulas which are a "multiple" of the simplest formula. For example, we saw in Chapter 2 that a molecule of the hydrocarbon ethylene contains two carbon and four hydrogen atoms; the molecular formula of ethylene is C_2H_4. In contrast, the simplest formula of this compound, as obtained from elementary analysis, is CH_2. The molecular formula of ethylene, C_2H_4, might be considered to be derived from its simplest formula, CH_2, by multiplying by 2. In general, the molecular formula of a substance is always a whole-number multiple of its simplest formula. The multiple may be 1 (as in H_2O, CO_2, and CCl_4), 2 (as in C_2H_4, H_2O_2, Cl_2), 3 (as in O_3, C_3H_6), or even 6 or 8 (as in C_6H_6 and C_8H_{16}). When the molecular formula of a substance is known, it is ordinarily used in preference to the simplest formula, since it gives us more information concerning the structure of the substance.

If we are to derive the molecular formula of a substance from its simplest formula, we must have independent evidence which enables us to decide upon the value of the multiplier referred to previously. The simplest way to obtain such information is to measure the molecular weight of the substance. To illustrate how molecular weight data may be combined with elemental analysis to yield molecular formulas, let us consider the two molecular compounds whose analysis has been described in this chapter, ethyl alcohol and hexane. The simplest formula of ethyl alcohol has been shown to be C_2H_6O; the corresponding formula weight is:

$$(2 \times 12) + (6 \times 1) + 16 = 46$$

Experimentally, it is found that the molecular weight of ethyl alcohol is 46. Consequently, the "multiplier" in this case must be 1; C_2H_6O is the molecular formula as well as the simplest formula of ethyl alcohol. In the case of hexane, the simplest formula is C_3H_7. The formula weight corresponding to C_3H_7 is:

$$(3 \times 12) + (7 \times 1) = 43$$

The molecular weight of hexane is found to be 86; it follows that the molecular formula of hexane must be twice the simplest formula or C_6H_{14}.

It is important to note that an approximate value of the molecular weight is sufficient to determine the molecular formula of a substance from its simplest formula. For example, a rather crude experiment which demonstrated that the molecular weight of hexane was in the range from 80 to 90 would be conclusive proof that its simplest formula should be multiplied by 2 rather than 1, 3, or some other whole number, in order to obtain the molecular formula.

3.6 THE MOLE

In Chapter 2, we considered three chemical mass units: gram equivalent weight, gram atomic weight, and gram molecular weight. A fourth quantity used extensively by chemists, particularly in dealing with mass and energy relationships in chemical reactions, is the **mole,** which may represent:

1. One gram formula weight of a *substance.*

Ar C_6H_{14}

G.A.W. Ar $= 39.95$ g. $= 1$ mole Ar $6 \times$ G.A.W. C $= 72.06$ g.

$14 \times$ G.A.W. H $= 14.11$ g.

G.M.W. $C_6H_{14} = 86.17$ g. $= 1$ mole C_6H_{14}

$CaCO_3$

$$\text{G.A.W. Ca} = \quad 40.08 \text{ g.}$$
$$\text{G.A.W. C} = \quad 12.01 \text{ g.}$$
$$3 \times \text{G.A.W. O} = \quad 48.00 \text{ g.}$$
$$\overline{\qquad\qquad\qquad} $$
$$100.09 \text{ g.} = 1 \text{ mole } CaCO_3$$

Note that for substances such as argon, which are built up of individual atoms, the terms mole and gram atomic weight are synonymous. For a molecular substance, the mole is identical with the gram molecular weight.

2. Avogadro's number of *particles.*

$$1 \text{ mole of Ar atoms} = 6.023 \times 10^{23} \text{ Ar atoms}$$
$$1 \text{ mole } C_6H_{14} \text{ molecules} = 6.023 \times 10^{23} \text{ } C_6H_{14} \text{ molecules}$$
$$1 \text{ mole of Ca}^{+2} \text{ ions} = 6.023 \times 10^{23} \text{ Ca}^{+2} \text{ ions}$$
$$1 \text{ mole of potatoes} = 6.023 \times 10^{23} \text{ potatoes}$$

Note that for substances made up of individual atoms (Ar) or molecules (C_6H_{14}), concepts 1 and 2 are equivalent. One mole of argon (39.95 g.) represents the weight of 6.023×10^{23} argon atoms; 1 mole of hexane molecules (6.023×10^{23} molecules) weighs 86.17 g. For ionic substances, the meaning of the mole differs, depending upon whether one is talking about the gram formula weight of the substance (1 mole $CaCO_3 = 100.09$ g.) or Avogadro's number of ions (1 mole $Ca^{+2} = 6.023 \times 10^{23}$ Ca^{+2} ions). Finally, for potatoes, marbles, Japanese beetles, or other objects of variable mass, the mole can be interpreted only as a number of particles.

Example 3.6 illustrates conversions between moles, grams, and numbers of particles.

Example 3.6. Calculate:
    a. the number of grams in 2.40 moles of potassium chromate, K_2CrO_4.
    b. the number of moles in 312 g. of $CaBr_2$.
    c. the number of electrons in 0.0820 mole of electrons.

Solution
    a. 1 mole $K_2CrO_4 = 2 \times$ G.A.W. K $+$ G.A.W. Cr $+ 4 \times$ G.A.W. O

$$= 194.20 \text{ g. } K_2CrO_4$$

no. of g. $K_2CrO_4 = 2.40$ moles $K_2CrO_4 \times \dfrac{194.20 \text{ g. } K_2CrO_4}{1 \text{ mole } K_2CrO_4} = 466 \text{ g. } K_2CrO_4$

b. 1 mole $CaBr_2$ = G.A.W. Ca + 2 × G.A.W. Br
$$= 199.9 \text{ g. } CaBr_2$$

no. of moles $CaBr_2$ = 312 g. $CaBr_2$ × $\dfrac{1 \text{ mole } CaBr_2}{199.9 \text{ g. } CaBr_2}$ = 1.56 moles $CaBr_2$

c. 1 mole electrons = 6.023×10^{23} electrons

no. of electrons = 0.0820 mole × $\dfrac{6.023 \times 10^{23} \text{ electrons}}{1 \text{ mole electrons}}$ = 4.94×10^{22} electrons

3.7   SUMMARY

The composition by weight of a compound can be determined by quantitative elementary analysis in which:

1. The compound is decomposed to give a residue consisting of an elementary substance. This method is used for many ionic compounds where the weight of metal produced from a weighed sample of the compound is determined. Decomposition may be brought about thermally, chemically, or electrically.

2. The compound is converted to a "reference" compound of known composition. Ionic substances may be converted to insoluble compounds such as $AgCl$, $BaSO_4$, or SnO_2. Molecular substances are often analyzed by combustion. One can, for example, determine the percentages of carbon and hydrogen in an organic compound by burning a weighed sample to form carbon dioxide and water.

Once the proportions by weight of the elements in a compound have been determined, the simplest formula can be calculated. To do this, it is convenient to first calculate the number of gram atomic weights of each element in a given weight of the compound. These numbers are in the same ratio as the numbers of atoms in the simplest formula.

The molecular formula of a substance is always an integral multiple (1, 2, 3, . . .) of the simplest formula. The "multiplier" is readily deduced if the molecular weight of the substance is known; one need only compare the measured molecular weight to the weight calculated for the simplest formula.

Another chemical mass unit, the mole, has been introduced in this chapter. The mole may be thought of as representing a definite weight in grams (one gram formula weight) or a definite number of particles (Avogadro's number, approximately 6.023×10^{23}).

PROBLEMS

3.1   Find the percentages by weight of the elements in the following compounds:
      a. HNO_3 b. $CaSO_4$ c. $C_{12}H_{22}O_{11}$ d. $CaCl_2 \cdot 6\,H_2O$

3.2   What weight of metal could be formed by decomposing:
      a. 12.0 g. of $SrCO_3$?   b. 1.82 g. of $Ni(NO_3)_2$?   c. 5.00 g. of $[Co(NH_3)_5Cl]Cl_2$?

3.3   An oxide of manganese is heated with carbon to give the pure metal and carbon dioxide. A sample of the oxide weighing 10.00 g. when treated in this way gives a residue weighing 6.32 g. What is the simplest formula of the oxide?

3.4   An impure sample of $CuCl_2$ weighing 1.600 g. is dissolved in water and electrolyzed to give 0.345 g. of copper. Assuming that the impurity contains no copper, calculate the percentage of $CuCl_2$ in the sample.

3.5   When a sample of a certain oxide of iron weighing 0.520 g. is heated in hydrogen, 0.364 g. of iron is formed. Calculate the simplest formula of the oxide and the number of grams of water formed in the reaction.

3.6   A sample of gallium bromide weighing 1.000 g. is dissolved in water and treated with excess silver nitrate solution. A total of 1.820 g. of silver bromide, AgBr, is formed. What is the simplest formula of gallium bromide?

3.7   A sample of barium iodide weighing 2.000 g. is dissolved in water and treated with an excess of dilute sulfuric acid. A total of 1.195 g. of insoluble barium sulfate, $BaSO_4$, is formed. What is the simplest formula of barium iodide?

3.8   When a certain compound containing cobalt, carbon, and oxygen is heated in air, it decomposes to form an oxide of cobalt. A sample of the compound weighing 2.500 g. when treated in this way gives off 0.928 g. of carbon dioxide and leaves an oxide residue weighing 1.686 g. Analysis shows the oxide to contain 73.4 per cent by weight of cobalt. Determine the simplest formula of the original compound and that of the oxide.

3.9   A certain hydrate of $CaSO_4$, i.e., $CaSO_4 \cdot x\ H_2O$, is heated to drive off the water. 1.000 g. of hydrate on heating is converted to 0.791 g. of anhydrous $CaSO_4$. What is the formula of the hydrate?

3.10   What information is necessary if one is to determine the empirical formula of a substance? the molecular formula?

3.11   A sample of a certain hydrocarbon weighing 2.32×10^{-3} g. is burned in oxygen to produce 7.77×10^{-3} g. of carbon dioxide. What is the simplest formula of the hydrocarbon? If its molecular weight is approximately 90 ± 5, what is its molecular formula?

3.12   An organic compound containing carbon, hydrogen, and chlorine is found to have a molecular weight of about 150. When 0.593 g. of this compound is burned in an absorption train, 1.063 g. of carbon dioxide and 0.145 g. of water are formed. Find the simplest and molecular formulas of the compound.

3.13   An organic chemist has prepared a compound which he believes to be either stearic acid, $C_{18}H_{36}O_2$, or oleic acid, $C_{18}H_{34}O_2$. If a sample of this compound weighing one tenth of a gram is to be analyzed by combustion in an absorption train, how accurately must the weight of water be determined to decide between these two possibilities?

3.14   Calculate the simplest formulas of compounds that have the following compositions:
    a. 19.3% Na, 26.8% S, 53.9% O   c. 19.2% P, 2.5% H, 78.3% I
    b. 79.3% Tl, 9.9% V, 10.8% O   d. 14.2% Ni, 61.3% I, 20.2% N, 4.3% H

3.15   Calculate:
    a. the mass in grams of 1.28 moles of $Ca(ClO_3)_2$.
    b. the number of moles in 169 g. of sugar, $C_{12}H_{22}O_{11}$.
    c. the total number of ions in 12.6 g. of $CaCl_2$.

*3.16   A mixture of SnO and SnO_2 weighing 1.000 g. is heated with hydrogen; the tin formed weighs 0.850 g. Calculate the percentage of SnO in the mixture.

*3.17   The spectrophotometric determination of the concentration of a species in solution makes use of Beer's Law, which may be stated in the form:

$$\log I/I_0 = -\mu c$$

in which I/I_0 is the fraction of light transmitted, c is the concentration in moles per liter, and μ is a proportionality constant. It is found that when light of a certain wavelength is passed through a solution containing 0.100 mole of Cu^{+2} ion per liter, 88.0 per cent of it is absorbed. Under similar conditions, another solution absorbs 65.0 per cent of the light passing through it. What is the concentration of Cu^{+2} in this solution?

*3.18   A research chemist prepares a compound which he believes to be

$$[Co(NH_3)_5NO_2]Cl_2 \cdot H_2O.$$

He sends it out for analysis and receives the following results:

	Sample 1	Sample 2
% N	30.12	30.22
% Co	21.2	21.2
% Cl	25.52	25.59

a. In your opinion, are these results consistent with the above formula?

b. Shortly before the analysis is received, the chemist performs a test which makes him suspect that the compound may actually be $[Co(NH_3)_5NO_3]Cl_2$. Can you, on the basis of the analytical results, distinguish between these two possibilities?

c. Suggest a way that one might be able to distinguish clearly between these two possibilities.

4 | CHEMICAL EQUATIONS

In the preceding two chapters, we have described, in words, several different chemical reactions. In this chapter, we shall consider how reactions can be interpreted in terms of what are known as chemical equations. Throughout the remainder of this text, extensive use will be made of such equations. In particular, we shall use balanced equations to express the relationship between the amounts of the different substances that participate in a reaction.

4.1 TRANSLATION OF REACTIONS INTO EQUATIONS

A chemical equation is an attempt to summarize, using chemical formulas, the essential features of a reaction. The process of translating a reaction into an equation is not nearly as simple as it may at first appear. Before an equation can be written, a great deal must be known about the corresponding reaction. In particular, the correct formulas and physical states of all reactants and products must be available. To illustrate, consider the reaction between hydrogen and oxygen, which may be translated into a chemical equation as follows:

1. On the left are written the correct formulas of the reactants, on the right the correct formulas of the products. If more than one reactant or more than one product is involved, the formulas are separated by + signs. An arrow is written to indicate the direction in which the reaction proceeds. In this particular case, the two elementary substances hydrogen and oxygen are made up of the diatomic molecules H_2 and O_2. The product of the reaction, water, consists of molecules of formula H_2O. Therefore:

$$H_2 + O_2 \longrightarrow H_2O \qquad (4.1a)$$

(Note that we do not write: $H + O \rightarrow H_2O$ because we know that the reacting species are diatomic molecules rather than individual atoms. In writing equations, we use molecular formulas to represent substances which are known to consist of molecules.)

2. We ordinarily prefer to work with "balanced" equations, that is, equations which conform to the Law of Conservation of Mass. A balanced equation is one that has the same number of atoms of each element on both sides. An equation such as the one above is balanced by writing coefficients in front of the formulas. These coefficients serve as multipliers for the entire formula.

A moment's reflection indicates that equation 4.1a can be balanced by writing:

$$2 H_2 + O_2 \longrightarrow 2 H_2O \tag{4.1b}$$

There are now 4 atoms of hydrogen (2×2) and 2 atoms of oxygen on both sides of the equation. The coefficient 1 is understood for O_2 in equation 4.1b just as the subscript 1 is understood for oxygen in the formula H_2O. It is of course true that the equations:

$$H_2 + \tfrac{1}{2} O_2 \longrightarrow H_2O \tag{4.1c}$$

$$4 H_2 + 2 O_2 \longrightarrow 4 H_2O$$

$$6.96 H_2 + 3.48 O_2 \longrightarrow 6.96 H_2O$$

are also balanced. Ordinarily, the equation that gives the simplest whole-number coefficients (equation 4.1b) is preferred. For certain purposes, however, we shall find it convenient to use an equation such as 4.1c in which the product has a coefficient of one.

3. Throughout this text, the physical states of reactants and products will be indicated by writing the letters (g), (1), or (s) to represent gas, liquid, or solid respectively. Thus, the equation for the reaction of hydrogen with oxygen to form water at atmospheric pressure and 25°C (approximately room temperature) becomes:

$$2 H_2(g) + O_2(g) \longrightarrow 2 H_2O(1) \tag{4.1}$$

If the reaction were carried out at 1000°C, at which temperature water can exist only as a gas, the correct equation would be:

$$2 H_2(g) + O_2(g) \longrightarrow 2 H_2O(g) \tag{4.2}$$

Unless otherwise stated, it will be assumed from now on that all reactants and products in an equation are at room temperature and atmospheric pressure. The letters (g), (1), and (s) will be written to indicate the stable state of each substance under these conditions.

As another example, consider the reaction between aluminum and oxygen. Knowing the formulas of reactants and products, we can write the unbalanced equation:

$$Al + O_2 \longrightarrow Al_2O_3$$

Note that the symbol Al is used to represent an atom in elementary metallic aluminum. For the ionic compound aluminum oxide, the simplest formula, Al_2O_3, is written. Balancing, we obtain:

$$4 Al + 3 O_2 \longrightarrow 2 Al_2O_3$$

Introducing the correct symbols for the physical states of the three substances, we arrive at the final equation.

$$4 Al(s) + 3 O_2(g) \longrightarrow 2 Al_2O_3(s) \tag{4.3}$$

It should be clearly noted that in order to arrive at equation 4.3, it is necessary to know that:

a. The fundamental building block in *solid* elementary aluminum (symbol, Al) is an atom.

b. The *gas* oxygen consists of diatomic molecules, formula O_2.

c. The *solid* compound aluminum oxide has the simplest formula Al_2O_3.

It can hardly be overemphasized that before attempting to represent reactions by means of equations, one must have a clear picture of precisely what is going on in the reaction. Students often fail to realize how much detailed chemical knowledge is required to write even the simplest of equations.

4.2   INTERPRETATION OF BALANCED EQUATIONS: PARTICLE RELATIONS

To illustrate how a balanced equation can be given a quantitative interpretation, consider a specific reaction: the combustion of ethane. When gaseous ethane, molecular formula C_2H_6, is burned in excess air, the products are water and carbon dioxide. From this information, it is possible to write an unbalanced equation for the combustion of ethane:

$$C_2H_6(g) + O_2(g) \longrightarrow CO_2(g) + H_2O(l)$$

Balancing gives:

$$2\ C_2H_6(g) + 7\ O_2(g) \longrightarrow 4\ CO_2(g) + 6\ H_2O(l) \qquad (4.4)$$

The question naturally arises as to what information can be deduced from equation 4.4. In what way is this balanced equation more useful to us than the unbalanced equation that immediately precedes it?

Perhaps the simplest relationship given by a balanced equation is that between the number of particles that react and are formed in the corresponding reaction. In equation 4.4, the coefficients 2, 7, 4, and 6 give the simplest whole-number relationship between the numbers of molecules of C_2H_6, O_2, CO_2, and H_2O participating in the reaction. That is:

2 molecules $C_2H_6 \simeq$ 7 molecules $O_2 \simeq$ 4 molecules $CO_2 \simeq$ 6 molecules H_2O

Not only do 2 molecules of C_2H_6 react with 7 molecules of O_2 to produce 4 molecules of CO_2 and 6 molecules of H_2O, but also:

20 molec. C_2H_6 + 70 molec. $O_2 \longrightarrow$ 40 molec. CO_2 + 60 molec. H_2O

1000 molec. C_2H_6 + 3500 molec. $O_2 \longrightarrow$ 2000 molec. CO_2 + 3000 molec. H_2O

2×10^{23} molec. C_2H_6 + 7×10^{23} molec. $O_2 \longrightarrow$

$$4 \times 10^{23} \text{ molec. } CO_2 + 6 \times 10^{23} \text{ molec. } H_2O$$

In general:

2x molec. C_2H_6 + 7x molec. $O_2 \longrightarrow$ 4x molec. CO_2 + 6x molec. H_2O (4.4a)

in which x can be any positive whole number.

Calculations involving particle relationships are further illustrated by Example 4.1.

Example 4.1.   For the combustion of ethyl alcohol, discussed in Chapter 3, calculate:
   a. the number of molecules of water formed from 11 molecules of ethyl alcohol.
   b. the number of molecules of oxygen required to produce 2.4×10^{23} molecules of carbon dioxide.

Solution.   Before any calculations can be carried out, a balanced equation must be written. Referring to Chapter 3, Section 3.3, we note that the molecular formula of ethyl alcohol is

C_2H_6O; the products formed when it burns are carbon dioxide (CO_2) and water (H_2O). Consequently, the unbalanced equation for the reaction is:

$$C_2H_6O(l) + O_2(g) \longrightarrow CO_2(g) + H_2O(l)$$

Balanced, it is $\quad C_2H_6O(l) + 3\,O_2(g) \longrightarrow 2\,CO_2(g) + 3\,H_2O(l)$

a. The relationship required, that between molecules of water and molecules of ethyl alcohol, is given by the coefficients of the balanced equation:

$$1 \text{ molecule } C_2H_6O \simeq 3 \text{ molecules } H_2O$$

$$\text{no. molecules } H_2O \text{ formed} = 11 \text{ molecules } C_2H_6O \times \frac{3 \text{ molecules } H_2O}{1 \text{ molecule } C_2H_6O}$$

$$= 33 \text{ molecules } H_2O$$

b. The conversion factor needed is that between molecules of O_2 and CO_2:

$$3 \text{ molecules } O_2 \simeq 2 \text{ molecules } CO_2$$

$$\text{no. molecules } O_2 = 2.4 \times 10^{23} \text{ molecules } CO_2 \times \frac{3 \text{ molecules } O_2}{2 \text{ molecules } CO_2}$$

$$= 3.6 \times 10^{23} \text{ molecules } O_2$$

The interpretation of balanced equations in terms of particle relationships is readily extended to reactions in which individual atoms participate as reactants or products. For example, in the equation for the combustion of elementary carbon:

$$C(s) + O_2(g) \longrightarrow CO_2(g) \tag{4.5}$$

we can say that for every *atom* of carbon that reacts, one *molecule* of oxygen is required and one *molecule* of carbon dioxide is formed. Similarly, the equation:

$$2\,AsH_3(g) \longrightarrow 2\,As(s) + 3\,H_2(g) \tag{4.6}$$

tells us that 2 *molecules* of arsine, AsH_3, produce 2 *atoms* of elementary arsenic and 3 *molecules* of hydrogen, or in general:

$$2 \text{ molecules } AsH_3 \simeq 2 \text{ atoms As} \simeq 3 \text{ molecules } H_2$$

The coefficient of the formula of an ionic compound appearing in an equation cannot be given a simple particle interpretation. To illustrate, consider the balanced equation for the reaction of lithium with oxygen:

$$4\,Li(s) + O_2(g) \longrightarrow 2\,Li_2O(s) \tag{4.7}$$

The coefficients on the left side of the equation indicate that 4 atoms of metallic lithium react with 1 molecule of oxygen, but the coefficient 2 preceding the formula for lithium oxide does not represent two particles of any type. Lithium oxide consists of two different particles, Li^+ and O^{-2} ions, rather than a single species. Consequently, the formula Li_2O, unlike Li and O_2, does not stand for an individual particle; rather, it represents an ionic compound in which Li^+ and O^{-2} ions are present in a 2:1 ratio. If one insists upon giving equation 4.7 a particle interpretation, the best that can be done is to say that $2 \times 2 = \underline{4}$ Li^+ ions and $2 \times 1 = \underline{2}$ O^{-2} ions in $Li_2O(s)$ are produced for every $\underline{4}$ lithium atoms and $\underline{1}$ oxygen molecule that react.

4.3 MASS RELATIONS

Moles of Reactants and Products

The mole, defined in Chapter 3 as the amount of matter in one gram formula weight of a substance, is a uniquely useful mass unit insofar as the interpretation of chemical equations is concerned. It can be shown that the coefficients of a balanced equation give the simplest ratio between the numbers of moles of the substances participating in the reaction. For example, equation 4.4, which has been taken to mean that:

$$\text{2 molecules } C_2H_6 + \text{7 molecules } O_2 \longrightarrow \text{4 molecules } CO_2 + \text{6 molecules } H_2O$$

$$(4.4b)$$

can be interpreted in terms of moles as:

$$\text{2 moles } C_2H_6 + \text{7 moles } O_2 \longrightarrow \text{4 moles } CO_2 + \text{6 moles } H_2O \qquad (4.4c)$$

The validity of the relation given by equation 4.4c can be demonstrated by going back to the fundamental relation (4.4a):

$$\text{2x molecules } C_2H_6 + \text{7x molecules } O_2 \longrightarrow \text{4x molecules } CO_2 + \text{6x molecules } H_2O$$

$$(4.4a)$$

This relation is valid for any positive, integral value of x; in particular, it applies when x is set equal to N, Avogadro's number (approximately 6.023×10^{23}).

$$\text{2N molecules } C_2H_6 + \text{7N molecules } O_2 \longrightarrow \text{4N molecules } CO_2 + \text{6N molecules } H_2O$$

But Avogadro's number of molecules, N, comprises 1 gram molecular weight or 1 mole of any molecular substance. Therefore:

$$\text{2 moles } C_2H_6 + \text{7 moles } O_2 \longrightarrow \text{4 moles } CO_2 + \text{6 moles } H_2O \qquad (4.4c)$$

Since one mole of any species (molecule, atom, or ion) always contains the same number of particles, it is possible to generalize the proof outlined above to apply to any balanced chemical equation. Thus, for equation 4.6, we have:

$$\text{2 moles } AsH_3 \longrightarrow \text{2 moles As} + \text{3 moles } H_2 \qquad (4.6c)$$

and for the reaction between lithium and oxygen (equation 4.7):

$$\text{4 moles Li} + \text{1 mole } O_2 \longrightarrow \text{2 moles } Li_2O \qquad (4.7c)$$

Calculations involving the numbers of moles of different substances participating in a reaction can be handled by the same "conversion factor" approach used previously with numbers of particles. Conversions between moles and numbers of particles (atoms, ions, or molecules) are readily made by keeping in mind the fact that 1 mole always represents 6.023×10^{23} particles. That is:

| 1 mole = N atoms | 1 mole = N molecules | 1 mole = N ions |

where $N = 6.023 \times 10^{23}$

Example 4.2. The reaction between aluminum and fluorine may be represented by the equation:

$$2 \text{ Al(s)} + 3 \text{ F}_2\text{(g)} \longrightarrow 2 \text{ AlF}_3\text{(s)}$$

For this reaction, calculate:

      a. the number of moles of AlF_3 produced from 1.45 moles of Al.
      b. the number of moles of F_2 required to form 2.82 moles of AlF_3.
      c. the number of molecules of F_2 required to react with 3.26 moles of Al.

Solution

      a. We need a conversion factor relating moles of Al to moles of AlF_3. This factor is given by the coefficients of the balanced equation:

$$2 \text{ moles Al} \simeq 2 \text{ moles AlF}_3$$

Hence: no. moles AlF_3 = 1.45 moles Al $\times \dfrac{2 \text{ moles AlF}_3}{2 \text{ moles Al}}$ = 1.45 moles $\mathbf{AlF_3}$

      b. Here again, the desired conversion factor is given by the coefficients:

$$3 \text{ moles F}_2 \simeq 2 \text{ moles AlF}_3$$

no. moles F_2 required = 2.82 moles AlF_3 $\times \dfrac{3 \text{ moles F}_2}{2 \text{ moles AlF}_3}$ = 4.23 moles $\mathbf{F_2}$

      c. This part of the problem is most readily approached in two steps. The first step involves the conversion of moles of Al to moles of F_2, using the conversion factor:

$$2 \text{ moles Al} \simeq 3 \text{ moles F}_2$$

Once the number of moles of F_2 has been established, the number of molecules is readily determined since 1 mole of $F_2 = 6.023 \times 10^{23}$ molecules F_2.

(Step 1)   no. moles F_2 = 3.26 moles Al $\times \dfrac{3 \text{ moles F}_2}{2 \text{ moles Al}}$ = 4.89 moles F_2

(Step 2)   no. molecules F_2 = 4.89 moles $F_2 \times \dfrac{6.023 \times 10^{23} \text{ molecules}}{1 \text{ mole}}$

$$= 2.95 \times 10^{24}$$

Note that it is not necessary to solve for the number of moles of F_2 in Step 1; the arithmetic could have been set up in a single expression:

no. molecules F_2 = 3.26 moles Al $\times \dfrac{3 \text{ moles F}_2}{2 \text{ moles Al}} \times \dfrac{6.023 \times 10^{23} \text{ molecules F}_2}{1 \text{ mole F}_2}$

$$= 2.95 \times 10^{24}$$

Grams of Reactants and Products

The usefulness of the mole as a weight unit in chemical calculations depends upon the fact that it represents a definite number of particles. It is this concept which has been emphasized in the foregoing discussion. However, for any given substance, the mole also represents a definite weight in grams. For example:

1 mole CO_2 = G.A.W. C + 2(G.A.W. O) = 12.01 g. + 32.00 g. = 44.01 g.

1 mole AlF_3 = G.A.W. Al + 3(G.A.W. F) = 26.98 g. + 57.00 g. = 83.98 g.

The fact that, for any substance, the mole can be assigned a certain weight in grams makes it possible to convert mole relationships in chemical reactions into gram relationships. To illustrate how this is done, let us return to the equation for the combustion of ethane:

$$2 \text{ C}_2\text{H}_6(\text{g}) + 7 \text{ O}_2(\text{g}) \longrightarrow 4 \text{ CO}_2(\text{g}) + 6 \text{ H}_2\text{O}(\text{l}) \qquad (4.4)$$

We have seen that this equation can be interpreted to mean that:

$$2 \text{ moles C}_2\text{H}_6 + 7 \text{ moles O}_2 \longrightarrow 4 \text{ moles CO}_2 + 6 \text{ moles H}_2\text{O} \qquad (4.4\text{c})$$

To find the corresponding relationship between grams of reactants and products, one need only, for each reactant and product, convert moles to grams:

1 mole $C_2H_6 = 24.02$ g. $+ 6.05$ g. $= 30.07$ g.   2 moles $C_2H_6 = 2(30.07$ g.$) = 60.1$ g. C_2H_6
1 mole O_2 $\qquad\qquad\qquad\qquad = 32.00$ g.   7 moles O_2 $\quad = 7(32.00$ g.$) = 224.0$ g. O_2
1 mole $CO_2 = 12.01$ g. $+ 32.00$ g. $= 44.01$ g.   4 moles $CO_2 = 4(44.01$ g.$) = 176.0$ g. CO_2
1 mole $H_2O = 2.02$ g. $+ 16.00$ g. $= 18.02$ g.   6 moles $H_2O = 6(18.02$ g.$) = 108.1$ g. H_2O

Hence, we have:

$$60.1 \text{ g. C}_2\text{H}_6 + 224.0 \text{ g. O}_2 \longrightarrow 176.0 \text{ g. CO}_2 + 108.1 \text{ g. H}_2\text{O} \qquad (4.4\text{d})$$

A comparison of equations 4.4c and 4.4d reveals two ways in which mole and gram relationships in chemical equations differ:

1. Mole relationships are given directly by the coefficients of the balanced equation and hence are simple, whole-number ratios. Gram relationships are more complex numerically. For example, while the mole ratio of C_2H_6 to CO_2 is $2:4$ or 0.500, the gram relationship is $60.1:176.0$ or 0.341.

2. According to the Law of Conservation of Mass, the total mass in grams of the products must be equal to that of the reactants. No such restriction applies to the numbers of moles of reactants and products, since the mass in grams of a mole differs from one substance to another. In the combustion of ethane (equation 4.4d), the total mass of reactants is 284.1 g. (60.1 g. + 224.0 g. = 284.1 g.); that of the products is the same (176.0 g. + 108.1 g. = 284.1 g.). On the other hand, a total of $2 + 7 = 9$ moles of reactants yields $4 + 6 = 10$ moles of products.

Example 4.3 illustrates mass conversions involving grams of reactants and products.

Example 4.3. Consider the reaction: $2\text{AsH}_3(\text{g}) \rightarrow 2\text{As}(\text{s}) + 3\text{H}_2(\text{g})$. Calculate:
    a. the number of grams of hydrogen formed from 6.00 g. of arsine.
    b. the number of grams of arsenic formed from 3.42 moles of arsine.

Solution
    a. We need to obtain a conversion factor relating grams of AsH_3 to grams of hydrogen. The coefficients of the balanced equation give a conversion factor in moles:

$$2 \text{ moles AsH}_3 \rightleftharpoons 3 \text{ moles H}_2$$

All we need do to arrive at the desired conversion factor is to convert moles to grams:

$$2 \text{ moles AsH}_3 = 2(74.92 + 3.02) \text{ g.} = 155.9 \text{ g.}$$

$$3 \text{ moles H}_2 = 3(2.016) \text{ g.} = 6.048 \text{ g.}$$

Consequently: 155.9 g. $AsH_3 \rightleftharpoons 6.048$ g. H_2

$$\text{no. grams H}_2 = 6.00 \text{ g. AsH}_3 \times \frac{6.048 \text{ g. H}_2}{155.9 \text{ g. AsH}_3} = 0.233 \text{ g. H}_2$$

From a slightly different point of view, we might consider this to be a three-step problem:

	Conversion	Conversion factor
(Step 1)	grams $AsH_3 \longrightarrow$ moles AsH_3	1 mole AsH_3 = 77.94 g. AsH_3
(Step 2)	moles $AsH_3 \longrightarrow$ moles H_2	2 moles $AsH_3 \simeq$ 3 moles H_2
(Step 3)	moles $H_2 \longrightarrow$ grams H_2	1 mole H_2 = 2.016 g. H_2

$$\text{g. } H_2 = 6.00 \text{ g. } AsH_3 \times \frac{1 \text{ mole } AsH_3}{77.94 \text{ g. } AsH_3} \times \frac{3 \text{ moles } H_2}{2 \text{ moles } AsH_3} \times \frac{2.016 \text{ g. } H_2}{1 \text{ mole } H_2} = 0.233 \text{ g. } H_2$$

$$\text{(Step 1)} \qquad \text{(Step 2)} \qquad \text{(Step 3)}$$

It is, of course, immaterial which procedure is followed; the analysis which seems most straightforward is the one to be preferred.

b. This may be visualized as a two-step process in which we first convert moles of AsH_3 to moles of As, using the coefficients of the equation, and then go from moles of As to grams of As, using the fact that 1 mole of As = 74.92 g. As.

(Step 1)   no. moles As = 3.42 moles $AsH_3 \times \dfrac{2 \text{ moles As}}{2 \text{ moles } AsH_3}$ = 3.42 moles As

(Step 2)   no. grams As = 3.42 moles As $\times \dfrac{74.92 \text{ g. As}}{1 \text{ mole As}}$ = 256 g. As

Relationships Involving Other Mass Units

While the gram is the fundamental unit of mass in the metric system, the English system of masses, based on the pound, finds application in a great many industrial laboratories. To the industrial chemist or engineer, the question, "How many pounds of carbon dioxide are formed from a pound of ethane?" is as important as the question, "How many grams of carbon dioxide are produced from a gram of ethane?" is to the student in a general chemistry laboratory. Fortunately, the answers to these questions are the same. In any chemical reaction, *mass relationships expressed in grams remain equally valid for any other unit of mass*. To illustrate, let us return to the combustion of ethane (reaction 4.4). It has been shown that:

$$60.1 \text{ g. } C_2H_6 + 224.0 \text{ g. } O_2 \longrightarrow 176.0 \text{ g. } CO_2 + 108.1 \text{ g. } H_2O \qquad (4.4d)$$

This expression states, among other things, that 60.1 g. of C_2H_6 is equivalent to 176.0 g. of CO_2. In other words, the mass ratio of C_2H_6 to CO_2 is:

$$\frac{60.1 \text{ g.}}{176.0 \text{ g.}} = \frac{60.1}{176.0}$$

The ratio 60.1:176.0 is dimensionless; it expresses the mass ratio of ethane to carbon dioxide not only in grams but also in pounds, tons, or any other unit of mass. That is, 60.1 parts by weight of C_2H_6 always reacts to produce 176.0 parts by weight of CO_2. So long as the masses of both substances are expressed in the same unit, this ratio will be valid. The same argument extends to the other mass relationships implied by equation 4.4d. Consequently:

$$60.1 \text{ lb. } C_2H_6 + 224.0 \text{ lb. } O_2 \longrightarrow 176.0 \text{ lb. } CO_2 + 108.1 \text{ lb. } H_2O$$

$$60.1 \text{ tons } C_2H_6 + 224.0 \text{ tons } O_2 \longrightarrow 176.0 \text{ tons } CO_2 + 108.1 \text{ tons } H_2O$$

4.4 THEORETICAL AND ACTUAL YIELDS

In the preceding section, the rhetorical question, "How many grams of carbon dioxide are formed from a gram of ethane?" was asked. Suppose you were the "student in the general chemistry laboratory" interested in answering this question. Presumably, you would do so by using the proper conversion factor (60.1 g. $C_2H_6 \simeq$ 176.0 g. CO_2) to arrive at an answer of 2.93 g. of carbon dioxide. That is:

$$1.00 \text{ g. } C_2H_6 \times \frac{176.0 \text{ g. } CO_2}{60.1 \text{ g. } C_2H_6} = 2.93 \text{ g. } CO_2$$

In making this calculation, it might not occur to you that one basic assumption is involved; it is assumed that *all* the ethane is converted to carbon dioxide according to the equation:

$$2 \, C_2H_6(g) + 7 \, O_2(g) \longrightarrow 4 \, CO_2(g) + 6 \, H_2O(l) \qquad (4.4)$$

The quantity of carbon dioxide produced may be significantly less than 2.93 g. if:

1. *Some of the ethane does not react.* This would be the case if insufficient oxygen were used to react with all the ethane. Calculation shows that 3.73 g. of oxygen are required to convert a gram of ethane to carbon dioxide; if less than 3.73 g. of oxygen were available, part of the ethane could not react.

Even though an excess of oxygen were used in this reaction, it is still possible that some of the ethane might fail to react. If one attempted to start the reaction at room temperature in the absence of a spark or other source of energy, reaction would occur so slowly that no appreciable quantity of products would be formed in a reasonable period of time.

2. *Side reactions, which lead to the formation of products other than carbon dioxide, consume part of the ethane.* A possible side reaction would be:

$$2 \, C_2H_6(g) + 5 \, O_2(g) \longrightarrow 4 \, CO(g) + 6 \, H_2O(l) \qquad (4.8)$$

This reaction consumes ethane without producing carbon dioxide; if it occurs to an appreciable extent, the amount of carbon dioxide formed from one gram of ethane will be significantly less than 2.93 g. It happens that reaction 4.8 is favored by low concentrations of oxygen and high temperatures; under extreme conditions, carbon monoxide, CO, may be a principal product of the oxidation of ethane.

In summary, it is quite unlikely, for a variety of reasons, that as much as 2.93 g. of carbon dioxide will be produced from one gram of ethane. This quantity, 2.93 g., is referred to as the **theoretical yield** of carbon dioxide; it is the maximum amount of that substance which can be produced from one gram of ethane. The **actual yield** of carbon dioxide in this reaction will ordinarily be less than the theoretical.

Example 4.4. A student attempting to prepare bromobenzene, C_6H_5Br, by the reaction of benzene, C_6H_6, with bromine:

$$C_6H_6(l) + Br_2(l) \longrightarrow C_6H_5Br(l) + HBr(g)$$

is instructed to weigh out 20.0 g. of benzene and 50.0 g. of bromine. What is the theoretical yield of bromobenzene (i.e., the maximum amount of C_6H_5Br that could be formed) in this experiment? If the student actually obtains 28.0 g. of bromobenzene, what is the per cent yield?

Solution. In order to calculate the theoretical yield, we must first decide which reagent to base our calculations on. From the coefficients of the equation, it is clear that one mole of bromine is required for every mole of benzene. In this experiment, there are available:

$$\frac{20.0}{78.1} \text{ moles} = 0.256 \text{ mole } C_6H_6 \qquad\qquad \frac{50.0}{159.8} \text{ moles} = 0.313 \text{ mole } Br_2$$

$$(1 \text{ mole } C_6H_6 = 78.1 \text{ g., } 1 \text{ mole } Br_2 = 159.8 \text{ g.})$$

Clearly, the bromine is in excess; the theoretical yield must then be calculated by determining how much bromobenzene can be produced from the amount of benzene available.

Referring again to the equation, it is clear that one mole of C_6H_6 could yield one mole of C_6H_5Br. We have calculated that 0.256 mole of C_6H_6 is available; it follows that the theoretical yield of C_6H_5Br must be 0.256 mole. Or, since one mole of C_6H_5Br weighs 157.0 g.:

$$\text{Theoretical yield} = 0.256 \text{ mole } C_6H_5Br \times \frac{157.0 \text{ g. } C_6H_5Br}{1 \text{ mole } C_6H_5Br} = 40.2 \text{ g. } C_6H_5Br$$

$$\% \text{ yield} = \frac{\text{Actual yield}}{\text{Theoretical yield}} \times 100 = \frac{28.0 \text{ g.}}{40.2 \text{ g.}} \times 100 = 69.7\%$$

(The remainder of the benzene is consumed in side reactions, producing dibromo- and tri-bromobenzenes, $C_6H_4Br_2$, $C_6H_3Br_3$.)

4.5   SUMMARY

The example that follows illustrates several of the important relationships discussed in this chapter.

Example 4.5. Trinitrotoluene, a solid explosive of molecular formula $C_7H_5N_3O_6$, is burned in a stream of oxygen. Analysis of the products reveals that a mixture of three gases, carbon dioxide, water vapor, and elementary nitrogen (N_2) is formed.
   a. Write a balanced equation for this reaction.
   b. Calculate the number of molecules of oxygen required to react with 2.70×10^5 molecules of trinitrotoluene.
   c. Calculate the number of moles of oxygen required to react with 1.67 g. of tri-nitrotoluene.
   d. Calculate the number of grams of carbon dioxide produced from 2.48 g. of tri-nitrotoluene, assuming that an excess of oxygen is used.
   e. Calculate the theoretical yield, in grams, of water produced by the reaction of 12.6 g. of trinitrotoluene with 10.2 g. of oxygen.

Solution
   a. From the information given, one can write the unbalanced equation:

$$C_7H_5N_3O_6(s) + O_2(g) \longrightarrow CO_2(g) + H_2O(g) + N_2(g)$$

   To balance, we first multiply the coefficient of the trinitrotoluene by 2 to give an integral number of molecules of H_2O and N_2:

$$2 \, C_7H_5N_3O_6(s) + {}_?O_2(g) \longrightarrow 14 \, CO_2(g) + 5 \, H_2O(g) + 3 \, N_2(g)$$

   Note that we now have a total of 33 oxygen atoms on the right as compared to 12 oxygen atoms tied up in the 2 molecules of trinitrotoluene on the left. This means that 21 oxygen atoms must be introduced on the left:

$$2 \, C_7H_5N_3O_6(s) + \tfrac{21}{2} \, O_2(g) \longrightarrow 14 \, CO_2(g) + 5 \, H_2O(g) + 3 \, N_2(g)$$

   Multiplying by 2 to get rid of the fractional coefficients, we have:

$$4 \, C_7H_5N_3O_6(s) + 21 \, O_2(g) \longrightarrow 28 \, CO_2(g) + 10 \, H_2O(g) + 6 \, N_2(g)$$

b. The required conversion factor is given by the coefficients of the balanced equation.

$$4 \text{ molecules } C_7H_5N_3O_6 \rightleftharpoons 21 \text{ molecules } O_2$$

$$\text{no. molecules } O_2 \text{ required} = 2.70 \times 10^5 \text{ molecules } C_7H_5N_3O_6 \times \frac{21 \text{ molecules } O_2}{4 \text{ molecules } C_7H_5N_3O_6}$$

$$= 1.42 \times 10^6 \text{ molecules } O_2$$

c. To obtain the necessary conversion factor, we note that:

$$4 \text{ moles } C_7H_5N_3O_6 \rightleftharpoons 21 \text{ moles } O_2$$

and $1 \text{ mole } C_7H_5N_3O_6 = 227.1 \text{ g.}$ (M.W. $C_7H_5N_3O_6 = 227.1$)

Hence: $4 \times 227.1 \text{ g. } C_7H_5N_3O_6 = 908.4 \text{ g. } C_7H_5N_3O_6 \rightleftharpoons 21 \text{ moles } O_2$

$$\text{no. moles } O_2 \text{ required} = 1.67 \text{ g. } C_7H_5N_3O_6 \times \frac{21 \text{ moles } O_2}{908.4 \text{ g. } C_7H_5N_3O_6}$$

$$= 0.0386 \text{ mole } O_2$$

d. We note from the balanced equation that:

$$4 \text{ moles } C_7H_5N_3O_6 \rightleftharpoons 28 \text{ moles } CO_2 \quad \text{ or } \quad 1 \text{ mole } C_7H_5N_3O_6 \rightleftharpoons 7 \text{ moles } CO_2$$

but, since 1 mole $C_7H_5N_3O_6$ weighs 227.1 g. and 1 mole CO_2 weighs 44.01 g.,

$$227.1 \text{ g. } C_7H_5N_3O_6 \rightleftharpoons 7 \times 44.01 \text{ g. } CO_2 = 308.1 \text{ g. } CO_2$$

$$\text{no. g. } CO_2 \text{ produced} = 2.48 \text{ g. } C_7H_5N_3O_6 \times \frac{308.1 \text{ g. } CO_2}{227.1 \text{ g. } C_7H_5N_3O_6} = 3.36 \text{ g. } CO_2$$

e. Our problem here is to determine which reagent to base our calculations on. There is available:

$$12.6 \text{ g. } C_7H_5N_3O_6 \times \frac{1 \text{ mole } C_7H_5N_3O_6}{227.1 \text{ g. } C_7H_5N_3O_6} = 0.0555 \text{ mole } C_7H_5N_3O_6$$

and $10.2 \text{ g. } O_2 \times \dfrac{1 \text{ mole } O_2}{32.0 \text{ g. } O_2} = 0.319 \text{ mole } O_2$

According to the balanced equation, we need 21 moles of O_2 for every 4 moles of $C_7H_5N_3O_6$. Consequently, for 0.0555 mole of $C_7H_5N_3O_6$:

$$\text{no. moles } O_2 \text{ required} = 0.0555 \text{ mole } C_7H_5N_3O_6 \times \frac{21 \text{ moles } O_2}{4 \text{ moles } C_7H_5N_3O_6}$$

$$= 0.291 \text{ mole } O_2$$

Clearly, the amount of O_2 available, 0.319 mole, is greater than that required, 0.291 mole. Consequently, we must base our calculations on the trinitrotoluene.

Referring again to the balanced equation, we see that:

$$4 \text{ moles } C_7H_5N_3O_6 \rightleftharpoons 10 \text{ moles } H_2O$$

Hence, the number of moles of H_2O formed is:

$$0.0555 \text{ mole } C_7H_5N_3O_6 \times \frac{10 \text{ moles } H_2O}{4 \text{ moles } C_7H_5N_3O_6} = 0.139 \text{ mole } H_2O$$

Since one mole of $H_2O = 18.0$ g., the theoretical yield of H_2O, in grams, is:

$$0.139 \text{ mole } H_2O \times \frac{18.0 \text{ g. } H_2O}{1 \text{ mole } H_2O} = 2.50 \text{ g. } H_2O$$

PROBLEMS

·4.1 Write balanced equations for each of the following reactions, following the procedure outlined in Section 4.1.
  a. The reaction that occurs when Fe_3O_4 is heated in a stream of hydrogen at 500°C. (cf. Example 3.1, Chapter 3).
  b. The reaction that occurs when lithium chlorate is heated to 300°C. (cf. Example 3.4, Chapter 3).
  c. The combustion of ammonia, which yields water vapor and a gas of molecular formula NO.
  d. The combustion of hexane (cf. Chapter 3).

4.2 Consider the reaction represented by the equation:

$$4 HCl(g) + O_2(g) \longrightarrow 2 Cl_2(g) + 2 H_2O(l)$$

  a. How many molecules of Cl_2 can be produced from 24 molecules of HCl?
  b. How many molecules of O_2 are required to form 36 molecules of H_2O?
  c. 6.0×10^{23} molecules of HCl will react with how many molecules of O_2?
  d. Suppose 52 molecules of HCl and 16 molecules of O_2 are present in a mixture. Which reactant is in excess? What is the maximum number of molecules of Cl_2 that can be produced from this reaction mixture?

· 4.3 In the combustion of propyl alcohol:

$$2 C_3H_8O(l) + 9 O_2(g) \longrightarrow 6 CO_2(g) + 8 H_2O(g)$$

  a. How many moles of CO_2 can be formed from 3.68 moles of propyl alcohol?
  b. How many moles of O_2 are required to react with 0.931 mole of propyl alcohol?
  c. How many molecules of H_2O can be formed from 1.58×10^{-5} moles of O_2?
  d. What is the maximum number of moles of CO_2 that can be formed from a mixture of 1.81 moles of propyl alcohol and 7.43 moles of O_2?

· 4.4 For the reaction:

$$3 NO_2(g) + H_2O(l) \longrightarrow 2 HNO_3(l) + NO(g)$$

  calculate:
  a. the number of grams of HNO_3 that can be formed from 12.0 g. of NO_2.
  b. the number of grams of H_2O required to react with 34.6 g. of NO_2.
  c. the number of moles of NO that can be formed from 1.64 g. of NO_2.
  d. the number of grams of HNO_3 that can be formed from 2.94 moles of NO_2.

4.5 Ammonia can be produced by heating ammonium chloride with calcium oxide:

$$2 NH_4Cl(s) + CaO(s) \longrightarrow 2 NH_3(g) + CaCl_2(s) + H_2O(g)$$

  a. How many grams of NH_4Cl are needed to produce 0.182 mole of NH_3?
  b. If it is desired to use a 50 per cent excess of calcium oxide, how many grams of CaO should be used to produce 0.182 mole of NH_3?

4.6 Carbon dioxide can be prepared by allowing concentrated sulfuric acid to drop on sodium hydrogen carbonate:

$$2 NaHCO_3(s) + H_2SO_4(l) \longrightarrow 2 CO_2(g) + Na_2SO_4(s) + 2 H_2O(l)$$

  a. If the $NaHCO_3$ used in this preparation is 94 per cent pure, how many grams of it will be required to form 10.0 g. of CO_2?
  b. If the sulfuric acid is used in the form of a water solution which is 52 per cent H_2SO_4 by weight and has a density of 1.26 g./ml., what volume of this solution must be used to produce 10.0 g. of carbon dioxide?

4.7   Consider the reaction:

$$Fe_2O_3(s) + 3\ C(s) \longrightarrow 3\ CO_2(g) + 2\ Fe(s)$$

a. How many tons of carbon are required to react with 920 lb. of Fe_2O_3?
b. How many tons of coke (96 per cent carbon) are required to react with one ton of iron ore which is 46 per cent by weight Fe_2O_3?
c. How many pounds of iron can be formed from 2.48×10^4 g. of Fe_2O_3?

4.8   Nitrobenzene, $C_6H_5NO_2$, can be prepared from benzene by the following reaction:

$$C_6H_6(l) + HNO_3(l) \longrightarrow C_6H_5NO_2(l) + H_2O(l)$$

a. If one starts with 10.0 g. of benzene and 15.0 g. of nitric acid, what is the theoretical yield of nitrobenzene?
b. If 8.15 g. of nitrobenzene are actually formed in this reaction, what is the percentage yield?

4.9   A student in the organic chemistry laboratory prepares ethyl bromide, C_2H_5Br, by reacting ethyl alcohol with phosphorus tribromide:

$$3\ C_2H_5OH(l) + PBr_3(l) \longrightarrow 3\ C_2H_5Br(l) + H_3PO_3(s)$$

He is told to react 24.0 g. of ethyl alcohol with 39.0 g. of phosphorus tribromide.
a. What is the theoretical yield of ethyl bromide?
b. If the student actually obtains 36.0 g. of C_2H_5Br, what is the percentage yield?

4.10 A student in the inorganic chemistry laboratory wishes to prepare 15 g. of the compound $[Co(NH_3)_5SCN]Cl_2$, starting with $[Co(NH_3)_5Cl]Cl_2$:

$$[Co(NH_3)_5Cl]Cl_2(s) + KSCN(s) \longrightarrow [Co(NH_3)_5SCN]Cl_2(s) + KCl(s)$$

He is instructed to use a 75 per cent excess of potassium thiocyanate, KSCN, and is told that he can expect to get a 63 per cent yield in the reaction. How many grams of the two starting materials should he use?

4.11 Consider the combustion of acetylene:

$$2\ C_2H_2(g) + 5\ O_2(g) \longrightarrow 4\ CO_2(g) + 2\ H_2O(g)$$

Complete the following table:

—— molecules C_2H_2 +	—— molecules O_2 →	—— molecules CO_2 +	10 molecules H_2O
1.46 moles C_2H_2 +	—— moles O_2 →	—— molecules CO_2 + —— moles	H_2O
—— grams C_2H_2 + 1560 molecules O_2 →	—— moles CO_2 + —— moles		H_2O
—— grams C_2H_2 + —— grams O_2 → 6.21 moles CO_2 + —— moles			H_2O
6.43 grams C_2H_2 + —— grams O_2 → —— grams CO_2 + —— grams			H_2O

*4.12 A student determines the formula of copper sulfide by heating a piece of copper wire weighing 0.536 g. with 0.438 g. of sulfur. The excess sulfur burns off as SO_2. What weight of SO_2 is formed:
a. if the formula of the sulfide formed is Cu_2S?
b. if the formula of the sulfide formed is CuS?

*4.13 A student is asked to prepare 0.250 mole of a pure compound C by the following reaction sequence:

$$2\ A \longrightarrow B \quad \text{and} \quad 3\ B \longrightarrow 2\ C$$

in which A and B represent two other compounds. He is told to expect to get a 71 per cent yield in the first step of this sequence and an 82 per cent yield in the second step. He is also expected to purify compound C by recrystallizing it from hot water; it is estimated that 22 per cent of it will be lost in the recrystallization. How many moles of A should he start with?

*4.14 The compound known as chromous acetate, $Cr(C_2H_3O_2)_2$, can be prepared by the following reaction:

$$CrCl_3 \cdot 6\ H_2O(s) + \tfrac{1}{2}\ H_2(g) + 2\ NaC_2H_3O_2(s) \longrightarrow$$

$$Cr(C_2H_3O_2)_2(s) + HCl(g) + 2\ NaCl(s) + 6\ H_2O(l)$$

a. A student starting with 30.0 g. of $CrCl_3 \cdot 6\ H_2O$ and 84.0 g. of sodium acetate, obtains 10.2 g. of chromous acetate. What is his percentage yield?

b. Referring to the description of this preparation, given in *Inorganic Syntheses*, Vol. 1, p. 122, suggest an explanation for the comparatively low yield.

5 | ENERGY CHANGES IN REACTIONS

One of the most important aspects of a reaction is the energy change that accompanies it. We are often far more interested in the amount of energy that can be obtained from a reaction than in the products formed. Fuel oil is burned in a furnace to produce heat rather than to serve as a source of carbon dioxide and water vapor. In the combustion of coal, our primary interest is in the amount of energy that can be obtained from a given weight of coal; we are much less concerned with the weight of ashes formed.

Almost without exception, chemical reactions, as they are ordinarily carried out in the laboratory, evolve or absorb energy in the form of heat. The study of the heat changes accompanying chemical reactions, known as thermochemistry, will occupy our attention throughout the first section of this chapter. Here, we will be particularly interested in the quantitative relationship between the heat change and the amounts of substances participating in the reaction.

In many cases, energy in a form other than heat is absorbed or evolved when a reaction takes place. For example, certain reactions require the absorption of light energy; in a relatively few reactions, light is spontaneously emitted. It is possible to carry out many reactions in such a way that a large fraction of the energy change takes the form of electrical or mechanical energy. Energy effects of these types will be discussed qualitatively in Section 5.2.

The energy change which we can see, feel, or otherwise detect in the surroundings when a reaction is carried out reflects a difference in chemical energies between reactants and products. A study of the chemical energies of substances helps us to decide in advance whether or not it is possible to carry out a reaction under a particular set of conditions. This is the ultimate purpose of the discipline, known as chemical thermodynamics, to which we shall give a brief introduction in the last sections of this chapter (Sections 5.3–5.5). In later chapters, we shall apply certain of the principles of thermodynamics in discussing the important topic of chemical equilibrium. In particular, we shall find the concept of free energy, introduced in Section 5.4, to be extremely useful in Chapters 14 and 21.

5.1 THERMOCHEMISTRY

Exothermic and Endothermic Reactions

From a thermochemical standpoint, it is possible to classify reactions into one or the other of two categories. A reaction which proceeds with the evolution of heat is referred to as an **exothermic** reaction; one in which heat is absorbed is called **endothermic.** The reactions of metals with oxygen are almost invariably exothermic; the decomposition to the elements of the corresponding metal oxides is endothermic.

The direction of the heat change in a chemical reaction is often indicated qualitatively by including the word "heat" in the equation:

$$2 \, Mg(s) + O_2(g) \longrightarrow 2 \, MgO(s) + heat \qquad (5.1)$$

$$2 \, HgO(s) + heat \longrightarrow 2 \, Hg(l) + O_2(g) \qquad (5.2)$$

Equation 5.1 represents an exothermic reaction, equation 5.2 an endothermic reaction.

When the direction of the heat change is expressed in this way, it always refers to the overall effect of the reaction. We know from experience that a piece of magnesium has to absorb heat before it can begin to react with oxygen. However, a much greater quantity of heat is liberated when the magnesium burns; the net effect is an evolution of heat.

Thermochemical Equations

We are often interested not only in the direction of the heat change in a reaction but also in the amount of heat absorbed or evolved. The magnitude of the heat change varies widely from one reaction to another. When four moles of silver and one mole of oxygen, originally at 25°C, react in an open container at atmospheric pressure to form two moles of silver oxide at the same temperature and pressure, 14.6 kilocalories of heat are evolved. The reaction of one mole of oxygen with an equivalent amount of zinc under the same conditions produces 166 kcal. These experimental observations may be expressed by writing:

$$4 \, Ag(s) + O_2(g) \longrightarrow 2 \, Ag_2O(s) + 14.6 \, kcal. \qquad (5.3)$$

$$2 \, Zn(s) + O_2(g) \longrightarrow 2 \, ZnO(s) + 166 \, kcal. \qquad (5.4)$$

Similarly, for the endothermic decomposition of mercuric oxide:

$$2 \, HgO(s) + 43.4 \, kcal. \longrightarrow 2 \, Hg(l) + O_2(g) \qquad (5.5)$$

Equations such as 5.3 to 5.5, in which the heat change is numerically specified, are referred to as **thermochemical equations.** The heat change in such an equation is always expressed in terms of moles of reactants and products. The 43.4 kcal. appearing in equation 5.5 is the amount of heat absorbed when two moles of mercuric oxide decompose to form two moles of mercury and one mole of oxygen.*

---

* The amount of heat absorbed or evolved in a reaction depends to a slight extent upon the pressure and temperature at which the reaction is carried out. Unless otherwise specified, the thermochemical equations written here will refer to the heat change observed when the reactants at 25°C and atmospheric pressure are converted to products at the same final temperature and pressure.

It is particularly important that the physical states of reactants and products be specified in writing a thermochemical equation. The magnitude of the heat effect is changed if the state of one of the products or reactants changes. For example, the formation of one mole of liquid water from the elements liberates 68.3 kcal. of heat. On the other hand, if the product is water vapor, only 57.8 kcal. are evolved:

$$H_2(g) + \tfrac{1}{2} O_2(g) \longrightarrow H_2O(g) + 57.8 \text{ kcal.} \tag{5.6}$$

$$H_2(g) + \tfrac{1}{2} O_2(g) \longrightarrow H_2O(l) + 68.3 \text{ kcal.} \tag{5.7}$$

The difference in the heat changes of the two reactions, 10.5 kcal., is precisely the amount of heat required to vaporize one mole of water at 25°C and 1 atm.

One of the fundamental laws of thermochemistry is that the amount of heat evolved or absorbed in a reaction is directly proportional to the amount of reactants consumed or products formed. Since it is known that 166 kcal. are evolved when two moles of zinc react with one mole of oxygen to form two moles of zinc oxide, it follows that exactly half as much heat, 83 kcal., is evolved when one mole of zinc oxide is formed; the reaction of three moles of oxygen with zinc evolves 3×166 kcal. $=$ 498 kcal., and so forth.

Example 5.1.   Using equation 5.5, calculate:
   a. the amount of heat absorbed when 3.84 moles of mercuric oxide decomposes.
   b. the number of grams of mercury produced by the absorption of 1.00 kcal. of heat.

Solution
   a. The problem is one of "converting" moles of HgO to kcal. of heat absorbed. The conversion factor is given by the equation:

$$2 \text{ moles HgO} \simeq 43.4 \text{ kcal.}$$

Hence: amount of heat absorbed $= 3.84 \text{ moles HgO} \times \dfrac{43.4 \text{ kcal.}}{2 \text{ moles HgO}} = 83.3 \text{ kcal.}$

   b. Here we wish to establish a relationship between the amount of heat absorbed and the number of grams of mercury produced. The equation relates heat absorbed to moles of mercury:

$$43.4 \text{ kcal.} \simeq 2 \text{ moles Hg}$$

But, since 2 moles of mercury weigh 2×200.6 g. $= 401.2$ g., the desired conversion factor must be:

$$43.4 \text{ kcal.} \simeq 401.2 \text{ g. Hg}$$

no. of grams Hg produced $= 1.00 \text{ kcal.} \times \dfrac{401.2 \text{ g. Hg}}{43.4 \text{ kcal.}} = 9.24 \text{ g. Hg}$

Thermochemical equations, in many of their properties, resemble ordinary algebraic equations. For example, since the heat change in a reaction is directly proportional to the amounts of reactants or products, it follows that both sides of a thermochemical equation can be multiplied by the same factor without affecting its validity. The equation:

$$H_2(g) + \tfrac{1}{2} O_2(g) \longrightarrow H_2O(l) + 68.3 \text{ kcal.} \tag{5.7}$$

can equally well be written:

$$2 H_2(g) + O_2(g) \longrightarrow 2 H_2O(l) + 136.6 \text{ kcal.} \tag{5.7a}$$

Similarly, the algebraic equation: $x + \tfrac{1}{2} y = z + 4$, remains equally valid if multiplied by 2 to give: $2x + y = 2z + 8$.

Three other ways in which thermochemical equations resemble algebraic equations are listed below.

1. Thermochemical equations remain valid if written in the reverse direction. Equation 5.7a, which says that 136.6 kcal. of heat are evolved when two moles of liquid water are formed from the elements, can be reversed to read:

$$2 H_2O(l) + 136.6 \text{ kcal.} \longrightarrow 2 H_2(g) + O_2(g)$$

indicating that this same quantity of heat, 136.6 kcal., must be absorbed in order to decompose two moles of water to the elements.

2. It is possible to add or subtract the same quantity from both sides of a thermochemical equation without affecting its validity. For instance, the equation for the formation of zinc oxide:

$$2 Zn(s) + O_2(g) \longrightarrow 2 ZnO(s) + 166 \text{ kcal.} \tag{5.4}$$

can equally well be written:

$$2 Zn(s) + O_2(g) - 166 \text{ kcal.} \longrightarrow 2 ZnO(s) \tag{5.4a}$$

The distinction between equations 5.4 and 5.4a may appear to be a trivial one. Where 5.4 states that 166 kcal. of heat are evolved in the formation of two moles of zinc oxide, 5.4a indicates that -166 kcal. are absorbed in the same reaction. Nevertheless, there are certain advantages in the interpretation suggested by equation 5.4a. In particular, we see that the amount of heat evolved in a reaction is equal in magnitude but opposite in sign to the amount of heat absorbed in the same reaction.

3. Two thermochemical equations can be added or subtracted to obtain a third equally valid equation. To illustrate the use of this principle, consider the following equations:

$$Sn(s) + Cl_2(g) \longrightarrow SnCl_2(s) + 83.6 \text{ kcal.} \tag{5.8}$$

and:

$$SnCl_2(s) + Cl_2(g) \longrightarrow SnCl_4(l) + 46.7 \text{ kcal.} \tag{5.9}$$

If we wish to obtain the amount of heat evolved when one mole of $SnCl_4$ is formed from the elements, it is only necessary to add equations 5.8 and 5.9:

$$Sn(s) + 2 Cl_2(g) \longrightarrow SnCl_4(l) + 130.3 \text{ kcal.} \tag{5.10}$$

Example 5.2 illustrates how these relationships can be used to calculate heat changes for reactions in which direct measurement would be difficult if not impossible.

Example 5.2.   A student is asked to determine the heat change for the formation of the organic compound C_5H_{12} (n-pentane) from the elements:

$$5 C(s) + 6 H_2(g) \longrightarrow C_5H_{12}(l) \tag{a}$$

Although this reaction cannot be carried out in the laboratory, the heat changes for the following reactions can be measured:

$$C_5H_{12}(l) + 8 O_2(g) \longrightarrow 5 CO_2(g) + 6 H_2O(l) + 837 \text{ kcal.} \tag{b}$$
$$C(s) + O_2(g) \longrightarrow CO_2(g) + 94 \text{ kcal.} \tag{c}$$
$$H_2(g) + \tfrac{1}{2} O_2(g) \longrightarrow H_2O(l) + 68 \text{ kcal.} \tag{d}$$

Show how the information given by thermochemical equations b, c, and d can be used to calculate the heat change corresponding to a.

Solution. We proceed exactly as we would with algebraic equations; our goal is to combine *b*, *c*, and *d* in such a way as to arrive at *a*. To do this, it will be convenient to start with *b* and eliminate the CO_2 and H_2O, neither of which appear in *a*. To get rid of the CO_2, we need only multiply *c* by 5 and subtract from *b*:

$$(b): \quad C_5H_{12}(l) + 8\ O_2(g) \longrightarrow 5\ CO_2(g) + 6\ H_2O(l) + 837 \text{ kcal.}$$
$$5 \times (c): \quad 5\ C(s) + 5\ O_2(g) \longrightarrow 5\ CO_2(g) \qquad\qquad + 470 \text{ kcal.}$$

Subtract: $C_5H_{12}(l) + 3\ O_2(g) - 5\ C(s) \longrightarrow 6\ H_2O(l) + 367 \text{ kcal.}$ (*e*)

To eliminate the water from equation *e*, we multiply *d* by 6 and subtract:

$$(e): \quad C_5H_{12}(l) + 3\ O_2(g) - 5\ C(s) \longrightarrow 6\ H_2O(l) + 367 \text{ kcal.}$$
$$6 \times (d): \quad 6\ H_2(g) + 3\ O_2(g) \qquad\qquad \longrightarrow 6\ H_2O(l) + 408 \text{ kcal.}$$

Subtract: $C_5H_{12}(l) - 6\ H_2(g) - 5\ C(s) \longrightarrow \qquad\quad - 41 \text{ kcal.}$

or: $C_5H_{12}(l) + 41 \text{ kcal.} \longrightarrow 6\ H_2(g) + 5\ C(s)$

Reversing, we obtain the desired thermochemical equation:

$$6\ H_2(g) + 5\ C(s) \longrightarrow C_5H_{12}(l) + 41 \text{ kcal.} \qquad\qquad (a)$$

Heats of Formation

There are many thousands of reactions for which heat changes have been experimentally determined. It would require a volume considerably larger than this text to list all of the corresponding thermochemical equations, any of which may be of value in studying a particular reaction. A more concise way of expressing thermochemical data involves tabulating quantities known as heats of formation. In this way, it is possible to list on a single page enough information to calculate heat changes for several thousand reactions.

The heat of formation (Hf) of a compound is defined as the amount of heat *absorbed* per mole when the compound is formed from the elementary substances. From the equations:

$$\tfrac{1}{2} N_2(g) + O_2(g) + 8.1 \text{ kcal.} \longrightarrow NO_2(g) \qquad\qquad (5.11)$$

$$Zn(s) + \tfrac{1}{2} O_2(g) \longrightarrow ZnO(s) + 83.2 \text{ kcal.} \qquad\qquad (5.12)$$

it is evident that the heats of formation of nitrogen dioxide and zinc oxide are $+8.1$ and -83.2 kcal./mole respectively. Since the formation of a compound from the elements usually evolves heat, the heat of formation of most compounds is a negative quantity (Table 5.1).

For many compounds, including zinc oxide (equation 5.12), it is possible to determine heats of formation by measuring the heat change involved in the direct reaction of the elements. Where a compound cannot be formed from the elements in a single step, the heat of formation may be obtained by following an indirect path. Such a path was indicated in Example 5.2, in which we found that by combining the thermochemical equations for the combustion of pentane, carbon, and hydrogen, one could arrive at the equation:

$$5\ C(s) + 6\ H_2(g) \longrightarrow C_5H_{12}(l) + 41 \text{ kcal.} \qquad\qquad (5.13)$$

indicating that the heat of formation of pentane is -41 kcal./mole.

Quite obviously, a list of heats of formation such as that given in Table 5.1 can be used to write thermochemical equations for reactions involving the synthesis of a compound from the elements. Knowing that the heat of formation of ammonia, NH_3, is -11.0 kcal./mole, it follows that 22.0 kcal. of heat must be evolved (-22.0 kcal. absorbed) when two moles of ammonia are formed from the elements, nitrogen and hydrogen, or:

$$3 H_2(g) + N_2(g) \longrightarrow 2 NH_3(g) + 22.0 \text{ kcal.} \tag{5.14}$$

TABLE 5.1   HEATS OF FORMATION (KCAL/MOLE) AT 25°C, 1 ATM.

$AgBr(s)$	-23.8	$C_2H_2(g)$	54.2	$H_2O_2(l)$	-44.8	$NH_3(g)$	-11.0
$AgCl(s)$	-30.4	$C_2H_4(g)$	12.5	$H_2S(g)$	-4.8	$NH_4Cl(s)$	-75.4
$AgI(s)$	-14.9	$C_2H_6(g)$	-20.2	$H_2SO_4(l)$	-193.9	$NH_4NO_3(s)$	-87.3
$Ag_2O(s)$	-7.3	$C_3H_8(g)$	-24.8	$HgO(s)$	-21.7	$NO(g)$	$+21.6$
$Ag_2S(s)$	-7.6	$n\text{-}C_4H_{10}(g)$	-29.8	$HgS(s)$	-13.9	$NO_2(g)$	$+8.1$
$Al_2O_3(s)$	-399.1	$n\text{-}C_5H_{12}(l)$	-41.4	$KBr(s)$	-93.7	$NiO(s)$	-58.4
$BaCl_2(s)$	-205.6	$C_2H_5OH(l)$	-66.4	$KCl(s)$	-104.2	$PbBr_2(s)$	-66.3
$BaCO_3(s)$	-291.3	$CoO(s)$	-57.2	$KClO_3(s)$	-93.5	$PbCl_2(s)$	-85.9
$BaO(s)$	-133.4	$Cr_2O_3(s)$	-269.7	$KF(s)$	-134.5	$PbO(s)$	-52.1
$Ba(OH)_2(s)$	-226.2	$CuO(s)$	-37.1	$KOH(s)$	-101.8	$PbO_2(s)$	-66.1
$BaSO_4(s)$	-350.2	$Cu_2O(s)$	-39.8	$MgCl_2(s)$	-153.4	$Pb_3O_4(s)$	-175.6
$CaCl_2(s)$	-190.0	$CuS(s)$	-11.6	$MgCO_3(s)$	-266	$PCl_3(g)$	-73.2
$CaCO_3(s)$	-288.5	$CuSO_4(s)$	-184.0	$MgO(s)$	-143.8	$PCl_5(g)$	-95.4
$CaO(s)$	-151.9	$Fe_2O_3(s)$	-196.5	$Mg(OH)_2(s)$	-221.0	$SiO_2(s)$	-205.4
$Ca(OH)_2(s)$	-235.8	$Fe_3O_4(s)$	-267.0	$MgSO_4(s)$	-305.5	$SnCl_2(s)$	-83.6
$CaSO_4(s)$	-342.4	$HBr(g)$	-8.7	$MnO(s)$	-92.0	$SnCl_4(l)$	-130.3
$CCl_4(l)$	-33.3	$HCl(g)$	-22.1	$MnO_2(s)$	-124.5	$SnO(s)$	-68.4
$CH_4(g)$	-17.9	$HF(g)$	-64.2	$NaBr(s)$	-86.0	$SnO_2(s)$	-138.8
$CHCl_3(l)$	-31.5	$HI(g)$	$+6.2$	$NaCl(s)$	-98.2	$SO_2(g)$	-71.0
$CH_3OH(l)$	-57.0	$HNO_3(l)$	-41.4	$NaF(s)$	-136.0	$SO_3(g)$	-94.5
$CO(g)$	-26.4	$H_2O(g)$	-57.8	$NaI(s)$	-68.8	$ZnO(s)$	-83.2
$CO_2(g)$	-94.1	$H_2O(l)$	-68.3	$NaOH(s)$	-102.0	$ZnS(s)$	-48.5

Heats of formation can also be applied to the calculation of heat changes for reactions in which more than one compound is involved. It can be shown that the *amount of heat absorbed* in any reaction is equal to the *sum of the heats of formation of the products minus the sum of the heats of formation of the reactants.*

$$\text{Heat absorbed} = \Sigma \text{ Hf products} - \Sigma \text{ Hf reactants} \tag{5.15}$$

Any elementary substance taking part in the reaction is omitted in taking these sums; the "heat of formation" of an elementary substance is, by definition, zero.

The application of equation 5.15 is illustrated by Example 5.3.

Example 5.3.   Using Table 5.1, calculate the heat changes for the reactions:
   a. $2 MgCl_2(s) + O_2(g) \longrightarrow 2 MgO(s) + 2 Cl_2(g)$
   b. $C_3H_8(g) + 5 O_2(g) \longrightarrow 3 CO_2(g) + 4 H_2O(l)$
Solution
   a. The amount of heat absorbed, according to equation 5.15, must be the difference between the heat of formation of two moles of MgO and the heat of formation of two moles of $MgCl_2$.

$$\text{Heat absorbed} = 2 \text{ Hf MgO} - 2 \text{ Hf MgCl}_2 = 2(-143.8 \text{ kcal.}) - 2(-153.4 \text{ kcal.})$$
$$= -287.6 \text{ kcal.} + 306.8 \text{ kcal.}$$
$$= +19.2 \text{ kcal.}$$

   or: $2 MgCl_2(s) + O_2(g) + 19.2 \text{ kcal.} \longrightarrow 2 MgO(s) + 2 Cl_2(g)$

b. Proceeding in the same way:

$$\text{Heat absorbed} = 3 \text{ Hf CO}_2(\text{g}) + 4 \text{ Hf H}_2\text{O}(\text{l}) - \text{Hf C}_3\text{H}_8(\text{g})$$
$$= 3(-94.1 \text{ kcal.}) + 4(-68.3 \text{ kcal.}) - (-24.8 \text{ kcal.})$$
$$= -531 \text{ kcal.}$$

It follows that 531 kcal. of heat are evolved for the reaction as written, i.e,

$$\text{C}_3\text{H}_8(\text{g}) + 5 \text{ O}_2(\text{g}) \longrightarrow 3 \text{ CO}_2(\text{g}) + 4 \text{ H}_2\text{O}(\text{l}) + 531 \text{ kcal.}$$

Experimental Measurement of Heat Changes

The amount of heat evolved in a reaction can be determined in an apparatus known as a **calorimeter.** An instrument of this type, in which the reaction is carried out inside a sealed metal "bomb," is shown schematically in Figure 5.1. The reactants, which may be gases, liquids, or solids, are charged into the bomb, which is then sealed, lowered into place, and surrounded with a known weight of water. Reaction is initiated by some suitable means; an electrically heated wire suffices for many gaseous reactants. The heat evolved in the reaction goes to raise the temperature of the calorimeter, including the bomb, and the water surrounding the bomb. The temperature increase is carefully measured; knowing the heat capacity of the calorimeter* and the water, we can calculate the amount of heat evolved in the reaction. Example 5.4 illustrates the calculations involved.

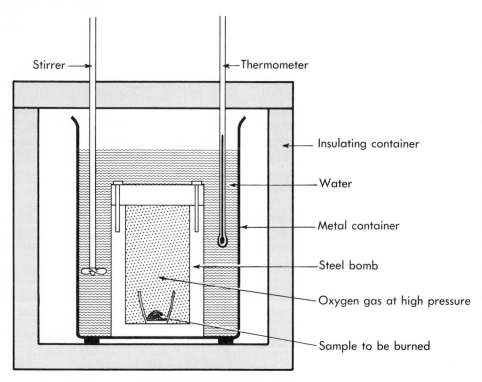

FIGURE 5.1 A bomb calorimeter.

---

* The heat capacity of the calorimeter can be determined by measuring the temperature increase when a reaction which evolves a known amount of heat is carried out in the apparatus. The combustion of benzoic acid, which gives off 6.315 kcal. per gram of benzoic acid, is frequently used for this calibration.

Example 5.4. It is found that when 1.008 g. of hydrogen is reacted with chlorine in a bomb calorimeter, the temperature rises from 25.00°C to 29.24°C. The calorimeter, which has a heat capacity of 210 cal./°C, contains 5.000 kg. of water. Calculate:

a. the amount of heat evolved.
b. the heat change for the reaction:

$$H_2(g) + Cl_2(g) \longrightarrow 2\,HCl(g)$$

Solution

a. The heat evolved by the reaction is absorbed in raising the temperature of the water and the calorimeter. That is:

heat evolved by reaction = heat absorbed by water
+ heat absorbed by calorimeter

(This equation neglects the small amount of heat absorbed by the hydrogen chloride formed in the reaction.) To calculate the heat absorbed by the water, we recall that 1.00 cal. is required to raise the temperature of 1 g. of water 1°C. The heat absorbed by 5000 g. in going from 25.00°C to 29.24°C, a temperature increase of 4.24°C, must be:

$$5000\ \text{g.} \times 4.24°C \times \frac{1.00\ \text{cal.}}{\text{g.} \times °C} = 21,200\ \text{cal.}$$

Since the heat capacity of the bomb is 210 cal./°C and its temperature, like that of the water, has increased by 4.24°C, it must have absorbed:

$$4.24°C \times \frac{210\ \text{cal.}}{°C} = 890\ \text{cal.}$$

Consequently: heat evolved = 21,200 cal. + 890 cal. = 22,100 cal.

b. We have seen that the reaction of 1.008 g., exactly one half mole, of H_2 with chlorine gives off 22,100 calories of heat. For one mole of H_2, the amount of heat evolved must be 44,200 cal. or 44.2 kcal.

$$H_2(g) + Cl_2(g) \longrightarrow 2\,HCl(g) + 44.2\ \text{kcal.}$$

(Strictly speaking, the quantity of heat appearing in a thermochemical equation applies, as pointed out previously, to the reaction carried out in an open container where reactants and products are at 1 atm. pressure. These conditions are not fulfilled in a bomb calorimeter. In this particular case, no significant error is introduced by neglecting this factor. With many reactions, it is necessary to make a small correction, the nature of which is described in Section 5.3.)

5.2 ENERGY CHANGES OTHER THAN HEAT

Although the energy change that accompanies a chemical reaction most often manifests itself in the form of heat, it may take different forms such as mechanical energy, electrical energy, or light.

Mechanical Energy. A spontaneous chemical reaction in which at least one of the products is a gas can, if made to occur in a confined space, transmit mechanical energy to the surroundings. The reaction of gasoline vapor with air in an automobile engine results in a miniature explosion in the cylinders; the mechanical energy imparted to the pistons by the gaseous combustion products serves to run the automobile. When the trigger of a rifle is pulled, a charge of explosive is set off which has sufficient energy to propel a bullet from the barrel at speeds as high as 1200 feet per second. The reaction of alcohol or gasoline with liquid oxygen in a rocket engine can serve as a source of energy to project a satellite out of the earth's atmosphere or send a guided missile to a target 4000 miles away.

An **explosive** is a material which, under the influence of thermal or mechanical shock, undergoes a rapid, exothermic decomposition accompanied by the evolution of hot gases which impart mechanical energy to the surroundings. So-called "low" explosives, of which ordinary gunpowder is an example, decompose by burning. High explosives, on the other hand, decompose by detonation; the reaction taking place is propagated by a shock wave traveling almost instantaneously through the body of the explosive. Since detonation occurs too quickly for oxygen of the air to participate in the reaction, a high explosive must contain within itself all the elements required for a spontaneous, exothermic reaction.

TABLE 5.2 PROPERTIES OF EXPLOSIVES

Common Name	Formula	Products	Energy (kcal./g.)	Pressure* (atm.)
Gunpowder	$2\ KNO_3$, 3 C, S	N_2, $3\ CO_2$, K_2S	0.50	6000
Ammonium nitrate	NH_4NO_3	N_2, $2\ H_2O$, $0.5\ O_2$	0.38	8300
TNT	$C_7H_5(NO_2)_3$	$1.5\ N_2$, $6\ CO$, $2.5\ H_2$, C	0.66	13400
Nitroglycerine	$C_3H_5(NO_3)_3$	$1.5\ N_2$, $3\ CO_2$, $2.5\ H_2O$, $0.25\ O_2$	1.53	15200
Picric acid	$C_6H_3O(NO_2)_3$	$1.5\ N_2$, $6\ CO$, H_2O, $0.5\ H_2$	0.85	16900
Lead azide	$Pb(N_3)_2$	$3\ N_2$, Pb	0.68	34800

* Pressure developed in a volume equal to that of the explosive itself.

Most of the compounds which are used as high explosives contain, in addition to oxygen, the three elements, carbon, hydrogen, and nitrogen. The products formed on detonation include elementary nitrogen and oxides of carbon and/or hydrogen. The oxygen atoms in the explosive combine preferentially with carbon to form carbon monoxide. In the case of TNT, in which there is only a limited amount of oxygen in the molecule, this is the only oxide formed:

$$C_7H_5(NO_2)_3(s) \longrightarrow 6\ CO(g) + C(s) + 2.5\ H_2(g) + 1.5\ N_2(g) \qquad (5.16)$$

If an explosive contains more than enough oxygen to convert all the carbon to carbon monoxide, water is formed. As an example, consider the detonation of picric acid:

$$C_6H_3O(NO_2)_3(s) \longrightarrow 6\ CO(g) + H_2O(g) + 0.5\ H_2(g) + 1.5\ N_2(g) \quad (5.17)$$

Finally, when sufficient oxygen is present, the products are carbon dioxide and water. In the case of nitroglycerin, detonation gives:

$$C_3H_5(NO_3)_3(l) \longrightarrow 3\ CO_2(g) + 2.5\ H_2O(g) + .25\ O_2(g) + 1.5\ N_2(g) \quad (5.18)$$

Contrary to popular opinion, the amount of energy given off when a high explosive is detonated is far less than that evolved in the combustion of conventional fuels. High explosives customarily give off energies in the range of 0.5 to 1.5 kcal./g. (Table 5.2); this is to be contrasted with the evolution of about 10 kcal./g. in the combustion of gasoline. Even sugar (heat of combustion = 4 kcal./g.) is a better energy source than TNT or nitroglycerine. The essential characteristic of a high explosive is not its high energy content but rather its ability to give off energy quickly under certain specified conditions.

Most high explosives, again contrary to popular belief, are relatively insensitive to shock. Picric acid or TNT may be heated to the melting point or struck with a sledgehammer without decomposing. Nitroglycerine is an exception; its sensitivity to shock is greatly reduced by absorbing it in infusorial earth or sawdust to form the product known as dynamite, first manufactured by Alfred Nobel in 1867. High explosives are ordinarily set off by small amounts of so-called "primary" explosives, such as lead azide, $Pb(N_3)_2$, which can be set off by a flame or slight shock. Primary explosives are extremely dangerous to work with and are always used in small quantities.

Electrical Energy.*   Many spontaneous chemical reactions can be carried out in such a way as to generate electrical energy. A familiar example is the reaction taking place in a lead storage battery:

$$Pb(s) + PbO_2(s) + 2\,H_2SO_4(l) \longrightarrow 2\,PbSO_4(s) + 2\,H_2O(l) \qquad (5.19)$$

This reaction produces sufficient electrical energy to operate the starting motor of an automobile. A different reaction taking place in an ordinary dry cell serves to operate a flashlight, a hearing aid, or a child's electric train.

Certain reactions can be initiated by the absorption of electrical energy in the form of a spark or arc discharge. Mixtures of gaseous hydrocarbons or of elementary hydrogen with oxygen are particularly sensitive to electrical ignition:

$$H_2(g) + \tfrac{1}{2}\,O_2(g) \longrightarrow H_2O(l) + 68.3\ \text{kcal.} \qquad (5.20)$$

The final result of reaction 5.20 is, of course, the evolution of energy. The electrical discharge serves only to supply the energy required for the first step of the reaction, which is probably the dissociation of an O_2 molecule into atoms.

The absorption of electrical energy plays a fundamental role in bringing about certain endothermic reactions carried out in electrical cells. For example, the decomposition of sodium chloride to the elements can be accomplished by passing a direct electric current through the molten salt:

$$NaCl(l) + 98.2\ \text{kcal.} \longrightarrow Na(l) + \tfrac{1}{2}\,Cl_2(g) \qquad (5.21)$$

Electrical energy must be supplied continuously to cause this nonspontaneous reaction to occur.

Light

1. PHOTOCHEMISTRY.   Reactions which can be brought about by the absorption of light energy are known as photochemical reactions. Light, like electrical energy, can bring about chemical changes in either of two quite different ways. In certain cases, the absorption of light serves only to get the reaction started by supplying the energy required to break the bonds holding the reactant particles together. An example of this type of photochemical reaction is that which occurs when a mixture of hydrogen and chlorine is exposed to ultraviolet light:

$$\tfrac{1}{2}\,H_2(g) + \tfrac{1}{2}\,Cl_2(g) \longrightarrow HCl(g) + 22\ \text{kcal.} \qquad (5.22)$$

---

* Electrochemical reactions will be discussed at greater length in Chapters 20 and 21.

The absorption of light causes the first step of the reaction, the dissociation of a Cl_2 molecule, to occur. Once a sufficient number of chlorine atoms have been produced to get the reaction started, the light source can be removed.

The process of photosynthesis illustrates a second, quite different, type of photochemical reaction in which light energy is converted to chemical energy. Visible light, absorbed by the green plant pigment, chlorophyll, brings about a nonspontaneous, endothermic reaction whose overall effect may be represented by the equation:

$$6 \ CO_2(g) + 6 \ H_2O(l) + 673 \ kcal. \longrightarrow C_6H_{12}O_6(s) + 6 \ O_2(g) \qquad (5.23)$$

The products of this reaction are complex organic substances known as carbohydrates, of which glucose, $C_6H_{12}O_6$, is but one example. Photosynthesis provides us with a basic source of fuels and foods. When carbohydrates are burned in the body, the reverse of reaction 5.23 occurs, thereby converting the chemical energy stored by photosynthesis into the thermal and mechanical energy needed to sustain life. Fuels such as wood, coal, and petroleum are produced by the decay of organic materials whose ultimate source was the photosynthesis reaction.

In discussing photochemical processes, it is convenient to consider light to be made up of discrete particles known as **photons,** whose energy is given by Planck's equation:

$$E = h\nu \qquad or \qquad E = \frac{hc}{\lambda} \qquad (5.24)$$

in which E = energy in ergs, ν = frequency of light in vibrations per second, h = Planck's constant (6.62×10^{-27} erg sec.), c = velocity of light (3.0×10^{10} cm./sec.), λ = wavelength in centimeters.

It was shown by Einstein that the first step in a photochemical reaction is the absorption of a single photon of light. The photon, by raising the reactant molecule to a higher energy state, supplies the energy necessary to get the reaction started. The "excited" molecule may then break down into smaller, more reactive particles. In the reaction of hydrogen with chlorine, experimental evidence indicates that it is the chlorine molecule which absorbs the photon:

$$Cl_2 + h\nu \longrightarrow Cl_2{}^*$$

The excited, high energy chlorine molecule,$Cl_2{}^*$, dissociates into chlorine atoms:

$$Cl_2{}^* \longrightarrow Cl + Cl$$

which react readily with hydrogen molecules by a mechanism to be discussed later.

If a photon is to initiate a reaction, it must ordinarily supply enough energy to break one of the bonds holding the atoms together in a reactant molecule. In most cases, this requires the absorption of at least 3.5×10^{-12} ergs (50 kcal./mole). In the case of the Cl_2 molecule, for example, 4.0×10^{-12} ergs (58 kcal./mole) is required to cause dissociation at room temperature. This rather large energy requirement explains why infrared radiation is ineffective in initiating photochemical reactions. The maximum amount of energy available to a photon in the infrared range ($\lambda = 8000$ Å or greater) is only 2.5×10^{-12} ergs. Visible light (4000 to 8000 Å) is somewhat more effective photochemically. Many reactions, the most important of which is the process of photosynthesis, may be brought about by the absorption of light in the visible region. Most photochemical reactions are initiated by ultraviolet light ($\lambda < 4000$ Å). The energy of a photon in the ultraviolet region ranges from

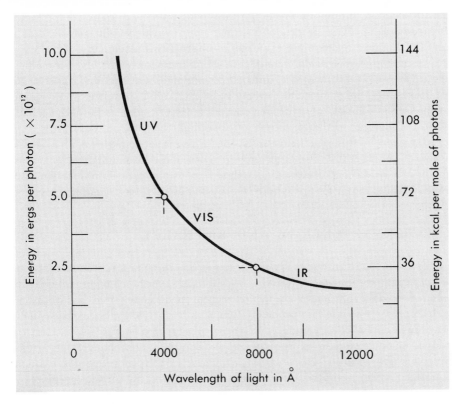

FIGURE 5.2 Dependence of energy of light on its wavelength.

5×10^{-12} ergs, sufficient to break apart such molecules as Cl_2 and HI, to 2×10^{-10} ergs, great enough to dissociate the most stable molecules known. An example of a reaction which is particularly sensitive to ultraviolet light is the photochemical decomposition of silver chloride:

$$AgCl(s) \longrightarrow Ag(s) + \tfrac{1}{2} Cl_2(g) \tag{5.25}$$

Freshly prepared silver chloride is unaffected by radiation in the red or infrared range; exposed to sunlight, which contains appreciable amounts of ultraviolet radiation, it develops the gray color characteristic of finely divided silver.

2. CHEMILUMINESCENCE. Occasionally, part of the energy evolved in a reaction is given off as light. For example, the combustion of magnesium evolves energy in the form of visible and ultraviolet radiation as well as heat. This reaction can be used as a source of ultraviolet light to initiate photochemical processes such as the reaction between hydrogen and chlorine.

Three hundred years ago, the German alchemist Brandt, hoping to obtain the philosopher's stone by the rather improbable method of heating urine, sand, and charcoal together, discovered instead a new substance with a remarkable ability to glow in the dark. Several years later, the famous English chemist Robert Boyle identified this substance as a new element to which he gave the name phosphorus (light giver). Although the term phosphorescence was derived from the name of this element, it is now known that the eery glow emanating from a sample of white phosphorus exposed to the air in a darkened room has a quite different origin than that from ordinary phosphors. The light results from the slow oxidation of the element to the oxide, P_4O_6. This process and similar ones in which light is evolved as the result of a chemical reaction are examples of **chemiluminescence.**

By far the most spectacular examples of chemiluminescence involve the oxidation of certain organic substances sold under the trade names of Luminal and Lophine. The latter compound (molecular formula $C_{21}H_{16}N_2$), when dissolved in alcohol and treated with a solution of hydrogen peroxide (H_2O_2) and sodium hypochlorite (NaOCl), undergoes oxidation to give off a brilliant green light. Very little, if any, heat is evolved in this reaction; this is one of the rare examples of the chemical emission of "cold light." The light emitted by fireflies has a similar origin, arising from the air oxidation of substances related to Luminal or Lophine. How such complex organic materials are synthesized by the lowly firefly remains a mystery.

5.3   INTERNAL ENERGY AND ENTHALPY

Up to this point in our study of energy effects in chemical reactions, we have focused attention almost exclusively on external energy changes which reveal themselves in the evolution or absorption of heat or other tangible forms of energy. We shall now approach this problem from a different viewpoint, considering the changes in chemical energy undergone by the substances participating in a reaction. We shall be interested in expressing and interpreting such changes for reactions taking place at *constant pressure and temperature*. These are the conditions most frequently encountered in the laboratory, where reactions are ordinarily carried out in an open container (constant atmospheric pressure) at a fixed temperature.

Internal Energy Change (ΔE)

The Law of Conservation of Energy requires that there be no net gain or loss of energy in a chemical reaction. This means that any external energy change which we can see, hear, or feel must be exactly compensated for by an internal energy change—a difference in energy between reactants and products. For example, when it is found that the reaction

$$Hg(l) + S(s) \longrightarrow HgS(s) \tag{5.26}$$

evolves 13.9 kcal. of energy, it follows that the internal energy of one mole of mercuric sulfide is 13.9 kcal. less than that of one mole of mercury and one mole of sulfur. Again, the fact that the reaction:

$$N_2(g) + O_2(g) \longrightarrow 2\,NO(g) \tag{5.27}$$

absorbs 43.2 kcal. means that the internal energy of the products (2 moles of NO) is 43.2 kcal. greater than that of the reactants (1 mole of N_2 + 1 mole of O_2).

The internal energy change accompanying a reaction is given the symbol ΔE. By convention, ΔE is given a negative sign if the energy of the products is less than that of the reactants and a positive sign if it is greater. This means that ΔE will be negative for a reaction in which energy is evolved externally and positive if it is absorbed. For the reactions just cited, ΔE is -13.9 kcal. and $+43.2$ kcal. respectively.

Although measurements of the energy changes in reactions yield information about differences in internal energy (ΔE) between reactants and products, they do

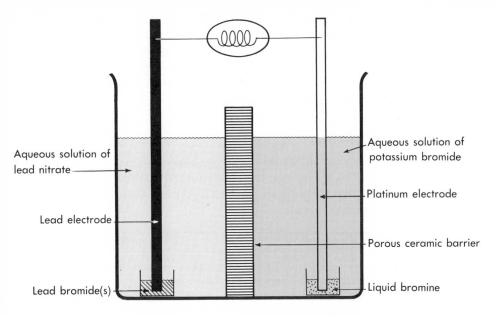

FIGURE 5.3 A cell producing electrical energy from the chemical reaction: $Pb(s) + Br_2(l) \rightarrow PbBr_2(s)$.

not enable us to establish absolute values for the internal energies of individual substances. There is, however, good reason to believe that a given quantity of a substance at a particular temperature and pressure has a definite, invariant internal energy. This belief rests upon the extremely important experimental observation that the *total amount of energy evolved or absorbed in a reaction is independent of the path by which the reaction is carried out.* To understand what this statement means, consider the reaction:

$$Pb(s) + Br_2(l) \longrightarrow PbBr_2(s) \qquad (25°C, \text{ 1 atm.}) \qquad (5.28)$$

If this reaction is carried out directly in the laboratory, all the energy given off is in the form of heat; 66.3 kcal. are liberated per mole of lead bromide formed. The same reaction, carried out by a different path, can serve as a source of electrical energy (Figure 5.3). In this case, the energy given off is in two forms; part of it is evolved as heat while the remainder is used to do electrical work such as operating a light bulb, running a motor, charging a condenser, and so on. The relative amounts of heat and electrical energy produced depend upon the nature of the electrical circuit, but it is always found that their sum is 66.3 kcal., the quantity of heat liberated when the reaction is carried out directly. If the circuit is so designed that the maximum possible amount of electrical work is done, it is found that 62.1 kcal. is utilized in this manner while the remaining 4.2 kcal. is dissipated as heat.

Summarizing what we have said about the internal energy change, ΔE:

1. ΔE represents the difference in internal energy between products and reactants. A positive value of ΔE means that the internal energy of the products is greater than that of the reactants. If the internal energy of the products is less than that of the reactants, ΔE is a negative quantity.

2. ΔE is ordinarily determined experimentally by obtaining the total energy change for the reaction. A positive ΔE corresponds to a reaction that absorbs energy from the surroundings; if energy is evolved to the surroundings, ΔE is negative.

3. ΔE is independent of the path by which the reaction is carried out. When a reaction is carried out in such a way that all the energy exchanged with the surroundings is in the form of heat, ΔE can, of course, be evaluated directly from the heat change. Frequently, however, other forms of energy (electrical energy, mechanical energy, and so on) are involved; these energy changes must be considered in obtaining the total change in internal energy.

Enthalpy Change (ΔH)

For a reaction carried out in an open container at a constant pressure and temperature, the total energy change, as reflected in ΔE, will include not only the heat effect but also any mechanical energy which is exchanged with the surroundings. To illustrate, consider the reaction:

$$KClO_3(s) \longrightarrow KCl(s) + \tfrac{3}{2} O_2(g) \qquad (25°C, 1 \text{ atm.}) \qquad (5.29)$$

When this reaction takes place in an open container such as a test tube, a small amount of mechanical energy is liberated by the oxygen gas in doing work against the atmosphere. The nature of this work may be visualized by imagining the reaction to take place in a cylinder equipped with a piston held down by the pressure of the atmosphere (Figure 5.4). As the reaction proceeds, there is a large increase in volume because of the gaseous oxygen produced. The piston rises and work is done against the atmosphere. One can calculate that the mechanical work done amounts to about 0.9 kcal. This quantity, added to the amount of heat evolved, 10.7 kcal., gives a total evolution of energy for this reaction of 11.6 kcal. Consequently, ΔE, which is equal to the total amount of energy *absorbed*, is -11.6 kcal.

Now, when we carry out a reaction in the laboratory in an open container, we do not ordinarily make any use of the mechanical work done against the atmosphere. In other words, we are more interested in the heat effect than we are in the total energy change. For this reason, among others, it is convenient to work with a quantity known as the change in "heat content" or, more commonly, the change in enthalpy, ΔH, defined so that it will be exactly equal to the *amount of heat absorbed when a reaction is carried out at constant temperature and pressure*. For reaction 5.29, in which 10.7 kcal. of heat are evolved, ΔH, the amount of heat absorbed, is -10.7 kcal.

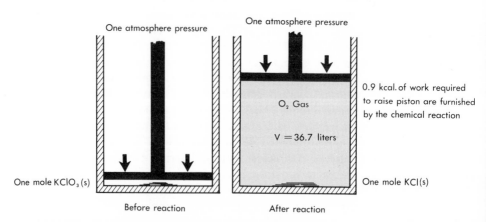

FIGURE 5.4 Expansion work done against atmosphere by the chemical reaction at 25°C: $KClO_3(s) \rightarrow KCl(s) + \tfrac{3}{2} O_2(g)$.

(cf. $\Delta E = -11.6$ kcal.). In general, we find that ΔH and ΔE rarely differ from each other by more than a few kilocalories at most; for many reactions, they are virtually identical.

It can be shown that for a reaction carried out at constant pressure, the two quantities ΔH and ΔE are related by the equation:

$$\Delta H = \Delta E + P\,\Delta V$$

in which P is the pressure against which the reaction is carried out and ΔV is the volume change for the reaction. For a reaction which results in an increase in volume (ΔV positive), ΔH will be slightly larger algebraically than ΔE. An example is reaction 5.29, in which $\Delta H = -10.7$ kcal., $\Delta E = -11.6$ kcal. Conversely, if the volume of the products is less than that of the reactants (ΔV negative), ΔH will be somewhat smaller than ΔE.

For reactions in which no gases are involved, ΔV is so small that ΔH and ΔE are equal to each other within experimental error. Consider, for example, reaction 5.28, which involves only solids and liquids (Pb, Br_2, $PbBr_2$). One can calculate that in this case, the $P\,\Delta V$ term amounts to only about 0.00035 kcal. in comparison to an overall energy change of 66.3 kcal. Even in certain gaseous reactions, notably that between hydrogen and chlorine to give hydrogen chloride (equation 5.22), the volume of the products is essentially identical to that of the reactants and the expansion work term effectively disappears. Only when a reaction results in a change in the number of moles of gas does the expansion work term become significant.

Enthalpy changes can be obtained directly from thermochemical equations of the type discussed in Section 5.1. The quantities of heat indicated in the equations

$$2\,Zn(s) + O_2(g) \longrightarrow 2\,ZnO(s) + 166 \text{ kcal.} \tag{5.4}$$

and

$$2\,HgO(s) + 43.4 \text{ kcal.} \longrightarrow 2\,Hg(l) + O_2(g) \tag{5.5}$$

refer to the heat changes observed when these reactions are carried out in an open container at a constant temperature and pressure (25°C, 1 atm.). Consequently, ΔH for these reactions must be -166 kcal. and 43.4 kcal. respectively. Note that since ΔH is equal to the amount of heat *absorbed* when a reaction is carried out at a constant temperature and pressure, it will be a positive quantity for an endothermic reaction (5.5) and will have a negative value for an exothermic reaction (5.4).

It was pointed out in Section 5.1 that the amount of heat absorbed in a reaction can be obtained by subtracting the sum of the heats of formation of the reactants from the sum of the heats of formation of the products. It follows that ΔH can be obtained in precisely the same way. That is:

$$\Delta H = \Sigma \text{ Hf products} - \Sigma \text{ Hf reactants} = \text{heat absorbed in reaction} \tag{5.30}$$
$$\text{(Constant T and P)}$$

Compare equation 5.15.

Example 5.5. Calculate ΔH for the reaction:

$$Fe_2O_3(s) + 3\,CO(g) \longrightarrow 2\,Fe(s) + 3\,CO_2(g) \quad (25°C, 1 \text{ atm.})$$

Solution. We note from Table 5.1 that:

Hf $Fe_2O_3(s) = -196.5$ kcal.,   Hf $CO(g) = -26.4$ kcal.,   Hf $CO_2(g) = -94.1$ kcal.

Applying equation 5.30, we have:

$$\Delta H = 3 \text{ Hf } CO_2 - (3 \text{ Hf } CO + \text{Hf } Fe_2O_3)$$
$$= -282.3 \text{ kcal.} - (-79.2 \text{ kcal.} - 196.5 \text{ kcal.})$$
$$= -6.6 \text{ kcal.}$$

Just as ΔE for a chemical reaction represents the difference between the internal energies of products and reactants, ΔH represents the difference in enthalpy between products and reactants. A positive value of ΔH corresponds to a reaction in which the enthalpy of the products is greater than that of the reactants. If, on the other hand, ΔH is found to be negative, it follows that the products must have an enthalpy less than that of the reactants. For example, the ΔH value of -22.1 kcal. for the reaction

$$\tfrac{1}{2} H_2(g) + \tfrac{1}{2} Cl_2(g) \longrightarrow HCl(g) \qquad (25°C, 1 \text{ atm.}) \qquad (5.22)$$

can be interpreted to mean that the enthalpy of one mole of HCl is 22.1 kcal. less than the total enthalpy of one half mole of hydrogen and one half mole of chlorine. This decrease in enthalpy is, of course, numerically equal to the amount of heat evolved in the reaction (22.1 kcal.); the evolution of heat occurs at the expense of a decrease in enthalpy.

The enthalpy of a substance, like its internal energy, has a fixed value at a particular temperature and pressure. This means that the enthalpy change, ΔH, like the change in internal energy, ΔE, is independent of the path by which the reaction is carried out. As a matter of fact, we anticipated this in Section 5.1, in which we pointed out that the amount of heat absorbed in the reaction

$$Sn(s) + 2 Cl_2(g) \longrightarrow SnCl_4(l) \qquad (25°C, 1 \text{ atm.}) \qquad (5.10)$$

can be determined by following an indirect path in which the tin is first converted to $SnCl_2$ which is then reacted with a second mole of elementary chlorine to give $SnCl_4$.

Qualitatively, one can interpret the sign of the enthalpy change for a reaction in terms of the relative strengths of the bonds holding the particles together in the products and reactants. If these bonds are stronger in the reactants than they are in the products, heat must be absorbed to bring about the reaction and ΔH is positive. Conversely, if the bonds holding the particles together in the products are stronger than those which must be overcome to break down the reactants, heat is evolved and ΔH is negative. As an example, consider the synthesis of hydrogen chloride from the elements (reaction 5.22). We interpret the negative value of ΔH for this reaction (-22.1 kcal.) to mean that the bonds holding the HCl molecules together in a mole of hydrogen chloride must be stronger than those in one half mole of H_2 and one half mole of Cl_2. Later, in Chapter 15, we shall consider the relationship between ΔH and "bond energies" in greater detail.

Summarizing our discussion of enthalpy changes, it may be well to emphasize that:

1. ΔH is equal to the amount of heat absorbed when a reaction is carried out directly at constant pressure and temperature. The numerical value of ΔH will ordinarily differ only slightly from that of ΔE.

2. ΔH can be calculated or measured by any of the methods discussed in Section 5.1 for determining the amount of heat absorbed in a reaction. Specifically, it can be calculated from heats of formation by using equation 5.30.

3. ΔH can be interpreted in terms of the relative strengths of the forces or bonds holding the atoms together in products and reactants. In general, if the bonds in the products are stronger than those in the reactants, the reaction will be exothermic and ΔH will be negative. If the bonds in the reactants are stronger than those in the products, we can expect an endothermic reaction and a positive value for ΔH.

5.4 SPONTANEITY OF REACTION: FREE ENERGY CHANGE

One of the most important questions that a chemist has to answer is whether a given reaction can take place under a particular set of conditions. The practicing chemist must expect to be asked questions such as:

Can lead bromide, $PbBr_2$, be formed by bringing the elements lead and bromine together at room temperature and atmospheric pressure?

Can silver oxide, Ag_2O, be decomposed to the elements by heating in an open container and, if so, what temperature will be required to bring about this reaction?

Questions such as these can, of course, be answered by direct experiment. However, such an approach may prove extremely tedious and may even be misleading. Negative results do not prove that a reaction cannot go; they may only indicate that under the conditions specified the reaction occurs too slowly to be detected.

We should like to be able to establish criteria to predict in advance whether or not a reaction can occur *spontaneously, that is whether it can take place directly, regardless of rate, in the absence of an external driving force.* We shall now consider how such criteria can be set up for reactions taking place at *constant temperature and pressure.*

Criteria of Spontaneity

Intuitively, we feel that the capacity of substances to react with each other should, in some way, be related to the energy change accompanying the reaction. A hundred years ago, many chemists were convinced that a reaction could occur only if the corresponding value of ΔH were negative, that is, if the reaction were exothermic. Endothermic reactions were believed to be impossible. Today, we know that the relation between spontaneity of reaction and energy change is a more subtle one. It is true, however, that almost all reactions* for which ΔH is negative are spontaneous at room temperature and atmospheric pressure. Consider, for example, the reaction:

$$2\,Ag(s) + \tfrac{1}{2}\,O_2(g) \longrightarrow Ag_2O(s) \qquad \Delta H = -7.31 \text{ kcal.} \qquad (5.31)$$

If finely divided silver is exposed, at 25°C, to oxygen at 1 atm. pressure, reaction occurs, albeit slowly, to form silver oxide. In contrast, the reaction:

$$N_2(g) + O_2(g) \longrightarrow 2\,NO(g) \qquad \Delta H = +43.2 \text{ kcal.} \qquad (5.32)$$

cannot occur under ordinary conditions; nitrogen will not spontaneously react with oxygen at room temperature and atmospheric pressure.

Although one can usually predict whether a reaction will be spontaneous at room temperature and atmospheric pressure by noting the sign of ΔH, this criterion cannot be applied generally at other temperatures and pressures. Referring again to equation 5.31, it is found experimentally that this reaction proceeds in the reverse

---

* Exceptions are known, particularly when ΔH is numerically small. For example, the reaction:

$$CO_2(g) + H_2(g) \longrightarrow CO(g) + H_2O(l) \qquad \Delta H = -0.6 \text{ kcal.}$$

can be shown to be nonspontaneous at 25°C and atmospheric pressure. The rule is generally inapplicable to physical changes; the evaporation of water at room temperature is a familiar example of a spontaneous endothermic physical change.

direction above 190°C. Again, at very low pressure, below about 2×10^{-4} atm., it is the decomposition of silver oxide rather than its synthesis which is spontaneous at room temperature. These changes in temperature and pressure have virtually no effect upon the magnitude of ΔH, which remains constant at -7.31 kcal. The behavior of the Ag-O_2-Ag_2O system is by no means unique. One finds in general that the spontaneity of a reaction, unlike the enthalpy change, is sensitive to variations in temperature and pressure. This clearly makes it impossible to use the sign of ΔH as an entirely general criterion to predict whether or not a reaction will take place. Quite clearly, we must search for some other, more general criterion of spontaneity if we are to estimate how changes in pressure and temperature will affect the tendency of a reaction to occur.

A better criterion of spontaneity for a chemical reaction can be deduced by focusing attention on the work that can be obtained from the reaction rather than upon the heat change that accompanies it. J. Willard Gibbs, the great American theoretician, was the first to point out that a reaction occurring at constant temperature and pressure will be spontaneous if useful* work can be obtained from it. It follows that if one can show, either by calculation or experiment, that a reaction, at a particular temperature and pressure, is *capable* of doing useful work, that reaction must be spontaneous. In other words, the reaction can proceed directly without absorbing energy in the form of work from the surroundings. Conversely, if work has to be supplied from an external source to make the reaction take place, the reaction cannot occur spontaneously.

To illustrate the principle stated above, let us return to the reaction:

$$Pb(s) + Br_2(l) \longrightarrow PbBr_2(s) \qquad (5.28)$$

This reaction can serve as a source of electrical energy if carried out in the electrical cell illustrated in Figure 5.3. As much as 62.1 kcal. of useful electrical work can be obtained in this manner. It follows that this reaction must be spontaneous when carried out directly. This is indeed the case; finely divided lead exposed to bromine in an open container reacts to form lead bromide. Note that as the reaction is ordinarily carried out, by mixing the reactants directly in a beaker or test tube, no useful work whatsoever is done. It is the fact that it is *possible* to carry out this reaction in such a way as to accomplish useful work that establishes its spontaneity.

In contrast to reaction 5.28, consider the decomposition of water:

$$H_2O(l) \longrightarrow H_2(g) + \tfrac{1}{2} O_2(g) \qquad (5.33)$$

which is known to be nonspontaneous at 25°C and 1 atm. One can calculate that in order for reaction to occur under these conditions, at least 56.7 kcal. of work has to be expended. This work may be supplied electrically; it is found experimentally that the amount of electrical energy required to decompose one mole of water is 56.7 kcal.

The relation between the spontaneity of a process and its capacity to produce useful work may be further illustrated by considering certain physical changes. All of us are familiar with the spontaneous tendency of water to run downhill. Work may be obtained from this process if the water falls against the blades of a paddle wheel which in turn is used to operate a direct current generator. If the water is

---

* The adjective "useful" excludes the expansion work, $P \Delta V$, which accompanies reactions carried out at constant pressure. In a reaction occurring in an open container, this work is required to push back the atmosphere; it cannot be utilized for any other purpose.

allowed to fall directly, no work is produced; this does not affect our conclusion that the process is capable of producing useful work.

Another example of a spontaneous physical change is the process of solution. While it may be difficult to visualize a mechanism for getting useful work out of the spontaneous tendency of two substances such as alcohol and water to dissolve in each other, it is easy to see that once this solution is formed, work would have to be expended to reverse the process, i.e., to separate the components.

Maximum Useful Work

It has been pointed out that at constant temperature and pressure, a reaction is spontaneous if useful work can be obtained from it. Stated another way, if the maximum amount of useful work, W', that can be obtained from a reaction is greater than zero, that reaction will occur:

$$W' > 0, \text{ reaction is spontaneous.}$$

If the quantity W' is less than zero (i.e., a negative quantity), the reaction cannot proceed spontaneously; work would have to be supplied from the surroundings to make it go. One could equally well say that under these conditions, the reverse reaction is spontaneous:

$$W' < 0, \text{ reverse reaction is spontaneous.}$$

If perchance, at the temperature and pressure specified, W' is zero, neither forward nor reverse reaction will proceed spontaneously. Regardless of how long one waits, no net change will occur in either direction. Under these conditions, the reaction is said to be at a state of equilibrium*: W' = 0, reaction is at equilibrium.

As this discussion implies, the maximum amount of useful work that can be obtained from a given reaction is a function only of the temperature and pressure at which it is carried out. For example, for the spontaneous reaction:

$$Pb(s) + Br_2(l) \longrightarrow PbBr_2(s) \tag{5.28}$$

at 25°C and 1 atm. pressure, W' has a fixed value which happens to be +62.1 kcal. At the same temperature and pressure, the nonspontaneous reaction:

$$H_2O(l) \longrightarrow H_2(g) + \tfrac{1}{2} O_2(g) \tag{5.33}$$

has associated with it a W' of −56.7 kcal.; at least this much useful work (electrical energy) must be expended to make the reaction go. Alternatively, one could say that for the reverse reaction, the synthesis of a mole of liquid water from the elements, W' would be +56.7 kcal. Finally, for the reaction:

$$Ag_2O(s) \longrightarrow 2 Ag(s) + \tfrac{1}{2} O_2(g) \tag{5.34}$$

at 190°C and 1 atm., W' is zero; it is impossible to obtain useful work from either the forward or reverse reaction at this temperature and pressure.

It is to be emphasized that W' represents only an upper limit to the amount of useful work that can be obtained from a reaction. The work actually done in the reaction will ordinarily be considerably smaller algebraically than W'. Thus, for reaction 5.28, the work done may have any value up to and including +62.1 kcal. It could, for example, be 0, +10, or +59.4 kcal.; it could not, however, be +63 kcal!

---

* The concept of chemical equilibrium will be touched on only briefly here and will be discussed in greater detail in Chapter 14.

Free Energy Change (ΔG)

The maximum amount of useful work that can be obtained from a process at constant temperature and pressure can be interpreted in terms of a difference in "free energy" (G)* between products and reactants.

$$\text{G products} - \text{G reactants} = \Delta G = -W' \tag{5.35}$$

The negative sign in this equation is introduced to be consistent with the convention that we have used for ΔE and ΔH. A decrease in internal energy (E products $<$ E reactants) is reflected in an evolution of energy in the surroundings; a decrease in free energy (G products $<$ G reactants) can lead to the production of useful work in the surroundings. The liberation of heat in a reaction carried out at constant pressure is accomplished at the expense of a decrease in enthalpy (H products $<$ H reactants); the harnessing of a reaction to produce useful work requires a decrease in free energy. Just as ΔE is a measure of the total amount of energy that can be obtained from a reaction, so ΔG is a measure of the amount of energy which is potentially available or "free" to do useful work.

The quantity ΔG can be regarded as the ultimate criterion for spontaneity of a reaction conducted at a constant pressure and temperature. Knowing that $\Delta G = -W'$, it follows from our discussion of maximum useful work that:

If:	Then:	Example:
ΔG is $-$	reaction is spontaneous	reaction 5.28, $\Delta G = -62.1$ kcal.
ΔG is $+$	reverse reaction is spontaneous	reaction 5.33, $\Delta G = +56.7$ kcal.
ΔG is 0	reaction is at equilibrium	reaction 5.34, $\Delta G = 0$

The free energy change for a reaction, like the change in internal energy or enthalpy, is independent of the path by which the reaction takes place. However, unlike ΔE and ΔH, ΔG can vary considerably with temperature and pressure. Consider, for example, reaction 5.34. We have stated that at 190°C and 1 atm., ΔG for this reaction is 0. It is found experimentally that ΔG becomes more negative with increasing temperature or decreasing pressure (Table 5.3). In contrast, ΔH for this reaction remains virtually constant at $+7.3$ kcal. over the entire range of temperatures and pressures covered in Table 5.3.

TABLE 5.3 VARIATION OF ΔG WITH TEMPERATURE
AND PRESSURE FOR THE REACTION:
$Ag_2O(s) \rightarrow 2\ Ag(s) + \frac{1}{2}\ O_2(g)$

T(°C)	P = 1 atm. ΔG(kcal.)	P = 0.01 atm. ΔG(kcal.)	P = 0.0001 atm. ΔG(kcal.)
25	+2.59	+1.22	−0.15
100	+1.40	−0.31	−2.02
190	0.00	−2.12	−4.24
300	−1.77	−4.39	−7.01
500	−4.94	−8.48	−12.02

* The symbol G is used in honor of J. Willard Gibbs, who first advanced many of the arguments concerning maximum useful work and its relation to the spontaneity of reactions. The symbolism here is somewhat confused by the fact that there are two different kinds of free energy. In addition to the "Gibbs free energy," which is the quantity we are concerned with, there is also a "Helmholtz free energy," usually given the symbol A, defined so that $-\Delta A$ becomes equal to the maximum *total* work obtainable from a reaction.

The data in Table 5.3 agree with our earlier qualitative statement that the decomposition of silver oxide, at 1 atm. pressure, is spontaneous above 190°C ($\Delta G-$); below 190°C, at 1 atm., where ΔG has a positive sign, the reverse reaction is spontaneous. One can also see that at a pressure of 0.0001 atm., the decomposition occurs spontaneously ($\Delta G-$) even at temperatures as low as 25°C. In other words, by pumping on silver oxide with a powerful enough vacuum pump, it should be possible to decompose it to the elements at room temperature. In practice, this is extremely difficult to do because the rate of reaction is so slow. It perhaps should be reemphasized that a negative value for ΔG tells us only that a reaction is capable of going at a particular temperature and pressure; it gives us no information whatsoever about the rate at which the reaction will occur.

Just as it is possible to obtain values for the enthalpy change, ΔH, from heat of formation data, so one can set up tables of free energies of formation of compounds from which free energy changes of reactions can be calculated. Since ΔG, unlike ΔH, is ordinarily sensitive to temperature and pressure, it is important to specify the conditions for which free energy of formation (Gf) data are valid. The values given in Table 5.4 are applicable at 25°C and 1 atm.

TABLE 5.4   FREE ENERGIES OF FORMATION (KCAL./MOLE) AT 25°C, 1 ATM.

$AgBr(s)$	-22.9	$CO(g)$	-32.8	$H_2O(g)$	-54.6	$NH_4Cl(s)$	-48.7
$AgCl(s)$	-26.2	$CO_2(g)$	-94.3	$H_2O(l)$	-56.7	$NO(g)$	20.7
$AgI(s)$	-15.9	$C_2H_2(g)$	50.0	$H_2S(g)$	-7.9	$NO_2(g)$	12.4
$Ag_2O(s)$	-2.6	$C_2H_4(g)$	16.3	$HgO(s)$	-14.0	$NiO(s)$	-51.7
$Ag_2S(s)$	-9.6	$C_2H_6(g)$	-7.9	$HgS(s)$	-11.7	$PbBr_2(s)$	-62.1
$Al_2O_3(s)$	-376.8	$C_3H_8(s)$	-5.6	$KBr(s)$	-90.6	$PbCl_2(s)$	-75.0
$BaCl_2(s)$	-193.8	$CoO(s)$	-51.0	$KCl(s)$	-97.6	$PbO(s)$	-45.1
$BaCO_3(s)$	-272.2	$Cr_2O_3(s)$	-250.2	$KClO_3(s)$	-69.3	$PbO_2(s)$	-52.3
$BaO(s)$	-126.3	$CuO(s)$	-30.4	$KF(s)$	-127.4	$Pb_3O_4(s)$	-147.6
$BaSO_4(s)$	-323.4	$Cu_2O(s)$	-35.0	$MgCl_2(s)$	-141.6	$PCl_3(g)$	-68.4
$CaCl_2(s)$	-179.3	$CuS(s)$	-11.7	$MgCO_3(s)$	-246	$PCl_5(g)$	-77.6
$CaCO_3(s)$	-269.8	$CuSO_4(s)$	-158.2	$MgO(s)$	-136.1	$SiO_2(s)$	-192.4
$CaO(s)$	-144.4	$Fe_2O_3(s)$	-177.1	$Mg(OH)_2(s)$	-199.3	$SnCl_4(l)$	-113.3
$Ca(OH)_2(s)$	-214.3	$Fe_3O_4(s)$	-242.4	$MgSO_4(s)$	-280.5	$SnO(s)$	-61.5
$CaSO_4(s)$	-315.6	$HBr(g)$	-12.7	$MnO(s)$	-86.8	$SnO_2(s)$	-124.2
$CCl_4(l)$	-16.4	$HCl(g)$	-22.8	$MnO_2(s)$	-111.4	$SO_2(g)$	-71.8
$CH_4(g)$	-12.1	$HF(g)$	-64.7	$NaCl(s)$	-91.8	$SO_3(g)$	-88.5
$CHCl_3(l)$	-17.1	$HI(g)$	0.3	$NaF(s)$	-129.3	$ZnO(s)$	-76.1
$CH_3OH(l)$	-38.7	$HNO_3(l)$	-19.1	$NH_3(g)$	-4.0	$ZnS(s)$	-47.4

It will be noted from Table 5.4 that the free energy of formation at 25°C and 1 atm. is negative for most compounds. This reflects the fact that most compounds are stable with respect to decomposition into the elements at room temperature and atmospheric pressure. In principle, any compound with a negative free energy of formation can be formed directly from the elements. For example, it should be possible to prepare ammonia (Gf = -4.0 kcal.) by reacting hydrogen with nitrogen at 25°C and 1 atm. In practice, this reaction occurs so slowly under these conditions that a mixture of the two elements can exist for many years without producing detectable quantities of ammonia.

Free energy changes can be calculated from Gf data in a manner entirely analogous to that used to obtain enthalpy changes from Hf data. That is:

$$\Delta G = \Sigma \, Gf \, products - \Sigma \, Gf \, reactants \qquad (5.36)$$

To illustrate, for the reaction:

$$4\,NH_3(g) + 5\,O_2(g) \longrightarrow 4\,NO(g) + 6\,H_2O(l)$$

$$\Delta G(25°C, 1\ atm.) = 4\,Gf\,NO(g) + 6\,Gf\,H_2O(l) - 4\,Gf\,NH_3(g)$$

$$= 4(20.7\ kcal.) + 6(-56.7\ kcal.) - 4(-4.0\ kcal.)$$

$$= -241.4\ kcal. \qquad \text{(reaction spontaneous)}$$

while for the reaction:

$$Fe_2O_3(s) + 3\,H_2(g) \longrightarrow 2\,Fe(s) + 3\,H_2O(l)$$

$$\Delta G(25°C, 1\ atm.)$$

$$= 3\,Gf\,H_2O(l) - Gf\,Fe_2O_3(s) = 3(-56.7) + 177.1 = +7.0\ kcal.$$

(Reaction does not occur at 25°C, 1 atm.)

5.5   RELATION BETWEEN ΔG AND ΔH: ENTROPY CONCEPT

We have seen that the free energy change, ΔG, represents the maximum amount of useful work that can be obtained from a reaction carried out at constant temperature and pressure; ΔH represents the heat change when such a reaction is carried out directly so that no useful work is done. It is almost obvious that these two quantities must be intimately related to one another. We shall now consider the nature of this relationship.

Relation Between ΔG and ΔH

In order to give a physical interpretation to the difference between ΔG and ΔH, let us refer to reaction 5.28, the synthesis of lead bromide from the elements. We have seen that at 25°C and 1 atm., ΔG and ΔH for this reaction are respectively −62.1 kcal. and −66.3 kcal. Consequently:

$$\Delta G - \Delta H = -62.1\ kcal. - (-66.3\ kcal.) = +4.2\ kcal.$$

But, it will be recalled from the discussion on p. 97 that 4.2 kcal. is precisely the amount of heat *evolved* when this reaction is carried out in such a way that a maximum amount of useful work is done. If we represent by Q' the amount of heat *absorbed* under these conditions, we can write:

$$\Delta G - \Delta H = -Q'$$

or

$$\Delta G = \Delta H - Q' \tag{5.37}$$

It can be shown that equation 5.37 is valid for any reaction. The change in free energy (ΔG) is always equal to the difference between the amount of heat absorbed (ΔH) when the reaction is carried out directly in such a way that no useful work is done and the amount of heat absorbed (Q') when the reaction is carried out in such a way that the maximum amount of useful work is done. The quantity Q', like ΔG and ΔH, depends only upon the states of reactants and products. From one point of view, it can be regarded as that fraction of the total enthalpy change which is not available for doing useful work; it must be subtracted from ΔH to obtain ΔG.

Depending upon the particular reaction, Q' may be either positive or negative. The fact that it is never, except by coincidence, equal to zero explains why ΔG and ΔH differ in magnitude. The absolute value of Q' for most chemical reactions at 25°C and 1 atm. is considerably smaller than that of ΔH. This means that for most reactions at room temperature and atmospheric pressure, ΔH and ΔG will have the same sign; i.e., exothermic reactions will be spontaneous. However, the magnitude of Q', unlike that of ΔH, is quite sensitive to changes in temperature; for many reactions, Q' changes with pressure as well. This explains why the sign of ΔG and consequently the direction in which a reaction proceeds spontaneously can change with temperature and pressure.

TABLE 5.5 VALUES OF ΔG, ΔH, AND Q' FOR CERTAIN REACTIONS AT 25°C, 1 ATM.

Reaction	ΔG (kcal.)	=	ΔH (kcal.)	−	Q' (kcal.)
$Pb(s) + Br_2(l) \rightarrow PbBr_2(s)$	−62.1		−66.3		−4.2
$\frac{1}{2} H_2(g) + \frac{1}{2} Cl_2(g) \rightarrow HCl(g)$	−22.8		−22.1		+0.7
$CO(g) + \frac{1}{2} O_2(g) \rightarrow CO_2(g)$	−61.5		−67.7		−6.2
$NO(g) \rightarrow \frac{1}{2} N_2(g) + \frac{1}{2} O_2(g)$	−20.7		−21.6		−0.9
$CaCO_3(s) \rightarrow CaO(s) + CO_2(g)$	+31.1		+42.5		+11.4
$H_2O(l) \rightarrow H_2(g) + \frac{1}{2} O_2(g)$	+56.7		+68.3		+11.6
$Ag_2O(s) \rightarrow 2 Ag(s) + \frac{1}{2} O_2(g)$	+2.59		+7.31		+4.72

Entropy Change (ΔS)

One can show experimentally that, at ordinary temperatures, the quantity Q' is very nearly directly proportional to the absolute temperature. The science of thermodynamics tells us that:

$$Q' = T \Delta S \tag{5.38}$$

where T is the absolute temperature in °K and ΔS is a quantity known as the change in **entropy.** The quantity ΔS, like ΔG and ΔH, is dependent only upon the states of products and reactants. It can be interpreted in terms of a difference in entropy between products and reactants.

$$\Delta S = S \text{ products} - S \text{ reactants}$$

The entropy change, ΔS, like the free energy change, ΔG, and the enthalpy change, ΔH, can have either a positive or a negative sign. In general, a positive value of ΔS corresponds to a process in which there is an increase in **randomness.** That is, if one goes from a more ordered to a more disordered or random structure, one can expect an increase in entropy ($\Delta S > 0$). Conversely, a physical or chemical change which results in the formation of a more ordered structure will be accompanied by a decrease in entropy.

A simple example of a physical change in which there is an increase in randomness is that of fusion, in which the rigid pattern of the solid is broken down to give the more mobile, random structure characteristic of the liquid state. Invariably, we find that when a solid melts there is an increase in entropy. The same is true for the processes of evaporation and sublimation, in which liquid or solid particles gain added freedom by moving into the gas state.

The interpretation of ΔS in terms of a change in disorder or randomness is less useful in dealing with chemical as opposed to physical changes. However, one does find that reactions in which gases are produced at the expense of solids or liquids are almost always accompanied by an increase in entropy. For example, the last three reactions listed in Table 5.5, all of which involve the formation of gaseous products from solid or liquid reactants, are each characterized by an increase in entropy (Q' positive, ΔS positive).

At room temperature and above, ΔS is, to a good degree of approximation, independent of temperature. This, of course, explains why the quantity Q' ($= T \Delta S$) is very nearly directly proportional to the absolute temperature. For reactions in which no gases are involved or in which there is no change in the number of moles of gas, such as

$$Pb(s) + Br_2(l) \longrightarrow PbBr_2(s)$$

or

$$\tfrac{1}{2} H_2(g) + \tfrac{1}{2} Cl_2(g) \longrightarrow HCl(g)$$

ΔS is essentially independent of pressure. On the other hand, ΔS for a reaction in which there is a change in the number of moles of gas is sensitive to changes in pressure. For example, for the reaction

$$Ag_2O(s) \longrightarrow 2 Ag(s) + \tfrac{1}{2} O_2(g)$$

at 25°C, one can show that ΔS changes by about 30 per cent when the pressure changes from 1 atm. to 0.01 atm.*

Gibbs-Helmholtz Equation

Our primary interest in the entropy change in a reaction lies in its relation to the free energy change. By combining equations 5.37 and 5.38, we arrive at the relation:

$$\Delta G = \Delta H - T \Delta S \qquad (5.39)$$

This relationship, known as the Gibbs-Helmholtz equation, is one of the most important in all of chemical thermodynamics. In particular, it helps us toward a better understanding of the driving force behind chemical reactions. We saw in Section 5.4 that the sign of the free energy change, ΔG, tells us whether or not a reaction is spontaneous at a particular temperature and pressure. Equation 5.39 tells us that ΔG can be broken down into two quantities:

1. **ΔH.** A negative value of ΔH, corresponding to an exothermic reaction, will tend to lead to a negative value of ΔG. This confirms the common observation that exothermic reactions, at ordinary temperatures and pressures, tend to be spontaneous.

2. **$T \Delta S$.** A positive value of ΔS will, according to equation 5.39, tend to make ΔG negative. We find that, other factors being equal, chemical or physical changes tend to go in such a way as to result in an increase in entropy (i.e., an increase in randomness). The spontaneous tendency of two pure substances to dissolve in each other is an example of a process in which the increase in entropy is the principal driving force.

---

* Although we shall not attempt to discuss how one can calculate the extent to which ΔS varies with pressure, see Problem 5.24.

We might sum up these observations by saying that matter tends to go spontaneously toward a condition of minimum energy (ΔH negative) and maximum disorder (ΔS positive). Putting it another way, if we wish to know whether a reaction will go spontaneously at a particular temperature and pressure, we must consider not only the relative strengths of the bonds holding the particles together in products and reactants, which determine the sign of ΔH, but also the relative freedom of motion of the particles in products and reactants, which determines the sign of ΔS.

In many physical and chemical changes, we find that ΔH and ΔS have the same sign. In this case, the sign of ΔG depends upon the magnitudes of the two terms in equation 5.39, and can be expected to change with temperature. To illustrate this situation, consider a familiar physical change, the melting of ice.

$$H_2O(s) \longrightarrow H_2O(l)$$

In this case, ΔH is positive; heat has to be absorbed to melt the ice. However, ΔS is also positive; the particles in the liquid state have greater freedom of motion than in the solid. Below 0°C, the first term in equation 5.39 predominates, ΔG is positive, and ice is stable. At 0°C, the quantity T ΔS becomes exactly equal to ΔH; ΔG is zero, and ice and water are in equilibrium with each other. Above 0°C, T ΔS is greater than ΔH, and ice melts spontaneously.

An example of a chemical change in which the sign of ΔG and hence the direction of spontaneity of reaction change with temperature is considered in Example 5.6.

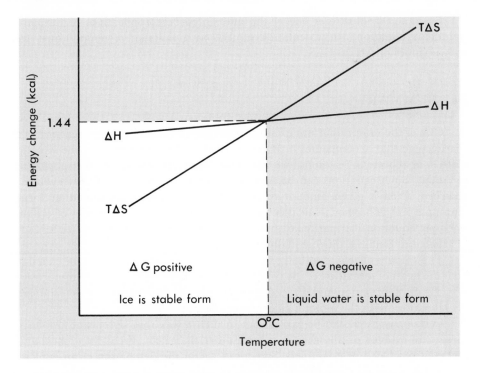

FIGURE 5.5   Thermodynamic quantities for the fusion of ice: $H_2O(s) \rightarrow H_2O(l)$.

Example 5.6. For the reaction $Ag_2O(s) \rightarrow 2\,Ag(s) + \frac{1}{2}\,O_2(g)$, it is known that, at 25°C and 1 atm., $\Delta H = +7.31$ kcal., $\Delta S = +0.0158$ kcal./°K. Using the Gibbs-Helmholtz equation and making the approximation that ΔH and ΔS are independent of temperature, calculate:

    a. ΔG at 25°C, 1 atm.

    b. ΔG at 300°C, 1 atm.

    c. the temperature at which ΔG at 1 atm. is zero.

Solution

    a.
$$\Delta G = \Delta H - T\,\Delta S$$

Substituting $\Delta H = +7.31$ kcal., $\Delta S = +0.0158$ kcal./°K and $T = 298$°K, we have:

$$\Delta G = 7.31 \text{ kcal.} - 298°K(0.0158 \text{ kcal.}/°K)$$
$$= 7.31 \text{ kcal.} - 4.72 \text{ kcal.}$$
$$= 2.59 \text{ kcal.}\quad \text{(Compare to the value in Table 5.4.)}$$

    b.
$$\Delta G = \Delta H - T\,\Delta S$$

But, $\Delta H = +7.31$ kcal., $\Delta S = +0.0158$ kcal./°K, $T = 573$°K

$$\Delta G = +7.31 \text{ kcal.} - 573°K(0.0158 \text{ kcal.}/°K)$$
$$= +7.31 \text{ kcal.} - 9.05 \text{ kcal.} = -1.74 \text{ kcal.}$$

    c. ΔG will be zero when $\Delta H = T\,\Delta S$ $\qquad +7.31$ kcal. $= T\,(+0.0158$ kcal./°K$)$

$$T = \frac{7.31}{0.0158}\,°K = 463°K = 190°C$$

At this temperature the reaction will not proceed in either direction; silver, silver oxide, and oxygen will be in equilibrium with each other at 190°C and 1 atm. Below 190°C, the synthesis of silver oxide from the elements will be spontaneous; above 190°C, the decomposition of silver oxide will occur.

Example 5.6 illustrates one of the most important applications of the Gibbs-Helmholtz equation; the calculation of ΔG, as a function of temperature, from known values of ΔH and ΔS.

5.6 SUMMARY

One of the most important quantities associated with a chemical reaction is the heat change that accompanies it. By incorporating heat changes into the equations written to represent reactions, we arrive at what are known as thermochemical equations. Such equations can be used to calculate the amount of heat evolved or absorbed when a given amount of reactant or product is consumed or formed (Example 5.1). Thermochemical equations have many of the properties of ordinary algebraic equations; in particular, two thermochemical equations can be added or subtracted to obtain a third, equally valid equation (Example 5.2).

The amount of heat absorbed or evolved in a chemical reaction can be calculated from the heats of formation of the compounds participating in the reaction (Example 5.3). Heats of formation and, indeed, heat changes in general, can be determined in the laboratory with the aid of a calorimeter (Example 5.4).

Certain reactions can be carried out in such a way that significant amounts of energy are evolved or absorbed in a form other than heat. Frequently, mechanical energy is produced or consumed. Sometimes, as in the detonation of an explosive, this energy change is dramatically evident. In other cases (Figure 5.4), the change in mechanical energy is less apparent. Many spontaneous reactions can serve to generate electrical energy (Figure 5.3); certain nonspontaneous reactions can be brought about by the absorption of electrical energy.

Certain spontaneous reactions, notably that between hydrogen and chlorine (reaction 5.22) may be set off by the absorption of light. In a few cases, the absorption of light energy can bring about a nonspontaneous reaction; photosynthesis (5.23) is the most important example of this type of process. Whatever the mechanism of a photochemical reaction, it is generally found that high energy (low wavelength) radiation is most effective; ultraviolet radiation ($\lambda = 100$ to 4000 Å) is more productive than infrared.

The science of chemical thermodynamics considers energy changes from the standpoint of the substances participating in the reaction. It puts particular emphasis on certain quantities which are independent of the path by which the reaction is carried out, i.e., depend only upon the nature and states of products and reactants. These thermodynamic quantities include:

1. The change in internal energy, ΔE, which represents the total amount of energy absorbed in a reaction.

2. The change in enthalpy, ΔH, which can be measured by determining the amount of heat absorbed when a reaction is carried out directly at a constant pressure. The change in enthalpy is readily calculated from heat of formation data (Example 5.5).

3. The change in free energy, ΔG, which is a measure of the maximum amount of useful work that can be obtained from a reaction ($\Delta G = -W'$). Of all the thermodynamic quantities, ΔG is perhaps the most important to the chemist, since its sign enables him to predict whether or not a reaction will be spontaneous at a particular temperature and pressure. The free energy change can be determined by measuring the maximum amount of useful work done when a reaction is carried out in an electrical cell (Figure 5.3); it can be calculated from free energies of formation.

4. The change in entropy, ΔS, which is a measure of the extent to which a reaction leads to an increase in randomness or disorder. The quantities ΔG, ΔH, and ΔS are related by the equation:

$$\Delta G = \Delta H - T \, \Delta S \qquad (T = \text{absolute temperature.})$$

This equation is particularly useful in calculations involving the variation of ΔG with temperature (Example 5.6).

PROBLEMS

5.1   Given the thermochemical equation: $SO_2(g) + \frac{1}{2} O_2(g) \rightarrow SO_3(g) + 23.5$ kcal.
   a. Calculate the amount of heat evolved when 1.65 moles of SO_2 burns in excess oxygen.
   b. How much heat is evolved in the formation of 6.38 moles of SO_3?
   c. How much heat is absorbed when 2.94 moles of SO_3 decomposes in the reverse reaction?
   d. Write a thermochemical equation corresponding to the above reaction for the combustion of two moles of SO_2.

5.2   In the reaction: $N_2(g) + O_2(g) \rightarrow 2\,NO(g)$, 21.6 kcal. of heat are absorbed per mole of NO formed. Calculate:
   a. The heat absorbed per gram of NO formed.
   b. The heat absorbed when one hundred grams of nitrogen reacts.
   c. The heat change for the reaction as represented by the equation, i.e., for the formation of two moles of NO.

5.3 In the combustion of ethyl alcohol, C_2H_5OH, 327 kcal. of heat are evolved for each mole of alcohol burned.
a. Calculate the heat evolved per gram of ethyl alcohol burned.
b. Calculate the heat evolved per gram of CO_2 formed.
c. Calculate the heat evolved per mole of H_2O formed.

5.4 One of the major constituents of gasoline, C_8H_{18}, has a heat of combustion of 1303 kcal. per mole.
a. Calculate the amount of heat evolved per gram of C_8H_{18} burned.
b. If C_2H_5OH and C_8H_{18} were selling at the same price per gram, which would be the more economical to use in an internal combustion engine?

5.5 Given the chemical reactions described by the following equations:

$$2 H_2(g) + O_2(g) \longrightarrow 2 H_2O(l) + 136 \text{ kcal.}$$
$$H_2O_2(l) \longrightarrow H_2O(l) + \tfrac{1}{2} O_2(g) + 23 \text{ kcal.}$$

Determine the heat effect in the following reaction:

$$H_2(g) + O_2(g) \longrightarrow H_2O_2(l)$$

What is the name given to the quantity just calculated?

5.6 Given the equations:

$$C_8H_{18}(l) + 12.5 O_2(g) \longrightarrow 8 CO_2(g) + 9 H_2O(l) + 1303 \text{ kcal.}$$
$$C(s) + O_2(g) \longrightarrow CO_2(g) + 94.1 \text{ kcal.}$$
$$H_2(g) + \tfrac{1}{2} O_2(g) \longrightarrow H_2O(l) + 68.3 \text{ kcal.}$$

Calculate the heat of formation, Hf, of C_8H_{18}.

5.7 Using the data in Table 5.1, calculate the heat effects for the following:
a. $CuS(s) + 2 O_2(g) \rightarrow CuSO_4(s)$
b. $2 CH_3OH(l) + 3 O_2(g) \rightarrow 2 CO_2(g) + 4 H_2O(l)$
c. $2 AgBr(s) + H_2O(l) \rightarrow Ag_2O(s) + 2 HBr(g)$

5.8 Using the data in Table 5.1, calculate the amount of heat evolved when:
a. One gram of ethyl alcohol, C_2H_5OH, burns to form $CO_2(g)$ and $H_2O(l)$.
b. 1.68 g. of acetylene, C_2H_2, burns to form $CO_2(g)$ and $H_2O(l)$.

5.9 A sample of methane, CH_4, weighing 1.60 g. is burned in a metal container weighing 9.05 kg. immersed in 8.68 kg. of water. The original temperature of container and water is 20.00°C; their final temperature is 22.21°C. If the container absorbs 0.101 cal. g.$^{-1}$ °C^{-1}, calculate the heat of combustion of one mole of methane.

5.10 When one gram of benzoic acid is burned in a calorimeter of the type shown in Figure 5.1, containing 2.30 kg. of water, the temperature rises from 25.00°C to 27.50°C. The heat of combustion of benzoic acid is 6.315 kcal./g. Calculate:
a. The heat capacity of the calorimeter in cal./°C.
b. The heat of combustion, in kcal./g., of a certain hydrocarbon, given that 1.08 g. of this compound when burned in the same calorimeter containing 2540 g. of water brings about a temperature increase of 4.28°C.

5.11 Write a balanced equation for the detonation of a sample of trinitrobenzene, $C_6H_3(NO_2)_3$ (cf. equations 5.16 to 5.18).

5.12 Using the data in Table 5.2, calculate the amount of energy given off when one mole of TNT detonates. Compare this to the heat of combustion of TNT, 821 kcal./mole. Explain the difference between these two quantities.

5.13 Calculate the wavelength of radiation which is just sufficient to break each of the following bonds. Use Planck's equation (5.24) and the conversion factor, 7.0×10^{-14} ergs/photon = 1 kcal./mole.

a. I—I bond (36 kcal./mole)   b. I—Cl bond (50 kcal./mole)   c. H—O bond (111 kcal./mole)   d. H—F bond (135 kcal./mole)
In what regions of the spectrum (ultraviolet, visible, infrared) would radiation of these wavelengths be found?

5.14 It is known that ΔE for the reaction $Zn(s) + I_2(s) \rightarrow ZnI_2(s)$ is -49.8 kcal. If this reaction is carried out in such a way that 29.4 kcal. of heat is evolved, how much work is done?

5.15 Calculate ΔH for each of the reactions listed in Problem 5.7.

5.16 Calculate ΔH for the combustion of one mole of benzoic acid, $C_7H_6O_2$ (cf. Problem 5.10).

5.17 For the reaction $Br_2(l) + I_2(s) \rightarrow 2 IBr(g)$, ΔH is $+19.5$ kcal. If this reaction is carried out at 25°C and 1 atm., in such a way that a maximum amount of useful work is done, 17.7 kcal. of heat is absorbed.
   a. Calculate Q', ΔG, and ΔS for this reaction.
   b. Is this reaction spontaneous at 25°C and 1 atm.?

5.18 Using the data in Table 5.4, calculate ΔG for each of the reactions listed in Problem 5.7. Which of these reactions are spontaneous at 25°C and 1 atm.?

5.19 Combining the results of Problems 5.15 and 5.18, calculate Q' and ΔS for each of the reactions considered.

5.20 For the reaction: $Pb(s) + Br_2(l) \rightarrow PbBr_2(s)$ at 25°C. and 1 atm., $\Delta H = -66.3$ kcal. and $\Delta S = -14.1$ cal./°K. Calculate Q' and ΔG under these conditions and compare to the values given in Table 5.5.

5.21 For the reaction: $Cu_2O(s) + \frac{1}{2} O_2(g) \rightarrow 2 CuO(s)$
   a. Calculate ΔH, using Table 5.1.
   b. Calculate ΔG at 25°C and 1 atm., using Table 5.4.
   c. Calculate Q' and ΔS under these conditions.
   d. Assuming ΔH and ΔS to be independent of temperature, calculate ΔG at 1500°K and 1 atm.
   e. Calculate the temperature at which ΔG, at 1 atm., is zero.
   f. Comment on the spontaneity of this reaction as a function of temperature.

*5.22 From the data of the previous problem, it can be deduced that the oxide containing the lower percentage of oxygen, Cu_2O, becomes more stable as the temperature is raised. This is generally true for the oxides and chlorides of elements such as copper, tin, and iron which form more than one compound with oxygen or chlorine. For example, at high temperatures, SnO_2 decomposes to SnO and oxygen; $SnCl_4$ decomposes to $SnCl_2$ and Cl_2. Can you suggest an explanation for this behavior in terms of the relationship between ΔS and randomness, as discussed in Section 5.5?

*5.23 In Section 5.5, it was stated that at ordinary temperatures, ΔS is nearly independent of temperature. Actually, for most reactions, as one approaches 0°K, ΔS goes to zero. Can you suggest an explanation in terms of the physical interpretation of ΔS?

*5.24 It can be shown that the variation of ΔS with pressure is given by the equation

$$\Delta S(P_2) - \Delta S(P_1) = 4.58 \, \Delta n_g \log_{10} P_1/P_2$$

in which $\Delta S(P_2)$ and $\Delta S(P_1)$ represent the entropy changes in cal./°K at two different pressures, P_2 and P_1 and Δn_g is the change in the number of moles of gas for the equation as written.
   For the reaction $Ag_2O(s) \rightarrow 2 Ag(s) + \frac{1}{2} O_2(g)$, at 25°C and 1 atm., ΔG, ΔH, and ΔS were given in the text as $+2.59$ kcal., $+7.31$ kcal., and $+0.0158$ kcal./°K respectively.
   a. Calculate ΔS at 0.01 atm.; at 0.0001 atm.
   b. Remembering that ΔH is independent of pressure, calculate ΔG at 25°C and 0.01 atm.; 25°C and 0.0001 atm. Compare to the values given in Table 5.3.

*5.25 Predict whether ΔS for the following reactions, at 25°C and 1 atm., will be positive or negative:
   a. $N_2O_4(g) \rightarrow 2 NO_2(g)$ b. $CaCl_2(s) + 6 H_2O(l) \rightarrow CaCl_2 \cdot 6 H_2O(s)$
   Predictions of this type are discussed by Prof. R. T. Sanderson in an article in the *Journal of Chemical Education*, Vol. 41, p. 13, 1964.

6 | THE PHYSICAL BEHAVIOR OF GASES

Depending on the temperature and pressure, pure substances will exist as solids, liquids, or gases. At low temperatures all substances become solids. In some intermediate temperature range they behave as liquids, and at high temperatures they are gaseous. What is "low" or "high" temperature for one substance is not necessarily "low" or "high" temperature for another, so that, while oxygen, ammonia, and carbon dioxide are gases at room temperature, iron, silicon carbide, and tungsten become gases only at temperatures in excess of 2000°C.

It is an experimental fact that in the gaseous state all pure substances exhibit remarkably similar physical behavior. This fact was used to good advantage when Avogadro's Law was applied to the problem of finding atomic weights. Indeed, much of the real foundation of chemistry was laid when scientists realized the far-reaching general laws that could be stated for gases. In this chapter we shall study some of the laws governing the physical behavior of gases.

6.1 SOME GENERAL PROPERTIES OF GASES

When a liquid is heated sufficiently it begins to boil and evaporate. In this process the substance is said to make a transition from the liquid to the gaseous state. During the change in state the particles in the liquid become free from one another and pass into space as molecules of gas. In general this process is accompanied by a great change in volume. If half a cupful of water is evaporated, the resulting water vapor (water in the gas phase), at one atmosphere pressure and 100°C, occupies a volume equal to that of a 50-gallon oil drum. Since molecules in the gas phase are the same size as they are in the liquid, it follows that the distances between them in the gas are much greater than they are in the liquid.

In view of the rather large distances between gas molecules, we might expect that compressing a gas would be fairly readily accomplished. Experimentally we find that this is so and that in general the volume of a gas varies inversely with the applied pressure; that is, doubling the pressure reduces the volume to about half its previous value. Similarly, if we double the amount (mass) of gas in a container we

114

find that the pressure approximately doubles. Increasing the temperature of a gas in a closed container will increase the pressure of the gas.

Gases can be expanded indefinitely and will always tend to occupy their containers completely and uniformly. If one milliliter of hydrogen gas at one atmosphere pressure is let into an evacuated 10,000-liter container, the hydrogen almost instantly diffuses to give a constant density and pressure throughout the container. The pressure of the gas would be very low under such conditions, about 10^{-7} atm., but could very easily be measured. You might wonder if the situation would have been the same if there had already been another gas at one atmosphere in the container. Under such circumstances the amount of hydrogen in any part of the container would ultimately be the same as if the container were initially evacuated, but the time required would be of the order of hours rather than a fraction of a second; the rate of diffusion of the hydrogen molecules would be very much reduced by the other gas molecules present.

All gases mix readily with one another to form completely homogeneous solutions. Ordinary air is such a solution. No one has ever been able to prepare a mixture of gases which tended to settle out into two or more regions of different composition. The situation is very different from that with mixtures of liquids and solids, in which solubilities of one substance in another are usually limited.

In the first part of this chapter we shall be concerned with describing in a quantitative way the physical properties of gases discussed here from a qualitative viewpoint. Then we will develop a theory, called the kinetic theory of gases, which explains in a simple way many of the relations we observe experimentally. The student may find it helpful to read about the theory along with his study of the laws that govern the behavior of gases.

6.2 ATMOSPHERIC PRESSURE AND THE BAROMETER

The most common gas we encounter, and the only one known until about 1750, is the air about us. This gas lies over the earth in a blanket about 50 miles thick. Like all earthly matter the air is subject to the gravitational pull of the earth. The air near the earth is compressed by the weight of the air above it. The pressure of the air at the earth's surface is by no means negligible and amounts to about 14.7 pounds per square inch; this means that our bodies are at all times subject to rather gigantic forces. The pressure of the atmosphere is not a constant, but varies with the height above sea level and with weather conditions. In Denver, Colorado (altitude, 5000 ft. above sea level) the atmospheric pressure is about 13.5 pounds per square inch. During a hurricane the pressure may become that low at sea level. Above about 10,000 feet breathing becomes uncomfortable for humans not accustomed to such altitudes, and for that reason modern aircraft have pressurized cabins. Military aircraft, which often operate at much higher altitudes, cannot be sufficiently pressurized (why?), and in such aircraft the personnel must wear pressurized suits and oxygen masks. At a height of 10 miles the atmospheric pressure is only about 10 per cent of that at sea level. Uncomfortable is not the word to describe the sensations of an unpressurized human being at such an altitude.

Although the facts of atmospheric pressure are really very simple, they were not clearly understood until about 1650. Men had learned earlier in a very practical way that they could not lift water more than about 33 feet with a suction pump; the reason for this was unknown, and the explanation given by philosophers was that

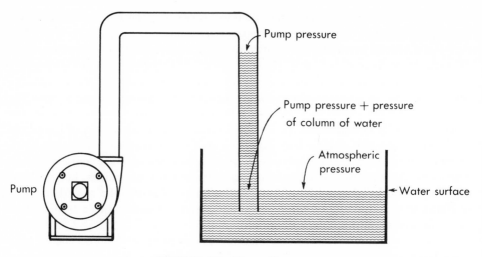

FIGURE 6.1   The suction pump.

"nature abhors a vacuum." Torricelli, an Italian scientist, showed that the limit on pumping heights exists because at the limiting height the pressure exerted by the atmosphere at the water surface is just balanced by the pressure exerted by the raised water column at the water surface. It is a natural law that in any liquid equal pressures must exist at equal heights. In the diagram in Figure 6.1 it is clear that at the water surface:

pressure outside tube = pressure inside tube

pressure of atmosphere = pressure at pump + pressure of column of water

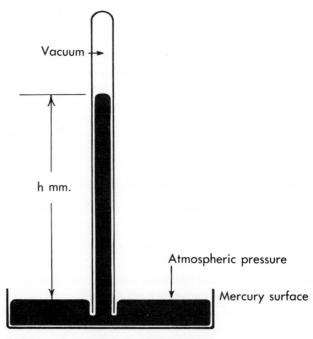

FIGURE 6.2   The barometer. Pressure of atmosphere = pressure of mercury column = h mm. Hg = 760 mm. Hg at standard atmospheric pressure and 0°C.

Torricelli recognized that the maximum height of the liquid column was essentially a measure of the atmospheric pressure and made a simple device for making the measurement conveniently. His device, called a **barometer,** is shown in Figure 6.2; it consists of a closed glass tube filled with mercury and inverted over a pool of mercury. Provided the tube is sufficiently long, liquid mercury flows into the reservoir when the tube is first inverted, leaving essentially a vacuum above the liquid; the height of the liquid column remaining in the tube is then directly proportional to the atmospheric pressure. Since the density of mercury is high, the height of the column is much less than with water and is, at one standard atmosphere pressure, 760 mm. if the mercury is at 0°C. It was several years before Torricelli's contemporaries accepted his reasoning and recognized the barometer as the scientific instrument it is; even today we use his barometer, essentially unmodified, as the standard instrument for the measurement of atmospheric pressure.

6.3 BOYLE'S LAW

One of the first laws ever discovered which related to the behavior of matter was stated in 1660 by Robert Boyle, an English natural philosopher. Boyle performed an experiment with air that is really very simple by modern standards. Using a glass tube and some liquid mercury arranged as in Figure 6.3, he found that the volume of entrapped air varied inversely with the pressure applied to it. Boyle did the experiment in a room in which the temperature was approximately constant and needed, in addition to his apparatus, only a barometer and a measuring rule. In order to interpret his data properly Boyle had to understand the role of atmospheric

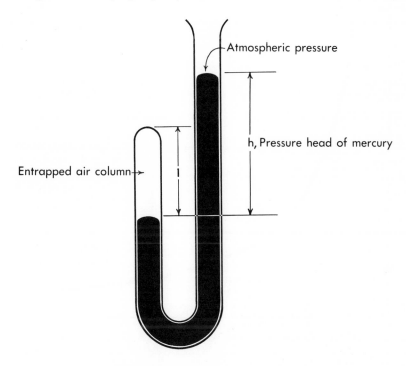

FIGURE 6.3 Boyle's experiment.

pressure in the experiment. Any schoolboy could repeat the experiment in the laboratory in a few hours, but even in these days it is just possible he might have difficulty in treating the data. (The interested student should try Problem 6.3 at the end of this chapter.) Boyle of necessity worked only with ordinary air, but when other gases were discovered it was found that they too showed an inverse relationship between volume and pressure at constant temperature. This relationship is called Boyle's Law.

In words, Boyle's Law states that: **The volume of a given mass of any gas at constant temperature varies inversely with the pressure or the product of the volume times the pressure of a given mass of any gas is a constant at constant temperature.**

In a mathematical equation we would say:

pressure × volume = a constant   (for a given mass of gas at constant T)

$$PV = k \quad \text{or} \quad V = k/P \tag{6.1}$$

In the equation, k is a constant at constant temperature and amount of gas; it may therefore be a function of both temperature and amount of gas.

Boyle's Law can be readily described by a graph. In Figure 6.4 we have plotted the volume of a given amount of gas as a function of pressure when the temperature is held constant. From the graph it is clear that as the gas pressure increases the volume decreases, in such a way that the product of P × V remains constant. If the pressure is increased fourfold, the volume decreases to one quarter its initial value. If the volume is increased by a factor of ten, the pressure decreases to one tenth its

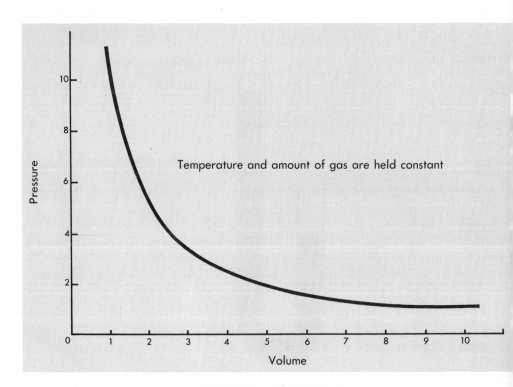

FIGURE 6.4 Boyle's Law.

initial value. The actual magnitude of the PV product depends on the dimensions of the pressure and volume and on the amount of gas and the temperature. The **constancy** of the PV product requires the **constancy** of the amount of gas and the temperature.

Robert Boyle was a remarkable person who, in addition to his discovery of the law which bears his name, made many contributions to scientific thought. One of the most important of these was a book entitled *The Sceptical Chemist* in which he challenged the then prevailing notion that salt, sulfur, and mercury were the true principles of nature. Although the science of the time was too primitive to allow him to do proper experiments in the area, he advanced the idea that matter was ultimately composed of particles of various sorts which could arrange themselves into groups, and that groups of one kind constituted a chemical substance. Boyle thus used concepts similar to those we have today and, by some, has been called one of the fathers of modern chemistry. We would prefer to reserve such a title for men like Dalton, Lavoisier, and Priestley, who performed chemical experiments to support their views.

6.4 CHARLES' LAW AND GAY-LUSSAC'S LAW

Boyle's Law, as we have mentioned, was discovered in 1660. It was not until about 100 years later that another quantitative relation for gas behavior was found. This relation involved the way in which the volume of a gas kept at constant pressure varied with the temperature. One might wonder why Boyle or his contemporaries did not proceed to investigate the effect of temperature on the properties of gases. Boyle did know that heating a gas would tend to increase its volume and checked to make sure that small temperature changes were unimportant in the experiments which led to his law. The difficulty was that, at that time, the concepts of heat and of temperature were not well understood. Any quantitative law involving temperature had to follow the development of the notion of temperature, the creation of a temperature scale, and a thermometer to measure the temperature. Science did not reach this level until about 1750, when several investigators made these important contributions. Men at that time began to be aware of the existence of gases other than air. (Interest in the discovery of such gases, particularly those lighter than air, was spurred by the development of the first balloons large enough to allow man to make his first air travels.) Progress in science is made in steps; these steps seem to have a natural order which is only rarely bypassed, and then only by men of extreme insight.

Between about 1780 and 1800 two French scientists, Charles and Gay-Lussac (who, incidentally, were both balloonists at one time or another), independently arrived at the law which bears their names. They found that **when a gas is heated at constant pressure from one given temperature to another, the fractional change in the volume is a constant independent of the gas being studied.** If the two temperatures involved are 0°C and 100°C, the increase in volume for any gas is always just about 37 per cent of the volume at 0°C.

If the change in temperature is 1°C rather than 100°C one finds that the increase in volume is very nearly 0.37 per cent of the volume at 0°C. A change of 2°C increases the volume by about 2×0.37 per cent or 0.74 per cent. The thoughtful student can see that these observations allow us to express the volume of a gas at constant pressure in terms of its centigrade temperature by the following equation:

$$V = V_0 + 0.0037\, V_0 t = V_0(1 + 0.0037t) \qquad (6.2)$$

in which V is the volume at t°C and V_0 the volume at 0°C.

This equation can be modified in an interesting manner to yield a very significant result regarding the nature of that property we call temperature. We can say that, at $t_1°C$,

$$V_1 = V_0(1 + 0.0037\ t_1)$$

and at $t_2°C$ and the same pressure on the same sample of gas,

$$V_2 = V_0(1 + 0.0037\ t_2)$$

Dividing the second equation by the first, we obtain

$$\frac{V_2}{V_1} = \frac{1 + 0.0037\ t_2}{1 + 0.0037\ t_1}$$

Now, if we divide both numerator and denominator of the right side of this equation by 0.0037, we see that, since $\dfrac{1}{.0037} = 273$,

$$\frac{V_2}{V_1} = \frac{273 + t_2}{273 + t_1}$$

The terms $273 + t_1$ and $273 + t_2$ can be very simply interpreted. They would be the *temperatures* as read on a new *temperature scale* on which *all centigrade temperatures were increased by* 273°. Such a temperature scale can be seen to have some real advantages over the ordinary centigrade scale. For gases the dependence of volume on temperature, in terms of the new scale, is readily expressed. If we let T on the new scale be $273 + t$, the equation becomes

$$\frac{V_2}{V_1} = \frac{T_2}{T_1} \tag{6.3}$$

It has been found that many natural laws are, like the foregoing relation, most simply written in terms of the temperature scale given by

$$T = 273 + t \tag{6.4}$$

and this scale has therefore been adopted for scientific use. T is called the **absolute** temperature, and can always be calculated by equation 6.4 from the centigrade temperature t. Degrees on the absolute temperature scale are called degrees absolute, °A, or degrees Kelvin, °K, in honor of Lord Kelvin, an English physicist, who arrived at the same scale of temperature on theoretical grounds.

The setting up of the absolute temperature scale completes our study of the temperature concept, but there are a few points which we should clear up before leaving the subject. What has really been done is to *define* the ratio of any two temperatures on the absolute scale to be equal to the ratio of the volumes that a given amount of gas at a fixed, low pressure would have at the two temperatures. If we then keep the same temperature interval as on the centigrade scale, namely 100°, between the freezing and boiling points of water, the absolute scale is completely determined. On this scale the precise value of the freezing point of water is 273.16°A. Absolute temperatures can, at least in principle, be determined with a gas volume thermometer and the foregoing conventions; from the absolute temperatures one can then calculate the centigrade temperatures. In practice the scales on the very best centigrade thermometers are made by calibration against a standard gas volume thermometer. Most thermometers are, however, made and calibrated by the procedure described in Chapter 1. This results, rather fortuitously, in fairly accurate thermometers, since the centigrade scale on the ordinary mercury-in-glass thermometer just happens to correspond fairly well to the centigrade scale as determined by the gas volume thermometer.

Since absolute temperatures can in principle be measured with any gas at low pressure, one of the objections to the temperature scale set up in Chapter 1 has been removed; one can now determine temperature independent of any given substance.

After studying this discussion of the dependence of gas volume on temperature and the development of the absolute temperature scale, the student might well ask what the law of Charles and Gay-Lussac actually is. Expressed in words, the law states that: **At constant pressure the volume of a given amount of gas is directly proportional to its absolute temperature.** In equation form

volume = a constant × temperature   (mass of gas and pressure held constant)

$$V = KT \quad \text{or} \quad V/T = K \tag{6.5}$$

The actual value of the constant K will depend on the amount of gas in the sample, the pressure, and the dimensions used.

As with Boyle's Law, the dependence of gas volume on temperature as given by Charles' Law can be readily illustrated with a graph. In Figure 6.5 we have plotted the volume of one mole of oxygen at one atmosphere pressure as a function of absolute temperature. Doubling the absolute temperature doubles the volume. Halving the volume at constant pressure would require that the absolute temperature also be halved.

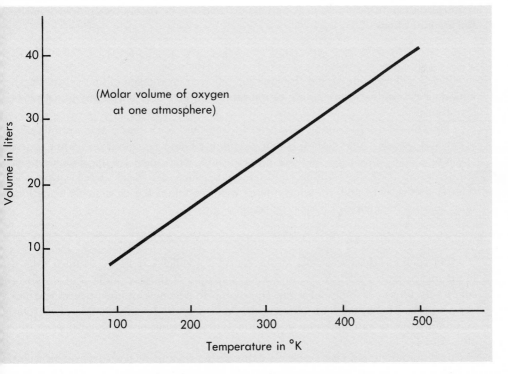

FIGURE 6.5 Charles and Gay-Lussac's Law.

In connection with Charles' Law, the question might arise about the volume the gas would have at very low temperatures. According to that law, as the temperature approaches 0°K the volume of the gas would also approach zero. Since this would be impossible without giving the gas an infinite density at 0°K, we might also wonder about the possibility of reaching the absolute zero of temperature. Actually, it is found that as we approach 0°K, or −273°C, all gases condense to liquids or solids having finite volumes at finite temperatures. It is also true, however, that a very tight theoretical argument can be presented which predicts the impossibility of attaining the absolute zero of temperature. Modern experimental results support this prediction; the lowest temperatures reached under the best conditions are about 0.001°K.

6.5 THE IDEAL GAS EQUATION

The laws of Boyle and Charles relate in two equations the pressure, volume, and temperature of a given amount of gas. We shall now show how these equations can be combined to obtain a more general law for the behavior of gases.

According to Boyle's Law (with temperature and amount of gas constant):

$$V = k/P \tag{6.1}$$

According to Charles' Law (with pressure and amount of gas constant):

$$V = KT \tag{6.5}$$

If the amount of gas in a container is doubled, holding pressure and temperature constant, the volume of the gas will be doubled. In general, the volume of a gas under given conditions will be proportional to the amount (mass) of gas present. This requires that both k and K in equations 6.1 and 6.5 be themselves proportional to the amount of gas. That is,

$$V = k'a/P = K'aT \quad (k'a = k; K'a = K) \tag{6.6}$$

in which a is the amount of gas. In equation 6.6 account is taken of the fact that both equations 6.1 and 6.5 must apply to the same sample of gas under any given set of conditions.

For equation 6.6 to be generally valid, it is necessary that a relationship exist between k' and K'; the relation is that k' equals cT and K' equals c/P, where c is a constant for any given gas and has a magnitude determined by the dimensions of temperature, pressure, volume, and amount which are used. Recognizing the relation between k' and K' allows us to write equation 6.6 as a single equation, summarizing the general physical behavior of gases,

$$V = acT/P \quad \text{or} \quad PV = acT \tag{6.6a}$$

For each gas there is a value of the constant c which can be determined from a single measurement of P, V, T, and a for a sample of the gas under a given set of conditions. Once c is found for a gas, equation 6.6a becomes an unequivocal relation between the volume, amount, temperature, and pressure for any sample of that gas and allows one to calculate any one of the four properties of the sample, given the other three.

It is found that if one agrees to express the amount of gas in terms of *moles*, rather than in some other mass unit such as grams, equation 6.6a takes on a remarkably simple form, in that under those conditions the constant c has the *same value for all gases*. This allows one to write a single equation applicable to all gases and offers such a distinct advantage that the amount of gas in equation 6.6a is invariably expressed as the number of moles, n. The constant c, which then becomes the same for all gases, is given the symbol R. In terms of the new symbolism, equation 6.6a has the form

$$PV = nRT \tag{6.7}$$

and is called the **Ideal Gas Law.**

The reason that the constant R in the Ideal Gas Law equation is not dependent on the kind of gas being studied follows from a fundamental postulate first stated in 1813 by Amadeo Avogadro, an Italian physicist. He recognized that Gay-Lussac's observations on the relative volumes of gases which react chemically (Section 6.6) could be most simply explained if **equal volumes of different gases under the same conditions of temperature and pressure contain equal numbers of molecules.** This postulate is now accepted as a basic principle of chemistry and is called Avogadro's Law.

Returning now to equation 6.6a,

$$V = acT/P$$

we can see that, if we take equal *volumes* of any two different gases at the same *temperature* and *pressure*, then P, V, and T for the two gases will obviously have equal values. By Avogadro's Law the number of molecules in the two samples will be equal; since a mole of gas always contains 6.023×10^{23} molecules, the number of moles of gas in the two samples must also be equal, and hence the amount, a, in moles, is the same in the two samples. Therefore, to give the right side of equation 6.6a the proper magnitude for the two gas samples, it is necessary that c be the same for the two gases and hence for all gases. Equation 6.7, with the proportionality constant expressed as R and the amount of gas expressed in moles, immediately follows.

In the Ideal Gas Law, R is called the **gas constant,** and has a numerical value which depends on the dimensions used for pressure and volume. In Table 6.1 we have listed the values of R which are obtained for several common sets of pressure-volume dimensions.

TABLE 6.1 VALUES OF THE GAS CONSTANT R IN VARIOUS DIMENSIONS

For Pressure in	and Volume in	R Has the Value
Atmospheres	liters	0.0821 l.-atm.*/mole · °K
Atmospheres	milliliters	82.1 ml.-atm./mole · °K
Millimeters of mercury	liters	62.3 l.-mm. Hg/mole · °K
Millimeters of mercury	milliliters	6.23×10^4 ml.-mm. Hg/mole · °K

* Liter-atmosphere.

The Ideal Gas Law is one of the more important relations in chemistry. Its importance lies in the fact that it relates in a definite way the pressure, volume, temperature, and amount of *any* gas, as long as the pressure of the gas is not too high. There are many possible applications of the Ideal Gas Law, making it a very powerful tool in the hands of one who understands it. At this point you may feel that the law is a rather complicated mathematical relation which probably has some theoretical significance but shows little promise of practical usefulness. Actually, as the student becomes familiar with the law by working with it, he will find it to be a rather simple relation and yet one which makes possible the solution of a large variety of problems.

The following examples illustrate some of the situations in which the Ideal Gas Law can be employed. In all cases we will take the value of R to be 0.0821 1-atm./ mole·°K and will, where necessary, convert the dimensions of pressure and volume accordingly.

Example 6.1. What volume will a sample of 240 ml. of argon occupy if its pressure is increased at 20°C from 0.10 atm. to 6.0 atm.?

Solution. For the argon in both states: $PV = nRT$

Initially: $\quad P_1 = 0.10$ atm.; $\quad V_1 = 240$ ml.; $\quad n_1 = n$; $\quad T_1 = T$ $\qquad P_1V_1 = nRT$

Finally: $\quad P_2 = 6.0$ atm.; $\quad V_2 = ?$; $\qquad n_2 = n$; $\quad T_2 = T$ $\qquad P_2V_2 = nRT$

Since both the temperature and amount of gas are held constant in this problem, the right sides of the two equations are equal, and so

$$P_1V_1 = P_2V_2$$

Substituting: 0.10 atm. $\times$ 240 ml. = 6.0 atm. $\times V_2$

$$V_2 = \frac{0.10 \text{ atm.} \times 240 \text{ ml.}}{6.0 \text{ atm.}} = 4.0 \text{ ml.}$$

This problem is typical of many encountered with gases. The state of the gas is changed, with one or more of its variables remaining fixed. By writing the gas law for the two states, one can usually quickly recognize the terms in the two equations which are equal and use that information and the given data to calculate the unknown quantity.

Example 6.2. A sample of hydrogen gas, collected at 100°C and 1.00 atm. pressure, has a volume of 350 ml. It is subsequently transferred to a 4.00-l. flask and cooled to 25°C. What pressure, in millimeters of mercury, will it exert in the flask?

Solution. For the hydrogen in the two states:

$$PV = nRT$$

Initially:

$$P_1 = 1.00 \text{ atm.}; V_1 = 350 \text{ ml.} \times \frac{1 \text{ l.}}{1000 \text{ ml.}} = 0.350 \text{ l.}; n_1 = n; T_1 = 273 + 100 = 373°K$$

$$P_1V_1 = nRT_1$$

Finally: $P_2 = ?$; $V_2 = 4.00$ l.; $n_2 = n$; $T_2 = 273 + 25 = 298°K$

$$P_2V_2 = nRT_2$$

In this problem nR is the same in the two states, and so,

$$\frac{P_1V_1}{T_1} = \frac{P_2V_2}{T_2}$$

Therefore,

$$P_2 = \frac{V_1}{V_2} \times \frac{T_2}{T_1} \times P_1$$

$$P_2 = \frac{0.350 \text{ l.}}{4.00 \text{ l.}} \times \frac{298°K}{373°K} \times 1.00 \text{ atm.} = 0.0700 \text{atm.} \times \frac{760 \text{ mm. Hg}}{1 \text{ atm.}} = 53.2 \text{ mm. Hg}$$

This problem is again one that involves a change in state of the gas. Here, however, the pressure, volume, and temperature all change, and the dimensions given are not the same in the two states. By carrying all dimensions in the calculations, we see that we must convert both volumes to the same units, if the volumes are to cancel properly. We could have, of course, converted P_1 to millimeters of mercury before making any calculations of P_2. *One must not, in any case, ignore the dimensions of the quantities in the calculation,* since they are as important as the numbers themselves, and must be expressed properly if the result is to have the proper dimensions.

The previous examples were concerned with changes in state of a given amount of gas. In such problems, n, the number of moles of gas, is constant, and the value of R need not be known, since R cancels from the calculation. The following problems are somewhat more complex and require full use of the Ideal Gas Law, including the value of R. They are illustrative of the large amount of information that the law allows one to obtain about gases.

Example 6.3. 2.50 g. of nitrogen gas are introduced into an evacuated 3.00-l. container at $-80°C$. Find the pressure in atmospheres in the container.

Solution. In this problem only one state is involved, and for it; PV = nRT

$$P = ?; \quad V = 3.00 \text{ l.}; \quad n = 2.50 \text{ g. N}_2 \times \frac{1 \text{ mole}}{28.0 \text{ g. N}_2} = 0.0893 \text{ mole}$$

$$R = 0.0821 \text{ l.-atm./mole} \cdot °K; \quad T = 273 - 80 = 193°K$$

Substituting: $P = \dfrac{nRT}{V} = \dfrac{0.0893 \text{ mole}}{3.00 \text{ l.}} \times 0.0821 \dfrac{\text{l.-atm.}}{\text{mole} \cdot °K} \times 193°K = 0.472 \text{ atm.}$

Here all the elements in the Ideal Gas Law enter the calculation directly; if one uses 0.0821 l.-atm./mole · °K for R, the dimensions of all the terms are of necessity those that appear in R, and any quantities which do not have those dimensions must be converted before substituting in the Gas Law.

Example 6.4. A lighter-than-air balloon is designed to rise to a height of 25 miles, at which point it will be fully inflated. At that altitude the atmospheric pressure is 2.40 mm. Hg and the temperature $-3°C$. If the full volume of the balloon is one hundred thousand liters, how many pounds of helium will be needed to inflate the balloon?

Solution. To calculate the number of pounds of helium required, we shall first use the Ideal Gas Law to obtain the number of moles, n, and then convert from moles to grams and finally to pounds.

Since balloons have flexible walls, the volume of the balloon will vary with the applied pressure, the pressure in the balloon being substantially equal to the outside atmospheric pressure. Hence, for the helium at a height of 25 miles;

$$P = 2.40 \text{ mm. Hg} \times \frac{1 \text{ atm.}}{760 \text{ mm. Hg}} = 0.00316 \text{ atm.}$$

$$V = 1.000 \times 10^5 \text{ l.}; \quad n = ?; \quad R = 0.0821 \text{ l.-atm./mole} \cdot °K; \quad T = 273 - 3 = 270°K$$

$$n = \frac{PV}{RT} = \frac{0.00316 \text{ atm.} \times 1.000 \times 10^5 \text{ l.}}{\dfrac{0.0821 \text{ l.-atm.}}{\text{mole} \cdot °K} \times 270°K} = 14.3 \text{ moles}$$

Since 1 mole of helium weighs 4.00 grams, the mass of helium is

$$14.3 \text{ moles} \times \frac{4.00 \text{ g.}}{1 \text{ mole}} = 57.2 \text{ g.} \times \frac{1 \text{ lb.}}{453.6 \text{ g.}} = 0.126 \text{ lb.}$$

6.6 OTHER APPLICATIONS OF THE IDEAL GAS LAW

There are some problems in which the use of the Ideal Gas Law is not quite so direct as in the previous examples. Two important cases involve the determination of the density of a gas under given conditions and the evaluation of its molecular weight from experimental data. These problems are readily treated if one recognizes the relationships between density or molecular weight and the variables in the Gas Law. These relations allow the statement of the law in terms of the density or molecular weight and other measured quantities.

Recalling that

$$\text{density} = \frac{\text{mass}}{\text{volume}}, \qquad \left(d = \frac{g}{V}\right)$$

and that

$$\text{number of moles} = \frac{\text{mass}}{\text{gram molecular weight}}, \qquad \left(n = \frac{g}{M}\right)$$

we can write the Ideal Gas Law as

$$PV = nRT = \frac{g}{M}RT \qquad \text{or} \qquad P = \frac{n}{V}RT = \frac{gRT}{VM} = d\frac{RT}{M} \qquad (6.8)$$

These equations are merely alternate forms of the Gas Law and involve no new concepts. Their use is illustrated in the following examples:

Example 6.5.   What is the density in grams per liter of sulfur dioxide at 25°C and 300 mm. Hg pressure?

Solution.   Solving equation 6.8 for density, $d = \dfrac{PM}{RT}$

For the SO_2 sample,   P = 300 mm. Hg × 1 atm./760 mm. Hg = 0.395 atm.

$$M_{SO_2} = (32.07 + 2 \times 16.00) \text{ g./mole} = 64.07 \text{ g./mole}$$

$$R = 0.0821 \text{ l.-atm./mole} \cdot °K; \quad T = 273 + 25 = 298°K$$

On substitution, $d = \dfrac{0.395 \text{ atm.} \times 64.07 \text{ g./mole}}{\dfrac{0.0821 \text{ l.-atm.}}{\text{mole} \cdot °K} \times 298°K} = 1.04 \text{ g./l.}$

Example 6.6.   A sample of chloroform weighing 0.5280 g. is collected as a vapor (gas) in a flask having a volume of 127 ml. At 75°C the pressure of the vapor in the flask is 754 mm. Hg. Calculate the molecular weight of chloroform.

Solution.   By the alternate form of the Gas Law we see that

$$M = g\frac{RT}{PV}$$

We have merely to express the variables in the equation in the proper dimensions and solve for the gram molecular weight by substitution.

$$g = 0.5280 \text{ g.}; \quad R = 0.0821 \text{ l.-atm./mole} \cdot °K; \quad T = 273 + 75 = 348°K$$

$$P = 754 \text{ mm. Hg} \times \frac{1 \text{ atm.}}{760 \text{ mm. Hg}} = 0.992 \text{ atm.}; \quad V = 127 \text{ ml.} \times \frac{1 \text{ l.}}{1000 \text{ ml.}} = 0.127 \text{ l.}$$

$$M = \frac{0.5280 \text{ g.} \times \dfrac{0.0821 \text{ l.-atm.}}{\text{mole} \cdot °K} \times 348°K}{0.992 \text{ atm.} \times 0.127 \text{ l.}} = 120 \text{ g./mole}$$

The calculated molecular weight of chloroform is, therefore, 120.

The data in Example 6.6 are typical of those obtained in one of the simplest experimental methods for the determination of molecular weights. In the experiment a few milliliters of a volatile liquid are placed in a flask fitted with a stopper in which there is a fine orifice (Figure 6.6). The flask is then heated in a water bath to a

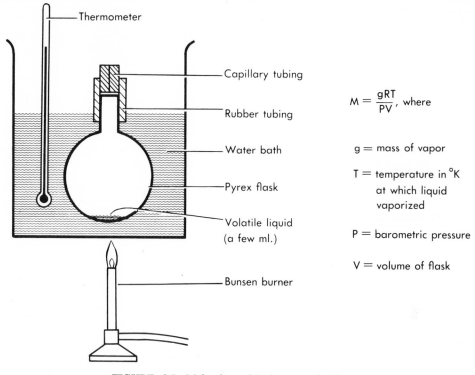

$M = \dfrac{gRT}{PV}$, where

g = mass of vapor

T = temperature in °K at which liquid vaporized

P = barometric pressure

V = volume of flask

FIGURE 6.6 Molecular weight by vapor density.

temperature somewhat above the boiling point of the liquid. The liquid evaporates, and its vapor replaces the air in the flask. After all the liquid has evaporated and the flask is filled with vapor, the flask is removed from the bath and let cool. The vapor condenses and air re-enters the flask. The mass of the vapor is taken as the difference between the mass of the flask containing the condensed vapor and its mass when dry. The method is an approximate one for several reasons, but when properly done gives results accurate to within a few per cent.

Another application of the gas laws arises in connection with our interpretation of chemical reactions. Given any chemical reaction we have seen that it is possible to calculate the relative masses of reactants and products as well as to state immediately the relative numbers of moles. Where gases are present it is possible to extend the interpretation of chemical reactions to include the volumes of the gases that would be involved under given conditions. The procedure is shown in the following example:

Example 6.7. One method for the commercial production of chlorine uses the electrolysis of molten sodium chloride. The chemical reaction that occurs is:

$$2\ NaCl(l) \longrightarrow 2\ Na(l) + Cl_2(g)$$

How many liters of chlorine, measured at 25°C and 1 atm., can be produced from one kg. of sodium chloride?

Solution. The chemical equation tells us that

$$2\ \text{moles NaCl} \longrightarrow 1\ \text{mole Cl}_2$$

$$117\ \text{g. NaCl} \longrightarrow 1\ \text{mole Cl}_2$$

Therefore, 117 g. NaCl $\simeq$ 1 mole Cl_2 and from 1000 g. NaCl we would obtain

$$1000 \text{ g. NaCl} \times \frac{1 \text{ mole } Cl_2}{117 \text{ g. NaCl}} = 8.55 \text{ moles } Cl_2$$

The chlorine will obey the Gas Law, PV = nRT, in which P = 1 atm.; V = ?; n = 8.55 moles; R = 0.0821 l.-atm./mole $\cdot$ °K; T = 298°K. Hence,

$$V = \frac{nRT}{P} = \frac{8.55 \text{ moles} \times \dfrac{0.0821 \text{ l.-atm.}}{\text{mole} \cdot °K} \times 298°K}{1 \text{ atm.}} = 209 \text{ l.}$$

In problems of this kind it is best to calculate the number of moles of gas produced or used up in the reaction and then to use the Gas Law to find the volume.

A rather interesting interpretation of chemical reactions can be made when the substances involved are all gases whose volumes are measured under the same conditions of temperature and pressure. Consider the following chemical reaction:

$$4 NH_3(g) + 5 O_2(g) \longrightarrow 4 NO(g) + 6 H_2O(g)$$

According to the usual interpretation, we would say

$$4 \text{ moles } NH_3 + 5 \text{ moles } O_2 \longrightarrow 4 \text{ moles } NO + 6 \text{ moles } H_2O$$

If all these gases are measured at the same temperature and pressure, their molar volumes will all be equal, say to some volume V_m liters. Under such conditions it would be true that

$$4 V_m \text{ l. } NH_3 + 5 V_m \text{ l. } O_2 \longrightarrow 4 V_m \text{ l. } NO + 6 V_m \text{ l. } H_2O$$

or, dividing through by V_m, simply

$$4 \text{ l. } NH_3 + 5 \text{ l. } O_2 \longrightarrow 4 \text{ l. } NO + 6 \text{ l. } H_2O$$

if all the gases are measured at the same temperature and pressure.

Volumes of gases, then, when measured under the same conditions, have the same simple numerical relationships that exist between moles of substances in chemical reactions. The remarkable fact is that, whereas the relation between moles is deduced from theory, that between volumes can be found experimentally. Indeed, in 1808 Gay-Lussac discovered the relationship and stated his Law of Combining Volumes: **In any chemical reaction involving gaseous substances the volumes of the various gases reacting or produced are in the ratios of small whole numbers.** (The gases are measured at the same temperature and pressure.)

In 1811, Avogadro, who saw the implications of Gay-Lussac's Law, stated his famous hypothesis, which, as we have noted in Chapter 2, can lead to correct and unequivocal values of atomic weights. Unfortunately, the chemists of the time were skeptical of the work of Gay-Lussac and Avogadro, and, by plausible but incorrect arguments, succeeded in discrediting it. The faulty line of reasoning used by Dalton was as follows:

It is proposed experimentally that, in the reaction between nitrogen and oxygen to form nitric oxide, one volume of nitrogen combines with one volume of oxygen to yield two volumes of nitric oxide. If this is so, then x atoms of nitrogen react with x atoms of oxygen to form 2x atoms of nitric oxide. Or, $\frac{1}{2}$ atom of nitrogen reacts with $\frac{1}{2}$ atom of oxygen to form 1 atom of nitric oxide. But, said Dalton, "thou canst not split an atom." Therefore, either the atomic theory is incorrect, or Gay-Lussac's experiment is faulty.

Dalton chose to believe the latter, and, in spite of the fact that Gay-Lussac's Law was later proved to be valid, the matter of atomic weights remained confused for 50 years. The situation was not straightened out until 1860, when Cannizzaro, recognizing clearly for the first time the distinction between atoms and molecules, properly interpreted Avogadro's Hypothesis and laid the foundation for the determination of atomic weights (Problem 2.23).

6.7 MIXTURES OF GASES: DALTON'S LAW OF PARTIAL PRESSURES

So far we have considered the physical properties of gaseous systems in which only one component is present. If several substances are present in a gaseous solution, one can still use the gas laws, but must properly take account of the presence of the different substances. Let us assume we have a gaseous mixture of A, B, and C, confined in a container of volume V. The Ideal Gas Law will apply to the mixture, provided we let n equal the total number of moles present. That is,

$$PV = nRT \quad \text{or} \quad P = \frac{nRT}{V}$$

in which P is the total pressure in the container and n equals $n_A + n_B + n_C$.

The three substances A, B, and C each contribute to the total pressure in the system. Their individual contributions, P_A, P_B, and P_C are obtainable by the Gas Law. We can say that

$$P_A = \frac{n_A RT}{V} \; ; \quad P_B = \frac{n_B RT}{V} \; ; \quad P_C = \frac{n_C RT}{V}$$

P_A, P_B, and P_C are called the **partial pressures** of A, B, and C in the container. The partial pressure of a gas is the pressure the gas would exert if it alone were present in the container at the same temperature as the mixture. It is clear that, since

$$P = \frac{nRT}{V} = (n_A + n_B + n_C)\frac{RT}{V} = \frac{n_A RT}{V} + \frac{n_B RT}{V} + \frac{n_C RT}{V}$$

it follows that

$$P = P_A + P_B + P_C$$

This equation is a mathematical statement of Dalton's Law of Partial Pressures, first proposed by John Dalton in 1807. In words the law is: **The total pressure in a container is equal to the sum of the partial pressures of the component gases.**

Dalton's Law makes it possible to handle very easily problems in which gaseous solutions are involved. The following examples illustrate typical applications.

Example 6.8. A ten-liter flask at 25°C contains a gaseous solution of carbon monoxide and carbon dioxide at a total pressure of 2.00 atm. If 0.20 mole of carbon monoxide is present, find its partial pressure and also that of the carbon dioxide.

Solution. By Dalton's Law $P = P_{CO} + P_{CO_2} = 2.00$ atm.

$$P_{CO} = n_{CO}\frac{RT}{V} = \frac{0.20 \text{ mole} \times \dfrac{0.0821 \text{ l.-atm.}}{\text{mole} \cdot {}^\circ\text{K}} \times 298 {}^\circ\text{K}}{10 \text{ l.}} = 0.49 \text{ atm.}$$

$$P_{CO_2} = P - P_{CO} = (2.00 - 0.49) \text{ atm.} = 1.51 \text{ atm.}$$

Example 6.9. Dry air contains about 78 per cent nitrogen, 21 per cent oxygen, and 1 per cent argon by volume. Find the partial pressures of nitrogen, oxygen, and argon in dry air at 25°C and 1.00 atm. pressure.

Solution. Composition of gaseous solutions is frequently given in percentages by volume. Stating that dry air contains 78 per cent nitrogen by volume means that, if air were fractionated into its components and the nitrogen obtained were brought to the same temperature and *total* pressure as the original sample of air, the volume of the nitrogen would be 78 per cent of that of the original sample.

For the whole sample of air

$$P = \frac{nRT}{V} \qquad n = n_{N_2} + n_{O_2} + n_{Ar}$$

For the nitrogen in the sample

$$P_{N_2} = \frac{n_{N_2}RT}{V}$$

Dividing the second equation by the first,

$$\frac{P_{N_2}}{P} = \frac{n_{N_2}}{n}$$

But we can also say

$$V = \frac{nRT}{P} \quad \text{and} \quad V_{N_2} = \frac{n_{N_2}RT}{P} = 0.78\ V$$

Therefore, it is true that

$$\frac{V_{N_2}}{V} = \frac{n_{N_2}}{n} = \frac{P_{N_2}}{P} = 0.78$$

$$P_{N_2} = 0.78\ P = 0.78 \times 1\ \text{atm.} = 0.78\ \text{atm.}$$

By similar reasoning,

$$P_{O_2} = 0.21\ \text{atm.} \qquad \text{and} \qquad P_{Ar} = 0.01\ \text{atm.}$$

Dalton's Law is often of practical use in experiments involving gases. In order to measure the amount of a gas produced in a chemical reaction one must collect the gas under known conditions. Probably the easiest way of doing this is to let the gas displace water is a system such as that shown in Figure 6.7. In this way one can measure the volume of gas at atmospheric pressure and known temperature. If the gas were pure, one could immediately use the Gas Law to calculate the number of moles produced by the reaction. However, under the conditions of the experiment the gas collected contains water vapor in addition to the gas of interest. The true pressure of the gas produced is, therefore, by Dalton's Law, equal to the total pressure minus the partial pressure of the water vapor. It is found experimentally that the pressure of water vapor in the presence of liquid water is a constant at a given temperature; its value can be obtained from a table and used in the calculation.

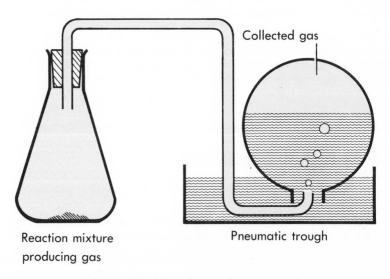

Reaction mixture producing gas   Pneumatic trough

FIGURE 6.7 The collection of gases over water.

(The pressure of vapor in equilibrium with its liquid is called the vapor pressure of the liquid and is discussed in detail in Chapter 12.) The following example is illustrative.

Example 6.10. In a laboratory experiment concentrated hydrochloric acid was reacted with aluminum. Hydrogen gas was evolved and was collected over water at 25°C; it had a volume of 355 ml. at a total pressure of 750 mm. Hg. How many moles of hydrogen were collected? At 25°C the vapor pressure of water is known to be about 24 mm. Hg.

Solution. By Dalton's Law $P = P_{H_2} + P_{H_2O}$

$$P_{H_2O} = 24 \text{ mm. Hg, the vapor pressure of } H_2O \text{ at } 25°C$$

Therefore

$$P_{H_2} = P - P_{H_2O} = (750 - 24) \text{ mm. Hg} = 726 \text{ mm. Hg}$$

$$= 726 \text{ mm. Hg} \times \frac{1 \text{ atm.}}{760 \text{ mm. Hg}} = 0.955 \text{ atm.}$$

By the Gas Law

$$P_{H_2} = \frac{n_{H_2}RT}{V} \qquad n_{H_2} = \frac{P_{H_2}V}{RT} = \frac{0.955 \text{ atm.} \times 0.355 \text{ l.}}{\dfrac{0.0821 \text{ l.-atm.}}{\text{mole} \cdot °K} \times 298°K} = 0.0138 \text{ mole}$$

$$n_{H_2} = 0.0138 \text{ mole}$$

6.8 REAL GASES

In this chapter we have applied the various gas laws to all gases, tacitly assuming that the laws were obeyed exactly. Under ordinary conditions (and in all problems involving gases in this text) the assumption is a very good one. Actually, however, all gases deviate to some extent from the ideal laws, by amounts that depend on the gas, its temperature, and its pressure. For gases in the vicinity of room temperature and 1 atm. pressure the deviation is small and at most a few per cent. Gases like oxygen and hydrogen, which boil far below 25°C, have molar volumes which are within 0.1 per cent of the value calculated by the Ideal Gas Law. Sulfur dioxide and chlorine, which boil at −10° and −35°C respectively, are, at 25°C and 1 atm., not so nearly ideal and have molar volumes which are 2.4 and 1.6 per cent lower than the ideal value.

It is possible to illustrate the behavior of real gases graphically by plotting PV/RT for a mole of gas as a function of pressure. Figure 6.8 is such a graph for several gases at 0°C. For a mole of ideal gas PV/RT would be a constant equal to one at all pressures. Actually, at relatively low pressures (less than 100 atm.) PV/RT is less than one in the vicinity of 25°C for all gases except hydrogen and helium and approaches one as the pressure approaches zero. The pressure of most gases at a given volume and temperature is, then, somewhat *less* than would be predicted by the Gas Law. This behavior is caused, we believe, by the small attractions (see Chapter 10) which exist between molecules even in the gas phase. As the temperature of the gas is lowered, the energy of motion of the molecules is lowered, and the effect of the attractive forces becomes more important, until, at the boiling point of the substance, the forces are large enough to cause the molecules to condense to a liquid. These forces in all cases tend to reduce the value of PV/RT and, in view of the foregoing line of reasoning, are important at temperatures near the boiling point of the substance. This qualitatively explains why SO_2 is less nearly ideal in its behavior than oxygen at 25°C. As the temperature of a gas is raised, the attractive forces become less and less significant; at very high temperatures the PV/RT behavior of all gases approaches that of hydrogen at 25°C, an effectively high temperature as far as the physical behavior of hydrogen is concerned.

The PV/RT behavior of gases at very high pressures (500 atm. and above) is shown at the right of Figure 6.8. For all gases, as the pressure is increased, PV/RT ultimately begins to increase, finally becoming much greater than the ideal value. Such an effect is best understood by considering the volumes of gas molecules. As we noted, in general the gas volume is much larger than the actual volume of the constituent gas molecules. However, the volume of the molecules is not zero (being roughly the volume of the liquid made by condensing the molecules), and, as the pressure increases, the volume of the molecules becomes a larger and larger fraction of the gas volume. The volume in which the gas molecules can actually move about is thus decreased by the volume taken up by the molecules, so the pressure of the gas at a given volume and temperature tends to be somewhat larger than predicted by the Gas Law. This effect becomes greater at high pressures and accounts for the high values of PV/RT at very high pressures. At intermediate pressures the attractive forces and finite molecular volume effects tend to counteract each other.

It is possible to write equations of state for gases which take account of both intermolecular attractions and finite molecular volumes. The simplest and best known of these relations is the Van der Waals equation, which for one mole of gas takes the form

$$P = RT/(V - b) - a/V^2 \qquad (6.10)$$

in which b and a are constants selected for each gas to give the best possible agreement between the equation and actual experimental behavior. The equation, in spite of its relative simplicity, gives good qualitative prediction of real gas behavior; the

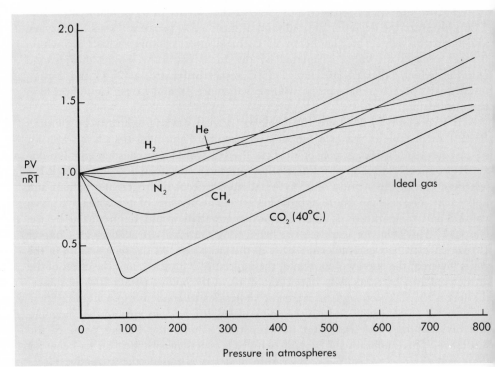

FIGURE 6.8 The behavior of real gases at 0°C.

constant b can be related to molecular volumés and a to molecular attractions. The Van der Waals equation is used in treating problems in which the nonideality of the gas is important and an analytical relation between P, V, and T is required.

The Limiting Density Method for Determining Molecular Weights

Historically, gas density measurements offered one of the best methods for the accurate determination of both molecular and atomic weights. Although it would appear that such determinations are inherently limited by the fact that all gases at finite pressures deviate from ideal behavior, it is possible, by a straightforward modification of the procedure used in Example 6.6, to devise an extremely accurate method for finding molecular weights.

One simply measures, very carefully and at a single temperature, the density of a gas at several low pressures. At each pressure an apparent molecular weight is calculated from the equation,

$$M_{app} = dRT/P \tag{6.8}$$

Each apparent molecular weight will be in error because of the deviation of the gas from ideality. Since the deviation decreases as pressure decreases, molecular weights calculated from data taken at the lower pressures will tend to be more nearly correct than those from higher pressures. Indeed, if the calculated apparent molecular weights are plotted against the pressure and the values extrapolated to zero pressure, the value of apparent molecular weight obtained at zero pressure would in principle be the correct molecular weight, since at zero pressure the gas would behave ideally. This approach, which is called the **limiting density method** for determining molecular weights, was used very successfully in the early part of this century, when no other accurate methods for the determination were available. Use of the method in finding molecular and atomic weights is illustrated in Problems 6.26 and 6.27.

6.9   THE KINETIC THEORY OF GASES

The fact that the Ideal Gas Law can be used to summarize reasonably accurately the physical behavior of all gases, no matter what their degree of molecular complexity, is a clear indication that the gaseous state of matter is a relatively simple one to attempt to treat from a theoretical point of view. There must be certain properties common to all gases which cause them to follow the same natural law and to exhibit so many generally similar characteristics.

One property common to all gases is their ability to move rapidly. The wind on a stormy day, the force of an explosion, the door that moves when another door in the house is opened, the speed with which the sound of a voice echoes across a valley; all these depend on the ease of motion of gases. It is easy to see why the early philosophers speculated on the motions of particles in matter and attempted to explain observed properties in terms of such motions. Without experiments to guide them they were, however, unable to develop any quantitative concepts.

With the experimental work on gases by Charles, Gay-Lussac, Graham, and others, enough information on gas behavior became available to allow the development of a theory of gases. Between 1850 and 1880, Maxwell, Boltzmann, Clausius, and others, using the notion that the properties of gases are the result of molecular motions, developed the kinetic theory of gases. The theory was shown to be consistent with the known laws of gas behavior and implied much about gases that was then unknown. Since the time of its creators, who, incidentally, rank among the very best theoreticians the world has known, the theory has only had to be modified to make it consistent with quantum theoretical principles. In its present form it is one of the most successful of scientific theories, ranking in stature with the Copernican theory for the motion of the planets and the atomic theory of the nature of matter.

Postulates of the Kinetic Theory of Gases

1. *Gases consist of molecules in continuous, random motion.* The molecules undergo collisions with one another and with the container walls. The pressure of a gas arises from the forces associated with wall collisions.

2. *Molecular collisions are elastic.* During collisions, there are no frictional losses which result in loss of energy of motion. The temperature of a gas insulated from its surroundings does not change.

3. *The average energy of translational motion of a gas molecule is proportional only to the absolute temperature.* The energy associated with the motion of a molecule from one place to another is dependent on the temperature but not on pressure or on the nature of the molecule.

In addition to these postulates it is often assumed that the volumes of molecules are negligible as compared to container volume and that molecules do not exert forces on each other except by collisions.

The postulates of the kinetic theory of gases are easily stated. Their implications are, however, by no means obvious, and can lead to extremely complicated mathematical problems. In this discussion we will be able to explore only a few of the simpler applications of the theory.

The Ideal Gas Law

Gas pressure, according to the kinetic theory, is the direct result of the forces associated with the collisions of molecules with the container walls. The molecules in a gas move about in a completely random manner, at speeds that are constantly changing due to molecule-molecule and molecule-wall collisions. To treat the forces resulting from molecular motion of this sort in a rigorous way requires mathematics of a very high level of sophistication; of necessity we will limit ourselves to a much-simplified model which is illustrative of the approach used and which yields the same results as the more complete treatment.

Let us first consider a system in which a single molecule is present in a cubic container, as in Figure 6.9. For simplicity we shall assume the molecule moves at a constant speed u and in a direction perpendicular to the end walls. If the mass of the molecule is m, each time it hits the right-hand wall of the container, it will exert an effective force of $2mu$. If the dimension of the container is a, the molecule must travel a distance of $2a$ between collisions with the right-hand wall. With the molecule bouncing back and forth across the container at a constant speed u, it will hit the right-hand wall $u/2a$ times per second. The total force exerted by the molecule on the wall will be the effective force per collision times the number of collisions occurring per second. That is, for the force, f, per molecule,

$$f = (2\,mu)(u/2a) = mu^2/a \qquad (6.11)$$

The molecule we have been considering would only exert force on the end walls of the container, since it would not hit the other walls. It is well known that the properties of a gas are the same in all directions, so that if our simple model is to have the observed properties of a gas, for every molecule moving in the direction we considered, there must be two other molecules present in the container, one moving in a vertical direction and the other moving normal to the plane of the paper and to the plane of the front and rear container walls. For n molecules, all moving at the

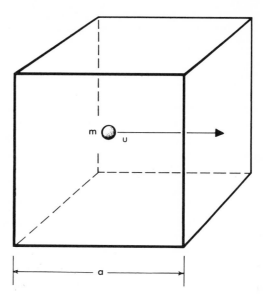

FIGURE 6.9 Molecule moving in a cubic box. The molecule of mass m travels, at a constant speed u, the distance of the dimension of the container, a.

same speed in the directions indicated, only $n/3$ would move in the direction perpendicular to the right-hand wall. The force on that wall will simply be the sum of the forces exerted by the individual molecules which strike it,

$$F = (n/3)f = (n/3)(mu^2/a) = nmu^2/3a \qquad (6.12)$$

The pressure on the wall is equal to the force divided by the wall area, which for a cubic box of dimension a is a^2. Therefore,

$$P = F/a^2 = nmu^2/3a^3 = nmu^2/3V \qquad (6.13)$$

in which V is the container volume. Equation 6.13 is also obtained in the complete kinetic theory treatment, with u being an average molecular speed. The equation is one of the main results of the theory, and relates the pressure and volume of a gas to the average speed of its molecules.

The Ideal Gas Law follows from equation 6.13 and the postulate of the kinetic theory that the average energy of translational motion of a gas molecule is dependent only on the absolute temperature and proportional to it. Mathematically, the postulate takes the form,

$$\epsilon = (\tfrac{1}{2})mu^2 = cT \qquad (6.14)$$

in which ϵ is the average molecular energy and c is a proportionality constant which has the same value for all molecules, whatever their nature.

By eliminating mu^2 from equation 6.13 by using equation 6.14, one obtains an equation of state for the gas,

$$PV = nmu^2/3 = 2n\epsilon/3 = (\tfrac{2}{3})ncT \qquad (6.15)$$

Recognizing that the number of molecules, n, equals the number of moles, n, multiplied by Avogadro's number, N,

$$PV = (\tfrac{2}{3})nNcT \qquad (6.16)$$

which is the Ideal Gas Law if the proportionality constant c is defined in magnitude to make R, the gas constant, equal to 2Nc/3. This development shows that the Ideal Gas Law is consistent with the kinetic theory, as indeed it should be.

Graham's Law

It is the characteristic of a successful theory that it can predict many of the experimental properties of the system to which it is applied. In the previous development the average molecular speed canceled from the equations so that no real evidence regarding molecular speeds was obtained. It is, however, possible to test that aspect of the theory in several ways. Probably the simplest of these involves the phenomena of diffusion and effusion.

If two different gases, in separate containers at the same temperature and pressure, are separated by stopcocks from a third gas confined at the same temperature and pressure, they will, when the stopcocks are opened, tend to diffuse into the third gas (see Figure 6.10). The rate of diffusion of each gas will be proportional to the average speed of its molecules. The less massive molecules will, according to equation 6.14, tend to move more rapidly than the heavier ones, and hence will diffuse more quickly. Hydrogen gas diffuses more quickly than does oxygen, as would be expected in light of the foregoing line of reasoning. Uranium hexafluoride, UF_6, with its very massive molecules, would diffuse much more slowly than would hydrogen or oxygen.

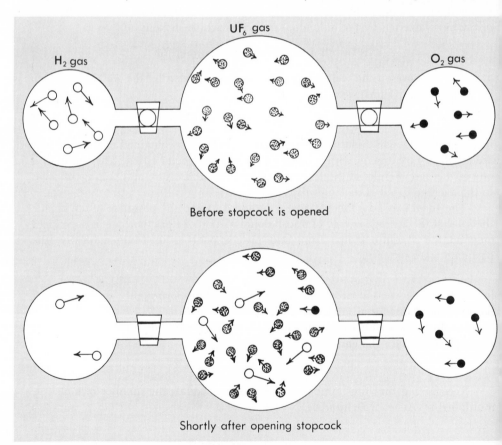

FIGURE 6.10 Diffusion of gases.

A quantitative test of the theory can be made if one measures the rate at which a gas will flow into a vacuum through a small opening in its container. This phenomenon is called **effusion,** and here also one would predict that the rate of effusion of a gas would be proportional to the average speed of its molecules. In this case, however, the rate could be measured by noting how rapidly the pressure in the container dropped and relating this to the number of molecules leaving the container in a given time interval. If the rates of effusion of two gases, A and B, were measured in the same container under similar conditions, we would predict that

$$\frac{\text{rate of effusion of A}}{\text{rate of effusion of B}} = \frac{\text{average speed of molecule A}}{\text{average speed of molecule B}} = \frac{u_A}{u_B} \qquad (6.17)$$

By equation 6.14, if gases A and B are studied at the same temperature,

$$m_A u_A^2 = 2cT = m_B u_B^2$$

or

$$\frac{u_A^2}{u_B^2} = \frac{m_B}{m_A} = \frac{m_B N}{m_A N} = \frac{M_B}{M_A} \qquad (6.18)$$

in which M_B and M_A are the molecular weights of B and A. If equation 6.18 is solved for the ratio of average molecular speeds, and this is substituted in equation 6.17, it is easily seen that

$$\frac{\text{rate of effusion of A}}{\text{rate of effusion of B}} = \left(\frac{M_B}{M_A}\right)^{1/2} \qquad (6.19)$$

This relation, that the rate of effusion of a gas varies inversely as the square root of its molecular weight, was essentially first observed experimentally by Thomas Graham in 1828. At that time molecular weights were not thoroughly understood, and Graham stated the relation in terms of the densities of the gases he studied. According to equation 6.8, the density of a gas and its molecular weight are related, so that if the equation is applied to A and B,

$$\begin{array}{l} M_B = d_B RT/P \\ M_A = d_A RT/P \end{array} \qquad \text{yielding} \qquad \frac{M_B}{M_A} = \frac{d_B}{d_A} \qquad (6.20)$$

if the densities of gases B and A are obtained under the same conditions of temperature and pressure. If the density ratio in equation 6.20 is substituted in equation 6.19, the law reported by Graham is obtained,

$$\frac{\text{rate of effusion of A}}{\text{rate of effusion of B}} = \left(\frac{d_B}{d_A}\right)^{1/2} \qquad (6.21)$$

when the densities of gases A and B are measured under the same conditions of temperature and pressure.

Graham's Law gives us an alternate method for the measurement of the molecular weights of gases, and one of its main uses is in this area. One needs merely to measure the rate of effusion of the unknown gas or vapor against the rate of a known reference gas. The procedure is straightforward and has found some practical application in industry in cases in which the purity of a gas is clearly reflected by its molecular weight. The following example is illustrative.

Example 6.11. In an effusion experiment it required 45 seconds for a certain number of moles of an unknown gas to pass through a small orifice into a vacuum. Under the same conditions it required 18 seconds for the same number of moles of oxygen to effuse. Find the molecular weight of the unknown gas.

Solution. The rates of effusion are inversely proportional to the times needed for the flow. Hence, by equation 6.19,

$$\frac{\text{rate}_X}{\text{rate}_{O_2}} = \frac{t_{O_2}}{t_X} = \left(\frac{M_{O_2}}{M_X}\right)^{1/2} \qquad \frac{18}{45} = \left(\frac{32}{M_X}\right)^{1/2} = 0.40$$

Squaring both sides, $\frac{32}{M_X} = 0.16$, and, therefore, $M_X = \frac{32}{0.16} = 200$.

During World War II, Graham's Law had a rather unexpected application in connection with a very complicated chemical problem. It had been found that the isotope of uranium having a relative mass of 235, U^{235}, had a nucleus unstable to collisions with neutrons. Such collisions result in a splitting of the uranium nucleus into lighter fragments (fission) and the liberation of large amounts of energy in the form of heat and γ-rays (see Chapter 23). It became clear that a bomb made of such a uranium isotope would be potentially extremely powerful, and hence the isolation of pure U^{235} was a necessity. Ordinary uranium contains only a small fraction of the U^{235} isotope, being about 99 per cent U^{238}. Due to the great chemical similarity of the isotopes of an element, the chemical resolution of uranium into its isotopes was not feasible, and some physical method was sought. Since the rate of diffusion of a gas varies with its molecular weight, the composition of a gas mixture coming through an orifice will not be the same as that in the original sample, and hence, the resolution of a gas mixture by successive diffusions is, at least in principle, possible. Preliminary diffusion experiments with uranium hexafluoride, UF_6, a volatile uranium compound, indicated that $U^{235}F_6$ could indeed be separated from $U^{238}F_6$ by diffusion, and an enormous plant was built for the purpose in Oak Ridge, Tennessee. In the process, UF_6 diffuses many thousands of times through porous barriers, with the lighter fractions moving on to the next stage and the heavier fractions being recycled through earlier stages. In this way a great deal of essentially pure U^{235} has been prepared and used to make nuclear power reactors and atomic weapons of all sorts.

Molecular Speeds

Of rather greater theoretical interest than the relative molecular speeds treated by Graham's Law are the actual average speeds of molecules. These can be calculated from equation 6.14 after substituting the value of c required to make the kinetic theory consistent with the Ideal Gas Law. Solving for u^2 in equation 6.14, we obtain, on letting c equal 3R/2N,

$$u^2 = 2cT/m = 2(3R/2N)(T/m) = 3RT/mN = 3RT/M$$

or

$$u = (3RT/M)^{1/2} \tag{6.22}$$

in which M is the gram molecular weight of the gas and R is the gas constant. From equation 6.22 it is clear that molecular speeds increase with increasing temperature, decrease with increasing molecular weight, and are not dependent on gas pressure. Simple substitution into the equation allows one to determine the average speed of any gas molecule at any given temperature.

Example 6.12. Find the average speed of an oxygen molecule in air at room temperature (25°C).

Solution. In order to give u the proper dimensions, cm./sec. in the metric system, the value of R used in equation 6.22 must be in absolute units. R will always have the dimensions of energy per mole per degree Kelvin, and in absolute units has a value of 8.31×10^7 ergs per mole per °K.* Using this value of R,

$$u = (3RT/M)^{1/2} = \left[\frac{3 \times \left(8.3 \times 10^7 \dfrac{\text{ergs}}{\text{mole} \cdot °K} \right) \times 298°K}{32 \text{ g./mole}} \right]^{1/2}$$

$$= 4.82 \times 10^4 \text{ cm./sec.} = 482 \text{ m./sec. or about 1000 miles per hour!}$$

According to the kinetic theory, molecular speeds are on the average very high by ordinary standards. It has been possible to test this prediction by several direct experiments, and the quantitative data obtained agree very well with the theoretical values. Qualitatively, the very high average speed of molecules appears reasonable when one considers the speed of sound in air. Since sound is propagated by molecular motion, one would expect that the speed of sound and that of the molecules in the gas through which it passes would be roughly equal. The speed of sound is about 800 miles an hour, which indeed is very close to the average speed of a nitrogen or oxygen molecule at 25°C.

Although it is very useful to be able to calculate an average speed for a gas molecule, you must remember that not all the molecules will be moving at that speed. At any moment the speeds of different molecules will cover a very wide range, with the speed and direction of motion of any given molecule changing many, many times each second as the result of collisions. It is possible, by an extension of the theory which led to equation 6.22 for the average molecular speed, to derive a much more complicated expression which predicts the likelihood that a molecule will have any given speed at any given moment. Some molecules, according to the theory, will have speeds well below the average, the large majority will have speeds near the average, and a small fraction will have speeds many times the average value. That fraction of molecules with high speeds and associated high energies of motion has an important effect on the rates at which chemical reactions occur and will be considered in this connection in Chapter 14.

PROBLEMS

6.1   A sample of hydrogen gas is confined in a 6.3-l. container at 0°C and 7.4 atm. pressure. What would its volume be at 0°C and a pressure of 1.0 atm.?

6.2   A sample of nitrogen collected in a McLeod gauge of 250 ml. volume is compressed at constant temperature to a volume of 0.30 ml. and a pressure of 1.0 cm. Hg. What was the pressure in atmospheres of the gas when collected?

---

* One erg equals 1 g. cm.²/sec.²

6.3 In Boyle's original experiment he measured the length (directly proportional to the volume) of a gas column as a function of the pressure head of mercury (Figure 6.3). The following table is taken from his data:

Length of gas column (1) (in cm.)	Pressure head (h) (in cm. Hg)	
48	0	(Barometric pressure
40	15.7	= 74.0 cm. Hg)
32	38.4	
24	75.5	
16	147.3	

Make calculations from these data which demonstrate the validity of Boyle's Law.

6.4 A gas in a cylinder is heated at a constant pressure of 1.00 atm. from 25°C to 150°C. If the gas initially has a volume of 24 l., find the final volume.

6.5 A 10.0-l. sample of steam at 100°C and 1.00 atm. pressure is cooled to 25°C and expanded until the pressure is 20 mm. Hg. If no water condenses, calculate the final volume of the water vapor.

6.6 Calculate the volume in liters of a mole of gas at 0°C and 1.00 atm. (This volume is sometimes called the molar volume of a gas at standard temperature and pressure, STP, and in some texts is used as the basis of calculations in problems involving gases. The Ideal Gas Law is a much more powerful tool in treating such problems, and is always used in more advanced studies of gas behavior.)

6.7 Calculate the density in grams per liter of ammonia gas, NH_3, at 25°C and 1.00 atm. pressure.

6.8 How many grams will the steam filling a 50-gal. oil drum at 100°C and one (1.00) atmosphere weigh? (1 gal. = 4.55 l.)

6.9 How many grams will the liquid water filling a 50-gal. oil drum at 25°C and 1.00 atm. weigh?

6.10 The oxygen in a 40.0-l. tank of compressed gas is at 2.00×10^3 lb./in.^{2} pressure. If the temperature of the tank is 25°C, how many pounds of oxygen does it contain?

6.11 Five milliliters of an unknown organic substance was vaporized at 90°C in a 275-ml. flask with a fine-holed stopper. After all the liquid was vaporized, the flask was cooled and weighed with the condensed liquid. The liquid was found to weigh 0.985 g. The barometric pressure in the laboratory was 752 mm. Hg. Calculate the molecular weight of the liquid from this data.

6.12 The molecular weight calculated in Problem 6.11 will be inaccurate for several reasons. Name as many reasons as you can and indicate the one which you think would have the most effect on the result.

6.13 Calculate the mass of air (M.W. = 29) at 25°C and 1.00 atm. in a room which is 5.0 m. × 4.0 m. × 2.0 m. in dimensions.

6.14 A 0.154-g. sample of $XH_2(s)$ reacts with water according to the following equation:

$$XH_2(s) + 2 H_2O(l) = X(OH)_2(s) + 2 H_2(g)$$

The hydrogen which is evolved is collected over water at 23°C and occupies a volume of 186 ml. at 746 mm. Hg total pressure. Find the number of moles of hydrogen which was evolved and the atomic weight of X. At 23°C the vapor pressure of water is 21 mm. Hg.

6.15 A gaseous mixture of carbon dioxide and carbon monoxide contains 25 mol per cent carbon dioxide. If the total pressure in the container is 6.0 atm., what are the partial pressures of each of the two gases?

6.16 When ammonium nitrite is heated in aqueous solution, the following reaction occurs:

$$NH_4^+ + NO_2^- = N_2(g) + 2\,H_2O(l)$$

If the nitrogen released by the reaction is collected over water at 23°C at a total pressure of 755 mm. Hg, how much ammonium nitrite must be reacted to produce 6.0 l. of wet gas?

⋏ 6.17 In the reaction:

$$N_2(g) + O_2(g) = 2\,NO(g)$$

how many liters of NO will be produced from 16 l. of N_2 if each of the gases is measured at 25°C and two atm. pressure?

6.18 How many grams of $O_2(g)$ can be recovered from 1.00×10^6 l. of air at 25°C and 750 mm. Hg pressure if the air is 21 per cent oxygen and 79 per cent nitrogen by volume?

⋄ 6.19 If an equimolar mixture of hydrogen and nitrogen is allowed to effuse down a capillary tube, which component will predominate in the effluent gas? Can you estimate the composition of the first effluent?

⋏ 6.20 It took 68 sec. for a given amount of a certain gas to effuse through a porous plug at 30°C and 96 sec. for the same number of moles of oxygen to effuse under the same initial conditions. Estimate the molecular weight of the gas.

6.21 For a mole of ideal gas, make:
a. A plot of P vs. T at V = 10 l.
b. A plot of PV vs. P at 25°C.
c. A plot of PV vs. V at 0°C.
d. A plot of PV vs. T.

⋏ 6.22 What properties of a gas determine:
a. The average speed of its molecules?
b. The average energy of its molecules?
c. The pressure it exerts?
d. The force of an average molecule-wall collision?

⋏ 6.23 Compare the mean speed of a fluorine molecule with that of a uranium hexafluoride, UF_6, molecule when both are present as gases in the same container. Compare the mean kinetic energies of the two molecules under the same conditions.

⋄ 6.24 How hot would a sample of sulfur dioxide gas have to be if its molecules were to have the same average speed as oxygen molecules at 27°C?

⋏ 6.25 How fast on the average are carbon tetrachloride molecules moving in the vapor at 150°C?

*6.26 In a classical experiment the density of carbon dioxide was carefully measured at 0°C at several low pressures, with the following results:

Pressure (atm.)	Density (g./l.)
1.00000	1.97676
0.66667	1.31485
0.33333	0.65596

At each pressure calculate, using 5-place logarithms or a desk calculator, the apparent molecular weight of carbon dioxide. (R equals 0.082056 l.-atm./mole · °K; 0°C equals 273.16°K) Make a graph of M.W.app. against the pressure and extrapolate the (straight) line to zero pressure. The value of M.W.app. at zero pressure is the "best" value for the molecular weight of CO_2, since at zero pressure the gas will behave ideally. Assuming the molecular formula of carbon dioxide and the atomic weight of oxygen, calculate the atomic weight of carbon from the molecular weight of CO_2 you obtained.

*6.27 At 27°C a certain gas has a density of 5.85 g./l. at 2.00 atm. pressure and a density of 11.90 g./l. at 4.00 atm. pressure. Use this data to find the best value you can for the molecular weight of the gas.

*6.28 Extimate the relative magnitudes of the Van der Waals constant b for the following gases: O_2, CO_2, H_2, CCl_4, H_2O. Do the same for the constant a for these gases.

*6.29 One of the postulates of the kinetic theory is that the average kinetic energy of motion through space (translational energy) of molecules in a gas is proportional only to the absolute temperature, with the same proportionality constant applying to all gases. Using the relations developed in this chapter, find an equation for the kinetic (translational) energy of a mole of gas in terms of known or measurable quantities. Given that the gas constant R has the value 1.987 cal./mole · °K, calculate the kinetic energy in calories for a mole of argon at 25°C and 1 atm.; for a mole of sulfur dioxide gas at 25°C and 2 atm. pressure.

*6.30 When a gas is heated at constant volume, all the heat that is absorbed by the gas serves to increase the energy of its molecules. If the molecules are monatomic, all the heat goes to increase their translational kinetic energy. Using the results of Problem 6.29, calculate the amount of heat required to raise the temperature of one mole of argon one °C when the gas is heated at constant volume. The observed value, which is called the heat capacity of argon at constant volume, is 3.01 cal./°C. The observed molar heat capacity at constant volume of SO_2 is 7.52 cal./°C. Can you suggest a reason for the difference between the values for the two gases?

*6.31 Absolute temperature scales can be set up on bases other than the one described in this chapter. For example, an absolute scale can be readily defined which is based on the Fahrenheit rather than the centigrade temperature scale. Find the absolute temperature at the freezing point of water on such a scale.

*6.32 A mole of nitrogen gas is confined in a ten liter container at 27°C. State the effect, qualitatively and then quantitatively, of each of the following changes on:
a. The average molecular speed.
b. The average molecular energy.
c. The force of an average molecule-wall collision.
d. The pressure of the gas.

The changes to be considered are:
a. The gas is compressed at 27°C to a volume of one liter.
b. The temperature of the gas is raised to 327°C.
c. Another mole of nitrogen is added to the container.
d. A mole of hydrogen is substituted for the nitrogen.

7 | THE PERIODIC CLASSIFICATION OF THE ELEMENTS

Thus far in our study of chemistry we have spent most of our efforts on the laws that govern chemistry. These laws allow us to predict the temperature-volume-pressure relationships in gases and the weight relations in known chemical reactions, and to find atomic weights and chemical formulas from experimental data. They do not, however, tell us much about the physical and chemical properties of specific chemical substances. Thus we find ourselves in the rather anomalous position of being able to calculate how much phosphine, PH_3, could be produced by the reaction between phosphorus and sodium hydroxide, given the equation for the reaction, without having any idea about the chemical properties of phosphine or even knowing whether it is a solid, a liquid, or a gas. Clearly a knowledge of chemistry must include familiarity with the actual properties of chemical substances as well as an understanding of theoretical principles.

The amount of information now available on the chemical properties and reactions of the pure substances is, considering the limitations of the human mind, essentially infinite. No present-day chemist can hope to be familiar with all the chemistry of all the pure substances. Each year the volume of information published in the chemical journals far exceeds the reading capacity of any individual. Much of this information is in very specialized areas and requires extensive reading of the previous literature before it can be understood. The professional chemist, realizing that he must be productive under these circumstances, makes an obvious compromise. Through his research and by study of the literature he becomes very well versed in the chemistry of his particular area of specialization. In order that he may relate other chemical research to his own work he also tries to obtain a useful general, if admittedly incomplete, working knowledge of chemical behavior.

If one accepts this compromise approach, the question arises as to how the choice of important information is to be made. One would hope that some broad generalizations of chemical behavior could be found, similar in character to the generalizations which were possible in the treatment of the physical properties of gases. This chapter illustrates how such generalizations can be shown to exist and how they can be used to classify and predict the chemical and physical properties of pure substances.

7.1 THE PERIODICITY OF PROPERTIES OF THE ELEMENTS

A search for possible generalizations regarding chemical behavior would probably begin with a study of the elementary substances, simply because there are only about a hundred elements and millions of pure substances. To expect at the outset that an examination of the properties of the elements would have fruitful results might well be considered a case of extreme optimism. So far our chemical theory has taken the elements as separate, independent entities. We have said very little about the nature of atoms or the possible relationships between them.

We begin our investigation by listing the first 25 elements in order of their atomic weights. With the notion that there may be some obvious, if unexpected, relations between the properties of the elementary substances, we also list several of their readily measured physical properties, including the density of the solid form of the element, its melting point, the normal boiling point, and the ionization energy, which is essentially the energy required to remove one electron from the atom of the element. These quantities are tabulated in Table 7.1 and are presented in graphic form in Figures 7.1 and 7.2.

TABLE 7.1 SOME PHYSICAL PROPERTIES OF THE LIGHTER ELEMENTS

Element	Order No.	Atomic Weight	Density of Solid (g./ml.)	Melting Point (°C)	Boiling Point (°C)	Ionization Energy (ev.)
H	1	1.008	0.08	−259	−253	13.6
He	2	4.003	0.13	−272	−269	24.6
Li	3	6.939	0.53	186	1340	5.4
Be	4	9.012	1.8	1350	1500	9.3
B	5	10.81	2.5	2300	2550	8.3
C	6	12.011	2.26	3500	?	11.3
N	7	14.007	1.03	−210	−196	14.5
O	8	16.00	1.43	−218	−183	13.6
F	9	19.00	1.3	−223	−187	17.4
Ne	10	20.183	1.0	−249	−246	21.6
Na	11	22.990	0.97	98	880	5.1
Mg	12	24.312	1.74	651	1110	7.6
Al	13	26.98	2.71	660	1800	6.0
Si	14	28.09	2.33	1420	2600	8.1
P	15	30.974	2.2	590	?	10.9
S	16	32.064	2.1	119	445	10.4
Cl	17	35.453	1.9	−102	−35	13.0
K	18 (19)	39.102	0.86	62	760	4.3
Ar	19 (18)	39.948	1.65	−189	−186	15.8
Ca	20	40.08	1.55	810	1215	6.1
Sc	21	44.96	~2.5	1200	~2400	6.6
Ti	22	47.90	4.5	1800	>3000	6.8
V	23	50.94	6.0	1710	~3000	6.7
Cr	24	52.00	7.1	1890	2500	6.8
Mn	25	54.94	7.2	1260	1900	7.4

Even a casual inspection of the graphs reveals that there is a certain amount of regularity in the properties of these substances. The properties do not vary randomly, but rather show a rough tendency to vary in some sort of cycle, being successively

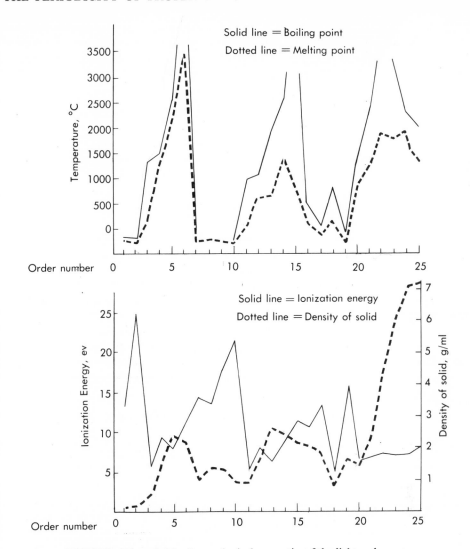

FIGURES 7.1 and 7.2   Some physical properties of the lighter elements.

relatively high and then relatively low. The same length of cycle is clearly present in the melting and boiling points, with minima at elements having order numbers of about 2, 10, and 19 and maxima at about numbers 6, 14, and 22. The density minima occur at order numbers 1, 11, and 18 and the maxima at 5, 13, and 25.

The ionization energy graph shows the most striking periodic character. The minima occur at order numbers 3, 11, and 18, and the maxima at numbers 2, 10, and 19. The steps in the curve from number 3 to number 10 are repeated between numbers 11 and 19, *except* that the ionization energy of element 18, potassium, is much too low. In fact, if elements number 18 and 19 are interchanged, the general appearance of the curve in the two cycles is very much the same. In the table the elements are ordered by their atomic weights; K, no. 18, = 39.102 and Ar, no. 19, = 39.948. These two atomic weights are correct to at least four places, so experimental error has not given the wrong order. However, potassium is also out of order in the graphs of the other properties, which would all be much more regular if elements no. 18 and 19 were interchanged. It seems possible that there is a natural order of the elements which is almost, but not quite, that of their atomic weights, and that, in the natural order, potassium is no. 19. With the notion that potassium, for some as yet unknown reason, is out of place in our list of elements, we shall arbitrarily interchange elements no. 18 and 19 in the list.

When this is done the regularity of the cycles in all the physical properties improves markedly. We get for

Physical Property	Maxima at Nos.	Minima at Nos.
Ionization energy	2, 10, 18	3, 11, 19

	Minima at Nos.	Maxima at Nos.
Melting point	2, 10, 18	6, 14, 22
Boiling point	2, 10, 18	6, 14, 22
Density	1, 11, 19	5, 13, 25

The cycle for ionization energy is now perfect, being eight elements long between maxima and between minima, with the smaller steps in the curve also spaced by eight elements. The other properties repeat in cycles varying in length from seven to twelve elements, with eight again being a reasonable average. The cycles for the four properties are also either completely in phase or out of phase.

This is the kind of variation observed with many of the physical properties of the elements. There does seem to be a periodic, or cyclic, character to the properties. In all cases potassium and argon fit into the cycles best when arranged in positions 19 and 18 respectively.

TABLE 7.2 FORMULAS OF SOME COMPOUNDS OF THE LIGHTER ELEMENTS

Element	Order No.	Formulas of Chlorides	Formulas of Oxides
H	1	HCl	H_2O, H_2O_2
He	2	—	
Li	3	$LiCl$	Li_2O, Li_2O_2
Be	4	$BeCl_2$	BeO
B	5	BCl_3 (B_4Cl_4, B_2Cl_4)*	B_2O_3
C	6	CCl_4 (C_2Cl_6)	CO_2, CO, C_3O_2
N	7	NCl_3	N_2O_5, N_2O, NO, N_2O_3, NO_2, N_2O_4
O	8	Cl_2O (ClO_2, ClO_3, Cl_2O_7)	O_2, O_3
F	9	ClF (ClF_3)	OF_2
Ne	10	—	
Na	11	$NaCl$	Na_2O, Na_2O_2, NaO_2
Mg	12	$MgCl_2$	MgO
Al	13	$AlCl_3$	Al_2O_3
Si	14	$SiCl_4$ (Si_2Cl_6)	SiO_2, SiO
P	15	PCl_3 (PCl_5)	P_2O_5, P_2O_3, P_2O_4
S	16	SCl_2 (S_2Cl_2, SCl_4)	SO_3, S_2O, S_2O_3, SO_2, S_2O_7
Cl	17	Cl_2	Cl_2O_7, Cl_2O, ClO_2, ClO_3
Ar	18	—	
K	19	KCl	K_2O, K_2O_2, KO_2
Ca	20	$CaCl_2$	CaO, CaO_2
Sc	21	$ScCl_3$	Sc_2O_3
Ti	22	$TiCl_2$, $TiCl_3$, $TiCl_4$	TiO_2, Ti_2O_3
V	23	VCl_2, VCl_3, VCl_4	VO, V_2O_3, VO_2, V_2O_5
Cr	24	$CrCl_2$, $CrCl_3$	CrO, Cr_2O_3, CrO_2, CrO_3
Mn	25	$MnCl_2$, $MnCl_3$	MnO, Mn_3O_4, Mn_2O_3, MnO_2, Mn_2O_7

* (The compounds in parentheses exist but do not fall on the line in Figure 7.3.)

So far our inquiry has been limited to the physical properties of the elementary substances. Our main concern, however, is with an organization, or generalization, of the chemical behavior of both elementary and compound substances. We now look into the question of whether the chemical properties of the elements show any regularities of the sort seen in the physical properties. Let us begin by simply writing down the formulas of some of the compounds of the elements being examined.

Many of these elements form both chlorides and oxides, and in Table 7.2 we have listed the formulas of these compounds.

In Figure 7.3 the data on the chlorides are presented graphically. Several of the elements form more than one chloride; the graph has been drawn both to go through the points for those elements which form only one or no compounds and also to be as symmetrical as possible. The cycles for composition of the chlorides are seen to be perfectly regular and eight elements in length. Similar graphs can be drawn for the oxides of these elements and for their other binary compounds. In all cases, the cycles are regular and the period is eight elements long.

If one investigates the physical properties of the chlorides, or other binary compounds, of these elements, he finds the same general periodic occurrence of similar properties that is observed for the elements themselves.

An extension of this kind of study to include all the elements reveals the existence of a similar, though somewhat less simple, periodicity of their chemical and physical properties. The experimental evidence supporting these regularities of properties is now indeed overwhelming, and can be summarized in the following statement, usually called the Periodic Law: **The elements, if arranged in order of their atomic weights, exhibit an evident periodicity of properties.**

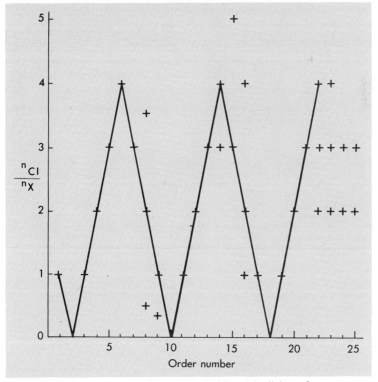

FIGURE 7.3   Atom ratios in the chlorides of the lighter elements.

7.2   HISTORY OF THE PERIODIC LAW

Several early chemists suspected the existence of the general relations which we have been discussing, but their supporting evidence at the time was so sketchy and the idea that such regularities were possible seemed so implausible that scientists paid them very little attention.

In 1817 Döbereiner reported that when certain groups of similar elements were arranged in groups of three, the atomic weight and other properties of the middle element were very close to the mean of the properties of the other two. The "triads" of elements then known were very limited in number, with calcium, strontium, and barium the best example, but in later years other "triads," such as lithium, sodium, and potassium, were discovered. You will remember that during the first half of the nineteenth century chemists, aided by the atomic theory and Lavoisier's work on combustion and the conservation of mass, were able to make very rapid progress. It was during this period that some 30 new elements were discovered. About 1860 Newlands, an English chemist, proposed that the elements occurred in sets of seven, but his "octaves," as they were called, had such a resemblance to the musical scale that the chemists of the time were so busy laughing they could not see that Newlands was right.

Between 1869 and 1871 Mendeleev, a Russian chemist, wrote a classic series of papers on the periodic properties of the elements. He included all the elements and used an approach very similar to that presented in this chapter. He was bold enough to assert that gaps in his arrangement corresponded to elements yet to be discovered and that experimental errors in atomic weights were responsible for the interchanges of positions of some of the elements. By noting the positions of the gaps, Mendeleev was able to predict many of the properties of the missing elements. Gallium, scandium, and germanium were among the elements predicted by Mendeleev and discovered in later years. In Table 7.3 we have listed the properties of germanium (then called ekasilicon) as predicted by Mendeleev, and the actual properties of that element as observed on its discovery in 1886. The agreement is truly remarkable. The success of predictions such as these removed any doubt of the validity of the concept of the periodicity of the properties of the elements; it explains the association of Mendeleev's name with the Periodic Law.

TABLE 7.3   THE PREDICTED AND OBSERVED PROPERTIES OF GERMANIUM

Property	Predicted by Mendeleev	Observed
Atomic weight	72	72.60
Density of metal	5.5	5.36
Color of metal	dark gray	gray
Formula of oxide	GeO_2	GeO_2
Density of oxide	4.7	4.703
Formula of chloride	$GeCl_4$	$GeCl_4$
Density of chloride	1.9	1.887
Boiling point of chloride	below 100°C	86°C
Formula of ethyl compound	$Ge(C_2H_5)_4$	$Ge(C_2H_5)_4$
Boiling point of ethyl compound	160°C	160°C
Density of ethyl compound	0.96	Slightly less than 1.0

7.3 THE PERIODIC TABLE

In order to emphasize their periodicity of properties, Mendeleev arranged the elements in horizontal rows of such length that elements of similar chemical properties fell directly beneath each other. This arrangement is still used and is called the **periodic table.** In the periodic table the elements in a given cycle, or period, are arranged in a horizontal row. The cycles for the lighter elements are most clearly shown in Figure 7.3. By convention, the first cycle of eight elements is taken to begin with lithium, element no. 3. The first row of eight elements is therefore

Li Be B C N O F Ne

The second cycle of eight elements in Figure 7.3 begins with sodium, element no. 11. Sodium is similar in its properties to lithium: both are soft metals of low density and melting point, both have relatively low ionization energies, both form chlorides with the formula XCl, and oxides with the formula X_2O. To indicate the similarity between sodium and lithium, sodium is placed immediately below lithium in the periodic table. If this is done, magnesium, element no. 12, falls below its counterpart, beryllium; aluminum below boron; and the rest of the elements in the second cycle of eight below their counterparts in the first cycle.

Elements like boron, carbon, and neon, which belong to the same cycle are said to be in the same **period;** elements which have similar properties, like lithium and sodium, or oxygen and sulfur, or neon and argon, are said to belong to the same **family** or **group.** To distinguish the families of elements they are given names; lithium and sodium belong to group 1A, beryllium and magnesium to group 2A, and so on up to neon and argon, which are in group 8A. Since hydrogen and helium are considered to be the only elements in the first cycle, they are said to make up the **first period.** Boron and fluorine are therefore in the **second period,** and magnesium, aluminum, and phosphorus are in the **third period.**

In the following table we have summarized these conventions by setting up the periodic table for the first 20 elements, indicating their groups and their periods.

TABLE 7.4 THE LIGHTER ELEMENTS IN THE PERIODIC TABLE

Group	1A	2A	3A	4A	5A	6A	7A	8A
1st period							H	He
2nd period	Li	Be	B	C	N	O	F	Ne
3rd period	Na	Mg	Al	Si	P	S	Cl	Ar
4th period	K	Ca						

Here we have included the first two elements, hydrogen and helium, in the table. Helium is clearly in the same family as neon and argon; these elements are all inert, or noble, gases. Hydrogen is put in group 7A, although, as we shall note later, it really belongs to no group. In the table we have put potassium and calcium, elements 19 and 20, in their proper places; they are clearly the first elements in the fourth period, with potassium in group 1A and calcium in group 2A.

At this point one might well be led to believe that the periodic table would be simply a rectangular array of the elements, eight elements across, with as many periods as needed to give a place to every element. This does not turn out to be the case. Following calcium there is a series of 10 elements, all metals, which do not seem to belong to any of the eight groups in the first three periods. Element 26, iron, would, if the fourth period were the same length as the third, be a noble gas like argon, neon, and helium, and it certainly has none of their properties. Figure 7.2 shows that the ionization energies of these 10 elements do not follow the two previous cycles.

Following these 10 elements we again encounter a series of elements which complete the fourth period begun by potassium and calcium. The period ends with elements 35 and 36, bromine and krypton; bromine has chemical properties very like those of chlorine and fluorine and belongs to group 7A. Krypton is a typical noble gas and hence a member of group 8A.

The elements following krypton are rubidium, with properties that make it a member of group 1A, and strontium, which fits well into group 2A. These two elements, then, begin the fifth period. Again in this period there is a series of ten elements that are not members of any of the A groups, followed by six elements that fit into groups 3A through 8A and complete the period. The last element in the fifth period is no. 54, xenon, a noble gas. The next element is cesium, which has all the properties of a 1A metal and begins the sixth period.

The overall structure of the periodic table for the first 54 elements can now be seen. The form is not as simple as we might have first thought, but it does have a high degree of symmetry nonetheless. The first period contains two elements; the second and third, eight elements each; the fourth and fifth, 18 elements each. The two series of 10 metals, in the fourth and fifth periods, fall into ten new groups, called the **transition metals.** The properties of the transition metals taken as a large group of elements are more similar than are the properties of the A elements, taken as a group. However, it is possible to note the existence of a cycle of properties in each of the two series of transition metals in the fourth and fifth periods, which justifies their classification into 10 families, each with one member in the fourth and one in the fifth periods.

Given the symmetry of the periodic table, one can make a sensible guess as to the number of elements in the sixth period, beginning with cesium. The numbers of elements in the first five periods are, as we have seen, in order, 2, 8, 8, 18, 18. The *increase* in the number of elements in the successive periods is 2, 6, and 10, as one goes to the first, from the first to the second, and from the third to the fourth periods. On this basis we would expect that, if the number of elements in the sixth period increases according to the simplest pattern, it will increase by 14, making the total number of elements in that period 32. That is just what is observed experimentally. Following barium, element no. 56, in group 2A, there is a series of 14 elements, called the **rare earths,** or lanthanides, then the series of 10 transition metals, and then six group A elements to complete the period. The situation in the sixth period appears to be repeated in the seventh, but that period is incomplete and contains several elements which do not exist in nature and whose properties are not well known.

In Table 7.5 and inside the rear cover of this book we have constructed the periodic table in accordance with our discussion. The transition metals are inserted in between groups 2A and 3A. The rare earths, elements 58 through 71, would rightly appear between the first and second transition metals in the sixth period, but to keep the length of the table manageable and also because the elements are very similar to one another, they are listed as a separate group, along with the equivalent series in the seventh period, at the bottom of the table.

TABLE 7.5 THE PERIODIC TABLE

1A	2A	3B	4B	5B	6B	7B	8	8	8	1B	2B	3A	4A	5A	6A	7A	8A
1 H 1.00797 ±0.00001																	2 He 4.0026 ±0.00005
3 Li 6.939 ±0.0005	4 Be 9.0122 ±0.00005											5 B 10.811 ±0.003	6 C 12.01115 ±0.00005	7 N 14.0067 ±0.0005	8 O 15.9994 ±0.0001	9 F 18.9984 ±0.0005	10 Ne 20.183 ±0.0005
11 Na 22.9898 ±0.0005	12 Mg 24.312 ±0.0005											13 Al 26.9815 ±0.0005	14 Si 28.086 ±0.001	15 P 30.9738 ±0.0005	16 S 32.064 ±0.003	17 Cl 35.453 ±0.001	18 Ar 39.948 ±0.0005
19 K 39.102 ±0.005	20 Ca 40.08 ±0.005	21 Sc 44.956 ±0.0005	22 Ti 47.90 ±0.005	23 V 50.942 ±0.0005	24 Cr 51.996 ±0.001	25 Mn 54.9380 ±0.0005	26 Fe 55.847 ±0.005	27 Co 58.9332 ±0.00005	28 Ni 58.71	29 Cu 63.54 ±0.005	30 Zn 65.37 ±0.005	31 Ga 69.72 ±0.005	32 Ge 72.59 ±0.005	33 As 74.9216 ±0.0005	34 Se 78.96 ±0.005	35 Br 79.909 ±0.002	36 Kr 83.80 ±0.005
37 Rb 85.47 ±0.005	38 Sr 87.62 ±0.005	39 Y 88.905 ±0.0005	40 Zr 91.22 ±0.005	41 Nb 92.906 ±0.0005	42 Mo 95.94 ±0.005	43 Tc (99)	44 Ru 101.07 ±0.005	45 Rh 102.905 ±0.0005	46 Pd 106.4 ±0.05	47 Ag 107.870 ±0.003	48 Cd 112.40 ±0.005	49 In 114.82 ±0.005	50 Sn 118.69 ±0.005	51 Sb 121.75 ±0.005	52 Te 127.60 ±0.0005	53 I 126.9044 ±0.0005	54 Xe 131.30 ±0.005
55 Cs 132.905 ±0.0005	56 Ba 137.34 ±0.005	57 La 138.91 ±0.005	72 Hf 178.49 ±0.005	73 Ta 180.948 ±0.0005	74 W 183.85 ±0.005	75 Re 186.2 ±0.005	76 Os 190.2 ±0.05	77 Ir 192.2 ±0.05	78 Pt 195.09 ±0.005	79 Au 196.967 ±0.0005	80 Hg 200.59 ±0.005	81 Tl 204.37 ±0.005	82 Pb 207.19 ±0.005	83 Bi 208.980 ±0.0005	84 Po (210)	85 At (210)	86 Rn (222)
87 Fr (223)	88 Ra (226)	89 Ac (227)															

Lanthanum Series

58 Ce 140.12 ±0.005	59 Pr 140.907 ±0.0005	60 Nd 144.24 ±0.005	61 Pm (147)	62 Sm 150.35 ±0.005	63 Eu 151.96 ±0.005	64 Gd 157.25 ±0.005	65 Tb 158.924 ±0.0005	66 Dy 162.50 ±0.005	67 Ho 164.930 ±0.0005	68 Er 167.26 ±0.005	69 Tm 168.934 ±0.0005	70 Yb 173.04 ±0.005	71 Lu 174.97 ±0.005

Actinium Series

90 Th 232.038 ±0.0005	91 Pa (231)	92 U 238.03 ±0.005	93 Np (237)	94 Pu (242)	95 Am (243)	96 Cm (247)	97 Bk (247)	98 Cf (249)	99 Es (254)	100 Fm (253)	101 Md (256)	102 No (253)	103 Lw (257)

Atomic Weights are based on C¹²—12.0000 and Conform to the 1961 Values of the Commission on Atomic Weights

Printed in U. S. A.

The Rare Earths

The rare earths, or lanthanides, are a group of 14 relatively uncommon metals with order numbers from 58 through 71. (Lanthanum, no. 57, is sometimes included.) These metals have very similar chemical and physical properties and, until the advent of ion-exchange columns, could not be efficiently separated.

In industry the metals are used mainly in the form of "misch metal," which is mainly a mixture of the lanthanides and a small amount of iron. Among the lanthanides in this material, cerium predominates with smaller amounts of lanthanum and neodymium and very small amounts of the other rare earths also present. Misch metal is useful in very small amounts (about 1 per cent) as an alloying agent with magnesium, where it serves to improve high-temperature properties. It is used in an alloy with iron in the "flints" of cigarette lighters and other devices which produce sparks by friction.

As pure oxides and salts, several of the rare earths are important as coloring agents in glass manufacture. Lanthanum oxide is an ingredient in some high refractive index glasses. Cerium oxide is used as a high quality abrasive in glass polishing and as an opacifying agent in ceramic enamels. Before the development of the incandescent lamp for lighting, ceria had very extensive use in the Welsbach incandescent gas mantle, now seen chiefly in gasoline camp lanterns.

7.4 SOME GENERALIZATIONS IN THE PERIOD TABLE

The principal purpose in building the periodic table was to place in the same vertical column those elements which appear in equivalent places in the cycles of properties. As we have noted, this results in having in the vertical columns elements which resemble one another in their properties. We have in this way made the very sort of generalization that was envisaged at the beginning of the chapter. For, by grouping similar elements together, one can study their chemistry as a group, rather than deal with the elements individually. As we shall see, there are limitations on the similarities between elements, but the principle of grouping them is a very useful one.

For purposes of discussion, the periodic table can be broken up into several regions. In the left-hand column of the table are the alkali metals, the most active of the metallic elements. They are soft, low-melting, ductile metals with characteristic luster and high electrical conductivity. They are also highly electropositive, which means that their atoms readily donate electrons to any electron-accepting, or electronegative, atoms. The elements in the second column are also metals, called the alkaline earths, with properties similar to those of the alkali metals; they are somewhat less reactive than the 1A metals, probably because they are somewhat less electropositive.

The large middle region of the periodic table is taken up by the transition elements, which are all metals. At the right side of the periodic table, in groups 4A through 8A are the elements which are nonmetals. These include all the elementary gases and those solids which are nonconductors of electricity. The elements in group 8A are all gases, and within the limitations discussed in Chapter 10, do not take part in chemical reactions; they are called the inert, or *noble* gases. The changes in physical properties within any given group of these elements are, except for group 8A, much more pronounced as one proceeds to higher periods than are the changes within a given family of metals, such as 2A or 6B. In group 5A, for example, nitrogen is a gas, phosphorus is a nonmetallic solid, arsenic exists in both metallic and nonmetallic allotropic modifications, and antimony and bismuth are usually classed as metals. The tendency toward increased metallic properties in the higher periods is also present in groups 4A, 6A, and 7A.

In view of the foregoing, one can generalize by saying that, within the periodic table, metallic character, as typified by high ductility, high electrical and thermal conductivity, and characteristic luster, decreases as one goes from group 1A to 8A in a given period. In the higher periods metallic character persists farther and farther to the right. This, and the existence of the transition and lanthanide elements, makes the number of nonmetallic elements much smaller than the properties of the lighter elements would have indicated, and essentially restricts them to the upper right-hand section of the periodic table.

Within any family there are, as we have noted, changes in the properties of its members as one goes to the higher periods. In general, however, these changes are smaller and more gradual than those observed for elements within a given period. This is particularly true for the ionization potentials of the elements, which tend to be related to their chemical reactivities. In the higher periods it is found, however, that the changes within a given period also become more gradual and smooth; especially is this true for the transition metals and the rare earths.

7.5 PREDICTIONS ON THE BASIS OF THE PERIODIC TABLE

One of the factors that established the validity of the periodic classification of the elements was Mendeleev's ability to predict the properties of some of the then undiscovered elements. His principle was simply that the properties within given groups vary in a regular fashion, and that, therefore, the unknown element would have properties which are a properly chosen average of the properties of the adjacent elements in the same family group. This principle is a very useful one, and we shall now show in a series of examples how Mendeleev might have predicted the properties of germanium on the basis of the properties of the related elements. Table 7.6 gives that portion of the periodic table in the vicinity of germanium.

TABLE 7.6 GERMANIUM IN THE PERIODIC TABLE

3A	4A	5A
Al	Si	P
Ga	Ge	As
In	Sn	Sb

Example 7.1. Predict the formula of germanium chloride.

Solution. Germanium is in group 4A, in the same family as silicon and tin, and, by our general principle, will tend to form compounds having the same formulas as those of silicon and tin. The chlorides of those two elements are known to have the following formulas:

$$SiCl_4, \quad Si_2Cl_6 \quad \text{and} \quad SnCl_2, \quad SnCl_4$$

Since $SiCl_4$ and $SnCl_4$ both exist, a likely formula for the germanium compound would be $GeCl_4$; the possibility that Ge_2Cl_6 and $GeCl_2$ also exist is suggested by the other formulas. Actually the ordinary chloride observed is $GeCl_4$. $GeCl_2$ has been reported, but is unstable.

Example 7.2.   Predict the normal boiling point of germanium tetrachloride, $GeCl_4$.

Solution.   The compounds most similar to $GeCl_4$ would be $SiCl_4$ (b.p. 58°C) and $SnCl_4$ (b.p. 114°C). Since germanium lies between silicon and tin in group 4A, we would expect that $GeCl_4$ would boil halfway between $SiCl_4$ and $GeCl_4$, that is, at the average of the two known boiling points. Therefore:

$$\text{predicted b.p. of } GeCl_4 = \frac{58 + 114}{2} = 86°C$$

The reported boiling point of $GeCl_4$ is, indeed, 86°C.

Example 7.3.   Estimate the atomic weight of germanium.

Solution.   The atomic weights of elements surrounding germanium are:

Al 26.98	Si 28.09	P 30.97
Ga 69.72	Ge —	As 74.92
In 114.82	Sn 118.69	Sb 121.75

If our approach is correct, gallium and arsenic should have atomic weights which are the averages of the atomic weights of aluminum and indium, and of phosphorus and antimony, respectively.

$$\text{predicted at. wt. of Ga} = \frac{26.98 + 114.82}{2} = 70.90 \quad (\text{observed at. wt.} = 69.72)$$

$$\text{predicted at. wt. of As} = \frac{30.97 + 121.75}{2} = 76.36 \quad (\text{observed at. wt.} = 74.92)$$

The predicted values are close to those observed, but are both high, the first by 1.18 units and the second by 1.44 units. We would expect that the similarly predicted value for germanium would also be high, by about 1.3 units. For Ge,

$$\text{simple predicted value} = \frac{28.09 + 118.69}{2} = 73.39$$

Correcting this value by the anticipated error of 1.3 units, we would make a "best estimate" of 72.1 for the atomic weight of germanium. The observed value is 72.59.

The procedures used in these examples can be employed to predict reasonably well the properties of germanium and its compounds, or for that matter, the properties of any other element and its compounds. In all cases the prediction is based on the properties of the related substances. (It must be admitted that germanium turns out to be an ideal element to use as an illustration of the power of the approach. Mendeleev was "lucky" in the sense that great scientists with good ideas recognize a promising situation when it arises.)

Correlation of Chemical Formulas

The possibilities for prediction that arise from the existence of the periodic table are particularly evident when one considers the formulas of chemical substances. The approach that is used is essentially that of Mendeleev, but has results that are more quantitatively reliable than are the predictions of physical properties.

Let us first examine the formulas of the group 1A chlorides and bromides. They are:

NaCl	KCl	RbCl	CsCl
NaBr	KBr	RbBr	CsBr

These formulas and indeed all the formulas of all alkali halides, the binary compounds between the 1A and 7A elements, can be represented by the general formula MX, where M is any 1A element and X is any 7A element. Thus, in order to be able to remember the formula of any alkali halide, one needs to know only the formula for one of them and realize the condition that the periodic table imposes.

A condition similar to that which fixes the formulas of the 1A–7A binary compounds is obeyed by the formulas of many inorganic compounds. This condition allows the correlation of the chemical formulas of substances in a very powerful way, and in its most general form is embodied in the following rule: *Given the formula of any inorganic compound, the replacement of any element in the compound by another in the same group will give the correct chemical formula for another compound.*

Given the formula for magnesium chloride, $MgCl_2$, one would correctly predict, on the basis of this rule, that the other 2A chlorides would have the formulas $CaCl_2$, $SrCl_2$, and $BaCl_2$, and that the 7A binary magnesium compounds would be MgF_2, $MgBr_2$, and MgI_2. The general formula for 2A–7A binary compounds would be predicted to be MX_2, as is observed.

The general relation is really far broader than this. It would imply, for instance, that since calcium molybdate has the formula $CaMoO_4$, that of barium molybdate would be $BaMoO_4$, that calcium chromate would have the formula $CaCrO_4$, and that strontium tungstate would have the formula $SrWO_4$. These formulas are all correct and follow directly on the substitutions of elements in the same family in the basic formula. It should be clear that the relation allows one to generalize chemical formulas and to make a great many formula predictions on the basis of a relatively small amount of information.

Like many general rules, the relation we have been using has some exceptions which must be kept in mind if it is to be most effective. The difficulty is that in some cases the relation predicts the existence of substances which do not occur or are extremely unstable. A simple example of such a failure is observed if carbon monoxide, CO, is used as a reference substance. The rule would predict the existence of a sulfide of carbon with the formula CS; this compound, if it exists at all, appears to be highly unstable. The fact that we would also predict the existence of substances with the formulas PbS and SnO, both of which are well known, may increase our confidence in the relation but does not remove the fact that an exception occurs. It is found by experience that exceptions such as that mentioned occur most frequently when the elements being substituted are the lighter nonmetals in groups 4A, 5A, and 6A, or are elements known to have several possible equivalent weights. Even under such circumstances, if the reference formulas used are for the most stable compounds containing the elements of interest, the predictions can be made with confidence. With practice and due allowance for its limitations, the student will find the general relation for systematizing chemical formulas a very useful one.

7.6   ANOMALIES AND LIMITATIONS OF THE PERIODIC CLASSIFICATION

The periodic table is a most useful tool for the organization of chemical knowledge. The fact that the chemical and physical properties of the elements and their compounds are correlated in the ways we have described makes possible the prediction of many chemical facts on the basis of a relatively small amount of information. In a very real sense an understanding of the periodic table enables the student to amplify his limited store of chemical facts to the point where he can, with effort, begin to develop a general perspective of all inorganic chemistry.

If, however, one is to make the most effective use of the periodic table, he must be aware of and take account of the various anomalies and limitations inherent in it. We have already considered one of these in the previous section on prediction of chemical formulas.

One of the anomalies in the table arises in the positions of some of the elements. In order to preserve the cyclic character of the properties of the elements, we found it necessary to interchange the positions of argon and potassium. There are three other instances in which similar interchanges are required if the elements are arranged in order of increasing atomic weights: the elements involved are iodine and tellurium, cobalt and nickel, and thorium and protoactinium. This anomaly disappears when the reasons for the existence of the periodic table become known, and the atomic number rather than atomic weight is used in ordering the elements. This important matter is discussed in the next chapter.

Another anomaly in the table is the position of hydrogen. We have listed it in group 7A, but it really cannot be placed in any group. It has some of the properties of the halogens, but it also behaves in some respects like the alkali metals. Hydrogen is a nonmetal, like the halogens; it is a reasonably good reducing agent, like the alkali metals. It forms compounds with the alkali metals, called hydrides, which are analogous to the alkali halides; its ion in aqueous solution is positively charged as are the alkali metal ions. The properties of hydrogen result from its being the first, and probably the simplest, of the elements, but its position in the periodic table is not at all well defined.

A similar anomaly is observed for the first member of each family of elements belonging to an A group. It is found that the chemical properties of these light elements differ from those of the family to which they belong to a much greater extent than would be anticipated on the basis of typical family behavior. Fluorine, the first well-established member of group 7A, forms compounds with other elements which have markedly different properties from the compounds of the other halogens with those elements. In Table 7.7 the properties of the silver and hydrogen compounds with the halogens are listed. Clearly, the listed properties of the fluorides are not consistent with those of the other halides.

TABLE 7.7 SOME PROPERTIES OF THE HALIDES OF SILVER AND HYDROGEN

Substance	Solubility in Water (moles/l., 25°C)	Substance	Normal Boiling Point (°C)	Extent of Dissociation in Water
AgF	14.6	HF	19	slight
AgCl	1.3×10^{-5}	HCl	−84	high
AgBr	5.8×10^{-7}	HBr	−67	high
AgI	9.3×10^{-9}	HI	−35	high

Similarly, nitrogen, the first member of group 5A, differs markedly from phosphorus, arsenic, and antimony in the same group. It is much less reactive chemically than any of the latter elements, and, fortunately for man, will not readily form compounds even with oxygen, which combines readily with the other members of group 5A. One can easily discover that oxygen, carbon, beryllium, and lithium, all first members of their families, differ in properties from their families in unpredictable ways.

PROBLEMS

7.1   What is meant by the term periodicity? What evidence is there for the existence of a periodicity of properties of the elements?

7.2   What is the periodic table? How did it originate?

7.3   What sorts of similarities would you expect among the elements of group 2A? 7A? What sorts of differences would you expect within these groups?

7.4   Where are the nonmetals in the periodic table? What fraction of the elements would be classified as nonmetals?

7.5   What are some of the uses of the periodic table?

7.6   What are some of the anomalies in the periodic table?

7.7   Look up the formulas of the hydrogen compounds of elements 3 through 17. For these compounds, plot the number of atoms of hydrogen per atom of the element versus the order number of the element. Compare your graph to Figure 7.3.

7.8   Plot the melting points, boiling points, and ionization potentials of the 7A elements, fluorine through iodine, versus atomic weight. Draw a smooth curve through your data. Use this curve to predict the melting point, boiling point, and ionization potential of astatine, the last member of this group.

7.9   Plot the melting points of the 1A metals as a function of their order numbers. What difference do you note in the general trend here as compared to that in Problem 7.8? Do the melting points of the 2A elements increase or decrease with increasing order number? How does the melting point of oxygen compare with that of sulfur? That of nitrogen with that of phosphorus? Can you make any generalization concerning the variation of melting point within a group as a function of the position of the group in the periodic table?

7.10 How would you use the periodic table and any other sources of information to predict the properties of arsine, AsH_3? For example, how would you go about predicting its boiling point?

7.11 Consider the element strontium in light of the periodic table. Predict, using the properties of the appropriate substances, the following properties of strontium and its compounds:
a. Atomic weight.   d. Formulas of the chloride and oxide.
b. Density of the solid metal.   e. Density of the oxide.
c. Melting point of the metal.   f. Melting point of the chloride.

7.12 Given the chemical formulas: H_2O, HCl, $CaCO_3$, Na_3PO_4, CO_2, Fe_2O_3, As_2O_3, and $KMnO_4$, predict the formulas of the following substances:
a. Hydrogen sulfide   f. Bismuth sulfide
b. Barium carbonate   g. Lithium arsenate
c. A sulfide of carbon   h. Sodium thioantimonate
d. Hydrogen fluoride   i. Potassium thiophosphate
e. Potassium phosphate   j. Sodium perrhenate
(When sulfur is substituted for oxygen in a compound, the prefix "thio" is often used.)

7.13 Name as many properties of elements as you can that are *not* periodic functions of their atomic numbers.

The information you will need to solve some of these problems can be found in:
Handbook of Chemistry and Physics, Chemical Rubber Co.
Handbook of Chemistry, N. A. Lange, McGraw-Hill Book Co.
International Critical Tables, McGraw-Hill Book Co.
Chemical Periodicity, R. T. Sanderson, Reinhold Publishing Corp.

THE
STRUCTURE
OF ATOMS

The periodic classification of the elements was the result of the realization that experimentally-obtained chemical knowledge could be correlated and organized in a very useful way. The periodic table is based on experimental fact, and, at the time of its origin, had no theoretical basis. It was not until the end of the nineteenth century that we began to have a definite theory for the periodic properties of the elements. This theory arose from new concepts of the nature and structure of atoms.

8.1 THE ATOMIC NUCLEUS

In Chapter 2 we briefly described the structure of atoms and the particles of which they are composed. Our purpose at the time was to present a background of information to aid your understanding of the sections on weight relations in chemical reactions. We now wish to study chemical bonding, and to do this we will need to develop the theory of the atom in considerably more detail.

In 1911 Ernest Rutherford and his students performed a series of experiments which profoundly influenced our ideas regarding the nature of atoms. Using a radioactive source, they let a beam of high-energy α-particles (He^{+2} ions) fall on a piece of thin gold foil. Then, with a fluorescent screen, they observed the degree to which the beam was scattered by the foil. Most of the α-particles went through the foil almost undeflected. A very few, however, were found to be reflected back from the foil at acute angles. The scientists measured the relative numbers of α-particles reflected at different angles by counting on the screen the scintillations caused by individual α-particles.

By a beautiful mathematical analysis of the rather large electrostatic forces required to explain the observed back scattering, Rutherford was able to conclude that:

1. The scattering was caused by a relatively massive particle with a diameter not exceeding 10^{-12} cm.
2. The charge on the particle was positive and had a magnitude equal to about half the atomic weight of the element of which the foil was made.

The experiment was repeated with foils of different elements from carbon to gold, and the results confirmed perfectly those which had been obtained with gold.

These were the experiments which established that an atom contains a tiny, positively charged massive particle, called the atomic **nucleus.** The atomic nucleus is surrounded by a sphere of negative charge. The negative charge had been previously shown by Thomson to be due to **electrons,** each of which has a very small mass and carries a characteristic amount of charge. Since atoms are electrically neutral, the positive charge on the nucleus is equal to the total negative charge on the surrounding electrons, and hence equal to an integral multiple of the charge on a single electron.

X-ray Spectra and Atomic Number

Rutherford's work established that the mass of the atom and the mass of its nucleus are essentially equal, since electrons were known to have only a tiny mass. His experiments, however, did not allow him to assign a precise positive charge to the nucleus. The magnitude of this charge was found in experiments with x-ray spectra.

If one lets a beam of high-energy electrons, accelerated by about 10,000 volts of potential, fall on a metal target, the atoms of the metal will be excited and will emit energy in the form of light. This light will differ from visible light in that it will have a much shorter wavelength. Visible light has a wavelength between 4000 and 8000 Å. The light emitted by the metal atoms has a wavelength of only about 1 Å.

Light generated by this method has many of the properties of ordinary light, but its very short wavelength enables it to penetrate matter to a much greater degree. Wilhelm Roentgen, who in 1895 did the first experiments with this kind of light, did not realize the nature of the radiation he was observing and so called it x-rays.

In 1912 it was proved that x-rays are indeed electromagnetic waves, or, simply, light waves, and in 1913 Bragg developed a method for measuring their wavelengths. That year a young English physicist, H. Moseley, investigated the x-rays which are emitted by different elements. He found, as had Bragg, that only at certain wavelengths did they have high intensity (we would say that the x-ray spectrum contained only a few lines) and that the positions of the strongest lines seemed to have some relation to the atomic weight of the element being studied. In attempting to find a relationship between the wavelengths of the x-rays emitted by an atom and its other properties, Moseley plotted the reciprocal of the shortest observed wavelength for each element against the square of its atomic weight (Figure 8.1). The line he obtained was nearly straight, but several elements fell off the curve. He then plotted the inverse of the shortest wavelength against the square of the **order number** of the element in the periodic table and found that again the line was essentially straight but that the points for *all the elements lay exactly on the line*!

Moseley's discovery was indeed significant. It established that the order number of an element in the periodic table could be found experimentally, and showed that the order we selected, which was based on properties, was actually correct. It also gave an unequivocal method for determining whether all the elements in a given region in the periodic table had been discovered, since breaks would occur on the graph at all missing elements.

The equation of the line relating x-ray wavelength to the order number of the element is very similar, and related, to an equation obtained by Niels Bohr in his

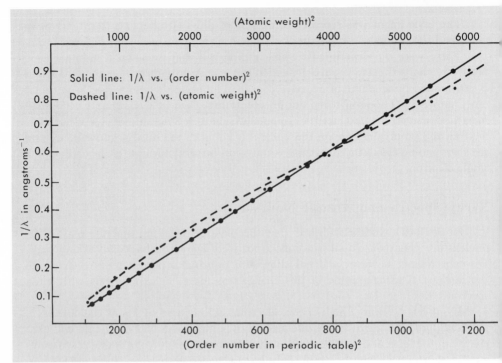

FIGURE 8.1 Moseley's data showing relationship between x-ray wavelengths and order numbers of the elements.

treatment of the hydrogen atom. (This will be discussed in Section 8.4.) Though we cannot go into the theory of x-ray spectra here, it was soon clear that Moseley's relation was most reasonably interpreted if the *order number of an element is numerically equal to the charge on its atomic nucleus*. This conclusion is completely consistent with Rutherford's work and is now an accepted part of atomic structural theory.

The realization that the order number of an element and its nuclear charge are one and the same simplifies our concept of the atom considerably. Since atoms are electrically neutral, the number of extranuclear electrons is equal to the nuclear charge, and hence also equal to the order number of the element. Since the order number of an element is of such significance it is given a special name; it is called the **atomic number** of the element. Hydrogen has an atomic number equal to 1. Sodium, eleventh in the list of elements, has atomic number 11; chlorine has atomic number 17. Moseley's work thus allows us to state that:

All sodium atoms have 11 electrons and nuclei having a charge of $+11$.

All chlorine atoms have 17 electrons and nuclei having a charge of $+17$.

All hydrogen atoms have 1 electron and nuclei having a charge of $+1$.

The *element* to which *an atom belongs* is, therefore, determined by its *number of electrons*, or its *nuclear charge*, and *not by its mass*. Stated another, completely equivalent, way, the *chemical properties* of an element are determined by the *number of electrons* possessed by its *atoms* and *not by the masses of those atoms*.

The Structure of Atomic Nuclei

In Chapter 2 we noted, in our discussion of methods for measuring atomic weights, that the masses of the isotopes of a given element were very nearly integral if one takes the mass of the C^{12} isotope to be 12.0000 (or as previously, the O^{16} isotope to be 16.0000). The rule is a general one and is illustrated in Table 8.1 for the isotopes of oxygen and magnesium.

TABLE 8.1 RELATIVE MASSES OF THE ISOTOPES OF OXYGEN
AND MAGNESIUM

	Oxygen			Magnesium	
Isotope	Mass	Per Cent Abundance	Isotope	Mass	Per Cent Abundance
O^{16}	15.9949	99.76	Mg^{24}	23.9847	78.6
O^{17}	16.9990	.04	Mg^{25}	24.9858	10.1
O^{18}	17.999	.20	Mg^{26}	25.9814	11.3

In view of the fact that isotopic masses are so nearly integral, it seems reasonable to propose that nuclei themselves are made up from an integral number of more basic particles. Two such particles, sometimes called fundamental particles, which appear to be reasonable components of atomic nuclei are the **proton** and the **neutron,** whose properties are given in Table 8.2. The proton is the nucleus of the ordinary hydrogen atom. The neutron is an uncharged particle having about the same mass as a proton. The neutron was discovered by Chadwick in 1932 and is produced in many reactions between nuclei.

TABLE 8.2 PROPERTIES OF TWO FUNDA-
MENTAL PARTICLES

Particle	Charge	Mass Number	Atomic Weight ($C^{12} = 12.0000$)
Proton	+1	1	1.00728
Neutron	0	1	1.00867

An interpretation of atomic nuclei on the basis of neutrons and protons is very straightforward. Each nucleus has a positive charge Z, equal to the atomic number of the element to which it belongs. It has a **mass number** A, equal to the integer nearest its atomic weight. Since the proton has a charge of $+1$ and is the only charged particle in the nucleus, there must be Z protons in all nuclei of atoms of *atomic number Z*. These contribute Z units of mass to the nucleus, since each proton has a mass number of unity. The remaining mass is made up by neutrons. If the total mass of the nucleus is A, $A - Z$ units will be due to neutrons. Since each neutron also has a mass number of unity, there will be $A - Z$ *neutrons* in nuclei of *mass number A* and *atomic number Z*.

Let us now describe the nuclei of the elements oxygen and magnesium. All *oxygen* atoms have atomic number *8*; the three isotopic atoms have mass numbers *16, 17,* and *18*. Therefore, all oxygen nuclei contain *8 protons*. The O^{16} nucleus contains $A - Z$, $16 - 8$, or *8 neutrons*. The O^{17} nucleus contains $17 - 8$, or *9 neutrons*, and the O^{18} nucleus will contain $18 - 8$, or *10 neutrons*.

Magnesium has atomic number 12 and isotopes of mass numbers 24, 25, and 26. Hence Mg^{24} nuclei contain 12 protons and 12 neutrons, Mg^{25} nuclei contain 12 protons and 13 neutrons, and Mg^{26} nuclei contain 12 protons and 14 neutrons. We have summarized these results in Table 8.3.

TABLE 8.3   COMPOSITION OF NUCLEI OF THE ISOTOPES
OF OXYGEN AND MAGNESIUM

Isotope	Atomic Number $= Z$	Mass Number $= A$	No. Protons $= Z$	No. Neutrons $= A - Z$
O^{16}	8	16	8	8
O^{17}	8	17	8	9
O^{18}	8	18	8	10
Mg^{24}	12	24	12	12
Mg^{25}	12	25	12	13
Mg^{26}	12	26	12	14

Although the nuclear model based on the proton and neutron as fundamental particles is satisfactory in many ways, it cannot really be said that nuclei contain protons and neutrons in the same way that water molecules contain hydrogen and oxygen atoms. Within the nucleus there is an interplay of enormous forces which prevent our identifying any specific particles, and although we could form, in principle, the O^{16} nucleus from 8 protons and 8 neutrons, the protons and neutrons would lose their identity in the act of combination. The structure of the atomic nucleus is, in spite of a great deal of time and effort spent on its investigation, still not thoroughly understood. In our discussions involving nuclei we shall assume the validity of our simple model and will find it adequate for any of our needs.

The student will find that, if he adds up the masses of the neutrons and protons present in a nucleus, the sum will be slightly greater than the observed mass of the nucleus. The difference in mass is directly related to the amount of energy required to decompose the nucleus into neutrons and protons. The stability of atomic nuclei is discussed in Section 23.6.

8.2   THE ELECTRONS IN ATOMS

The knowledge that the atomic number of an element is equal to the number of electrons surrounding its atomic nucleus allows us to determine the number of electrons associated with the atom of any element. These electrons are responsible for the chemical properties of both isolated and chemically combined atoms, and so are of great chemical importance. The properties of electrons in atoms and molecules have been the subject of extensive research, both experimental and theoretical, during all of this century, but it must be admitted that at present our knowledge of the detailed electronic structure of all but the simplest atoms is still incomplete. Much progress has been made on this problem, but much more remains to be accomplished. In this book we will present some of the common current models for electron arrangements in atoms and molecules, and will find them very useful in interpreting the chemical and physical properties of pure substances.

The main obstacle to our understanding of the properties of chemical substances in terms of the electrons and nuclei of which they are composed is that small particles, like atoms, molecules, nuclei, and particularly electrons, appear to obey different laws regarding energy and motion than do larger particles, like billiard balls and rotating bicycle wheels. Systems with which we are ordinarily concerned, with masses many, many times those of atoms and molecules, follow essentially exactly the laws of motion first formulated by Isaac Newton which now constitute that part of physics called **classical mechanics.** Small particles obey the laws of a somewhat different kind of mechanics, called **quantum mechanics.** (Actually it turns out that classical mechanics is in a very real sense a special case of quantum mechanics and is valid for all but those particles which have exceedingly small masses.) Quantum mechanics is part of a general theory, called the **quantum theory,** proposed early in this century to explain the anomalous experimental behavior of electrons and other small particles. Some experiments which led to the quantum theory will be considered in the next section, after we have stated and discussed some of the underlying principles of the theory that are of chemical interest.

The Quantum Theory

1. *Atoms and molecules can only exist in certain allowed states, characterized by definite amounts of energy. When an atom or molecule changes its state, it must absorb or emit an amount of energy just sufficient to bring it to another allowed state.*

⚹Atoms and molecules can, as we have seen, possess various kinds of energy. One form of energy of particular importance when considering atomic structure arises from the motion of electrons about the atomic nucleus and from the charge interactions among the electrons and between the electrons and the nucleus. This kind of energy is called **electronic energy.** Only certain values of electronic energy are allowed to an atom. When an atom goes from one allowed electronic state to another, it must absorb or emit just enough energy to bring its own energy to that of the final state.

Analogous considerations apply to the other forms of energy possessed by atoms, molecules, and other small particles. Translational energy of motion, rotational and vibrational energy, in addition to electronic energy, are subject to the limitations of the quantum theory.

The energy of systems that can exist only in discrete states is said to be **quantized.** A change in the energy level of such a system involves the absorption or emission of a **quantum** of energy.

2. *The allowed energy states of atoms and molecules can be described by sets of numbers called quantum numbers.*

The mathematical solutions, as obtained by quantum mechanics, to problems regarding the energies of atoms and molecules usually result in sets of integral numbers, which serve to denote the allowed states and to allow calculation of their energies. These numbers are called **quantum numbers.**

Associated with each electronic state of an atom is a group of quantum numbers, identifying the state. In the usual model, the quantum numbers are associated with the individual electrons in the atom. Each electron is assigned a set of quantum numbers according to a set of rules. A statement of all the quantum numbers of all the electrons in an atom is used to designate the energy level, or quantum state, of the atom.

Similarly, the various translational, rotational, vibrational, and electronic energy states of molecules or other small particles can be described by the appropriate sets of quantum numbers. Ordinarily only one kind of energy and one set of quantum numbers are considered at a time, but to specify completely the state of a water molecule would require a statement of the quantum numbers associated with its translational energy, its rotational energy, its vibrational energy, and its electronic energy.

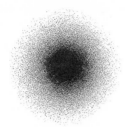

FIGURE 8.2 "Electron cloud" surrounding nucleus of a typical atom.

3. *Although the energies of atoms and molecules can, in principle, be calculated exactly, the positions and paths of their electrons cannot be predicted. At best, all that can be determined is the probability of finding the electrons in any particular geometric arrangement.*

In the analysis of the motion of ordinary macroscopic systems it is possible to calculate exactly the position of the system as a function of time, given its initial state and the forces acting. This does not seem to be possible for a system in which the masses are as small as those of electrons. For an atom we can only hope to calculate how likely it is that the electrons will be in any given spatial arrangement, which is much less informative than being able to predict the routes the electrons will follow. We sometimes describe atoms pictorially by drawing a "cloud of charge" around the nucleus, letting the density of the "cloud" be proportional to the likelihood of finding an electron at that point in space. Figure 8.2 is an illustration of that sort.

8.3 EXPERIMENTAL BASIS OF THE QUANTUM THEORY

Now that we have stated some of the principles of the quantum theory it should be helpful to your understanding of the theory to examine some of the experiments and theoretical relations on which it is based. There are actually a great many experiments which are best explained by the theory; among them should be mentioned black body radiation, the photoelectric effect, atomic spectra, and the several kinds of molecular spectra. Though these are all important phenomena, we shall restrict our attention here mainly to atomic spectra, postponing a discussion of the other experiments to more advanced courses of study in physics and chemistry. Atomic spectra bear directly on the problem of atomic structure and nicely illustrate an area of experiment in relation to the general quantum theory.

Atomic Spectra

As we saw in Section 8.1, x-rays are emitted by atoms when they are hit by high-energy electrons. The emission of light by excited atoms is a general phenomenon. The nature of the light emitted depends on the excitation which is used.

If we should heat any metal in a furnace or in a flame, it will, depending on its temperature, give off visible light; at 1000°C it will look red, at 1500°C it will appear essentially white. If the emitted light is examined with a spectroscope, a device which breaks up light into its component colors, it is found to contain essentially all colors. More precisely, we would say that, over the region in which the metal radiates, its **spectrum** is **continuous,** containing light at all *wavelengths*. (The radiation from such an incandescent source is very analogous to so-called black body radiation mentioned earlier; the explanation of the characteristics of this radiation was one of the first triumphs of the quantum theory.)

Not all emitters of light radiate at all wavelengths. If we observe in a spectroscope the light emitted by sodium chloride when it is placed in a flame, say from a Bunsen burner, we see only a few bright lines, which indicate the few wavelengths at which sodium atoms, excited by the flame, are emitting. In this case we are seeing the **atomic spectrum** of sodium, which since it contains light at only a few wavelengths, is said to be **discrete.**

Atomic spectra are emitted when atoms are mildly excited; this can be accomplished in a flame, in a spark, or by electrons which have been accelerated by falling through a few volts of potential. Our common fluorescent lights and mercury vapor highway lights give off light of this sort, with well-resolved components, or lines (Figure 8.3).

Atomic spectra have been known and studied since the spectroscope was invented in 1860 by the German scientists Kirchhoff and Bunsen. They recognized that the atomic spectrum of one element differed from that of another. By using this fact, they and others were able to use this new instrument to discover several new elements, among them cesium, rubidium, thallium, and indium.

The existence and properties of atomic spectra are very readily treated by the quantum theory. According to the theory, an atom, say the sodium atom, can exist

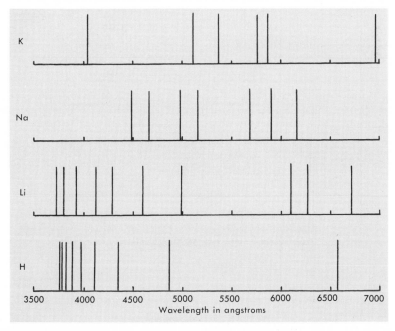

FIGURE 8.3   Atomic spectra of hydrogen and some alkali metals in the visible region.

only in certain states, which occur at levels of energy characteristic of the sodium atom. By absorbing or emitting energy in the proper amount, the atom can make transitions from one energy level to another. When a gas containing sodium atoms is heated to a high temperature or is exposed to fast-moving electrons, some of the sodium atoms will, by collisions, tend to absorb energy and become excited, moving in the process to higher allowed electronic energy levels. Once excited, the atoms will be unstable and will tend to return to lower electronic energy levels, ultimately reaching the lowest allowed level, which is usually called the ground state of the atom. Under excitation, the sodium gas will quickly reach a state of dynamic equilibrium, in which some atoms are releasing energy at the same rate as it is being absorbed by others.

One of the ways in which electronically excited sodium atoms can lose energy is by radiating it as light. In a process in which an excited atom makes a transition to a lower energy level, a photon of light may be emitted. The photon will have some of the characteristics of a particle, and will have an energy given by an equation you may recall from Chapter 5,

$$E = hc/\lambda \qquad (5.24)$$

in which E is the photon energy, h is Planck's constant, c is the velocity of light, and

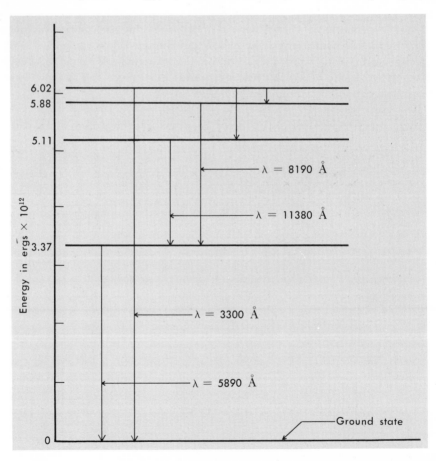

FIGURE 8.4 Some transitions and spectral lines for a few low-lying energy levels of the sodium atom.

λ is the wavelength of the photon. This equation was first proposed by Einstein in 1905 in the very early days of the quantum theory; it was based on his assumption that interchanges of energy between radiation and matter take place in discrete units called light quanta, with energies given by the foregoing equation. The relation is a basic postulate of the quantum theory and is consistent with many different kinds of experiments.

Atomic spectra are believed to consist of the radiation resulting from transitions made by electronically excited atoms from higher to lower allowed energy levels. Since each kind of atom has a set of energy levels characteristic of it, the atomic spectrum of an element will serve to identify that element. In Figure 8.4 we have arranged, in somewhat simplified form, some of the lower electronic energy levels of the sodium atom, along with the transitions that are observed between those levels. Each transition gives rise to a line in the atomic spectrum of sodium, with the wavelength we have indicated. One of the lines in the sodium spectrum in Figure 8.3 is due to a transition shown in Figure 8.4. The actual energies of the levels were determined by noting that in general several spectral lines are associated with each allowed energy level; this means that, if the theory is correct, there must be mathematical relations between the energies of photons emitted by sodium atoms. (You may be able to recognize some of these in the figure.) By using these relations, and there are many which must be satisfied, it is possible to use the atomic spectrum of an element to determine an unequivocal set of energy levels to be associated with its atoms. In spite of the fact that some atomic spectra are very complex, containing thousands of lines, the spectra of essentially all the atoms and many of the ions of the elements have been unraveled and explained in terms of a relatively small number of energy levels.

Regularities in Atomic Spectra

Beginning about 1880 it was recognized that there is a certain amount of order in atomic spectra. It was found possible in some cases to sort out the lines in a spectrum into series to each of which several lines could be assigned on the basis of wavelength, intensity, and breadth. In the atomic spectrum of sodium one discusses the so-called principal (intense), sharp, and diffuse series. It was also found that the spectra of elements in the same group in the periodic table were qualitatively similar.

In 1885 Balmer found a very remarkable relationship between the wavelengths of the lines in the atomic spectrum of hydrogen (Figure 8.3). He showed that one could mathematically express the wavelengths of the nine then known lines in the atomic spectrum of hydrogen by the following equation:

$$\lambda = b[(n^2/(n^2 - 4)]$$

in which λ is the wavelength, b is a constant, and n is an integer and has the values 3, 4, 5, and so on, for the first, second, third, ..., lines in the hydrogen spectrum.

Balmer's formula for the series of lines which now bears his name predicts the wavelengths exceedingly well. In Table 8.4 we have tabulated the calculated and observed wavelengths in the series. Balmer's equation undoubtedly gives the most nearly exact prediction of experimental quantities in all physical science, and its discovery gave others great incentive to look for other such relations. To this day none have been found that approach the Balmer formula in exactness.

TABLE 8.4   CALCULATED AND OBSERVED WAVELENGTHS (IN Å) IN
THE BALMER SERIES FOR HYDROGEN

$$\lambda_{calc} = 3646.00\, n^2/(n^2 - 4)$$

Line	n	λ_{obs}	λ_{calc}	Line	n	λ_{obs}	λ_{calc}
1	3	6562.79	6562.80	6	8	3889.06	3889.07
2	4	4861.33	4861.33	7	9	3835.40	3835.40
3	5	4340.47	4340.48	8	10	3797.91	3797.92
4	6	4101.74	4101.75	9	11	3770.06	3770.65
5	7	3970.07	3970.09				

8.4 THEORIES OF THE ELECTRONIC STRUCTURE OF ATOMS

By the beginning of this century knowledge of atomic structure had advanced to the point at which scientists could begin to speculate on the way in which positive and negative charges were arranged in atoms. Part of the problem was solved when Rutherford demonstrated the existence of atomic nuclei. It was only two years later, in 1913, that Niels Bohr presented a theory for the structure of the hydrogen atom that added greatly to our ideas regarding the behavior of the electrons in atoms.

Bohr based his approach on Rutherford's nuclear atom and on Planck's suggestion that atoms and other small particles can only possess certain definite amounts of energy. By making some rather drastic assumptions about the motion of the

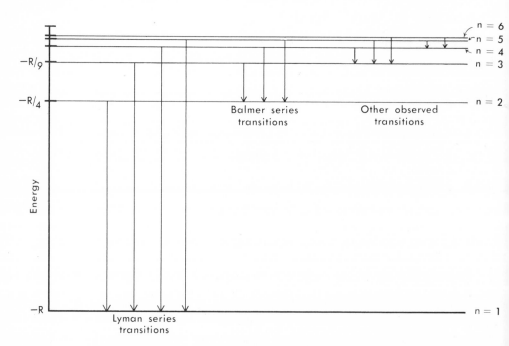

FIGURE 8.5   Some energy levels and transitions of the hydrogen atom.

hydrogen electron about its nucleus, Bohr was able to derive a relation for the possible energies of the hydrogen atom. By Bohr's theory, the energy levels of the hydrogen atom are given by the equation

$$E = -R/n^2$$

in which R is a constant obtainable from the theory and n is a quantum number equal to 1, 2, 3, 4 . . . . In Figure 8.5 we have shown the energy levels of hydrogen as given by Bohr's equation. According to the theory, the atomic spectrum of hydrogen arises from transitions made by hydrogen atoms from higher to lower energy levels. When the lower state is that for which n = 2, these transitions can be shown to predict the Balmer series. When the lower state is that associated with n = 1, or 3, or 4, other series are predicted, and are verified by experiment.

Bohr's treatment of hydrogen allowed him to predict quantitatively the allowed energy levels of the hydrogen atom. From the energies he was able to predict the atomic spectrum of hydrogen.

Bohr assumed that a hydrogen atom consists of an effectively stationary central positive nucleus, the proton, about which the single negative hydrogen electron moves in a circular orbit. By calculating the conditions under which the electrostatic attractive force between proton and electron was balanced by the centrifugal force due to the motion of the electron, he was able to find a relation for the total energy of the atom. To make the predicted spectrum of hydrogen agree with that which is observed, he had to postulate a condition on the motion of the electron.

Mathematically, we can summarize Bohr's theory for hydrogen as follows:

The force of electrostatic attraction between proton and electron is, by Coulomb's Law,

$$e^2/r^2 \qquad (8.1)$$

in which e is the charge on the electron (Figure 8.6). The centrifugal force due to orbital motion of the electron is, by Newton's Law,

$$mv^2/r \qquad (8.2)$$

At equilibrium, the two forces are equal:

$$e^2/r^2 = mv^2/r, \quad \text{or} \quad mv^2r = e^2 \qquad (8.3)$$

The kinetic energy of motion of the electron is

$$\tfrac{1}{2}mv^2 \qquad (8.4)$$

The potential energy due to electrostatic forces between proton and electron is

$$-e^2/r \qquad (8.5)$$

The total energy of the atom is the sum of the kinetic and potential energies:

$$E = \tfrac{1}{2}mv^2 + (-e^2/r) \qquad (8.6)$$

By equation 8.3,

$$\tfrac{1}{2}mv^2 = \tfrac{1}{2}e^2/r,$$

so, for the total energy:

$$E = -e^2/2r \qquad (8.7)$$

This was as far as Bohr could go without making any new assumptions. To solve for the specific energies he assumed arbitrarily that, for the electron,

$$mvr = nh/2\pi \qquad (8.8)$$

in which n is an integer and may take on any integral value, and h is Planck's constant, known at that time to have a value of about 6.6×10^{-27} erg second.

To solve for allowed values of r, square equation 8.8, obtaining

$$m^2v^2r^2 = n^2h^2/4\pi^2 \qquad (8.9)$$

Dividing equation 8.9 by equation 8.3, we obtain:

$$r = n^2h^2/4\pi^2e^2m \qquad (8.10)$$

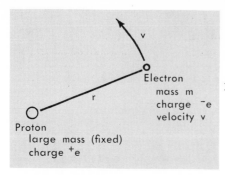

FIGURE 8.6   Bohr's model of the hydrogen atom.

Now substituting for r in equation 8.7

$$E = -e^2/2(n^2h^2/4\pi^2e^2m) = -2\pi^2e^4m/n^2h^2 = -R/n^2 \tag{8.11}$$

Equation 8.11 is Bohr's classic equation for the energy of a hydrogen atom. It predicts that the atom can exist only at energies given by integral values of the quantum number n.

By the quantum theory, atomic spectra arise from changes in the energy of an atom, according to the equation

$$\Delta E = E_2 - E_1 = hc/\lambda \tag{8.12}$$

in which c is the velocity of light, λ is the wavelength of the emitted light, and the subscripts 2 and 1 refer to higher and lower energy states respectively. Substituting in equation 8.12 with equation 8.11,

$$E_2 - E_1 = -R((1/n_2^2) - (1/n_1^2)) = hc/\lambda = R(n_2^2 - n_1^2)/n_1^2n_2^2 \tag{8.13}$$

Solving equation 8.13 for the wavelength,

$$\lambda = \frac{hc}{R}\left[\frac{n_1^2n_2^2}{n_2^2 - n_1^2}\right] = \frac{h^3c}{2\pi^2me^4}\left[\frac{n_1^2n_2^2}{n_2^2 - n_1^2}\right] \tag{8.14}$$

Letting $n_1 = 2$, and substituting known modern values of h, c, m, and e into equation 8.14

$$\lambda = \frac{(6.6251 \times 10^{-27})^3 \times 2.9979 \times 10^{10} \times 10^8}{2 \times (3.1416)^2 \times 9.1085 \times 10^{-28} \times (4.8028 \times 10^{-10})^4}\left[\frac{4n^2}{n^2 - 4}\right]$$

$$\lambda = 3645\left[\frac{n^2}{n^2 - 4}\right] \quad (\text{in Å}) \tag{8.15}$$

The agreement between equation 8.15 and Balmer's formula is remarkable, considering the complexity of Bohr's equation. There can be little doubt that, irrespective of the theory from which it follows, equation 8.11 describes the energies that can be associated with the hydrogen atom very well indeed. If n_1 is given the value 1, or 3, or 4, other series of spectral lines can be predicted for hydrogen. The wavelengths of the lines in these series, like those in the Balmer series, are in very good agreement with Bohr's equation.

Bohr's theory for the structure of the hydrogen atom, and all other one-electron species like He+ and Li+2, was highly successful, and scientists of the day must have felt that they were on the verge of being able to predict all atomic spectra. However, it soon became obvious that the extension of Bohr's ideas to atoms with two or more electrons gave, at best, only qualitative agreement with experiment. We have at present no theory which successfully predicts the allowed energies of atoms in general, in spite of an enormous amount of research on the problem.

Our present approach to the electronic structure of atoms and molecules is based on wave mechanics, and involves solutions to an equation, called the **wave equation,** which was discovered by Erwin Schrödinger in 1926. Using his equation, Schrödinger was also able to solve for the allowed energies of the hydrogen atom and obtained the same solution as Bohr did. In contrast to Bohr's theory, the wave equation can be applied to other atoms and molecules. Unfortunately, the extension to these other systems has turned out to be more difficult in fact than in principle, since the form of the wave equation for other systems is in general so complicated mathematically as to be insoluble, even with the most modern electronic computers. However, in the relatively few cases in which an essentially exact solution has been possible, there is excellent agreement with experiment; this has led scientists to believe that the wave equation approach to atomic and molecular properties is a correct, albeit complicated, one.

The wave equation for a one-particle system is

$$\nabla^2\psi + \frac{8\pi^2m}{h^2}(E - V)\psi = 0$$

In the equation, E and V are the total and potential energies of the system respectively, m is the mass of the particle, h is the physical constant called Planck's constant, and ψ is a function, called the wave function, which is related to the probability of finding the particle at any point in space. ∇^2 is a so-called differential operator, which in Cartesian coordinates takes the form

$$\nabla^2 = \frac{\partial^2}{\partial x^2} + \frac{\partial^2}{\partial y^2} + \frac{\partial^2}{\partial z^2}$$

The wave mechanical problem is to find the values of ψ and E which satisfy the wave equation. In any given system there will in general be many possible functions that are proper ψ's, each with its own value of the energy. Each ψ and E belong to an allowed energy state of the system.

8.5 ELECTRON CONFIGURATIONS IN ATOMS

The wave mechanical solution to the hydrogen atom problem allows us to associate quantum numbers, analogous to the quantum number n in the Bohr theory, with the energy levels of the hydrogen atom. These quantum numbers describe the properties of the atom in its allowed states in a brief but informative way. Once the description of the hydrogen atom was obtained in this way, it became clear that similar descriptions of the other atoms in the periodic table were desirable. Since it did not prove possible to solve wave mechanically for the energy levels of atoms other than hydrogen, the descriptions which have been developed are necessarily approximations, based on the implications obtained from the hydrogen atom solution and the observed properties of atoms. In this section we will show how one proceeds to determine these descriptions of the electron arrangements in atoms.

We assume that the electrons in an atom can be assigned quantum numbers associated with their states in the atom. The description of the electronic structure, or the **electron configuration,** of the atom is simply a statement of all the quantum numbers of all its electrons. The problem thus becomes one of describing atomic electrons in terms of quantum numbers.

It can be shown that associated with a single electron in an atom there are four quantum numbers, which give information regarding its energy and motion. Only two of these numbers have an appreciable effect on the energy of the atom, and these are the only ones used in elementary discussions of atomic structure. In this section we will restrict ourselves to the evaluation of these two quantum numbers for each electron.

The first, or **principal,** quantum number is denoted by the letter n. Both the energy of the electron and the size of the region in which it moves are determined primarily by n, and both increase with increasing n. The principal quantum number is always integral and can have the values 1, 2, 3, and so on, but not zero. Electrons with the same principal quantum number move about in roughly the same region and are said to be in the same **shell** or **level.** Both theory and experiment indicate that the capacities of the shells for electrons are limited and increase with increasing n. The actual capacities are well known and are given in Table 8.5.

Each shell of electrons can be resolved into one or more **subshells** or **sublevels.** The subshells are denoted by the second, or **orbital** quantum number, which is given the symbol l. The orbital quantum number is related to the principal quantum number n; for any given value of n, l can have the values $n - 1, n - 2, n - 3, \ldots, 0$. The capacities of the various subshells are also limited, and are fixed by the value of l. An $l = 0$ subshell can hold two electrons, an $l = 1$ subshell can hold six, an $l = 2$ can hold 10, and an $l = 3$ subshell can hold 14 electrons. In Table 8.5 we have indicated the subshells and their capacities for each value of n in accord with these rules. It is interesting to note that as a result of the conditions limiting the number of subshells in a given shell and the number of electrons in each subshell, there are always $2n^2$ electrons in a shell with quantum number n.

TABLE 8.5 CAPACITY OF ATOMIC SHELLS FOR ELECTRONS

n	Total Number of Electrons in Shell	Number of Electrons in Subshells				
		$l = 0$	1	2	3	4
1	2	2	—	—	—	—
2	8	2	6	—	—	—
3	18	2	6	10	—	—
4	32	2	6	10	14	—

An electron entering an atom will assume the lowest allowed energy, and will take on the set of quantum numbers associated with that lowest energy state. Independent of the particular atom under consideration, it is possible to associate qualitatively each set of quantum numbers with a relative energy value, and so to arrange the states having these quantum numbers in order of increasing energy. This has been done in Figure 8.7.

From Figure 8.7 it is clear that, as we noted earlier, the energy increases with principal (first) quantum number. The energy also increases slightly with increasing orbital (second) quantum number. (It turns out that the increase with increasing l value is sufficient to make the energy of the 3, 2 subshell greater than that of the 4, 0 subshell.)

In any atom we will have electrons populating one or more of the subshells shown in Figure 8.7. To describe the electron configuration of an atom we need merely to state the number of electrons in each of the subshells. We shall now show how the electron configurations of some typical atoms are determined on the basis of the various rules we have been considering.

The simplest of all atoms is the hydrogen atom, with its one electron. In the ordinary H atom this electron will be in the state of lowest energy, the 1, 0 state. We would say that the electron configuration of the H atom is 1, 0. For some reason,

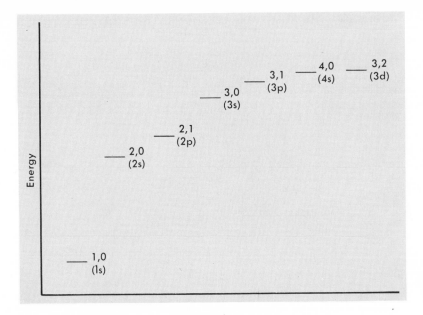

FIGURE 8.7 Relative energies of electronic subshells.

probably traditional, we do not express electron configurations quite this way. The notation for the principal (first) quantum number is as we have written it, but a new symbol is used for the orbital (second) quantum number. Electrons for which $l = 0$ are called **s electrons**; if $l = 1$, they are called **p electrons**; for $l = 2$, they are called **d electrons**; if their l value is **3**, they are called **f electrons.** The symbols s, p, d, and f come from the sharp, principal, diffuse, and fundamental series observed by spectroscopists early in this century. Spectroscopists were among the first to describe atoms in this way, and their notation has persisted. On this basis the electron in the ordinary hydrogen atom is a **1s electron,** and the *electron configuration* of the H atom is simply **1s.** If the hydrogen atom were excited to a higher energy level, its electron would assume the quantum numbers associated with that higher level, perhaps 2s or 2p. (The atom would be unstable in such a state and would tend to return quickly to the lowest, or ground, state by radiating light or by some other means. Electron configurations of atoms are understood to refer to the ground state unless a specific exception is indicated.)

Helium, atomic number 2, has, of course, two electrons in its atom. These will both fit into the lowest subshell, and so both will have quantum numbers 1s. The electron configuration of helium is written $1s^2$.

The three electrons in lithium atoms cannot all have 1s quantum numbers, since only two electrons can fit into the same s subshell. Two of the electrons go into the 1s subshell, filling it, and the third electron goes into the 2s subshell, which is the one of next higher energy. The electron configuration of Li is, therefore, $1s^2 2s$.

The 2s subshell is filled at beryllium, atomic number 4, whose electron configuration is $1s^2 2s^2$. Boron atoms, with five electrons, have two 1s electrons, two 2s electrons, and the fifth electron is, as you would expect, a 2p electron. The electron configuration of B atoms is $1s^2 2s^2 2p$.

The electron configurations of the rest of the elements in the periodic table are determined in a similar way. Given the atomic number of the element, and hence

TABLE 8.6 THE ELECTRON CONFIGURATIONS OF THE ATOMS
OF THE ELEMENTS

Element	Atomic Number	1s	2s	2p	3s	3p	3d	4s	4p	4d	4f	5s
H	1	1										
He	2	2										
Li	3	2	1									
Be	4	2	2									
B	5	2	2	1								
C	6	2	2	2								
N	7	2	2	3								
O	8	2	2	4								
F	9	2	2	5								
Ne	10	2	2	6								
Na	11				1							
Mg	12				2							
Al	13		Neon		2	1						
Si	14		core		2	2						
P	15				2	3						
S	16				2	4						
Cl	17				2	5						
Ar	18	2	2	6	2	6						
K	19							1				
Ca	20							2				
Sc	21						1	2				
Ti	22						2	2				
V	23						3	2				
Cr	24						5	1				
Mn	25		Argon				5	2				
Fe	26		core				6	2				
Co	27						7	2				
Ni	28						8	2				
Cu	29						10	1				
Zn	30						10	2				
Ga	31						10	2	1			
Ge	32						10	2	2			
As	33						10	2	3			
Se	34						10	2	4			
Br	35						10	2	5			
Kr	36	2	2	6	2	6	10	2	6			
Rb	37											1
Sr	38											2
Y	39									1		2
Zr	40									2		2
Cb	41			Krypton						4		1
Mo	42			core						5		1
Tc	43									6		1
Ru	44									7		1
Rh	45									8		1
Pd	46									10		
Ag	47									10		1
Cd	48									10		2

TABLE 8.6 (*Contd.*)

Element	Atomic Number		4d	4f	5s	5p	5d	5f	6s	6p	6d	7s
							Populations of Subshells					
In	49		10		2	1						
Sn	50		10		2	2						
Sb	51		10		2	3						
Te	52		10		2	4						
I	53		10		2	5						
Xe	54		10		2	6						
Cs	55		10		2	6			1			
Ba	56		10		2	6			2			
La	57		10		2	6	1		2			
Ce	58		10	2	2	6			2			
Pr	59		10	3	2	6			2			
Nd	60		10	4	2	6			2			
Pm	61		10	5	2	6			2			
Sm	62		10	6	2	6			2			
Eu	63		10	7	2	6			2			
Gd	64		10	7	2	6	1		2			
Tb	65		10	9	2	6			2			
Dy	66		10	10	2	6			2			
Ho	67		10	11	2	6			2			
Er	68		10	12	2	6			2			
Tm	69		10	13	2	6			2			
Yb	70		10	14	2	6			2			
Lu	71		10	14	2	6	1		2			
Hf	72		10	14	2	6	2		2			
Ta	73		10	14	2	6	3		2			
W	74	Krypton core	10	14	2	6	4		2			
Re	75		10	14	2	6	5		2			
Os	76		10	14	2	6	6		2			
Ir	77		10	14	2	6	9					
Pt	78		10	14	2	6	9		1			
Au	79		10	14	2	6	10		1			
Hg	80		10	14	2	6	10		2			
Tl	81		10	14	2	6	10		2	1		
Pb	82		10	14	2	6	10		2	2		
Bi	83		10	14	2	6	10		2	3		
Po	84		10	14	2	6	10		2	4		
At	85		10	14	2	6	10		2	5		
Rn	86		10	14	2	6	10		2	6		
Fr	87		10	14	2	6	10		2	6		1
Ra	88		10	14	2	6	10		2	6		2
Ac	89		10	14	2	6	10		2	6	1	2
Th	90		10	14	2	6	10		2	6	2	2
Pa	91		10	14	2	6	10	2	2	6	1	2
U	92		10	14	2	6	10	3	2	6	1	2
Np	93		10	14	2	6	10	5	2	6		2
Pu	94		10	14	2	6	10	6	2	6		2
Am	95		10	14	2	6	10	7	2	6		2
Cm	96		10	14	2	6	10	7	2	6	1	2
Bk	97		10	14	2	6	10	9	2	6		2
Cf	98		10	14	2	6	10	10	2	6		2
Es	99		10	14	2	6	10	11	2	6		2
Fm	100		10	14	2	6	10	12	2	6		2
Md	101		10	14	2	6	10	13	2	6		2

the number of electrons in its atoms, one assigns the electrons to the subshells in order of their increasing energies, filling each one before beginning the next. The order of the subshells is that in Figure 8.7; a more complete list is given below:

1s, 2s, 2p, 3s, 3p, 4s, 3d, 4p, 5s, 4d, 5p, 6s, 4f, 5d, 6p, 7s, 5f, 6d

For example, let us determine the electron configuration for iron atoms, atomic number 26. There are two 1s electrons, two 2s, six 2p, two 3s, six 3p, and two 4s electrons, filling the first six subshells, and requiring 20 electrons. The other six electrons will go into the 3d subshell. The electron configuration of iron, Fe, atoms is, therefore, $1s^2 2s^2 2p^6 3s^2 3p^6 4s^2 3d^6$.

The electron configurations of ions are very analogous to those of atoms and are determined in the same way. Electron configurations depend in general only on the number of electrons in the species and not on either its charge or the charge of its nucleus. The configuration of the B^+ ion is therefore the same as that of the Be atom, $1s^2 2s^2$. That of B^{+2} is $1s^2 2s$; of B^{+3}, $1s^2$. The electron configuration of an ion is ordinarily the same as that of the atom which has the same number of electrons.

In Table 8.6 we have listed the electron configurations of the elements of atomic number 1 through 101. The configurations in general follow the rules we have given. The major exceptions occur for those elements which have configurations with near-full or near-half-full d subshells. It appears that there is an additional stability in a subshell which is full or half full, which tends to cause electrons to be promoted to achieve such configurations. This effect is observed in chromium and copper, at. nos. 24 and 29 in the first series of transitions metals; those atoms have an extra d electron, promoted from the 4s subshell. In the fifth and sixth periods the effect is somewhat more pronounced.

Other Electron Quantum Numbers: The Concept of Atomic Orbitals

At the beginning of this section we mentioned that, although electrons have four quantum numbers, knowledge of two of these, the principal quantum number n and the orbital quantum number l, is sufficient to allow one to deal with the energies and electron configurations of atoms. If, however, one is interested in the spatial relationships of atoms in molecules which result from chemical bonding, it is useful to consider the other two quantum numbers. They are also of importance to our understanding of the theory of electron configurations.

The third quantum number, which is called the magnetic quantum number and has the symbol m, appears, like the first two, in the solution to the wave equation for the hydrogen atom (the properties of the quantum numbers n, l, and m are indeed based on the implications of that solution). The quantum number m is related to the quantum number l by the condition

$$m = 1, 1 - 1, 1 - 2, \ldots -(1 - 1), -1$$

Since l is integral, m is integral, and, for a given value of l, m can assume any one of 2l + 1 values. So if,

l = 0, m can equal 0
l = 1, m can equal 1, 0, or −1
l = 2, m can equal 2, 1, 0, −1, or −2
l = 3, m can equal 3, 2, 1, 0, −1, −2, or −3

In light of these ideas, let us consider a single electron in an atom; for an example we choose the outer electron in the lithium atom, whose configuration is $1s^2 2s$. In the lowest energy, or ground, state, the outer electron will be $2s(n = 2, 1 = 0)$. For this electron the m quantum number will of necessity be 0; it would be proper to describe the 2s electron as a 2, 0, 0 electron, specifying its first three quantum numbers. The electron cloud associated with the 2s electron is spherical, much like that in Figure 8.2. Such an electron is said to be in an **s orbital,** which means that its electron cloud is like that illustrated in the figure.

If the lithium atom is excited by heat or electrical energy, it can go to a higher energy level. In this process, in general only the outer electron, 2s, will change its quantum numbers, since the inner 1s electrons are far more stable energetically (see Section 8.6). In the excitation process the electron might become a 2p, a 3s, a 3p, a 3d electron, or might go into still higher energy states. We shall presume that it becomes a 2p electron.

In the 2p state, since $1 = 1$, the m quantum number can have any one of three possible values, 1, 0, or -1. The energy of the 2p electron will be independent of what value the m quantum number has, but, interestingly enough, the orientation of the electron cloud associated with the 2p electron will depend on the value of m. There are three possible orientations of the electron cloud associated with a 2p electron, each at right angles to the other two. The clouds may be considered to be concentrated along the x, y, and z axes in the manner indicated in Figure 8.8.

The 2p electron associated with the cloud along the x axis is said to be in a p_x orbital. Similarly, it might be in a p_y or p_z orbital if it were associated with the cloud along the y or z axes. Clearly the three orbitals are equivalent in energy and differ only in orientation. In a strong magnetic field, such as is used in the Zeeman effect, the energies of the orbitals can be distinguished and are found to vary as theory would predict.

Summarizing and generalizing, an s electron can be said to occupy an s orbital and will have an associated electron cloud which is spherically symmetrical. A p electron will occupy a p_x, p_y, or p_z orbital, which will have an electron cloud concentrated about the x, y, or z axes. A d electron can occupy, by virtue of its possible five m values, one of five d orbitals, each of which has a characteristic orientation in space.

So far we have considered three of the four quantum numbers possessed by an electron. The fourth is called the electron spin quantum number, and is to be associated with the spin of the electron on its own axis. The spin quantum number is

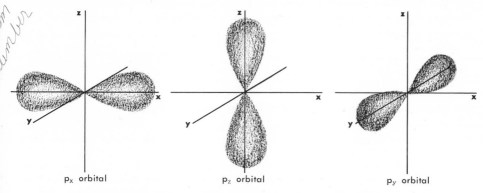

p_x orbital p_z orbital p_y orbital

FIGURE 8.8   Electron clouds associated with p electrons.

independent of n, l, and m, and can assume one of two possible values, $+\frac{1}{2}$ or $-\frac{1}{2}$, depending on the direction of rotation about its axis. The spin quantum number differs from the other three in that unlike n, l, and m, it does not appear in the wave mechanical solution to the hydrogen atom problem. It was first postulated to explain properties of atomic spectra and has proved to be necessary for our understanding of many experiments. Though our understanding of the physical significance of the spin quantum number is somewhat less than that for the other quantum numbers, its existence is of basic importance to the theory of atomic structure.

The Pauli Exclusion Principle

In order to obtain the electron configurations of atoms, one must, in addition to recognizing the existence of the four quantum numbers for an electron, establish rules for the limits on the capacities of electronic subshells in an atom. What is it that prevents all the electrons in an atom from going into the 1s subshell, which clearly has the lowest energy? There must be an additional rigorous condition on the properties of electrons that prevents this from occurring. This condition was first stated by Pauli in 1925.

According to Pauli, **no two electrons in an atom can have the same set of quantum numbers.** This means that within any given orbital, where the n, l, and m quantum numbers are fixed, there can be no more than two electrons, and these must have spins of $+\frac{1}{2}$ and $-\frac{1}{2}$. The rule was deduced by Pauli on experimental grounds, as being necessary for the explanation of the observed properties of atoms. Although there has never been a theoretical explanation of the rule, it is now very well established, and is called the *Pauli Exclusion Principle.*

By the Pauli Exclusion Principle every filled atomic orbital will contain two electrons with opposed spins; such electrons are said to be *paired.* Associated with an s subshell there is only one orbital, since when l = 0, m = 0; therefore, the capacity of an s subshell is two electrons, or one electron pair. For a p subshell there are three possible orbitals (m = 1, 0, −1), each with a capacity of two electrons. A p subshell may contain up to six electrons, which will occur in three pairs. Similarly, a d subshell, with which there are five associated orbitals, will have a capacity of 10 electrons, and an f subshell, with seven orbitals, can contain up to 14 electrons. It was by this approach that the capacities of the subshells in Table 8.5 were determined.

The Pauli Principle gives rise to the structures of atoms and may well be an important factor in determining molecular geometries. The principle can be interpreted as implying that electron pairs will tend to occur in molecules at maximum distances from other paired electrons. Application of this rule, without regard to the geometries of the atomic orbitals involved, can lead to the prediction of many molecular structures. It is also possible to discuss molecular structure in terms of atomic orbital geometries. In this book both approaches to the problem of molecular geometry will be used extensively in later chapters.

Some Comments on the Electron Configuration Theory

The theory of electron configurations associates the electrons in an atom with quantum states appropriate to their energies and space properties. The electron configuration of an atom describes as best we can at present the properties of an atom in terms of the properties of its electrons. Associated with each electron quantum state there is its set of quantum numbers and a cloud of negative charge, whose density at any point is proportional to the probability of finding the electron at that point in space. An atom, according to the model, consists of a positive nucleus surrounded by a cloud of negative charge resulting from the superposition of the charge clouds associated with each of its electrons.

Since the charge clouds for different sets of quantum numbers, or different quantum states, may differ in their properties, particularly in the distance from the atomic nucleus at which they have appreciable densities, our notion of the electronic structure of the atom is not quite so nebulous as it might first appear. Theory tells us that electrons with high principal quantum number n have high energy and, on the average, are much more likely to be found in regions relatively distant from the nucleus than are electrons with low n values. On this basis we can assign electrons to regions, which are usually called "shells" or "levels," one shell or level for each value of n, with shells associated with low n values near the nucleus and those with higher n values more distant. To discriminate between electrons in the same shell (same n value) but different values of the quantum number l, we use the term "same subshell" or "same sublevel" to denote those electrons with the same values of both n and l. Since the regions over which the charge clouds for electrons have appreciable density are not at all sharply defined, "shell" terminology is somewhat unfortunate, since to the novice it implies more than it should. We use the shell notation because it is very convenient, and we must simply remember the meaning of the term in light of this discussion. In this and subsequent chapters we shall occasionally use the terms "level" and "sublevel" in place of "shell" and "subshell"; this terminology is perhaps better in principle, in view of the fact that electron configurations describe energy levels, but has the disadvantage that when used in this context "level" must be taken to mean that group of states having a given n value. Similarly, "sublevel" will mean that group of states with the same values of both n and l.

There is one difficulty with the electron configuration theory that should be mentioned. The theory is based on the assumption that the electrons in an atom can be described by assigning them quantum numbers. This means that in the theory we consider the electrons to have properties as individuals. (Indeed the quantum numbers we use and the interpretations we give them are based on the wave mechanical solution of the one-electron problem, and hence involve only the electron-nucleus interactions.) In such an atomic model the electronic properties of the atom will be simply equal to the sum of the properties of all the electrons in the atom, with individual electron properties determined by solutions to one-electron problems. Such a model is clearly incorrect, since in an atom there are important electron-electron charge interactions and electron-electron spin interactions, as well as the electron-nucleus charge interaction covered by the model. So far, the theory of atomic structure has been unable to treat properly electron-electron interactions in atoms. Such interactions are usually considered to be "averaged in" when one interprets electron configurations. The qualitative structure of atoms, involving the existence of shells and their populations, does not seem to be appreciably altered by such an averaging; this explains the usefulness of electron configurations. Clearly, however, the necessity for such an averaging renders impossible the use of electron configurations in quantitative calculations of atomic energy levels and atomic dimensions.

8.6 EXPERIMENTAL SUPPORT FOR ELECTRON CONFIGURATIONS

The electronic configurations of atoms are based on theoretical evidence, particularly the wave mechanical solution to the hydrogen atom problem, and on experimental evidence, mainly atomic spectra. The configurations are also closely related, as we shall see in the next section, to the chemical properties of the elements.

It would take us too far afield to show the detailed relations between atomic spectra and electron configurations. However, very similar relations are obtained in investigations of the ionization energies of atoms and ions. The ionization energy, sometimes called the ionization potential, of a particle is a direct measure of the energy required to remove an electron from that particle. A given element will have several ionization energies, one for each electron in its atom. The first ionization energy of sodium is equal to the energy required to remove the outermost, 3s, electron from the atom; the second ionization energy measures the energy required to remove

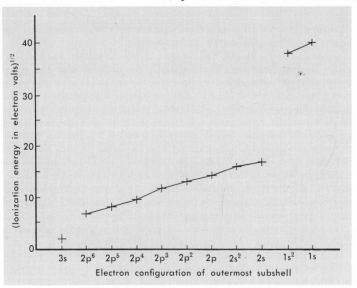

FIGURE 8.9   The ionization energies of sodium.

a 2p electron from Na$^+$; the third, the energy needed to remove a second 2p electron from Na^{+2}, and so on. As the charge on the ion increases, the ionization energy increases. In Figure 8.9 we have plotted the square roots of the ionization energies of sodium as a function of the electron being removed.

According to the theory, the electron configuration of sodium, at. no. 11, would be $1s^2 2s^2 2p^6 3s$. Electrons would be present in three shells, with n values of 1, 2, and 3, with higher-energy electrons having higher n values. The first electron to be removed, being a 3s electron, would be expected to come off relatively easily. Then one would predict there would be a group of eight electrons, in the 2p and the 2s subshells, each of which would be somewhat less easily removed than the one before it, but which would not be grossly different in character from one another as far as energy of removal is concerned. The last two electrons, in the n = 1 shell, would be very tightly bound and could only be removed with difficulty.

Figure 8.9 clearly supports the theory. The ionization energies are grouped as expected, indicating the three shells in which electrons are found; with careful examination one can discern a difference between the 2p and the 2s electrons.

More striking, if somewhat more complicated, experimental evidence for the shell structure of atoms can be obtained if one plots the square roots of all the known ionization energies of atoms having atomic numbers from 1 to 20 as a function of atomic number. This has been done in Figure 8.10.

There are several ways in which this large amount of data concerning ionization energies might be interpreted. Probably the simplest and most revealing is to connect, as we have done in the figure, the ionization energies of species having the *same number of electrons*. Since electron configuration depends only on number of electrons, the configurations of such species will be the same, and their ionization energies will differ only because their nuclear charges differ. All species with the same electron configurations form an **isoelectronic series.** An example of such a series is Li, Be$^+$, B^{+2}, C^{+3}, N^{+4}, O^{+5}, and F^{+6}, all of which have three electrons, and whose ionization energies are given in Figure 8.10 by the line labeled 2s, for the electron being removed.

The simple pattern of lines in Figure 8.10 clearly reflects the general fact that isoelectronic species are closely related in their energy properties, as would be expected if they have the same electron configurations. The lines are nearly straight, and, for series with the same principal quantum number on the outermost electron, nearly parallel. This means, for instance, that, given the ionization energies of Li and Be⁺, we could predict with good accuracy the ionization energies of all other species having three electrons. The fact that we can make this kind of prediction implies the general rule that many properties of an ion are more to be associated with the atom with which it is isoelectronic than with the parent atom. Na⁺ indeed behaves much more like the Ne atom than like the Na atom.

The lines in Figure 8.10 fall into three families, with two, eight, and eight lines. The first two lines are associated with the electrons we have called 1s and 1s². The next group of eight lines contains three subgroups, of two, three, and three lines. The first two of these lines give the ionization energies of the 2s and 2s² electrons; the next three lines are for the 2p, 2p², and 2p³ electrons; the last group completes the sextet of 2p electrons. We interpret the spacing between the two sets of three lines as being due to the added stability of the half-filled 2p subshell. There are certainly eight electrons having a principal quantum number of 2. The third group of eight lines, which we would associate with 3s and 3p electrons, is similar in its properties to the previous group. Our data would tell us that there are at least eight electrons with 3 as principal quantum number.

The properties of the ionization energies of atoms and ions are consistent with the theory of electron configurations and support the validity of the classifications we have made. The quantum theory does not at present allow us to predict quantitatively the ionization energies of isoelectronic series, but it does afford an excellent qualitative explanation of the experimental observations.

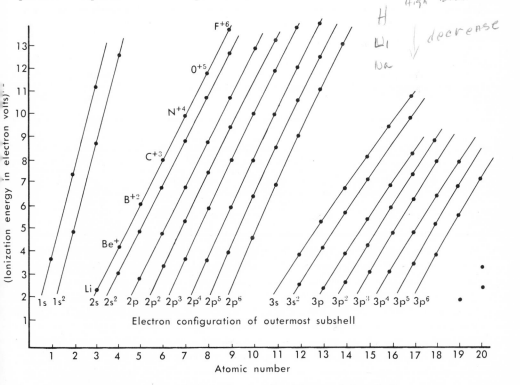

FIGURE 8.10 The ionization energies of elements 1 through 20.

8.7   THE ELECTRONIC STRUCTURE OF ATOMS AND THE PERIODIC TABLE

In the previous section we associated the electronic configurations of atoms with one of their physical properties, their ionization energies. Probably the most striking support of such configurations, however, comes from a study of the chemical properties of the elements.

When substances undergo a chemical reaction, a rearrangement of the electrons in the reacting atoms or molecules takes place, and the result is a system which is somewhat more stable than the reactants. The difference in stability is given by the energy, or heat, which must be removed from the reaction products to lower their temperature to that of the reactants. In chemical changes the energy liberated is of the order of 100 kcal. per mole of reactant. The formation of a mole of liquid water from gaseous hydrogen and oxygen, a vigorous reaction, evolves about 68 kcal. The combustion of a mole of methane evolves 210 kcal. In terms of electron volts per molecule these energies are, respectively, about 3 and about 9 ev. These energies are about of the same order of magnitude as the ionization potentials of the electrons in the outermost shell of an atom, but considerably smaller than the ionization potentials of the inner electrons.

From these observations one can conclude with some confidence that when atoms take part in chemical reactions it is only the outer electrons that are appreciably affected. The stability of inner shells is simply too high for them to be appreciably influenced by only a few electron volts of energy. This reasoning leads us to believe that, since only the outermost shells of electrons participate in chemical reactions, *the chemical properties of the atoms are primarily to be associated with their electron configurations in the outermost shell.*

As soon as one examines the periodic table in the light of the outer electron configurations of atoms it becomes obvious that the relationship between chemical properties and configuration of electrons is close indeed. Consider, for instance, the electron configurations of the alkali metals (Table 8.7).

TABLE 8.7   THE ELECTRON CONFIGURATIONS OF THE ALKALI METALS

Element	Atomic Number	Configuration
Li	3	$1s^2 2s$
Na	11	$1s^2 2s^2 2p^6 3s$
K	19	$1s^2 2s^2 2p^6 3s^2 3p^6 4s$
Rb	37	$1s^2 2s^2 2p^6 3s^2 3p^6 3d^{10} 4s^2 4p^6 5s$
Cs	55	$1s^2 2s^2 2p^6 3s^2 3p^6 3d^{10} 4s^2 4p^6 4d^{10} 5s^2 5p^6 6s$

For each of the alkali metals atoms the electron configuration in the outermost shell is ns. These are the only elements with such a configuration, and by their chemical properties clearly belong in the same family.

As with the alkali metal family, each family of atoms has its own particular electron configuration in its outermost shell. The difference in electronic structure between members of a given family is only in the number of inner shells. Indeed, *if the elements are arranged in a table according to the outer electron configurations of their atoms, with atoms having the same outer configuration placed in the same vertical column, and atoms with the same number of shells in the same row, the table of all the elements has a form identical to that of the periodic table.*

The basis on which we constructed the periodic table was primarily chemical. The foundations on which we built the electron configurations of the atoms are partly theoretical and partly physical. The fact that the periodic table can be derived by grouping atoms by outer electron configuration is strong evidence in support of the following very important generalization: *The chemical properties of an atom are determined primarily by the electron configuration in its outermost shell. The periodicity of properties of the elements is the result of the periodicity of the electron configurations in their outermost shell.*

8.8   THE CORRELATION OF ATOMIC AND PHYSICAL PROPERTIES WITH ELECTRON CONFIGURATIONS

A knowledge of electronic configurations in atoms is extremely useful in all areas of chemistry. It allows us to correlate and predict many of the physical and chemical properties of atoms and molecules in a truly remarkable way. In the next few chapters we shall discuss the applicability of the theory to problems of chemical bonding. Here we shall show how electron configurations can be used to aid our understanding of atomic sizes.

According to our model, the electrons in an atom are arranged in shells and subshells around the nucleus, at distances which increase as their principal quantum numbers increase. The electrons and the nucleus obey, within the quantum-mechanical limits, the laws of electrostatics. Electrons, being of like charge, repel each other, and electrons and nuclei are attracted to each other because of their unlike charges. Mathematically, these forces are: For electron-electron repulsion,

$$F_R = e^2/r^2$$

and for electron-nucleus attraction,

$$F_A = Ze^2/r^2$$

in which $-e$ is the electronic charge, Ze the nuclear charge, and r the interparticle distance. In addition, the force between a charge and a group of charged concentric spheres is proportional to the total net charge of the spheres (Figure 8.11). In this atomic model (admittedly very simplified), Figure 8.11 can be considered to resemble an atom, with its nuclear charge (q_1) shielded from the outermost electrons $(-Q)$ by the charge on the inner electron shells $(-q_2 -q_3)$.

On the basis of our model let us now consider sizes of atoms. In any given group in the periodic table we can predict that the atomic diameters will increase as the number of electron shells increases. The reason for the increase is clearly shown by the examination of the electronic structures of the group 1A elements (Table 8.8). Each of these elements has a single s electron outside a closed shell or a closed p subshell. These subshells are relatively closer to the nucleus than is the outermost electron and so shield the electron from much of the nuclear charge. If the shielding were perfect the outermost s electron would move in a field of essentially a $+1$ charge and the atom would behave as would a hydrogen atom, its electron having

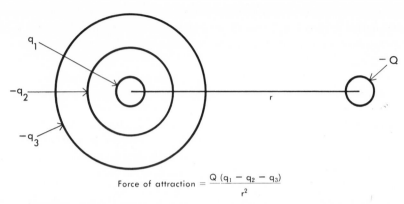

$$\text{Force of attraction} = \frac{Q\,(q_1 - q_2 - q_3)}{r^2}$$

FIGURE 8.11 Shielding of charge of nucleus by inner electronic subshells.

the same quantum number as the outermost s electron. Since the average distance of the electron from the hydrogen nucleus increases rapidly with increasing value of n, the size of the alkali metal atoms should increase with increasing principal quantum number of the outermost electron, and hence should increase with increasing period. The shielding is not perfect since the atomic shells are not sharply defined, but the general line of reasoning is valid enough to properly predict the increase in atomic size with period.

TABLE 8.8 RADII OF THE ALKALI METALS

	Li	Na	K	Rb	Cs
Configuration in outermost shell	2s	3s	4s	5s	6s
Atomic radius in Å	1.52	1.86	2.31	2.44	2.62

A similar argument can be applied to atoms of elements in the same period, that is, with the same number of shells but differing configurations in the outermost shell. A good example would be the third period shown in Table 8.9.

In each of these atoms the electron configuration in the inner shells is the same, $1s^2 2s^2 2p^6$. Since electrons in the same shell do not shield the nucleus from each other, the shielding effect on the outermost, often called **valence,** electrons is also of the same magnitude in all of these atoms. This means that, since the nuclear charge of the atoms increases from left to right, the valence electrons of these atoms are attracted by an increasing positive charge (the size of the positive charge would be $Z - 10$ if the shielding were perfect), and hence move closer and closer to the nucleus. The ever-decreasing size of the atoms across the row supports this reasoning. Argon appears to be an exception to the rule; the reason for the exception is that the

TABLE 8.9 RADII OF ELEMENTS IN THE THIRD PERIOD

	Na	Mg	Al	Si	P	S	Cl	Ar
Outer configuration	3s	$3s^2$	$3s^2 3p$	$3s^2 3p^2$	$3s^2 3p^3$	$3s^2 3p^4$	$3s^2 3p^5$	$3s^2 3p^6$
Atomic radius in Å	1.86	1.60	1.43	1.17	1.10	1.04	0.99	(1.54)

radii of the other elements are those observed for bonded atoms, whereas the argon radius was found from the density of solid argon. (See Chapter 10 for a discussion of the methods used in determining atomic dimensions.)

Other facts about atomic radii are also made reasonable by analysis in terms of electron configurations. (In some rows of the periodic table the electrons go into inner shells rather than the outermost one. As one proceeds across such a period from one element to the next, both the nuclear charge and the population of the inner shell change by the same amount, making for only a small change in the shielding effect on the outermost electrons.) Since the electrons in such outermost shells have very

TABLE 8.10 RADII AND IONIZATION POTENTIALS OF SOME TRANSITION AND RARE EARTH METALS

Element	Atomic Radius (Å)	Ionization Energy (ev.)	Element	Atomic Radius (Å)	Ionization Energy (ev.)
Sc	1.60	6.7	Ce	1.82	6.54
Ti	1.46	6.81	Pr	1.82	5.8
V	1.31	6.71	Nd	1.82	6.3
Cr	1.25	6.74	Pm		
Mn	1.29	7.41	Sm		
Fe	1.26	7.83	Eu	2.04	5.7
Co	1.25	7.8	Gd	1.79	6.7
Ni	1.24	7.61	Tb	1.77	6.7
Cu	1.28	7.68	Dy	1.77	6.8
Zn	1.33	9.36	Ho	1.76	
			Er	1.75	
			Tm	1.74	
			Yb	1.93	6.2
			Lu	1.74	
(3d shell being filled)			(4f shell being filled)		

similar environments, one would expect that for such atoms the sizes and the ionization energies would be substantially constant. The transition metals and the rare earths are examples of elements that should, and do, show this behavior. In the rare earths the 4f subshell is gradually being filled as one crosses the period; this results in a very small decrease in the atomic radii of these elements. This difference in size, though small, has been sufficient to allow for separation of these elements by ion exchange, and is given the name **lanthanide contraction.** A similar small shrinkage occurs in the transition metals, where d subshells are being filled.

The electron configuration theory can be applied successfully to explain other atomic properties, but the correlation of atom sizes is an excellent example of how the theory can be used.

PROBLEMS

8.1 What experimental evidence do we have for the existence of:
   a. Atomic nuclei?   b. Extranuclear electrons?   c. Neutrons in atomic nuclei?

8.2 Characterize each of the following as to charge, mass, and size:
   a. The electron
   b. The proton
   c. The alpha particle
   d. The fluorine atom
   e. The fluorine nucleus
   f. The O^{17} nucleus

8.3   Given that the atomic number of manganese is 25, what can be said about the nuclear composition of manganese atoms? What can be said about Mn^{55} atoms?

8.4   Characterize each of the following particles as to number of extranuclear electrons, number of protons and number of neutrons in the nucleus, and charge on the nucleus:

$$_{19}K^{39} \quad _{16}S^{34} \quad _3Li^7 \quad Na^+ \quad Cl^- \quad (Sn^{118})^{+4}$$

If complete characterization is not possible, indicate the reason.

8.5   How might one produce an atomic spectrum for carbon? Of what practical use is such a spectrum? Of what theoretical use?

8.6   What does the "electron cloud" in Figure 8.2 represent? How does the electron cloud picture of a hydrogen atom differ from Bohr's model for that atom?

8.7   How do the laws governing the motion and energy of the electrons in a lithium atom differ from the laws governing the motion and energy of the planets in the solar system?

8.8   What are quantum numbers? Where do they originate? How are they used? How many quantum numbers does an electron have in an atom? Name a possible set of quantum numbers for an electron in a carbon atom. What properties of the electron can be associated with each of its quantum numbers?

8.9   What is meant by the statement, "The electron configuration of the oxygen atom is $1s^22s^22p^4$"? What are the electron configurations of the following atoms and ions?

$$N \quad P \quad H \quad Ar \quad Cl^- \quad K^+ \quad Cu \quad Sn^{+4}$$

8.10 What would be the electron configuration of each of the above species in its first excited state?

8.11 What property of an atom prevents all its electrons from going into the 1s energy level? What sorts of properties would you expect for atoms if the 1s level were the only level in which electrons were ordinarily found?

8.12 What is an orbital? What is the geometry of an s orbital? A p orbital? How many electrons can there be in a p orbital? In what ways, if any, do the electrons in a p orbital differ?

8.13 What are isoelectronic species? How are they similar? How do they differ? Name a species isoelectronic with the potassium atom; with the Fe^{+2} ion. How do the properties of isoelectronic species support the theory of electron configurations?

8.14 Given that the ionization energy of the Be atom is 9.28 ev. and that of B^+ ion is 25.00 ev., predict the ionization energy of the N^{+3} ion and that of the Li^- ion The latter quantity is called the electron affinity of the lithium atom and is a measure of the tendency for the Li atom to acquire an electron.

8.15 What evidence do we have that the chemical properties of atoms are primarily determined by the electrons in their outermost shells?

8.16 What is the relationship between the electron configurations of atoms and the periodic table?

8.17 Using the electron configurations of the atoms and the laws of electrostatics, predict which species in each of the following pairs would have the larger diameter:
a. F or Cl   b. C or N   c. C or Si   d. Na or Mg^+ e. Na or F^-

8.18 How does the electron configuration theory for atoms explain the fact that the atoms of the rare earths are so nearly alike in their properties?

*8.19 Using Bohr's equation 8.15, calculate the wavelengths of the first and second lines in the Balmer series. Compare your results with those in Table 8.4. Calculate the wavelength of the first line in the Lyman series, n = 2 to n = 1.

*8.20 Using the Bohr theory, calculate the radius of an H atom in its ground state. Calculate the speed of an H atom electron in the ground state. How do the radius and speed vary with the quantum number n?

*8.21 Using quantum theoretical principles, calculate the wavelengths of the lines associated with the two transitions in the sodium atom shown with unspecified wavelengths in Figure 8.4.

*8.22 Iron atoms have a characteristic x-ray wavelength at 1.932 Å; the analogous line in the x-ray spectrum of silver occurs at 0.558 Å. An unknown metal has the line at 0.708 Å Find the atomic number of the metal.

*8.23 X-ray spectra are thought to be caused by the ejection of inner electrons from an atom by a beam of very energetic electrons. When, for example, an n = 1 electron is removed from the atom, electrons in higher shells tend to make a transition to the n = 1 level, thereby lowering the energy of the system and emitting x-ray photons. The situation is very similar to that occurring in hydrogen atoms when the Lyman series is excited. One of the strong x-ray lines for an element will be the result of an n = 2 to n = 1 transition, the same transition responsible for the first line in the Lyman series. In the x-ray transition, the electron which makes the quantum jump is not appreciably influenced in its energy by any atomic electrons except the remaining 1s electron, which shields the atomic nucleus and decreases its effective charge by one unit. (Shielding here is essentially perfect.)

Develop a relation, analogous to equation 8.14, for a one-electron system in which the nuclear charge is Z rather than 1. Using this relation, predict the wavelength in the copper x-ray spectrum which is associated with the n = 2 to n = 1 transition.

*8.24 Suppose that the spin quantum number could have the values $+\frac{1}{2}$, 0, and $-\frac{1}{2}$. Assuming that the rules governing the possible values of the other quantum numbers and the order in which the various levels are filled remain unchanged:
   a. What would be the capacity of an s subshell? A p subshell? A d? An f?
   b. What would be the capacity of the n = 3 shell?
   c. What would be the electron configuration of the element of atomic number 5? 10?
   d. What would be the atomic number of the element which would most closely resemble in chemical and physical properties the element of atomic number 5?
   e. Using electron configurations, construct a "periodic table" for the first 40 elements.

9 | IONIC BONDING

In Chapter 2, we considered briefly some of the different forces which hold atoms together in elementary and compound substances. Now that we have developed a clearer picture of the electronic structure of atoms, we are better able to understand the nature of these forces. Such forces, called chemical bonds, will occupy our attention throughout this and the two following chapters.

Chemical bonds arise from interactions between electrons of atoms. Perhaps the simplest type of bond and one of the strongest is that which arises when electrons are transferred from one atom to another. The result of such a transfer is the formation of positively and negatively charged particles called ions. These ions are held together by powerful electrostatic forces called ionic bonds.

In discussing ionic bonding in this chapter, we shall concentrate upon the monatomic ions which result from the transfer of electrons from atoms of metallic elements to atoms of nonmetallic elements. We shall be particularly concerned with:

1. The prediction of the charges ($+1$, -2, and so on) of the monatomic ions formed by various elements. A knowledge of such charges leads immediately to the simplest formulas of ionic compounds.

2. The properties of individual ions and of the ionic compounds that they form.

9.1 VALENCE ELECTRONS: ELECTRON DOT SYMBOLS

When atoms combine with one another, their electronic structures undergo rearrangements of one type or another. Frequently, it is only the electrons in the outermost shell (principal energy level) that are involved. These particular electrons are sufficiently important to be given a special name: **valence electrons.** For the A group elements, the number of valence electrons per atom is given by the group number. For example, atoms of lithium, sodium, and potassium in group 1A all have one valence electron; those of fluorine, chlorine, bromine, and iodine in group 7A of the periodic table have seven.

In discussing chemical bonding and the reactions of elements with each other, we frequently indicate the number of valence electrons in an atom by sprinkling dots, circles, or x's around the symbol of the element. Such "electron dot symbols," sometimes irreverently referred to as "flyspeck formulas," are given below for the atoms of the elements of atomic number 11 to 17:

$$\text{Na·} \quad \text{·Mg·} \quad \text{·Al·} \quad \text{·Si·} \quad \text{:P·} \quad \text{:S:} \quad \text{:Cl:}$$

In this notation, the symbol of the element represents the nucleus and the inner electron core of the atom; only the valence electrons are shown. The dots used to represent the latter are distributed in a regular pattern around the four sides of the symbol. When we are dealing with individual atoms, we shall write the electron dot symbols in such a way as to give the maximum number of single, unpaired electrons.

9.2 NOBLE-GAS ELECTRONIC STRUCTURES

It has been pointed out that reactions between elements involve rearrangements in the electronic structures of their atoms. When reaction occurs, atoms of the two elements involved tend to acquire stable electronic structures. The question then arises whether there are any electronic configurations which are particularly stable and hence particularly likely to be formed when atoms react with each other.

There is indeed one type of electronic structure that is peculiarly stable, that of the noble gases. Helium, neon, argon, and the other members of this group are unique in two respects. In the first place, the noble gases are composed of individual atoms with little interaction between them. Furthermore, these elements are extremely unreactive; the lower members do not form stable binary compounds with any other elements.* Both of these facts indicate that noble-gas atoms have extremely stable electronic structures; they resist interactions with other atoms which would result in changes in these structures.

TABLE 9.1 ELECTRONIC STRUCTURES OF THE NOBLE GASES

Element	Populations of Principal Energy Levels					
	1st	2nd	3rd	4th	5th	6th
$_2$He	2					
$_{10}$Ne	2	8				
$_{18}$Ar	2	8	8			
$_{36}$Kr	2	8	18	8		
$_{54}$Xe	2	8	18	18	8	
$_{86}$Rn	2	8	18	32	18	8

In view of the stability of the noble-gas structure, it might be expected that atoms of other elements, in reacting with each other, would tend to acquire such a structure. This is confirmed experimentally; atoms of elements which are 1 to 4 electrons removed from a noble-gas configuration ordinarily react so as to acquire such a structure. One way in which this can happen is through the formation of ions, which will be discussed in Section 9.3.

It will be noted that each of the noble gases except helium has eight electrons in its outermost principal energy level. This is often referred to as a "stable octet"

---

* Recently, it has been found that the higher members of the noble-gas group (Kr, Xe, Rn) react with fluorine to form stable binary compounds. The structures of certain of these compounds are discussed in Chapter 10.

of electrons. The tendency of other elements to acquire a noble-gas structure through chemical reaction, first suggested by the American physical chemist G. N. Lewis, is often referred to as the "octet rule."

9.3 MONATOMIC IONS WITH NOBLE-GAS STRUCTURES

Ions with Neon Structure

The electronic structures of atoms of elements of atomic number 8 to 13 are as follows:

Element	Electronic Structure	Shell Populations	Valence Electrons
$_8$O	$1s^2$ $2s^2$ $2p^4$	2, 6	6
$_9$F	$1s^2$ $2s^2$ $2p^5$	2, 7	7
$_{10}$Ne	$1s^2$ $2s^2$ $2p^6$	2, 8	
$_{11}$Na	$1s^2$ $2s^2$ $2p^6$ $3s^1$	2, 8, 1	1
$_{12}$Mg	$1s^2$ $2s^2$ $2p^6$ $3s^2$	2, 8, 2	2
$_{13}$Al	$1s^2$ $2s^2$ $2p^6$ $3s^2$ $3p^1$	2, 8, 3	3

It is evident that an atom of oxygen can achieve the stable octet of neon by acquiring two more electrons; a fluorine atom can accomplish the same result by picking up one extra electron. The resulting particles are negative ions (**anions**) with charges of -2 and -1 respectively. In terms of electron dot symbols, these processes are represented as:

$$: \overset{\cdot}{\underset{\cdot}{O}} : + 2e^- \longrightarrow (: \overset{\cdot\cdot}{\underset{\cdot\cdot}{O}} :)^{-2} \tag{9.1}$$

$$: \overset{\cdot\cdot}{\underset{\cdot}{F}} : + e^- \longrightarrow (: \overset{\cdot\cdot}{\underset{\cdot\cdot}{F}} :)^- \tag{9.2}$$

While it might be expected that oxygen and fluorine atoms would have a strong tendency to form negative ions with the neon structure, it is clear that there must be a source of electrons available if this process is to take place. Examination of the electronic structures of sodium, magnesium, and aluminum reveals three likely sources. Atoms of these elements by losing one, two, and three electrons respectively form positive ions (**cations**) with electronic structures identical to that of the neon atom:

$$\text{Na} \cdot \longrightarrow \text{Na}^+ + e^- \tag{9.3}$$

$$\cdot \text{Mg} \cdot \longrightarrow \text{Mg}^{+2} + 2e^- \tag{9.4}$$

$$\cdot \overset{\cdot}{\text{Al}} \cdot \longrightarrow \text{Al}^{+3} + 3e^- \tag{9.5}$$

When the metals sodium, magnesium, or aluminum come in contact with fluorine or oxygen, reactions occur in which electrons are transferred from metal to nonmetal atoms. Such reactions result in the formation of solids containing positively and negatively charged ions which have the stable octet of neon. The simplest formulas of the ionic compounds formed are readily deduced from the charges of the ions. For example, since the reaction between sodium and fluorine results in the formation of ions with charges of $+1$ and -1 respecively, sodium fluoride must contain an equal number of Na^+ and F^- ions and hence must have the simplest formula NaF. The product of the reaction of aluminum with fluorine must have the simplest formula AlF_3, containing three fluoride ions with a -1 charge for every $+3$ aluminum ion.

In terms of electron dot symbols, the reactions just described between atoms of the elements may be represented as:

$$Na \cdot \longrightarrow Na^+ + e^-$$

$$:\overset{..}{F}: + e^- \longrightarrow (:\overset{..}{F}:)^-$$

$$Na \cdot + :\overset{..}{F}: \longrightarrow Na^+ + (:\overset{..}{F}:)^- \qquad NaF \qquad\qquad (9.6)$$

$$2\,Na \cdot \longrightarrow 2\,Na^+ + 2\,e^-$$

$$:\overset{..}{O}: + 2\,e^- \longrightarrow (:\overset{..}{O}:)^{-2}$$

$$2\,Na \cdot + :\overset{..}{O}: \longrightarrow 2\,Na^+ + (:\overset{..}{O}:)^{-2} \qquad Na_2O^* \qquad (9.7)$$

$$\cdot Mg \cdot \longrightarrow Mg^{+2} + 2\,e^-$$

$$2 :\overset{..}{F}: + 2\,e^- \longrightarrow 2(:\overset{..}{F}:)^-$$

$$\cdot Mg \cdot + 2 :\overset{..}{F}: \longrightarrow Mg^{+2} + 2(:\overset{..}{F}:)^- \qquad MgF_2 \qquad (9.8)$$

$$\cdot Mg \cdot \longrightarrow Mg^{+2} + 2\,e^-$$

$$:\overset{..}{O}: + 2\,e^- \longrightarrow (:\overset{..}{O}:)^{-2}$$

$$\cdot Mg \cdot + :\overset{..}{O}: \longrightarrow Mg^{+2} + (:\overset{..}{O}:)^{-2} \qquad MgO \qquad (9.9)$$

$$\cdot Al \cdot \longrightarrow Al^{+3} + 3\,e^-$$

$$3 :\overset{..}{F}: + 3\,e^- \longrightarrow 3(:\overset{..}{F}:)^-$$

$$\cdot Al \cdot + 3 :\overset{..}{F}: \longrightarrow Al^{+3} + 3(:\overset{..}{F}:)^- \qquad AlF_3 \qquad (9.10)$$

$$2 \cdot Al \cdot \longrightarrow 2\,Al^{+3} + 6\,e^-$$

$$3 :\overset{..}{O}: + 6\,e^- \longrightarrow 3(:\overset{..}{O}:)^{-2}$$

$$2 \cdot Al \cdot + 3 :\overset{..}{O}: \longrightarrow 2\,Al^{+3} + 3(:\overset{..}{O}:)^{-2} \qquad Al_2O_3 \qquad (9.11)$$

* At ordinary temperatures, the product of the reaction between sodium and oxygen is sodium peroxide, Na_2O_2. Only at quite high temperatures does sodium form the normal oxide, Na_2O. These reactions will be discussed in greater detail in Chapter 15.

It may be noted that in the overall reactions for the formation of these compounds there is no net gain or loss of electrons. The number of electrons lost by the metal atoms taking part in the reaction is in each case exactly equal to the number of electrons gained by atoms of the nonmetallic element. For example, in the formation of Al_2O_3, the six electrons given up by the two aluminum atoms are taken on by the three oxygen atoms.

Other Ions with Noble-Gas Configurations

It has been pointed out that the reactions of the metals sodium, magnesium, and aluminum with the nonmetals fluorine and oxygen lead to the formation of positive and negative ions, all of which have a noble-gas structure. One might then argue by analogy that the reaction of any metal with 1, 2, or 3 valence electrons with any nonmetal in group 6A or 7A of the periodic table should give the same result. The ions which these elements are capable of forming are listed in Table 9.2.

TABLE 9.2 IONS WITH NOBLE-GAS CONFIGURATIONS

Noble Gas	−2 Ion	−1 Ion	+1 Ion	+2 Ion	+3 Ion
He		H^-	Li^+	Be^{+2}	
Ne	O^{-2}	F^-	Na^+	Mg^{+2}	Al^{+3}
Ar	S^{-2}	Cl^-	K^+	Ca^{+2}	Sc^{+3}
Kr	Se^{-2}	Br^-	Rb^+	Sr^{+2}	Y^{+3}
Xe	Te^{-2}	I^-	Cs^+	Ba^{+2}	La^{+3}
Rn	Po^{-2}	At^-	Fr^+	Ra^{+2}	Ac^{+3}

From Table 9.2 the simplest formulas of a great many binary compounds formed between metals and nonmetals are readily deduced. For example, using the principle of electroneutrality, one can predict for sodium hydride, calcium iodide, and lanthanum sulfide the simplest formulas NaH, CaI_2, and La_2S_3 respectively (cf. NaF, MgF_2, Al_2O_3).

It is found experimentally, using the techniques described in Chapter 3, that the formulas of such compounds are in excellent agreement with predictions based on Table 9.2. In the majority of cases, the properties of the compounds are those to be expected of ionic substances (Section 9.5). Calcium iodide, like magnesium fluoride, is a high-melting-point solid capable of conducting electricity either in the molten state or in water solution. Sodium hydride is quite similar in appearance, physical properties, and crystal structure to sodium fluoride or sodium chloride.

In a few instances, compounds formed by the elements included in Table 9.2 have properties more typical of molecular than ionic substances. This is particularly true of the binary compounds formed by beryllium and aluminum, two elements which are on the borderline between metals and nonmetals. Aluminum bromide, simplest formula $AlBr_3$, shows none of the typical properties of ionic compounds. We shall find in Chapter 10 that this particular compound and many others like it are molecular rather than ionic. The agreement of the simplest formula with predictions based on an ionic structure is, in a sense, fortuitous.

9.4   SIZES OF IONS

The fact that it is impossible to obtain a sample of matter made up of only one kind of ion poses a fundamental difficulty in the experimental determination of ionic sizes. One can, by x-ray diffraction, determine the distance between centers of oppositely charged ions in a crystal. For example, from data obtained on sodium fluoride, the internuclear distance between a $+1$ sodium ion and a -1 fluoride ion can be calculated to be 2.31 Å. However, without further information, it is impossible to say how much of this distance is to be attributed to the radius of the sodium ion and how much to the fluoride ion. The same problem arises regardless of the ionic compound chosen; one always obtains only the sum of the radii of two different ions.

Qualitatively, it is reasonable to suppose that a sodium ion should have a smaller radius than a fluoride ion. The two ions have identical electronic structures (10 electrons each); they differ only in the composition of their nuclei. The greater positive charge of the sodium nucleus (11 protons) as compared to that of fluorine (9 protons) would be expected to draw the electrons in more tightly, resulting in a smaller ionic radius for Na$^+$. Accordingly, one would predict that less than half of the internuclear distance in sodium fluoride should be assigned to the sodium ion with the larger fluoride ion accounting for the remainder.

Professor Pauling has refined this simple picture to predict quantitatively the relative sizes of ions such as Na$^+$ and F$^-$ which have identical electronic structures. He considers the two ionic radii to be inversely proportional to their "effective nuclear charges." The latter represent nuclear charges adjusted for the screening effect of electrons in inner electronic levels. These electrons partially insulate those

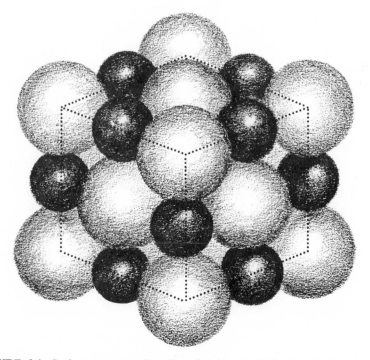

FIGURE 9.1   Ionic arrangement in sodium fluoride crystal: in the crystal each sodium ion (black sphere) is surrounded by six fluoride ions (light sphere) and each fluoride ion by six sodium ions.

in the outermost level from the nucleus, thereby diminishing the attractive force of the nucleus pulling on the valence electrons. For ions with the neon structure, it has been calculated that this factor effectively cancels out the charge of about 4.5 of the protons in the nucleus. This leads to an "effective nuclear charge" of $11.0 - 4.5 = 6.5$ for the Na^+ ion and $9.0 - 4.5 = 4.5$ for the F^- ion. Taking the radii of these two ions to be inversely proportional to their effective nuclear charges:

$$\frac{r\ Na^+}{r\ F^-} = \frac{r\ Na^+}{2.31\ Å - r\ Na^+} = \frac{4.5}{6.5}$$

Solving, we find

$$r\ Na^+ = 0.95\ Å \quad \text{and} \quad r\ F^- = 1.36\ Å$$

By a similar approach, it is possible to establish ionic radii for various monatomic ions. A list of such radii (taken from Linus Pauling, *The Nature of the Chemical Bond*, Cornell University Press, Ithaca, N.Y., 3rd edition, 1960) is given in Table 9.3.

TABLE 9.3 ATOMIC AND IONIC RADII

Atoms	Protons	Electrons	Atomic Radius (Å)	Ion	Protons	Electrons	Ionic Radius (Å)
H	1	1	0.37	H^-	1	2	2.08
He	2	2	0.93				
Li	3	3	1.52	Li^+	3	2	0.60
Be	4	4	1.11	Be^{+2}	4	2	0.31
O	8	8	0.66	O^{-2}	8	10	1.40
F	9	9	0.64	F^-	9	10	1.36
Ne	10	10	1.12				
Na	11	11	1.86	Na^+	11	10	0.95
Mg	12	12	1.60	Mg^{+2}	12	10	0.65
Al	13	13	1.43	Al^{+3}	13	10	0.50
S	16	16	1.04	S^{-2}	16	18	1.84
Cl	17	17	0.99	Cl^-	17	18	1.81
Ar	18	18	1.54				
K	19	19	2.31	K^+	19	18	1.33
Ca	20	20	1.97	Ca^{+2}	20	18	0.99
Sc	21	21	1.60	Sc^{+3}	21	18	0.81
Se	34	34	1.17	Se^{-2}	34	36	1.98
Br	35	35	1.14	Br^-	35	36	1.95
Kr	36	36	1.69				
Rb	37	37	2.44	Rb^+	37	36	1.48
Sr	38	38	2.15	Sr^{+2}	38	36	1.13
Y	39	39	1.80	Y^{+3}	39	36	0.93
Te	52	52	1.37	Te^{-2}	52	54	2.21
I	53	53	1.33	I^-	53	54	2.16
Xe	54	54	1.90				
Cs	55	55	2.62	Cs^+	55	54	1.69
Ba	56	56	2.17	Ba^{+2}	56	54	1.35
La	57	57	1.87	La^{+3}	57	54	1.15

Table 9.3 suggests several generalizations concerning the sizes of ions:
1. A series of particles such as O^{-2}, F^-, Ne, Na^+, Mg^{+2} and Al^{+3}, all of which have the same electronic structure, show a steady decrease in radius (1.40, 1.36,

1.12, 0.95, 0.65, 0.50 Å) with increasing nuclear charge (8, 9, 10, 11, 12, 13). The increased nuclear charge tends to pull the outer electrons closer to the nucleus.

2. The radii of negative ions are larger than those of the corresponding non-metal atoms (see Chapter 10, Section 10.4, for a discussion of this effect).

3. Positive ions are considerably smaller than the atoms from which they are derived. The conversion of a metal atom to a positive ion with a noble-gas structure involves the removal of an entire outer electron shell with a consequent reduction in size.

4. Within a given vertical group of the periodic table, there is a steady increase in ionic radius with increasing atomic number. This same effect is, of course, observed with atomic radii.

Frequently, ionic radii obtained from Table 9.3 are not entirely consistent with

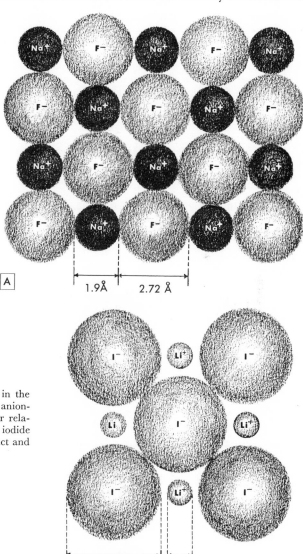

FIGURE 9.2 A. A plane in the sodium fluoride crystal showing anion-cation contact and ionic diameter relations. B. A plane in the lithium iodide crystal showing anion-anion contact and ionic diameter relations.

experimentally observed internuclear distances. For example, the distance between nuclei in LiCl, 2.57 Å, is about 7 per cent greater than that calculated by taking the sum of the radii of the Li^+ and Cl^- ions.

$$0.60 \text{ Å} + 1.81 \text{ Å} = 2.41 \text{ Å}$$

Similarly, the internuclear distances in LiBr and LiI (2.75 Å, 3.02 Å) are found to be somewhat greater than those calculated from ionic radii (2.55 Å for LiBr, 2.76 Å for LiI).

Discrepancies of this sort arise whenever the positive ion is much smaller than the negative ion. In such cases, the negative ions approach one another closely enough in the crystal lattice to introduce repulsive forces which increase the internuclear distance. If the ratio of the radii of the + and − ions is less than about 0.41, there is actually anion-anion contact in the crystal rather than cation-anion contact.

In principle, one of the most straightforward methods of obtaining ionic radii is to measure the internuclear distance between anions in a crystal in which there is anion-anion contact. Dividing this distance by two gives directly a value for the anion radius. For example, one could establish a value for the radius of the I^- ion by taking one half of the I^- to I^- distance (4.24 Å) in LiI. The value calculated in this manner, 2.12 Å, agrees reasonably well with that listed in Table 9.3.

9.5 PROPERTIES OF IONIC COMPOUNDS

Ionic compounds, without exception, are:

High-melting solids. Their melting points range from several hundred to over 2000°C.

Good electrical conductors in the liquid state. Molten ionic compounds have electrical conductivities many millions of times greater than those of nonionic compounds. To cite one example, molten NaCl has a conductivity about 10^{18} times that of the molecular compound CCl_4.

We shall now examine more closely these two characteristic properties of ionic compounds.

Melting Points

The relatively high melting points of ionic compounds are a consequence of the strong electrical forces between oppositely charged ions in the crystal lattice. High temperatures must be reached before the ions can be separated to give the freedom of motion characteristic of the liquid state.

According to Coulomb's Law, the attractive force between oppositely charged particles is directly proportional to their charges and inversely proportional to the square of the distance between them. Applied to ions in a crystal lattice, the relation becomes:

$$f = \text{constant} \times \frac{q_1 \times q_2}{(r_+ + r_-)^2} \qquad \begin{array}{l} (q_1, q_2 = \text{charges of } + \text{ and } - \text{ ions}) \\ (r_+, r_- = \text{radii of } + \text{ and } - \text{ ions}) \end{array} \qquad (9.12)$$

According to equation 9.12, interionic forces should be greatest for small ions of high charge; the melting points of ionic compounds might be expected to show the same effect. Complications arise because of a factor (the partial covalent character of ionic bonds) to be discussed in Chapter 10, but, in general, this prediction is confirmed. If one compares the compounds NaCl and BaO, for which the sums of the ionic radii are nearly the same but the charge products differ by a factor of four, it is found that barium oxide has a considerably higher melting point (Table 9.4). The size effect is illustrated by a comparison of MgO and BaO; the smaller radius of the Mg^{+2} ion as compared to the Ba^{+2} ion results in a stronger attraction for the O^{-2} ion and, consequently, a higher melting point.

TABLE 9.4 EFFECT OF IONIC SIZE AND CHARGE ON MELTING POINT

Compound	Charges of Ions	$r_+ + r_-$ (Å)	Melting Point (°C)
NaCl	+1, −1	0.95 + 1.81 = 2.76	800
BaO	+2, −2	1.35 + 1.40 = 2.75	1920
MgO	+2, −2	0.65 + 1.40 = 2.05	2800

Electrical Conductivities

Perhaps the best evidence for the existence of ions in a compound such as sodium chloride is its ability to conduct an electric current when melted or dissolved in water. In either the molten state or water solution, the current is carried by the ions (Na^+ and Cl^-), which are free to move under the influence of an electrical field.

It should be emphasized that the mechanism of conduction in molten salts is entirely different from that in metals. (In the latter, it is electrons rather than ions which carry the current) The fact that most metals have conductivities at least a thousand times greater than that of molten sodium chloride implies that ions offer more resistance to flow than do electrons.

Metallic and ionic conductors differ in still another important respect. The passage of a direct electric current through fused or dissolved salts results in a chemical reaction at the electrodes. With molten sodium chloride, the reaction products are elementary sodium and chlorine. A somewhat more complicated reaction takes place when a direct current passes through a water solution of sodium chloride (cf. Chapter 20). In contrast, no chemical change whatsoever occurs when electrons flow through a metallic conductor.

Ionic compounds are ordinarily nonconductors in the solid state at room temperature. However, as the temperature is raised, there is usually a significant increase in conductivity. Solid sodium chloride at the melting point (800°C) has a conductivity about 10^{10} times that at 25°C.

The increase in conductivity with increase in temperature of ionic solids can be explained in terms of defects in the crystal structure. These defects, which arise when ions are missing or out of place, make it easier for ions to move through the solid under the influence of an electrical field. The number of such defects increases sharply with rising temperature, paralleling the increase in conductivity. A few ionic solids, notably the oxides and sulfides of the heavy metals, have a high enough conductivity at room temperature to be classified as semiconductors. Lead sulfide is one such compound; crystals of PbS (galena) were used in the early days of radio as semiconductors. Here again, conductivity in the solid is due to imperfections in the crystal lattice (cf. Chapter 12).

9.6 OTHER TYPES OF IONS

So far in this chapter, we have restricted our discussion of ionic bonding almost exclusively to monatomic ions with noble-gas structures. Before leaving this topic, it is important to point out that there are many monatomic ions which have electronic structures different from those of the noble gases. Again, there are a great many polyatomic ions, i.e., ions containing more than one atom. A few ions in each of these two categories are described here.

Stable Cations with Non-Noble-Gas Structures

The metals located to the right of group 3B in the periodic table have too many valence electrons to achieve a noble-gas structure by losing electrons. Yet, in many of the compounds of these metals, there is evidence for the existence of monatomic positive ions. For example, silver fluoride, AgF, is a high-melting solid (m.p. = 435°C) with a high electrical conductivity in the liquid state. We interpret this evidence to mean that in this compound there are Ag^+ ions, combined with an equal number of F^- ions. The same sort of evidence leads us to believe that the compounds CuCl and $MnCl_2$ are made up of ions (Cu^+ and Cl^-; Mn^{+2} and Cl^-).

The electronic structures of some of the more important ions of the transition and post-transition metals are listed in Table 9.5. It will be noted that the electronic structures of many (e.g., Cu^+, Zn^{+2}, Ag^+, Cd^{+2}, Sn^{+2}, Tl^+, Pb^{+2}) but by no means all (e.g., Mn^{+2}, Fe^{+2}, Co^{+2}, Ni^{+2}, Cu^{+2}) of these ions are characterized by a completed sublevel. Just as such ions as Na^+, Mg^{+2}, and Al^{+3} have the completed p-level characteristic of the noble-gas structure, so Cu^+, Zn^{+2}, Ag^+, and Cd^{+2} have a completed d-level; Sn^{+2}, Pb^{+2}, and Tl^+ have a completed s-level.

TABLE 9.5 MONATOMIC POSITIVE IONS WITH NON-NOBLE-GAS STRUCTURES

Ion	Total e⁻	\multicolumn{6}{c}{Populations of Principal Levels}

Ion	Total e⁻	1st	2nd	3rd	4th	5th	6th
Mn^{+2}	23	2	8	$3s^2\ 3p^6\ 3d^5$			
Fe^{+2}	24	2	8	$3s^2\ 3p^6\ 3d^6$			
Co^{+2}	25	2	8	$3s^2\ 3p^6\ 3d^7$			
Ni^{+2}	26	2	8	$3s^2\ 3p^6\ 3d^8$			
Cu^{+2}	27	2	8	$3s^2\ 3p^6\ 3d^9$			
Cu^+	28	2	8	$3s^2\ 3p^6\ 3d^{10}$			
Zn^{+2}	28	2	8	$3s^2\ 3p^6\ 3d^{10}$			
Ag^+	46	2	8	18	$4s^2\ 4p^6\ 4d^{10}$		
Cd^{+2}	46	2	8	18	$4s^2\ 4p^6\ 4d^{10}$		
Sn^{+2}	48	2	8	18	$4s^2\ 4p^6\ 4d^{10}$	$5s^2$	
Tl^+	80	2	8	18	32	$5s^2\ 5p^6\ 5d^{10}$	$6s^2$
Pb^{+2}	80	2	8	18	32	$5s^2\ 5p^6\ 5d^{10}$	$6s^2$

It should be emphasized that although many of the transition and post-transition metals are capable of forming positive ions such as those listed above, the bonding in many of their compounds is not primarily ionic. We find that many of the binary compounds of these metals have melting points and electrical conductivities in the liquid state which are inconsistent with a simple ionic structure. An example of such a compound is $\underline{GaCl_3}$; though we might be tempted to postulate the existence of discrete Ga^{+3} ions in this compound, the experimental evidence clearly shows it to be molecular rather than ionic in nature.

Polyatomic Ions

Many of the ions most frequently encountered in inorganic chemistry contain more than one atom. The structures of ions of this type will be discussed in Chapters 10 and 19. The names and charges of a few of the more common polyatomic ions are given in Table 9.6.

TABLE 9.6 POLYATOMIC IONS

Ammonium, NH_4^+	Hydrogen sulfate, HSO_4^-	Dichromate, $Cr_2O_7^{-2}$	Phosphate, PO_4^{-3}
Mercurous, Hg_2^{+2}	Hydrogen carbonate, HCO_3^-	Chromate, CrO_4^{-2}	
	Hydroxide, OH^-	Sulfate, SO_4^{-2}	
	Nitrate, NO_3^-	Sulfite, SO_3^{-2}	
	Chlorate, ClO_3^-	Carbonate, CO_3^{-2}	
	Perchlorate, ClO_4^-	Peroxide, O_2^{-2}	
	Acetate, $C_2H_3O_2^-$		
	Cyanide, CN^-		
	Permanganate, MnO_4^-		

9.7   SUMMARY

When elements react with each other, their atoms tend to acquire stable electronic configurations. One of the most important of these is the noble-gas structure. In this chapter, we have considered one way in which atoms of reacting elements can attain this structure: the transfer of electrons from metal to nonmetal atoms to give $+$ and $-$ ions. A simple example of such a process is the interaction between atoms of sodium and fluorine to give Na^+ and F^- ions, both of which have the electronic structure of the noble gas neon:

$$Na\cdot(2, 8, 1) + \overset{\cdot\cdot}{:}\underset{\cdot}{F}:(2, 7) \longrightarrow Na^+(2, 8) + (\overset{\cdot\cdot}{:}\underset{\cdot\cdot}{F}:)^-(2, 8)$$

Ionic compounds are commonly formed by the transfer of electrons from metal atoms with 1, 2, or 3 valence electrons to nonmetal atoms having 6 or 7 valence electrons. For example, the elements lithium, magnesium, and aluminum react with fluorine and oxygen to form ionic compounds of formulas LiF, Li_2O, MgF_2, MgO, AlF_3, and Al_2O_3.

The relative sizes of different ions may be deduced from their electronic structures. Positive ions are always smaller than the atoms from which they are formed; the reverse is true of negative ions. In a series of isoelectronic ions, such as O^{-2}, F^-, Na^+, Mg^{+2}, Al^{+3}, ionic radius decreases with increasing nuclear charge. When a metal forms more than one positive ion, the one of higher charge is always the smaller (e.g., Fe^{+3} is smaller than Fe^{+2}). Within a given group of the periodic table, the ionic radius ordinarily increases with increasing atomic number.

Ionic compounds are solids at room temperature, reflecting the strong electrical forces holding them together. Their melting points depend upon the sizes and charges of the ions of which they are composed. In general, it is found, as Coulomb's Law (equation 9.12) predicts, that the melting point increases as the charges of the ions increase and their radii decrease. Another characteristic property of ionic compounds is their ability to conduct a current when melted.

Although the transition and post-transition metals show less tendency to form ions than do the metals in groups 1A and 2A, certain binary compounds of these metals are ionic. The positive ions in these compounds do not, of course, have noble-gas structures. In several cases, however, ions of these metals are found to have electronic structures in which the outermost sublevel (d or s) is completely filled.

PROBLEMS

9.1   Predict the formula of the ionic compound formed by:
    a. Magnesium and hydrogen c. Potassium and astatine   e. Lithium and tellurium
    b. Scandium and sulfur   d. Barium and oxygen   f. Lanthanum and oxygen

9.2   Give the electronic structures, by sublevels, for each of the following:
    Rb^+, Sc^{+3}, Ca^{+2}, Cu^+, In^+, Y^{+3}, Cr^{+2}, Cl^-, Se^{-2}, O^{-2}, Br^-

9.3   A certain element of atomic number 37 exists in all its compounds as a $+1$ ion. Without referring to the periodic table, give the atomic numbers of:
    a. Two other elements which form cations with this same electronic structure.
    b. Two other elements which form anions with this same electronic structure.
    c. An element whose atoms have this same electronic structure.
    d. Three other elements which form $+1$ ions of smaller radius than that formed by element 37.
    e. Two other elements which form $+1$ ions of larger radius than that formed by element 37.

9.4   Complete and balance the following equations:
    a. $Na(s) + S(s) \longrightarrow$
    b. $K(s) + I_2(s) \longrightarrow$
    c. $Al(s) + O_2(g) \longrightarrow$
    d. $Ba(s) + F_2(g) \longrightarrow$
    e. $Sr(s) + O_2(g) \longrightarrow$

9.5   Give the simplest formula of each of the following compounds.
    a. Ammonium bromide   d. Scandium acetate   g. Calcium hydroxide
    b. Ammonium sulfate   e. Aluminum nitrate   h. Nickel chloride
    c. Magnesium carbonate f. Lithium phosphate   i. Zinc sulfate

9.6   For each of the following sets of ions and atoms, indicate, without referring to Table 9.3, which you would expect to have the largest radius.
    a. Na^+, Ne, F^- c. Mg, Al^{+3}, Mg^{+2} e. Co^{+2}, Ni^{+2}, Fe^{+2}
    b. K^+, Ca^{+2}, Sc^{+3} d. Cl^-, Cl, S^{-2} f. Zn, Zn^{+2}, Cd

9.7   Referring to Table 9.3 and using the rule that anion-anion contact will occur when the radius ratio of cation to anion is less than 0.41, determine in which of the following alkali halides the anions will be touching.
    a. NaF   b. NaI   c. LiBr   d. KI   e. LiCl

9.8   Predict which member of each of the following pairs will have the higher melting point.
    a. NaCl or NaBr   c. CaO or KCl   e. KI or NaBr
    b. ZnO or ZnS   d. BaO or CaO   f. LiF or NaI

9.9   Explain why the electrical conductivity of ionic compounds increases sharply when they are melted.

9.10 Referring to Figure 9.1:
   a. Calculate the volume, in cc., of a cube containing 10^8 Na^+ ions and 10^8 F^- ions along each edge.
   b. How many Na^+ and F^- ions would there be in this cube?
   c. Using the atomic weights of sodium and fluorine in combination with Avogadro's number, calculate the mass of the ions in this cube.
   d. Combining the results of (a) and (c), calculate the density of sodium fluoride. The observed density is 2.79 g./cc.

*9.11 Ionic compounds, in either the solid or the liquid state, are relatively poor conductors of heat, in comparison to metals. Suggest an explanation for this (cf. Chapter 11, Section 11.5).

*9.12 Ionic compounds are extremely brittle; when struck sharply with a hammer, an ionic crystal shatters. Suggest an explanation for this (cf. Chapter 11, Section 11.5).

*9.13 Above 450°C, cesium chloride has the structure shown in Figure 9.1. Below 450°C, cesium chloride crystallizes in a different pattern in which the lattice can be considered to be made up of Cl^- ions arranged in a simple cubic structure with Cs^+ ions at the center of each cube formed by eight Cl^- ions. Can you suggest why the structure of cesium chloride changes in this way?

*9.14 In the text, it was stated that if the radius ratio of cation to anion was less than about 0.41, one would have anion-anion rather than cation-anion contact in a crystal of the type shown in Figure 9.1. Derive, by simple geometry, the precise value of the radius ratio for which there will be both cation-anion and anion-anion contact.

10

COVALENT BONDING: MOLECULAR SUBSTANCES

In Chapter 9, we discussed the formation of ionic bonds by the transfer of electrons from a metal to a nonmetal atom. In this chapter, we shall turn our attention to a quite different type of chemical bond formed by the sharing of pairs of electrons between atoms of the nonmetallic elements. Such electron-pair or **covalent** bonds exist in a wide variety of both elementary and compound substances.

Perhaps the simplest example of the covalent bond is that found in the diatomic hydrogen molecule, whose structure in electron dot notation may be represented as:

$$H : H$$

The two electrons written between the hydrogen nuclei comprise a covalent or electron-pair bond. Each hydrogen atom contributes its unpaired 1s electron to the formation of this bond. It will be noted that in the H_2 molecule, both atoms are surrounded by two electrons, the number present in an atom of the noble gas helium. Covalent bonding, like ionic bonding, frequently results in both atoms acquiring a stable, noble-gas electronic structure.

The diatomic molecules of the halogens (F_2, Cl_2, Br_2, I_2) have electronic structures basically similar to that of the hydrogen molecule. In elementary fluorine, for example, two atoms, each with seven valence electrons, combine to form the F_2 molecule, in which each fluorine atom is surrounded by a total of eight valence electrons:

$$:F: + :F: \longrightarrow :F:F: \tag{10.1}$$

In this way, both atoms acquire the stable electronic configuration of the noble gas neon. Here, as with hydrogen, two identical atoms, each with an unpaired valence electron, in this case, a 2p electron, form a diatomic molecule held together by a covalent bond.

Covalent bonding is by no means restricted to elementary substances. Unlike atoms with unpaired electrons can combine to form molecules containing electron-pair bonds. As a simple example, consider the HF molecule which forms the basic structural unit of gaseous hydrogen fluoride. Here, a hydrogen atom with a single valence electron combines with a fluorine atom (seven valence electrons) to form a diatomic molecule with a covalent bond joining the two atoms:

$$H\cdot \ + \ :\overset{\cdot\cdot}{\underset{\cdot\cdot}{F}}: \ \longrightarrow \ H:\overset{\cdot\cdot}{\underset{\cdot\cdot}{F}}: \tag{10.2}$$

In the HF molecule, as in H_2 and F_2, both atoms acquire a stable noble-gas structure by sharing a pair of electrons.

Covalent bonding need not result in the formation of molecular substances. In certain solids, referred to as *atomic* or *macromolecular* crystals, all the atoms are held together by covalent bonds. The compound substance quartz (silicon dioxide) has a network structure in which each silicon atom is bonded to four oxygens and each oxygen to two silicons. There are no small, discrete molecules in silicon dioxide: there is no break in the interlocking network of silicon to oxygen bonds until the faces of the crystal are reached. Each atom, by sharing electron pairs with its neighbors, acquires a stable octet.

As one might expect, the physical and chemical properties of substances held together by covalent bonds vary widely. In this chapter, we shall devote the major part of our attention to covalent bonding in molecular substances. We shall be interested in relating the properties of such binary molecular compounds as HF, CO_2, SO_2, and H_2O to the electronic structures, shapes, and sizes of their molecules.

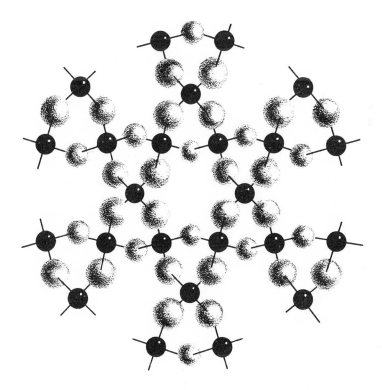

FIGURE 10.1 Crystal structure of silicon dioxide. (Sisler, H. H., *Electronic Structure, Properties and the Periodic Law*, Reinhold Publishing Corporation, New York, 1963.)

10.1   ELECTRON DISTRIBUTION IN THE COVALENT BOND

Bonds between Like Atoms (H_2, F_2)

The electron dot notation for the H_2 molecule: H : H is somewhat misleading insofar as it implies that the two electrons are located in fixed positions between the hydrogen nuclei. The electrons are, of course, in constant motion; at any given moment, they may be located at any of various points in the vicinity of the nuclei.

A more exact picture of the electron distribution in the hydrogen molecule may be derived from quantum mechanics. For this very simple molecule, consisting of two protons and two electrons, it is possible to calculate rather accurately the probability of finding an electron in any given region of the molecule. The results of such a calculation are shown schematically in Figure 10.2.

We see from Figure 10.2 that the electrons are much more likely to be found between the nuclei than at the far ends of the molecule. This situation is frequently described by saying that the electron clouds corresponding to the 1s orbitals of the two hydrogen atoms overlap in the region between the nuclei. Quantum mechanical calculations attribute much of the stability of the covalent bond here and in other molecules to this overlapping of electron clouds.

For the F_2 molecule, containing 18 electrons and an equal number of protons, it is impossible to obtain from quantum mechanics an exact picture of the electron distribution. Nevertheless, one can arrive at a reasonably accurate picture of the bonding electrons. A "density map" for these two 2p electrons, one contributed by each atom, closely resembles that shown in Figure 10.2 for the H_2 molecule. There is a high probability of finding the bonding electrons in the region between the two nuclei. Moveover, they are as likely to be found in the vicinity of one nucleus as the other. The remaining electrons in the molecule appear to be relatively unaffected by the formation of the covalent bond. Half of them still "belong" to one fluorine atom and half to the other.

Bonds between Unlike Atoms (HF)

The electron distribution in the HF molecule differs in one very important respect from that in molecules of elementary hydrogen and fluorine. Experimental evidence indicates that the density of the electron cloud formed by the overlap of the bonding electrons is concentrated in the vicinity of the fluorine nucleus. In other words, the two electrons making up the covalent bond are closer, on the average, to the fluorine than to the hydrogen nucleus. As a result, the fluorine atom carries a

FIGURE 10.2   Electron density in H_2 molecule.

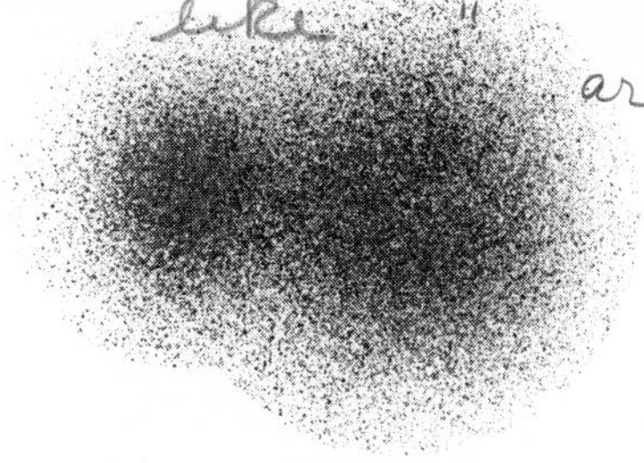

all covalent bond between unlike atoms are polar
" " " like " are non polar

FIGURE 10.3   Electron density in polar molecule
(only valence electrons are shown).

partial negative charge while the hydrogen atom has a partial positive charge of equal
magnitude. The molecule as a whole is electrically neutral.

Covalent bonds such as that in <u>HF</u> in which the <u>shared electrons are unsymmetrically distributed</u> are referred to as **polar.** <u>Symmetrical bonds</u> such as those in
<u>H$_2$</u> and F$_2$ are <u>called</u> **nonpolar.** The polarity of the covalent bond in HF is a
consequence of the fact that fluorine has a greater attraction for electrons than does
hydrogen. Since atoms of two different elements always differ in their affinity for
electrons, covalent bonds between unlike atoms are always polar. Only when the
atoms joined are identical is the bond nonpolar.

H F - polar, because unsymmetrical
H$_2$, F$_2$ nonpolar   "   symmetrical

Extent of Polarity: Electronegativity Values

The extent of polarity of a covalent bond can be interpreted in terms of the
relative electronegativity (attraction for electrons) of the two atoms involved. Where
the atoms are identical, as in the F$_2$ molecule, the difference in <u>electronegativity is
zero and the bond is nonpolar.</u> In the ClF molecule, the bonding electrons are only
slightly displaced toward the fluorine, which has a slightly greater attraction for
electrons than does chlorine. When the two atoms differ widely in electronegativity,
as in the HF molecule, the polarity of the bond is much more pronounced.

An ionic bond may be regarded as an extreme case of a polar covalent bond in
which the bonding electrons are so much closer to the more electronegative atom
that, for all practical purposes, an electron transfer has taken place. The term
partial ionic character is often used to describe the extent of polarity of a covalent bond.
Thus, we may say that the bond joining two different atoms is 50 per cent ionic to
indicate that it is halfway between a pure ionic and a nonpolar covalent bond.
In another case, in which the atoms involved differ more widely in electronegativity,
the bond may be described as 90 per cent ionic, implying that the transfer of electrons
to the more electronegative element is virtually complete.

The attraction of an element for electrons can be measured in various ways.
One method, based on the strength of the bond formed between two different
elements, leads to an electronegativity scale first suggested by Professor Pauling.
On this scale, each element is assigned an *electronegativity value* ranging from 0.7 to
4.0. The larger the electronegativity value of an element, the greater is its attraction
for bonding electrons. <u>Fluorine,</u> the element whose atoms most strongly attract
electrons, has the <u>highest electronegativity value, 4.0.</u> Electronegativity increases
from left to right in a given period of the periodic table and decreases as one moves
down a given group.

A scale of relative electronegativities can be used to estimate the partial ionic
character of a bond. The greater the difference in electronegativity between two
elements, the more ionic will be the bond joining them. The relationship between these

E. N   increase →
decrease

H						
2.1						

Li	Be	B	C	N	O	F
1.0	1.5	2.0	2.5	3.0	3.5	4.0

Na	Mg	Al	Si	P	S	Cl
0.9	1.2	1.5	1.8	2.1	2.5	3.0

K	Ca	Sc	Ge	As	Se	Br
0.8	1.0	1.3	1.8	2.0	2.4	2.8

Rb	Sr	Y	Sn	Sb	Te	I
0.8	1.0	1.2	1.8	1.9	2.1	2.5

Cs	Ba	La–Lu	Pb	Bi	Po	At
0.7	0.9	1.0–1.2	1.9	1.9	2.0	2.2

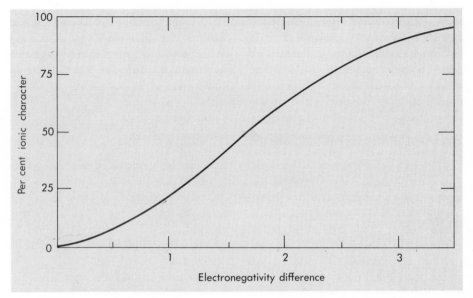

FIGURE 10.4   Top part of figure shows values of electronegativity of some of the elements. Lower portion shows relation between amount of ionic character in a chemical bond and electro-negativity difference of bonded atoms.

two variables is shown graphically in Figure 10.4. A difference of 1.7 electronegativity units corresponds to a bond that has approximately 50 per cent ionic character.

It is clearly an oversimplification to refer to a bond between two elements as being ionic or covalent. Consider, for example, the bonding in compounds formed by the reaction of a 1A or 2A metal with a nonmetal in group 6A or 7A. The difference in electronegativity values ranges from a minimum of 0.6 for the beryllium-tellurium pair to a maximum of 3.3 for cesium and fluorine. The percentage of ionic character in the bonds formed between these pairs of elements shows a corresponding variation, ranging from about 10 per cent for BeTe to 95 per cent for CsF.

The difference in electronegativity between oxygen or fluorine on the one hand and a 1A or 2A metal on the other in all cases exceeds 1.7 units, the value correspond-ing to 50 per cent ionic character. In this sense, the bonding in the oxides and fluorides of these metals is predominantly ionic. The same statement applies to the oxide and fluoride of aluminum in group 3A, where electronegativity differences of 2.0 and 2.5 units correspond to about 65 per cent and 80 per cent ionic character in Al_2O_3 and AlF_3 respectively. The situation is quite different with the chloride,

bromide, and iodide of aluminum; in each of these three compounds, electronegativity differences less than 1.7 units imply that the bonding is predominantly
covalent.

10.2 ELECTRONIC STRUCTURES OF SOME SIMPLE MOLECULES

It is possible to deduce the formulas and electronic structures of a great many
molecular substances by making use of the fact that atoms, in sharing electrons to
form covalent bonds, tend to acquire noble-gas structures. The application of this
simple principle is particularly straightforward in the case of the molecular compounds formed by hydrogen with the nonmetals in groups 4A, 5A, 6A, and 7A of the
periodic table.

The large number of binary compounds formed between hydrogen and the
nonmetals are invariably molecular in nature. In each case, the hydrogen atom,
with its single unpaired electron, achieves the electronic structure of helium by
acquiring a share in a second electron contributed by a nonmetal atom. With the
halogens, this leads to the formation of diatomic molecules of general formula HX:

$$H \circ + \; :\ddot{X}: \;\longrightarrow\; H \!\circ\! \ddot{X}: \qquad (HF, HCl, HBr, HI) \qquad (10.3)$$

($\circ$ = electron supplied by hydrogen, $\cdot$ = electron supplied by halogen)

It will be noted that the fluorine atom in the hydrogen fluoride molecule is surrounded
by a stable octet of electrons, as is the case in the fluoride ion. The major difference
is that in forming the HF molecule, fluorine acquires a share in eight electrons; in the
F$^-$ ion, it has complete control over all eight electrons.

When hydrogen combines with an element such as oxygen in group 6A with
six valence electrons, two hydrogen atoms, each with one valence electron, must
combine with a single nonmetal atom in order to give a noble-gas structure. The
resulting molecule contains two covalent bonds:

$$2\,H \circ + \; :\ddot{O}: \;\longrightarrow\; H \!\circ\! \ddot{O} \!\circ\! H \qquad (H_2O, H_2S, H_2Se, H_2Te) \qquad (10.4)$$

An atom of a 5A element with five valence electrons must acquire a share in 3 more
electrons to reach a stable octet. We find that three atoms of hydrogen are required
to satisfy an atom of an element such as nitrogen:

$$3\,H \circ + \; :\dot{\ddot{N}}\cdot \;\longrightarrow\; \begin{matrix} H \\ \circ\cdot \\ H \!\circ\! N \!\circ\! H \\ \cdot\cdot \end{matrix} \qquad (NH_3, PH_3, AsH_3, SbH_3, BiH_3) \qquad (10.5)$$

A similar argument explains the formation of compounds such as methane, CH_4,
and silane, SiH_4, formed by hydrogen with the 4A elements:

$$4\,H \circ + \; \cdot\dot{C}\cdot \;\longrightarrow\; \begin{matrix} H \\ \circ\cdot \\ H \!\circ\! C \!\circ\! H \\ \circ\cdot \\ H \end{matrix} \qquad (10.6)$$

In writing the electronic structures of molecules such as these, the electron pair forming the covalent bond is often represented by a straight line joining the two atoms. For HF, H_2O, NH_3, and CH_4, we have:

$$H—\overset{..}{\underset{..}{F}}: \qquad H—\overset{..}{\underset{..}{O}}—H \qquad H—\overset{..}{\underset{\underset{H}{|}}{N}}—H \qquad H—\overset{\overset{H}{|}}{\underset{\underset{H}{|}}{C}}—H$$

Water and ammonia are not the only compounds which hydrogen forms with the elements oxygen and nitrogen. The less stable compounds, hydrogen peroxide, H_2O_2, and hydrazine, N_2H_4, are also known. Molecules of these substances, like those of water and ammonia, satisfy the requirement that the constituent atoms have noble-gas structures.

$$H—\overset{..}{\underset{..}{O}}—\overset{..}{\underset{..}{O}}—H \qquad\qquad H—\overset{..}{\underset{\underset{H}{|}}{N}}—\overset{..}{\underset{\underset{H}{|}}{N}}—H$$

Herein lies a key to the experimental observation that (two nonmetals frequently form more than one molecular compound.) In covalent bonding, it is often possible for atoms of different elements to acquire noble-gas structures by combining in more than one ratio. A striking illustration is offered by the elements hydrogen and carbon; thousands of different compounds containing only these two elements have been isolated. All of these hydrocarbons, like the simplest member of the series, methane, are built up of molecules in which each atom has a noble-gas structure. Examples include:

| Ethane | Propane | Isooctane |

Atoms of the halogens, like those of hydrogen, require the addition of a single electron to reach a noble-gas structure. Consequently, it is hardly surprising that the halogens should form molecular compounds entirely analogous in formula and electronic structure to the corresponding hydrogen compounds (See Table 10.1).

10.3 ORBITALS USED IN BOND FORMATION: sp³ HYBRID BOND ORBITALS

In Chapter 8, we discussed the electron distribution in nonbonded, gaseous atoms in terms of the atomic orbitals in which the various electrons are located. It will be recalled, for example, that an s sublevel consists of one such orbital, while a p sublevel is divided into three orbitals. Since every orbital has a capacity of two electrons, there are two s electrons and six p electrons associated with each energy level. The principle that, in any incomplete sublevel, there will be as many half-filled orbitals as possible,

TABLE 10.1 ELECTRONIC STRUCTURE OF CHLORINE AND
HYDROGEN COMPOUNDS OF F, O, N, AND C

H Compound	Cl Compound	Compound Containing Both H and Cl
HF H:F:	ClF :Cl—F:	
H$_2$O H—O—H	Cl$_2$O :Cl—O—Cl:	HOCl H—O—Cl:

NH$_3$ H—N—H
        H
	NCl$_3$:Cl—N—Cl:
	        :Cl:
		NH$_2$Cl H—N—Cl:
		        H

H
CH$_4$ H—C—H
        H
	:Cl:
	CCl$_4$:Cl—C—Cl:
	        :Cl:
		H
		CHCl$_3$:Cl—C—Cl:
		        :Cl:

enables one to deduce the following electron distributions for the isolated atoms of the nonmetals in the second period of the periodic table.

	1s	2s	2p		
$_9$F	(· ·)	(· ·)	(· ·)	(· ·)	(·)
$_8$O	(· ·)	(· ·)	(· ·)	(·)	(·)
$_7$N	(· ·)	(· ·)	(·)	(·)	(·)
$_6$C	(· ·)	(· ·)	(·)	(·)	( )

From the diagram, it is apparent that a free fluorine atom has one half-filled 2p orbital and consequently one unpaired electron. Similarly, atoms of oxygen, nitrogen, and carbon have two, three, and two unpaired electrons respectively.

The question arises whether this concept of atomic orbitals can be extended to describe the electron distribution in bonded atoms. This question can be answered in the affirmative; indeed, our only justification for introducing atomic orbitals in the first place was to explain or at least rationalize the formation of electron-pair bonds. Unfortunately, the way in which these orbitals are utilized in bonding is not nearly as straightforward as was once assumed.

Simplified Picture of Bonding Orbitals

From the simplest point of view, one can expect covalent bond formation to take place when atoms with half-filled orbitals come together. For example, two fluorine atoms, each with a half-filled 2p orbital, combine to give a stable diatomic molecule in which all the electrons are paired. Again, when a hydrogen atom with a half-filled 1s orbital approaches a fluorine atom possessing a half-filled 2p orbital, the electron clouds of these two orbitals overlap to give the stable covalent bond that holds the

HF molecule together. On the other hand, atoms of helium and neon, neither of which have any half-filled orbitals, show no tendency to combine with each other.

Using the foregoing criterion for covalent bond formation, it would seem that an atom should form only enough bonds to "pair" all of its unpaired electrons. That is, one electron-pair bond should be formed for every unpaired electron in the isolated atom. Referring to the diagram we can see that this would require that a fluorine atom, with one unpaired electron, form one electron-pair bond. Similarly, an oxygen atom would be expected to form two bonds and a nitrogen atom three. These predictions are confirmed experimentally (cf. Table 10.1). They are also consistent with the octet rule, since the formation of one bond by fluorine, two by oxygen, and three by nitrogen gives these atoms stable octets.

	1s	2s	2p		
$_9$F	(· ·)	(· ·)	(· ·)	(· ·)	[(· ∘)]
$_8$O	(· ·)	(· ·)	(· ·)	[(· ∘)	(· ∘)]
$_7$N	(· ·)	(· ·)	[(· ∘)	(· ∘)	(· ∘)]

(Orbitals involved in bond formation are enclosed by solid lines.)

Following the argument just outlined, the bonds formed by fluorine, oxygen, and nitrogen would be referred to as p bonds, since the bonding electrons occupy p orbitals.

This simple picture breaks down when one attempts to extend it to carbon. From a naïve point of view, the carbon atom, with two unpaired electrons, would be expected to form only two "p" bonds, leaving one 2p orbital vacant. Instead, carbon invariably forms four electron-pair bonds in stable molecules.

One comparatively straightforward way out of this dilemma is to postulate that, prior to bond formation, one of the 2s electrons of carbon is "promoted" to a vacant 2p orbital.

	1s	2s	2p		
$_6$C	(· ·)	(·)	(·)	(·)	(·)

Such a structure, with four unpaired electrons, can account for the formation of four covalent bonds by the carbon atom.

	1s	2s	2p		
$_6$C	(· ·)	[(· ∘)	(· ∘)	(· ∘)	(· ∘)]

One might, of course, object that the promotion of a 2s electron to a 2p orbital would be improbable from an energy standpoint. However, it seems likely that the formation of two additional stable bonds would liberate more than enough energy to compensate for that lost in "exciting" the carbon atom prior to reaction.

Hybrid Bond Orbitals

The explanation just offered for the tetracovalency of carbon is unsatisfactory in one respect. It implies that one of these bonds, which could be described as an s bond, should differ inherently from the other three p bonds. Experimentally, it is found that the four bonds formed by carbon in such molecules as CH_4 and CCl_4

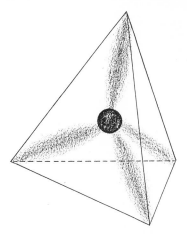

FIGURE 10.5 Electron density in sp³ hybrid orbital.

are identical in every respect. In methane, for example, the four carbon-to-hydrogen bonds have the same length, the same strength, and are oriented in space in the same direction to each other.

The evidence just cited leads us to the conclusion that the four orbitals used for bond formation by the carbon atom must be equivalent to each other. We describe this situation by saying that one s and three p orbitals in the non-bonded carbon atom are "hybridized" to give four new bonding orbitals which are identical with each other. These four orbitals are referred to as **sp³ hybrid** orbitals. It should be clearly understood that even though the sp³ orbitals are formed by combining s and p orbitals, they have their own unique properties, distinct from those of their parents. For example, it can be shown that whereas s orbitals are spherical in nature and p orbitals are directed at right angles to each other, sp³ orbitals are directed toward the corners of a tetrahedron.

There is a good deal of evidence to suggest that sp³ hybridization takes place in many atoms other than those which have four valence electrons. The fact that the bond angles in water and ammonia are very nearly tetrahedral (cf. Section 10.4) suggests that whenever an atom is surrounded by an octet of electrons, the four electron pairs occupy sp³ hybrid orbitals. If the bonds formed by oxygen in water or nitrogen in ammonia were pure p bonds, one would expect them to be oriented at right angles to each other (Figure 8.8).

The stability of sp³ bonding orbitals can be invoked to explain the octet rule which we have found so useful for predicting the formulas of simple molecular substances. By filling four sp³ bonding orbitals, a fluorine, oxygen, nitrogen, or carbon atom surrounds itself with an octet of electrons and thereby attains a stable, noble-gas structure.

In later sections of this chapter and in succeeding chapters, we shall have occasion to refer to other types of hybrid bond orbitals in addition to sp³ hybrids. All such orbitals arise from a particular combination of atomic orbitals. In each case, bonding electrons, by occupying hybrid orbitals, achieve a lower energy than would be the case if they were to fit into the unhybridized orbitals characteristic of individual atoms.

In attempting to describe the electron distribution in molecules, we have focused attention on the atomic orbitals of individual atoms, modifying them in a relatively simple way to arrive at a physical picture of the orbitals occupied by the bonding electrons in a molecule. This approach, known as the *atomic orbital* or *valence bond* method, has the advantage of simplicity and leads to conclusions which are in accord with experimental evidence for many molecules. However, for certain more complex molecules the atomic orbital approach has proved to be unsatisfactory.

Within the past several years, a somewhat more sophisticated approach to covalent bonding, known as the *molecular orbital* treatment, has become popular, particularly with organic chemists. In deriving the electronic structure of a molecule by this method, all the electrons are considered to belong to the molecule as a whole. These electrons are then distributed among a set of energy levels, called molecular orbitals, which are analogous to the atomic orbitals used to describe the energies of electrons in isolated atoms.

To illustrate qualitatively the difference between the two approaches, consider the hydrogen fluoride molecule. The atomic orbital approach considers what happens to the unpaired electrons of hydrogen and fluorine atoms as they approach each other. These atoms are assumed to retain their identity in the molecule, having undergone relatively minor modifications in electronic structure. In the molecular orbital approach, on the other hand, the hydrogen fluoride molecule is considered to be made up of two nuclei with charges of $+1$ and $+9$ respectively surrounded by a total of 10 electrons distributed among molecular orbitals characteristic of the molecule as a whole.

The molecular orbital approach, in principle, is a more exact method of deriving the electron distribution in molecules than is the valence bond approach. In practice, the approximations that must be made to get a meaningful solution to the complex mathematical equations involved in the molecular orbital treatment reduce its validity to a level comparable to that of the valence bond method. For that reason, among others, we shall continue to emphasize the simpler valence bond picture in discussing the electronic structures of molecules. From time to time, however, we will present some of the results of the molecular orbital treatment when they help to clarify problems of molecular structure.

10.4 SIZES AND SHAPES OF MOLECULES

Many of the physical properties of molecular substances are directly related to the sizes and shapes of their molecules. Molecular geometry in turn depends upon the distances between atoms joined by covalent bonds and, when there is more than one bond, upon the angles between bonds.

Covalent Bond Distance

The equilibrium distance of separation of the nuclei in the H_2 molecule can be calculated from spectroscopic data to be 0.74 Å. Dividing this distance by 2 gives a value of 0.37 Å for what is defined as the **covalent radius** of an individual hydrogen atom. It is perhaps not surprising that the covalent radius of hydrogen is significantly

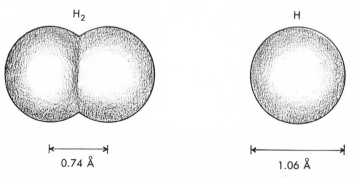

FIGURE 10.6 Dimensions of hydrogen molecule and hydrogen atom.

smaller than the Bohr radius, 0.53 Å. The covalent bond within the H_2 molecule tends to compress the electron cloud and bring the nuclei closer together.

Covalent radii of the halogens may be calculated in much the same way as that of hydrogen, taking one half the interatomic distance in the diatomic halogen molecules. (As one might expect, the covalent radius increases steadily from fluorine (0.64 Å) to iodine (1.33 Å).) It is interesting to compare the covalent radii of these elements to the so-called Van der Waals radii, which are obtained by taking one half the distance between nuclei in adjacent molecules in the crystal. (The Van der Waals radius is roughly twice the covalent radius, reflecting the fact that the forces between molecules are much weaker than the covalent bonds within a molecule.)

By making measurements on the proper substances, it is possible to obtain the covalent radii of all the nonmetals in groups 4A, 5A, and 6A of the periodic table, as well as hydrogen and the halogens. In the case of carbon, for example, one takes half of the interatomic distance in the diamond crystal, in which all the carbon atoms are linked together by covalent bonds. For nitrogen and oxygen, calculation of the covalent radius can be based upon measurements carried out on molecules of hydrazine and hydrogen peroxide, which contain a N—N and an O—O bond respectively. For many of these elements, Van der Waals radii are available as well. Table 10.2 summarizes the data for the various nonmetals.

TABLE 10.2 COVALENT AND VAN DER WAALS RADII OF THE NONMETALS (Å)

	Group 4A Cov.	V.D.W.		Group 5A Cov.	V.D.W.		Group 6A Cov.	V.D.W.		Group 7A Cov.	V.D.W.
C	0.77	—	N	0.70	1.5	O	0.66	1.4	F	0.64	1.4
Si	1.17	—	P	1.10	1.9	S	1.04	1.9	Cl	0.99	1.8
Ge	1.22	—	As	1.21	2.0	Se	1.17	2.0	Br	1.14	2.0
			Sb	1.41	2.2	Te	1.37	2.2	I	1.33	2.2

A comparison of Table 10.2 with Table 9.3 reveals that for the nonmetals, the covalent radius is identical with the atomic radius. Indeed, the atomic radius of a nonmetal is *defined* as its covalent radius. It may be noted further that the Van der Waals radii listed in Table 10.2 are very nearly equal to the ionic radii of the nonmetals listed in Table 9.3. This is perhaps not too surprising; to a chlorine atom in a particular molecule, a second chlorine atom located in an adjacent molecule would "look" very much like a chloride ion, surrounded as it is by eight valence electrons. From this point of view, it is readily understood why, for the nonmetals, the ionic radius (∼ V.D.W. radius) is invariably larger than the atomic radius (≡ covalent radius).

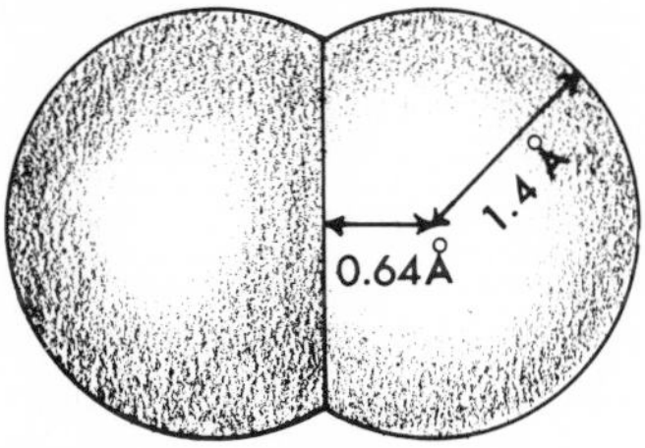

FIGURE 10.7 Dimensions in fluorine molecule. Van der Waals radius = 1.4 Å, covalent radius = 0.64 Å.

The "atomic radii" of the noble gases given in Table 9.3 of the previous chapter are actually Van der Waals radii, determined by measuring the distance between adjacent atoms in the solid forms of these elements. They are, on the average, about 0.3 Å smaller than the Van der Waals radii of the halogens immediately preceding the noble gases in the periodic table (e.g., Ne = 1.12 Å, F = 1.4 Å). The recent discovery of the covalently bonded compounds of the heavier noble gases should make it possible to assign covalent radii to these elements. In the case of xenon, it has been shown experimentally that the Xe—F bond distance in the compound XeF_4 is 1.92 Å. This gives a calculated covalent radius for Xe of 1.28 Å.

$$r\ Xe = d\ Xe{-}F \quad - r\ F$$
$$= 1.92\ \text{Å} \quad - 0.64\ \text{Å} = 1.28\ \text{Å}$$

Significantly, this is 0.05 Å *smaller* than the covalent radius of iodine, the element directly preceding xenon in the periodic table. Clearly, the abnormally high "atomic radii" of the noble gases, referred to earlier, fall into line with those of other elements when measured under comparable conditions.

For the simple molecules discussed in the preceding section, it is found that the distance between two different atoms joined by a covalent bond is very nearly equal to the sum of the two covalent radii. For example, in the HCl molecule, one can calculate a distance of separation of the hydrogen and chlorine nuclei of:

$$0.37\ \text{Å} + 0.99\ \text{Å} = 1.36\ \text{Å}$$

The experimental value is 1.27 Å. In methane, CH_4, and carbon tetrachloride, CCl_4, the agreement is considerably better:

Bond	Internuclear Distance Calculated	Experimental
C—H in CH_4	0.77 Å + 0.37 Å = 1.14 Å	1.10 Å
C—Cl in CCl_4	0.77 Å + 0.99 Å = 1.76 Å	1.76 Å

Bond Angles

From a knowledge of covalent radii alone, it is possible to derive a satisfactory physical picture of diatomic molecules such as H_2, Cl_2, and HCl. However, with molecules such as H_2O, NH_3, and CH_4 which contain more than two atoms, we must be concerned not only with bond distances but with bond angles as well. In the case of the water molecule, for example, it is important to know whether the three atoms are in a straight line, as would be the case if the angle between the two covalent bonds were 180°, or arranged in a triangular pattern, corresponding to a bond angle less than 180°.

For the relatively simple molecules that we have discussed up to this point, one can predict bond angles quite accurately by following the principle that the *four pairs of electrons comprising a stable octet tend to direct themselves towards the corners of a regular tetrahedron*. The simplest way to explain this tendency is to attribute it to a mutual repulsion of the electron clouds containing pairs of electrons; the tetrahedral arrangement is the one which serves to put the four pairs of electrons as far apart as possible. Alternatively, we can adopt the point of view suggested in Section 10.3 that the four valence pairs of the octet occupy sp^3 orbitals; one can show from quantum mechanical calculations that these four hybrid orbitals should be oriented at a tetrahedral angle to each other.

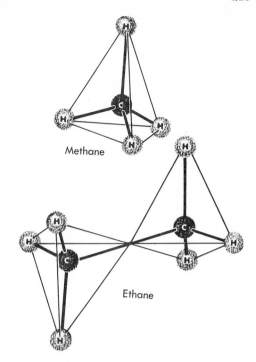

Methane

FIGURE 10.8 Molecular geometry in
methane and ethane.

Ethane

Applying this principle to molecules such as CH_4, CCl_4, or $CHCl_3$, one can
predict that the four bonds formed by the central carbon atom will be at the tetrahedral angle of 109° to each other, which turns out to be the case. Extending this idea
to molecules containing more than one carbon atom, we arrive at spatial arrangements
such as those shown in Figure 10.8.

In a molecule such as NH_3 or NF_3, one would expect to find the three atoms
surrounding the nitrogen at three of the four corners of a tetrahedron with the unshared pair of electrons directed toward the fourth corner. This means that the
four atoms in these molecules would form a pyramid with a triangular base; the
nitrogen atom would be located above the plane of the equilateral triangle formed
by the three hydrogen or fluorine atoms. Experimentally, it is found that the bond
angle in NH_3 is 107° and that in NF_3 is 103°, as compared to the predicted value of
109°. The H—O—H bond angle in water, 105°, is also slightly less than the
tetrahedral angle.

In writing electron dot formulas for molecules, an attempt is often made to
indicate the bond angles. Thus, we have:

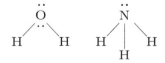

The fact that the bond angles in NH_3 and H_2O are somewhat less than the tetrahedral
angle of 109° has been attributed to the influence of the unshared pairs of electrons in these
molecules. The electron cloud formed by the unshared pair in the NH_3 molecule may be
expected to spread out over a greater volume than that of the three pairs involved in covalent
bond formation. Consequently, it should tend to repel the clouds formed by the bonding
electrons rather more strongly than they repel each other, thereby drawing the three shared
pairs slightly closer together and reducing the angles between them. This effect should be more

pronounced in the H_2O molecule, in which there are two unshared pairs of electrons around the oxygen atom as compared to the lone unshared pair surrounding the nitrogen atom in NH_3.

One might expect the distortion of the tetrahedral angle by unshared electron pairs to be particularly important when bonding electrons are relatively far removed from each other. Under these conditions, repulsive forces between the bonding electrons are relatively weak, and it should be somewhat easier to reduce the bond angle. Experimentally, this prediction is confirmed. Compare, for example, the bond angle of 107° in NH_3 to that of 103° in NF_3. In the latter molecule, the bonding electrons, concentrated around the highly electronegative fluorine atoms located at the far corners of the molecule, are much farther apart than in NH_3. Again, consider the PH_3 molecule, in which both the increased size and reduced electronegativity of the central atom (P vs. N) tends to drive the three pairs of bonding electrons apart and thereby weaken the repulsive forces between them. The H—P—H bond angle in PH_3 is only 93°, some 14° less than the H—N—H angle in NH_3. A similar effect may explain why the bond angles in H_2S, H_2Se, and H_2Te (92°, 91°, 89°) are so much smaller than that in H_2O (105°).

Polarity of Molecules

We have previously considered the polarity of covalent bonds: now that we have some idea of the spatial distribution of atoms in molecules, we are in a position to consider the polarity of molecules themselves. A polar molecule is one in which there is a separation of positive and negative charge, that is, $+$ and $-$ poles. A simple example is the HF molecule; the fact that the bonding electrons are somewhat closer to the fluorine atom gives it a partial negative charge, while the hydrogen atom acts as a positive pole. In general, any diatomic molecule in which the two atoms differ from each other will be polar. The more electronegative atom will act as a negative pole, while the less electronegative atom serves as the positive pole. Examples include HCl and HF; in both cases, the atom written last in the formula acts as the negative pole. Only when the atoms joined are identical, as in the elementary substances hydrogen and fluorine, will diatomic molecules (H_2, F_2) be nonpolar.

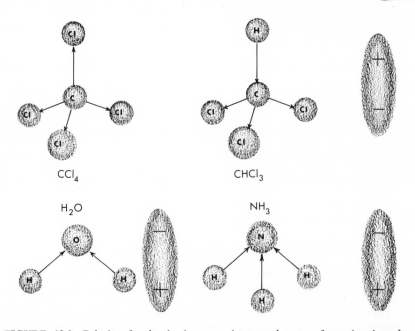

CCl₄   CHCl₃

H₂O   NH₃

FIGURE 10.9 Polarity of molecules (arrows point toward center of negative charge).

When a molecule contains more than two atoms, it is more difficult to decide whether or not it is polar. Here, one must consider not only the polarity of the covalent bonds in the molecule but also the orientation of these bonds with respect to one another. (A symmetrical molecule will be nonpolar even though the bonds within it are polar.) Consider, for example, the CCl_4 molecule. The four carbon to chlorine bonds are polar; the bonding electrons are slightly displaced towards the chlorine atoms. However, since the four chlorines are arranged about the central carbon atom in a symmetrical, tetrahedral pattern, the polar bonds cancel each other. The CCl_4 molecule has no + and − poles; it is nonpolar.

If one of the chlorine atoms in CCl_4 is replaced by a hydrogen, the symmetry of the molecule is destroyed. The chloroform molecule, $CHCl_3$, unlike CCl_4, is polar. Molecules of H_2O and NH_3 are also polar; the geometry here is such that the polar covalent bonds do not compensate for each other. In the H_2O molecule, the negative pole is located at the oxygen atom, while the positive pole is situated midway between the two hydrogen atoms.

One can distinguish polar from nonpolar molecules by studying their behavior in an electrical field. When a substance made up of polar molecules is placed in a field such as that between the plates of a condenser (Figure 10.10), the molecules act as *dipoles*, tending to line up with their positive poles oriented towards the negative plate and their negative poles toward the positive plate. This behavior may be described by saying that the molecule has a **dipole moment** which causes it to turn into a preferred position in an electrical field. Nonpolar molecules, having no permanent centers of positive and negative charge, show little tendency to orient themselves in an electrical field and are said to have a dipole moment of zero.

TABLE 10.3 DIPOLE MOMENTS (DEBYE UNITS)

H_2	0	HF	2.00	H_2O	1.84	CH_3Cl	1.86
Cl_2	0	HCl	1.03	H_2S	0.92	CH_2Cl_2	1.59
CO_2	0	HBr	0.79	NH_3	1.46	$CHCl_3$	1.15
CH_4	0	HI	0.38	PH_3	0.55	CCl_4	0

(A molecule in which unit + and − charges are separated by 0.21 Å has a dipole moment of one Debye Unit.)

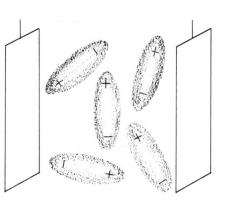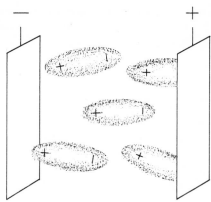

Field off   Field on

FIGURE 10.10 Orientation of polar molecules in electrical field.

10.5 STRUCTURES OF MORE COMPLEX MOLECULES

To this point, our study of molecular substances has been restricted to a few relatively simple molecules. The molecules whose electronic structures, sizes, and shapes we have considered have the following properties in common:

1. They are held together by single covalent bonds; that is, there is a single pair of bonding electrons between each pair of atoms in the molecule.

2. The covalent bonds present are formed by each atom contributing one unpaired electron to the shared pair.

3. Each atom in the molecule has a noble-gas configuration.

There are a great many molecular substances in which one or more of these conditions are not fulfilled. We shall now consider the electronic structures and geometries of some of these molecules.

Ethylene (C_2H_4) and Acetylene (C_2H_2): Multiple Bonds

There are three known hydrocarbons containing two carbon atoms. Ethylene and acetylene, like ethane, which was discussed earlier, are gases at STP. However, they differ from ethane, C_2H_6, in molecular formula, electronic structure and spatial arrangement of atoms.

If we attempt to write electronic structures for C_2H_4 and C_2H_2 molecules analogous to that given in Section 10.2 for ethane, we find that there are not enough valence electrons available to give a single bonded structure in which each atom has a noble-gas configuration. Noting that each carbon atom has four valence electrons and each hydrogen atom one, we might write for C_2H_4:

$$H \overset{\cdot}{\underset{\circ \cdot}{\circ}} C \overset{\cdot}{:} \underset{\circ \cdot}{C} \overset{\cdot}{\circ} H$$
$$H \quad H$$

in which each carbon atom is surrounded by seven valence electrons rather than an octet. A similar structure for C_2H_2:

$$H \overset{\cdot}{\underset{\cdot}{\circ}} C \overset{\cdot}{:} \underset{\cdot}{C} \overset{\cdot}{\circ} H$$

puts only six valence electrons around each carbon atom.

This unsatisfactory situation can be remedied by moving the unshared electrons on each carbon atom into the region between the two nuclei:

$$H \overset{\circ}{:} C : : C \overset{\circ}{:} H \quad \text{and} \quad H \overset{\circ}{:} C : : : C \overset{\circ}{:} H$$
$$H \quad H$$

These structures are consistent with the idea that each atom in the molecule should have a noble-gas electronic configuration. Experimental evidence indicates these structures to be correct. The group of four electrons shared by the two carbon nuclei in the C_2H_4 molecule is referred to as a **double** covalent **bond**; the group of six electrons shared by the two carbon atoms in C_2H_2 is called a **triple bond.** The structures of these molecules may be written:

$$H—C{=}C—H \qquad\qquad H—C{\equiv}C—H$$
$$| \quad |$$
$$H \quad H$$

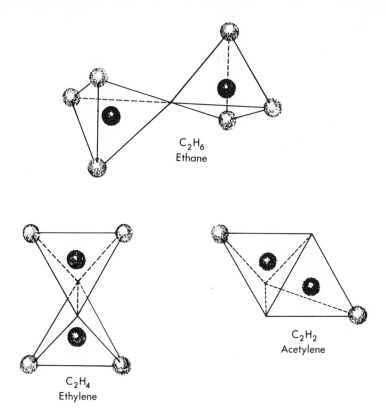

FIGURE 10.11 Molecular geometry in ethane, ethylene, and acetylene: C_2H_6, tetrahedra share a corner; C_2H_4, tetrahedra share an edge; C_2H_2, tetrahedra share a face.

The multiple bonds in ethylene and acetylene have a marked effect on the geometry of the molecules. The distance between the carbon atoms is only 1.20 Å in C_2H_2 and 1.33 Å in C_2H_4 as compared to 1.54 Å in C_2H_6. The shape of the molecule is also affected; C_2H_4 is planar while C_2H_2 is linear.

The spatial arrangement of the atoms in molecules of C_2H_6, C_2H_4, and C_2H_2 may be demonstrated quite simply. If we take two regular tetrahedra and place them next to each other so that two corners coincide, we obtain the ethane molecule. If the tetrahedra are placed so that an edge is shared, the ethylene molecule results; sharing a face gives the acetylene structure with a triple bond between the carbons. It may be noted that sharing an edge brings the two carbon atoms closer together, while sharing a face further reduces the C—C distance. Note also the planar arrangement of atoms in C_2H_4 and the linear pattern in C_2H_2 (Figure 10.11).

In studying the structures of molecular substances, we shall encounter many other examples of multiple-bond formation. Atoms of nitrogen, oxygen, and sulfur as well as carbon are capable of forming double or triple bonds. The following general rules apply in all cases:

1. Multiple bonds arise when there are too few valence electrons available to give each atom a noble-gas configuration in a completely single-bonded structure. Double bond formation removes a deficiency of two electrons, triple bond formation a deficiency of four.

2. The distance between two atoms joined by a double or triple bond is less than the single bond distance for the same two atoms. Furthermore, the bond angles are distorted from those observed in single-bonded structures.

Oxides of Sulfur (SO_2, SO_3): Resonance and Coordinate Covalent Bonds

Of the six different oxides of sulfur that have been reported, only the dioxide, SO_2, and the trioxide, SO_3, are sufficiently stable to merit attention in an elementary text. Sulfur dioxide is a gas at room temperature and atmospheric pressure, condensing to a liquid at $-10°C$. Sulfur trioxide is readily obtained in all three physical states; its melting point is $17°C$ and its normal boiling point $45°C$.

Molecules of both these substances are two electrons shy of the number required for a completely single-bonded structure. Sulfur dioxide has 18 valence electrons (six contributed from each atom) while sulfur trioxide has a total of 24. A triatomic molecule in which there are no multiple bonds would require 20 electrons, a molecule in which there are four atoms, 26 (see, for example, the structures of Cl_2O and NCl_3, in Table 10.1). Accordingly, one would expect to find double bonds in both SO_2 and SO_3:

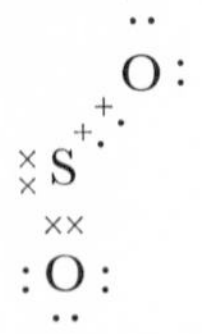

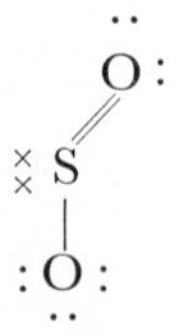

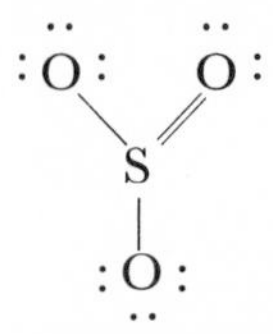

The structures written here do not provide an entirely satisfactory explanation of the properties of these molecules. On the basis of the proposed structure for SO_2, one would expect the distances between the sulfur atom and the two oxygens to differ. The sulfur should be closer to the double-bonded oxygen than to the oxygen attached by a single bond. Experimentally, it is found that the two bond distances are exactly the same.

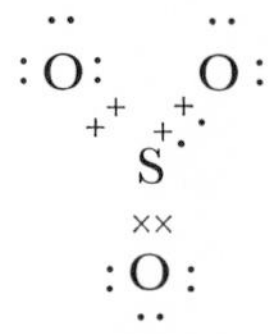

The sulfur to oxygen distance in SO_2, 1.43 Å, is intermediate between that calculated for a single and a double bond. This suggests that each of the bonds in the SO_2 molecule is a "hybrid," intermediate between a single and a double bond. There is no simple way to indicate this in writing the electronic structure of the molecule. What is commonly done is to write two structures:

with the understanding that the actual electronic structure is intermediate between these. Structures such as these are referred to as **resonance** forms. The word resonance is used to describe the phenomenon in which a single electronic structure does not suffice to describe the properties of a substance.

A similar situation arises with SO_3; experimental evidence indicates that all three bonds in the molecule are equivalent. The sulfur to oxygen distance is the same in all three cases. Furthermore, the molecule has a dipole moment of zero, which indicates that it must have a completely symmetrical structure. This evidence is interpreted to mean that the three resonance forms:

$$:\ddot{O} \qquad \ddot{O}: \qquad :\ddot{O} \qquad \ddot{O}: \qquad :\ddot{O} \qquad \ddot{O}:$$

$$\overset{\diagdown}{\underset{\displaystyle :\ddot{O}:}{S}}{}^{\diagup} \quad \longleftrightarrow \quad \overset{\diagdown}{\underset{\displaystyle :\ddot{O}:}{S}}{}^{\diagup} \quad \longleftrightarrow \quad \overset{\diagdown}{\underset{\displaystyle :\ddot{O}:}{S}}{}^{\diagup}$$

make equal contributions to the actual structure of the molecule. We may say that each bond in SO_3 has "$\frac{1}{3}$ double bond" and "$\frac{2}{3}$ single bond" character.

The concept of resonance can be applied to many molecules discussed previously. For example, instead of saying that the bond in HF is "60 per cent ionic," we could describe the situation by saying that this molecule is a resonance hybrid of the two forms:

$$H : \ddot{F} : \quad \longleftrightarrow \quad H^+(:\ddot{F}:)^-$$

Covalent   Ionic

in which the ionic form makes a 60 per cent contribution to the actual structure of the molecule.

We shall encounter many other examples of molecules whose electronic structures can best be represented as hybrids of two or more resonance forms. It should be clearly understood that resonance forms do not imply different kinds of molecules. Sulfur trioxide contains only one type of molecule whose electronic structure is intermediate among those of the three resonance forms written here.

One other aspect of the electronic structures of the SO_2 and SO_3 molecules is worthy of attention; the source of the bonding electrons. Referring to the foregoing electron dot structures, it may be noted that in each case the two electrons forming a single covalent bond between sulfur and oxygen are supplied by the sulfur atom. This contrasts with the bonds previously discussed in which each atom contributes one electron to the shared pair. A bond formed by electrons supplied by a single atom is referred to as a **coordinate covalent bond.**

One of the important consequences of coordinate covalent bonding is its tendency to increase the number of bonds formed by the atom furnishing the electrons. Consider, for example, the sulfur atom with its six valence electrons. Sulfur, by utilizing its two unpaired electrons to form two ordinary covalent bonds, surrounds itself with eight valence electrons, thereby acquiring a noble-gas structure. This happens, for example, in the formation of the H_2S molecule:

$$\cdot \ddot{S} \cdot + 2\, H \circ \longrightarrow H \overset{\cdot\cdot}{\underset{\cdot\cdot}{S}} H$$

Two unshared pairs of electrons remain on the sulfur atom. If one of these pairs of electrons is used to form a coordinate covalent bond, as in SO_2, the total number of bonds formed by sulfur is increased to three. If both pairs are used, as in SO_3, the sulfur atom forms four bonds, two of which are of the coordinate covalent type.

A similar situation arises with a halogen atom, which has seven valence electrons. A bromine atom can acquire a noble-gas structure by forming a single covalent bond as in molecules of Br_2, HBr, or CBr_4. This leaves the bromine with three unshared pairs of electrons, one or more of which may be used to form a coordinate covalent bond. In aluminum bromide (molecular formula Al_2Br_6, simplest formula $AlBr_3$):

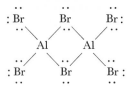

each of the two central bromine atoms forms two bonds, one of which is of the coordinate covalent type. In this way, the bromine atoms serve as a bridge holding the molecule together.

Oxides of Carbon (CO, CO_2)

Both of the common oxides of carbon are gases at room temperature and atmospheric pressure. Carbon dioxide is unusual in that the liquid is stable only at pressures above 1 atm.; the solid (Dry Ice) sublimes at $-78°C$ at atmospheric pressure.

In both oxides, the number of valence electrons (10 for CO, 16 for CO_2) is four less than that required for a single-bonded structure (14 for a diatomic, 20 for a triatomic molecule). In CO_2, this deficiency can be remedied either by the formation of two double bonds or one triple bond. The actual molecule is a hybrid of the three resonance forms:

$$: O{=}C{-}\ddot{O}: \longleftrightarrow :\ddot{O}{=}C{=}\ddot{O}: \longleftrightarrow :\ddot{O}{-}C{\equiv}O:$$

The principal contribution is made by the symmetrical, double-bonded structure. The fact that carbon dioxide has no dipole moment shows that the molecule is linear; the two carbon to oxygen dipoles cancel each other.

In the CO molecule, the electron deficiency can be alleviated by the formation of a triple bond:

$$: C{\equiv}O:$$

This is the only structure which can be written to give each atom a noble-gas configuration. It appears, however, that such forms as:

$$: C{=}\ddot{O}: \quad \text{and} \quad : \ddot{C}{-}\ddot{O}:$$

make at least a small contribution. The carbon to oxygen bond distance is somewhat greater than one would predict for a pure triple bond.

Oxides of Nitrogen: Odd Electron Molecules

Of the several known oxides of nitrogen, nitric oxide, a colorless gas which condenses at $-152°C$ to form a blue liquid, is one of the more interesting from a theoretical standpoint. The NO molecule is often described as an "odd electron molecule" since it contains an odd number of valence electrons (11). Clearly, one cannot write a noble-gas electronic configuration for such a molecule. Resonance forms:

$$\cdot \ddot{N}{=}\ddot{O}: \longleftrightarrow :\ddot{N}{=}\ddot{O} \cdot$$
$$\text{(I)} \qquad\qquad \text{(II)}$$

in which the unpaired electron is assigned to either the nitrogen or the oxygen atom have been suggested. Presumably, structure I is more important than structure II, since oxygen is more electronegative than nitrogen.

Nitrogen dioxide, NO_2, like nitric oxide, is an odd-electron molecule; it has a total of 17 valence electrons. The NO_2 molecule is best regarded as a resonance hybrid to which the following structures contribute:

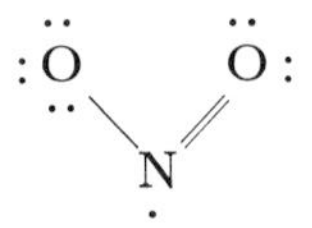

The fact that nitrogen dioxide readily dimerizes to form N_2O_4, whose electronic structure is known to be:

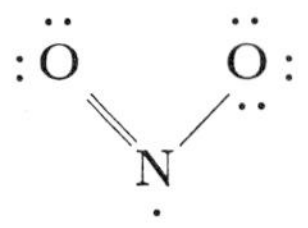

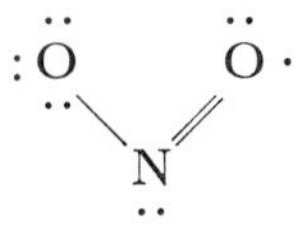

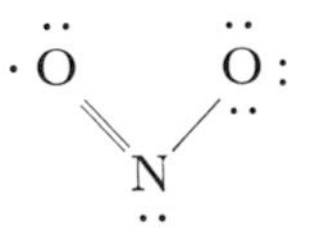

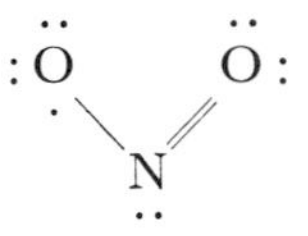

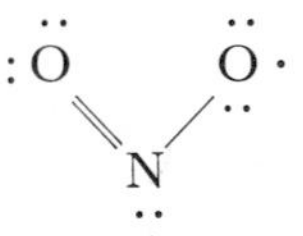

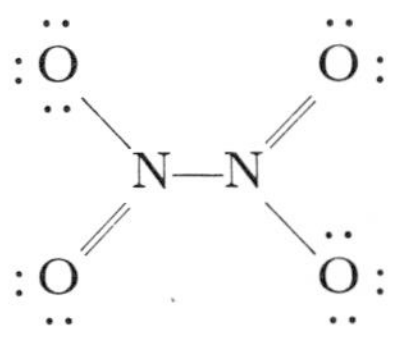

tends to emphasize the importance of structures I and II in which there is an unpaired electron on the nitrogen atom. Dimerization is favored at low temperatures; it is estimated from gas density measurements that at 135°C, 99 per cent of the molecules are in the NO_2 form (brown), while at the boiling point, 21°C, two thirds of the molecules exist as the colorless dimer, N_2O_4.

The existence of molecules such as NO and NO_2 in which there are unpaired electrons can be attributed at least in part to the extensive possibilities for resonance in these molecules. It is known, both from theory and experiment, that substances which are best represented as resonance hybrids are more stable than would otherwise be expected. The bonds in CO_2 and SO_2 are found to be stronger than comparable bonds in other compounds of these elements in which the possibility of resonance does not exist. The extra "resonance energy" is particularly large when, as in NO_2, a large number of approximately equivalent resonance forms contribute to the structure of the molecule.

Of the other oxides of nitrogen, by far the most important is nitrous oxide, N_2O, commonly called "laughing gas." This compound, which may be prepared by gently heating ammonium nitrate:

$$NH_4NO_3(s) \longrightarrow N_2O(g) + 2\ H_2O(g) \tag{10.7}$$

is used as a pressurizing gas in "instant whip" cream, where its high solubility in water and low chemical reactivity are utilized. The N_2O molecule is believed to be a resonance hybrid:

$$:N{=}N{=}\overset{..}{O}: \longleftrightarrow :N{\equiv}N{-}\overset{..}{\underset{..}{O}}:$$

Halides of Boron and Beryllium: sp^2 and sp Hybrid Orbitals

The physical properties of boron trifluoride, notably its volatility (m.p. = $-129°C$, b.p. = $-99°C$) and extremely low conductivity in the liquid state, reveal it to be a molecular rather than an ionic compound. Gas density measurements on the vapor indicate a molecular weight of 68, corresponding to the molecular formula BF_3. Spectroscopic studies have shown that the BF_3 molecule is planar, with three equivalent boron to fluorine bonds oriented at angles of 120° to each other.

By following a line of reasoning analogous to that used in Section 10.3 to explain the bonding in carbon compounds, one can arrive at a picture of the electron distribution in the BF_3 molecule consistent with the experimental evidence already cited. An isolated boron atom has the orbital electronic structure

	1s	2s	2p		
$_5B$	$(\cdot\,\cdot)$	$(\cdot\,\cdot)$	$(\cdot\ )$	$(\ )$	$(\ )$

By promoting one of the 2s electrons to an unfilled 2p orbital, we arrive at a structure which explains why boron forms three bonds

	1s	2s	2p		
$_5B$	$(\cdot\,\cdot)$	$(\cdot\ )$	$(\cdot\ )$	$(\cdot\ )$	$(\ )$

If we now hybridize the 2s and two of the 2p orbitals to form a total of three equivalent sp^2 hybrid bond orbitals, we can explain why the three bonds formed by boron in BF_3 are equivalent

	1s	2s	2p		
$_5B$	$(\cdot\,\cdot)$	$(\cdot\,\circ)$	$(\cdot\,\circ)$	$(\cdot\,\circ)$	$(\ )$

It can be shown from quantum mechanical calculations that three hybrid sp^2 orbitals should be oriented at angles of 120° to each other. Alternatively, one can consider that the angle of 120° is exactly that required to put the three sp^2 orbitals as far apart as possible, just as the tetrahedral angle represents the manner in which four sp^3 orbitals can be located as far from each other as possible.

From the foregoing diagram, it is obvious that boron, in forming three covalent bonds with fluorine, does not acquire a noble-gas structure. Looking at the electron dot representation of the BF_3 molecule,

$$
\begin{array}{ccc}
:\overset{\cdot\cdot}{F} & & \overset{\cdot\cdot}{F}: \\
\cdot\cdot\diagdown & & \diagup\cdot\cdot \\
 & B & \\
 & | & \\
 & :\overset{}{F}: & \\
 & \cdot\cdot &
\end{array}
$$

one would predict that boron trifluoride would have a strong tendency to acquire a stable octet of electrons by forming a fourth covalent bond. This is precisely what happens when BF_3 is brought in contact with ammonia; a solid addition compound, BF_3NH_3

$$
\begin{array}{cccc}
 & :\overset{\cdot\cdot}{F}: & H & \\
 & | & | & \\
:\overset{\cdot\cdot}{F}-B & : & N-H & \\
 & | & | & \\
 & :\overset{}{F}: & H & \\
 & \cdot\cdot & &
\end{array}
$$

is formed, in which there is a coordinate covalent bond between the boron and nitrogen atoms. The geometry of this molecule is similar to that of ethane; the boron atom is located at the center of a tetrahedron surrounded by four stable sp^3 orbitals.

Beryllium, like boron, forms a volatile fluoride. The vapor consists of BeF_2 molecules in which the two beryllium-fluorine bonds are of the same length and are oriented at an angle of $180°$ to each other.

$$: \overset{..}{\underset{..}{F}}-Be-\overset{..}{\underset{..}{F}} :$$

The bonds in BeF_2 are best described as "sp" hybrids; the electrons involved in bond formation occupy two hybrid orbitals formed by combining one 2s orbital with one 2p orbital of the isolated beryllium atom.

		1s	2s	2p		
isolated atom:	$_4$Be	$(\cdot\,\cdot)$	$(\cdot\,\cdot)$	$(\ )$	$(\ )$	$(\ )$
promotion of e$^-$:	$_4$Be	$(\cdot\,\cdot)$	$(\cdot\ )$	$(\cdot\ )$	$(\ )$	$(\ )$
sp hybrid bonds:	$_4$Be	$(\cdot\,\cdot)$	$(\cdot\,\circ)$	$(\cdot\,\circ)$	$(\ )$	$(\ )$

Here again, as in sp^3 and sp^2 hybridization, the sp orbitals orient themselves so as to be as far apart as possible. With only two orbitals involved, this amounts to a linear orientation, i.e., an angle of $180°$ between the orbitals.

The concept of sp^2 and sp hybrid orbitals can be applied to certain of the molecules which we have considered previously. In particular, one can explain the planar nature of the ethylene molecule and the linearity of the acetylene molecule by assuming the existence in these substances of sp^2 and sp hybridization respectively. This would mean that three of the bonds formed by carbon in C_2H_4 would be sp^2 hybrids; the other bond between the carbon atoms would be a p bond formed by the overlap of the p orbitals of the double-bonded atoms. In the case of acetylene, C_2H_2, we would have two sp hybrid bonds, one joining carbon to hydrogen, the other between the two carbon atoms. The two remaining bonds in the acetylene molecule, linking the two carbon atoms, would be pure p bonds.

$$\begin{array}{cc} H & H \\ \diagdown & \diagup \\ & C=C \\ \diagup & \diagdown \\ H & H \end{array} \qquad\qquad H-C\equiv C-H$$

— = sp^2 bond   — = sp bond
— = p bond   — = p bond

Halides of Sulfur and Phosphorus: Use of d Orbitals in Bonding

The nonmetals in the second period of the periodic table (F, O, N, C) almost always achieve a stable, noble-gas electronic configuration as a result of covalent bond formation. They do this, as we have seen, by utilizing a 2s and three 2p orbitals. Exceptions to the octet rule are more numerous with the nonmetals of the third period. Atoms of these elements have low-lying 3d orbitals which can be used for bonding in addition to the 3s and 3p orbitals. Consequently, we find that these elements, particularly phosphorus and sulfur, form several stable molecules in which the central, nonmetal atom is surrounded by more than four pairs of valence electrons.

On the basis of the octet rule, one would predict that the reaction of phosphorus with chlorine would lead to the formation of a compound of molecular formula PCl_3.

$$: \overset{\displaystyle \cdot}{\underset{\displaystyle \cdot}{P}} \cdot \qquad 3 : \overset{\displaystyle \cdot \cdot}{\underset{\displaystyle \cdot \cdot}{Cl}} \cdot \longrightarrow \quad : \overset{\displaystyle \cdot \cdot}{\underset{\displaystyle \cdot \cdot}{Cl}} - \underset{\displaystyle | }{P} - \overset{\displaystyle \cdot \cdot}{\underset{\displaystyle \cdot \cdot}{Cl}} :$$

$$: \overset{\displaystyle \cdot \cdot}{\underset{\displaystyle \cdot \cdot}{Cl}} :$$

Phosphorus trichloride is indeed formed when chlorine gas is bubbled through molten phosphorus. However, if this compound is exposed to chlorine at room temperature, further reaction occurs to give phosphorus pentachloride, PCl_5.

$$PCl_3(l) + Cl_2(g) \longrightarrow PCl_5(s) \qquad\qquad (10.8)$$

In forming the PCl_5 molecule, a phosphorus atom, with five valence electrons, acquires a share in five more electrons contributed by the chlorine atoms, thereby surrounding itself with a total of 10 valence electrons. These electrons occupy one 3s orbital, three 3p orbitals, and a 3d orbital.

3s	3p			3d				
P $(\cdot \circ)$	$(\cdot \circ)$ $(\cdot \circ)$ $(\cdot \circ)$		$(\cdot \circ)$	( )	( )	( )	( )

These bonding orbitals may be described as sp^3d hybrid orbitals. Quantum mechanical calculations suggest that these orbitals should be directed toward the corners of a trigonal bipyramid (Figure 10.12). Such an arrangement also satisfies the requirement that the bonding electrons be as far away each other as possible. Experimentally, it is found that the PCl_5 molecule in both the vapor and liquid states has this structure. The analogous compound PF_5 is known and appears to have the same bonding and geometry as PCl_5.

Sulfur reacts directly with fluorine to give the extremely stable compound sulfur hexafluoride, molecular formula SF_6. In this molecule, it is evident that the sulfur atom must be surrounded by a total of 12 valence electrons, six contributed by the sulfur atom itself and six by the fluorine atoms forming electron-pair bonds with

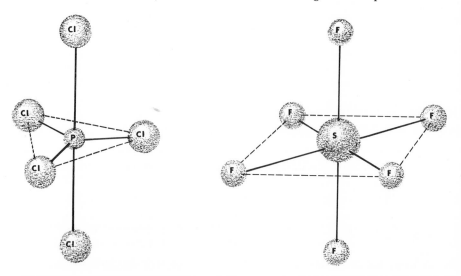

FIGURE 10.12   Molecular geometry in phosphorus pentachloride and sulfur hexafluoride.

sulfur. This requires that two 3d orbitals in addition to a 3s and three 3p orbitals be used in bonding.

	3s	3p				3d		
S	$(\cdot\,\circ)$	$(\cdot\,\circ)$ $(\cdot\,\circ)$ $(\cdot\,\circ)$			$(\cdot\,\circ)$ $(\cdot\,\circ)$	$(\ )$	$(\ )$	$(\ )$

The bonding orbitals used by sulfur in the SF_6 molecule are described as sp^3d^2 hybrids. Again, we find that these orbitals are directed in such a way as to be separated from each other as much as possible. This requirement, with six orbitals, leads to an octahedral structure (Figure 10.12). We shall find in Chapter 19 that this structure is an extremely common one. Indeed, if we were to tabulate the structures of all inorganic ions and molecules, octahedral and tetrahedral configurations taken together would far outnumber all others.

In Table 10.4 are listed the formulas of various nonmetal fluorides in which the central atom is surrounded by more than eight valence electrons.

TABLE 10.4 BINARY FLUORIDES INVOLVING
d ORBITALS

One d Orbital Used			Two d Orbitals Used		
5A	6A	7A	5A	6A	7A
PF_5	SF_4	ClF_3	—	SF_6	—
AsF_5	SeF_4	BrF_3	—	SeF_6	BrF_5
SbF_5	TeF_4	—	—	TeF_6	IF_5

Examining the compounds listed in Table 10.4, one might speculate whether it could be extended to include the noble gases, which lie directly to the right of the halogens in the periodic table. As heretical as this idea might have seemed to chemists of a generation ago, it has recently been found that fluorides of certain of the noble gases can indeed be prepared and have the formulas that one would predict by extrapolation from Table 10.4. Xenon difluoride, XeF_2, analogous in electronic structure to SbF_5, TeF_4 and the so-far unknown compound IF_3, can be prepared from the elements by a photochemical reaction. It is a stable, molecular solid which sublimes without decomposition at 25°C. The compounds KrF_4 and XeF_4, which fall in the series $SeF_6 \rightarrow BrF_5 \rightarrow KrF_4$ and $TeF_6 \rightarrow IF_5 \rightarrow XeF_4$, have also been prepared.

10.6 STRUCTURES OF POLYATOMIC IONS*

In Chapter 9, we mentioned briefly certain species called polyatomic ions, which may be defined as charged particles containing two or more atoms. The atoms within these ions are held together by covalent bonds. The principles that govern the electronic structures, sizes and shapes of polyatomic ions are the same as those which we have used throughout this chapter in discussing molecular structure. Indeed, for every polyatomic ion listed in Table 9.6, it is possible to cite a molecule which has the same electronic structure and geometry.

---

* A particular type of polyatomic ion, known as a complex ion, is discussed in Chapter 19.

Electronic Structure

We can deduce the electronic structure of a polyatomic ion in precisely the way that we have obtained the electronic structures of molecules. The first step is to count the number of valence electrons in the ion, taking into account its charge. The problem then becomes one of distributing these electrons in such a way that each atom acquires a noble-gas structure or other stable electronic configuration.

As a simple example, let us consider the hydroxide ion, OH^-. Since this ion has a charge of -1, it must contain one electron more than those supplied by the neutral atoms (six for oxygen, one for hydrogen). Therefore, the number of valence electrons in the ion must be:

$$6 + 1 + 1 = 8$$

By using two of these electrons to form a covalent bond and assigning the other six to the oxygen atom, we arrive at a structure which gives both atoms a noble-gas configuration:

$$(: \overset{\cdot\cdot}{\underset{\cdot\cdot}{O}}—H)^-$$

It may be noted that the hydroxide ion has the same electronic structure as the HF molecule in which there are also a total of eight valence electrons available (seven from F, one from H).

The hypochlorite ion, ClO^-, offers a slightly more complicated case. Here, there are a total of 14 valence electrons:

$$7 \text{ (from Cl atom)} + 6 \text{ (from O atom)} + 1 \text{ (charge of ion)} = 14$$

This is exactly the number required to give a single-bonded structure in which both atoms have a noble-gas configuration (compare the Cl_2 molecule, which also has 14 valence electrons).

$$(: \overset{\cdot\cdot}{\underset{\cdot\cdot}{O}}—\overset{\cdot\cdot}{\underset{\cdot\cdot}{Cl}} :)^-$$

The electronic structures of the other oxyanions of chlorine, ClO_2^-, ClO_3^-, and ClO_4^-, are readily derived by adding to the ClO^- ion successive oxygen atoms, each with its six valence electrons, so as to make use of the unshared pairs of electrons on the chlorine atom:

$$ClO_2^- \qquad\qquad ClO_3^- \qquad\qquad ClO_4^-$$

For each of these ions, it is possible to cite a neutral molecule with a similar electronic structure. Corresponding to the ClO_4^- ion, for example, is the CCl_4 molecule, which contains the same number of atoms, five, and the same number of valence electrons, 32.

The SO_3^{-2} and SO_4^{-2} ions contain the same number of atoms and valence electrons as the ClO_3^- and ClO_4^- ions respectively. Hence, it is hardly surprising that these oxyanions of sulfur have electronic structures identical with those of the corresponding oxyanions of chlorine:

SO_3^{-2} no. valence $e^- = 6$ (S atom) $+ 3 \times 6$ (3 O atoms) $+ 2$ (charge of ion) $= 26$

SO_4^{-2} no. valence $e^- = 6$ (S atom) $+ 4 \times 6$ (4 O atoms) $+ 2$ (charge of ion) $= 32$

$$(:\overset{..}{\underset{..}{O}}-\overset{..}{S}-\overset{..}{\underset{..}{O}}:)^{-2} \qquad (:\overset{..}{\underset{..}{O}}-\overset{\overset{\overset{..}{O}:}{|}}{S}-\overset{..}{\underset{..}{O}}:)^{-2}$$

$$\qquad :\overset{..}{\underset{..}{O}}: \qquad\qquad\qquad :\overset{..}{\underset{..}{O}}:$$

Counting the number of valence electrons available in the carbonate ion, CO_3^{-2}:

$$4 \text{ (C atom)} + 3 \times 6 \text{ (3 O atoms)} + 2 \text{ (charge of ion)} = 24$$

we find that there are two fewer electrons than the number, 26, required to give each atom a noble-gas configuration in a completely single-bonded structure. It may be recalled that this situation was encountered with the SO_3 molecule. In the CO_3^{-2} ion, as in SO_3, the electron deficiency is remedied by the formation of one double bond; the carbonate ion is a resonance hybrid of the three forms:

$$(:\overset{..}{O}-C=\overset{..}{O}:)^{-2} \longleftrightarrow (:\overset{..}{O}-C-\overset{..}{O}:)^{-2} \longleftrightarrow (:\overset{..}{O}=C-\overset{..}{O}:)^{-2}$$

$$\quad :\overset{..}{\underset{..}{O}}: \qquad\qquad\qquad :\overset{..}{\underset{..}{O}}: \qquad\qquad\qquad :\overset{..}{\underset{..}{O}}:$$

The nitrate ion, NO_3^-, has the same number of valence electrons, 24, as the carbonate ion and is isoelectronic with it.

Perhaps the most familiar polyatomic cation is the ammonium ion, NH_4^+, which occurs as a structural unit in such compounds as ammonium chloride, NH_4Cl, ammonium nitrate, NH_4NO_3, and ammonium sulfate, $(NH_4)_2SO_4$. The electronic structure of the NH_4^+ ion is readily derived. The neutral atoms supply a total of nine valence electrons (five from the nitrogen, one from each of four hydrogens). Deducting one electron to account for the $+1$ charge of the ion leaves a total of eight, which is just sufficient to give a structure in which the nitrogen atom is covalently bonded to four hydrogens. Compare:

$$\left[\begin{array}{c} H \\ | \\ H-N-H \\ | \\ H \end{array} \right]^+ \qquad \text{and} \qquad \begin{array}{c} H \\ | \\ H-C-H \\ | \\ H \end{array}$$

Finally, we may consider a rather unique polyatomic cation in which two metal atoms are joined by covalent bonds. In the mercurous ion, Hg_2^{+2}, there is an electron-pair bond between the two mercury atoms:

$$(Hg:Hg)^{+2}$$

This ion may be formed by a reaction in which a mercury atom with two 6s electrons combines with a Hg^{+2} ion:

$$Hg: + Hg^{+2} \longrightarrow Hg_2^{+2} \qquad\qquad (10.9)$$

Sizes and Shapes

The principles that govern the geometry of neutral molecules apply to poly-atomic ions as well. With few exceptions, the spatial arrangement of atoms in an oxyanion is identical with that of a molecule containing the same number and type of covalent bonds. For each of the ions shown in Figure 10.13, it is possible to cite a molecule in which the atoms are arranged in the same pattern.

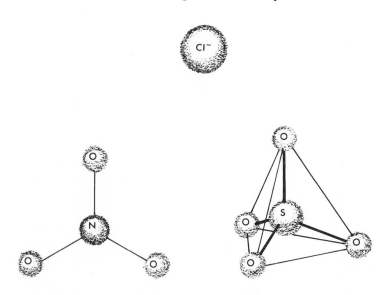

FIGURE 10.13   Geometry of the chloride, nitrate, and sulfate ions.

Two examples may suffice to illustrate this point. Consider first the similarity between the SO_4^{-2} ion and the CCl_4 molecule. Both of these particles consist of a central atom joined by single covalent bonds to four identical atoms. The SO_4^{-2} ion, like the CCl_4 molecule, has a tetrahedral structure in which the four like atoms (O, Cl) are symmetrically distributed about the central atom (S, C). Again, compare the carbonate ion, CO_3^{-2}, and the sulfur trioxide molecule, SO_3, which have similar electronic structures. Both of these particles are planar with the three oxygens arranged symmetrically about the central atom.

The bond distances in oxyanions held together by single bonds can often be predicted quite accurately from covalent radii. For example, the observed chlorine-to-oxygen distance in the ClO_2^- ion is 1.64 Å, in good agreement with the calculated value of 1.65 Å.

$$\text{covalent radius Cl} + \text{covalent radius O} = 0.99 \text{ Å} + 0.66 \text{ Å} = 1.65 \text{ Å}$$

In many cases, the bond distance in an oxyanion is found to be significantly shorter than the sum of the single bond radii. In the SO_4^{-2} ion, the sulfur to oxygen distance is only 1.44 Å as compared to the calculated distance of 1.70 Å.

$$\text{covalent radius S} + \text{covalent radius O} = 1.04 \text{ Å} + 0.66 \text{ Å} = 1.70 \text{ Å}$$

It has been suggested that the abnormally short bond lengths in the SO_4^{-2} ion are a result of partial double bond character. The resonance forms:

$$
\begin{bmatrix} & & :\!\overset{\cdot\cdot}{O}\!: & & \\ :\!\overset{\cdot\cdot}{O}\!-\!\overset{|}{S}\!=\!\overset{\cdot\cdot}{O}\!: & \\ & & \overset{|}{\underset{\cdot\cdot}{:\!O\!:}} & \end{bmatrix}^{-2} \quad \text{and possibly} \quad \begin{bmatrix} & & :\!\overset{\cdot\cdot}{O}\!: & & \\ :\!\overset{\cdot\cdot}{O}\!=\!\overset{|}{S}\!=\!\overset{\cdot\cdot}{O}\!: & \\ & & \overset{|}{\underset{\cdot\cdot}{:\!O\!:}} & \end{bmatrix}^{-2}
$$

are believed to make a significant contribution to the actual structure of the ion.

10.7 PHYSICAL PROPERTIES OF MOLECULAR SUBSTANCES: FORCES BETWEEN MOLECULES

Molecular substances differ generally from ionic compounds in two respects:

1. They are poor conductors of electricity. This is, of course, a consequence of the fact that neutral molecules cannot carry an electrical current. It is true that water solutions of certain polar molecular compounds are electrical conductors. In all such cases, however, the current is carried by ions formed by a chemical reaction with water.

2. Molecular substances as a class are relatively volatile. Many of them are gases at room temperature and atmospheric pressure; others are liquids or solids of appreciable vapor pressure. In contrast, ionic compounds are invariably high-melting solids.

The volatility or, more specifically, the melting points and boiling points, of molecular substances are directly related to the forces between molecules.

Interatomic vs. Intermolecular Forces

The generally low melting and boiling points of molecular substances are a direct consequence of the weak forces between molecules. They imply nothing about the forces within a molecule, which are strong. Consider, for example, elementary hydrogen, which is made up of diatomic molecules. To melt or boil hydrogen, it is necessary only to overcome the attractive forces holding the molecules together, rigidly in the solid, loosely in the liquid state. The low melting ($-259°C$) and boiling point ($-253°C$) of hydrogen reflect the weakness of these forces. They reveal nothing about the strength of the covalent bond between hydrogen atoms in the H_2 molecule, since this bond remains intact when hydrogen melts or boils. The greater strength of interatomic as opposed to intermolecular forces is implied by the fact that at temperatures as high as $2400°C$, only about one per cent of the H_2 molecules are dissociated into atoms. A comparison of the energy of dissociation, 104 kcal./mole, with the energy of sublimation, 0.122 kcal./mole, gives another indication of the relative magnitudes of these forces.

The distinction between interatomic and intermolecular forces is further illustrated by comparing the volatility of molecular solids to that of typical "atomic crystals." Carbon dioxide, in which only the weak intermolecular forces need be overcome to break down the molecular lattice, sublimes at $-78°C$. In silicon dioxide, covalent bonds must be broken to melt the solid; here the melting point is $1700°C$.

Trends in Melting and Boiling Points

Among molecular substances, it is found that the melting point, boiling point, heat of fusion, and heat of vaporization all tend to increase with molecular weight. Consider, for example, the halogens (Table 10.5).

TABLE 10.5 PHYSICAL PROPERTIES OF THE HALOGENS

Element	Molecular Weight	Melting Point (°C)	Boiling Point (°C)	Heat of Fusion (kcal./mole)	Heat of Vaporization (kcal./mole)
F_2	38	−223	−187	0.38	2.80
Cl_2	71	−102	−35	1.63	4.79
Br_2	160	−7	59	2.59	7.17
I_2	254	113	184	4.01	10.50

A further illustration of this effect appears in a comparison of the volatilities of different hydrocarbons. Those of low molecular weight, such as CH_4, C_2H_6, C_3H_8, and C_4H_{10} are gases at room temperature and atmospheric pressure. Hydrocarbons containing from 5 to 18 carbon atoms are liquids of steadily decreasing volatility (b.p. $C_5H_{12} = 36°C$, $C_{18}H_{38} = 308°C$). Paraffin wax is a mixture of solid hydrocarbons of even higher molecular weight.

Another factor affecting the volatility of molecular substances is their polarity. (Compounds built up of polar molecules melt and boil at slightly higher temperatures than nonpolar substances of comparable molecular weight.)

TABLE 10.6 BOILING POINTS OF POLAR VS. NONPOLAR SUBSTANCES

Nonpolar			Polar		
Formula	M.W.	B.P. (°C)	Formula	M.W.	B.P. (°C)
N_2	28	−196	CO	28	−192
SiH_4	32	−112	PH_3	34	−85
GeH_4	77	−90	AsH_3	78	−55
Br_2	160	59	ICl	162	97

The effect of polarity on melting or boiling point is ordinarily small enough to be obscured by differences in molecular weight. For example, in the series HCl → HBr → HI, boiling point increases steadily with molecular weight despite decreasing polarity. In molecular compounds in which hydrogen is bonded to a small, highly electronegative atom (N, O, F), polarity has a more pronounced effect on volatility. Hydrogen fluoride, despite its low molecular weight, has the highest boiling point of all the hydrogen halides. Water and ammonia also have abnormally high boiling points compared to those of the other hydrides of the 6A and 5A elements. In these three cases, the effect of polarity reverses the normal trend to be expected on the basis of molecular weight alone.

As one might expect, the substances which are most difficult to condense to liquids or solids are those in which the basic structural unit is both light in weight and nonpolar. Such substances include the nonmetallic elements of low molecular weight (H_2, b.p. $= -253°C$; N_2, b.p. $= -196°C$; O_2, b.p. $= -183°C$; F_2, b.p. $= -187°C$) and the lower members of the noble-gas group (He, b.p. $= -269°C$; Ne, b.p. $= -246°C$; Ar, b.p. $= -186°C$).

An explanation of these trends in volatility lies in the nature of the forces holding molecular substances together. These forces, for reasons which we shall now consider, increase in magnitude with the mass and polarity of the molecule.

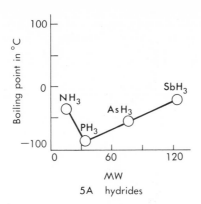

5A hydrides

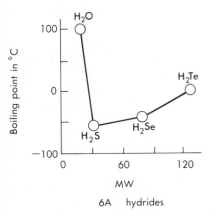

6A hydrides

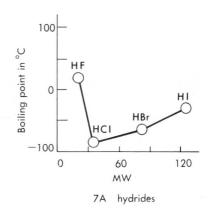

7A hydrides

FIGURE 10.14 Boiling points of nonmetal hydrides.

Types of Intermolecular Forces

Dipole Forces. The effect of polarity on the physical properties of molecular substances is readily explained in terms of the dipole forces existing between polar molecules. It has been pointed out that such molecules tend to line up in an electrical field. A similar orientation exists in a crystal composed of polar molecules. In solid iodine chloride, for example, the ICl molecules are aligned in such a way that the iodine atom (+ pole) of one molecule is adjacent to the chlorine atom (− pole) of the next molecule.

The electrostatic attraction holding neighboring molecules together in an iodine chloride crystal is similar in origin to that between adjacent ions in solid sodium chloride. However, the dipole forces between polar molecules in ICl are an order of magnitude weaker than the ionic bonds in NaCl. In the former case, the unequal electronegativities of iodine and chlorine produce only partial + and − charges within the molecule. In NaCl, on the other hand, a complete transfer of electrons leads to ions with full + and − charges.

When iodine chloride is heated to 27°C the comparatively weak dipole forces are no longer able to hold the molecules in rigid alignment and the solid melts. Dipole forces remain significant in the liquid state, in which the polar molecules are still relatively close to each other. Only in the gas, in which the molecules are very far apart, do the electrical forces become negligible. Consequently, the boiling points as

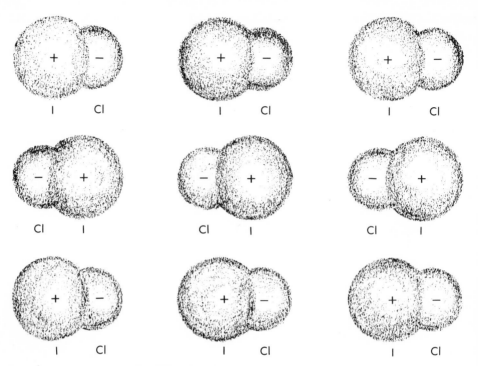

FIGURE 10.15   Cross section of ICl crystal.

well as the melting points of polar compounds such as ICl are higher than those of nonpolar substances of comparable molecular weight (Table 10.6).

Hydrogen Bonds. The abnormal properties of hydrogen fluoride, water, and ammonia result from the presence in these substances of an unusually strong type of intermolecular force. This attractive force, exerted between the hydrogen atom of one molecule and the fluorine, oxygen, or nitrogen of another, is sufficiently unique to be given a special name, the hydrogen bond. There are two reasons why the hydrogen bond is stronger than ordinary dipole forces:

1. The difference in electronegativity between hydrogen (2.1) and fluorine (4.0), oxygen (3.5), or nitrogen (3.0) is great enough to cause the bonding electrons in HF, H_2O, and NH_3 to be markedly displaced from the hydrogen. Consequently, the hydrogen atoms in these molecules, insofar as their interaction with adjacent molecules is concerned, behave almost like bare protons. The hydrogen bond is strongest in HF, in which the difference in electronegativity is greatest, and weakest in NH_3, in which the difference in electronegativity is smallest.

2. The small size of hydrogen allows the fluorine, oxygen, or nitrogen atom of one molecule to approach the hydrogen atom of another molecule very closely. It is significant that hydrogen bonding appears to be limited primarily to compounds containing these three elements, all of which have comparatively small atomic radii. The larger chlorine and sulfur atoms, with electronegativities (3.0, 2.8) similar to that of nitrogen, show little or no tendency to form hydrogen bonds in such compounds as HCl and H_2S.

Many of the abnormal properties of water are a consequence of hydrogen bonding. Its high surface tension and viscosity are directly related to the strength of these intermolecular forces. The comparatively high heat capacity of water can be explained in terms of the energy required to break hydrogen bonds, which become less numerous as the temperature is raised. When water boils, the remaining hydrogen bonds are broken. This requires the absorption of 10.5 kcal./mole, more than twice the heat of vaporization of hydrogen sulfide.

When water freezes to ice, an open, hexagonal pattern of molecules results. Each oxygen atom in the ice crystal is bonded to four hydrogens, two by ordinary covalent bonds at a distance of 0.99 Å and two by hydrogen bonds 1.77 Å in length. The large proportion of "empty space" in the ice structure explains the curious fact that ice is less dense than liquid water. Indeed, water starts to decrease in density if cooled below 4°C, indicating that the transition from a closely packed to an open structure occurs gradually over a temperature range rather than taking place abruptly at the freezing point. It is believed that even in water at room temperature, some of the molecules are oriented in an open, icelike pattern. More and more molecules assume this pattern as the temperature is lowered. Below 4°C, the transition

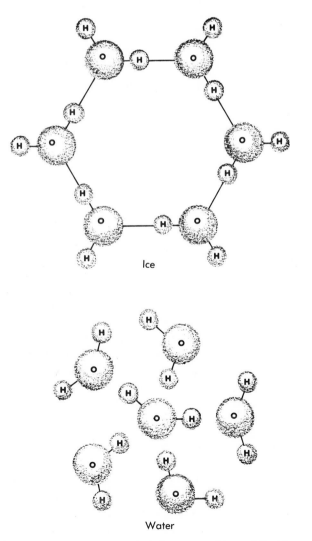

Ice

Water

FIGURE 10.16   Plane projection of geometry of ice and liquid water.

to the open structure predominates over the normal contraction on cooling, and liquid water expands as its temperature is lowered toward 0°C.

Hydrogen bonding occurs in a great many molecular substances containing hydrogen and fluorine, oxygen, or nitrogen. Hydrogen cyanide, HCN, is an example of a ternary compound in which hydrogen bonding between adjacent molecules has a profound effect on physical properties. The boiling point of hydrogen cyanide is 26°C, some 222°C higher than that of elementary nitrogen, a nonpolar substance of comparable molecular weight.

Van der Waals Forces. The two types of intermolecular forces already discussed can exist only between polar molecules. A different type of attractive force must be postulated to explain the existence in the liquid and solid states of such nonpolar substances as bromine and iodine. Since the melting and boiling points of nonpolar substances tend to increase with molecular weight, it may be inferred that the magnitude of this force increases with the mass or size of the molecule. The fact that the volatility of polar as well as nonpolar substances decreases with increasing molecular weight suggests that this third type of intermolecular force must be common to all molecular substances.

The intermolecular force whose characteristics have just been deduced is known as a Van der Waals force. Its origin is more difficult to visualize than that of the dipole force or hydrogen bond. Like them, it is basically electrical in nature. However, while hydrogen bonds and dipole forces arise from an attraction between permanent dipoles, Van der Waals forces are due to what might be called temporary or instantaneous charge separations.

It has been pointed out that over a period of time, the two bonding electrons in a nonpolar molecule such as H_2 are as close to one nucleus as the other; the molecule has no permanent dipole moment. However, at any given moment, the electron cloud may be concentrated at one end of the molecule (position 1A in Figure 10.17). A fraction of a second later, it may be located at the opposite end of the molecule (position 1B). The situation is analogous to that of a person watching a tennis match from a position directly in line with the net. At one instant, his eyes are focused on the player to his left; a moment later, they shift to the player on his right. Over a period of time, he looks to one side as often as the other; the "average" position of focus of his eyes is straight ahead.

The instantaneous concentration of the electron cloud on one side or the other of the center sets up a temporary dipole in the H_2 molecule. This in turn induces a similar dipole in an adjacent molecule. When the electron cloud in the first molecule is at position 1A, the electrons in the second molecule are attracted to 2A. As the first electron cloud shifts to 1B, the electrons of the second molecule are pulled back to 2B. These temporary dipoles, both oriented in the same direction, lead to an attractive force between the molecules, the Van der Waals force.

The strength of Van der Waals forces depends upon the ease with which the electronic distribution in a molecule can be distorted or "polarized" by a temporary dipole set up in an adjacent molecule. As one might expect, the ease of polarization depends primarily upon the size of the molecule. Large molecules in which the electrons are far removed from the nuclei are more readily polarized than small, compact molecules in which the nuclei exert greater control over the position of the electrons. In general, molecular size and molecular weight parallel one another; hence, the experimental observation that Van der Waals forces increase in magnitude with molecular weight.

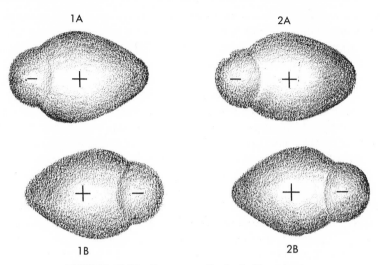

FIGURE 10.17 Temporary dipoles in H_2 molecules.

Of the three types of intermolecular forces, the only one operative between nonpolar molecules is, of course, the Van der Waals force. Even with polar molecules, this force is often the most important. For example, it is estimated that in HBr, about 95 per cent of the attractive force between molecules is of the Van der Waals type; the other 5 per cent is accounted for by dipole forces. Even in HCl, dipole forces contribute only about 15 per cent to the total intermolecular attractive forces. Only where hydrogen bonding is involved do Van der Waals forces play a minor role. In water, about 80 per cent of the intermolecular attraction can be attributed to hydrogen bonding and only 20 per cent to Van der Waals forces.

10.8 SUMMARY

The particles in a great many elementary and compound substances are held together by strong forces known as covalent bonds. Such bonds arise when two atoms, both with unpaired electrons, share them to form an electron pair. The stability of the covalent bond can be explained in terms of the overlap of the clouds corresponding to these electrons. The atoms joined may be identical, as in the H_2 molecule, in which case the bond is said to be nonpolar. When two different atoms are joined by a covalent bond, as in the HF molecule, the bonding electrons are displaced toward the more electronegative atom, giving rise to a polar bond. The greater the difference in electronegativity, the greater will be this displacement (Figure 10.4).

The orbitals used by nonmetal atoms in covalent bond formation are most frequently s and p orbitals. Nonmetal atoms located below the second period of the periodic table sometimes use d orbitals as well. In covalent bond formation, the atomic orbitals of isolated atoms are ordinarily combined in a particular manner to give hybrid bonding orbitals. Among these are the sp^3 hybrid orbitals which are occupied in molecules in which the central nonmetal atom has a noble-gas structure.

It is often possible to predict the formulas of molecular substances by using the octet rule. Frequently, however, two nonmetals form more than one compound, reflecting the fact that atoms can ordinarily achieve a stable octet by combining in more than one ratio. The reverse problem, that of assigning a plausible electronic structure to a molecule in which the nonmetal atoms are known to obey the octet rule, can be approached in a systematic manner. One simply counts the number of valence electrons and distributes them in such a way as to give each atom a noble-gas structure. It is readily shown that in a molecule containing n atoms, none of which are hydrogen, $6n + 2$ valence electrons are required to give a completely single-bonded structure. Thus, we can deduce that the molecules Cl_2, Cl_2O, NCl_3 and CCl_4 (n = 2, 3, 4, 5) have just enough valence electrons (14, 20, 26, 32) to have all their constituent atoms joined by single bonds. When the number of valence electrons is 2 fewer than required for single bond formation, as in SO_2 (18 valence electrons, n = 3) or SO_3 (24 valence electrons, n = 4), one can expect to find a double covalent bond. An electron deficiency of 4 can be remedied by forming two double bonds, as in CO_2, or a triple bond, as in CO. The electronic structures of polyatomic ions can be deduced by following the same procedure.

Frequently it is found that no single electronic structure satisfactorily explains all the properties of a molecule. In such cases, two or more structures, known as resonance forms, are written with the understanding that the true structure of the molecule lies somewhere between these extremes. Resonance increases the stability of a molecule; the existence of such odd-electron molecules as NO and NO_2 may be partially explained in this way.

The number of ordinary covalent bonds formed by a nonmetal atom depends upon the number of electrons it requires to achieve a noble-gas structure. Atoms of the 7A elements acquire the one extra electron they need by forming one bond; the 6A elements attain a noble-gas structure by forming two bonds; the 5A elements three; and the 4A elements, four. It is possible, through the formation of coordinate covalent bonds, for an atom to increase its bonding capacity. A sulfur atom, by donating electrons to oxygen, can form a total of three electron-pair bonds in SO_2 and four in SO_3.

The shapes and sizes of molecules and polyatomic ions depend upon the covalent radii of atoms and, where two or more bonds are present, upon the angle between these bonds. The distance between centers of atoms within a molecule is invariably smaller than that between atoms in adjacent molecules. The bond angles in single-bonded molecules in which each atom has a noble-gas structure are very nearly tetrahedral. These angles are distorted by multiple bond formation, which also leads to a shortening of internuclear distances within a molecule.

Diatomic molecules of compound substances are polar; that is, one end of the molecule carries a partial positive charge, the other a partial negative charge. The polarity of a molecule containing more than one covalent bond depends not only on the polarity of these bonds but also upon the angles between them. Certain symmetrical molecules such as CCl_4 and CO_2 are nonpolar despite the fact that each bond within the molecule is itself polar.

Many of the physical properties of molecular substances, in particular their volatility, depend upon the strength of the attractive forces between molecules. Intermolecular forces include dipole forces, hydrogen bonds, and Van der Waals forces. Dipole forces exist between polar molecules; they result from the attraction of the positive pole of one molecule for the negative pole of another. A hydrogen bond may be regarded as an unusually strong dipole force between the hydrogen atom of one molecule and a small, highly electronegative atom (F, O, N) of an adjacent molecule. Van der Waals forces, which exist in all molecular substances, result from the tendency for one molecule to induce a temporary dipole in another by distorting the electron distribution. Experimentally, it is found that, as a result of dipole forces, polar molecular substances tend to melt and boil at somewhat higher temperatures than nonpolar substances of comparable molecular weight. This effect is particularly pronounced when hydrogen bonding is present, as in water, ammonia, and hydrogen fluoride. The general increase in melting and boiling point with molecular weight may be attributed to an increase in the magnitude of the Van der Waals forces with increasing molecular size.

PROBLEMS

10.1 Using only the periodic table, state toward which atom the bonding electrons will be displaced in each of the following bonds.
a. N—O   b. O—S   c. S—S   d. P—F

10.2 Using the electronegativity table given in the text, arrange the following bonds in order of increasing polarity:
Mg—O   S—O   C—H   As—F   N—Cl

10.3 From the graph given in Figure 10.4, predict the approximate percentage of ionic character in each of the following bonds.
a. H—F   b. H—C   c. H—N

10.4 Give the molecular formulas and electron dot structures of:
a. Hydrogen sulfide.
b. Oxygen difluoride.
c. Three different compounds containing nitrogen, hydrogen, and/or chlorine, in which there is one and only one nitrogen atom per molecule.
d. A compound of empirical formula CH_3.
e. Two different compounds both having the empirical formula CH_4N.

10.5 Using a table of covalent radii, arrange the following diatomic molecules according to increasing size:
HCl H_2 Cl_2 Br_2.

10.6 Sketch geometric representations of the following molecules.
a. CCl_4 b. NCl_3 c. C_2H_2 d. H_2S e. BF_3 f. PBr_5 g. SeF_6

10.7 Which of the following molecules would you expect to be polar?
a. CF_4 b. P_4 c. CH_2Cl_2 d. CH_3Cl e. CO_2 f. $BeBr_2$

10.8 Which of the following molecules would have a permanent dipole moment?
a. CO   b. SF_6 c. SO_2 d. SO_3

10.9 How many valence electrons are there in each of the following species?
a. N_2O b. CH_3F c. $(SCN)_2$ d. H_2NOH e. SO_3^{-2} f. BF_4^-

10.10 Assuming that each atom in the following molecules has a noble-gas configuration, draw electron dot structures for:
a. $AsCl_3$ b. SeO_2 c. CH_3Cl d. HCN   e. Al_2I_6 f. O_3

10.11 Assuming that each atom in the following polyatomic ions has a noble-gas configuration, draw electron dot structures for:
a. NO_3^- b. PO_4^{-3} c. BrO_3^- d. O_2^{-2} e. SO_3^{-2}

10.12 What, if anything, is wrong with each of the following electron dot structures?

a. Na : Cl :

b. : Cl : B : Cl :
   : Cl :

c. (H : H : F :)⁻

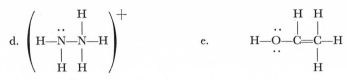

10.13 Of the molecules and ions included in Problems 10.10 and 10.11, which would you expect to exhibit resonance? Explain your reasoning.

10.14 Give an example of a particle, other than one specifically mentioned in this chapter, which
a. Contains a double bond.   d. Exhibits resonance.
b. Contains a triple bond.   e. Uses d orbitals in bonding.
c. Contains a coordinate covalent bond.

10.15 List the hybrid orbitals used by the element whose symbol is written first in each of the following species.
a. C_2H_6 b. NH_4^+ c. SiF_6^{-2} d. BeI_2 e. BF_4^- f. BBr_3

10.16 Draw resonance forms for:
a. CO_2 b. NO_3^- c. NO_2^- d. O_3

10.17 Write reasonable electronic structures for the following species, each of which is known to contain an unpaired electron.
a. ClO_2 b. O_2^- c. NO_3 d. CH_3

10.18 Give the electronic structure of the species formed when:
a. A proton is added to the ammonia molecule.
b. A proton is added to the HSO_4^- ion.
c. A proton is abstracted from an HSO_4^- ion.
d. A molecule of boron trichloride reacts with a chloride ion.

10.19 Draw, to scale, a two-dimensional model of an iodine crystal, containing four molecules.

10.20 Which of the following species would you *not* expect to obey the octet rule?
a. SiO_4^{-2} b. I_3^- c. S_2^{-2} d. SF_5^- e. $COCl_2$ f. BeF_3^-

10.21 Indicate the orbitals used in bonding by the central atom in:
a. KrF_4 b. ClF_3 c. IF_5 d. SiF_6^{-2} e. SiF_4

10.22 Predict which compound in each of the following pairs will have the higher boiling point. In each case, explain your reasoning.
a. LiCl or CCl_4 c. CO_2 or SiO_2 e. CCl_4 or $SiCl_4$
b. PH_3 or AsH_3 d. HCl or F_2 f. HCN or HCl

10.23 What kind of attractive force or chemical bond must be broken to:
a. Melt calcium chloride?   d. Boil hydrogen fluoride?
b. Melt carbon dioxide?   e. Dissolve I_2 in water?
c. Melt silicon dioxide?   f. Dissolve I_2 in CCl_4?

10.24 Explain, in terms of intermolecular forces, why:
a. Most molecular compounds are volatile.
b. Hydrogen fluoride has a higher boiling point than hydrogen bromide.
c. Symmetrical molecules usually boil at lower temperatures than unsymmetrical molecules of comparable mass.
d. An ice cube floats in a glass of water.

*10.25 A certain compound analyzes as follows: 54.5 per cent C, 13.6 per cent H, 31.8 per cent N. The density of its vapor at 227°C and 1 atm. pressure is about 2.1 g./l. Suggest at least two possible structural formulas for this compound. How could you determine experimentally which of these formulas is correct?

*10.26 There are three known compounds of molecular formula $C_2H_2Cl_2$, but only one of formula C_2H_3Cl. Explain this in terms of molecular structure (cf. Chapter 24).

*10.27 The density of gaseous hydrogen fluoride at 28°C and 1 atm. is 2.30 g./l. What information does this yield concerning intermolecular forces in hydrogen fluoride?

*10.28 A compound called diborane has the molecular formula B_2H_6. Suggest a reasonable electronic structure for this compound (cf. Linus Pauling, *The Nature of the Chemical Bond*, Cornell University Press, Ithaca, N.Y., 3rd edition, 1960).

*10.29 One of the less commonly known interhalogen compounds is iodine pentafluoride, IF_5. How many pairs of electrons are there around the central iodine atom in a molecule of IF_5? What symmetry would you expect these electrons to assume? What would be the resulting structure to be predicted for the IF_5 molecule?

*10.30 Iodine heptafluoride, IF_7, is one of the very few substances in which seven atoms are bound to a central atom. By extension of the reasoning used in rationalizing the structures of substances like PCl_5 and SF_6, suggest a likely structure for IF_7.

*10.31 A molecule whose structure is still in doubt at the present writing (February, 1966) is XeF_6. This molecule does not appear to have octahedral symmetry. By consideration of your solution to Problem 10.30, suggest a likely alternative structure for XeF_6.

11 | PARTICLE STRUCTURE OF THE ELEMENTS

Elements can be classified on the basis of particle structure into four principal categories. The simplest structure is that of the noble gases, which are made up of individual atoms. A second structure, shown by many of the more electronegative elements, has as its basic unit a small, discrete molecule. Hydrogen and the halogens, discussed in Chapter 10, fall into this category, being built up of diatomic molecules. In this chapter, we shall extend our study of molecular elementary substances to include oxygen, nitrogen, and sulfur.

A third structure, shown by carbon and several other nonmetallic elements, gives rise to what are called atomic or macromolecular crystals, in which all the atoms are joined together by a network of covalent bonds. We shall be interested in certain physical properties, including the phenomenon of semiconductivity, shown by elements with this structure.

The last section of this chapter is devoted to a discussion of the metallic elements, in which one encounters a type of bonding quite different from any previously

Periodic Table

	1A	2A	3B	4B	5B	6B	7B	8B	8B	8B	1B	2B	3A	4A	5A	6A	7A	8A	
																	2	1	He
Li	4	4											3	3	2	2	2	1	Ne
Na	4	4											4	3	2 3	2	2	1	Ar
K	4	4	4	4	4	4	4	4	4	4	4	4	4	3	2 3 4	2 3	2	1	Kr
Rb	4	4	4	4	4	4	4	4	4	4	4	4	4	4	2 3 4	2 3	2	1	Xe
Cs	4	4	4	4	4	4	4	4	4	4	4	4	4	4	4			1	Rn

FIGURE 11.1 Types of bonding in the elements: 1 = individual atoms, 2 = molecules, 3 = atomic crystals, 4 = metals.

described. We shall consider the nature of the metallic bond and see how it leads to the characteristic properties associated with metals.

11.1 NOBLE GASES

The fact that these elements are composed of isolated, neutral atoms with weak Van der Waals forces between them makes the physical properties of the noble gases quite analogous to those of such nonpolar molecular substances as hydrogen and nitrogen. They are all gases at room temperature and atmospheric pressure. Like the halogens, their melting and boiling points increase steadily with increasing formula weight.

TABLE 11.1 PHYSICAL PROPERTIES OF THE NOBLE GASES

Element	Atomic Weight	Melting Point (°C)	Boiling Point (°C)	Critical Temp. (°C)	Heat of Vapor (cal./mole)
He	4.003	−272	−269	−268	24
Ne	20.183	−249	−246	−229	416
Ar	39.948	−189	−186	−122	1500
Kr	83.80	−169	−152	−63	2200
Xe	131.30	−140	−109	17	3200
Rn	222	−71	−62	104	4300

11.2 MOLECULAR ELEMENTARY SUBSTANCES: H, F, Cl, Br, I, O, S, N

The properties of the diatomic molecules of elementary hydrogen (H_2) and the halogens (F_2, Cl_2, Br_2, I_2) were discussed at length in Chapter 10.

Oxygen (O_2, O_3)

O_2. Elementary oxygen under ordinary conditions exists as diatomic molecules. A reasonable structure for the O_2 molecule with its 12 valence electrons would appear to be:

$$: \overset{..}{O} = \overset{..}{O} :$$

Such a structure is indeed the only one which gives both oxygen atoms a noble-gas configuration. Nevertheless, experimental evidence indicates that this is not a satisfactory picture of the O_2 molecule.

Oxygen, in both the gaseous and liquid states, shows a small but measurable attraction towards a magnetic field. This property, known as *paramagnetism*, is characteristic of substances containing unpaired electrons.* It is shown, for example, by nitric oxide, NO, and nitrogen dioxide, NO_2, both of which have unpaired electrons (Chapter 10, Section 10.5). The paramagnetism of oxygen argues against a

---

* Molecules such as H_2 and Cl_2, in which all the electrons are paired, are slightly repelled by a magnetic field. This behavior is referred to as *diamagnetism*.

structure such as that just written for the O_2 molecule, in which all the electrons are paired. Quantitative studies on the magnetic properties of oxygen indicate the presence of two unpaired electrons in the O_2 molecule, suggesting a structure such as:

$$: \overset{..}{O} — \overset{..}{O} :$$

in which neither oxygen atom has a noble-gas configuration.

O_3. If oxygen is passed through a silent electrical discharge, a new gas with a pungent odor is produced. This substance, called ozone, has physical properties quite different from those of ordinary oxygen, yet analysis shows it to contain only oxygen atoms. Gas density measurements on ozone indicate a molecular weight of 48, just 3/2 that of ordinary oxygen. On this basis, it is evident that ozone is a form of elementary oxygen in which there are three atoms per molecule (O_3) rather than two (O_2).

The existence of elementary oxygen in two different forms in the same physical state is an example of a general phenomenon known as **allotropy.** Ozone and ordinary oxygen are referred to as allotropic forms of the element. As we shall see, the phenomenon of allotropy is shown by a great many nonmetallic elements.

The ozone molecule can best be described as a resonance hybrid of the two contributing forms:

(bond angle = 127°, bond distance = 1.26 Å)

The two oxygens at the ends of the molecule are equidistant from the central atom. The bond distance is intermediate between that calculated for a single and a double bond.

TABLE 11.2 PHYSICAL PROPERTIES OF O_2, O_3

	Melting Point (°C)	Boiling Point (°C)	Density at STP (g./l.)	Solubility in Water at STP (moles/l.)
O_2	−218	−183	1.429	0.00218
O_3	−251	−112	2.145	0.00022

The formation of ozone is a highly endothermic process:

$$3 \ O_2(g) + 69.0 \ \text{kcal.} \longrightarrow 2 \ O_3(g) \tag{11.1}$$

The energy which must be absorbed to bring about this reaction may be supplied electrically or in the form of ultraviolet light. Small amounts of ozone can be detected in the vicinity of a spark coil or high voltage transformer.

A layer of ozone formed by the interaction of atmospheric oxygen with the ultraviolet portion of sunlight is known to exist in the upper atmosphere, about 14 miles above the surface of the earth. This ozone layer forms only a tiny fraction of the total atmosphere; it has been estimated that if it were concentrated in a pure band at sea level, it would be less than a tenth of an inch thick. Nevertheless, it exerts a profound influence on life as we know it. Ozone strongly absorbs ultraviolet radiation, which is harmful to body cells. At the other end of the spectrum, it absorbs infrared radiation. The greater part of the energy radiated from the earth's surface is in the infrared range; the presence of the ozone layer in the atmosphere helps to prevent this energy from escaping into outer space. Water vapor and carbon dioxide behave similarly; were it not for the presence of these three gases in the atmosphere, our climate would be a great deal colder.

Although ozone is potentially unstable with respect to decomposition into ordinary oxygen, this decomposition is ordinarily quite slow, since the first step in the conversion:

$$O_3(g) + 24.7 \text{ kcal.} \longrightarrow O_2(g) + O(g) \qquad (11.2)$$

is highly endothermic. The reactive oxygen atoms produced by reaction 11.2 account for the fact that ozone is much more reactive than ordinary oxygen. Ozone has been used on a small scale to purify drinking water by oxidizing and thus destroying harmful bacteria.

Sulfur

Sulfur, like oxygen, exhibits allotropy. In the solid state, two different crystalline forms are possible, rhombic and monoclinic sulfur. Both are composed of octagonal ring molecules of formula S_8:

(In this diagram and those that follow, the two unshared electron pairs associated with each sulfur atom are not shown.)

The two forms differ only in the pattern in which the molecules pack in the crystal.

Rhombic and monoclinic sulfur are in equilibrium with each other at a temperature of 96°C. Above this temperature, the monoclinic form is stable; below 96°C, the transformation to rhombic sulfur is spontaneous. Monoclinic crystals, separated from molten sulfur at its freezing point (119°C), may be preserved for some time if the melt is quickly cooled to room temperature, where the rate of conversion to the rhombic form is quite slow.

The free-flowing, pale yellow liquid formed when sulfur melts is composed of the same S_8 molecules that are present in the solid. However, upon heating to about 160°C, sulfur undergoes an unusual transformation. The liquid becomes so viscous that it cannot be poured; at the same time its color changes to a deep reddish-brown. These changes result from the formation of another form of liquid sulfur in which large numbers of atoms are linked together to form a long-chain **polymer.** Two steps are involved in this transition. First, the S_8 ring molecules break up to form eight-membered chains:

$$(11.3)$$

in which the terminal sulfur atoms have unpaired electrons. Two such chains adjacent to each other can then link together to form a double chain of 16 atoms:

$$(11.4)$$

Since this process leaves unpaired electrons on the terminal sulfur atoms, the chains can continue to grow to 24, 32, 40, . . . sulfur atoms. Liquid sulfur at temperatures between 160°C and 250°C contains a high proportion of such polymeric chains, varying in length from eight to several thousand atoms. Entanglements between neighboring chains prevent free flow, producing a highly viscous liquid. The deep color is attributed to the absorption of light by the unpaired electrons at the ends of the chains.

Above 250°C, the viscosity of liquid sulfur decreases; at the boiling point, 445°C, it again becomes free-flowing. Over this temperature range, the long chains break into smaller fragments:

$$(11.5)$$

The shorter chains show less tendency to overlap and interlock with each other, thereby reducing the viscosity. The color steadily deepens as the boiling point is approached, reflecting the increased number of unpaired electrons produced when the chains break.

If liquid sulfur at a temperature between 160° and 250°C is quickly cooled by pouring into water, a rubbery mass commonly referred to as "plastic sulfur" separates. This material consists of long-chain molecules which did not have time to rearrange to the ring molecules characteristic of solid sulfur at room temperature. Over a period of a day or two, the plastic sulfur loses its elasticity as it is transformed to rhombic crystals.

Nitrogen

All the available evidence indicates that the nitrogen molecule with 10 valence electrons has the structure:

$$: N \equiv N :$$

The distance between the nitrogen atoms joined by a triple bond is 1.09 Å, considerably less than the N—N single-bond distance of 1.47 Å. The triple bond in the nitrogen molecule is unusually strong. The energy required to dissociate the N_2 molecule is 225 kcal., more than six times that calculated for a N—N single bond. The high energy of dissociation of the N_2 molecule explains why nitrogen is the least reactive of molecular elementary substances.

11.3   ELEMENTS   FORMING   ATOMIC   (MACROMOLECULAR) CRYSTALS: C, Si, Ge, Sn

Carbon

The arrangement of atoms in the two crystalline forms of carbon, diamond, and graphite, is shown in Figure 11.2. In diamond, each carbon atom is covalently bonded to four other atoms. The nonvolatility of diamond (sublimes at ~3500°C) reflects the difficulty of breaking these bonds. Like most atomic crystals, diamond is extremely hard; it will scratch all other minerals. Tips of highspeed cutting tools and dies are often set with tiny diamonds; these tools can be used repeatedly without losing their cutting edge.

The layer structure shown by graphite reflects the fact that the carbon atoms are themselves bonded in layers. Each atom is joined to three neighboring atoms in the same plane by strong covalent bonds; one of these is a double bond which resonates among the three possible positions.)There are no bonds between layers; adjacent planes of carbon atoms are held together by weak Van der Waals forces. The ability of these layers to slip readily over one another makes graphite soft. When one writes with a "lead" pencil, thin layers of graphite rub off on the paper. In spite of its softness, graphite has an extremely high melting point (~3500°C). In order to melt graphite, the strong bonds within the layers must be broken.

Diamond has a considerably higher density (3.51 g./ml.) than graphite (2.26 g./ml.). The lower density of graphite results from the wide spacing between adjacent layers (3.40 Å). Within a given layer, the atoms in graphite are slightly closer together than in diamond (1.42 Å vs. 1.54 Å).

At room temperature and atmospheric pressure, graphite is the stable form of carbon. Under these conditions, diamond should, in principle, be transformed to graphite. Fortunately for the owners of diamond rings, this transition occurs at an infinitesimal rate under ordinary conditions. At high temperatures, the rate of conversion increases markedly; a sample of diamond maintained at 1800°C changes rapidly into graphite. For understandable reasons, no one has ever become excited

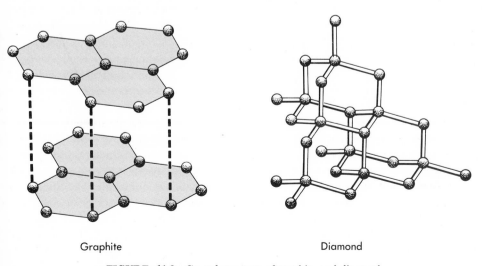

Graphite   Diamond

FIGURE 11.2   Crystal structure of graphite and diamond.

over the commercial possibilities of this process. The more difficult task of converting graphite to diamond has aroused more enthusiasm.

Since diamond has a greater density than graphite, its formation is favored by high pressures. One can calculate that at 25°C, a pressure of 8000 atm. should be sufficient to accomplish this transition. Higher temperatures are required to bring about the conversion of graphite to diamond in a finite amount of time. Unfortunately, at high temperatures the pressure required for conversion increases; at 2800°C, a pressure of 100,000 atm. is needed. In 1954, scientists at the General Electric laboratories were able to achieve sufficiently high temperatures and pressures to bring about the conversion of graphitic material to diamond. The synthetic diamonds produced by this process are extremely small, but suitable for industrial purposes.

Several amorphous forms of carbon can be prepared; lampblack and charcoal are two of the more familiar. These materials show no ordered crystal pattern and contain varying amounts of impurities. However, x-ray studies have shown that the carbon atoms in the amorphous forms are arranged in an irregular hexagonal pattern similar in many respects to that of graphite.

Silicon, Germanium, and Tin

Elementary silicon, germanium, and the gray allotropic form of tin crystallize in the diamond pattern. Gray tin, the stable form of the element below 13°C, is extremely brittle, crumbling readily to a fine powder. Tin objects, maintained at low temperatures for long periods of time, disintegrate because of the transition from the metallic form (white tin) to the gray modification. This phenomenon, referred to as "tin disease," makes tin unsuitable for use as a structural metal in very cold climates.

Defect Crystals

The brittleness of gray tin may be attributed to the large number of crystal defects inherent in its structure. When tin is cooled below 13°C, the transition from the white to gray form takes place at a great many points separated from each other by a few atomic diameters. By the time a few atoms have arranged themselves in the tetrahedral pattern characteristic of gray tin, the microcrystal thus formed intersects another. When this happens, the tetrahedral arrangement of atoms is disturbed; comparatively few bonds are formed across the intersections. A large crystal of gray tin consists of an agglomeration of thousands of tiny crystals held together by relatively weak forces. When such a crystal is struck even a mild blow, it disintegrates into a finely divided microcrystalline powder.

Defects of a quite different type are responsible for the semiconducting properties of silicon and germanium. Small amounts of impurities incorporated into the crystal lattice of these elements convert them from insulators to semiconductors, widely used in such devices as transistors, thermistors, and solar batteries.

Extremely pure samples of germanium or silicon are nonconductors since they contain virtually no free electrons. The four valence electrons of each atom are tightly held in the covalent bonds formed with neighboring atoms; the core electrons are held too tightly by the nuclei to be available for conduction. This situation changes drastically when small numbers of foreign atoms (as few as 1 in 10^6) are introduced into the crystal. In order to understand how this comes about, let us

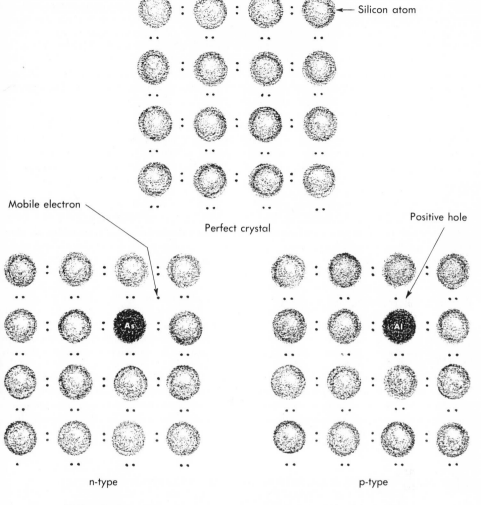

← Silicon atom

Mobile electron

Positive hole

Perfect crystal

n-type   p-type

FIGURE 11.3 Schematic drawing of semiconductors derived from silicon.

Ge Zn
Si ↑ 3 +type

Bo -p
+type

examine how the crystal structure of a 4A element is disturbed by the introduction of atoms of a 5A or 3A element.

An atom of arsenic or antimony with its five valence electrons can fit into the tetrahedral lattice of germanium or silicon only if it gives up its extra electron. This electron is relatively free to move throughout the crystal under the influence of an electrical field, giving rise to an *n-type semiconductor* (current carried by the flow of negative charge). If an atom of boron or other element with three valence electrons is introduced into the lattice, a quite different situation arises. An electron deficiency is created at the site occupied by the foreign atom; it is surrounded by seven valence electrons rather than eight. Physicists describe the introduction of such a defect in terms of the formation of a "positive hole" in the lattice. In an electrical field, an electron moves from a neighboring atom to fill this hole. In so doing, it creates an electron deficiency around the atom which it leaves. Conduction in this type of defect crystal, a *p-type semiconductor*, can be visualized as a movement of positive holes through the lattice.

A semiconductor in which there is a junction between an electron-rich and an electron-deficient region acts as a rectifier, capable of converting alternating to direct current. Such an "n-p" junction can be formed by starting with a silicon disc impregnated with a small amount of arsenic (an n-type semiconductor) and introducing a trace of boron (a p-type semiconductor) on one side of the disc. Electrons flow readily from the electron-rich region containing arsenic to the electron-deficient area created by the presence of boron atoms. Potentials as high as 1000 volts are incapable of bringing about electron flow in the opposite direction.

Perhaps the best known of all semiconductor devices is the transistor, in which n-p-n or p-n-p junctions are created by forming a sandwich of alternate electron-rich and electron-poor regions. A transistor amplifies an electric current in much the same way as a vacuum tube. The small size of transistors makes them ideal for use in hearing aids, miniature radios, and electronic components of missiles or satellites. Their increasing use in television and radio receivers, in which they compete with vacuum tubes, reflects the greater durability and lower energy consumption of transistors.

The electrical conductance or, conversely, the resistance of all types of semiconductors is extremely sensitive to temperature. The resistance of a typical semiconductor decreases by as much as 4 per cent per °C at room temperature; that of copper wire increases by only one tenth of that amount under the same conditions. Semiconductor devices known as thermistors have been developed to take advantage of this property. Accurate resistance readings taken in a circuit including thermistors make it possible to estimate temperature changes to 0.0001°C or better. The small size of thermistors makes them suitable for temperature measurements in restricted spaces. A thermistor inserted into the tip of a glass probe can be used to measure temperatures in various parts of the human body. Thermistors can be taped to the skin or soldered to metal surfaces to measure surface temperatures.

Quite recently, it has been found that a semiconductor whose surface contains an n-p junction can convert radiant energy to electrical energy. This principle is used in the solar battery, which promises to be an important power source in the interplanetary space vehicles of the future. Light striking a crystal of germanium or silicon impregnated with an electron-rich impurity such as arsenic ejects some of the loosely held electrons. These electrons are collected at the surface, which is coated with a thin, transparent layer of a p-type semiconductor such as boron. The electrons then pass through an electrical circuit where their energy is used to do useful work.

11.4 ELEMENTS FORMING BOTH ATOMIC AND MOLECULAR CRYSTALS: P, As, Sb

The element phosphorus can exist in three different allotropic forms known as white, red, and black phosphorus. Of these, the white and red modifications are by far the more important; black phosphorus is stable only at very high pressures. "Yellow" phosphorus, believed at one time to be a distinct allotropic form of the element, is now known to be a mixture resulting from a slow transition, at room temperature, of white phosphorus to the more stable red form.

White phosphorus is a soft, waxy substance with a low melting point (44°C) and boiling point (280°C). It is readily soluble in such nonpolar organic solvents as carbon tetrachloride and carbon disulfide. The chemical reactivity of white phosphorus is so great that it is commonly stored under water to protect it from the oxygen of the atmosphere. A piece of white phosphorus exposed to air in a dark room glows as a result of the evolution of light accompanying its exothermic oxidation. In World War II, pieces of paper soaked in a solution of white phosphorus in carbon disulfide were used as incendiary "calling cards." The heat given off by the oxidation of the white phosphorus served to ignite first the carbon disulfide and then the paper.

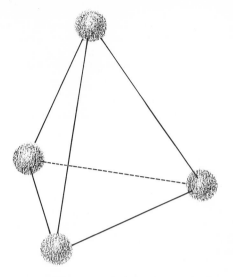

FIGURE 11.4   Structure of P_4 molecule.

The high volatility, solubility in nonpolar solvents, and chemical reactivity of white phosphorus show it to be a molecular substance. Molecular weight determinations reveal that there are four atoms per molecule. X-ray diffraction measurements indicate a tetrahedral structure for the P_4 molecule with each phosphorus atom bonded to three others (Figure 11.4).

White phosphorus is extremely toxic; as little as 0.1 g. taken internally can be fatal. Direct contact with the skin produces painful burns which are slow to heal. Inhaling the vapor leads to decay of the bone structure, particularly around the nose and jaw. To make matters worse, phosphorus vapor is a cumulative poison; persons exposed to low concentrations may show no symptoms of phosphorus poisoning for several years. Despite its toxicity, white phosphorus was at one time widely used in the manufacture of matches. Laws were eventually passed prohibiting its use for this purpose; a nontoxic sulfide of phosphorus, P_4S_3, is now used instead.

The properties of red phosphorus contrast strikingly with those of the white form. Red phosphorus is higher melting (m.p. = 590°C at 43 atm.), insoluble in organic solvents, and stable to oxidation at temperatures below about 250°C. The low volatility of red phosphorus makes it much less toxic than the white form.

As its physical and chemical properties imply, red phosphorus is a polymeric solid in which large numbers of phosphorus atoms are joined by a network of covalent bonds. Each phosphorus atom is joined to three others, as in white phosphorus, but bonding extends throughout the entire crystal instead of being confined to a discrete molecule. To melt or dissolve red phosphorus, it is necessary to break covalent bonds between phosphorus atoms. These bonds must also be broken before reaction with oxygen can occur.

Arsenic and Antimony

The two elements lying directly below phosphorus in group 5A exhibit the same type of allotropy as does phosphorus. "Yellow," "black" and "gray" allotropic forms are known for both arsenic and antimony. The yellow modifications are believed to be similar to white phosphorus in that they are made up of tetratomic molecules. The black forms have a structure equivalent to that of red phosphorus, while the gray forms show metallic properties.

11.5 METALS

The metals, which comprise about three fourths of the known elements, show a unique type of bonding different from any considered up to this point. Before discussing metallic bonding, it may be helpful to summarize the more important properties of metals. From these properties, it is possible to deduce a great deal about the arrangement of particles in metals and the forces between these particles.

General Properties

It is difficult if not impossible to draw a sharp dividing line between the metallic elements on the one hand and nonmetals on the other. Nevertheless, one can list several general properties which are possessed to a greater or lesser degree by all metals. These include:

1. High Electrical Conductivity. The metallic elements as a group have electrical conductivities greater by several orders of magnitude than those of typical nonmetals. Lead, one of the poorest metallic conductors, has a conductivity nearly 4000 times that of the metalloids silicon and germanium.

TABLE 11.3 RELATIVE ELECTRICAL
CONDUCTIVITIES OF SOLID
ELEMENTS (Pb = 1)

Metals		Nonmetals	
Ag	13.6	graphite	0.016
Cu	13.0	Si	0.00026
Al	8.4	Ge	0.00025
Zn	3.7	I	1.7×10^{-14}
Fe	2.2	diamond	4.4×10^{-20}
Pb	1.0	S	1.1×10^{-22}

The high conductivity of metals implies the presence of a large number of electrons which are relatively free to move under the influence of an electric current. This in turn indicates a type of bonding quite different from that in the nonmetals, in which the outermost electrons are tied up in covalent bonds.

2. High Thermal Conductivity. Of all solids, metals are by far the best conductors of heat. Frying pans and kettles are made of metals such as copper, aluminum, or iron; the insulating handles of these utensils are constructed from such nonmetallic materials as wood, glass, or plastic.

TABLE 11.4 RELATIVE THERMAL
CONDUCTIVITIES OF SOLIDS
(Pb = 1)

Metals		Other Solids	
Ag	12.2	graphite	0.087
Cu	11.1	glass	0.022
Al	6.1	wood	0.013
Zn	3.2	sand	0.012
Fe	2.0	S	0.009
Pb	1.0	paper	0.004

Comparison of Tables 11.3 and 11.4 reveals that the various metals fall in the same order whether arranged according to decreasing thermal or electrical conductivity. This suggests that the mechanism of conduction of heat in metals is similar to that of electrical conduction.

3. Luster. Polished metal surfaces are excellent reflectors of light and hence present a shiny appearance. Most metals appear to have a silvery white color when illuminated by ordinary light, indicating that light of all wavelengths is being reflected. A few metals, notably gold and copper, absorb some light in the blue region of the spectrum and hence have a yellow color.

4. Ductility, Malleability. Metals are ductile (capable of being drawn out into wire) and malleable (capable of being hammered into thin sheets). Nonmetallic solids tend to shatter if drawn out or hammered. The ductility and malleability of metals indicates that in these elements it is relatively easy for layers of atoms to slide over one another.

5. Emission of Electrons. All metals, if heated to sufficiently high temperatures, eject electrons. This property, referred to as *thermionic emission*, is used in the ordinary vacuum tube in which electrons emitted by a hot metal filament travel to a positively charged plate.

Many metals emit electrons at room temperature when exposed to light of the proper frequency. The 1A metals in particular are sensitive to light. This so-called *photoelectric effect* is used in an "electric eye" photocell to convert light into electrical energy. A beam of light striking a negatively charged cesium electrode causes electrons to flow to a positively charged collecting plate. When the light is cut off temporarily, the flow of current stops, a switch is thrown, and a traffic light turns green or a supermarket door opens.

The photoelectric and thermionic effects offer additional evidence for a metallic structure in which the electrons are relatively mobile.

6. Formation of Positive Ions in Reactions. Metals, in reacting with nonmetallic elements, lose electrons to form positive ions. This property, exhibited to varying degrees by all metals, offers chemical evidence in support of the idea that electrons are readily separated from the metal lattice.

Crystal Structure of Metals: Coordination Number

With very few exceptions, metals crystallize in one or another of three different geometric patterns. Two of these are "closest-packed" arrangements, i.e., patterns in which spheres representing metal atoms are packed so as to leave as little free space as possible. To understand why there are two such arrangements, consider Figure 11.5. Here, a portion of a single layer of spheres, packed as tightly as possible, is indicated by the circles marked B. A second closest-packed layer can be added directly above the one shown by placing spheres so that their centers lie directly above the points labeled A. There are now two different ways in which we can add a third layer, below the plane of the paper:

1. The spheres can be placed so that they line up perfectly with the uppermost layer; i.e., their centers fall directly below the points labeled A. In this structure, the pattern repeats itself every two layers; one might represent this as ABABAB . . . . This arrangement is called **hexagonal closest packing** (hcp).

2. The spheres in the third layer can be placed so that their centers lie directly beneath the points marked C. In this structure, the pattern repeats itself every three layers; the arrangement can be represented as ABCABC . . . . This is referred to as

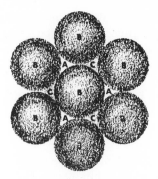

Closest packing: hexagonal = ABA
cubic = ABC

FIGURE 11.5 Packing pattern of atoms in metallic crystals.

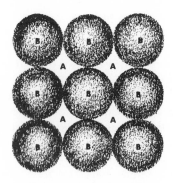

Body-centered cubic: ABA

cubic closest packing or, alternatively, as **face centered cubic** (fcc), since it can be constructed by fitting together cubes in which there is an atom at each corner and one at the center of each face (Figure 11.6).

A third type of packing shown by many metals is described as **body-centered cubic** (bcc). This structure can be synthesized by fitting together cubes in which there are atoms at each corner and one in the center. The body-centered cubic structure is somewhat more "open" than the two closely packed structures already referred to. One can calculate that whereas 74 per cent of the volume in the fcc or hcp structures is occupied by the atoms themselves, only about 68 per cent of the volume in the bcc structure is filled by the atoms (Chapter 12, Problem 12.25). In other words, there is an additional 6 per cent of "empty" space in the body-centered cubic structure since the atoms are not packed as closely as possible.

The structures just described are represented in three dimensions in Figure 11.6. From the figure, it is possible to deduce, for each structure, the coordination number of a metal atom, i.e., the number of atoms immediately surrounding a given atom. For the two closest-packed structures, hcp and fcc, this number is 12. This is perhaps easiest to see in the model representing hexagonal closest packing, where it is obvious that an atom at the center of a hexagon is surrounded by six atoms in its own layer, three atoms in the layer above and three atoms in the layer below. An atom in the body-centered cubic structure has a coordination number of 8; if we concentrate on an atom in the center of a cube, the eight atoms touching it are those at the corners of the cube.

We see then that the coordination number of an atom in a metallic crystal is either 8 or 12 depending upon the particular pattern in which the metal atoms arrange themselves. These coordination numbers are much higher than those of nonmetallic elements, in which the number of nearest neighbors is determined by the number of covalent bonds formed by the central atom. In silicon, for example, each atom is bonded to four others to give a coordination number of 4.

The relatively high densities of metals as compared to nonmetals may be attributed to the close packing of metal atoms. Compare, for example, the two elements aluminum and silicon. The aluminum atom is both lighter (At. Wt. Al = 27.0, Si = 28.1) and larger (atomic radius Al = 1.43 Å, Si = 1.17 Å) than the

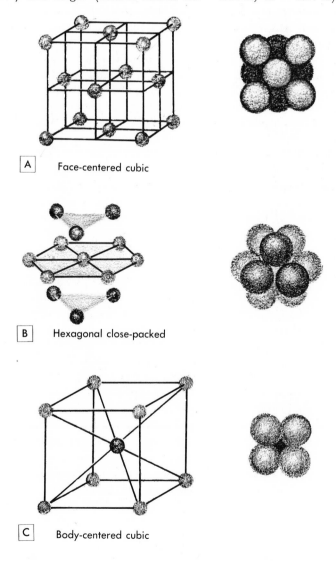

A   Face-centered cubic

B   Hexagonal close-packed

C   Body-centered cubic

FIGURE 11.6   Crystal structures of metals (top view at right).

silicon atom. Nevertheless, the density of aluminum (2.71 g./ml.) is greater than that of silicon (2.33 g./ml.). The explanation of this apparent anomaly lies in the way in which the atoms are packed. Each aluminum atom has 12 nearest neighbors as compared to four for silicon. Consequently, there is much less "empty space" in the aluminum lattice, resulting in a higher density.

The Metallic Bond

The types of chemical bonding previously considered arise from interactions between valence electrons of atoms. These are the electrons which are bound least tightly to the nucleus. Accordingly, it is reasonable to suppose that it is the valence electrons of the metallic elements which participate in bond formation between metal atoms. On this basis, an atom of a 1A metal would have one electron available for bonding, an atom of a 2A metal two, and so on.

It is by no means obvious how interactions between valence electrons can lead to stable chemical bonds between metal atoms. The possibility of ionic bonding, which would require the transfer of electrons from one atom to another, can be discarded immediately. Since all the atoms in a metal are alike, it is unreasonable to suppose that one atom would give up electrons to another.

A more likely possibility would be for adjacent metal atoms to share electrons, thereby forming a covalent bond. This is, of course, precisely what happens with nonmetallic elements. However, there is a fundamental objection to the formation of conventional electron-pair bonds in metals; there simply are not enough valence electrons to go around. Consider, for example, the metal cesium, each atom of which has one valence electron available for bond formation. In a crystal of cesium, which has a body-centered cubic structure, each cesium atom is surrounded by eight others, all of which have equally valid claims to the single available electron. In order for a cesium atom to form ordinary covalent bonds with its eight neighbors, it would need eight valence electrons rather than one.

There remains one alternative for a cesium atom; it can share its valence electron equally with all eight neighboring atoms. In this way, a cesium atom forms what might be described as one eighth of an electron-pair bond with each of these atoms. Introducing the concept of resonance, one can picture the valence electron of cesium as being shared equally by each of the eight surrounding atoms.

In barium, in which two valence electrons are available to share with eight nearest neighbors, one can expect to find two eighths or one fourth of an ordinary electron-pair bond between adjacent atoms. The situation in aluminum, which has three valence electrons and crystallizes in the face-centered cubic system with a coordination number of 12, is similar to that in barium. The three valence electrons of an aluminum atom are shared with each of its 12 neighbors, forming what can be described as one fourth of an ordinary covalent bond with each of these neighbors.

Electron-Sea Model. The picture of metallic bonding that has just been presented implies that the bonding electrons are not tied down to a particular pair of atoms as is the case in ordinary covalent bonding, but are spread out over a relatively wide region. This concept has led to what is known as the electron-sea model of metallic bonding. From this point of view, the metallic lattice can be visualized as consisting of a regular array of positive ions (i.e., metal atoms minus their valence electrons) anchored in position like bell buoys in a mobile "sea" of

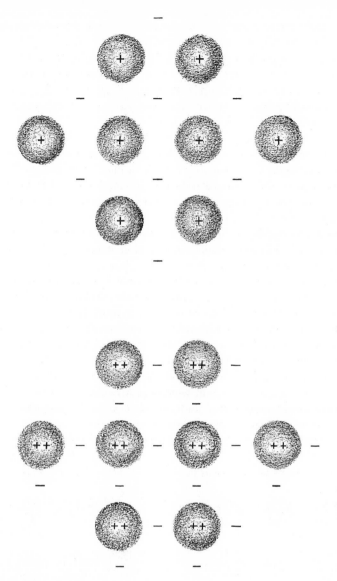

FIGURE 11.7 Schematic diagram of electronic structure of metals (cesium and barium).

electrons. The valence electrons can wander throughout the lattice in much the same way that gas molecules are able to move freely throughout their container. The metal ions are held together by a sort of "electron glue" composed of the valence electrons.

Many of the characteristic properties of metals are explained quite adequately by this admittedly oversimplified picture of metallic bonding. In particular, the high mobility of the valence electrons explains the high electrical conductivity of metals. Under the influence of an electrical field, it is possible for these electrons to move through the lattice, thereby conducting a current. The high thermal conductivity of metals is another consequence of the freedom of motion of the valence electrons. Heat energy is transferred through the metal by collisions between electrons. Since the valence electrons are responsible for the conduction of both thermal and electrical energy, it is hardly surprising that the metals that are the best electrical conductors are also the best conductors of heat (Tables 11.3 and 11.4).

The property of metallic luster is readily explained in terms of the electron-sea model. Since the electrons are not tied to a particular bond with a characteristic energy, they are able to absorb and re-emit light of all wavelengths. A metal thereby becomes a virtually perfect reflector; the silvery color that we associate with metals can be attributed to their high reflectance.

The picture of a metallic lattice as consisting of a regular array of positive ions embedded in a sea of mobile electrons offers a simple explanation of the malleability and ductility of metals. Consider, for example, a metal crystal in which the atoms in adjacent layers have the positions indicated in 1A, Figure 11.8. Under an applied stress, the ions in the upper layer move through a distance equivalent to one atomic diameter, taking the position shown in 1B. Since the valence electrons are mobile, they are free to move along with the metal ions to give a structure entirely equivalent to the original one. For this reason, metals offer comparatively little resistance to distortions produced by the slippage of crystal planes. Contrast this situation to that which exists in ionic crystals. If one attempts to move one layer of ions across another, ions of like charge come in contact with each other (position 2B, Figure 11.8). The strong electrostatic repulsions created by this situation shatter the crystal.

Given sufficient energy, it is possible for valence electrons to completely escape from the metallic lattice. This energy can be supplied as light (photoelectric effect) or heat (thermionic effect). Alternatively, a nonmetal atom approaching close to the surface of a metal may be able to detach an electron. In doing so, the nonmetal atom is converted to a negative ion, while a positive ion is left behind in the lattice. The formation of an ionic compound can be visualized quite simply as being due to a flow of electrons from the metal lattice to nonmetal atoms.

Even though the electron-sea model qualitatively explains many of the characteristic properties of metals, it is inadequate in certain respects. In particular, it is difficult to explain, in terms of this model, why the molar heat capacity of metals is

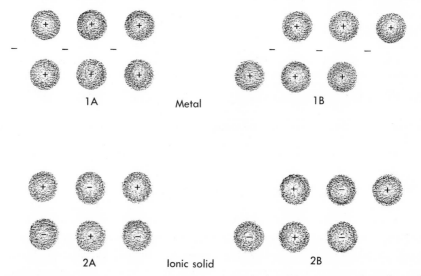

FIGURE 11.8 Movement of crystal planes. In an ionic solid, movement through one ionic diameter brings ions of like charge in contact with each other. In metals, in which the negative charges are free to move, the movement of a plane of atoms produces little change in the crystal structure.

not considerably higher than that of nonmetals. One would suppose that if the electrons in a metal were all free to move throughout the crystal, they should make a significant contribution to the heat capacity. In the case of calcium, for example, one can calculate that the heat capacity on the basis of a free-electron model should be nearly twice the observed value of 6.2 cal./mole.

Band Theory of Metals. A more sophisticated picture of the electron distribution in metals can be derived from quantum-mechanical considerations. This picture, a refinement of the "electron-sea" model just described, starts with the same fundamental assumptions. It considers that the valence electrons in a metal are associated, not with a particular atom, but with the crystal as a whole. The essential refinement of the band theory is that it assigns these electrons to discrete energy levels. These energy levels are similar to atomic orbitals in one respect; each level has a capacity of two electrons. However, they differ from atomic orbitals in being much closer together in energy. The absorption of an almost infinitesimal amount of energy can raise an electron in a metal from a particular energy level to the next higher level.

These energy levels are grouped into *bands* or zones. The number of levels within each band is equal to the number of atoms in the sample. For a metal crystal of finite size, there will be a huge number of levels in any given band. Since the band itself covers an energy range of only a few electron volts, this means that there is a tremendous number of closely spaced energy levels within the band.

To illustrate the application of the band theory to metals, let us consider a sample of sodium weighing 23.0 g. and therefore containing Avogadro's number of atoms (6.02×10^{23} atoms). Since each sodium atom has one valence electron, this means that in this sample there will be 6.02×10^{23} electrons to be distributed among energy levels. Recalling that the number of levels in any given band is equal to the number of atoms in the sample, we deduce that there will be an equal number, 6.02×10^{23}, of levels within the lowest band. The valence electrons fit into these levels, two electrons being paired in each level. Consequently, in the absence of an external energy source, the valence electrons will fill only half the levels in the first band. This will, of course, be true regardless of the number of atoms in the sample; in any crystal of sodium metal, half the energy levels in the first band are unoccupied.

When a crystal of sodium with the ground state electronic structure just described is placed in an electrical field, a few electrons acquire enough energy to move up into higher, unoccupied levels within the first band. These high-energy electrons are the ones that carry an electrical current. The high conductivity of sodium can be attributed to the presence of a large number of energy levels differing only slightly in energy from the occupied levels. Comparatively little energy is required to promote the few electrons needed to conduct an electric current or transfer thermal energy through the metal.

While it is relatively easy to promote a few electrons in sodium to higher, unoccupied levels, most of the electrons are located in levels buried so deeply within the first band that they cannot readily be promoted. This explains why the electrons in a metal under ordinary conditions make only a small contribution to the heat capacity. When the temperature of the metal is raised, the vast majority of the electrons remain in their original energy levels and so absorb no heat.

The electron distribution in a sample of magnesium, in which each atom has two valence electrons, is somewhat more complex than that of sodium. One might

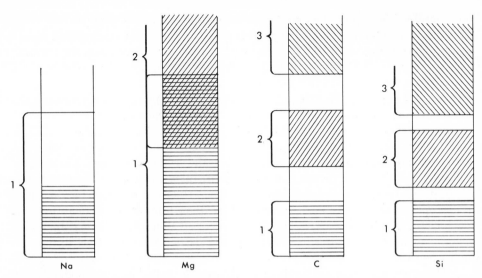

FIGURE 11.9 Schematic diagram of band structure of metals. In sodium and magnesium there are a large number of empty levels only slightly higher in energy than the filled levels. In carbon and silicon the gap between empty and filled levels is comparatively large.

expect to find all the energy levels in the first band filled with two electrons each. It turns out, however, that the second band of magnesium overlaps the first in energy; the lower levels of the second band have energies somewhat less than those of the higher levels of the first band. Consequently, the first band of magnesium is not entirely filled with electrons in the ground state. Magnesium, like sodium, has a large number of empty levels differing only slightly in energy from the filled ones. The amount of energy required to promote electrons is relatively small, so magnesium, like sodium, is a good electrical conductor.

The overlapping of energy bands is characteristic of almost all metallic conductors. In contrast, nonmetallic solids are characterized by large gaps between successive bands. With carbon, for example, there is a sharp break of about 6 ev. between the second and third bands. In the ground state, the valence electrons (four per carbon atom) completely fill the two lowest bands, a pair of electrons occupying each level. The comparatively large amount of energy required to promote an electron into an unoccupied level in the third band makes carbon an insulator rather than a conductor of electricity. Silicon, in which the energy gap is narrowed (Figure 11.9) to about 1 ev., is a semiconductor.

PROBLEMS

11.1 Referring to Figure 11.1, can you make any generalization concerning the region of the periodic table where the elements form metallic bonds? Atomic crystals? Molecular crystals? Can you offer any generalizations in terms of electronic structure?

11.2 One of the topics discussed in this chapter is that of allotropy. Give examples of elements which have allotropic forms differing in:
a. Crystal structure in the solid state.
b. Molecular weight in the gaseous state.
c. Molecular weight in the liquid state.
d. Type of bonding in the solid state.

11.3 a. It was at one time believed that ozone had a ring structure:

What evidence can you think of which would tend to support such a structure?
What experimental observation appears to refute this structure?

b. If someone were to propose that ozone had the structure:

how would you go about testing this possibility?

11.4 The molecular weight of sulfur at 25°C has been found to be 256, within experimental error. In each of the following temperature regions, would you expect the molecular weight of sulfur to be approximately 256, significantly less than 256, or significantly greater than 256?
a. 25–96°C.   b. 96–119°C.   c. 119–250°C.   d. 250–445°C.   e. 445–1000°C.

11.5 Explain, in terms of electronic structure and bonding, why:
a. Diamond is more dense than graphite.
b. The carbon atoms within a layer of graphite are closer together than are those in diamond.
c. The coordination number of the carbon atoms in graphite is lower than that in diamond.
d. Graphite is a very soft substance even though it has a high melting point.
e. Graphite can be converted to diamond at high pressures.

11.6 Suppose a small number of atoms of each of the following elements were incorporated into a silicon crystal. Would you expect this to result in the formation of a semiconductor and, if so, would it be of the n- or p-type?
a. Sn   b. B   c. P   d. Se   e. Be

11.7 Referring to the discussion of changes in enthalpy and entropy (Chapter 5), predict the sign of ΔH and ΔS for each of the following:
a. The introduction of atoms of aluminum into a silicon crystal.
b. Raising the temperature of liquid sulfur above 250°C.
c. The formation of diamond from an amorphous form of carbon such as lampblack.

11.8 Explain in terms of electronic structure and bonding why:
a. White phosphorus is more volatile than red phosphorus.
b. White phosphorus is more reactive chemically than red phosphorus.
c. White phosphorus is more soluble in organic solvents than is red phosphorus.
d. Neither form of phosphorus is appreciably soluble in water.

11.9 Explain, first in terms of the electron-sea model and then in terms of the band theory, why:
a. Metals are good conductors of electricity.
b. Metals are good conductors of heat.
c. Metals have shiny surfaces.
d. Metals tend to form positive ions in reacting with nonmetals.

11.10 Explain, in terms of the bonding involved, why:
a. Graphite and lead are both malleable while diamond is not.
b. Magnesium has a higher melting point than sodium.
c. Elements of high density, almost without exception, are metals.

11.11 Assuming that the following pairs of metals have the same type of packing, which would you expect to have the higher density?
a. Mg or Ti   b. Cu or Ag   c. Ba or Fe

11.12 Metallic manganese at a temperature of 1130°C and a pressure of 1 atm., undergoes a change in crystal structure from face-centered cubic to body-centered cubic. Would you expect this transition to be accompanied by an increase or decrease in density? Would you expect the transition temperature to be raised or lowered by an increase in pressure?

11.13 What is the coordination number of:
a. The sulfur atom in solid sulfur?
b. The phosphorus atom in white phosphorus?
c. The oxygen atom(s) in ozone?

*11.14 The electrical conductivity of lead is 10^{22} times that of sulfur; the thermal conductivity of lead is only about 100 times that of sulfur. Can you suggest an explanation for the great difference in these two ratios?

*11.15 Look up in a handbook or other reference source the melting points of the metals in the fourth period, starting with potassium and going through zinc. Assuming that there is a correlation between melting point and number of valence electrons, what can you say concerning the variation in this number as one moves along from potassium to zinc?

*11.16 One way in which metal atoms could pack would be a simple cubic structure with an atom at the corner of each cube.
a. What would be the coordination number of an atom in this structure?
b. Draw diagrams similar to those in Figures 11.5 and 11.6 to describe this structure.
c. Can you suggest why such a structure is rarely found in nature?

*11.17 Assuming that the ozone in the atmosphere would occupy a layer 0.1 in. thick if it were concentrated at the surface of the earth (radius = 8000 miles), calculate an approximate value for the total mass of the ozone in the atmosphere.

12

LIQUIDS AND SOLIDS: CHANGES IN STATE

In Chapter 6, we discussed the laws governing the physical behavior of gases and the interpretation of these laws in terms of the kinetic theory. In succeeding chapters, we have had frequent occasion to refer to substances in the liquid and solid states. We are now ready to discuss the properties of these two condensed states of matter. In doing so, we shall be particularly interested in:

1. The particle structure of liquids and solids and its influence upon their physical properties.

2. The equilibria between the gaseous, liquid, and solid phases of a pure substance.

12.1 NATURE OF THE LIQUID STATE

The structure of liquids is less well established than that of gases or solids. Despite a great deal of research in this area, we still do not have a clear picture of the way in which molecules are arranged in the most common liquid, water. We do, however, have a reasonably detailed knowledge of the average distances between particles in a liquid. Moreover, we can estimate, with considerable accuracy, the magnitude of the forces between particles in a liquid. It is these two aspects of liquid structure which we shall now consider.

(At ordinary temperatures and pressures, the particles in a liquid are much closer together than in a gas)(Figure 12.1). The closer approach of particles in the liquid as opposed to the gaseous state provides a simple explanation for many of the observed differences in behavior of these two states of matter. In particular, it explains why:

1. The density of liquids is ordinarily much greater than that of gases. Compare, for example, the density of liquid water at 100°C and 1 atm., 0.958 g./ml., to that of water vapor at the same temperature and pressure, as calculated from the Ideal Gas Law:

$$d = \frac{PM}{RT} = \frac{(1 \text{ atm.})(18.0 \text{ g./mole})}{\left(82.1 \dfrac{\text{ml. atm.}}{\text{mole} \times {}^\circ\text{K}}\right)(373^\circ\text{K})} = 0.000588 \text{ g./ml.}$$

2. Liquids diffuse into each other much more slowly than do gases. If one pours concentrated sulfuric acid carefully down the inside of a beaker containing water,

263

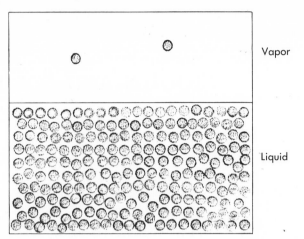

FIGURE 12.1   Spacing of particles in liquid and vapor at ordinary pressures.

two layers can be maintained almost indefinitely despite the fact that the two liquids are soluble in each other. The small amount of free space between molecules in the liquid tends to prevent one liquid from diffusing into another. In contrast, diffusion in the gaseous state, in which the molecules are widely separated, occurs much more rapidly.

3. Liquids are much less compressible than gases. At 25°C, an increase in pressure from 1 to 2 atm. decreases the volume of a sample of liquid water by only 0.0045 per cent. The same change in pressure decreases the volume of an ideal gas by 50 per cent. In the gas, in which most of the space is unoccupied to begin with, an increase in pressure drastically reduces the volume; liquids, in which the molecules are much closer together, are virtually incompressible.

4. Liquids expand less when heated than do gases. The density of liquid water at 100°C is only about 4 per cent less than that at 0°C. An ideal gas, in going through this same temperature change at constant pressure, expands by $\frac{100}{273}$ or about 37 per cent.

Since the attractive forces between molecules are inversely related to the distances separating them, we would expect intermolecular forces to be much stronger in the liquid than in the gaseous state. This is, of course, the case; we find that energy must be supplied to overcome these forces and thereby convert a liquid to a vapor. One can calculate that the attractive energy due to Van der Waals forces between carbon tetrachloride molecules in the vapor at 25°C and 1 atm. is of the order of a few *calories* per mole. In the liquid, on the other hand, it amounts to several *kilocalories* per mole.

The amount of heat required to vaporize a mole of liquid against a constant external pressure (e.g., in an open container) is referred to as the **heat of vaporization.** The heat of vaporization is a measure of the strength of the intermolecular forces holding molecules in the liquid state. Compare, for example, the heat of vaporization of water, 10.5 kcal./mole,* to that of methane, 2.0 kcal./mole. The difference between these two quantities reflects the strong hydrogen bonding in water superimposed upon the Van der Waals forces which account for all the intermolecular attraction in methane.

---

* The heat of vaporization of a liquid varies to some extent with temperature. In the case of water, it is 10.7 kcal./mole at 0°C, 10.5 kcal./mole at 25°C, and 9.7 kcal./mole at 100°C.

The attractive force acting on a molecule at the surface of a liquid is considerably smaller than that in the interior, where the number of surrounding molecules is approximately twice as great. A molecule at the surface experiences an unbalanced attractive force tending to pull it into the body of the liquid. This explains why liquids tend to achieve as small a surface as possible. Small drops of water falling through air or through a liquid with which water is immiscible take on the shape of a sphere, thereby achieving the smallest possible surface-to-volume ratio.

The work required to expand the surface of a liquid by unit area is referred to as its surface tension (γ). This quantity is ordinarily expressed in ergs/cm.^{2} ($\equiv$ dynes/cm.) The surface tension, like the heat of vaporization, is a measure of the strength of intermolecular forces. Water, in which these forces are comparatively strong, has a high surface tension, considerably greater than that of most organic liquids. This explains, at least in part, why organic liquids tend to "wet" or spread out over solid surfaces much more readily than does water. Mercury, with a surface tension even higher than that of water, is a notoriously poor wetting agent; it forms spherical drops even on clean glass surfaces.

measure of strength of intermolec. forces
1) heat, vaporization
2) surface tension

TABLE 12.1 HEATS OF VAPORIZATION AND
SURFACE TENSIONS OF LIQUIDS

Liquid	ΔH vap. (kcal./mole)*	γ(ergs/cm.^{2}) at 20°C.
Mercury	14.2	475
Water	9.7	72.8
Pyridine	8.5	38.0
Benzene	7.3	29.0
Ether	6.2	17.0

* The heat of vaporization is given at the normal boiling point (cf. Table 12.2).

12.2 LIQUID-VAPOR EQUILIBRIUM

All of us are familiar with the process of evaporation, in which a volatile liquid, placed in an open container, spontaneously passes into the vapor phase. Let us now consider this physical change from a molecular viewpoint.

According to the kinetic theory, the molecules in a liquid will have a certain average kinetic energy at a given temperature. Some of the molecules, however, have energies considerably above the average. A few of these fast-moving, high-energy molecules will manage to escape through the surface of the liquid, passing into the vapor state. In an open container, these molecules tend to diffuse into the surrounding atmosphere rather than to return to the liquid. The escape of high-energy molecules from the liquid lowers the temperature and hence the average kinetic energy of its molecules—evaporation is a cooling process. However, under ordinary conditions, heat flows to the liquid from the surroundings, restoring the temperature and average kinetic energy to their original values. More high-energy molecules escape from the liquid into the atmosphere; the process of evaporation continues until all the liquid is gone.

Now let us consider what happens when a volatile liquid is placed in a closed container rather than an open vessel (Figure 12.2). As before, some of the molecules of the liquid will spontaneously pass through the surface into the space above it. This time, however, the molecules in the vapor are unable to escape from the container; some of them will pass back into the liquid. At first the movement of molecules will be primarily in one direction, from liquid to vapor. Gradually, however, the rate at which molecules re-enter the liquid approaches that at which they leave. If a constant temperature is maintained in a closed container, the rates of evaporation and condensation eventually become equal. When this happens, we say that **equilibrium** has been established between the liquid and the vapor above it. Once equilibrium is attained, there is no further change in the number of molecules in either the liquid or the vapor state.

Having developed a kinetic picture which leads us to believe that a state of equilibrium will be reached between liquid and vapor confined in a closed container at constant temperature, it is interesting to speculate as to what will happen if we change the volume of the container, maintaining constant temperature. Let us place the liquid in a container (Figure 12.2b) whose volume is such that the space occupied by the vapor is exactly twice that in our original system (Figure 12.2a). Once again, we predict that an equilibrium will be established such that the number of molecules passing into the vapor in a given time will be exactly balanced by the number returning to the liquid. However, since the volume in which the vapor molecules move is twice as great as before, a particular molecule will have only half as great a chance of returning to the liquid in a given time. It would seem that in order to achieve the same balance as before, the total number of molecules in the vapor would have to be doubled. In general, we would predict that, at equilibrium, the number of molecules in the vapor would be directly proportional to its volume.

$$n_g = \text{constant} \times V \qquad (12.1)$$

(n_g = no. of molecules in vapor of volume V)

Equation 12.1 can, of course, be rearranged to read

$$n_g/V = \text{constant} = C_g \qquad (12.2)$$

This equation predicts that the number of molecules per unit volume in the vapor should be constant at a given temperature. Stated another way, our kinetic-molecular picture of liquid-vapor equilibrium leads us to the conclusion that the *concentration of molecules in the vapor* (C_g) *should be a constant, independent of volume, for a given liquid at a particular temperature.*

Let us now ask ourselves what is likely to happen to the concentration of molecules in the vapor if the temperature is raised. We shall find in Chapter 14 that even a relatively small increase in temperature greatly increases the fraction of molecules having very high energies (Figure 14.6, p. 343). This means that the number of molecules capable of escaping from the liquid and consequently the rate of vaporization will be increased by raising the temperature. In order to maintain equilibrium between vaporization and condensation, the number of molecules per unit volume in the vapor must increase accordingly. We would predict, then, that an increase in temperature should increase the equilibrium concentration of molecules in the vapor (Figure 12.2c).

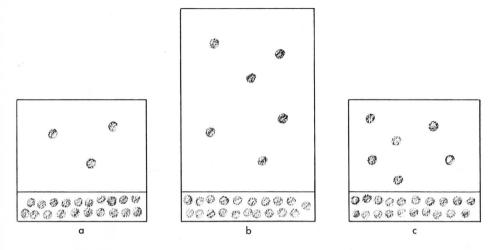

FIGURE 12.2   Kinetic-molecular interpretation of liquid-vapor equilibrium.

Vapor Pressure

The kinetic-molecular picture of liquid-vapor equilibrium that we have developed predicts that the concentration of molecules in the vapor will be constant, independent of volume, at a given temperature, and will increase with temperature. To check the validity of our reasoning, we should like to confirm our predictions experimentally. Unfortunately, the concentration of molecules in a vapor is a somewhat awkward quantity to measure directly in the laboratory. We prefer to work with a function such as pressure, which can more readily be measured.

The pressure of a vapor (gas) at a given temperature is uniquely determined by its concentration. One can perhaps see this most readily by referring to the ideal gas equation in the form:

$$P = \frac{nRT}{V} = \frac{n_g}{N}\frac{RT}{V} = C_g \frac{RT}{N}$$

which tells us that the pressure at a given temperature can be directly calculated from the quantity n_g/V, the concentration of gas molecules in the container.

Following this line of reasoning, we can restate our conclusions reached from the kinetic-molecular approach as follows: *The pressure of the vapor above a liquid at equilibrium, referred to as the vapor pressure of the liquid, will have a characteristic value, independent of volume, at a particular temperature and will increase with temperature.*

The validity of this statement can be checked experimentally in an apparatus of the type shown in Figure 12.3, which consists of a cylinder fitted with a piston to allow changes in volume, a manometer for the measurement of pressure, and a heating device with which we can maintain a fixed temperature throughout the system. The apparatus is designed so that it can be evacuated to remove air.

Let us suppose that the apparatus shown in Figure 12.3 is evacuated and a mole of liquid benzene added. The temperature is maintained at 50.0°C. We observe that the liquid level drops at first but soon reaches a constant value. The gas pressure read on the manometer rises quickly to 272 mm. Hg, where it remains steady. In other

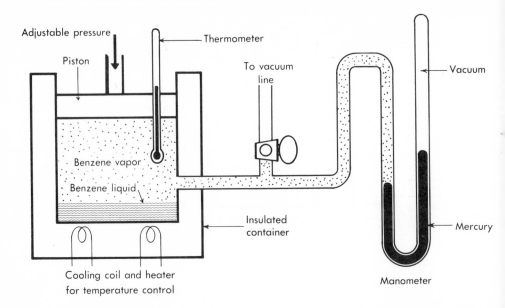

FIGURE 12.3   Schematic diagram of apparatus for studying phase equilibria.

words, the system reaches a position of equilibrium, exactly as we predicted; a constant equilibrium pressure of vapor is established. We deduce that at 50.0°C the vapor pressure of benzene is 272 mm. Hg. Had we used water instead of benzene in the apparatus, we would have found the equilibrium pressure to be 92.5 mm. Hg, the vapor pressure of water at 50.0°C.

Now let us see what happens when we change the volume of this system by raising or lowering the piston, maintaining a constant temperature of 50.0°C. If the volume is increased from, let us say, 5 l. to 10 l., the manometer still reads 272 mm. Hg. In accordance with our predictions based on the kinetic-molecular model, we find that, regardless of the extent to which we increase the volume, the pressure remains constant as long as there is any liquid present to maintain equilibrium with the vapor. Only if the piston is raised to the point where all the liquid is vaporized does the pressure drop below 272 mm. Hg; further volume increase gives a gas pressure which decreases according to the Ideal Gas Law. Similarly, if we decrease the volume of the system by lowering the piston, the manometer reads 272 mm. Hg as long as both liquid and vapor are present (Figure 12.4).

Having established that the vapor pressure of a liquid such as benzene is independent of volume, let us see what happens when the temperature is changed. We find, as kinetic theory predicts, that the equilibrium pressure of vapor above liquid benzene rises markedly with increasing temperature, reaching 760 mm. Hg at 80.1°C and 1500 mm. Hg at 104°C. At lower temperatures, the vapor pressure is lower, being 80 mm. Hg at 21.3°C. Again, the equilibrium pressure at a given temperature is independent of container volume as long as both liquid and vapor are present.

The behavior of all liquid-vapor systems as a function of volume and temperature is very similar to that of benzene. *The vapor pressure of any pure liquid is a constant at a given temperature and increases with increasing temperature* (Figure 12.5).

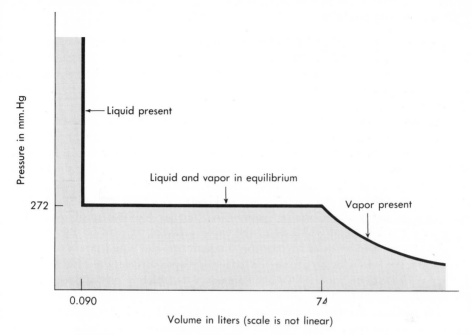

FIGURE 12.4 Pressure-volume behavior of benzene system at 50°C.
(Based on one mole benzene.)

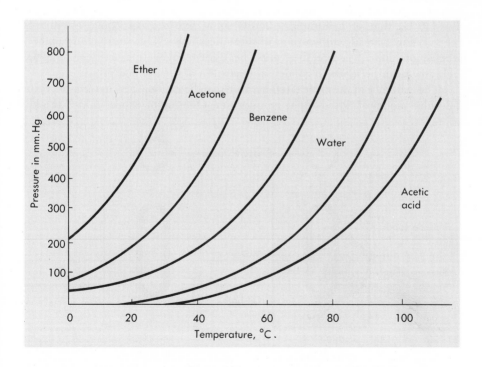

FIGURE 12.5 Dependence of vapor pressure on temperature for some typical liquids.

Critical Temperature

We have just considered the effect of temperature upon a liquid-vapor system at equilibrium, pointing out that the vapor pressure increases with temperature. One might wonder whether there is any upper limit to the existence of the liquid state. In other words, is it possible to reach a temperature so high that the liquid no longer exists?

To answer this question, we might conduct the following experiment. Let us seal a sample of benzene in a pressure-tight metal container fitted with a window through which observations can be made (Figure 12.6). The apparatus is immersed in an oil bath whose temperature can be raised at a controlled rate; the pressure within the apparatus is read on a gauge. As the temperature is increased, the pressure steadily rises, following the curve shown in Figure 12.5. The level of liquid drops somewhat as vaporization occurs. Nothing spectacular happens until we reach a temperature of 289°C, at which point the vapor pressure, as read on the gauge, is about 47.9 atm. Suddenly, as we pass this temperature, the liquid phase completely disappears. We are no longer able to see the liquid-vapor surface; the entire container is filled with benzene vapor. This phenomenon is completely reversible; if we cool the container to 289°C, the liquid appears as suddenly as it disappeared on heating.

The behavior described for benzene is typical of all liquids. For every substance, there is a temperature called the **critical temperature,** above which the liquid phase cannot exist. The pressure at that temperature, which is the maximum vapor pressure that the liquid can exert, is referred to as the critical pressure. Critical temperatures and pressures vary widely from one substance to another. For water, the critical temperature is 374°C; the vapor pressure of water at that temperature (its critical pressure) is 218 atm. On the other hand, oxygen has a critical temperature of −119°C; that of helium is −268°C, only five degrees above absolute zero. The very low critical temperatures of substances like oxygen and helium make their liquefaction difficult, since they must be cooled below their critical temperature before they can be made to condense, regardless of the applied pressure.

The existence of the critical temperature can be rationalized in terms of a kinetic-molecular model of liquid-vapor equilibrium. One might expect that if the kinetic

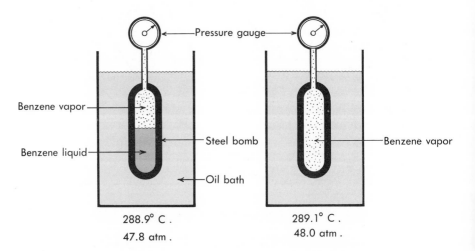

FIGURE 12.6 Behavior of benzene at its critical point.

energy of the molecules were increased sufficiently, they would no longer be able to stay in the condensed, liquid state. By increasing the temperature, we reach a critical kinetic energy, the point at which the attractive forces between molecules are no longer able to hold them together in the liquid.

Boiling Point

If a liquid is heated in an open container rather than in a closed system of the type we have been discussing, it will still tend to vaporize so as to establish its vapor pressure above the surface. If the temperature is raised sufficiently, bubbles of vapor will form in the liquid and rise to the surface. When this happens, we say that the liquid is boiling.

We find experimentally that the temperature at which a liquid boils depends upon the pressure above it. To understand why this is the case, let us refer to Figure 12.7. For a vapor bubble to form within the liquid, the pressure within the bubble, P_1, must be at least equal to the pressure above the liquid, P_2.*

$$P_1 = P_2 \quad \text{for a boiling liquid}$$

But, P_1 is simply the vapor pressure of the liquid. Consequently, we deduce that a *liquid boils at a temperature at which its vapor pressure becomes equal to the pressure above its surface.* If the pressure at the surface is constant, the boiling point of the liquid must also be constant. If the pressure is equal to one standard atmosphere (760 mm. Hg), the liquid boils at a temperature referred to as its normal boiling point. In the case of water, the vapor pressure reaches 760 mm. Hg at a temperature of exactly 100°C. The normal boiling point of benzene, 80.1°C, is somewhat lower; that of oxygen, −183°C, is a great deal lower.

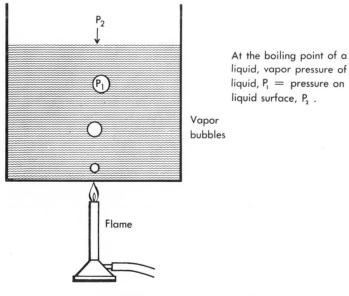

At the boiling point of a liquid, vapor pressure of liquid, P_1 = pressure on liquid surface, P_2.

FIGURE 12.7 A boiling liquid.

* Actually, for the bubble to be stable, the pressure within it must be slightly greater than the total pressure at the point where the bubble is formed, which in turn will be slightly greater than the pressure at the surface.

Since a liquid will boil whenever its vapor pressure is equal to that at its surface, the boiling point can be changed by changing the applied pressure. Both water and benzene will boil at room temperature in a container which is being evacuated with a vacuum pump. Chemists often purify compounds which are unstable at their normal boiling points by boiling them at low pressures, and, hence, low temperatures, and condensing their vapors. It is, of course, possible to raise the boiling point of a liquid by increasing the applied pressure. At 2 atm. pressure water boils at about 120°C. The sensible housewife often uses a pressure cooker, a device in which the pressure on water can be raised to over 1 atm. Under the conditions in the cooker, the water boils at a temperature above 100°C and the cooking reaction takes place more rapidly. It should now be obvious why, when the boiling point of a liquid is recorded, the pressure on the liquid must also be recorded.

The normal boiling point of a liquid is, of course, always lower than its critical temperature. However, if we examine a series of liquids, we find that these two temperatures are directly related to each other. For most liquids, we find that:

$$\left(\text{normal boiling point } (°K) \approx \tfrac{2}{3} \times \text{critical temperature } (°K) \right)$$

We can also relate, at least qualitatively, the normal boiling point of a liquid to its vapor pressure at room temperature. Liquids such as ether which have a high vapor pressure at 20°C, will reach a vapor pressure of 760 mm. Hg at a comparatively low temperature. Relatively nonvolatile liquids such as mercury must be heated to a high temperature to reach this same vapor pressure.

As Table 12.2 indicates, there is also a correlation between the heat of vaporization of a liquid and its normal boiling point. In general, a liquid in which strong intermolecular forces contribute to a high heat of vaporization will have a high boiling point, a high critical temperature, and a low vapor pressure at room temperature.

TABLE 12.2 PHYSICAL PROPERTIES OF LIQUIDS RELATED TO
INTERMOLECULAR FORCES

Liquid	Normal b.p. (°K)	Critical Temperature (°K)	Vapor Pressure at 20°C (mm. Hg)	Heat of Vaporization (kcal./mole)
Mercury	630	~1750	0.0012	14.2
Water	373	647	17.5	9.7
Benzene	353	562	75	7.3
Ether	308	467	442	6.2
Ethane	184	305	27000	3.5
Oxygen	90	154	—	1.6
Helium	4.2	5.2	—	0.08

12.3 NATURE OF THE SOLID STATE

The density of a substance in the solid state is ordinarily somewhat greater than that of the liquid (Table 12.3). This implies that the particles in the solid are slightly closer together than they are in the liquid. The difference is small; the increase in density on solidification seldom exceeds 5 to 10 per cent. A few substances, of which water is the most notable example (cf. Chapter 10, Section 10.7), expand on freezing because of the formation of a relatively "open" solid structure.

TABLE 12.3 DENSITIES OF SOLIDS VS. LIQUIDS*

	Solid (g./ml.)	Liquid (g./ml.)
Mercury	14.2	13.6
Benzene	1.005	0.894
Sodium chloride	2.0	1.55
Water	0.917	1.000
Bromine	3.9	3.2

* Densities given at the melting point.

The fact that heat must be absorbed to melt a solid implies that the attractive forces between particles are stronger in the solid than in the liquid state. It should be noted, however, that the heat absorbed on melting, referred to as the **heat of fusion,** is ordinarily only a small fraction of the heat of vaporization (Table 12.4). This indicates that the difference in attractive forces in the solid and liquid states is relatively small; the major portion of these forces is not overcome until the molecules pass into the vapor, in which they are widely separated from one another.

TABLE 12.4 SOME TYPICAL HEATS OF FUSION AND VAPORIZATION*

	Heat of Fusion (kcal./mole)	Heat of Vaporization (kcal./mole)	ΔH fus./ΔH vap.
Sodium chloride	6.9	43	0.16
Bromine	2.6	9.0	0.29
Benzene	2.55	8.27	0.31
Water	1.44	10.7	0.13
Mercury	0.56	13.5	0.04

* Values given at the melting point.

The most obvious structural difference between solids on the one hand and liquids on the other is the rigidity characteristic of the solid state. While the particles in a liquid have sufficient translational energy to allow them to move past one another, motion of this type cannot ordinarily occur in a solid. In a perfect crystal, the particles are restricted to vibrating about a fixed point. The amplitude of this vibration increases with temperature, but never becomes great enough for one particle to slip past another.

Crystal Structure

Solids tend to crystallize in definite geometric forms which can frequently be seen by the naked eye. In ordinary table salt, one can distinguish small, cubic crystals of sodium chloride; large, beautifully formed crystals of such minerals as quartz (SiO_2) and fluorite (CaF_2) are found in nature. Even in finely powdered solids, it is ordinarily possible to observe distinct crystal forms under a microscope.

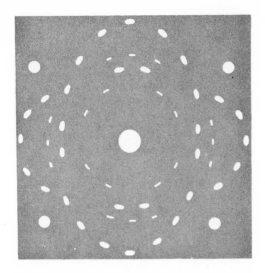

FIGURE 12.8 Diffraction pattern of NaCl. (From Sienko, M. J. and Plane, R. A., *Chemistry*, 2nd edition, McGraw-Hill Book Company, Inc. New York.)

The existence of crystals with distinct geometric forms implies that the particles making up the crystal are arranged in a definite, three-dimensional pattern. One can sometimes deduce what this pattern must be from the crystal form. A great deal more information concerning the packing of particles can be obtained by x-ray diffraction, which is one of the most powerful structural tools available to the chemist.

X-rays are diffracted by a crystal in somewhat the same way that ordinary light is spread out by a diffraction grating. Those of you who have had a course in physics will recall that visible light striking a glass plate ruled with a large number of closely spaced parallel lines is broken up by diffraction into a series of beams, provided the spacing between the lines is of the same order of magnitude as the wavelength of the light. Von Laue, in 1912, suggested that crystals, which are made up of layers of particles a few angstroms apart, should act as a diffraction grating for x-rays, which have wavelengths of 0.1 to 10 Å. This reasoning was soon confirmed experimentally. Figure 12.8 shows a typical diffraction pattern obtained by passing a beam of x-rays through a crystal of sodium chloride.

In 1913, W. L. Bragg adapted the technique of x-ray diffraction to the determination of crystal structures. The principle which he used is embodied in the so-called Bragg equation which relates the angle of diffraction to the distance between successive layers of atoms or ions in the crystal.

$$\sin \theta = \frac{n\lambda}{2d} \qquad (12.3)$$

In this equation, θ is the angle between the beam and the layer of atoms, λ is the wavelength of the x-rays, d is the distance between successive layers, and n is an integer (1, 2, 3, . . .) known as the order number of the particular beam.

By measuring the angles at which x-rays of known wavelength are diffracted by a crystal, one can calculate from equation 12.3 the distances between planes of atoms or ions. In this way, values can often be obtained for atomic and ionic radii. It is more difficult to deduce the geometric pattern in which the particles are arranged. The basic problem is that the x-ray beam "sees" not one but many different series of layers of particles oriented at various angles to each other. Consequently, an x-ray beam, in passing through a crystal, is broken up into a large number of diffracted

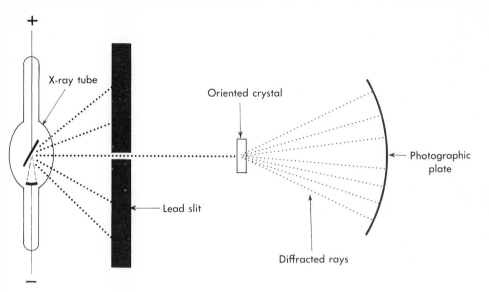

FIGURE 12.9 Schematic diagram of x-ray diffraction from a single crystal.

beams. Nevertheless, by studying the relative intensities of the various beams, x-ray crystallographers have been able to unravel the particle structure of a wide variety of crystals.

The basic information which comes out of x-ray diffraction studies concerns the dimensions and geometric form of what is known as the **unit cell,** the smallest unit which, repeated over and over again in three dimensions, generates the crystal lattice. Perhaps the easiest unit cell to visualize is the simple cubic cell, which consists of eight identical particles arranged at the corners of a cube. Two variations on this structure, body-centered and face-centered cubes, were discussed in Chapter 11. A few other unit cells are shown in Figure 12.10.

Substances which crystallize in the same geometric form are said to be **isomorphous** with each other. If the atoms or ions involved are of approximately the same size, isomorphous substances may form mixed crystals in which one particle is substituted more or less randomly for another. Calcium carbonate, $CaCO_3$, and

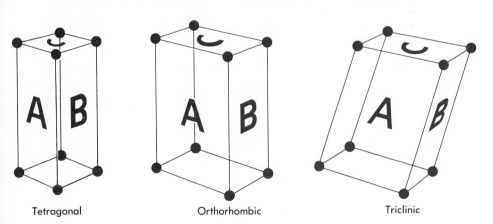

Tetragonal   Orthorhombic   Triclinic

FIGURE 12.10 Some common unit cells in crystals.

magnesium carbonate, $MgCO_3$, both of which form hexagonal crystals, are frequently found in nature in the form of mixed crystals in the mineral dolomite.

[Many substances are capable of crystallizing in more than one form, depending upon the temperature and pressure. This general phenomenon is referred to as **polymorphism;** when it is exhibited by elementary substances such as carbon (diamond and graphite) or sulfur (rhombic or monoclinic crystals), it is called allotropy (cf. Chapter 11).]

Types of Lattices

For many purposes, we are more interested in the types of forces holding particles together in a crystal than we are in the geometric arrangement of the particles. From this point of view, one can distinguish four lattice types, each of which has been discussed previously.

1. **Molecular** (I_2, CO_2, etc.). Small, discrete molecules are held together by relatively weak dipole or Van der Waals forces.

2. **Macromolecular** (C, SiO_2, etc.). All the atoms in the crystal are covalently bonded to each other.

3. **Metallic** (Na, Al, etc.). An array of positive ions is held together by relatively mobile valence electrons.

4. **Ionic.** Oppositely charged ions are held together by strong electrostatic forces. The ions may be monatomic (Na^+, Ca^{+2}, Cl^-, F^-, etc.) or polyatomic (NH_4^+, SO_4^{-2}, NO_3^-, etc.).

Many ionic compounds, when crystallized from aqueous solution, include water molecules as an integral part of the crystal lattice. Such compounds are called **hydrates.** Since the water molecules occupy definite positions in the lattice, the ratio of moles of water to moles of salt is fixed and is either an integer or a simple fraction. The formulas and colors of some typical hydrates are given in Table 12.5.

TABLE 12.5 IONIC HYDRATES

Formula	Color	Formula	Color
$Na_2SO_4 \cdot 10\ H_2O$	white	$CuSO_4 \cdot 5\ H_2O$	blue
$MgSO_4 \cdot 7\ H_2O$	white	$CuSO_4 \cdot 3\ H_2O$	blue
$CaSO_4 \cdot 2\ H_2O$	white	$CuSO_4 \cdot H_2O$	white
$CaSO_4 \cdot \frac{1}{2}\ H_2O$	white	$CoCl_2 \cdot 6\ H_2O$	pink
$NaI \cdot 2\ H_2O$	white	$NiSO_4 \cdot 7\ H_2O$	green

As Table 12.5 indicates, many salts can form more than one hydrate. The form which crystallizes from solution depends upon the conditions, particularly the temperature, at which the crystallization is carried out. As the temperature rises, the relative amount of hydrated water in general decreases, usually by integral amounts at fixed temperatures. Along this same line, it is commonly observed that hydrates when heated in air lose water of crystallization in this same, stepwise fashion, eventually yielding the anhydrous compound. Many hydrates are sufficiently unstable to lose water at room temperature when exposed to dry air. This phenomenon is referred to as **efflorescence.**

In certain hydrates, the principal function of the water molecules seems to be to fill holes in the crystal lattice. In $NaI \cdot 2\ H_2O$, for example, the water molecules fit into spaces between the small Na^+ ions (radius = 0.95 Å) and the large I^- ions (radius = 2.16 Å). More commonly, the water molecules are held by relatively strong forces to the ions, usually the cations. The fact that $CuSO_4 \cdot 5 H_2O$, unlike anhydrous $CuSO_4$, is strongly colored implies an electronic interaction between the water molecules and the surrounding ions. In this particular hydrate, four of the water molecules appear to be joined to a Cu^{+2} ion through coordinate covalent bonds to form what is known as an "aquo complex ion," $Cu(H_2O)_4^{+2}$ (see Chapters 16 and 19). The other water molecule is associated with the SO_4^{-2} ion, presumably through hydrogen bond formation.

Defect Crystals

A perfect crystal, in which all of the particles are exactly where they are supposed to be and every lattice site is occupied by the proper particle, is an extremely useful model for discussing the structure of solids. However, a perfect crystal, like an ideal gas, is an abstraction; the crystals we work with in the laboratory contain imperfections, no matter how carefully they are prepared. These defects, even if relatively few in number, can profoundly affect the physical and chemical properties of a solid substance.

In Chapter 11, it was pointed out that minute quantities of aluminum or arsenic in a macromolecular crystal of silicon cause a tremendous increase in electrical conductivity. The same effect can be achieved by introducing certain foreign ions into ionic crystals. By "doping" crystals of nickel oxide with small amounts of lithium, some of the Ni^{+2} ions can be replaced by Li^+ ions, thereby producing a semiconductor.

Even in the absence of foreign particles, a crystal will contain defects. Consider, for example, an ionic crystal which, if it were perfect, would consist of an equal number of + and − ions arranged in a completely ordered geometric pattern (Figure 12.11a). In practice, we can expect to find, at any finite temperature, defects of the types shown in Figure 12.11b and c. The so-called Frenkel defect, illustrated schematically in Figure 12.11b, results from the displacement of an ion from its normal lattice site to an "interstitial" position. The migration of a cation

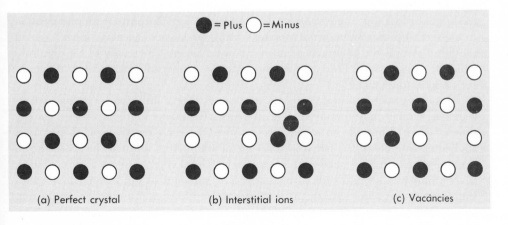

● = Plus ○ = Minus

(a) Perfect crystal   (b) Interstitial ions   (c) Vacancies

FIGURE 12.11 Two-dimensional representation of some common defects in crystalline lattices.

and an anion from the interior to the surface of a crystal, leaving two vacancies in the crystal lattice, produces what is known as a Schottky defect (Figure 12.11c).

The defects shown here do not affect the stoichiometry of an ionic crystal; in each case, we are left with an equal number of + and − ions and hence an atom ratio of exactly 1:1. In practice, we find that ionic defect crystals frequently deviate from the exact stoichiometry required by the Law of Constant Proportions. The oxides and sulfides of the heavier metals commonly show either a slight deficiency or a slight excess of metal atoms (cf. Chapter 2, Section 2.3). Zinc oxide (ZnO) prepared by heating an excess of the metal with oxygen at high temperatures, may contain up to 0.03 per cent of excess zinc; nickel oxide (NiO) is ordinarily slightly deficient in metal.

The excess zinc incorporated into nonstoichiometric zinc oxide crystals is believed to be present as interstitial zinc atoms or, if you wish, interstitial Zn^{+2} ions to which two electrons are loosely bound (Figure 12.12). The metal deficiency in nonstoichiometric nickel oxide appears to result from positive ion vacancies in the NiO crystal; scattered throughout the crystal are sites from which Ni^{+2} ions are missing. In order to maintain electrical neutrality, excess positive charges must be associated with these sites. The chemist describes this situation by saying that in the immediate vicinity of a Ni^{+2} ion vacancy there are two Ni^{+3} ions.

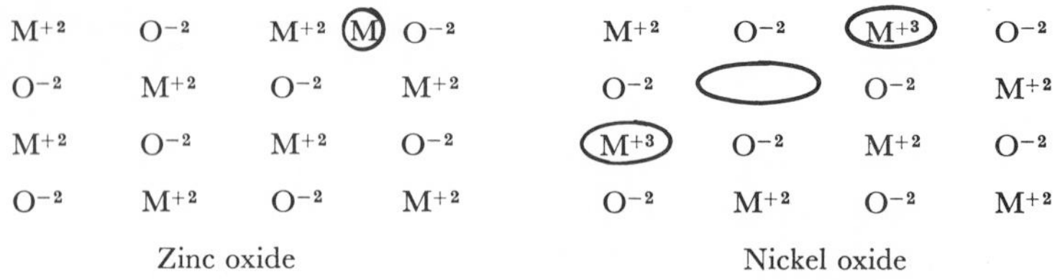

FIGURE 12.12 Lattice defects in some nonstoichiometric oxides.

Defects of the type we have described can lead to important changes in the properties of ionic crystals. In particular, they account for:

1. Diffusion. The introduction of imperfections into a crystal greatly facilitates diffusion in the solid state. An interstitial ion can jump from one position to another and thereby move across the crystal. Vacancies can also "move"; as an ion fills a vacant site by moving into it, another vacancy is created at the site from which the ion moved. Thus, as ions move across the crystal, the vacancy moves in the opposite direction.

From the standpoint of chemistry, the promotion of diffusion by crystal defects is perhaps their most important consequence. Reactions involving solids usually proceed by a diffusion-controlled mechanism. One such reaction which has been studied extensively is that between silver metal and molten sulfur. It has been shown that the silver sulfide formed in this reaction is "permeable" to silver atoms. That is, silver atoms are able to diffuse through the silver sulfide so as to come in contact with sulfur atoms and react with them. Were it not for diffusion, the reaction would stop as soon as a thin layer of silver sulfide formed at the silver-sulfur interface.

2. Semiconductivity. Under the influence of an electrical field, ions can move across a crystal and thereby carry a current. In nonstoichiometric crystals of zinc oxide or nickel oxide, electronic conduction is also possible. The electrons associated with interstitial Zn^{+2} ions are relatively mobile and make zinc oxide with a slight excess of zinc an n-type semiconductor, analogous to silicon containing a slight amount of arsenic. Nonstoichiometric nickel oxide is a p-type semiconductor; here it is the positive hole which migrates, presumably through the transfer of an electron from a Ni^{+2} ion to an adjacent Ni^{+3} ion.

3. Color. Certain ionic crystals which are transparent if extremely pure become colored when defects are introduced. If one heats a rock salt crystal to a high temperature in the presence of sodium vapor and cools it slowly to room temperature, the crystal takes on a blue color, which is believed to be due to the presence of colloidally dispersed sodium. If the crystal is quenched to cool it quickly to room temperature, it takes on a yellow color which has been attributed to the presence of electrons trapped in sites normally occupied by chloride ions. These electrons absorb light in the blue region of the spectrum; light passing through the crystal is rich in the yellow wavelength region.

4. Fluorescence. Certain defect crystals when exposed to high-energy radiation absorb part of the energy and emit the remainder in the form of visible light. This phenomenon is referred to as fluorescence if the emission of light is virtually instantaneous. When there is a time lag between absorption and emission, it is called phosphorescence. One of the most important phosphorescent materials is zinc sulfide, used commercially in television picture tubes. A slight excess of zinc atoms or a trace of foreign ions such as Cu^{+2} is necessary if zinc sulfide is to act as a phosphor; careful purification of zinc sulfide crystals renders them inactive.

12.4 SOLID-VAPOR EQUILIBRIUM

We ordinarily think of the transition from the solid to the vapor state as occurring in two steps, the melting of the solid to a liquid followed by vaporization of the liquid. However, it is entirely possible for a solid to pass directly to the vapor; this type of phase change is referred to as *sublimation.* All of us have seen this process occur with solid carbon dioxide (Dry Ice), which seems to disappear when exposed at room temperature. Iodine is another substance which sublimes readily; if crystals of iodine are placed in a stoppered bottle at room temperature, one can observe the purple color of iodine vapor as it forms above the crystals. It is perhaps less generally realized that the substance water can and often does sublime. On a winter day when the temperature is well below freezing, snow passes directly to water vapor without going through the liquid as an intermediate. High quality dehydrated foods are now being prepared by the process known as freeze-drying, in which water vapor is removed from the frozen material at very low temperatures and pressures.

Vapor Pressure of Solids

A solid placed in a closed container at a constant temperature will establish equilibrium with its vapor. When equilibrium is reached, we find that the vapor exerts a constant, fixed pressure, referred to as the vapor pressure or, sometimes, the sublimation pressure, of the solid. The vapor pressure of a solid, like that of a liquid, increases with temperature. To study the variation of vapor pressure with tempera-ture, we can use the same apparatus employed with liquids (Figure 12.3). If we

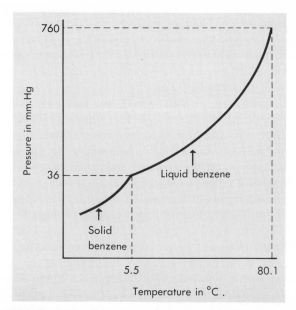

FIGURE 12.13   Vapor pressures of solid and liquid benzene.

introduce solid benzene at a temperature of, let us say, 0°C, we find that upon reaching equilibrium, it establishes a vapor pressure of 24 mm. Hg. Upon raising the temperature to 5.5°C, the vapor pressure of the solid rises to 36 mm. Hg; at temperatures below 0°C, the vapor pressure decreases slowly, reaching 10 mm. Hg at −12°C. In Figure 12.13, we have shown the vapor pressure curves for both solid and liquid benzene. It will be noted that the two curves have the same general form. The vapor pressure curve of the solid is, of course, displaced toward lower temperatures and pressures.

Heat of Sublimation

The amount of heat absorbed when a solid passes directly to the vapor state at a constant pressure is referred to as its heat of sublimation. We find experimentally that for a given amount of a substance at a particular temperature, the heat of sublimation (ΔH subl.) is equal to the sum of the heat of fusion (ΔH fus.) plus the heat of vaporization (ΔH vap.)

$$\left| \Delta H \text{ subl.} = \Delta H \text{ fus.} + \Delta H \text{ vap.} \right| \tag{12.4}$$

For 1 mole of benzene at 5.5°C, these quantities are respectively 10.82 kcal., 2.55 kcal., and 8.27 kcal.

Equation 12.4 illustrates the principle referred to earlier that the heat change (more exactly, the enthalpy change) for a process depends only upon the final and initial states and not upon the path. Thus, the heat required to convert solid benzene to benzene vapor at 5.5°C and 36 mm. Hg is independent of whether this phase change occurs directly (sublimation) or passes through the liquid as an intermediate (fusion and evaporation).

12.5 SOLID-LIQUID-VAPOR EQUILIBRIUM

Referring to Figure 12.13, we note that the vapor pressure curves of solid and liquid benzene intersect at a temperature of 5.5°C and a pressure of 36 mm. Hg. This is referred to as the triple point of benzene because it is the only temperature and pressure at which solid, liquid, and vapor can exist in equilibrium with each other in a system containing only pure benzene.

The triple point of benzene can be reached experimentally in any of several ways. One might, for example, cool the liquid-vapor system described in Section 12.2 to a temperature of 5.5°C, at which point the liquid will exert a pressure of 36 mm. Hg. If one attempts to remove heat from this system, it is found that a new phase, solid benzene, appears. The temperature (and the pressure) remain constant until all the liquid has solidified. Only then is it possible to lower the temperature of the system by removing heat. Conversely, one can approach the triple point by heating the solid until a temperature of 5.5°C and a vapor pressure of 36 mm. Hg are reached. The addition of further heat to the system serves only to melt the solid; the temperature and pressure remain constant until the solid has disappeared.

Each pure substance has a characteristic triple point. That of water is 0.0075°C and 4.58 mm. Hg, the point at which ice, liquid water, and water vapor are in equilibrium with each other. The triple point of carbon dioxide occurs at −56.6°C and 5.1 atm. This explains why a piece of Dry Ice, exposed to the atmosphere in a warm room, sublimes instead of melting; its sublimation pressure reaches 1 atm. at a temperature of −78°C, far below the triple point. (In general, substances which have high triple point pressures such as carbon dioxide, iodine, and naphthalene, are readily sublimed.)

12.6 SOLID-LIQUID EQUILIBRIA

We have seen from the foregoing discussion that solid and liquid benzene are in equilibrium with each other at a temperature of 5.5°C and a pressure of 36 mm. Hg. The question arises whether the equilibrium temperature can be changed by increasing the external pressure. Experimentally, we find that it is indeed possible to do this, although the effect is quite small. In the case of benzene, the equilibrium temperature increases by about 0.026°C per atmosphere. In other words, if one were to increase the external pressure to 1 atm., the temperature would have to be increased by about 0.026°C in order to maintain equilibrium between solid and liquid. At a pressure of 50 atm., the equilibrium temperature would rise to about 1.3°C above the triple point or 6.8°C.

The temperature at which the liquid and solid phases of a pure substance are in equilibrium with each other at a given pressure is referred to as the **melting point** of the solid, or, alternatively, the **freezing point** of the liquid. Melting points are ordinarily measured in an open container at atmospheric pressure. Consequently, the melting points which we find recorded in the literature will ordinarily represent the temperature at which solid and liquid are in equilibrium at an external pressure of 1 atm. For most substances, the melting point under these conditions is virtually identical with the triple point. In the case of benzene, as we have pointed out, the difference amounts to only 0.026°C. With water, the change is even smaller. The

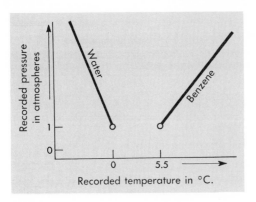

FIGURE 12.14 Effect of pressure on the melting points of water and benzene.

temperature at which ice and water are at equilibrium with each other in an open container in contact with air is defined as exactly 0°C; it will be recalled that the triple point of water is +0.0075°C.

Even though the effect of pressure upon the melting point of a substance is very small, we are often interested in the direction of this effect. We would like to be able to predict, without resort to experiment, whether the melting point of a substance will be increased or decreased by increasing the external pressure. This can be done very simply by applying the principle that an increase in pressure will favor the formation of the more dense phase. In the case of benzene, in which the solid is more dense than the liquid (Table 12.3), an increase in pressure favors the solid. This means that at higher pressures, the solid will become stable at temperatures above the normal melting point; i.e., the melting point will be raised by increasing the pressure. The behavior of benzene is typical of that of most substances, since the solid phase is usually more dense than the liquid.

We recall that water is unusual in that the liquid phase is more dense than the solid; an ice cube floats in a glass of water. We would then predict that the melting point of ice should decrease with pressure; i.e., at high pressures the liquid should be stable at temperatures below the normal melting point. This is confirmed experimentally; the melting point of ice decreases by about 1°C for every 134 atm. of applied pressure. This effect can be demonstrated strikingly by suspending two heavy weights from a wire stretched across a block of ice. In a short time, the wire passes completely through the block of ice, which appears to be unchanged. What happens is that the pressure exerted by the weights melts a thin layer of ice around the wire. As the wire falls, the pressure above it drops and the ice re-forms.

12.7 PHASE DIAGRAMS

We have now completed our discussion of the various possible equilibria that are observed in a system containing one pure substance. It is possible to summarize all that has been said in a graphic way, by means of what is known as a phase diagram. In Figure 12.15, the phase diagram for benzene (a typical pure substance), is illustrated. One can regard this diagram as being constructed by putting together the various curves noting solid, liquid, and vapor relationships for pure benzene.

The coordinates in a phase diagram are the temperature and the pressure (the scales of both coordinates have been adjusted to bring all the important points on the diagram). The purpose of the diagram is to describe the state in which benzene will exist under any given conditions of temperature and pressure. Properly inter- preted, the diagram does this very satisfactorily. For example, let us determine the state in which benzene would be found at 200°C and 2 atm. pressure. We locate the point on the diagram corresponding to these conditions (A) and note that it is in the region labeled Vapor; this means that benzene under such conditions will exist only as a vapor. Any set of conditions of temperature and pressure falling in the vapor region will make benzene occur in only one phase and that will be vapor. Similarly, benzene in any state lying in the regions labeled Liquid or Solid (B or C, for example) will exist solely as a liquid or a solid respectively. For sets of conditions lying on the lines in the phase diagram, benzene can exist in two phases in equilibrium. Along the line separating the liquid and vapor regions, systems containing benzene in both the liquid and the vapor phases can exist; this line is indeed the vapor pressure curve for liquid benzene and can be used to find the vapor pressure at any temperature. The normal boiling point of a liquid will always be on that line at the temperature corresponding to a vapor pressure of one atm. For benzene this point is at 80.1°C (D). The vapor pressure curve ends at the critical temperature of the liquid, since above that temperature the liquid does not exist, and of course has no vapor pressure. On the diagram this is E (289°C and 47.90 atm.).

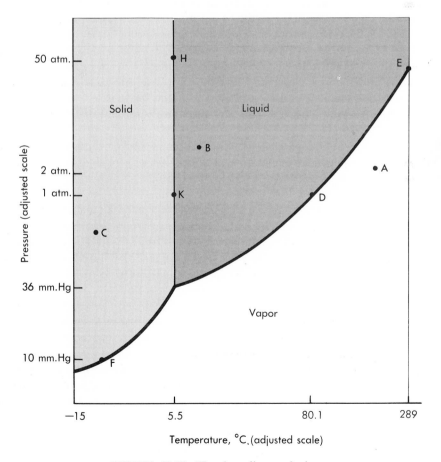

FIGURE 12.15   The phase diagram for benzene.

Along the solid-vapor line two-phase equilibria involving solid and gaseous benzene can occur. This line is the sublimation pressure curve for benzene and from it we can say that the sublimation pressure of benzene at $-12°C$ is about 10 mm. Hg (F). The solid-vapor and liquid-vapor equilibrium lines meet at the triple point of benzene, $5.5°C$ and 36 mm. Hg, where solid, liquid, and vapor coexist in equilibrium. Clearly this is the only point at which this can occur. Rising very nearly vertically from the triple point is the solid-liquid line, essentially the melting-point curve for benzene as a function of total pressure. The line is very nearly straight and inclined very slightly to the right. We see that the melting point of benzene at 1 atm. (K) is very nearly $5.5°C$ and at 50 atm. (H) is about $6.8°C$.

The phase diagrams for other pure substances are very similar in appearance to that for benzene and are interpreted in the same way. Depending on whether the solid is more, or less, dense than the liquid, the slope of the solid-liquid equilibrium line will be positive, as it is for benzene, or negative, as it is for water. For benzene the melting point thus increases with pressure, while for water it decreases.

12.8 NONEQUILIBRIUM PHASE BEHAVIOR

The phase changes which we have considered in this chapter have been assumed to take place under equilibrium conditions. In practice, the phase changes that we observe in the laboratory or in the world around us occur at temperatures and pressures at least slightly removed from equilibrium. When one actually does experiments of the type we have described, he frequently finds that the systems do not behave in quite the manner predicted by the phase diagram. A liquid being vaporized may not boil smoothly, particularly at low pressures. Instead, it may superheat to temperatures above the calculated boiling point and then "bump" and boil furiously. A very pure liquid on cooling does not start to freeze exactly at its freezing point; it has to be supercooled below that temperature before crystallization occurs. Cooling a vapor to a temperature at which its pressure slightly exceeds the vapor pressure may not bring about condensation.

Nonequilibrium behavior is thought to be caused by the system being unable to respond fast enough to maintain equilibrium. For a cooled liquid to crystallize, some centers, or nuclei, on which crystallization can occur, are needed. These centers may be dust particles, other solid impurities, or small crystals of the substance itself. In a very pure liquid, such centers will be missing and the liquid will supercool. As an extreme example, very pure water can be supercooled to as low as $-40°C$ without freezing.

For a liquid to boil, there must be centers at which bubbles can form. These centers may be microscopic bubbles of dissolved gas, dust particles, or sharp crystal edges or corners. When a liquid is to be distilled, one ordinarily adds a small quantity of an inert solid such as marble or porcelain. These solids offer a large surface on which vapor bubbles can form. In the absence of such a surface, pronounced super-heating can occur. Water which has been thoroughly purged of dust particles and gas bubbles has been heated in an open capillary tube to a reported temperature of $270°C$ without boiling.

From a practical standpoint, one of the most frustrating examples of non-equilibrium behavior is the failure of water in the atmosphere to condense and fall as rain at equilibrium temperatures and pressures. A cloud in the upper atmosphere consists of an aggregate of many billions of tiny water droplets approximately 0.1 mm. in diameter. These droplets will not spontaneously coalesce to form drops large enough to fall through the atmosphere. Precipitation is ordinarily initiated by the formation of tiny ice crystals which grow at the expense of the droplets. This means that for precipitation to occur, the temperature within the cloud must be reduced to at least 0°C. In practice, because of supercooling, ice crystals do not form unless the temperature drops to at least -15°C. This means that the water droplets in clouds, particularly on warm days or in hot, arid regions, frequently evaporate without condensing into large drops. To prevent this, clouds are sometimes seeded with condensation nuclei.

One popular method of cloud seeding involves the use of Dry Ice. The sublimation of solid carbon dioxide absorbs enough heat from the cloud to lower the temperature below that required for ice crystal formation. Another substance which is frequently used is finely divided silver iodide, which has a crystal structure similar to that of ice. The presence of silver iodide presumably tends to prevent supercooling and hence allows ice crystals to form at temperatures close to 0°C.

PROBLEMS

12.1 Explain, in terms of the kinetic-molecular model, why:
    a. Liquids are much less compressible than gases.
    b. Liquids have a surface tension.
    c. The vapor pressure of a liquid is independent of volume.
    d. The vapor pressure of a liquid increases with temperature.
    e. Heat is absorbed when a liquid vaporizes.

12.2 The density of liquid xenon at its normal boiling point, -109°C, is 3.06 g./ml.
    a. Calculate the volume of one mole of liquid xenon at -109°C and 1 atm.
    b. Using the Ideal Gas Law, calculate the volume of a mole of xenon vapor at -109°C and 1 atm.
    c. Assuming that xenon atoms can be treated as spheres with a radius of 1.90 Å, calculate the volume of a mole of xenon atoms.
    d. From your answers to a, b, and c, calculate the percentages of the total volume in liquid and gaseous xenon at -109°C and 1 atm. which is occupied by the atoms.

12.3 A sample of water vapor in equilibrium with liquid water at 20°C. is expanded from a volume of 1.0 liter to a volume of 2.0 liters. Assuming equilibrium is maintained at 20°C, what change, if any, occurs in:
    a. The number of molecules in the vapor?
    b. The concentration of molecules in the vapor?
    c. The pressure exerted by the vapor?
    d. The average kinetic energy of the molecules in the vapor?

12.4 If in Problem 12.3 the temperature were increased instead of the volume, what would be your answers to a, b, c, and d?

12.5 A sample of water vapor at 100°C and 50.0 mm. Hg pressure is cooled at constant volume.
    a. What will be its pressure at 50°C (v.p. water at 50°C = 92.5 mm. Hg)?
    b. What will be its pressure at 20°C (v.p. water at 20°C = 17.5 mm. Hg)?

12.6 A tin can, originally full of air at 20°C and 750 mm. Hg, is half-filled with water and immediately stoppered.
    a. What will be the total pressure inside the can when equilibrium is established at 20°C?
    b. If the stoppered can is heated to 50°C, what will be the total pressure inside it?

12.7 A certain liquid has a vapor pressure of 240 mm. Hg at 20°C. A sample of 0.100 mole of this liquid is placed in an evacuated, one-liter container at 20°C.
 a. Using the Ideal Gas Law, calculate the number of moles of vapor which will be present at equilibrium under these conditions (neglect the volume of the liquid).
 b. If the volume of the container is slowly increased, maintaining a constant temperature, at what point will all the liquid be vaporized?
 c. What will be the pressure inside the container when the volume is two liters?
 d. What will be the pressure inside the container when the volume is ten liters?

12.8 Two liquids A and B have vapor pressures at 20°C of 12 mm. Hg and 242 mm. Hg respectively. Which of these liquids would you expect to have:
 a. The higher normal boiling point?
 b. The higher critical temperature?
 c. The higher surface tension at 20°C?
 d. The larger heat of vaporization?

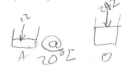

12.9 Explain why:
 a. Ethane is ordinarily transported in cylinders as a liquid but oxygen is not.
 b. Pressure cookers are more widely used in Denver, Colorado, than in Hartford, Connecticut.

12.10 For so-called normal liquids, in which there is no hydrogen bonding or other abnormally strong intermolecular force, the heat of vaporization, in calories per mole, is approximately 21 times the normal boiling point in degrees Kelvin.
 a. Using the data in Table 12.2, comment on the extent of hydrogen bonding in water, benzene, and ether.
 b. What can you say about the extent of hydrogen bonding in ammonia and hydrogen chloride, for which ΔH vap. at the normal boiling point (−33°C, −85°C) is respectively 327 cal./g. and 106 cal./g.?

12.11 If 4.00 g. of steam at 100°C is added to 20.0 g. of ice at 0°C, calculate the final temperature of the system, given that the heat of vaporization of water at 100°C is 540 cal./g., the heat of fusion of ice is 80 cal./g. at 0°C, and the specific heat of liquid water is 1.00 cal. $\cdot$ g.$^{-1}$ $\cdot$ °C^{-1}.

12.12 Calculate the total amount of heat which must be absorbed to convert a mole of ice at 0°C to steam at 100°C:
 a. Using the data given in Problem 12.11.
 b. Using the data given in Table 12.4 and taking the specific heat of water vapor to be 0.45 cal. $\cdot$ g.$^{-1}$ $\cdot$ °C^{-1}. Follow the path: water (s, 0°C) → water (1, 0°C) → water (g, 0°C) → water (g, 100°C).

12.13 From the data in Table 12.4, calculate the heat of sublimation of ice at 0°C. Why does this differ slightly from the quantity calculated in Problem 12.12?

12.14 Explain why:
 a. The normal melting point of a solid is almost identical with the triple point temperature.
 b. External pressure has a much greater effect on the boiling point than on the melting point.
 c. A substance whose triple point pressure is relatively high often sublimes when it is heated rather than melting.

12.15 Under what conditions might it be possible for liquid water to freeze while it is boiling?

12.16 It is commonly observed that driving on ice is most dangerous when the temperature is very close to the freezing point. Suggest a possible explanation.

12.17 State whether or not it is possible for:
 a. A liquid to exist at a temperature above the critical point.
 b. A liquid to exist at a temperature below the triple point.
 c. A gas to exist at a temperature below the critical point.
 d. A solid to exist at a temperature above the triple point.

e. A substance which has a triple pressure point of .2 atm. to exist in the liquid state in an open container.

12.18 A sample of pure benzene is at a pressure of 36 mm. Hg and a temperature of 5.5°C. Referring to the phase diagram of benzene (Figure 12.15), state precisely what will happen if:
a. Heat is removed from the system at constant pressure.
b. Heat is added to the system at constant pressure.
c. The pressure is increased at constant temperature.
d. The temperature is increased at constant pressure.

12.19 Construct a phase diagram for water.

*12.20 The formation of defects in a perfect crystal is an endothermic process ($\Delta H+$). Would you expect ΔS for this process to be positive or negative? Using the Gibbs-Helmholtz equation (Chapter 5), can you explain why at least a small number of defects are found in any crystal at a temperature above $0°K$? What would you expect to happen to the number of defects as the temperature is increased?

12.21 A beam of x-rays obtained by bombarding platinum with electrons has a wavelength of 0.182 Å. Calculate the angle of diffraction for n = 1, 2, and 3 when this x-ray beam strikes a crystal in which the layers of atoms are 1.60 Å apart.

12.22 In discussing crystal lattices, it is important to know how many atoms or ions should be assigned to a particular unit cell. This number is always less than the number shown when the unit cell is drawn, because certain atoms are shared by more than one unit cell. For example, an atom at the corner of a cubic unit cell is shared by eight adjacent unit cubes and hence only one eighth of it should be assigned to a particular cell. Following this reasoning, how many atoms should be assigned to a simple cubic unit cell? A face-centered cubic unit cell? A body-centered cubic unit cell?

12.23 The metal cesium crystallizes in a body-centered cubic unit cell 6.05 Å on an edge.
a. What is the volume of the unit cell?
b. How many atoms should be assigned to this unit cell (cf. Problem 12.22)?
c. What volume is occupied by a mole of cesium atoms?
d. What is the calculated density of cesium (observed density = 1.9 g./ml.)?
e. What is the atomic radius of cesium? (Note that a cesium atom in the center of this cube is touching each of the atoms at the corners.)
f. Explain how x-ray diffraction data can be used to determine Avogadro's number.

12.24 Determine the simplest formula of an ionic compound in which:
a. The unit cell consists of a cube in which there are cations (C) at each corner and an anion (A) at the center of the cube.
b. The unit cell consists of a cube in which there are cations (C) at each corner and anions (A) at the center of each face.

*12.25 Calculate the fraction of empty space or "free volume" in a crystal made up of simple cubic unit cells; body-centered cubic unit cells; face-centered cubic unit cells. Consider the volume of the atoms assigned to each cell in comparison to the volume of the cell itself.

*12.26 The energy of vaporization, ΔE, is actually a more direct measure of the intermolecular forces in a liquid than is the heat of vaporization, ΔH. Why? Using the equation $\Delta H = \Delta E + p\Delta V$ and the Ideal Gas Law, show that for the vaporization of 1 mole of liquid:

$$\Delta H \text{ vap.} = \Delta E \text{ vap.} + RT$$

Calculate ΔE vap. for water at 20°C.

*12.27 Using the data in Table 12.1, calculate the amount of work, in ergs, which must be done to create one sq. cm. of surface in liquid water. Convert this amount of energy to kilocalories. Assuming that approximately half as much energy must be supplied to bring a molecule to the surface as to vaporize it, calculate the amount of energy, in kilocalories, required to bring one molecule of water to the surface. On this basis, what would be the average area occupied by a water molecule at the surface? From what you know about the atomic radii of hydrogen and oxygen, does the number you have just calculated seem physically reasonable?

*12.28 The variation of the vapor pressure of a liquid with temperature may be expressed by the equation:

$$\log_{10} \frac{P_2}{P_1} = \frac{\Delta H \text{ vap. } (T_2 - T_1)}{2.3 \ R \ T_2 T_1}$$

in which P_2 and P_1 are the vapor pressures at temperatures T_2 and T_1, expressed in °K, and R is the gas constant in cal./mole °K (1.987).

a. Knowing that the normal boiling point of benzene is 80.1°C and that its heat of vaporization is 7.3 kcal./mole, calculate the vapor pressure of benzene at 50°C.

b. Explain how one could use this equation in combination with the rule referred to in Problem 12.10 to estimate the vapor pressure of a liquid at a particular temperature, knowing only its normal boiling point.

13 | SOLUTIONS

Up to this point, we have been primarily concerned with the structures and properties of pure substances. From now on, we shall be dealing increasingly with chemical changes taking place in solution. In this chapter, we shall develop the background for a discussion of solution chemistry by studying the structure and physical properties of solutions.

A solution was defined in Chapter 1 as a homogeneous mixture of two or more substances. In this connotation, the adjective "homogeneous" ordinarily means uniform to visual observation by eye or microscope. From a structural point of view, homogeneity implies that:

1. The particles of the various components are of molecular size, of the order of 50 Å or less in diameter.

2. These submicroscopic particles, which may be atoms, ions, or molecules, are distributed in a more or less random pattern, showing little if any long-range order.

Both of these criteria must be met by a true solution. In a solution formed by adding benzene (C_6H_6) to toluene (C_7H_8), the particles are individual molecules 6 to 8 Å in diameter. These molecules are distributed in a random pattern throughout the liquid phase; there is no tendency for large clusters of benzene or toluene molecules to aggregate in one portion of the solution. In a suspension, either or both of these criteria are not met. To cite a familiar example, fog is formed by the clustering of thousands upon thousands of water molecules into droplets large enough to be visible to the eye.

13.1 SOLUTION PHASES

Solutions may exist in any of the three states of matter; gas, solid, or liquid. The physical and chemical properties of **gaseous** solutions have been treated previously (Chapter 6) and will not be discussed further here.

Solid solutions are more common than is generally realized; many familiar alloys fall into this category. The "nickel" coin is actually a solid solution containing 25 per cent by weight of nickel dissolved in copper. Brass is a solid solution of up to 40 per cent of zinc in copper. Two structural types of solid solutions can be distinguished:

1. **Substitutional solid solutions,** in which one type of particle is substituted, more or less randomly, for another. Metals whose atoms are of about the same size

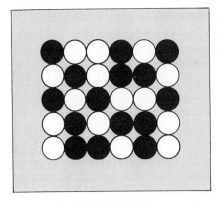
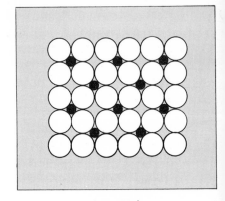

Substitutional   Interstitial

FIGURE 13.1   Two-dimensional representation of two kinds of solid solution.

tend to form solutions of this type. If one cools a melt containing nickel (at. rad. = 1.24 Å) and copper (at. rad. = 1.28 Å), a completely homogeneous solid phase is produced regardless of the proportions of the two metals. On the other hand, lead (at. rad. = 1.75 Å) is completely insoluble in solid copper. Microscopic examination of an alloy prepared by heating these two metals together shows it to be a heterogeneous mixture of crystals of the two elements.

2. **Interstitial solid solutions,** in which small, foreign atoms fit into empty spaces in a regular crystal lattice. A commercially important example of an interstitial solid solution is that formed by carbon (at. rad. = 0.77 Å) with iron (at. rad. = 1.26 Å). Iron, below 912°C, crystallizes in a body-centered cubic structure (α-iron or ferrite) in which the interstices are too small to accommodate carbon atoms. At 912°C, the iron undergoes a crystal modification to a face-centered cubic structure (γ-iron or austenite) with larger interstices capable of dissolving up to 2 per cent by weight of carbon. If an alloy of this composition is cooled rapidly by quenching, the carbon remains in solution, giving a hard, brittle steel.

The chemist most frequently deals with solutions in the liquid rather than the gaseous or solid state. Frequently, liquid solutions are subdivided according to the physical states of the pure components. We may have a solution in which the components are liquids (gasoline, alcohol-water). One component may be a gas (soda-water) or a solid (salt water). It is even possible to have a liquid solution in which neither component, at the temperature and pressure of the solution, is a liquid. A familiar example is the solution formed when calcium chloride or sodium chloride is used to "melt" ice below 0°C.

The remainder of this chapter will be devoted to a discussion of the properties and structures of liquid solutions, particularly those in which water is a major constituent. Before making such a study, it will be helpful to consider some of the terms used to describe the composition of solutions.

13.2   SOLUTION TERMINOLOGY

Solvent and Solute

While there are no rigid rules dictating which component of a solution shall be called the solute and which the solvent, certain conventions are ordinarily followed.

In a gas-liquid or solid-liquid solution, the liquid is referred to as the solvent. This choice reflects the way in which we visualize the solution process; it is natural to think of carbon dioxide or sodium chloride as "dissolving" in water rather than the reverse.

If both components of a solution are themselves liquids, the designations "solute" and "solvent" are more ambiguous and are seldom used without qualification. Frequently, the component present in greater amount is referred to as the solvent. In a solution containing 1 g. of ethyl alcohol in 100 g. of water, one ordinarily speaks of the water as the solvent and the alcohol as the solute. If the amounts of alcohol and water are more nearly equal or if one wishes to consider a series of alcohol-water solutions covering the entire composition range, the choice becomes less clear-cut and must be specified.

Dilute and Concentrated Solutions

Although the adjectives dilute and concentrated are frequently used to refer to the composition of solutions, they are seldom given an exact meaning. Neither, for that matter, can they be restricted to a particular concentration range; about all that one can say is that a dilute solution of A in B contains a lower concentration of A than does a concentrated solution of A in the same solvent.

In a few cases, the terms dilute and concentrated have taken on a quantitative meaning. Dilute and concentrated solutions of certain acids and bases, labeled as such in the general chemistry laboratory, have the concentrations specified in Table 13.1.

TABLE 13.1 CONCENTRATIONS OF LABORATORY ACID AND BASE SOLUTIONS

		Solute	Moles Solute (per liter)	Per cent Solute (by weight)	Density (g./ml.)
Hydrochloric acid	conc.	HCl	12	36	1.18
	dilute		6	20	1.10
Nitric acid	conc.	HNO₃	16	72	1.42
	dilute		6	32	1.19
Sulfuric acid	conc.	H₂SO₄	18	96	1.84
	dilute		3	25	1.18
Ammonia	conc.	NH₃	15	28	0.90
	dilute		6	11	0.96

Saturated, Unsaturated, and Supersaturated Solutions

A saturated solution of a solute A is one which is in equilibrium with undissolved A. The simplest way to prepare a saturated solution at 25°C of, let us say, sodium chloride in water, is to bring an excess of the solid into contact with water at that temperature and stir until no more NaCl goes into solution. The resulting solution, which contains 36.2 g. of sodium chloride per 100 g. of water, is said to be saturated with sodium chloride. Addition of further solid sodium chloride fails to change its concentration in solution.

If one attempts to carry out an experiment of the type just described with alcohol and water at 25°C it is found that equilibrium cannot be established. Regardless of the relative amounts of alcohol and water added, only one layer forms. The two liquids are soluble in each other in all proportions; there is no such thing as a saturated solution of alcohol in water or water in alcohol. As we shall see later, this behavior is not uncommon with liquid-liquid solutions; one might look upon it as the rule rather than the exception.

[An **unsaturated** solution contains a lower concentration of solute than a saturated solution.] A solution at 25°C containing less than 36.2 g. of sodium chloride per 100 g. of water is said to be unsaturated with respect to sodium chloride. It is not in a state of true equilibrium; if an unsaturated solution is brought into contact with solute its concentration increases to approach saturation.

[A **supersaturated** solution in one which contains a higher concentration of solute than a saturated solution.] Supersaturated solutions most commonly arise when a solid is dissolved in a liquid. To illustrate one method of preparing a supersaturated solution, consider a specific example, that of sodium acetate, $NaC_2H_3O_2$, dissolved in water. At 20°C, a saturated solution contains 46.5 g. of sodium acetate per 100 g. of water; at higher temperatures, the solubility of sodium acetate is considerably greater. If one heats 80 g. of this salt with 100 g. of water until it is completely dissolved (a temperature of about 50°C is required) and then cools carefully to 20°C, the excess solute remains in solution. This supersaturated solution can be maintained indefinitely so long as there are no nuclei upon which crystallization can start (cf. the phenomenon of supercooling, described in Chapter 12). If a small seed crystal of sodium acetate is added, crystallization takes place until equilibrium is attained by the formation of a saturated solution.

13.3   CONCENTRATION UNITS

The physical and chemical properties of solutions depend to a large extent upon the relative amounts of solute and solvent present. For this reason, in any quantitative work involving solutions, it is important to specify concentrations. This can be done either by stating the relative amounts of solute and solvent or, alternatively, the amount of one component relative to the total amount (mass or volume) of solution.

In this chapter, we shall have occasion to use three different concentration units in each of which the amount of solute is expressed in moles. These are: the mole fraction, molality, and molarity.

Mole Fraction

The mole fraction of component A in a solution, designated as X_A, is given by the expression:

$$X_A = \frac{\text{no. of moles of A}}{\text{total no. moles of all components}} \tag{13.1}$$

Example 13.1 illustrates how this defining equation can be used to calculate the mole fractions of substances in solution or to give directions for the preparation of a solution containing components at specified mole fractions.

Example 13.1

    a. Calculate the mole fractions of ethyl alcohol, C_2H_5OH, and water, H_2O, in a solution prepared by adding 50.0 g. of ethyl alcohol to 50.0 g. of water.

b. How should one prepare an ethyl alcohol–water solution in which the mole fraction of ethyl alcohol is 0.300?

Solution

a. Since 1 mole C_2H_5OH = 46.0 g. and 1 mole H_2O = 18.0 g.

$$\text{no. moles } C_2H_5OH = 50.0 \text{ g.} \times \frac{1 \text{ mole}}{46.0 \text{ g.}} = 1.09$$

$$\text{no. moles } H_2O = 50.0 \text{ g.} \times \frac{1 \text{ mole}}{18.0 \text{ g.}} = 2.78$$

Using equation 13.1:

$$X \; C_2H_5OH = \frac{1.09}{1.09 + 2.78} = 0.282$$

$$X \; H_2O = \frac{2.78}{1.09 + 2.78} = 0.718$$

Note that: $X \; C_2H_5OH + X \; H_2O = 1$. The sum of the mole fractions of all the components of a solution will always be equal to unity.

b. A mole fraction of C_2H_5OH of 0.300 requires that there be 0.300 mole of C_2H_5OH in a total of 1.000 mole of solution; this in turn means that for every 0.300 mole of C_2H_5OH there must be $(1.000 - 0.300) = 0.700$ mole of H_2O.

$$.300 \text{ mole } C_2H_5OH = .300 \times 46.0 \text{ g. } C_2H_5OH = 13.8 \text{ g. } C_2H_5OH$$

$$.700 \text{ mole } H_2O = .700 \times 18.0 \text{ g. } H_2O = 12.6 \text{ g. } H_2O$$

One could prepare such a solution by adding alcohol to water in a mass ratio of 13.8 : 12.6. Depending upon the amount of solution required, one might add 13.8 g. of C_2H_5OH to 12.6 g. of H_2O, 27.6 g. of C_2H_5OH to 25.2 g. of water, and so on.

If all of the particles in a solution are molecules, the mole fraction becomes identical with the molecule fraction. Thus, in an alcohol-water solution in which the mole fraction of alcohol is 0.3, three out of every 10 particles in the solution are alcohol molecules; the other seven are water molecules (Figure 13.2).

Molality

Molality (m) is defined as the number of moles of solute per kilogram of solvent. Mathematically:

$$m = \frac{\text{no. of moles solute}}{\text{no. of kg. solvent}} \tag{13.2}$$

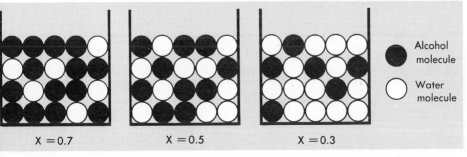

FIGURE 13.2 Schematic drawing showing relative numbers of alcohol and water molecules in solutions of various mole fractions of alcohol.

Example 13.2. Calculate the molality of a solution prepared by dissolving 20.4 g. of NaCl in 192 g. of water.

Solution

$$1 \text{ mole NaCl} = 58.45 \text{ g. NaCl}$$

$$\text{no. moles NaCl} = 20.4 \text{ g. NaCl} \times \frac{1 \text{ mole NaCl}}{58.45 \text{ g. NaCl}} = 0.349$$

$$\text{no. kg. H}_2\text{O} = 0.192$$

From equation (13.2):

$$\text{molality NaCl} = \frac{0.349}{0.192} = 1.82$$

As Example 13.2 implies, a solution of a given molality can be prepared by dissolving a known weight of solute in a predetermined weight of solvent. The precision with which the concentration is known is limited only by that of the balance used to make the weighings. One of the advantages of molality as a concentration unit is that it is independent of temperature; a one molal solution prepared at 20°C will retain the same molality at 100°C, provided there is no loss of solute or solvent on heating.

Molarity

Concentrations of reagents in the general chemistry laboratory are most often specified in terms of molarity (M), which is defined as the number of moles of solute per liter of solution, or:

$$M = \frac{\text{no. of moles solute}}{\text{no. liters solution}} \tag{13.3}$$

Example 13.3

    a. What is the molarity of a solution prepared by dissolving 16.0 g. of $BaCl_2$ in sufficient water to give 450 ml. of solution?

    b. How should one prepare 20.0 l. of 6.0 M NaOH solution, starting with solid NaOH?

    c. How should one prepare 1.0 l. of 0.50 M NaOH solution, starting with the solution in b?

Solution

    a.

$$1 \text{ mole BaCl}_2 = 137.3 \text{ g.} + 70.9 \text{ g.} = 208.2 \text{ g.}$$

$$\text{no. moles BaCl}_2 = 16.0 \text{ g. BaCl}_2 \times \frac{1 \text{ mole BaCl}_2}{208.2 \text{ g. BaCl}_2} = 0.0769$$

$$\text{no. l. solution} = 0.450$$

By equation 13.3:

$$M = \frac{0.0769}{0.450} = 0.171$$

  b. From equation 13.3, we have:

$$\text{no. moles NaOH} = (\text{M NaOH})\ (\text{Volume of solution in liters})$$

$$= 6.0\ \frac{\text{moles}}{\text{l.}} \times 20.0 \text{ l.} = 120 \text{ moles NaOH}$$

It follows that one should weigh out 120 moles (4800 g.) of NaOH and dissolve in sufficient water to give 20.0 l. of solution.

c. Clearly, the more concentrated solution (6.0 M) must be diluted with water to give a 0.50 M solution. The question is: What volume of 6.0 M solution should one start with to prepare one liter of 0.50 M solution? To answer this question, we note that the number of moles of solute is not changed by dilution. In the final solution, we have:

$$0.50 \ \frac{\text{mole}}{\text{l.}} \times 1.0 \text{ l.} = 0.50 \text{ mole NaOH}$$

All that remains is to calculate what volume of 6.0 M NaOH must be taken to give 0.50 mole of NaOH:

$$\text{volume (in liters)} = \frac{\text{no. moles solute}}{\text{molarity}} = \frac{0.50}{6.0} = 0.083 \text{ l.}$$

Hence, one should take 0.083 l. (83 ml.) of the 6.0 M solution and dilute with water to give a final volume of 1.0 l. of the 0.50 M solution.

The volume measurements referred to in Example 13.3 can often be carried out with sufficient accuracy using a graduated cylinder or beaker. Where greater accuracy is required, a volumetric flask of the type shown in Figure 13.3 may be used. The flask is designed to hold a specified volume of liquid when filled to the mark inscribed on the narrow neck. With a flask of this type and an ordinary analytical balance, one can prepare solutions to a given molarity within 0.1 per cent or better.

FIGURE 13.3 Volumetric flask.

Since the volume of a liquid is more easily measured than its mass, laboratory reagents whose concentrations need not be known too accurately are usually made up to a specified molarity rather than a given molality. Furthermore, as we shall see later (Chapter 18), molarity is a very convenient unit for calculations involving the relative quantities of two solutions that react with each other. Consequently, we find that many of the standard solutions used in analytical laboratories have their concentrations expressed in molarity, often to three or more significant figures. Since the volume of a solution ordinarily increases with temperature, it follows that, for very exact work, the temperature at which a solution of a given molarity was prepared should be specified. The molarity of a solution can readily be converted to molality if its density is known (Example 13.4).

Example 13.4.   The density of a 0.0600 M solution of potassium iodide in water is 1.006 g./ml. at 20°C. Calculate the molality of the solution.

Solution.   In order to obtain the molality, we must know the number of moles of KI per kilogram of water. Let us base our calculations on one liter of solution.

$$\text{no. moles KI} = 0.0600$$

To obtain the mass of water in one liter of solution, we first note that since the solution has a density of 1.006 g./ml., the total mass of one liter of solution must be 1006 g. To find the mass of water, we must subtract from 1006 g. the mass of KI. Noting that one mole of KI weighs 166 g., we have:

$$\text{mass of KI} = 0.0600 \text{ mole} \times \frac{166 \text{ g.}}{\text{mole}} = 10.0 \text{ g.}$$

hence,

$$\text{mass of water} = 1006 \text{ g.} - 10 \text{ g.} = 996 \text{ g.}$$

To calculate the molality:

$$m = \frac{\text{no. moles KI}}{\text{no. kg. water}} = \frac{0.600}{0.996} = 0.0602$$

As this example implies, the molarity of a solute in a dilute water solution is virtually the same as its molality. For more concentrated solutions or with a solvent other than water, concentrations expressed in these two units may differ widely from each other.

A fourth concentration unit, which happens to be particularly useful in quantitative analysis, is normality, defined as the number of gram equivalent weights of solute per liter of solution:

$$N = \frac{\text{no. of G.E.W. solute}}{\text{no. liters solution}}$$

We shall postpone further discussion of normalities of solutions to Chapter 18, Section 18.2.

13.4 PRINCIPLES OF SOLUBILITY

The prediction of the extent to which one substance will dissolve in another is one of the most fascinating and, at the same time, one of the most frustrating problems in chemical theory. The following brief discussion of this topic deals with solubility in the liquid state and is subdivided according to whether the solute is a liquid, a gas, or a solid.

Liquid-Liquid

A major portion of the driving force behind the solution process in this case can be attributed to the spontaneous tendency for matter to go to a more random, less ordered state. When one liquid dissolves in another, the molecules of the two substances become thoroughly mixed; in this sense, we have gone from a more ordered to a less ordered system. Thermodynamically, we say that when one liquid dissolves in another, there is an increase in entropy.

If the change in entropy were the only factor determining solubility, we might expect all liquids to be infinitely soluble in each other. From another point of view, we can readily see why this is not the case. We have pointed out that the molecules in a pure liquid are held together by attractive forces. Energy has to be absorbed to overcome these forces so that the two different kinds of molecules can mix with each other. Unless the attractive forces between molecules in the solution are at least as strong as those in the pure liquids, energy has to be absorbed for solution to occur. This will tend to reduce the spontaneity of the solution process and can lead to limited solubility.

In discussing the solubility of two liquids in each other, it is sometimes stated that "like dissolves like." A more meaningful way of expressing this same idea is to say that substances which have similar molecular structures and, consequently, intermolecular forces of about the same magnitude, will be soluble in each other in all proportions. An illustration of this rule is furnished by the liquid aliphatic hydrocarbons of general formula C_nH_{2n+2} (C_5H_{12}, C_6H_{14} ... $C_{18}H_{38}$), all of which are completely miscible with each other. Molecules of these nonpolar substances are held together by Van der Waals forces which increase only slightly with molecular size. The forces between C_5H_{12} molecules in pure liquid pentane are very nearly the same as those between C_5H_{12} and C_8H_{18} molecules in a solution of pentane in octane. A pentane molecule readily passes into solution in octane because it undergoes virtually no change in environment in the solution process.

Moderate differences in polarity between solute and solvent seem to have little effect on solubility. Aliphatic hydrocarbons of the type just discussed are as soluble in chloroform ($CHCl_3$, dipole moment = 1.15 Debye unit) as they are in each other or in carbon tetrachloride (CCl_4, dipole moment = 0). This reflects the weakness of dipole forces, which make only a minor contribution to the total attractive force between $CHCl_3$ molecules. The fact that the heats of vaporization and surface tensions of chloroform and carbon tetrachloride are virtually identical implies that the intermolecular forces in $CHCl_3$ and CCl_4 are nearly the same. It is about as easy to "break into" the liquid structure of $CHCl_3$ as it is in CCl_4 and consequently the two liquids show similar solvent properties despite a considerable difference in polarity.

If one attempts to dissolve a hydrocarbon in water, the situation is quite different. In order to dissolve appreciable quantities of, let us say, pentane in water, one would have to break the strong intermolecular hydrogen bonds holding water molecules together. The large amount of energy required to do this would not be restored in any step of the solution process; the Van der Waals forces in solution between C_5H_{12} and H_2O molecules are probably weaker than those between C_5H_{12} molecules in liquid pentane. Consequently, pentane and other hydrocarbons are only very slightly soluble in water; at 25°C, the mole fraction of pentane in a saturated water solution is 0.00003. It is commonly supposed that the few molecules of pentane that dissolve do so by fitting, with minimum distortion, into "holes" in the hydrogen-bonded water structure. This is suggested by the fact that the heats of solution per mole of most liquid hydrocarbons in water are very nearly zero.

Of the relatively few organic liquids which dissolve readily in water, the majority are oxygen-containing compounds of low molecular weight. Two familiar examples are the alcohols containing one and two carbon atoms,

Methyl alcohol   Ethyl alcohol

both of which are soluble in water in all proportions. Methyl and ethyl alcohol each contain an −OH group, as does water. Even more important, both these compounds are known to be hydrogen-bonded in the liquid state. Consequently, it is hardly surprising that they dissolve readily in water; one would expect the intermolecular forces between alcohols and water in solution to be roughly comparable to those in the pure liquids.

Solid-Liquid

Unlike liquid-liquid pairs, in which we frequently find that the two components are soluble in each other in all proportions, it is always possible to prepare a saturated solution of a solid in a liquid. In other words, there is always a finite limit to the solubility of a solid in a liquid. Moveover, we invariably find that a solid is less soluble in a given liquid than is a liquid of similar structure.

The limited solubility of solids in liquids is readily explained if one imagines the process by which a solid "A" goes into solution in a liquid solvent "B" as taking place in two steps:

(Step 1) Solid A melts to form pure, liquid A.

$$A(s) \longrightarrow A(l)$$

(Step 2) Liquid A dissolves in B to form a liquid solution:

$$A(l) + B(l) \longrightarrow \text{liquid solution of A in B}$$

Step 1 is clearly nonspontaneous at any temperature at which solid A is the stable phase. It follows that the combination of Step 1 and Step 2, which represents the solution process for a solid, is less spontaneous than Step 2 by itself, which is the only step involved when a liquid dissolves.

Following the reasoning we have just outlined, one can deduce that the relative solubilities of different solids in a given solvent at room temperature should be inversely related to their melting points. The greater the difference between the melting point of a solid and the temperature at which its solubility is measured, the less spontaneous Step 1 will be. Consequently, high-melting solids, in which this temperature difference is comparatively great, should be less soluble than solids whose melting points are closer to room temperature. The validity of this reasoning is confirmed by data such as those in Table 13.2, which compare the solubilities of a series of solid hydrocarbons in a nonpolar hydrocarbon solvent, benzene.

TABLE 13.2 SOLUBILITIES OF SOLID
HYDROCARBONS IN BENZENE AT 25°C.*

Solute	Melting Point (°C)	X Solute
Anthracene	218	0.008
Phenanthrene	100	0.21
Naphthalene	80	0.26
Biphenyl	69	0.39

* Mole fraction of solid in saturated solution.

In applying this rule relating melting point to solubility, one must, of course, be careful to restrict it to solids whose particle structures are reasonably similar. With this limitation, it applies surprisingly well.

In comparing the relative solubilities of a given solid in a series of liquid solvents, one must take into account the factors discussed previously in connection with liquid-liquid systems. (Nonpolar solids are most soluble in solvents of low polarity) hydrogen-bonded liquids are poor solvents for solid hydrocarbons. Compare, for example, the solubility of naphthalene in benzene at 20°C (X naphthalene = 0.24) to that in methyl alcohol (X naphthalene = 0.018) and in water (X naphthalene = 4.8 × 10^{-6}). Ionic solids are considerably more soluble in water than they are in organic solvents. We shall postpone until Chapter 16 a general discussion of the solubilities of ionic compounds in water.

Gas-Liquid

Following the reasoning outlined for solid-liquid and liquid-liquid solutions, one can arrive at the following conclusions regarding the solubilities of gases in liquids:

1. The higher the boiling point of the gas (i.e., the closer it is to the liquid state) the more soluble it will be in a given solvent.

2. The best solvent for a given gas will be the one whose intermolecular forces are most similar to those of the gaseous solute.

TABLE 13.3 SOLUBILITY OF THE INERT GASES IN BENZENE AND WATER AT 25°C AND 1 ATM.*

Gas	Boiling Point (°C)	Solvent Benzene	Water
He	−269	0.76 × 10^{-4}	0.069 × 10^{-4}
Ne	−246	1.14 × 10^{-4}	0.082 × 10^{-4}
Ar	−186	8.9 × 10^{-4}	0.25 × 10^{-4}
Kr	−152	27.3 × 10^{-4}	0.45 × 10^{-4}
Xe	−109	110 × 10^{-4}	0.86 × 10^{-4}
Rn	−62	310 × 10^{-4}	1.63 × 10^{-4}

* Mole fraction of gas in saturated solution.

Both of these principles are illustrated by the solubility data for the inert gases given in Table 13.3. Note the steady increase in solubility with boiling point (He < Ne < Ar < Xe < Kr < Rn) for both solvents. The reduced solubility of all these gases in water as compared to benzene reflects the strong intermolecular hydrogen bonding in water; in the nonpolar solvent benzene, as in the inert gases themselves, the attractive forces between particles are of the Van der Waals type.

13.5 EFFECT OF TEMPERATURE AND PRESSURE ON SOLUBILITY

The mutual solubilities of two substances, A and B, depend not only upon their chemical and physical properties, but also upon the external conditions of temperature and pressure. The effects of these two variables upon solubility are readily deduced if one regards the solution process as an equilibrium:

$$A + B \rightleftharpoons \text{solution}$$

and applies the principles discussed in Chapter 12 concerning the influence of temperature and pressure upon physical equilibria.

Temperature

In any equilibrium, an increase in temperature favors the endothermic process. Applied to the solution process, this means that if heat is absorbed when A dissolves in B:

$$A + B + \text{heat} \rightleftharpoons \text{solution}$$

an increase in temperature will increase the solubility of A in B. Conversely, if dissolving A in B liberates heat:

$$A + B \rightleftharpoons \text{solution} + \text{heat}$$

an increase in temperature will favor the reverse process; i.e., it will reduce the solubility. Unfortunately, there are no infallible rules for predicting whether the formation of a solution from the pure components will absorb or evolve heat.

The solubility of solids in liquids almost always increases with temperature. To explain this, it is convenient, once again, to imagine the solution process as occurring in two steps:

(Step 1) $A(s) \longrightarrow A(l)$

(Step 2) $A(l) + B(l) \longrightarrow$ liquid solution of A in B

Step 1, the melting of the solid, is invariably endothermic. If the heat change in Step 2 is endothermic or small, as will ordinarily be the case, the net solution process will absorb heat, and solubility will increase with temperature. Exceptions are known, particularly when A and B interact strongly with each other, but they are comparatively rare.

It is difficult to predict in advance whether the solubility of a gas in a liquid will increase or decrease with temperature. Many examples of both types of behavior are known (Figure 13.4). To appreciate the problems involved, imagine, as before, a two-step process:

(Step 1) $A(g) \longrightarrow A(l)$

(Step 2) $A(l) + B(l) \longrightarrow$ liquid solution of A in B

Step 1, the condensation of a gas to a liquid, is exothermic. Step 2, as already pointed out, is usually endothermic. Under these conditions, the direction of the net heat change depends upon the relative amounts of heat evolved in Step 1 and absorbed in Step 2. In the case of helium dissolving in benzene, the heat absorbed in forming a cavity in the solvent large enough to accommodate an He atom (Step 2) is greater than the heat evolved when the gas condenses: the overall process is endothermic and solubility increases with temperature. In the helium-water system, the heat change in Step 2 virtually vanishes, presumably because the few gas molecules which dissolve do so by fitting into cavities already present in the water structure. Consequently, the overall process is exothermic and solubility decreases with increasing temperature.

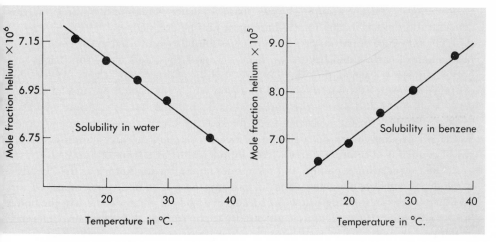

FIGURE 13.4 Temperature dependence of solubility of helium in water and benzene.

Pressure

As pointed out in Chapter 12, pressure has little effect on the position of equilibria involving only condensed phases, i.e., liquids and solids. The volume change accompanying the solution process in liquid-liquid or solid-liquid systems is so small that very large pressure changes are required to produce a detectable change in solubility.

Experimentally, it is found that, at moderate pressures, the solubility of a gas in a liquid is directly proportional to its partial pressure in the gas phase over the solution.

$$P_a = k\, C_a \tag{13.4}$$

in which P_a = partial pressure of gas, C_a = concentration of gas in solution, and k is a constant. A simple kinetic explanation of equation 13.4 (Henry's Law) is shown in Figure 13.5. Doubling the partial pressure of a gas over a solution amounts

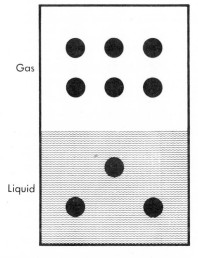
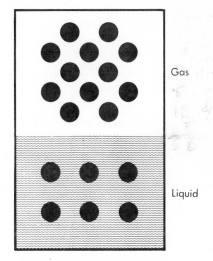

FIGURE 13.5 Schematic drawing showing effect of pressure of a gas on its solubility in a liquid.

to doubling its concentration in the gas phase. In order to maintain equilibrium, the concentration of gas in the liquid phase must also be doubled.

The influence of partial pressure upon gas solubility is utilized in the commercial production of carbonated beverages. Beer, certain wines, and many soft drinks are bottled under a carbon dioxide pressure slightly greater than 1 atm. When the container is open, exposing the liquid to air, in which the partial pressure of CO_2 is very small (0 to .001 atm.), the carbon dioxide bubbles out of solution, giving a froth or "head." Pressurized containers for shaving cream, insecticides, and other household products work on a similar principle. Opening a valve causes dissolved gas to come out of solution, carrying the liquid with it as a foam or spray.

The excruciatingly painful and sometimes fatal affliction known as the "bends" is another consequence of the effect of pressure on gas solubility. Compressed air breathed by divers working below the surface of a body of water dissolves in the body fluids and tissues. If the diver ascends rapidly to the surface, the excess air comes out of solution in the form of tiny bubbles which impair circulation and affect nerve impulses. One way of minimizing this effect is to substitute a mixture of helium and oxygen for the compressed air supplied to the diver. Helium, which has a much lower boiling point than nitrogen, is only about $\frac{1}{5}$ as soluble in body fluids as in nitrogen. Consequently, much less gas comes out of solution on decompression.

13.6 ELECTRICAL CONDUCTIVITIES OF WATER SOLUTIONS

Solutes are often classified as to the conductivity of their water solutions into three categories: nonelectrolytes, strong electrolytes, and weak electrolytes.

Nonelectrolytes. Substances which dissolve as molecules and hence give water solutions which are nonconducting are classed as nonelectrolytes. Most, but not all, covalent solutes are of this type. Examples include methyl alcohol, CH_3OH; sugar, $C_{12}H_{22}O_{11}$; and urea, $CO(NH_2)_2$.

Strong Electrolytes. Substances which exist in water solution almost exclusively in the form of ions are referred to as strong electrolytes. Their electrical conductivities, even at concentrations as low as 0.1 M, are at least 100,000 times that of pure water. Conduction is due to the movement of ions through the solution.

Any compound which exists as ions in the solid state can be expected to act as a strong electrolyte in water solution. Compounds in this category include NaCl (Na^+, Cl^-), BaI_2(Ba^{+2}, I^-), and $Cu(NO_3)_2$ (Cu^{+2}, NO_3^-). Certain covalently bonded substances react with water to form high concentrations of ions. Strong electrolytes of this type include hydrochloric acid (HCl molecules in the gas state, H^+ and Cl^- ions in solution) and nitric acid (HNO_3 molecules in the pure liquid, H^+ and NO_3^- ions in solution). We shall have more to say about this type of substance when we discuss acids and bases in Chapter 17.

The electrical conductivity of a water solution of a strong electrolyte depends upon several factors, including the charges of the ions, their concentrations, and their mobilities. To illustrate the effect of charge, let us compare the conductivities of solutions of NaCl, $MgSO_4$ and Na_2SO_4. Since the ions in $MgSO_4$(Mg^{+2}, SO_4^{-2}) have a charge twice as great as those in NaCl(Na^+, Cl^-), one might expect the conductivity of a magnesium sulfate solution to be roughly twice that of a sodium chloride solution of the same molarity. By the same reasoning, one could argue that the conductivities of equimolar mixtures of $MgSO_4$ and Na_2SO_4 should be about the same; two Na^+ ions should make a contribution about equal to that of one Mg^{+2} ion. Experimentally, these predictions are confirmed, provided one works with very dilute solutions. The conductivities of 0.001 M solutions of $MgSO_4$, Na_2SO_4, and NaCl are in the ratio 1.8:2.0:1.0. In more concentrated solutions, the relative conductivities of solutions of these salts deviate from what one might expect on the basis of their charge type for reasons which we shall consider in Section 13.7.

Weak Electrolytes. Substances which exist in water solution as an equilibrium mixture of ions and molecules are called weak electrolytes. An example is hydrogen fluoride: a water solution of this compound contains a relatively small number of H^+ and F^- ions in equilibrium with HF molecules (cf. Chapter 17).

13.7   COLLIGATIVE PROPERTIES OF DILUTE SOLUTIONS*

Certain properties of solutions are found to depend primarily upon the concentrations of solute particles rather than upon the nature of these particles. These are called colligative properties. In discussing such properties, it is convenient to distinguish between solutions of nonelectrolytes on the one hand and electrolytes on the other.

Nonelectrolytes

Vapor Pressure of Solvent

It is invariably found that the vapor pressure of water above a solution of a nonelectrolyte is lower than that of pure water at the same temperature. Moveover, careful studies carried out with dilute solutions of nonvolatile solutes show that the amount by which the vapor pressure of the solvent is lowered is:

1. *Directly proportional* to the *concentration* of solute. For example, the vapor pressure of water above a 0.10 M solution of sugar at 25°C is 0.043 mm. Hg less than that of pure water; the vapor pressure lowering in a 0.20 M sugar solution at the same temperature is 0.086 mm. Hg.

2. *Independent* of the *nature* of the solute. A 0.10 M solution of urea at 25°C, like a 0.10 M solution of sugar, has a vapor pressure 0.043 mm. Hg less than that of pure water.

These two observations, which are generally valid for all dilute solutions of nonelectrolytes, show vapor pressure lowering to be a colligative property.

The relationship between solvent vapor pressure and concentration can be expressed mathematically as:

$$P_1 = X_1 P_1^\circ \tag{13.5}$$

$$P_1^\circ - P_1 = \text{vapor pressure lowering} = X_2 P^\circ \tag{13.6}$$

---

* As pointed out earlier in this chapter, the adjective dilute does not have a precise quantitative meaning. The laws developed in this section are best regarded as limiting laws which are approached more and more closely as the solution becomes more dilute. In practice, equations 13.5 to 13.9 are generally applicable to within at most a few per cent at concentrations as high as 1 molal.

in which P_1 = vapor pressure of solvent in solution; $P_1^°$ = vapor pressure of pure solvent; X_1 and X_2 = mole fractions of solvent and solute respectively. Equations 13.5 and 13.6 are, of course, equivalent, as may be shown by substituting: $X_1 = 1 - X_2$ in 13.5 and rearranging to obtain 13.6. Equation 13.5, known as Raoult's Law, lends itself more readily to a simple kinetic explanation, while equation 13.6 is somewhat more useful in calculations of the type illustrated by Example 13.5.

Example 13.5. Calculate the vapor pressure lowering and the vapor pressure of a solution containing 100 g. of sugar, $C_{12}H_{22}O_{11}$, in 500 g. of water at 25°C.

Solution. In order to use equation 13.6, we need to know the vapor pressure of pure water (23.76 mm. Hg at 25°C) and the mole fraction of sugar. To obtain the mole fraction of sugar, we note that, since the molecular weight of sugar is 342:

$$\text{no. moles sugar} = 100 \text{ g.} \times \frac{1 \text{ mole}}{342 \text{ g.}} = 0.292$$

$$\text{no. moles } H_2O = 500 \text{ g.} \times \frac{1 \text{ mole}}{18.0 \text{ g.}} = 27.8$$

$$\text{X sugar} = \frac{0.292}{0.292 + 27.8} = 0.0104$$

Therefore, vapor pressure lowering = 0.0104×23.76 mm. Hg = .247 mm. Hg

vapor pressure of solution = $(23.76 - .25)$ mm. Hg = 23.51 mm. Hg

Equation 13.5 (Raoult's Law) may be interpreted in a manner entirely analogous to that used earlier with Henry's Law of gas solubilities. Considering the equilibrium between solvent molecules in solution and in the gas phase (Figure 13.6), it seems entirely reasonable that the concentration in the gas phase, as measured by the solvent vapor pressure, should be directly proportional to the concentration in solution, as measured by the mole fraction of solvent. In this case, we are able to evaluate the proportionality constant as being the vapor pressure of the pure solvent, i.e., the vapor pressure when the mole fraction of solvent is one.

Raoult's Law can, in principle, be applied to solutions of nonelectrolytes in which both components are volatile. If both solute and solvent obey Raoult's Law:

$$P_1 = X_1 P_1^° \quad \text{and} \quad P_2 = X_2 P_2^°$$

The total vapor pressure over such a solution is obtained by adding the two partial pressures:

$$P_1 + P_2 = P \text{ tot} = X_1 P_1^° + X_2 P_2^°$$

Solutions which obey this equation are said to be *ideal*.

In practice, very few solutions behave ideally. Although the solvent ordinarily obeys Raoult's Law in dilute solution, the solute seldom does so. Instead, the solute vapor pressure

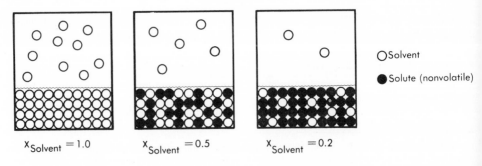

$X_{Solvent} = 1.0$ $X_{Solvent} = 0.5$ $X_{Solvent} = 0.2$ ○ Solvent   ● Solute (nonvolatile)

FIGURE 13.6 Schematic drawing showing relation between solvent mole fraction and solvent vapor pressure above solution.

follows a more general expression equivalent to Henry's Law:

$$P_2 = k\,X_2$$

in which k is a constant which may be greater or less than $P_2°$, the vapor pressure of pure solute, but is seldom equal to it. It is not difficult to see why this should be the case. When a small amount of solute is dissolved in a large amount of solvent, the solute molecules find themselves in an environment quite different from that of the pure solute. The *escaping tendency* of the solute, or its vapor pressure, is determined by the attractive forces between the solute molecule and the solvent particles which surround it. These forces may be greater or less than those in the pure solute, but they will rarely be exactly equal to the solute-solute attractive forces.

Boiling Point

A water solution of a nonvolatile* solute invariably boils at a higher temperature than pure water at the same external pressure. Moreover, the boiling point elevation, in dilute solution, is found to be directly proportional to solute concentration. The general relation between these two quantities for water solutions of nonelectrolytes is usually expressed in terms of the molality of solute:

$$\Delta T_b = 0.52°C\,(m) \tag{13.7}$$

where ΔT_b is the boiling point elevation in °C, and m is the molality. An analogous relationship is found to apply to all dilute solutions of nonelectrolytes, regardless of the solvent. The constant appearing in equation 13.7 is a function of the solvent; it is generally larger than 0.52°C for organic solvents (Table 13.4).

TABLE 13.4 MOLAL FREEZING POINT AND BOILING
POINT CONSTANTS

Solvent	Freezing Point (°C)	Freezing Point Constant (°C)	Boiling Point (°C)	Boiling Point Constant (°C)
Water	0	1.86	100	0.52
Acetic acid	17	3.90	118	2.93
Benzene	5.5	5.10	80	2.53
Cyclohexane	6.5	20.2	81	2.79
Camphor	178	40.0	208	5.95

The boiling point elevation associated with solutions of nonvolatile solutes is readily explained in terms of the vapor pressure lowering. Since the solution, at any given temperature, has a vapor pressure lower than that of the pure solvent, a higher temperature must be reached before the solution boils, that is, before its vapor pressure becomes equal to the external pressure. Moreover, since the extent of vapor pressure lowering is directly proportional to solute concentration, one would expect to find the same type of linear relationship between boiling point elevation and solute concentration. Figure 13.7 illustrates this reasoning graphically.

Freezing Point

Dilute water solutions freeze at temperatures below 0°C. The freezing point lowering in a dilute solution, like vapor pressure lowering and boiling point elevation, is directly proportional to solute concentration. The equation for water solutions of

---

* If the solute is volatile (methyl alcohol or acetone, for example), it will contribute to the total vapor pressure above the solution and will ordinarily lower the boiling point.

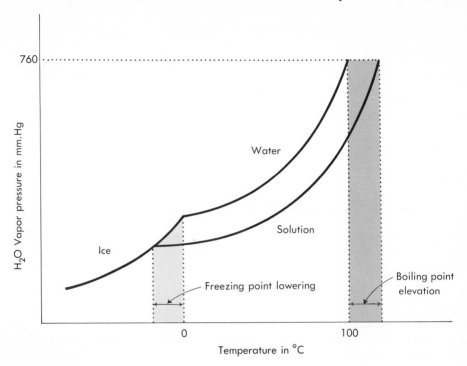

FIGURE 13.7 Dependence of freezing point and boiling point of aqueous solutions on vapor pressure lowering.

nonelectrolytes is:

$$\Delta T_f = 1.86°C \ (m) \tag{13.8}$$

The constant in this equation, like that in equation 13.7, depends on the solvent (Table 13.4).

The freezing point depression, like boiling point elevation, is a direct consequence of the lowering of the solvent vapor pressure by a solute. The freezing point of a solution from which pure solvent crystallizes out* is that temperature at which the solvent has the same vapor pressure in the two phases, liquid solution and solid solvent. Since the solvent vapor pressure in solution is depressed, its vapor pressure will become equal to that of the solid solvent at a lower temperature. Again, since vapor pressure lowering is directly proportional to solute concentration, one would expect to find a similar relationship between freezing point lowering and concentration (Figure 13.7).

The use of equations 13.7 and 13.8 in calculations involving freezing and boiling points of solutions of nonelectrolytes is illustrated by Example 13.6.

Example 13.6. Calculate the freezing point and boiling point, at 760 mm. Hg, of a solution of 2.60 g. of urea, $CO(NH_2)_2$ in 50.0 g. of water.

Solution. To use equations 13.7 and 13.8, one must first calculate the molality. Noting that the molecular weight of urea is 60.0, we have:

$$\text{no. moles urea} = 2.60/60.0 = 0.0433$$

$$m = \frac{\text{no. moles urea}}{\text{no. kg. water}} = \frac{0.0433}{0.050} = .866$$

---

* If a solid solution separates on freezing, this argument will not be valid. In practice, it is almost always pure ice that separates when dilute aqueous solutions freeze.

Hence:

$$\Delta T_b = 0.52°C \times .866 \qquad = 0.45°C$$
$$\Delta T_f = 1.86°C \times .866 \qquad = 1.61°C$$
$$b.p. = 100.00°C + 0.45°C \quad = 100.45°C$$
$$f.p. = 0.00°C - 1.61°C \qquad = -1.61°C$$

Osmotic Pressure

Imagine an experiment in which two beakers, one containing pure water, the other a sugar solution, are placed under a bell jar (Figure 13.8). As time passes, it is found that the liquid level in the beaker containing the solution rises, while the level of pure water in the other beaker falls. Eventually, by evaporation and condensation, all this water is transferred to the solution; at the end of the experiment, the beaker that contained pure water is empty.

The driving force behind the process just described is the difference in vapor pressure of water in the two beakers. Water moves spontaneously from a region in which its vapor pressure is high (pure water) to a region in which its vapor pressure is low (sugar solution). The air in the bell jar is permeable only to water molecules; the nonvolatile solute is unable to move from one beaker to the other.

The apparatus shown at the bottom of Figure 13.8 can be used to achieve a result similar to that found in the bell jar experiment. Here, the sugar solution is separated from the pure water by a semipermeable membrane, which may be an animal bladder, a slice of vegetable tissue, or a piece of parchment. This membrane, by a mechanism which is poorly understood, allows solvent molecules to pass through

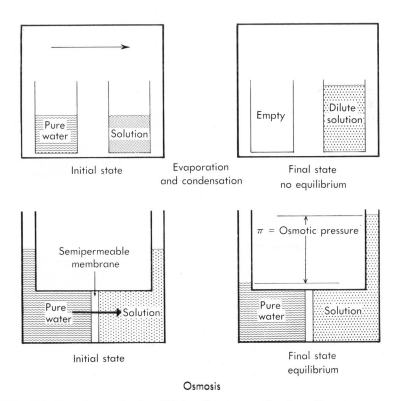

FIGURE 13.8 Experiments showing diffusion of water toward regions of lower vapor pressure.

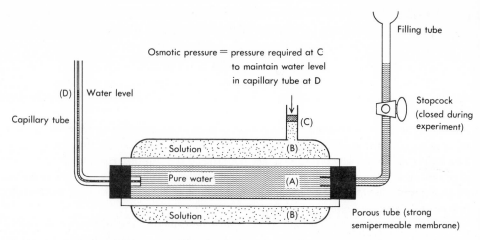

FIGURE 13.9   Apparatus for measurement of high osmotic pressures.

it preferentially. As before, water moves from a region in which its vapor pressure or mole fraction is high to a region in which its vapor pressure or mole fraction is low. This process, taking place through a semipermeable membrane, is referred to as **osmosis.** In general, the term osmosis is used to describe any process in which one component of a solution moves preferentially through a barrier or membrane which is permeable only to it. The component moves from a region in which its mole fraction is high toward a region in which its mole fraction is low.

The passage of water molecules through a membrane into a solution may be prevented by applying pressure to the solution. The external pressure which is just sufficient to prevent osmosis is referred to as the **osmotic pressure** of a solution. Osmotic pressure may be measured in an apparatus such as that shown in Figure 13.9. The inner, porous tube, A, contains within it a strong, semipermeable membrane consisting of a film of copper(II) ferrocyanide, $Cu_2Fe(CN)_6$. This insoluble film is formed by allowing solutions containing Cu^{+2} and $Fe(CN)_6^{-4}$ ions to diffuse into each other through the walls of the tube. The tube is filled with pure water; the compartment, B, surrounding the tube is filled with the solution whose osmotic pressure is to be measured. Pressure is applied to the solution at C so as to maintain a constant level (D) in the capillary attached to the tube containing pure water. This pressure is, by definition, the osmotic pressure.

It is found experimentally that the osmotic pressure of a dilute nonelectrolyte solution, like vapor pressure lowering, boiling point elevation, and freezing point lowering, is a colligative property. The osmotic pressure is directly proportional to the concentration of solute and independent of its nature; the equation relating osmotic pressure of a solution to its concentration may be written in the form:

$$\pi = MRT \tag{13.9}$$

in which π = osmotic pressure, M = molarity, R = gas constant (0.0821 l.-atm./mole °K), and T = temperature in °K. It may be noted that since the molarity is equal to the number of moles of solute per liter of solution, i.e., M = n/V, this equation can be written in the form:

$$\pi V = nRT$$

which is formally identical with the Ideal Gas Law, pV = nRT (Chapter 6).

Substitution into equation 13.9 shows that the osmotic pressure, even in dilute solution, is comparatively great. In a 0.10 M solution at 25°C, for example,

$$\pi = 0.10 \frac{\text{moles}}{\text{l.}} \times 0.0821 \frac{\text{l.-atm.}}{\text{mole-°K}} \times 298°\text{K} = 2.45 \text{ atm.}$$

A pressure of 2.45 atm. is equivalent to a column of water 83 feet high. This may give some indication of the driving force behind osmosis and the difficulties involved in measuring osmotic pressure accurately with ordinary membranes.

Osmosis plays a vital role in many biological processes. Nutrient and waste materials are transported by osmosis through the cell walls of animal tissues, which show varying degrees of permeability to different solutes. A striking example of a natural osmotic process is afforded by observing under a microscope the behavior of blood cells placed in pure water. Water passes through the walls to dilute the solution inside the cell, which swells and eventually bursts, releasing its red pigment. If the blood cells are placed in a concentrated sugar solution, the reverse process occurs; the cells shrink and shrivel up as water moves out into the sugar solution. To avoid effects such as these, solutions used in intravenous feeding must be carefully adjusted in concentration so that they have the same osmotic pressure as the solution inside the cells.

Plant as well as animal cell walls can act as semipermeable membranes. Flowers immersed in sugar or salt solution wilt as they are dehydrated by osmosis; if transferred to pure water, they appear to regain their freshness as water moves back into the cells. It has been suggested that the flow of sap up a tree results from osmosis; the movement of water through the roots into the concentrated nutrient solution inside could easily develop an osomotic pressure sufficient to push fluid to the top of the highest tree.

Determination of Molecular Weights from Colligative Properties

In previous chapters, we discussed the determination of molecular weights from gas density data. While this method works quite well for gases or volatile liquids, it cannot be applied to solids such as sugar or urea which decompose on heating. An alternative approach, applicable to a wide variety of nonelectrolytes, involves the measurement of the colligative properties of their solutions. For example, from the measurement of the freezing point lowering of a solution of known composition, one can calculate the molecular weight of the solute, making use of equation 13.8. Example 13.7 illustrates the calculations involved.

Example 13.7. A solution of 1.250 g. of a certain nonelectrolyte in 20.0 g. of water freezes at −1.06°C. Calculate the molecular weight of the solute.

Solution. From the information given, we can readily calculate the molality, using equation 13.8. Knowing the molality, we can then calculate the number of moles of solute present. Since the number of grams of solute is given, it should then be possible to determine the number of grams per mole, i.e., the gram molecular weight of the solute.

(Step 1) $\Delta T_f = 1.86°C \times m = 1.06°C$

$$m = \frac{1.06}{1.86} = 0.570 = \frac{\text{no. moles solute}}{\text{no. kg. solvent}}$$

Step (2) no. moles solute $= m \times$ no. kg. solvent

$$= (0.570)(0.0200) = 0.0114$$

(Step 3) 0.0114 moles $= 1.250$ g.

$$\text{no. of grams in 1 mole} = 1 \text{ mole} \times \frac{1.250 \text{ g.}}{.0114 \text{ mole}} = 110 \text{ g.}$$

M.W. $= 110$

It is, of course, possible to determine molecular weights from measurements of the vapor pressure lowering, boiling point elevation or the osmotic pressure of a solution, using the appropriate equation (13.6 to 13.9) relating the particular colligative property to the concentration of solute. Freezing point lowerings are perhaps most commonly used because the effect is comparatively large (compare, for example, the constants for the freezing point lowering, 1.86°C, and the boiling point elevation, 0.52°C, for water solutions) and readily measured. For nonelectrolytes which are insoluble in water, it is usually possible to choose a suitable organic solvent. Camphor, which has a particularly large freezing point depression constant, 40.0°C is often used.

Osmotic pressure measurements are frequently used to determine the molecular weights of polymeric materials, in which the molar concentration of solute is ordinarily extremely low. Consider, for example, a solution containing 10 g. of a polymer of molecular weight 10,000 dissolved in 1 kg. of water. One can calculate that such a solution would have a molality of 0.0010; its osmotic pressure would be approximately 0.025 atm. (19 mm. Hg) as compared to a freezing point lowering of only 0.0019°C. The principal difficulty associated with osmotic pressure measurements has always been that of finding a membrane which is both semipermeable and strong enough to withstand pressure. Recently, instruments have come on the market which are capable of measuring osmotic pressures of solutions of polymers covering a wide range of molecular weights.

Electrolytes

We have seen that in dilute solutions of nonelectrolytes, the vapor pressure lowering, boiling point elevation, freezing point depression, or osmotic pressure are directly proportional to the concentration of solute particles. If one extends this relationship to electrolyte solutions, it would seem that, at a given molality, a salt such as sodium chloride should have a greater effect on the colligative properties of water than a nonelectrolyte such as sugar. If one dissolves a mole of sugar in water, *one* mole of solute molecules is obtained; one mole of NaCl, on the other hand, produces *two* moles of ions. Again, one would predict that a 1 molal solution of $CaCl_2$ (*three* moles of ions per mole of solute) should have a lower vapor pressure, a higher boiling point, a lower freezing point, and a greater osmotic pressure than a 1 molal solution of NaCl.

Qualitatively, the predictions we have just made are confirmed experimentally. A 1 molal solution of sodium chloride has a lower vapor pressure than a 1 molal solution of sugar; the vapor pressure of a 1 m solution of calcium chloride is still lower. Many electrolytes form saturated solutions whose vapor pressures are so low that the solids pick up water when exposed to moist air. This phenomenon, known as **deliquescence,** is common with very soluble electrolytes of high charge type. Calcium chloride, for example, forms a saturated solution with a vapor pressure only 20 per cent that of pure water; if the dry salt is exposed to air in which the relative humidity is greater than 20 per cent it deliquesces. The saturated solution continues to take on water until its vapor pressure is equal to that of the water in the air, that is, until equilibrium is reached.

The freezing point of an electrolyte solution, like the vapor pressure, is normally lower than that of a nonelectrolyte at the same molality. Sodium chloride or calcium chloride is commonly used to remove ice from the highway after a snowstorm.

Quantitatively, one might expect that the equations (13.6 to 13.9) which relate the colligative properties of nonelectrolyte solutions to their concentrations could be adapted to electrolytes by introducing a multiplier, n, equal to the number of moles of ions formed from 1 mole of electrolyte. Thus, we would have, for the freezing point lowering and boiling point elevation:

$$\Delta T_f = n(1.86°C)m \tag{13.10}$$

$$\Delta T_b = n(0.52°C)m \tag{13.11}$$

in which n = 2 for NaCl, KCl, MgSO$_4$, n = 3 for CaCl$_2$, H$_2$SO$_4$, and so on. Experimentally, it is found that the observed freezing point lowerings, even in quite dilute solution, are somewhat smaller than these equations would predict (Table 13.5).

TABLE 13.5 FREEZING POINTS OF SOLUTIONS
OF KCl AND MgSO$_4$

m	ΔT$_f$ Observed		n Calculated (equation 13.10)	
	KCl	MgSO$_4$	KCl	MgSO$_4$
0.005	0.0182	0.0158	1.96	1.70
0.01	0.0361	0.0301	1.94	1.62
0.02	0.0714	0.0573	1.92	1.54
0.05	0.175	0.132	1.88	1.42
0.10	0.346	0.246	1.86	1.32
0.20	0.682	0.454	1.83	1.22
0.50	1.67	1.00	1.80	1.08

It is evident from the data in Table 13.5 that, for both KCl and MgSO$_4$, n, as calculated from the freezing point lowering, is less than the expected value of 2, approaching this as a limit in very dilute solution. Stated another way, at finite concentrations, the observed freezing point lowering is less than that calculated from equation 13.10 with n = 2. It may also be observed that the deviations from ideal behavior are considerably greater for MgSO$_4$, in which we are dealing with +2 and −2 ions, than with KCl (+1, −1 ions). Conductivity data for solutions of these two salts show precisely the same trends.

The deviations of colligative properties of electrolyte solutions from the simple relationships predicted on the basis of completely independent solute particles have been explained in various ways. Arrhenius in 1887 suggested that strong electrolytes were incompletely dissociated in solution. According to the Arrhenius theory, a solution of potassium chloride should consist of an equilibrium mixture of K$^+$ ions, Cl$^-$ ions and KCl molecules:

$$KCl \rightleftharpoons K^+ + Cl^-$$

At high concentrations, enough KCl molecules would be present to make the conductivity or freezing point lowering appreciably less than that calculated on the basis of complete dissociation.

In the first two decades of the twentieth century, x-ray studies conducted on solid salts such as potassium chloride showed them to be made up of individual ions

(K+, Cl−) rather than molecules. This evidence tended to discredit the Arrhenius picture of electrolyte solutions. If K+ and Cl− ions exist as separate entities in the solid state, it is difficult to understand why they should combine to form molecules in solution. By 1920, it was generally conceded that strong electrolytes were completely dissociated in solution and that there must be some other explanation for the observed anomalies in conductivities and colligative properties.

A quantitative explanation of the properties of dilute solutions of strong electrolytes was put forth by Debye and Hückel in 1923. Their theory was based on the idea that, as a result of electrical attraction between positive and negative ions, there are in solution around a given ion more ions of opposite than of like charge. An ion in solution will surround itself with an **ionic atmosphere** containing an excess of oppositely charged ions. The existence of such an atmosphere lowers the conductivity of the solution by reducing the mobility of the ions; it has a similar though less obvious effect on such colligative properties as freezing point lowering and boiling point elevation. One would expect, in agreement with experiment, that ionic atmosphere effects would be most pronounced in concentrated solutions of electrolytes of high charge.

Debye and Hückel, by taking into account the effect of the ionic atmosphere, were able to derive an equation for the variation with concentration of such properties as conductivity and freezing point lowering. The equations they proposed worked quite well in very dilute solutions, below about 0.01 m. Various modifications of the Debye-Hückel equations, notably that of Onsager for the conductivity of electrolyte solutions, extended their range to as high as 0.1 m. In more concentrated solutions, however, all attempts to extend the Debye-Hückel treatment have proved unsatisfactory.

Recently, in attempting to explain the properties of concentrated solutions of electrolytes, chemists have gone back to an earlier concept proposed by Bjerrum in 1909. He suggested that in concentrated solutions, a considerable fraction of the electrolyte could be tied up in the form of "ion-pairs." Thus when solid $MgSO_4$ dissolves to give a concentrated solution, it may dissolve primarily as $Mg^{+2}SO_4^{-2}$ ion pairs rather than as individual Mg^{+2} and SO_4^{-2} ions. The strength of the electrostatic forces holding the ion pair together should be directly related to the charge to size ratio of the ions. Small ions of high charge such as Mg^{+2} would be expected to form ion pairs more readily than large ions of low charge such as K+. The ratio of ion pairs to free ions increases with concentration, in agreement with observed trends in conductivity and colligative properties.

It is now generally realized that a comprehensive structural model of electrolyte solutions must include not only ion-ion interactions (the ionic atmosphere of Debye or the ion pair of Bjerrum) but also interactions between ions and polar solvent molecules. In this connection, there is considerable evidence to indicate that ions may distort the peculiar hydrogen-bonded structure of water. Until we know more about the molecular structure of liquid water, it seems unlikely that we will be able to give a completely satisfactory explanation for the properties of electrolyte solutions.

Despite the observed deviations of electrolyte solutions from equation 13.10, it is possible to use freezing point measurements to decide upon the mode of ionization of a salt in water solution. Consider, for example, the compound sodium hydrogen carbonate, $NaHCO_3$. One might postulate two different ways in which this compound could ionize in water:

$$NaHCO_3(s) \longrightarrow Na^+ + HCO_3^- \qquad (13.12)$$

or:

$$NaHCO_3(s) \longrightarrow Na^+ + H^+ + CO_3^{-2} \tag{13.13}$$

To decide between these two possibilities, one could measure the freezing point of a dilute solution of $NaHCO_3$. If the ionization follows equation 13.12, the freezing point should be approximately equal to that of an NaCl solution of the same concentration. If, on the other hand, $NaHCO_3$ forms three ions in solution, as required by equation 13.13, one would expect to observe a freezing point lowering similar to that of Na_2CO_3. Experimentally, it is found that the freezing point of a 0.01 m solution of $NaHCO_3$ is $-0.038°C$, very nearly equal to that of a 0.01 m NaCl solution $(-0.036°C)$ and markedly different from that of 0.01 m $Na_2CO_3(-0.051°C)$. The freezing point data imply that equation 13.12 must accurately represent the ionization of $NaHCO_3$ in water. This conclusion is confirmed by conductivity measurements, which show that the conductivity of 0.01 M $NaHCO_3$ is very nearly equal to that of 0.01 M NaCl, but considerably lower than that of 0.01 M Na_2CO_3.

13.8 SUMMARY

A mixture which appears homogeneous to the eye or microscope is said to be a solution. The particles in a solution are 50 Å or less in diameter and, in any macroscopic portion of the solution, are randomly distributed. The concentration of solute in a solution may be expressed in many different ways. The concentration units considered in this chapter are mole fraction (equation 13.1), molality (equation 13.2), and molarity (equation 13.3).

Two liquids in which the intermolecular attractive forces are similar in magnitude are ordinarily soluble in each other in all proportions. Limited solubility in liquid-liquid systems arises when the two components differ significantly in intermolecular attractive forces, particularly when one of the components is hydrogen-bonded and the other is not. Gases and solids have finite solubilities in liquids; the closer the gas or solid is to the liquid state, the greater is its solubility. Thus, low-melting solids and high-boiling gases tend to be most soluble in liquids.

If the solution process is endothermic, solubility increases with temperature; if it is exothermic an increase in temperature brings about a decrease in solubility. Pressure has little effect on solubility except when gases are involved; the solubility of a gas in a liquid is directly proportional to its partial pressure.

For a solution of a nonvolatile nonelectrolyte, the vapor pressure is lower, the boiling point higher, and the freezing point lower than for the pure solvent. The vapor pressure lowering, boiling point elevation, and freezing point lowering in dilute solution are all directly proportional to the concentration of solute, as is the osmotic pressure (the pressure required to prevent solvent from passing through a semipermeable membrane from a region of high vapor pressure to a region of low vapor pressure). Equations 13.6 to 13.9, which relate these colligative properties to concentration, can be used to calculate molecular weights from experimental data on freezing point lowerings, etc., as illustrated in Example 13.7.

Solutions of electrolytes have freezing point lowerings (or boiling point elevations) considerably higher than those of nonelectrolytes of the same molality. The freezing point lowering in electrolyte solutions is somewhat lower than one would expect on the basis of complete dissociation into ions which act as totally independent entities.

PROBLEMS

13.1 Explain briefly what is meant by each of the following terms:
   a. Supersaturated solution   f. Ionic atmosphere
   b. Raoult's Law   g. Osmotic pressure
   c. Henry's Law   h. Substitutional solid solution
   d. Interstitial solid solution   i. Ion pair
   e. Colligative property   j. Weak electrolyte

13.2 Referring to Table 13.1:
   a. Suggest a reason for the fact that the molarity of dilute H_2SO_4 is set at one-half the molarity of dilute HCl and dilute HNO_3.
   b. Confirm by calculation that a solution of hydrochloric acid containing 36 per cent by weight of HCl and having a density of 1.18 g./ml. is 12 M in HCl.
   c. Describe how one would prepare 12 l. of dilute NH_3 from concentrated NH_3.

13.3 The solubility of potassium nitrate in water at 20°C is 2.77 moles/l. A solution of this salt is prepared by dissolving 155 g. at 80°C to form 375 ml. of solution. Upon cooling to 20°C, no solid separates until a tiny crystal of KNO_3 is added, whereupon all of the excess solute comes out of solution. How many grams of solute separate?

13.4 Describe how you would prepare each of the following solutions:
   a. A 1.20 molar solution of NaCl in water.
   b. A 1.20 molal solution of NaCl in water.
   c. A 0.20 M solution of $NiSO_4$ in water (the stockroom does not carry anhydrous $NiSO_4$; it does, however, have $NiSO_4 \cdot 6\,H_2O$).
   d. A solution of KOH in CH_3OH in which the mole fraction of KOH is 0.20.

13.5 Calculate the mole fractions of all substances and the molality of the underlined substance in each of the following solutions:
   a. 1.00 mole of C_2H_5OH and 6.00 moles of water.
   b. 1.80 moles of $\overline{NaBr}$ and 512 g. of water.
   c. 16.0 g. of $\overline{CCl_4}$, 12.9 g. of $CHCl_3$ and 19.1 g. of C_6H_{14}.

13.6 Complete the following table. All of the data refer to water solutions.

Solute	Grams Solute	Moles Solute	Volume Solution	Molarity
$NaNO_3$	25	—	—	1.2
$NaNO_3$	—	—	16 l.	0.023
KBr	91	—	450 ml.	—
KBr	—	0.420	—	1.8

13.7 If you were asked to prepare 50 ml. of 0.30 M KCl solution and were given a bottle of solid KCl, a supply of distilled water, a 0.20 M KCl solution, and a 0.40 M solution of KCl, describe four different methods which you could use. Which of these methods would be the fastest?

13.8 A certain solution is prepared by dissolving 15.2 g. of NaCl in 197 g. of water. The density of the resulting solution is 1.012 g./ml. Calculate the mole fraction of NaCl, the molality of NaCl, and the molarity of NaCl.

13.9 Predict which member of each of the following pairs of solutes will be more soluble in carbon tetrachloride at 20°C and 1 atm:
   a. Benzene or hydrogen peroxide.
   b. Anthracene or biphenyl (cf. Table 13.2).
   c. Helium or argon (cf. Table 13.3).
   d. Methane or propane.
   e. Sodium fluoride or anthracene.
   Repeat your predictions for water as a solvent.

13.10 A student wishes to recrystallize a certain organic solid by preparing a saturated solution in benzene at 50°C and cooling to room temperature. He finds that the addition of a small amount of benzene to the solid results in an increase in temperature. On the basis of this observation, would you advise him to follow his original recrystallization scheme?

13.11 The solubility of methane in hexane at 20°C and 1 atm. pressure is 0.024 mole/l. Estimate the solubility at 20°C and 15 atm.

13.12 Can you suggest a thermodynamic explanation for the fact that all gases are completely soluble in each other while many liquids are not?

13.13 Explain briefly why heat is always given off when a supersaturated solution of a solid in a liquid, prepared at a higher temperature, crystallizes at room temperature.

13.14 Water saturated with air (20 per cent O_2, 80 per cent N_2) at 20°C contains 8.9 × 10^{-3} g./l. of dissolved oxygen. Estimate the solubility of pure oxygen in water at a pressure of 25 atm. and a temperature of 20°C.

13.15 Calculate the vapor pressure of benzene above a solution containing 10.0 g. of naphthalene, $C_{10}H_8$, in 100 g. of benzene, C_6H_6, at 25°C. The vapor pressure of pure benzene at 25°C is 97.0 mm. Hg.

13.16 Two organic liquids, A and B, have vapor pressures at 25°C of 150 mm. Hg and 250 mm. Hg respectively. Assuming Raoult's Law applies to both components, draw a graph of:
a. The partial pressure of A over the solution vs. the mole fraction of A from $X_A = 0$ to $X_A = 1$.
b. The partial pressure of B vs. mole fraction of A.
c. The total pressure over the solution vs. the mole fraction of A.

13.17 A beaker containing 20 g. of sugar in 100 g. of water and another containing 10 g. of sugar in 100 g. of water are placed under a bell jar and allowed to stand until equilibrium is reached. How much water will be transferred from one beaker to another?

13.18 Calculate the boiling points at 760 mm. Hg and the freezing points of the following solutions.
a. 50.0 g. of sugar, $C_{12}H_{22}O_{11}$, in 50.0 g. of water.
b. 0.32 g. of glucose, $C_6H_{12}O_6$, in 20.0 g. of water.
c. 16.0 g. of NaCl in 185 g. of water, assuming ideal behavior.

13.19 How many quarts of ethylene glycol, $C_2H_6O_2$ (density = 1.12 g./ml.), should be added to five gallons of water (density = 1.0 g./ml.) to make up an antifreeze which will protect an automobile radiator down to −20°C? At what temperature will this solution boil?

13.20 A student determines the molecular weight of a certain nonelectrolyte by dissolving 5.23 g. of it in 168 g. of water and measuring the freezing point of the solution to be −0.510°C. What is the molecular weight of the nonelectrolyte?

13.21 When 5.30 g. of an organic solute are dissolved in 200 g. of benzene, the freezing point of the solution is 4.20°C.
a. What is the molecular weight of the solute?
b. If the compound contains 9.4 per cent H and 90.6 per cent C, what is its molecular formula?

13.22 Ammonia when placed in water ionizes as follows: $NH_3 + H_2O \rightarrow NH_4^+ + OH^-$. Calculate the percentage ionization of NH_3 in a 0.010 molal solution from the fact that it freezes at −0.0193°C.

13.23 A storage battery contains a solution of H_2SO_4 (38 g. of H_2SO_4 per 100 g. of water). At this concentration, the apparent value of n is 2.50. At what temperature will the battery contents freeze?

13.24 Arrange the following water solutions in order of decreasing freezing point, assuming ideal behavior.

0.01 m sugar   0.01 m Li_2SO_4 0.02 m urea   0.01 m AlF_3

13.25 Calculate the osmotic pressure of a solution containing 5.00 g. of sugar, $C_{12}H_{22}O_{11}$, in one liter of solution at $20\,^{\circ}C$.

*13.26 An inorganic chemist prepares a compound which he believes to be $[Co(NH_3)_5F]F_2 \cdot H_2O$. The compound could, however, be $[Co(NH_3)_5H_2O]F_3$. Describe two different physical methods which he might use to distinguish between these two possibilities.

*13.27 Assuming that osmosis is responsible for sap rising in a tree, calculate the approximate height to which the sap can rise if it is 0.10 M in sugar and the water outside the tree contains dissolved solids equivalent to a 0.02 M solution of sugar.

*13.28 A cell containing 1.68 g. of sugar, $C_{12}H_{22}O_{11}$, in 20.0 g. of water and another containing 2.45 g. of a nonvolatile nonelectrolyte in 24.0 g. of water are placed in an evacuated container and allowed to come to equilibrium. It is found that the total mass of the sugar solution at equilibrium is 24.9 g. Calculate the molecular weight of the nonelectrolyte.

*13.29 The Debye-Hückel theory, applied to the calculation of the freezing point lowering, ΔT_f, of a solution of KCl, predicts the following relation:

$$\Delta T_f = (\Delta T_f)_{ideal}\,(1 - 0.39\,\sqrt{m})$$

in which $(\Delta T_f)_{ideal}$ is the freezing point lowering predicted by equation 13.10 with n = 2, and m is the molality. Calculate ΔT_f from this equation at m = 0.005, 0.01, and 0.05 and compare to the values given in Table 13.5.

14

EQUILIBRIUM IN CHEMICAL SYSTEMS: RATES OF CHEMICAL REACTIONS

In Chapter 12 the physical equilibria that are possible in one-component systems were discussed. It was noted that, under certain conditions, a pure substance could exist stably in two, or even three, states of aggregation in the same container. At $-112°C$, and 0.81 atm., the triple point of xenon, solid, liquid, and gaseous xenon can coexist indefinitely. Gaseous xenon, on being introduced into an evacuated container at $-107°C$, the boiling point of xenon, will condense to a liquid when the xenon pressure reaches 1 atm.; addition of more xenon will not raise the pressure in the system, but will increase the amount of liquid present. If the container is closed and held at $-107°C$, the pressure will remain at 1 atm., and the relative amounts of liquid and gas will remain fixed. Such systems as these are in a state of **physical equilibrium.**

When a system contains substances which react chemically, a situation analogous to that obtaining in cases of physical equilibrium can arise. One finds that, at a given temperature, a chemical reaction may proceed in a closed container only to a certain point and no further. At that point there will be present amounts of each reactant and product which do not change with time. These species coexist stably in a state of **chemical equilibrium.**

The relative amounts of the substances present in a system in chemical equilibrium are in general related to one another and to the temperature and pressure. In this chapter we will be concerned with describing and discussing these very important relations.

14.1 AN EXAMPLE OF CHEMICAL EQUILIBRIUM: THE HI-H_2-I_2 SYSTEM

The simplest systems exhibiting chemical equilibrium contain only gases. One such system is that in which the species present are hydrogen iodide, HI, hydrogen, H_2, and iodine, I_2. At temperatures of about $520°C$, these three substances are gaseous, and, if placed in a container, will react chemically to a state of

317

equilibrium. The reaction which occurs is:

$$2 \, HI(g) \rightleftharpoons H_2(g) + I_2(g)$$

The two arrows mean that, depending on conditions, equilibrium will be attained by reaction to the right, using up HI, or to the left, using up H_2 and I_2.

In order to illustrate the properties of systems in chemical equilibrium we shall set up HI-H_2-I_2 systems in various ways, always at the same temperature, 520°C, and always in the same container, which will be taken to have a volume of 20 l. We shall admit various amounts of HI, H_2, and I_2, and then measure those amounts after equilibrium has been reached.

System I. Two (2.00) moles of HI are admitted at 520°C, to the evacuated 20-l. container. The HI partially decomposes, at first rapidly, then more slowly, to form H_2 and I_2. After a period of time, the amounts of all three substances reach values which are steady and do not change further with time. The system is then in a state of chemical equilibrium. Experimentally we find that in that state there are present 1.60 moles of HI, 0.20 mole of H_2, and 0.20 mole of I_2. Figure 14.1 indicates schematically how the amounts of HI, H_2, and I_2 vary with time as the reaction proceeds.

Another possible way to set up the system would be to start with the products of the reaction, H_2 and I_2. If all the HI in System I decomposed, one mole of H_2 and one mole of I_2 would be produced. It is interesting to see what happens when those substances are used to make up the system.

System II. One (1.00) mole H_2 and one (1.00) mole I_2 are introduced into the empty container at 520°C. In this case the chemical reaction to form HI proceeds, and the amounts of H_2 and I_2 decrease with time. Equilibrium is attained when there are 1.60 moles of HI, 0.20 mole of H_2, and 0.20 mole of I_2 present.

In System II the same amounts of HI, H_2, and I_2 are present at equilibrium as were there in System I. In System II we started with the products of the complete dissociation of the HI used in System I. Systems I and II illustrate the general experimental fact that the *final equilibrium state of a system of fixed overall composition is independent of the nature and amounts of the species initially present*. Systems I and II both

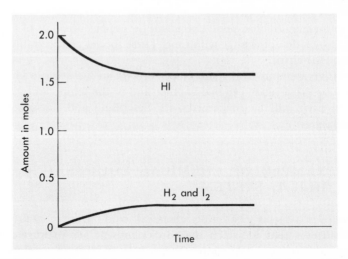

FIGURE 14.1   The HI-H_2-I_2 system: attainment of equilibrium at 520°C.

TABLE 14.1 EQUILIBRIA AT 520°C IN HI-H$_2$-I$_2$
SYSTEMS OF SAME OVERALL INITIAL COMPOSITIONS

System	Initial No. of Moles			Equilibrium No. of Moles		
	HI	H$_2$	I$_2$	HI	H$_2$	I$_2$
I	2.00	0	0	1.60	0.20	0.20
II	0	1.00	1.00	1.60	0.20	0.20
III	1.00	0.50	0.50	1.60	0.20	0.20
IV	0.50	0.75	0.75	1.60	0.20	0.20
V	0.67	0.67	0.67	1.60	0.20	0.20

contain two gram atoms of hydrogen and two gram atoms of iodine: that is, they have
the same overall composition. Therefore, although the kinds and amounts of species
initially present differ greatly, the equilibrium states are identical.

In view of this generalization, we can predict that each of the systems in Table
14.1, which differ initially but have the same overall composition, will have the same
equilibrium state.

The overall composition of Systems I to V is obviously not the only one possible.
In Table 14.2 are listed the initial and equilibrium states of several other possible
systems containing HI, I$_2$, and H$_2$.

TABLE 14.2 EQUILIBRIA AT 520°C IN HI-H$_2$-I$_2$ SYSTEMS
WITH DIFFERENT OVERALL INITIAL COMPOSITIONS

System	Initial No. of Moles			Equilibrium No. of Moles			Moles H$_2$ × Moles I$_2$ (Moles HI)^2
	HI	H$_2$	I$_2$	HI	H$_2$	I$_2$	
VI	1.00	1.00	0	0.970	1.015	0.015	0.016
VII	1.00	0.00	1.00	0.970	0.015	1.015	0.016
VIII	1.00	1.00	1.00	2.40	0.30	0.30	0.016
IX	3.00	1.00	1.00	4.00	0.50	0.50	0.016
X	0	2.00	1.00	1.894	1.053	0.053	0.016
I	2.00	0	0	1.60	0.20	0.20	0.016

In Systems VI to X the initial and equilibrium compositions are all different
from those in Systems I to V, and one would certainly wonder whether there could
possibly be any relation which applies to all of the systems considered.

Amazingly enough, there is. If, for Systems I to X in their equilibrium states, one
multiplies the number of moles of H$_2$ present by the number of moles of I$_2$ present, and
then divides by the square of the number of moles of HI present, one obtains essentially
the same number, about 0.016 in all cases! Apparently, associated with the HI-H$_2$-I$_2$
systems at 520°C in a 20-l. container there is a number which is related to the number
of moles of each of the species present at equilibrium. If other systems of different
initial amounts of HI, H$_2$, and I$_2$ are let into the container (as long as the overall
composition contains some H atoms and some I atoms), chemical reaction to
equilibrium at 520°C will result in amounts of HI, H$_2$, and I$_2$ which, when treated as
before, will yield the same number as previously obtained.

The fact that such a number exists means that, associated with the HI-H$_2$-I$_2$
equilibrium, there is a condition on the amounts of these three substances that can
coexist in a container. A mixture of HI, H$_2$, and I$_2$, on being let into a container,

will react chemically until the relative amounts of those substances present satisfy the condition. The importance of the condition lies in the fact that one cannot arbitrarily fix the amounts of HI, H_2, and I_2 that will coexist stably in a container, but must take account of the fact of the condition governing their relative magnitudes. The necessity for considering the condition when dealing with a chemical system in equilibrium has, as we shall see, many very important chemical implications.

This rather unexpected property of the HI-H_2-I_2 system can be generalized to include all systems which involve chemical equilibria. For every chemical reaction there is an associated *number* analogous to the one we have found. *Ordinarily, the number* which is obtained for a given reaction at a given temperature is a *function of the volume of the container.* The situation is similar to that which arises in the treatment of liquid-vapor systems in equilibrium. The *number of moles* of vapor in equilibrium with a liquid in a container at a given temperature is dependent on the nature of the liquid *and* the volume of the container. As we saw in Chapter 12, however, the *vapor pressure* of the liquid at a given temperature is *not* dependent on the container volume (see Example 14.4).

This suggests that if, instead of dealing with amounts of gas in moles in equilibrium systems, one works with the partial pressures of those gases, the numbers which would be obtained by proceeding as we did with the HI-H_2-I_2 system would also be independent of container volume. This is indeed found to be the case (Section 14.4). It is possible to set up the numbers associated with equilibrium reactions in gases in terms of the partial pressures of the reacting gases and show that such numbers, like the vapor pressure of pure liquid, are not dependent on the volume of the container used. Indeed, in advanced courses, treatment of gaseous equilibria is carried out in terms of the partial pressures of the involved gases.

Since beginning students are not so familiar with gas pressures as with amounts of substances, an alternate procedure for dealing with the constants associated with chemical equilibria is ordinarily used. Instead of setting up the numbers on the basis of gas pressure, one determines them on the basis of gas *concentrations*, the number of moles of gas per unit volume of container. The constants so obtained are, since concentration is proportional to pressure, also independent of container volume, and are the ones most frequently used in elementary discussions. The use of concentrations in formulating these numbers has the advantage that no change in procedure is necessary for the discussion of chemical equilibria in liquid solutions; in working with such systems concentrations in moles per liter are almost always used.

14.2 THE LAW OF CHEMICAL EQUILIBRIUM

Summarizing and generalizing the discussion of the previous section, we can state that, *in a system in which a chemical reaction can occur between gases A, B, C, and D, according to the equation:*

$$aA + bB \rightleftharpoons cC + dD$$

the equilibrium concentrations of all reactants and products will be such that

$$\frac{[C]^c[D]^d}{[A]^a[B]^b} = K_c \qquad (14.1)$$

in which [A], [B], [C], and [D] are the equilibrium concentrations of species A, B, C, and D, and a, b, c, and d are the coefficients in the chemical equation. K_c is a constant independent of the volume and initial composition and is only a function of temperature. The equation is called the Law of Chemical Equilibrium.

The Law of Chemical Equilibrium, sometimes called the Law of Mass Action, was first suggested by Guldberg and Waage, Norwegian chemists, in 1846 in a rather ambiguous form. It was later shown that it follows rigorously from thermodynamics. It has been checked thoroughly by experiment, and, properly interpreted, can be applied to any system in chemical or physical equilibrium.

K_c, the constant in the law, is called the **equilibrium constant** for the reaction. The essence of the Law of Chemical Equilibrium is that such a constant exists, that **there is a condition on a chemical equilibrium system that must be satisfied by the reactants and products which are in equilibrium. In any equilibrium, the concentrations of reactants and products will achieve, by virtue of reaction in the forward or reverse directions, values which satisfy the Law of Chemical Equilibrium: chemical reactions will proceed up to that point and no further.** The law has far reaching implications and is one of the most important relations in all of chemistry. In this and succeeding chapters, we shall make considerable use of the law in treating chemical problems.

In order to treat a system in chemical equilibrium, one must be able to write the equation for the chemical reaction which is involved. Once this is known, the expression for the equilibrium constant, K_c, can be formulated by application of equation 14.1. In the combustion of hydrogen gas to form a mole of water vapor, the pertinent equation would be:

$$H_2(g) + \tfrac{1}{2} O_2(g) \rightleftharpoons H_2O(g) \tag{14.2}$$

By equation 14.1:

$$K_c = \frac{[H_2O]}{[H_2] \times [O_2]^{1/2}} \tag{14.3}$$

At 25°C, K_c can be shown to have a value of about 10^{40}. This means that in a container in which hydrogen, oxygen, and water vapor are present in equilibrium at 25°C, the concentrations of hydrogen and oxygen are very low compared to the concentration of water vapor, since:

$$K_c = \frac{[H_2O]}{[H_2][O_2]^{1/2}} = 10^{40} \tag{14.4}$$

Reactions such as this one, with enormous equilibrium constants, effectively proceed to completion, since so little of the reactants is left at equilibrium.

Consider now the reaction by which water vapor decomposes at 25°C, the reverse of reaction 14.2

$$H_2O(g) \rightleftharpoons H_2(g) + \tfrac{1}{2} O_2(g) \tag{14.5}$$

in which

$$K_c' = \frac{[H_2][O_2]^{1/2}}{[H_2O]} \tag{14.6}$$

Since the equilibrium state of this system must be independent of the direction in which we write the equation (indeed, independent of whether we start with water vapor or the hydrogen and oxygen from which the vapor could be formed), the concentrations in equations 14.6 and 14.4 must be the same if these two systems have the same overall composition. Therefore:

$$K_c' = \frac{1}{K_c} = \frac{1}{10^{40}} = 10^{-40} \tag{14.7}$$

This illustrates the general rule that the equilibrium constant associated with the equation for the reaction proceeding in *one* direction is the *reciprocal* of the constant for the reaction proceeding in the *reverse* direction.

Consideration of equation 14.6 and the value of K_c' allows one to conclude that the concentrations of hydrogen or oxygen in equilibrium with water vapor are very small. For this reason, the reaction at 25°C by which water vapor decomposes to the elements is assumed to proceed to a negligible extent.

Many chemical reactions have equilibrium constants of intermediate value. In systems in which such reactions occur there will be appreciable amounts of both reactants and products present at equilibrium. It is with such systems that discussions of equilibrium properties are primarily concerned.

14.3 SOME APPLICATIONS OF THE LAW OF CHEMICAL EQUILIBRIUM

Most problems requiring a quantitative application of the Law of Chemical Equilibrium involve either calculating equilibrium constants, given some equilibrium conditions in a system, or calculating equilibrium conditions in a system, given the initial conditions and the equilibrium constant for the reaction which occurs. The following examples illustrate the problems that arise and the method of attack.

Example 14.1. If a mole of H_2O and a mole of CO are let into a five liter container at 986°C, 44 per cent of the water reacts with the carbon monoxide according to the equation:

$$H_2O(g) + CO(g) \rightleftharpoons H_2(g) + CO_2(g)$$

Calculate the equilibrium constant, K_c, for the reaction.

Solution. For this type of problem, it is useful to construct a table describing the system at each stage of the reaction. In the table are listed the *amounts in moles* of all reactants and products present initially, the changes in these amounts which occur as the reaction proceeds to equilibrium, and finally, the amounts present in the equilibrium system. For this problem, the table takes the form:

	Initial	Gain	Loss	Equilibrium
H_2O	1.00		0.44	0.56
CO	1.00		0.44	0.56
H_2	0	0.44		0.44
CO_2	0	0.44		0.44

44 per cent of one mole is 0.44; hence 0.44 mole of H_2O reacted. Since the chemical equation involves species in a 1:1:1:1 ratio, this is the number of moles of CO reacted and the number of moles of H_2 and CO_2 formed.

$$K_c = \frac{[H_2][CO_2]}{[H_2O][CO]} = \frac{(0.44/5)\,(0.44/5)}{(0.56/5)\,(0.56/5)} = 0.63$$

Example 14.2. At 520°C, K_c equals 0.0156 for the gaseous reaction

$$2\,HI(g) \rightleftharpoons H_2(g) + I_2(g)$$

In an experiment, two (2.00) moles of HI are introduced into an evacuated 10.0 l. container. Calculate the concentrations and total numbers of moles of HI, H_2, and I_2 in the container at equilibrium. What is the fraction of HI which decomposes?

Solution.   In this problem, only the reactant HI is initially present. The HI will decompose until the amounts of H_2 and I_2 formed are sufficient to satisfy the Law of Chemical Equilibrium. At that point, equilibrium will be established, and no further decomposition of HI will be observed.

The amount of HI which decomposes is an unknown, and we shall call that amount 2x moles. *By the chemical equation for the reaction,* decomposition of 2x moles of HI will produce x moles of H_2 and x moles of I_2. Here, as in Example 14.1, it is convenient to set up a table:

	Initial	Gain	Loss	Equilibrium
HI	2		2x	2 − 2x
H_2	0	x		x
I_2	0	x		x

The equilibrium amount of HI is $2 - 2x$, since the amount initially present, 2 moles, is decreased by the decomposition of 2x moles. Therefore, at equilibrium, in a 10.0 l. container,

$$\frac{[H_2][I_2]}{[HI]^2} = K_c = 0.0156 = \frac{(x/10)(x/10)}{\left(\frac{2-2x}{10}\right)^2}$$

$$\frac{x^2}{(2-2x)^2} = 0.0156 \qquad \frac{x}{2-2x} = (0.0156)^{1/2} = 0.125$$

$$x = 0.125(2 - 2x) = 0.25 - 0.25x$$

$$1.25x = 0.25, \qquad x = 0.20$$

The calculation tells us that at equilibrium:

number of moles $H_2 = x = 0.20$ mole $[H_2] = \dfrac{0.20 \text{ moles}}{10.0 \text{ l.}} = 0.020 \dfrac{\text{mole}}{\text{l.}}$

number of moles $I_2 = x = 0.20$ mole $[I_2] = \dfrac{0.20 \text{ mole}}{10.0 \text{ l.}} = 0.020 \dfrac{\text{mole}}{\text{l.}}$

number of moles HI $= 2 - 2x = 1.60$ moles $[HI] = \dfrac{1.60 \text{ moles}}{10.0 \text{ l.}} = 0.160 \dfrac{\text{mole}}{\text{l.}}$

The fraction of HI which dissociates is equal to the amount reacted divided by the initial amount:

$$\text{fraction HI dissociated} = 2x/2 = 0.40/2 = 0.20 \text{ or } 20\%$$

By using the procedure of this example, the student can confirm all the data listed in Tables 14.1 and 14.2 (see also Example 14.3).

Example 14.3.   One (1.00) mole each of HI, H_2, and I_2 are placed in a 1.00 l. container and allowed to come to equilibrium at 520°C. What is the final state of the system?

Solution.   It was pointed out in Example 14.2 that, at 520°C, K_c for the reaction:

$$2 \text{ HI(g)} \rightleftharpoons H_2(g) + (I_2(g))$$

is 0.0156. In other words, at equilibrium:

$$\frac{[H_2] \times [I_2]}{[HI]^2} = 0.0156$$

Under the conditions specified in this problem, the initial concentration quotient is:

$$\frac{(\text{conc. } H_2)(\text{conc. } I_2)}{(\text{conc. } HI)^2} = \frac{(1.00)(1.00)}{(1.00)^2} = 1.00$$

Since this quotient, 1.00, is considerably greater than the equilibrium constant, 0.0156, it is perhaps obvious that some H_2 and I_2 must be converted to HI to establish equilibrium. To decide how much H_2 and I_2 react, we proceed, as before, to set up an equilibrium table. If we let the amount of H_2 which reacts be x:

	Initial	Gain	Loss	Equilibrium
HI	1.00	2x		1.00 + 2x
H_2	1.00		x	1.00 − x
I_2	1.00		x	1.00 − x

Since the volume of the container is 1.00 l., we have:

$$\frac{\left(\dfrac{1.00 - x}{1.00}\right)\left(\dfrac{1.00 - x}{1.00}\right)}{\left(\dfrac{1.00 + 2x}{1.00}\right)^2} = 0.0156$$

Extracting the square root of both sides:

$$\frac{1.00 - x}{1.00 + 2x} = 0.125$$

and solving,

$$x = 0.70$$

In other words, 0.70 mole of H_2 reacts with 0.70 mole of I_2 to form 1.40 mole of HI. At equilibrium (see equilibrium table), we have:

$$(1.00 - 0.70) \text{ mole } H_2 = 0.30 \text{ mole } H_2 \qquad (1.00 - 0.70) \text{ mole } I_2 = 0.30 \text{ mole } I_2$$

$$(1.00 + 1.40) \text{ mole HI} = 2.40 \text{ mole HI}$$

Examples 14.2 and 14.3 illustrate how one can use the equilibrium constant to predict the extent of reaction. In Example 14.2 we found that when 2 moles of HI were admitted into an evacuated 10.0 l. container at 520°C, 20 per cent of the HI decomposed to establish equilibrium. In Example 14.3 we showed that when one starts with one mole each of H_2, I_2, and HI in a 1.0 l. container, 70 per cent of the H_2 (0.70 mole) reacts with I_2 to form HI.

From a qualitative standpoint, Examples 14.2 and 14.3 illustrate how one can use the equilibrium constant to predict the direction in which a reaction will proceed under a particular initial set of conditions. In Example 14.2 we found that starting with pure HI, reaction proceeds in the direction:

$$2 \text{ HI(g)} \longrightarrow H_2(g) + I_2(g)$$

to establish equilibrium. Under the quite different conditions of Example 14.3 the reaction proceeds in the opposite direction:

$$H_2(g) + I_2(g) \longrightarrow 2 \text{ HI(g)}$$

until equilibrium is established. In general, one can say that whenever the **concentration quotient,**

$$\frac{\text{conc. } H_2 \times \text{conc. } I_2}{(\text{conc. HI})^2}$$

is _less_ than the equilibrium constant, K_c, the reaction will proceed so as to form H_2 and I_2 by decomposition of HI. If the quotient is _greater_ than K_c, reaction will occur in the opposite direction to form more HI. If, perchance, the concentration quotient is exactly equal to the equilibrium constant, no net reaction will occur. For the general reaction:

$$aA(g) + bB(g) \rightleftharpoons cC(g) + dD(g)$$

we can distinguish three possibilities:

1. $\dfrac{(\text{conc. C})^c(\text{conc. D})^d}{(\text{conc. A})^a(\text{conc. B})^b} < K_c$ Reaction proceeds to right to attain equilibrium.

2. $\dfrac{(\text{conc. C})^c(\text{conc. D})^d}{(\text{conc. A})^a(\text{conc. B})^b} = K_c$ No reaction: system is at equilibrium.

3. $\dfrac{(\text{conc. C})^c(\text{conc. D})^d}{(\text{conc. A})^a(\text{conc. B})^b} > K_c$ Reaction proceeds to left to attain equilibrium.

The value of the concentration quotient as calculated from initial concentrations of reactants and products will determine whether a given reaction will proceed to right or left in accord with the above relations.

14.4 CHANGES IN SYSTEMS IN EQUILIBRIUM

It has been shown in the previous section how one can make calculations of equilibrium conditions if initial conditions and an equilibrium constant are given. It is also possible to begin with an equilibrium system and alter it so that it is no longer in equilibrium, causing reaction to occur until equilibrium is reattained. This could be done by increasing or decreasing the amount of one or more of the reactants or products in the equilibrium system. One could also increase or decrease the volume of the container in which the equilibrium exists. A substance which takes no part in the equilibrium could be added. And, finally, the temperature of the equilibrium system could be changed. A quantitative attack on the results of changes of the kinds we have mentioned is usually based on the Law of Chemical Equilibrium, and involves the same general approach as in the previous section.

Le Chatelier's Principle

It is also possible to discuss these changes qualitatively, using either the equilibrium Law or a general rule known as Le Chatelier's Principle. Le Chatelier's Principle states that *if a system in chemical equilibrium is altered in any way, the system will respond in such a way as to minimize the effect of the change.* If, for instance, one adds one of the substances present in an equilibrium system to that system, the equilibrium will shift in such a way as to consume part of the added substance. If an equilibrium system is compressed, reaction will tend to occur to reduce the net increase in pressure in the system. If the system is heated, reaction will occur so as to minimize the rise in temperature of the system. By use of Le Chatelier's Principle it is relatively easy to predict in a qualitative way the changes which will occur when an equilibrium system is disturbed. In this book we will discuss changes in equilibrium systems both on the basis of the Equilibrium Law and on the basis of Le Chatelier's Principle.

Example 14.4. Phosphorus pentachloride, PCl_5, decomposes partially to phosphorus trichloride, PCl_3, and chlorine at elevated temperatures, where all the substances are gases. The equation for the reaction is

$$PCl_5(g) \rightleftharpoons PCl_3(g) + Cl_2(g)$$

At a certain temperature in a 10.0 l. container the concentration of PCl_5 in a system in equilibrium is 0.80 mole/l.: the concentration of PCl_3 is 0.20 mole/l. and that of Cl_2 is 0.20 mole/l.

What would happen qualitatively, and quantitatively to the concentrations of all species if

    a. Two (2.00) moles of PCl_5 were added to the system?
    b. Two (2.00) moles of Cl_2 were added to the system?
    c. The container volume was decreased to 5.0 l?

Solution. At final equilibrium, *no matter which change is made*, the Equilibrium Law will be obeyed.

$$K_c = \frac{[PCl_3][Cl_2]}{[PCl_5]} = \frac{(0.20)(0.20)}{(0.80)} = 0.050$$

The amounts of PCl_5, PCl_3, and Cl_2 initially present at equilibrium are 8.0 moles, 2.0 moles, and 2.0 moles respectively.

    a. To these amounts are added two moles of PCl_5. If no reaction occurred, there would be 10 moles of PCl_5 in the 10-l. container, or its concentration would be raised to 1.0 mole/l. Substituting the values 0.20, 0.20, and 1.0 into the concentration quotient yields a value of .04, which is smaller than the value of K_c, 0.050. Therefore, since the equation must be satisfied at equilibrium, we can say qualitatively that some of the PCl_5 must decompose after the addition of the two moles, lowering its concentration below 1.0 and thereby raising the concentrations of the PCl_3 and Cl_2. In applying Le Chatelier's Principle one would reach the same conclusion by recognizing that part of the added PCl_5 would be consumed by reaction, thereby reducing the net increase in its concentration.

    The quantitative solution is somewhat more difficult, and we again resort to an equilibrium table, considering the initial amounts to be those present *after* the addition of the PCl_5 and *before* its partial decomposition to reattain equilibrium.

	Initial	Gain	Loss	Equilibrium
PCl_5	10	—	x	$10 - x$
PCl_3	2	x	—	$2 + x$
Cl_2	2	x	—	$2 + x$

At equilibrium:

$$\frac{[PCl_3][Cl_2]}{[PCl_5]} = 0.050 = \frac{\left(\dfrac{2+x}{10}\right)\left(\dfrac{2+x}{10}\right)}{\left(\dfrac{10-x}{10}\right)}$$

    This equation can be solved by the quadratic formula. The value of x which is obtained is 0.21. Therefore, the equilibrium amounts of PCl_5, PCl_3, and Cl_2 are 9.8, 2.2, and 2.2 moles respectively, and their concentrations are 0.98, 0.22, and 0.22 mole/l. respectively, in agreement with the qualitative prediction.

    b. When Cl_2 is added, the equilibrium is again disturbed, resulting in too large a value for the concentration quotient. Equilibrium can only be attained if some Cl_2 reacts with PCl_3, decreasing the latter's concentration and raising that of the PCl_5. For a quantitative result we construct the equilibrium table as before.

	Initial	Gain	Loss	Equilibrium
PCl_5	8	x	—	$8 + x$
PCl_3	2	—	x	$2 - x$
Cl_2	4	—	x	$4 - x$

Substituting into the equilibrium equation:

$$\frac{[PCl_3]\,[Cl_2]}{[PCl_5]} = 0.050 = \frac{\left(\dfrac{2-x}{10}\right)\left(\dfrac{4-x}{10}\right)}{\left(\dfrac{8+x}{.10}\right)}$$

Solution of the resulting quadratic yields a value of x equal to 0.69 mole. Therefore, $[PCl_5] = 0.87$, $[PCl_3] = 0.13$, and $[Cl_2] = 0.33$ mole/l.

c. When the volume of the container is decreased to 5.0 l., the concentrations of all species are momentarily doubled, becoming 1.60, 0.40, and 0.40 mole/l. If no reaction occurred, the concentration quotient would equal 0.10, twice K_c. To reach equilibrium again, the amounts of PCl_3 and Cl_2 must be reduced by combining to form PCl_5. If Le Chatelier's Principle were used, one would note that the pressure increase created by the volume change would be met by a shift in the equilibrium system in the direction which would decrease the final pressure. Since reaction of PCl_3 with Cl_2 to form PCl_5 decreases the number of moles of gas in the system, and hence the pressure of the system, that reaction will occur. The quantitative treatment is again readily accomplished by setting up the equilibrium table:

	Initial	Gain	Loss	Equilibrium
PCl_5	8	x	—	$8+x$
PCl_3	2	—	x	$2-x$
Cl_2	2	—	x	$2-x$

Using the equilibrium equation:

$$\frac{[PCl_3]\,[Cl_2]}{[PCl_5]} = 0.05 = \frac{\dfrac{(2-x)}{5}\times\dfrac{(2-x)}{5}}{\dfrac{(8+x)}{5}}$$

Solving, we find that $x = 0.54$ mole, yielding $[PCl_5] = 1.71$, $[PCl_3] = 0.29$, and $[Cl_2] = 0.29$ mole/l.

The qualitative results obtained for the PCl_5-PCl_3-Cl_2 system can be generalized to cover all gaseous systems. Whenever a reactant is added at constant volume to an equilibrium mixture, the concentrations of products will increase and that of all other reactants will decrease. The net increase in the concentration of added reactant will be less than if no equilibrium were present. If a reaction product is added to an equilibrium mixture, the concentrations of all reactants will increase and that of all other products will decrease. The net increase in concentration of the added product will be less than if no equilibrium were present.

If the volume of the container for the system is decreased, the concentrations of all reactants and products will momentarily increase, as will the total pressure in the system. A chemical reaction will take place in the direction which counteracts the pressure increase, and so will proceed in the direction which decreases the total number of moles of gas present. Decrease in volume of the PCl_5-PCl_3-Cl_2 system favors formation of PCl_5, since to form 1 mole of PCl_5 2 moles of gas are consumed, 1 mole of PCl_3 and 1 mole of Cl_2. If the volume of the container is increased, the reaction to reattain equilibrium will occur so as to increase the total number of moles of gas present. In the event that the number of moles of reactants equals the number of moles of products in the chemical equation, a change in volume will have no effect on the total amounts of any species present, although of course their concentrations will change.

Addition of a substance which does not react with any of the species present in an equilibrium system will not disturb the equilibrium, since the concentrations of the reacting species are not affected and the equilibrium constant expression remains satisfied. If helium were pumped into a PCl_5-PCl_3-Cl_2 equilibrium system at constant volume, no change in the concentrations of any of the substances involved in the equilibrium would occur. In order for any substance to influence a chemical equilibrium system it must be either a reactant or a product of the reaction involved, or it must react chemically with one or more of the reactants or products.

The notions underlying the behavior of systems in chemical equilibrium are both among the most important and the most difficult of all the concepts to be mastered in an elementary course. In later chapters, the principles which have been presented here will be applied to different chemical systems to aid our understanding of why they behave as they do. The student should, at this point, make every effort to obtain a real understanding of the basic principles governing the qualitative and quantitative properties of simple gaseous systems in chemical equilibrium so that, when these ideas are extended to other systems, they will appear to be extensions of basic concepts rather than a new group of notions, unrelated to earlier knowledge.

Equilibrium Constants Involving Partial Pressures: K_p. In discussing gaseous equilibria, chemists sometimes use equilibrium constants involving concentration units other than those found in the expression for K_c (moles/l.). In particular, an equilibrium constant, designated as K_p, in which concentrations are expressed in terms of partial pressures, is often employed. For the equilibrium:

$$aA(g) + bB(g) \rightleftharpoons cC(g) + dD(g)$$

we may write:

$$K_p = \frac{[p_C]^c [p_D]^d}{[p_A]^a [p_B]^b}$$

in which the terms in square brackets represent equilibrium partial pressures of C, D, A, and B in atmospheres.

Even though all our calculations concerning gaseous equilibria will be made in terms of K_c, it is useful to examine briefly certain of the properties of K_p. For a given equilibrium system, the numerical values of K_p and K_c will often differ significantly from each other. Using the Ideal Gas Law to obtain the relation between gas pressure and concentration, we see that:

$$p_A = \frac{n_A}{V} RT = [A]RT$$

in which p_A is the partial pressure in atmospheres of a gas in a mixture, R the gas constant (0.0821 l.-atm./mole × °K), and T the absolute temperature. On setting up K_p in terms of the foregoing relations, it is readily seen that for any reaction:

$$K_p = K_c (RT)^{\Delta n}$$

in which Δn is the change in the number of moles of gas as the reaction proceeds from left to right. Thus, we have:

$2 H_2O(g) \rightleftharpoons 2 H_2(g) + O_2(g)$	$\Delta n = +1$	$K_p = K_c(RT)$
$H_2(g) + I_2(g) \rightleftharpoons 2 HI(g)$	$\Delta n = 0$	$K_p = K_c$
$N_2(g) + 3 H_2(g) \rightleftharpoons 2 NH_3(g)$	$\Delta n = -2$	$K_p = K_c/(RT)^2$

K_p, like K_c, can be used to determine the extent or direction of a reaction under a particular set of conditions. For example, knowing that K_p for the reaction:

$$N_2(g) + 3 H_2(g) \rightleftharpoons 2 NH_3(g)$$

is 9.5 at 300°C, i.e.:

$$\frac{[p\ NH_3]^2}{[p\ N_2]\ [p\ H_2]^3} = 9.5$$

we can predict that if nitrogen, hydrogen, and ammonia, each at a partial pressure of 1 atm., are mixed at 300°C, reaction will proceed from left to right according to the foregoing equation. That is, some of the nitrogen will react with hydrogen to form ammonia and thereby establish equilibrium.

From a slightly different point of view, we could say that since K_p corresponding to the previous equation has a value of 9.5, the reaction:

$$N_2(g, 1\ atm.) + 3\ H_2(g, 1\ atm.) \longrightarrow 2\ NH_3(g, 1\ atm.)$$

will proceed spontaneously at 300°C. In other words, it should be possible to prepare ammonia at 1 atm. pressure by passing the elements at that pressure through a reaction vessel maintained at 300°C. Indeed, under these conditions, one can expect to produce ammonia at an equilibrium pressure considerably greater than 1 atm.

The line of reasoning just outlined suggests a simple physical interpretation of the magnitude of the equilibrium constant, K_p: *If K_p for a given reaction is greater than 1, that reaction will be spontaneous under "standard conditions," i.e., reactants and products each at 1 atm. pressure. If K_p is less than 1, the reverse reaction will be spontaneous under these conditions.*

For the general reaction:

$$aA(g) + bB(g) \rightleftharpoons cC(g) + dD(g)$$

we can write:

If $K_p > 1$, then $aA(1\ atm.) + bB(1\ atm.) \rightarrow cC(1\ atm.) + dD(1\ atm.)$

$K_p = 1$, no reaction will occur under standard conditions.

$K_p < 1$, then $cC(1\ atm.) + dD(1\ atm.) \leftarrow aA(1\ atm.) + bB(1\ atm.)$

The Relation between K_p and the Standard Free Energy Change, $\Delta G°$. It will be recalled from the discussions of Chapter 5 that the sign of the free energy change, ΔG, of a reaction is a criterion of spontaneity for that reaction. A negative free energy change corresponds to a spontaneous reaction; if the sign of ΔG is positive, the reverse reaction will be spontaneous under the conditions specified. For the general reaction:

$$aA(g) + bB(g) \rightleftharpoons cC(g) + dD(g)$$

we can write:

If $\Delta G° < 0$, then $aA(1\ atm.) + bB(1\ atm.) \rightarrow cC(1\ atm.) + dD(1\ atm.)$

$\Delta G° = 0$, no reaction will occur under standard conditions.

$\Delta G° > 0$, then $cC(1\ atm.) + dD(1\ atm.) \rightarrow aA(1\ atm.) + bB(1\ atm.)$

in which $\Delta G°$ is the free energy change at standard conditions, i.e., all gaseous products and reactants at a partial pressure of 1 atm.

Comparing the expressions written above for K_p and $\Delta G°$, it is perhaps obvious that these two quantities might be functionally related. It can be shown by thermodynamics that the following relation between them exists:

$$\Delta G° = -RT \ln K_p \qquad (14.8)$$

where R is the gas constant (1.987 cal./mole°K), T is the absolute temperature and $\ln K_p$ is the natural logarithm of K_p. (See Appendix 1 for a discussion of natural logarithms.) If $K_p > 1$, $\ln K_p$ will be positive and $\Delta G°$ negative; if $K_p = 1$, $\ln K_p = 0$, and $\Delta G° = 0$; if $K_p < 1$, $\ln K_p$ will be negative and $\Delta G°$ positive.

Equation 14.8 is useful in that it can be used to calculate K_p from free energy data. From a known value of K_p, K_c can then be determined. At 25°C, where free energy data are available, substitution of numerical values for R and T and conversion to ordinary logarithms gives equation 14.8 the form:

$$\Delta G° \text{ (cal.)} = -(1.987)(298)(2.303) \log_{10} K_p$$

$$\Delta G° \text{ (cal.)} = -1364 \log_{10} K_p \quad \text{(at 25°C)} \qquad (14.9)$$

We shall find equation 14.9 to be particularly useful for discussing the spontaneity and extent of oxidation-reduction reactions in solution (Chapter 21).

14.5   THE EFFECT OF TEMPERATURE ON CHEMICAL EQUILIBRIA

So far our attention has been directed toward equilibrium systems at a constant temperature. Under such conditions the equilibrium constant, K_c, remains constant, independent of any changes of concentrations of reactants or products which might be made. Many equilibria are studied under constant temperature conditions, but it is of importance to know what effect changes in temperature can have on equilibrium systems.

It is found experimentally and predicted by thermodynamics that temperature can have a very great influence on the magnitude of equilibrium constants. The equilibrium constant for a reaction will increase with increasing temperature if that reaction is endothermic, that is, if the system absorbs heat when the reaction occurs at constant temperature. If the reaction is exothermic, evolving heat, then a rise in temperature will cause a decrease in the size of the equilibrium constant. These conclusions are consistent with Le Chatelier's Principle which would predict that heating an equilibrium system would cause the equilibrium to shift to the right for endothermic reactions and to the left for exothermic reactions, thereby minimizing the temperature rise in the system.

Most decomposition reactions, in which molecules break down to smaller particles, are endothermic, and hence tend to proceed to a greater degree at high temperatures. In Table 14.3 are listed several reactions we have considered, with their associated heat effects and the effect of temperature on K_c. In Figure 14.2, log K_c is plotted as a function of temperature for those reactions.

The laws of thermodynamics allow us to derive an analytic function expressing the dependence of the equilibrium constant on the temperature at which the reaction occurs. For K_p the function is:

$$\ln K_{p2}/K_{p1} = \frac{\Delta H}{R}\left(\frac{1}{T_1} - \frac{1}{T_2}\right) \tag{14.10}$$

in which ΔH is the heat absorbed when the reaction proceeds to completion at constant pressure, R is the gas constant, T is the absolute temperature, and the subscripts 2 and 1 refer to the final and initial temperatures of the system. If we let T_1 be 298°K (25°C) and T_2 be the temperature at which we need information, equation 14.10 can be restated, making use of equation 14.9 and the relations used in obtaining it. The result is

$$\log_{10} K_p = \frac{\Delta H - \Delta G°}{1364} - \frac{\Delta H}{4.606\ T} \tag{14.10a}$$

TABLE 14.3 HEAT EFFECTS AND DEPENDENCE OF K_c ON TEMPERATURE FOR SOME TYPICAL REACTIONS

Reaction	Heat Effect (kcal.)	Effect of Temperature Increase on K_c
$PCl_5(g) \rightarrow PCl_3(g) + Cl_2(g)$	22.1 absorbed	increase
$2\ HI(g) \rightarrow H_2(g) + I_2(g)$	2.5 absorbed	increase
$H_2O(g) + CO(g) \rightarrow H_2(g) + CO_2(g)$	9.8 evolved	decrease
$2\ H_2O(g) \rightarrow 2\ H_2(g) + O_2(g)$	115.6 absorbed	increase

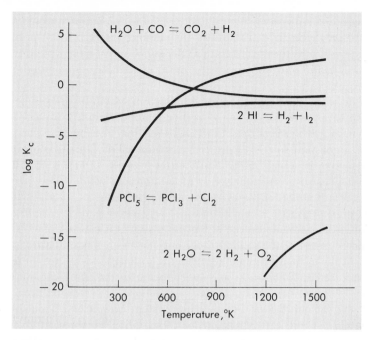

FIGURE 14.2 Temperature dependence of the equilibrium constant for some chemical reactions involving gases.

in which K_p is the equilibrium constant at the temperature T and ΔH and $\Delta G°$ are the standard enthalpy and free energy changes in calories for the reaction at 25°C. Using Tables 5.1 and 5.4, one can calculate K_p at any temperature T for any reaction for which the thermodynamic data are given. Values of K_c at the temperature T can be readily found from those of K_p by making use of the relation derived previously (p. 328):

$$K_c = K_p(RT)^{-\Delta n}$$

It was in this manner that the data for Figure 14.2 were obtained.

14.6 EQUILIBRIA INVOLVING PHASES OTHER THAN GASES: HETEROGENEOUS EQUILIBRIA

In most chemical reactions not all the reactants and products are gases. Frequently the participants in a chemical equilibrium system are pure solids, or pure liquids, or are solutes in an aqueous solution. The treatment of equilibria in such systems is very similar to that we have employed for completely gaseous systems. It will be briefly described here and considered further in later chapters.

Probably the simplest heterogeneous chemical reaction involves only gases and pure solids. A typical example would be the reaction in which carbon disulfide is formed from the elements at high temperatures:

$$C(s) + S_2(g) \rightleftharpoons CS_2(g)$$

The equilibrium system contains solid carbon in the presence of certain concentrations of S_2 gas and CS_2 gas. The influence of the gases on the system is the same as in an all-gas equilibrium system. That is, increasing the amount of S_2 would tend to drive the equilibrium to the right; increasing the amount of CS_2 by, say, pumping it into the system would shift the equilibrium to the left. Compressing the system would not shift the equilibrium since the number of moles of gas is the same on both sides of the chemical equation.

The role of the solid carbon in the equilibrium system remains to be considered. Its effect on the system is established as soon as solid carbon is present and will not change as more carbon is added. One might say that the effective concentration of the carbon is constant since it is present as a pure solid. The situation is completely analogous to that observed in the equilibrium between a pure solid and its vapor; the pressure of carbon dioxide gas in a container in which there is solid carbon dioxide is not a function of the amount of solid present. At any given temperature, the sublimation pressure, or concentration, of carbon dioxide is constant. The effect of the solid carbon dioxide on the equilibrium system is constant and established by the presence of some of the solid; it does not vary with the amount of solid. In the same way, in the carbon disulfide equilibrium, so long as some carbon is present, its effect on the system is constant, and independent of the actual amount of solid in the system.

Since the carbon disulfide equilibrium system cannot be altered by adding or removing solid carbon, the expression for the equilibrium constant for the reaction cannot involve the concentration of solid carbon as a variable. The effect of the solid is constant and can be considered to be included in K_c. The expression for K_c is formulated simply in terms of the gases present and according to the same rule as for an all-gas system. By applying equation 14.1 to the gases in the carbon disulfide system, one arrives at the following expression for the equilibrium constant:

$$K_c = \frac{[CS_2]}{[S_2]}$$

Problems involving the carbon disulfide equilibrium are handled by using this expression for K_c and taking proper account of the stoichiometry of the reaction in the same manner as that employed with all-gas systems.

In treating any equilibrium system in which pure solids or pure liquids are present with gases, the effects of the solids and liquids can be taken to be constant and included in K_c. The expression for K_c will include only the gaseous reactants and products. Below we have formulated the expressions for K_c for several reactions in which pure solids and liquids are present as reactants or products along with one or more gases:

$$CaCO_3(s) \rightleftharpoons CaO(s) + CO_2(g) \qquad\qquad K_c = [CO_2]$$
$$2\ CaSO_4(s) \rightleftharpoons 2\ CaO(s) + 2\ SO_2(g) + O_2(g) \qquad\qquad K_c = [SO_2]^2[O_2]$$
$$2\ Mo(s) + CH_4(g) \rightleftharpoons Mo_2C(s) + 2\ H_2(g) \qquad\qquad K_c = [H_2]^2/[CH_4]$$
$$C(s) + CO_2(g) \rightleftharpoons 2\ CO(g) \qquad\qquad K_c = [CO]^2/[CO_2]$$
$$2\ BrCl(g) \rightleftharpoons Br_2(l) + Cl_2(g) \qquad\qquad K_c = [Cl_2]/[BrCl]^2$$

When an equilibrium system includes substances which are present as solutes in a liquid solution, the concentrations of those substances, which may be neutral molecules or ions, are ordinarily variable. Such substances participate in chemical equilibrium in the same way as gases, and their concentrations occur in the expression for the equilibrium constant according to the same rules as apply to gases. Pure solids or pure liquids, when they participate in reactions which involve solutes, are treated as in gas-solid systems. Below we have listed some common reactions which can occur in aqueous solution along with the expressions for the equilibrium constants (unless otherwise specified, all species are solutes):

$$H_2S \rightleftharpoons H^+ + HS^- \qquad K_c = \frac{[H^+][HS^-]}{[H_2S]}$$

$$AgCl(s) \rightleftharpoons Ag^+ + Cl^- \qquad K_c = [Ag^+][Cl^-]$$

$$H_2O(l) \rightleftharpoons H^+ + OH^- \qquad K_c = [H^+][OH^-]$$

Equilibria such as these can be treated qualitatively and quantitatively by the same principles and methods as were applied to gaseous systems. The equilibrium properties of aqueous solutions form a very important part of chemistry, and, directly or indirectly, will be the subject of much of the rest of this book.

14.7 NONEQUILIBRIUM PROCESSES: THE RATES OF GASEOUS REACTIONS

In considering equilibrium systems we tacitly assumed that the rates of the reactions involved were fast enough to ensure the attainment of equilibrium in a reasonable amount of time. In general, one can expect that reactions between relatively small gas molecules or between ions will proceed rapidly to an equilibrium state. However, not all chemical reactions occur quickly, nor do they occur at the same rate under different conditions.

Some reactions are infinitesimally slow. A mixture of hydrogen and oxygen at room temperature will remain unreacted for centuries even though the equilibrium constant for the reaction to form water is highly favorable: if the reaction is once started, say by a spark, then it goes very rapidly, but it will not begin of itself unless the temperature is markedly increased. It is indeed fortunate that some reactions are exceedingly slow at ordinary temperatures. The wooden table on which I am writing is surely not in chemical equilibrium with the air in this room: the equilibrium state would be one in which all the carbon atoms in the table were in carbon dioxide gas molecules and all the hydrogen atoms were in water molecules. All living things owe their existence to the fact that, by the expenditure of energy at relatively low temperatures, reactions can be made to occur in the direction opposite to that favored by the equilibrium constant. The substances which make up the living organism are frequently thermodynamically unstable, but the slow rate at which they decompose to stabler substances enables the organism to live and grow.

The study of reaction rates, sometimes called **chemical kinetics,** is at present one of the most active areas of chemical research. Incentive for such research has in recent years been increased by the development of instrumental methods, particularly vapor phase chromatography and mass spectroscopy, capable of rapid identification and quantitative analysis of the chemical substances present in reaction mixtures. Instruments using these and other approaches have made possible much more complete and definitive investigations of chemical reaction rates, and have enabled chemists to learn a great deal about the sometimes very complex paths by which chemical reactions occur. In the rest of this chapter we will first consider some experimentally observed properties of systems undergoing chemical reaction, particularly with regard to the effects of changing experimental conditions on rate of reaction. Then we will discuss some of the theories which have been proposed to explain these observations.

14.8 THE MEANING OF REACTION RATE

In order to discuss rates of chemical reactions intelligently one must understand what the term reaction rate means in a quantitative sense. One can speak qualitatively of fast or slow reactions, but this is not sufficient when it is necessary to express rates of reaction in mathematical terms. The concept of reaction rate is not particularly simple or straightforward and is probably most easily introduced by working with a specific example.

Let us consider the gaseous reaction:

$$CO + NO_2 \longrightarrow CO_2 + NO$$

If, at about 430°C, some carbon monoxide and some nitrogen dioxide are let into an evacuated container, it is found that, as time passes, the concentrations of carbon monoxide and nitrogen dioxide decrease, while those of carbon dioxide and nitric oxide increase. (Analysis of this system could be made at different times by sampling the gas, cooling it quickly to stop the reaction, and passing it into either a vapor chromatography apparatus, which could analyze easily for all four components, or into an absorption spectrometer which, if it operates in the infrared region could also analyze for all components, or if it operates in the visible region could analyze for that gas which is colored, namely the nitrogen dioxide.) The rate of change of all the concentrations is most rapid at the beginning of the reaction, and approaches zero as equilibrium is reached. For this reaction at 430°C, K_c is very large (about 10^{17})

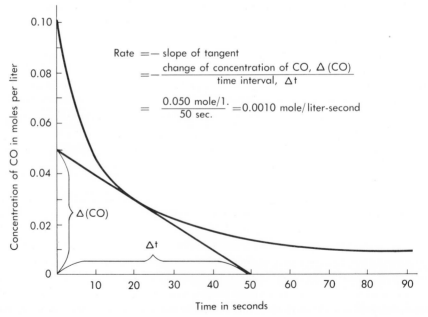

FIGURE 14.3   Determination of the rate of the chemical reaction: $CO + NO_2 \rightarrow CO_2 + NO$.

so the reaction goes essentially to completion. In Figure 14.3 the concentration of carbon monoxide is plotted as a function of time for a system at 430°C which initially contained 0.10 mole/l. of CO and 0.10 mole/l. of NO_2.

The **rate** of a chemical reaction is the *change per unit of time* of the *concentration* of one of the reactants or products in the reaction. In our example the rate would be the change in concentration of the CO, or the NO_2, or the CO_2, or the NO, which occurs in one second. Due to the stoichiometry of the reaction all these changes are equal in magnitude and can differ only in sign: by convention the rate is always taken to be a positive quantity, so, if we were to write the rate in terms of a reactant, it would be minus the change of concentration per second. (If the stoichiometry were such that different numbers of moles of reactants or products were taking part in the reaction, the rate would be based on any one substance chosen arbitrarily and could be readily expressed in terms of any other.)

Clearly, in light of Figure 14.3, the rate of the reaction at time equals 20 seconds is not the same as the rate at time equals 10, or 40 seconds. The rate decreases with time and must be evaluated in such a way as to give the change taking place at the time that is of interest. The rate is determined by finding the **slope** of the concentration vs. time curve at a particular time. The slope is most readily found by drawing a tangent to the curve at that time. In Figure 14.3 we have drawn a tangent to the curve at time equals 20 seconds. The slope of the curve equals the slope of the tangent, and, by Figure 14.3:

$$\text{rate} = -\text{slope of tangent} = -\frac{\text{change of concentration of CO, } \Delta(CO)}{\text{time interval, } \Delta t}$$

$$\text{rate} = \frac{0.050 \text{ mole/l.}}{50 \text{ sec.}} = 0.0010 \text{ mole/l.-sec.}$$

Reaction rates can be determined for any reaction at any time by proceeding as we did in this example. To find the rate it is necessary to know the concentration of any one reactant or product as a function of time.

The rate of a given chemical reaction is dependent on several factors, of which reactant concentration or state of subdivision, temperature, and the possible presence of catalysts are among the most important. We are now in a position to look in some detail into the effect of each of these factors on reaction rate.

14.9   THE DEPENDENCE OF REACTION RATE ON CONCENTRATION: THE ORDER OF A CHEMICAL REACTION

In the previous section we noted that, as time passed, the rate of the reaction between carbon monoxide and nitrogen dioxide decreased. From Figure 14.3 it is also clear that, as the concentration of carbon monoxide decreased, the rate of reaction decreased. The decrease in rate was indeed the result of the smaller CO concentration, and is illustrative of the general rule that the rate of a given reaction will increase, or decrease, as the concentration of any reactant is increased, or decreased. The mathematical relation between rate of reaction and reactant concentrations turns out to be a relatively simple one, and can be found by examining the initial rates of reaction that are obtained at a given temperature for different

TABLE 14.4 INITIAL RATES OF REACTION BETWEEN
CO AND NO_2 AT 430°C

(CO) (moles/l.)	(NO_2) (moles/l.)	Rate of Reaction (moles/l.-sec.)
0.10	0.10	0.012
0.20	0.10	0.024
0.40	0.10	0.048
0.10	0.20	0.024
0.10	0.30	0.036

initial reactant concentrations. In Table 14.4 are listed some initial rates of reaction observed for the CO-NO_2 system at 430°C.

If the initial concentration of the NO_2 is kept constant, the rate of the reaction is seen to double if the concentration of the CO is doubled and to quadruple if the concentration of CO is increased by a factor of four. Similarly, if the concentration of CO is kept constant, doubling the concentration of the NO_2 doubles the rate. By virtue of this kind of dependence, all the data in Table 14.4 can be summarized in the equation:

$$\text{rate} = 1.2(CO)(NO_2) \text{ moles/l.-sec.}$$

The rate of the reaction is proportional to the concentration of the carbon monoxide and to the concentration of the nitrogen dioxide. The proportionality constant, 1.2 l./mole-sec., is called the **rate constant** for the reaction at 430°C, the temperature at which the investigation was carried out.

Rate equations similar to the one we have just derived can be written for many chemical reactions. In general, for the reaction:

$$aA(g) + bB(g) \longrightarrow cC(g) + dD(g) \tag{14.11}$$

$$\text{rate} = k(A)^n(B)^m$$

in which n and m are integers (0, 1, 2, and possibly 3) and k is the rate constant. If n = 1, we say that the reaction is **first order** with respect to A. If m = 2, the reaction is **second order** with respect to B. The *overall* order of the reaction equals *n plus m*. In the CO-NO_2 system, the reaction is first order with respect to both CO and NO_2 and is second order overall. Experimentally it is found that the order of a reaction with respect to a given reactant is not necessarily related to the stoichiometric coefficient of that reactant in the chemical equation. The values of n and m have no clear connection with the values of a and b, although for some reactions, of which the CO-NO_2 reaction is an example, the values are found to correspond.

TABLE 14.5 ORDERS OF SOME TYPICAL
REACTIONS INVOLVING GASES

Reaction	Overall Order
$CH_3CHO \rightarrow CH_4 + CO$	second
$2\,HI \rightarrow H_2 + I_2$	second
$2\,N_2O_5 \rightarrow 4\,NO_2 + O_2$	first
$SO_2Cl_2 \rightarrow SO_2 + Cl_2$	first

The order of a reaction with respect to each reactant is one of the first kinetic properties of a reaction that is determined. Many, but not all, reactions have integral orders. The order of a reaction may appear to change during the course of a reaction, particularly if the products of the reaction undergo further change or if the value of K_c, the equilibrium constant for the reaction, is not very large. The orders of a great many reactions have been determined and those for some typical reactions are listed in Table 14.5. The data indicate clearly the lack of correlation between reaction order and stoichiometry.

By the use of calculus one can obtain mathematical expressions for the concentrations of reactants as a function of time for many reactions, given the order of the reaction with respect to each reactant. The rate of a reaction in calculus notation is equal to the decrease in the derivative of the concentration of a reactant with respect to time. For the first-order reaction:

$$A \longrightarrow B$$

$$\text{rate} = -\frac{d(A)}{dt} = k(A)$$

This is also the rate law obeyed by substances undergoing radioactive decay. In Chapter 23 it is shown that the expression for (A) as a function of time is

$$\log_{10} \frac{(A)}{(A)_0} = -\frac{kt}{2.3} \qquad \text{or} \qquad (A) = (A)_0 \times 10^{-kt/2.3}$$

in which $(A)_0$ is the initial reactant concentration. In a first order reaction the concentration of the reactant decreases exponentially with time.

By means of calculus, similar expressions can be found for reactant concentrations for reactions following other simple kinetics. For complex reactions, involving several reactants or nonintegral orders, such expressions cannot in general be obtained.

In the case of a reaction occurring between a gas and a solid, or a liquid and a solid, the reaction must take place on the solid surface. Under these conditions we find that the rate of reaction is dependent on both the concentration of the reactant in the gas or liquid phase and the amount of solid surface available for reaction. For a given mass of solid, as one would expect, a much higher reaction rate is generally obtained with a finely powdered solid than with a few large crystals. Powdered zinc, heated to 300°C in a crucible, burns in air to form white, threadlike particles of zinc oxide. Oxidation of mossy zinc occurs only at much higher temperatures. A more spectacular illustration of this effect is offered by pyrophoric lead, a finely divided form of the metal produced by the thermal decomposition of certain lead salts. This material ignites spontaneously in air at room temperature; bulk samples of lead are oxidized very slowly even at temperatures near its melting point. Gas-solid reactions are often complicated by the fact that the reaction product does not leave the solid surface rapidly; this, of course, makes kinetic studies difficult and accounts for the fact that most quantitative kinetic data involve homogeneous systems.

14.10   THE DEPENDENCE OF REACTION RATE ON TEMPERATURE

The rates of chemical reactions are profoundly influenced by the temperature at which the reaction is carried out. An increase in temperature invariably increases the rate, to the extent that a reaction which requires months at room temperature might well occur in hours at 100°C. As a general, very approximate, rule, one can assume that the reaction rate will about double for every 10°C rise in temperature. Clearly a rise in temperature of 200°C can produce an enormous increase in the rate of a reaction.

The quantitative treatment of the dependence of reaction rate on temperature can be carried out by measuring the initial rate at different temperatures and the same initial reactant concentrations. Equivalently, and ordinarily, one measures the rate constant k at different temperatures. The results of a temperature study of the rate constant of the CO-NO_2 reaction are given in the middle column of Table 14.6.

TABLE 14.6 TEMPERATURE DEPENDENCE
OF THE RATE CONSTANT FOR THE
CO-NO_2 REACTION

Temperature (°C)	k_{obs} (l./mole-sec.)	k_{calc} (l./mole-sec.)
385	0.276	0.29
445	2.38	2.31
490	8.80	8.60
510	14.5	14.6
527	21.6	23.1

From the ratio of the rate constants at 527° and 385°C one can say that, as a result of the 142°C rise in temperature, the rate of the reaction was increased about 80-fold. A further, rather more important, quantitative relation between reaction rate and temperature is made apparent if one plots the logarithm of the rate constant as a function of the reciprocal of the absolute temperature. In Figure 14.4 it is shown that such a plot for the CO-NO_2 reaction results in an essentially straight line; mathematically, one would say that for that reaction the logarithm of the rate constant varies linearly with the reciprocal of the absolute temperature. This kind of

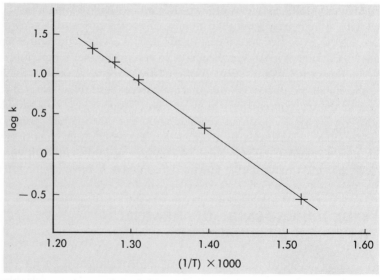

FIGURE 14.4 Temperature dependence of the reaction rate constant: a test of the validity of the Arrhenius equation in the CO-NO_2 reaction.

relation was first observed by Arrhenius and is found to be a kinetic property of many reactions. Such reactions are said to obey the **Arrhenius equation**; the equation may be stated in several equivalent ways:

$$\log k = -A/T + \log B \qquad \text{with} \qquad k = B \times 10^{-A/T}$$
$$\text{or, in terms of natural logarithms,} \qquad (14.12)$$
$$\ln k = -C/RT + \ln B \qquad \text{with} \qquad k = B \times e^{-C/RT}$$

in which e is the base of natural logarithms and R is the gas constant. Since, as we shall see in Section 14.12, it turns out to be possible to assign a physical significance to the constant C in equation 14.12, the Arrhenius equation is usually stated in terms of natural logarithms or as an exponential to the base e (see Appendix 1).

The specific form of equation 14.12 for the CO-NO$_2$ system can be found by choosing the constants B and C so as to obtain the best fit of the equation to the line in Figure 14.4. The equation which is obtained if energy units in the exponential terms are calories is

$$k = 1.3 \times 10^{10} \times e^{-32000/RT} \text{ l./mole-sec.} \qquad (14.12a)$$

The values of the rate constant as calculated from equation 14.12 are in the last column of Table 14.6. Considering the difficulty in measuring reaction rates accurately and the fact that the rate constant changes by a large factor over the temperature range used, the agreement with experiment must be considered very good.

14.11 CATALYSTS AND THE RATES OF CHEMICAL REACTIONS

One of the important problems the industrial or academic research chemist must solve is to make the reaction in which he is interested proceed rapidly enough to yield the desired product in a reasonable amount of time. The most obvious solution to such a problem, as indicated in the previous section, would be to increase the temperature of the reacting system until an adequate rate is achieved. Within limits such an approach is often useful, but it frequently is the case that reactants which at one temperature yield one set of products will, at a higher temperature, yield quite another set. The reasons for such behavior are that the reactants are often unstable at the higher temperature and decompose more rapidly than they react with each other, or that, at the higher temperature, other reactions occur more rapidly than the one which dominates at the low temperature. In many cases, therefore, it proves necessary to resort to other means to achieve satisfactory rates of desired reactions. The approach to this problem which has turned out to be most practical is one which, at least at first, would appear to be most impractical indeed.

Relatively early in the development of chemistry it was discovered that small amounts of certain substances, particularly metallic or metallic oxide powders, can have drastic effects on the rates of chemical reactions. Such substances, which are called **catalysts,** are, in principle, not consumed during a reaction, but participate in it in such a way as to increase, or possibly decrease, its rate. Since the catalyst is not a reactant or product in the overall reaction, it cannot alter the equilibrium constant or the final equilibrium state of the reacting system; what it does is decrease the time required for the system to attain equilibrium.

To illustrate the process of catalysis, consider the synthesis of water from the elements. Although the gas-phase reaction between hydrogen and oxygen is, in principle, spontaneous at temperatures below 2000°C, the two gases can be confined together in a glass vessel for long periods of time with no visible evidence of reaction. If a piece of copper foil is inserted into the gas mixture at 200°C, reaction occurs almost instantaneously. Finely divided platinum is even more effective; insertion of a platinum gauze into the hydrogen-oxygen mixture brings about reaction at room temperature. Careful weighing of the copper or platinum before and after reaction reveals no change in mass, indicating that these metals are acting as true catalysts.

One of the first commercially important processes based on the use of catalysts was the synthesis of ammonia by the Haber process early in this century. This proved to be but the first of a long series of processes for the production of important chemical substances in which catalysts play a vital role. The discovery of catalysts for specific reactions proved to be an important factor in the growth of the chemical industry, making possible the production, often by simple direct reactions, of many substances which had previously required complicated syntheses or were only available from natural sources. In the petroleum industry in particular, catalysts have been useful, both for improving the quality of motor fuels and for increasing the amount of fuel obtainable from a given amount of petroleum (see Chapter 24). At present the majority of the commercially significant processes employed by the world's chemical industry are based on catalysts, and a substantial fraction of the research effort of industrial chemists is devoted to catalyst development. Much of this research is still essentially empirical, but in recent years there has been some success in developing catalysts tailored to specific purposes. In Table 14.7 we have listed some important industrial reactions for which the catalysts are known, along with the temperatures at which the reactions are carried out. The reactions involving ethanol, C_2H_5OH, illustrate the fact that the proper choice of catalyst can frequently change the product obtained from given reactants.

TABLE 14.7 CATALYTIC CONDITIONS FOR SOME INDUSTRIALLY
IMPORTANT REACTIONS

Reaction	Used in Manufacture of	Catalyst and Temperature (°C)
$2 SO_2 + O_2 \rightarrow 2 SO_3$	sulfuric acid	Pt at 450
Hardening of liquids fats	shortening, margarine, and soap	Ni at 180
$CO + 2 H_2 \rightarrow CH_3OH$	methanol	$ZnO + Cr_2O_3$ at 380
$C_2H_5OH \rightarrow C_2H_4 + H_2O$	ethylene (polyethylene)	Al_2O_3 at 350
$C_2H_5OH \rightarrow CH_3CHO + H_2$	acetaldehyde (CH_3CHO)	Ni at 350
Ethylbenzene $\rightarrow$ styrene	polystyrene	Cu at 650

Within living organisms are found some of the most remarkable catalysts. These make possible the many very complex chemical reactions by which the organisms grow, move, respond, and indeed exist. These catalysts are exceedingly efficient, extremely selective, and, unlike most catalysts, are active at relatively low temperatures. Biochemists have discovered and isolated many such catalysts, which are called enzymes. In most cases the structures of these substances are unknown; they all appear to be proteins, and are often given names which are indicative of their catalytic function. Thus, the sugar maltose, $C_{12}H_{22}O_{11}$, is hydrolyzed to glucose by the body in the presence of the enzyme maltase; lactose, a sugar with the same molecular formula, requires the enzyme lactase for its hydrolysis under similar conditions.

14.12 THE COLLISION THEORY OF REACTION RATES

A successful theory for reaction rates should explain the experimental observations we have been discussing in the preceding sections. It should account for the existence of integral reaction orders and should allow the prediction of the orders of specific reactions. It should explain the great temperature dependence of reaction rates and enable one to predict rate constants for given reactions from essentially first principles. It should deal with the properties of catalysts and afford clues as to good catalysts for specific reactions. Although none of the theories which have been proposed can claim to meet all these requirements, some of them have been remarkably successful in dealing with certain aspects of this rather complicated area of chemistry. In this section we will confine our discussion to one of the older, simpler theories for rates of reactions, based on the kinetic theory of gases, which was considered briefly in Chapter 6. This theory is called the **collision theory** of gas reactions, and, although it is not completely satisfactory, it is physically reasonable and aids our understanding of several important features of chemical reactions.

According to the collision theory, chemical reactions occur as a result of collisions between reactant molecules. Only those collisions which involve molecules having sufficiently high kinetic energy are assumed likely to result in reaction. The *rate of reaction*, the number of molecules reacting per second in a given volume, is simply equal to the *number of collisions* occurring per second in that volume *times* the *fraction* of those collisions *which have sufficient energy*. The kinetic theory can be used to find expressions for both of these quantities.

Let us first consider the number of CO-NO_2 collisions, Z, which would occur in one second in a one-liter container in which there are CO and NO_2 molecules. (Collisions between two CO molecules or two NO_2 molecules cannot result in reaction and are ignored.) If, for example, our initial sample contains only a relatively few CO molecules and a great many NO_2 molecules, then the number of CO-NO_2 collisions would clearly double if the concentration of CO molecules were doubled. Similarly, if the sample were initially mainly CO, doubling the concentration of NO_2 would also double the number of collisions occurring per second. By this line of reasoning the number of collisions between NO_2 and CO molecules is clearly proportional to the concentrations of both NO_2 and CO molecules and would obey the relation:

$$Z = K(CO)(NO_2) \qquad (14.13)$$

in which K is some function depending only on the dimensions of the two molecules and their average speeds (the function can be found from kinetic theory, but need not concern us here, since we are mainly interested in the dependence of Z on concentration).

Having found an expression for the collision number, Z, we turn our attention to the relation between chemical reaction rates and the energies involved in molecular collisions. We noted earlier than many reactions are ordinarily extremely slow, even though the possible products of such reactions are much more stable than are the

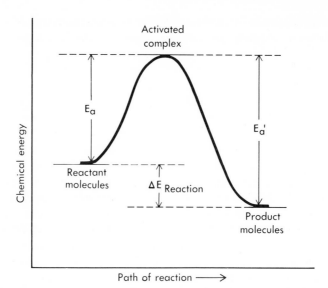

FIGURE 14.5   Energy changes during chemical reaction which proceeds via an activated complex.

reactants. Clearly, it is not equilibrium considerations which govern the concentrations of reactants in such systems, since under equilibrium conditions the systems could not exist.

The accepted theoretical reason for the essential nonoccurrence of many reactions which are thermodynamically favored is that, under the experimental conditions, the reactant molecules do not collide with sufficient energy to undergo reaction. During the reaction process molecules must come into close proximity and chemical bonds must be broken or weakened. Both of these effects require energy, which must ordinarily be furnished by the kinetic energy associated with molecular collisions. The energy needed to bring the reactant molecules to the point at which they can undergo reaction to form products is called the **activation energy**, E_a, for the reaction. Collisions occurring with an associated energy of E_a or greater can result in chemical reaction; collisions with an associated energy of less than E_a are elastic. Reactant molecules, furnished the energy E_a by a collision, pass through a transition state during which they exist as a transitory, unstable species called an **activated complex.** In the CO-NO_2 reaction the activated complex may be considered to be a pseudomolecule containing one CO and one NO_2 molecule in close interaction, with a chemical energy E_a above that of the separated CO and NO_2 molecules. Once formed, the activated complex will decompose very quickly either to form products or the original reactants. In Figure 14.5 the situation is illustrated schematically.

In the figure the energies of reactants, products, and the activated complex are indicated. Reactants, on being furnished energy E_a, can become activated and then release energy E_a' as the product molecules are formed. ΔE, the difference in energy between reactants and products, is the heat effect in the reaction. E_a' would be the activation energy for the reverse reaction.

According to the collision theory, chemical reactions are the result of those molecular collisions which occur with an associated kinetic energy of E_a, the activation energy, or greater. You will recall from Chapter 6 that in a gas most molecules have speeds near some average value, but that some molecules have very high speeds. It is these high speed molecules, with their high kinetic energies, which are believed to be responsible for chemical reactions. Many years ago, James Clerk Maxwell derived a rather complicated mathematical expression which describes the manner in which molecular speeds are distributed among the molecules in a gas. This expression is called the Maxwellian distribution function for molecular speeds, and states the fraction of molecules which at any instant will have any given speed; the fraction depends on the temperature, the speed, and the mass of the molecules.

It is possible to derive, given the Maxwellian distribution function for speed, an analogous function for molecular energies. This is shown in Figure 14.6 at two temperatures, with the relative number of molecules having a given energy plotted as a function of energy. As with molecular speeds, there are some molecules with low kinetic energies, most molecules have energies near some average value, and some molecules have relatively high energies. As the temperature increases, the average energy increases and the distribution function has appreciable magnitude at higher energy values. In the figure we have indicated the energy of activation, E_a. The area under the curve to the right of E_a will include all molecules with sufficient energy to react. It is clear that this number will increase rapidly with increasing temperature and will decrease rapidly as E_a increases. The fraction, f, of molecules having energy equal to or greater than E_a can be determined from the distribution function and is to a good approximation given by the relation:

$$f = e^{-E_a/RT} \qquad (14.14)$$

in which e is the base of natural logarithms and R is the gas constant.

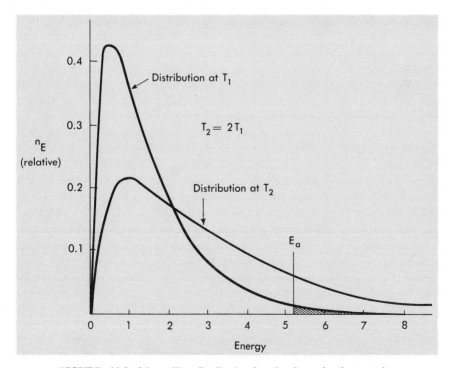

FIGURE 14.6   Maxwellian distribution function for molecular energies.

By the collision theory, rate of reaction is equal to the product of the collision number Z and the fraction f:

$$\text{rate} = Z \times f$$

By equations 14.13 and 14.14 for the CO-NO_2 reaction, the collision theory predicts:

$$\text{rate} = K(CO)(NO_2)e^{-E_a/RT} \tag{14.15}$$

Experimentally you will recall that for that reaction,

$$\text{rate} = k(CO)(NO_2) \quad \text{and} \quad k = 1.3 \times 10^{10} \times e^{-32000/RT}$$

or

$$\text{rate} = 1.3 \times 10^{10}(CO)(NO_2)e^{-32000/RT}$$

which, if we let 1.3×10^{10} equal K and 32000 cal./mole equal E_a, the energy of activation, agrees completely with the theoretical result.

The collision theory thus allows one to explain the observed order in the NO_2-CO reaction as well as the manner in which the rate constant varies with temperature. It is even possible to attempt to predict the actual value of k, by calculating K from the kinetic theory; the value obtained is somewhat larger than that which is observed. You will note that the activation energy for the reaction was not determined theoretically but was found by experiment. This is always the case, although, as here, the activation energy is typically what would be required to break a bond in a reactant molecule. From bond energy data one would predict that to break a mole of N—O single bonds would take about 45 kcal., which is of the order of magnitude of the activation energy.

Mechanisms of Chemical Reactions

Although the collision theory appears to explain many important features of chemical reaction rates, it has some deficiencies which should be mentioned. Whereas the simple theory would predict that all reactions are second order overall, many reactions, particularly those involving thermal decomposition of a single substance, are first order; other reactions are of other integral or fractional orders. Even for second order reactions, the value of the rate constant k as calculated by the kinetic theory may be several orders of magnitude too large.

An essential weakness of the simple theory is that it oversimplifies the path, or mechanism, by which reactions occur. It is now known that many, probably most, reactions occur in not one, but several steps, each of which has its own kinetic properties. By applying the collision theory to each of the steps in the mechanism of the reaction and then mathematically calculating the resultant overall order and activation energy of the reaction, one can make a much more realistic attack on the rate problem and often achieve very good correlation between theory and experiment.

The ultimate aim of the reaction kineticist is to establish an unambiguous mechanism for the chemical reaction being studied. This is a much larger problem than determining activation energy and order of the reaction for each reactant. One must consider the possible presence and effects of intermediate substances which react rapidly with other species present; possible equilibria among reactants, products, and intermediates; and possible catalysis by container walls or other substances. Having acquired all pertinent experimental data, the kineticist attempts to establish a reaction mechanism which agrees with all experimental observations. He then performs other experiments implied by his mechanism, such as checking for the presence of proposed intermediates or the rate properties of one step in the reaction, to see whether he can obtain support for or evidence against the mechanism. In some cases, by a very thorough investigation, it has been possible to develop a reaction mechanism which is clearly preferable to all others. In other cases several mechanisms appear to be equally good. At present relatively few reactions have been completely characterized kinetically. In recent years chemists have begun studying some of the very simplest reactions, those which might well be steps in many reaction mechanisms; this research is frequently conducted by the use of molecular beams, where the reactions are carried out between molecules with well-defined speeds and directions of motion.

A gas phase reaction which has received a great deal of attention is that for the thermal decomposition of nitrogen pentoxide:

$$2 \, N_2O_5 \longrightarrow 4 \, NO_2 + O_2$$

This reaction is first order at all temperatures and all but very very low pressures. It does not appear to be catalyzed by the container or other solids, nor is it affected by the presence of other substances. Since it is first order, it clearly cannot be explained by simple collision theory. Several mechanisms have been proposed for this reaction, but the following seems to be in best agreement with the experimental facts:

$$2 \, N_2O_5 \underset{k_2}{\overset{k_1}{\rightleftharpoons}} N_2O_5{}^* + N_2O_5 \qquad \begin{aligned} \text{rate}_1 &= k_1(N_2O_5)^2 \\ \text{rate}_2 &= k_2(N_2O_5{}^*)(N_2O_5) \end{aligned} \qquad \text{(a)}$$

$$N_2O_5{}^* \underset{k_4}{\overset{k_3}{\rightleftharpoons}} NO_2 + NO_3 \qquad \begin{aligned} \text{rate}_3 &= k_3(N_2O_5{}^*) \\ \text{rate}_4 &= k_4(NO_2)(NO_3) \end{aligned} \qquad \text{(b)}$$

$$NO_2 + NO_3 \underset{\text{slow}}{\overset{k_5}{\longrightarrow}} NO_2 + O_2 + NO \qquad \text{rate}_5 = k_5(NO_2)(NO_3) \qquad \text{(c)}$$

$$NO + NO_3 \underset{\text{fast}}{\overset{k_6}{\longrightarrow}} 2 \, NO_2 \qquad \text{rate}_6 = k_6(NO)(NO_3) \qquad \text{(d)}$$

In reaction a, N_2O_5 molecules are activated by collisions to an unstable high energy state, described by $N_2O_5{}^*$, from which they can react on the next collision to re-form ordinary N_2O_5 or can dissociate according to reaction b. Rate constant $k_2 \gg k_1$, so that $(N_2O_5{}^*)$ is very small at all times. Reaction a proceeds to an equilibrium, so that

$$\text{rate}_1 = \text{rate}_2 \qquad \text{and} \qquad (N_2O_5{}^*) = (k_1/k_2)(N_2O_5)$$

In reactions 3 and 4, activated N_2O_5 molecules dissociate and are reformed, again attaining an equilibrium state:

$$\text{rate}_3 = \text{rate}_4 \qquad \text{and} \qquad (NO_2)(NO_3) = (k_3/k_4)(N_2O_5{}^*) = (k_3/k_4)(k_1/k_2)(N_2O_5)$$

The equilibria in a and b are assumed to be attained very rapidly, with only very small amounts of $N_2O_5{}^*$ and NO_3 being formed. The only slow step in the mechanism is c, which determines the observed rate of the reaction. In c:

$$\text{rate}_5 = k_5(NO_2)(NO_3) = k_5(k_3/k_4)(k_1/k_2)(N_2O_5) = k'(N_2O_5)$$

which has the observed order. The actual rate of the reaction is twice rate$_5$, since for every mole of NO_3 used up in c another mole will be used in d. This means that, since NO_3 is only formed in b, 2 moles of N_2O_5 will react for every mole consumed in c.

The mechanism of the N_2O_5 reaction is typical of proposed mechanisms for many reactions. Intermediates such as NO_3 and $N_2O_5{}^*$, which are unstable and not detected chemically, appear to be very commonly present, and in many instances equilibria are involved. In some reactions, which are called chain reactions, an active species, generated in the first step of the reaction mechanism, will participate in product-forming steps and then will be regenerated, to be used again and again to form product. The classic example of a chain reaction is that between hydrogen and chlorine gas, which is initiated by the absorption of a quantum of ultraviolet light:

$$Cl_2 + hv \longrightarrow 2 Cl \qquad \text{initiation step}$$

$$\left.\begin{array}{l} Cl + H_2 \longrightarrow HCl + H \\ H + Cl_2 \longrightarrow HCl + Cl \end{array}\right\} \text{chain propagation steps}$$

$$2 Cl \longrightarrow Cl_2 \qquad \text{termination step}$$

In this reaction Cl atoms, regenerated in the second propagation step, react with H_2 molecules up to a million times before they are destroyed by recombination with other Cl atoms (see p. 360).

Mechanism of Catalysis

Before leaving the subject of reaction rates we should mention the application of rate theory to the problem of catalysis. A typical catalyst will, as we have seen, increase the rate of a given reaction, often very selectively. The catalyst surface is characterized by large area and sites capable of adsorbing the reactant molecules. In the reaction between hydrogen and oxygen as catalyzed by platinum, it is postulated that oxygen molecules adsorb on the platinum surface, with the formation of the unstable oxide PtO. Hydrogen molecules are then able to react with this oxide, forming water and regenerating the catalyst. The activation energy for this two-step process is much less than for the direct reaction and is responsible for the highly increased rate. In many reactions, including most biological reactions, it is very likely that the high specificity of the catalyst is the result of a good fit between the atomic arrangement in the catalyst and that of the adsorbed reactant molecules.

PROBLEMS

14.1   If certain amounts of HI, H_2, and I_2 are admitted to an evacuated 10.0 l. container at 520°C and undergo chemical reaction until equilibrium is attained:
   a. What, if anything, can be said about the initial concentrations of HI, H_2, and I_2?
   b. What, if anything, can be said about the equilibrium concentrations of HI, H_2, and I_2?

14.2   State the Law of Chemical Equilibrium in words. State in words how it applies to the HI-H_2-I_2 system.

14.3   Formulate expressions for the equilibrium constant, K_c, for each of the following reactions:
   a. $2 CO(g) + O_2(g) \rightleftharpoons 2 CO_2(g)$
   b. $H_2(g) + Cl_2(g) \rightleftharpoons 2 HCl(g)$
   c. $2 NO(g) \rightleftharpoons N_2(g) + O_2(g)$
   d. $CO(g) + 2 H_2(g) \rightleftharpoons CH_3OH(g)$
   e. $H_2(g) \rightleftharpoons 2 H(g)$
   f. $CH_4(g) + 2 H_2S(g) \rightleftharpoons CS_2(g) + 4 H_2(g)$

14.4   One mole H_2 and one mole I_2 are let into an evacuated 5.0 l. container at 520°C, and react to equilibrium.
   a. How many moles of HI are produced by the reaction ($K_c = 0.0156$)?
   b. What is the final concentration of I_2?
   c. What percentage of the I_2 is used up in the reaction?

14.5   A mole of HI and a mole of H_2 are admitted to an evacuated 10.0 l. container at 520°C. Find the equilibrium concentrations of HI, H_2, and I_2. How many grams of I_2 are formed by the reaction to equilibrium?

14.6   To the system in Problem 14.5 is added another mole of HI. Qualitatively, what happens to the concentrations of HI, H_2, and I_2 in the container?

14.7   When phosgene, $COCl_2$, is present in a system at elevated temperatures, it dissociates to some extent due to the following reaction:

$$COCl_2(g) \rightleftharpoons CO(g) + Cl_2(g)$$

a. In view of the properties of equilibrium systems, what can be said about the concentrations of $COCl_2$, CO, and Cl_2 in a container in which there is some $COCl_2$?
b. What effect, if any, would the following changes cause in the concentrations of the species present in the container in a:
   1. CO is added to the container.   3. The container volume is doubled.
   2. N_2 is added to the container.   4. $COCl_2$ is added to the container.

14.8   When a mole of nitrogen tetroxide is introduced into an evacuated 10.0 l. container at 55°C, 30 per cent of it dissociates according to the equation:

$$N_2O_4(g) \rightleftharpoons 2\ NO_2(g)$$

a. Formulate the expression for the equilibrium constant, K_c, to be associated with this reaction.
b. What are the equilibrium concentrations of N_2O_4 and NO_2 in the container?
c. Find the value of K_c for the reaction at 55°C.
d. What is the density of the gas in the container in grams per liter?
e. The volume of the container is decreased to 5.0 l.
   1. What happens to the value of K_c?
   2. What happens to the fraction of N_2O_4 which dissociates?
   3. What is the new concentration of NO_2?
f. If the dissociation reaction for N_2O_4 is endothermic, what will happen to the concentrations of N_2O_4 and NO_2 in the 10.0 l. container as the temperature is raised to 100°C?

14.9   Consider the gaseous reaction:

$$CO(g) + H_2O(g) \rightleftharpoons CO_2(g) + H_2(g)$$

At 420°C a mole of CO and a mole of H_2O are introduced into an evacuated 5.0 l. container. After reaction to equilibrium, the system is found to contain 0.75 mole of CO_2.
a. Find the equilibrium constant, K_c, for this reaction at 420°C.
b. CO_2 is added to the system until its equilibrium concentration is doubled.
   1. How many moles of CO_2 are required?
   2. How much hydrogen is present after equilibrium is attained?
c. The volume of the container is increased to 20 l. for the system in a.
   1. What happens to K_c?
   2. What happens to the amount of CO_2 present? To the concentration of CO_2?

14.10 Ten grams of I_2 and 0.20 g. H_2 are heated to 520°C in a 3.0 l. container. How many grams of HI will be present in the container at equilibrium?

14.11 One mole of PCl_5 is let into an evacuated 25-l. container, where it dissociates partially according to the following reaction:

$$PCl_5(g) \rightleftharpoons PCl_3(g) + Cl_2(g)$$

If the equilibrium constant, K_c, for the reaction is 0.050, find the equilibrium concentration of Cl_2 in the container. What fraction of the PCl_5 has dissociated?

14.12 Formulate expressions for the equilibrium constants to be associated with the following reactions:
   a. $Ag_2O(s) \rightleftharpoons 2\ Ag(s) + \frac{1}{2}\ O_2(g)$
   b. $SnO_2(s) + 2\ H_2(g) \rightleftharpoons Sn(s) + 2\ H_2O(g)$
   c. $Pt(s) + Cl_2(g) \rightleftharpoons PtCl_2(g)$
   d. $Br_2(1) + H_2(g) \rightleftharpoons 2\ HBr(g)$

14.13 Formulate expressions for the equilibrium constants to be associated with the following reactions:
   a. The dissociation of gaseous water to the elements.
   b. The vaporization of water.
   c. The sublimation of solid carbon dioxide.
   d. The dissociation of liquid water to its ions.
   e. The solution of sugar in water.

14.14 Would you expect the solubility of barium sulfate, $BaSO_4$, to be higher or lower in water than in a solution of sodium sulfate? Why? in a solution of potassium nitrate? Why?

14.15 Define the following terms:
   a. Reaction rate   d. Activation energy
   b. Order of a reaction   e. Reaction mechanism
   c. Rate constant   f. Catalyst

14.16 For the reaction: $SO_2Cl_2(g) \rightarrow SO_2(g) + Cl_2(g)$

   explain clearly how you would proceed experimentally to find the rate of the reaction at any time. How would you determine the reaction order? the rate constant of the reaction?

14.17 In the decomposition of N_2O_5 at 45°C, according to the equation:

$$2\ N_2O_5(g) \longrightarrow 4\ NO_2(g) + O_2(g)$$

   the following concentration data were obtained:

t(in seconds)	(N_2O_5) (in moles/l.)	t(in seconds)	(N_2O_5) (in moles/l.)
0	0.250	800	0.152
200	0.223	1000	0.134
400	0.198	1200	0.120
600	0.174		

   a. Find the rate of the reaction at t = 500 seconds.
   b. Show that the reaction is first order.
   c. Find the rate constant for the reaction.
   d. Find (N_2O_5) at t = 2000 sec.

14.18 In the reaction: $2\ NO_2Cl(g) \longrightarrow 2\ NO_2(g) + Cl_2(g)$

   a. How would the rate of the reaction depend on NO_2Cl if the reaction is first order? If it is second order?
   b. If the reaction is first order and the initial concentration of NO_2Cl is doubled, what effect will the change have on the initial reaction rate?

14.19 If one step in the mechanism of a chemical reaction among gases is

$$Br_2(g) + H(g) \longrightarrow HBr(g) + H(g)$$

   what would be the expression for the rate of the reaction according to the collision theory? What would be the order of the reaction with respect to Br_2? With respect to HBr?

14.20 What are some of the successful features of the collision theory? What are some of its limitations?

14.21 What explanation do we have for the fact that the rates of reactions depend so greatly on the temperature?

14.22 Why are catalysts so important in the processes used in the chemical industry?

*14.23 Show that for a chemical reaction, $K_p = K_c(RT)^{\Delta n}$, in which Δn is the change in the number of moles of gas in the chemical equation for the reaction; $\Delta n = n_{gas\ products} - n_{gas\ reactions}$

*14.24 In the reaction; $Ag_2O(s) \rightleftharpoons 2\ Ag(s) + \frac{1}{2}\ O_2(g)$, the equilibrium pressure of O_2 increases as the temperature is raised.
  a. Find, using the data in Table 5.4, the equilibrium pressure of O_2 above solid Ag_2O at 25°C.
  b. Find the temperature at which the equilibrium pressure would become one atm. (Data needed for this part of the problem is in Table 5.1.)

*14.25 Find K_c at 25°C for the following reactions from the data in Table 5.4:
  a. $2\ SO_2(g) + O_2(g) \rightleftharpoons 2\ SO_3(g)$ d. $H_2O(l) \rightleftharpoons H_2O(g)$
  b. $PCl_5(g) \rightleftharpoons PCl_3(g) + Cl_2(g)$ e. $H_2O(g) \rightleftharpoons H_2(g) + \frac{1}{2}\ O_2(g)$
  c. $2\ NH_3(g) \rightleftharpoons N_2(g) + 3\ H_2(g)$ f. $2\ HgO(s) \rightleftharpoons 2\ Hg(l) + O_2(g)$

*14.26 Use the thermodynamic data in Tables 5.1 and 5.4 to find the normal boiling point of water. Then from the data, find the vapor pressure in mm. Hg of water at 25°C.

*14.27 Show that equation 14.12a follows from the data in Table 14.6.

*14.28 According to the collision theory, what interpretation would be given to the terms in equation 14.12a?

*14.29 Predict the order of a reaction with respect to the amount of catalyst used. Defend your answer.

*14.30 Show that the time required for half of a reactant to be consumed in a first order reaction is independent of the initial reactant concentration. On what property of the reaction does the "half-life" depend?

*14.31 In the first order decomposition of ethyl bromide, C_2H_5Br, it took 38 minutes for half the C_2H_5Br to break down at a given temperature. How long would it take for three fourths of the C_2H_5Br to decompose? For 90 per cent?

*14.32 The following reaction is second order:

$$2\ NO_2(g) \longrightarrow 2\ NO(g) + O_2(g)$$

  a. Write the equation for the rate of the reaction as a function of NO_2 concentration.
  b. Derive the expression for the dependence of the concentration of NO_2 on time.
  c. If, at a given temperature, 1.0 mole of NO_2 in a 10.0 l. container was 50 per cent decomposed in an hour, how long would it take for it to be 75 per cent decomposed? 90 per cent decomposed?

15 | REACTIONS OF ELEMENTS WITH EACH OTHER

Throughout the remainder of this text, we shall be concerned with various kinds of chemical reactions. In this chapter, we shall survey one particular type of reaction, that between pairs of elementary substances. Particular emphasis will be given to:

1. The formulas and properties of binary compounds resulting from the reactions of elements with each other.
2. The mechanisms by which such reactions occur.
3. The energy changes involved as related to the strength of the bonds in reactants and products.

Much of the material covered in this chapter has been touched on briefly in earlier chapters. In particular, we shall make frequent reference to the material on ionic and covalent bonding discussed in Chapters 9 and 10. We shall, however, find it necessary to introduce certain new concepts. To start with, it will be useful to define the terms oxidation and reduction.

15.1 OXIDATION AND REDUCTION

Loss and Gain of Electrons

It was pointed out in Chapter 9 that the formation of the ionic compound sodium fluoride from sodium and fluorine atoms can be represented in electron dot notation as:

$$\text{Na} \cdot + \cdot \ddot{\text{F}} : \longrightarrow \text{Na}^+ + (: \ddot{\text{F}} :)^- \tag{15.1}$$

It is clear that in this process, a sodium atom has transferred an electron to a fluorine atom.

$$\text{Na} \cdot \longrightarrow \text{Na}^+ + e^- \tag{15.1a}$$

$$\cdot \ddot{\text{F}} : + e^- \longrightarrow (: \ddot{\text{F}} :)^- \tag{15.1b}$$

Any reaction between atoms which leads to the formation of ions may be analyzed similarly. For example, the reaction between magnesium and oxygen atoms

$$\cdot \text{Mg} \cdot + : \dot{\text{O}} : \longrightarrow \text{Mg}^{+2} + (: \ddot{\text{O}} :)^{-2} \tag{15.2}$$

may be broken down into two half-reactions:

$$\cdot Mg \cdot \longrightarrow Mg^{+2} + 2e^- \qquad (15.2a)$$

and
$$:\overset{..}{O}: + 2e^- \longrightarrow (:\overset{..}{O}:)^{-2} \qquad (15.2b)$$

Processes such as 15.1a and 15.2a which involve the *loss of electrons* are referred to as **oxidation** half-reactions; atoms of lithium and magnesium lose electrons to become positively charged ions. The processes represented by 15.1b and 15.2b, which involve the *gain of electrons*, are referred to as **reduction** half-reactions; atoms of fluorine and oxygen in gaining electrons are said to be reduced. The overall reactions 15.1 and 15.2, in which oxidation and reduction occur simultaneously, are called **oxidation-reduction** reactions or more briefly "redox" reactions. In any oxidation-reduction reaction there can be no net gain or loss of electrons. For example, when lithium reacts with oxygen, two lithium atoms are oxidized to Li^+ ions for every oxygen atom reduced to an O^{-2} ion.

Oxidation:
$$2\,Li \cdot \longrightarrow 2\,Li^+ + 2\,e^- \qquad (15.3a)$$

Reduction:
$$:\overset{..}{O}: + 2\,e^- \longrightarrow (:\overset{..}{O}:)^{-2} \qquad (15.3b)$$

Overall reaction:
$$2\,Li \cdot + :\overset{..}{O}: \longrightarrow 2\,Li^+ + (:\overset{..}{O}:)^{-2} \qquad (15.3)$$

We shall shortly find that it is possible to broaden the meaning of the terms oxidation and reduction so that any reaction in which elementary substances participate, regardless of the type of bonding involved, can be classified as an oxidation-reduction reaction. To accomplish this, it is necessary to introduce a new concept known as oxidation number.

Oxidation Number

The chemical equation written for the reaction between hydrogen and fluorine:

$$\tfrac{1}{2}\,H_2(g) + \tfrac{1}{2}\,F_2(g) \longrightarrow HF(g) \qquad (15.4)$$

bears at least a superficial resemblance to that for the reaction of lithium with fluorine:

$$Li(s) + \tfrac{1}{2}\,F_2(g) \longrightarrow LiF(s)$$

Indeed, the two reactions themselves have much in common. In both, there is an exchange of electrons between atoms. The major difference between the two reactions lies in the extent to which electron transfer takes place. In the case of lithium and fluorine, an electron is donated by a lithium atom to a fluorine atom, forming the pair of ions Li^+ and F^-. When hydrogen reacts with fluorine, the valence electron of hydrogen is shared with fluorine to form the covalently bonded HF molecule. This distinction is one of degree rather than kind. The electrons in the covalent bond are displaced strongly toward the fluorine atom. The electronic environment of the fluorine atom in the HF molecule is not markedly different from that in the F^- ion:

$$:\overset{..}{\underset{..}{F}}:^- \qquad H\ :\overset{..}{\underset{..}{F}}:$$

So far as "electron bookkeeping" is concerned, it is reasonable to assign both bonding electrons in the HF molecule to the fluorine atom. This is equivalent to assigning a -1 charge to the fluorine, which now has one more valence electron (eight) than the neutral fluorine atom (seven). The hydrogen atom, deprived of its valence electron by this assignment, could then be said to have a charge of $+1$.

Many years ago, chemists adopted the accounting system that we have just outlined to assign electrons in covalently bonded substances. The concept of **oxidation number** was introduced to refer to the charge an atom would have if the bonding electrons were assigned arbitrarily to the more electronegative element. In the HF molecule, hydrogen is said to have an oxidation number of $+1$, fluorine an oxidation number of -1. In water, the bonding electrons are assigned to the more electronegative oxygen atom:

$$H \quad :\overset{\displaystyle ..}{\underset{\displaystyle ..}{O}}: \quad H$$

This gives oxygen an oxidation number of -2 (8 valence e^- vs. 6 e^- in the neutral atom) and hydrogen an oxidation number of $+1$ (0 e^- vs. 1 e^- in the neutral atom). In a nonpolar covalent bond, the bonding electrons are split evenly between the two atoms:

$$:\overset{\displaystyle ..}{\underset{\displaystyle ..}{F}}\cdot \quad \cdot\overset{\displaystyle ..}{\underset{\displaystyle ..}{F}}: \qquad \text{oxidation no. } F = 0$$

It should be emphasized that the oxidation number of an atom in a covalently bonded substance is a manmade concept. Unlike the charge of an ion, the oxidation number of an element cannot be determined experimentally. The hydrogen atom in the HF or H_2O molecule does not carry a full positive charge; its oxidation number of $+1$ in these molecules may be regarded as a "pseudocharge."

In principle, one could obtain oxidation numbers for the various atoms in any covalently bonded compound whose electronic structure is known simply by assigning valence electrons to the more electronegative atom. In practice, such a method of assignment is neither convenient nor necessary. Instead, oxidation numbers are assigned according to certain arbitrary rules which, while consistent with the scheme we have described, are much simpler to apply. The following rules make it possible to assign oxidation numbers to atoms in any substance regardless of the structure or type of bonding involved.

1. *The oxidation number* of an element in an elementary substance is 0.* For example, the oxidation number of chlorine in Cl_2 or of phosphorus in P_4 is zero.

2. *The oxidation number of an element in a monatomic ion is equal to the charge of that ion.* In the ionic compound NaCl, sodium has an oxidation number of $+1$, chlorine an oxidation number of -1. The oxidation numbers of aluminum and oxygen in Al_2O_3 (Al^{+3}, O^{-2} ions) are $+3$ and -2 respectively.

3. *Certain elements have the same oxidation number in all or almost all their compounds.* The 1A metals always exist as $+1$ ions in their compounds and hence are assigned an oxidation number of $+1$. By the same token, the 2A elements always have oxidation numbers of $+2$ in their compounds. Fluorine, the most electronegative of all elements, has an oxidation number of -1 in all its compounds. Oxygen, second only to fluorine in electronegativity, ordinarily is assigned an oxidation number of -2 (certain exceptions will be pointed out later).

---

* Many authors prefer to speak of the *oxidation state* of an element in contrast to the *oxidation number* of an atom. We shall follow the common practice of using these terms interchangeably.

Hydrogen, in its compounds with metals such as NaH and CaH_2, exists as a -1 ion and therefore has an oxidation number of -1. In its compounds with the nonmetals, hydrogen is assigned an oxidation number of $+1$.

4. *The sum of the oxidation numbers of all the atoms in the formula of a substance is 0.* To illustrate the application of this rule, consider the ionic compound sodium selenide, Na_2Se. Knowing the oxidation number of sodium in this compound to be $+1$, we have:

$$2(+1) + \text{oxidation no. Se} = 0 \qquad \text{oxidation no. Se} = -2$$

Again, for the compound V_2O_5, in which the oxidation number of oxygen is -2:

$$2(\text{oxidation no. V}) + 5(-2) = 0 \qquad \text{oxidation no. V} = +5$$

As an example of a somewhat more complex situation, consider the ternary compound potassium dichromate, $K_2Cr_2O_7$:

$$2(\text{oxidation no. K}) + 2(\text{oxidation no. Cr}) + 7(\text{oxidation no. O}) = 0$$
$$2(+1) + 2(\text{oxidation no. Cr}) + 7(-2) = 0$$

Solving: $$\text{oxidation no. Cr} = +6$$

A corollary to this rule states that the sum of the oxidation numbers of the atoms in a polyatomic ion is equal to the charge of that ion. Consider, for example, the permanganate ion, MnO_4^-:

$$\text{oxidation no. Mn} + 4(-2) = -1 \qquad \text{oxidation no. Mn} = +7.$$

Oxidation States of the Elements

The common oxidation states of the elements are tabulated in Figure 15.1. The oxidation states shown by different elements can be correlated with their position in the periodic table as follows:

1. The highest oxidation number that an element can have is ordinarily given by its group number. For example, chromium, in group 6B, has a maximum oxidation number of $+6$ (CrO_3, K_2CrO_4, $K_2Cr_2O_7$). The highest oxidation number of chlorine, in group 7A is $+7$ (Cl_2O_7, $HClO_4$). This rule is based on the fact that the group number ordinarily gives the total number of electrons that must be lost for an atom to acquire the structure of the preceding noble gas or, in the case of elements at the lower right of the periodic table, a structure with 18 electrons in the outermost level.

A major exception to this rule involves the group 1B elements, which can have oxidation numbers of $+2$ ($CuCl_2$) or even $+3$ ($AuCl_3$).

2. For the elements in groups 3A to 7A of the periodic table, an oxidation number two less than the maximum is common. Thus, thallium in group 3A commonly shows an oxidation number of $+1$ (TlCl, and so on); lead in group 4A tends to attain an oxidation number of $+2$ (as in $PbCl_2$). This general rule may be attributed to the tendency for an element to lose only the p electrons in the outermost energy level, retaining the two s electrons in that level. For example, lead, with two 6s and two 6p electrons, achieves an oxidation number of $+2$ by losing control over the two electrons in the 6p level.

3. For the nonmetals, the minimum oxidation number is equal to the number of

electrons that must be gained to give a noble-gas structure (7A, -1; 6A, -2; 5A, -3; 4A, -4). The elements of groups 6A and 7A almost always exhibit this oxidation number in the binary compounds that they form with metals (Cl, -1, S, -2, and so on).

4. As one passes from left to right in the periodic table, there is a general tendency for the number of stable oxidation states of the elements to increase. The 1A and 2A metals at the far left of the table show only one oxidation state in their compounds ($+1$ for 1A, $+2$ for 2A). The transition metals, located near the center of the periodic table, commonly have two or more stable oxidation states. Iron, for example, forms one series of compounds ($FeCl_2$, $FeSO_4$, and so on) in which it has an oxidation number of $+2$ and another ($FeCl_3$, $Fe_2(SO_4)_3$, Fe_2O_3, and so on) in which its oxidation number is $+3$. The nonmetals ordinarily exhibit several different oxidation states. To cite one example, chlorine can have oxidation numbers of $+7$, $+5$, $+3$, $+1$ or -1 ($HClO_4$, $HClO_3$, $HClO_2$, $HClO$, HCl).

5. Among the transition metals, there is a general tendency for the higher oxidation states to become more stable as one moves down a given group. For example, among the group 6B elements, we find that the $+6$ state becomes more stable as we

H -1 $+1$																H $+1$ -1	He
Li $+1$	Be $+2$										B $+3$	C $+4$ $+2$ -2 -4	N $+5$ $+4$ $+3$ $+2$ $+1$ -3	O -1 -2	F -1	Ne
Na $+1$	Mg $+2$										Al $+3$	Si $+4$ $+2$ -2 -4	P $+5$ $+3$ -3	S $+6$ $+4$ $+2$ -2	Cl $+7$ $+5$ $+3$ $+1$ -1	Ar
K $+1$	Ca $+2$	Sc $+3$	Ti $+4$ $+3$ $+2$	V $+5$ $+4$ $+3$ $+2$	Cr $+6$ $+3$ $+2$	Mn $+7$ $+4$ $+3$ $+2$	Fe $+3$ $+2$	Co $+3$ $+2$	Ni $+2$	Cu $+2$ $+1$	Zn $+2$	Ga $+3$	Ge $+4$ -4	As $+5$ $+3$ -3	Se $+6$ $+4$ -2	Br $+5$ $+1$ -1	Kr $+4$ $+2$
Rb $+1$	Sr $+2$	Y $+3$	Zr $+4$	Cb $+5$ $+3$	Mo $+6$	Tc $+7$ $+6$ $+4$	Ru $+4$ $+3$	Rh $+3$	Pd $+4$ $+2$	Ag $+1$	Cd $+2$	In $+3$	Sn $+4$ $+2$	Sb $+5$ $+3$ -3	Te $+6$ $+4$ -2	I $+7$ $+5$ $+1$ -1	Xe $+6$ $+4$ $+2$
Cs $+1$	Ba $+2$		Hf $+4$	Ta $+5$	W $+6$	Re $+7$ $+6$ $+4$	Os $+8$ $+4$ $+3$	Ir $+4$ $+3$	Pt $+4$ $+2$	Au $+3$ $+1$	Hg $+2$ $+1$	Tl $+3$ $+1$	Pb $+4$ $+2$	Bi $+3$	Po $+2$	At -1	Rn
1A	2A	3B	4B	5B	6B	7B		8B		1B	2B	3A	4A	5A	6A	7A	8A

FIGURE 15.1 Oxidation states of the elements.

move from chromium to molybdenum to tungsten, while the $+3$ state becomes less stable in the same order. Again, among the elements in the iron subgroup, only the two higher members, ruthenium and osmium, show an oxidation number of $+8$; iron itself forms few stable compounds in which its oxidation number is greater than $+3$.

Oxidation and Reduction: General Definition

The concept of oxidation number leads directly to a working definition of the terms oxidation and reduction. **Oxidation** is defined as an *increase in oxidation number*, **reduction** as a *decrease in oxidation number*. Reactions in which one element increases in oxidation number at the expense of another are referred to as oxidation-reduction reactions. Two simple examples are:

$$2\,Al(s) + 3\,Cl_2(g) \longrightarrow 2\,AlCl_3(s) \quad \text{Al oxidized (oxidation no. } 0 \longrightarrow +3)$$
$$\text{Cl reduced (oxidation no. } 0 \longrightarrow -1) \quad (15.5)$$

$$4\,As(s) + 5\,O_2(g) \longrightarrow As_2O_5(s) \quad \text{As oxidized (oxidation no. } 0 \longrightarrow +5)$$
$$\text{O reduced (oxidation no. } 0 \longrightarrow -2) \quad (15.6)$$

These definitions are, of course, compatible with the earlier interpretation of oxidation and reduction in terms of the loss and gain of electrons. An element which loses electrons inevitably increases in oxidation number; the gain of electrons always results in a decrease in oxidation number. By defining oxidation and reduction in terms of changes in oxidation number, the scope of oxidation-reduction reactions is greatly increased. In particular, any reaction in which an elementary substance participates, either as a reactant or product, falls into this category. Furthermore, the use of oxidation number simplifies the electron bookkeeping in oxidation-reduction reactions. For example, analysis of the reaction:

$$HCl(g) + HNO_3(l) \longrightarrow NO_2(g) + \tfrac{1}{2}\,Cl_2(g) + H_2O(l) \quad (15.7)$$

in terms of oxidation numbers reveals immediately that chlorine is oxidized (oxidation no. $= -1$ in HCl, 0 in Cl_2) while nitrogen is reduced (oxidation no. $= +5$ in HNO_3, $+4$ in NO_2). It is much more difficult to decide precisely which atoms are "losing" or "gaining" electrons.

In discussing oxidation-reduction reactions, the phrases *oxidizing agent* and *reducing agent* are frequently used to designate the species responsible for oxidation and reduction. We speak of chlorine in reaction 15.5 and oxygen in 15.6 as being oxidizing agents, since they bring about the oxidation of aluminum and arsenic respectively. In these reactions, aluminum and arsenic act as reducing agents, being responsible for the reduction of chlorine and oxygen. In the more complex reaction represented by 15.7, the species which is oxidized, HCl, acts as a reducing agent; HNO_3, which undergoes reduction, is the oxidizing agent.

15.2 REACTIONS OF NONMETALS WITH EACH OTHER

In compounds formed by the reaction of two nonmetals with each other, the atoms are held to each other by electron-pair bonds. In certain cases, all the atoms are bonded together to give a nonvolatile, macromolecular crystal. More frequently, a small number of atoms are joined to each other to form a discrete molecule. The structures and properties of a variety of molecular compounds were considered in Chapter 10. We shall now consider some of the reactions by which these compounds are formed, paying particular attention to the rate and spontaneity of reaction.

Bond Energies

In order for a reaction to occur between two nonmetals, the bonds joining the atoms in the elementary substances must be broken. This is often difficult to accomplish; in the case of nitrogen, for example, 225 kcal./mole must be absorbed to break the bonds holding the N_2 molecules together. This implies that the early stages of reactions involving elementary nitrogen are highly endothermic. Reactions of nitrogen with other nonmetals are ordinarily slow-starting because of the large activation energy involved. In contrast, the most reactive of the nonmetals, fluorine, has one of the lowest dissociation energies; only about 37 kcal./mole are required to break apart the F_2 molecule. Reactions involving elementary fluorine often occur with explosive violence because of the relatively small amount of energy required to get the reaction started.

The strength of the bonds holding the atoms together in a nonmetal affects not only the rate at which it reacts with another element but also the stability of the compound formed. The overall energy change in any reaction represents the difference between the energy evolved when "new" bonds are formed and that absorbed when the "old" bonds holding the reactants together are broken. The stronger the bonding in the elementary substances, the smaller will be the net evolution of energy in the formation of a binary compound. The strong bond in the N_2 molecule not only makes it difficult to initiate reactions involving elementary nitrogen but also tends to reduce the stability of compounds of nitrogen. In practice, it is found that nitrogen reacts directly with only two nonmetals, hydrogen and oxygen. Both of these reactions require either high temperatures and special catalysts or both to occur at a reasonable rate; the products, ammonia and nitric oxide, can be quite easily decomposed to the elements.

When the new bonds formed in a binary compound are particularly strong one can expect a covalent compound to be stable with respect to thermal decomposition. One of the strongest covalent bonds is that between hydrogen and fluorine. The large amount of energy given off in the reaction:

$$H_2(g) + F_2(g) \longrightarrow 2\ HF(g) + 129\ \text{kcal.} \tag{15.8}$$

represents the difference between the energy evolved in forming the bonds in two moles of HF (270 kcal.) and that absorbed in breaking the bonds in one mole of H_2 (104 kcal.) and one mole of F_2 (37 kcal.). The hydrogen fluoride molecule is one of the most stable known; it is not appreciably dissociated at temperatures as high as 3000°C. This situation may be contrasted with that in nitrogen trichloride, NCl_3, an extremely explosive compound which is unstable at all temperatures:

$$2\ NCl_3(g) \longrightarrow N_2(g) + 3\ Cl_2(g) + 111\ \text{kcal.} \tag{15.9}$$

The bonds in the elementary substances N_2 and Cl_2 are so much stronger than those in NCl_3 that the decomposition of nitrogen trichloride rather than its synthesis results in an evolution of energy.

Table 15.1 lists the bond energy* (energy absorbed per mole of bonds broken) for a series of covalent bonds. Such a table can be used, in much the same way as a table of heats of formation, to calculate energy changes for reactions involving gaseous molecular substances. Example 15.1 illustrates how this is done.

Example 15.1. Calculate, using Table 15.1, the energy changes corresponding to the following reactions:

a. $H_2(g) + I_2(g) \rightarrow 2\ HI(g)$

b. $3\ H_2(g) + N_2(g) \rightarrow 2\ NH_3(g)$

Solution. In each case, the net energy change is obtained by subtracting the energy absorbed in breaking old bonds from that evolved in forming new bonds.

a. Two moles of H—I bonds are formed, evolving 2(71 kcal.) = 142 kcal. 1 mole of H—H bonds and 1 mole of I—I bonds are broken: energy absorbed = 104 kcal. + 36 kcal. = 140 kcal. Net *evolution* of energy = 142 kcal. − 140 kcal. = 2 kcal.

b. In a molecule of NH_3, there are three N—H bonds. Hence, in forming 2 moles of NH_3, 6 moles of N—H bonds are formed; energy evolved = 6 × 93 kcal. = 558 kcal. Bonds broken: 3 moles H—H, 1 mole N≡N. Energy absorbed = 3(104 kcal.) + 225 kcal. = 537 kcal. Net *evolution* of energy = 558 kcal. − 537 kcal = 21 kcal.

TABLE 15.1   BOND ENERGIES (kcal./mole)

H—H	104	I—I	36	H—Si	70
C—C	83	H—F	135	Br—Cl	52
C=C	143	H—Cl	103	I—Cl	50
C≡C	196	H—Br	88	O—Cl	49
N—N	38	H—I	71	S—Cl	60
N≡N	225	H—O	111	N—Cl	48
O—O	33	H—Se	66	P—Cl	79
S—S	51	H—S	81	C—Cl	79
F—F	37	H—N	93	Si—Cl	86
Cl—Cl	58	H—P	76	C—O	84
Br—Br	46	H—C	99	C=O	173

In using a table of bond energies to make calculations such as those illustrated by Example 15.1, two important limitations concerning bond energies must be kept in mind. In the first place, they are directly applicable only when all the reactants and products are gaseous. If one of the substances involved in the reaction is a solid or a liquid, intermolecular forces as well as bond energies must be considered. In other words, a correction must be made for the amount of heat evolved when the gas condenses. Furthermore, for most reactions, bond energy calculations give only an approximate value for the energy change. The energy required to break a particular bond depends to some extent upon the other bonds present in the molecule. For example, the strength of the N—H bond in ammonia, NH_3, is not exactly the same as in hydrazine, N_2H_4. Deviations of this type become particularly important in molecules which cannot be represented by a single structural formula, i.e., resonance hybrids. The energy required to dissociate the SO_2 molecule into atoms is significantly greater than that calculated on the basis of one S-to-O single bond and one S-to-O double bond. This energy difference is the resonance energy referred to earlier.

The concept of resonance energy can be used in a somewhat different context to explain the great amount of energy evolved in the formation of a polar molecule such as HF. If the bond in HF were a pure covalent bond, i.e., if the bonding electrons were equally shared, one

---

* Strictly speaking, the bond energy represents an enthalpy change (ΔH) rather than a change in internal energy (ΔE).

might expect the bond energy in HF to be the average of that in the nonpolar molecules H_2 and F_2. If this were the case, the formation of hydrogen fluoride from the elements would neither evolve nor absorb energy. That is, the energy change for the reaction:

$$H_2(g) + F_2(g) \longrightarrow 2\ HF(g)$$

would be zero. In practice, the H—F bond is some 64.5 kcal. stronger than the average for the H—H and F—F bonds (Table 15.1), so that the foregoing reaction evolves a total of 2×64.5 kcal. $= 129$ kcal. This "extra" 64.5 kcal. represents the resonance energy associated with the hybrid structures:

$$H^+ F^- \leftrightarrow H—F$$

In a sense, then, the evolution of energy in the formation of hydrogen fluoride can be ascribed to the partial ionic character of the HF bond. In this connection, it is significant that in the HI molecule, in which the two atoms have similar electronegativities, the resonance energy virtually disappears:

bond energy H—I = 71 kcal.

$$\text{Average bond energy H—H} + \text{I—I} = \frac{(104 + 36)\ \text{kcal.}}{2} = 70\ \text{kcal.}$$

resonance energy = 1 kcal.

The table of electronegativities presented in Chapter 10 was set up by quantitatively relating resonance energies of the type just described to differences in electronegativity. The equation used by Professor Pauling was:

$$E_r = 23\ (Xa - Xb)^2$$

in which Xa and Xb represent the electronegativities of elements A and B and E_r is the resonance energy of the A—B bond, i.e., the difference between the A—B bond energy and the average of the A—A and B—B bond energies.

In the remainder of this section, we shall use bond energies in discussing the reactions of hydrogen and oxygen with various nonmetals. Many of these reactions are frequently carried out in the general chemistry laboratory; others are of considerable industrial importance.

Reactions of Hydrogen with Nonmetals

Hydrogen fails to react directly with any of the nonmetals in group 4A, primarily because of the great strength of the covalent bonds holding the atoms together in macromolecular crystals of carbon, silicon, and germanium. The reactivity of hydrogen towards the elements in groups 5A, 6A, and 7A is directly related to their electronegativity. In the presence of a platinum catalyst, hydrogen (e.n. = 2.1) and oxygen (e.n. = 3.5) react explosively and quantitatively; the reactions of hydrogen with the other nonmetals in group 6A (sulfur, e.n. = 2.5; selenium, e.n. = 2.4; tellurium, e.n. = 2.1), even under optimum conditions, give a poor yield of product. For this reason, the binary hydrogen compounds of the higher 6A elements are ordinarily prepared by other methods (cf. Chapter 18).

The only 5A element which reacts directly with hydrogen is nitrogen (e.n. = 3.0). The hydrides of the other nonmetals in this group, all of which are close to hydrogen in electronegativity (P = 2.1, As = 2.0, Sb = 1.8), are prepared by indirect means. These compounds all have positive heats of formation (Hf PH_3 = +2.1 kcal., AsH_3 = +41 kcal., SbH_3 = +34 kcal.) and readily decompose to the elements on heating (Figure 15.2).

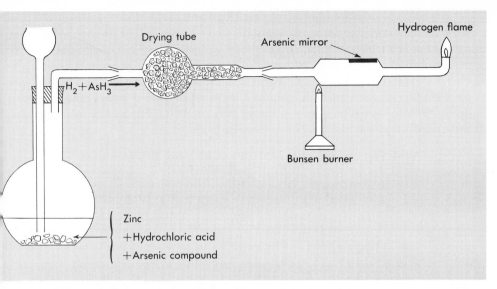

FIGURE 15.2 The Marsh test for arsenic. Arsine, AsH_3, is produced when an arsenic-containing compound is added to hydrochloric acid in the presence of zinc. The arsine decomposes to the metal when heated, forming a mirror which serves as a test for the presence of arsenic.

From a practical standpoint, by far the most important reactions of elementary hydrogen are those which it undergoes with nitrogen and the halogens. We shall now consider these reactions in some detail, paying particular attention to the rate and extent of reaction.

Nitrogen

$$N_2(g) + 3\ H_2(g) \rightleftharpoons 2\ NH_3(g) + 22.0\ \text{kcal.} \tag{15.10}$$

Over six million tons of ammonia are produced annually in this country by the reaction represented by equation 15.10. The industrial process used today to convert atmospheric nitrogen to ammonia is essentially similar to that worked out by the German chemist Fritz Haber in 1913. The success of Haber and his co-workers in making this reaction feasible on a large scale made Germany independent of outside sources of nitrogen compounds, particularly nitrates, which are used to make explosives, and undoubtedly had a great deal to do with Germany's ability to wage World War I.

The problem faced by Haber was that of finding experimental conditions under which nitrogen would react rapidly with hydrogen to give a reasonably high yield of ammonia. Calculations show that at room temperature and atmospheric pressure, the position of the equilibrium strongly favors the formation of ammonia. Unfortunately, under these conditions, the rate of reaction is virtually zero. The rate at which equilibrium is reached can, of course, be increased by raising the temperature. However, since reaction 15.10 is exothermic, high temperatures reduce the yield of ammonia (Table 15.2). High pressures, on the other hand, have a favorable influence on both the rate of the reaction and the position of the equilibrium. An increase in pressure makes it possible to attain equilibrium more rapidly because it increases the concentrations of the gases involved; it also increases the relative amount of ammonia present at equilibrium, since the forward reaction represented by 15.10 results in a decrease in the number of moles of gas.

Haber concluded on the basis of data like that in Table 15.2 that direct synthesis of ammonia from the elements was industrially feasible. The reaction was to be carried out at a moderately high temperature with a catalyst, to hasten the attainment of equilibrium, and at high pressures to increase the yield of ammonia. Much of Haber's research was devoted to finding a suitable catalyst; he also had to deal with the metallurgical problem of developing alloy steels capable of withstanding pressures up to 300 atm. at temperatures in the vicinity of 400°C. His success in overcoming these difficulties won him the Nobel prize in 1918.

TABLE 15.2 EFFECT OF TEMPERATURE AND PRESSURE ON THE YIELD OF AMMONIA IN THE HABER PROCESS ($[H_2] = 3 [N_2]$)

		Mole % NH_3 in Equilibrium Mixture				
°C	K_c	10 atm.	50 atm.	100 atm.	300 atm.	1000 atm.
200	650	51	74	82	90	98
300	9.5	15	39	52	71	93
400	0.5	4	15	25	47	80
500	0.08	1	6	11	26	57
600	0.014	0.5	2	5	14	13

In a modern ammonia synthesis plant, nitrogen and hydrogen are reacted at a temperature of 400 to 450°C and pressures of 200 to 600 atm. Various catalysts have been used; perhaps the most common is a specially prepared mixture of iron, potassium oxide, and aluminum oxide. Ammonia is separated from the gaseous reaction mixture by condensing it out as a liquid (b.p. = −33°C); the unreacted hydrogen and nitrogen are recycled to raise the yield of ammonia.

A major portion of the ammonia produced in this country is used to prepare nitric acid, a fundamental starting material for the manufacture of almost all high explosives. The so-called Ostwald process for the preparation of nitric acid makes use of the following series of reactions:

$$4 NH_3(g) + 5 O_2(g) \longrightarrow 4 NO(g) + 6 H_2O(g) \quad \text{(1000°C, Pt catalyst)}$$
$$2 NO(g) + O_2(g) \longrightarrow 2 NO_2(g) \quad \text{(NO allowed to cool in air)}$$
$$3 NO_2(g) + H_2O(l) \longrightarrow 2 HNO_3(l) + NO(g) \quad \text{(NO}_2 \text{ passed into water)}$$

Halogens

$$H_2(g) + X_2(g) \longrightarrow 2 HX(g) \tag{15.11}$$

The reactions of hydrogen with the halogens lend themselves particularly well to an analysis of the factors that govern the ease with which a reaction occurs; the rate of reaction and the stability of the products. Experimentally, it is observed that both these factors become less favorable as one moves from fluorine to iodine.

The reaction of hydrogen with chlorine has been studied extensively. The elements react very slowly in the dark at room temperature. However, if a mixture of the two gases is exposed to bright sunlight or heated to 200°C, reaction takes place almost instantaneously. This behavior is explained by the reaction mechanism, the first step of which involves the dissociation of a chlorine molecule:

(Step 1) $: \overset{..}{\underset{..}{Cl}} : \overset{..}{\underset{..}{Cl}} : \longrightarrow : \overset{.}{\underset{..}{Cl}} : + : \overset{.}{\underset{..}{Cl}} :$

The rupture of the covalent bond in the Cl_2 molecule absorbs 58 kcal./mole (the Cl—Cl bond energy). This high energy requirement explains why the reaction takes place so slowly in the dark at room temperature. Exposure to the ultraviolet radiation contained in sunlight or to thermal energy at 200°C produces a sufficient number of chlorine atoms to initiate the second step, the reaction of a chlorine atom with a hydrogen molecule:

(Step 2) $: \overset{\cdot}{\underset{\cdot\cdot}{Cl}} : \, + H : H + 1 \text{ kcal} \longrightarrow H : \overset{\cdot\cdot}{\underset{\cdot\cdot}{Cl}} : \, + H \cdot$

This step occurs rapidly, since only 1 kcal. (the difference between the H—H bond energy, 104 kcal./mole and that of the HCl bond, 103 kcal./mole) is required to bring it about. The hydrogen atom formed reacts immediately with a chlorine molecule:

(Step 3) $H \cdot + \, : \overset{\cdot\cdot}{\underset{\cdot\cdot}{Cl}} : \overset{\cdot\cdot}{\underset{\cdot\cdot}{Cl}} : \longrightarrow H : \overset{\cdot\cdot}{\underset{\cdot\cdot}{Cl}} : \, + \, : \overset{\cdot}{\underset{\cdot\cdot}{Cl}} : \, + 45 \text{ kcal.}$

Steps 2 and 3, occurring over and over again in the gaseous mixture, account for the formation of the product, hydrogen chloride, and the overall evolution of energy:

$$H : H + \, : \overset{\cdot\cdot}{\underset{\cdot\cdot}{Cl}} : \overset{\cdot\cdot}{\underset{\cdot\cdot}{Cl}} : \longrightarrow 2 \, H : \overset{\cdot\cdot}{\underset{\cdot\cdot}{Cl}} : \, + 44 \text{ kcal.}$$

A few chlorine atoms (about one for every 10^{11} Cl_2 molecules), produced in Step 1, are sufficient to set off the reaction. Reactions of this type in which an extremely small number of highly reactive particles bring about the formation of a large amount of product are known as **chain reactions.** The chain consisting of Steps 2 and 3 can be broken by processes such as:

$$H \cdot + \, : \overset{\cdot}{\underset{\cdot\cdot}{Cl}} : \longrightarrow H : \overset{\cdot\cdot}{\underset{\cdot\cdot}{Cl}} :$$

or: $: \overset{\cdot}{\underset{\cdot\cdot}{Cl}} : \, + \, : \overset{\cdot}{\underset{\cdot\cdot}{Cl}} : \longrightarrow \, : \overset{\cdot\cdot}{\underset{\cdot\cdot}{Cl}} : \overset{\cdot\cdot}{\underset{\cdot\cdot}{Cl}} :$

or: $H \cdot + H \cdot \longrightarrow H : H$

in which the reactive particles, hydrogen and chlorine atoms, are used up.

Fluorine and bromine react with hydrogen in much the same way as does chlorine. The chain reaction is more readily initiated with fluorine, since the F—F bond energy is only 37 kcal./mole as compared to 58 kcal./mole for Cl—Cl. Consequently, fluorine and hydrogen react explosively at temperatures as low as 20°K. Bromine reacts more slowly with hydrogen than does chlorine, despite the lower dissociation energy (46 kcal./mole) of the Br_2 molecule. The inhibiting factor here is the increased amount of energy required for the second step of the reaction:

$$: \overset{\cdot}{\underset{\cdot\cdot}{Br}} : \, + H : H + 16 \text{ kcal.} \longrightarrow H : \overset{\cdot\cdot}{\underset{\cdot\cdot}{Br}} : \, + H \cdot$$

The amount of energy absorbed in this step is 15 kcal. greater than for the corresponding step in the reaction of chlorine with hydrogen, reflecting the weakness of the H—Br bond (bond energy = 88 kcal./mole) as compared to the H—Cl bond (103 kcal./mole).

In the case of iodine, the step:

$$: \overset{\cdot}{\underset{\cdot\cdot}{I}} : \, + H : H + 33 \text{ kcal.} \longrightarrow H : \overset{\cdot\cdot}{\underset{\cdot\cdot}{I}} : \, + H \cdot$$

is so difficult to accomplish that a chain reaction takes place only at extremely high temperatures. Under ordinary conditions, reaction results from collisions between H_2 and I_2 molecules and the rate of reaction is quite slow.

Turning from rate of reaction to stability of products, it is found that the hydrogen halides become less stable as one passes from hydrogen fluoride to hydrogen iodide.

TABLE 15.3 PERCENTAGE OF HX
DISSOCIATED INTO H_2 AND X_2

Temperature (°C)	HF	HCl	HBr	HI
200	—	—	—	13
600	—	—	0.04	22
1000	—	0.01	0.4	25
2000	0.00006	0.4	4	30

As Table 15.3 indicates, hydrogen iodide is the only member of the series which is appreciably dissociated below 1000°C. This means that the reactions of hydrogen with fluorine, chlorine, and bromine are essentially irreversible at ordinary temperatures. Of the four hydrogen halides, HF, HCl, and HBr can be prepared in good yield by the direct reaction of the elements with each other; HI cannot be prepared satisfactorily in this way. To obtain a reasonable rate of reaction, a temperature of at least 200°C must be attained. At this temperature, the reaction of hydrogen with iodine is incomplete; the reaction mixture contains appreciable quantities of unreacted hydrogen and iodine.

The thermal stabilities of the hydrogen halides can be correlated with the amounts of heat evolved when they are formed from the elements. (HF = 64 kcal./mole, HCl = 22 kcal./mole, HBr = 13 kcal./mole, HI = 1 kcal./mole). The steady decrease from HF to HI is due in large measure to the decreasing strength of the H—X bond (Table 15.1).

Reactions of Oxygen with Nonmetals

Oxygen can be made to react with all of the nonmetals except the halogens. In the case of nitrogen, the reaction:

$$N_2(g) + O_2(g) + 43.2 \text{ kcal.} \rightleftharpoons 2 \text{ NO}(g) \tag{15.12}$$

does not occur spontaneously at ordinary temperatures, Nitric oxide, NO, can be made in 2 per cent yield by passing a mixture of nitrogen and oxygen through an electric arc at 2000°C. Small quantities of this compound can be detected in the atmosphere after a thunderstorm.

Unless the temperature and pressure are carefully controlled, the reaction of oxygen with a nonmetal frequently yields a mixture of two or more oxides. When phosphorus burns in air, for example, the principle product, P_4O_{10}, is contaminated with small amounts of a lower oxide, P_4O_6. High temperatures and low oxygen concentrations favor the formation of an oxide in which the nonmetal is in a lower oxidation state. The compound P_4O_6 (oxidation no. P = +3) can be made in relatively pure form by burning phosphorus in a limited supply of air at a high temperature. The highly toxic compound carbon monoxide, CO, (oxidation no. C = +2) is formed at concentrations up to several per cent in the region directly above the coal bed in a furnace where the temperature is a maximum and the supply of air is limited. Further up the furnace, carbon monoxide, cooling in excess air, is converted to carbon dioxide, CO_2 (oxidation no. $C = +4$). This same reaction sequence takes place in an ordinary Bunsen burner; the intensely hot, bluish-colored cone directly above the tip of the burner consists mainly of CO which is burning to CO_2 as it comes in contact with the surrounding air.

The reaction of sulfur with oxygen is extremely important from an industrial standpoint, since it forms the basis for the preparation of sulfuric acid. When sulfur is heated in an open container above its melting point, it catches fire, forming a choking gas made up principally of sulfur dioxide.

$$S(l) + O_2(g) \longrightarrow SO_2(g) \tag{15.13}$$

Up to 2 per cent of sulfur trioxide is formed simultaneously. To prepare this compound in good yield, sulfur dioxide is further reacted with oxygen.

$$SO_2(g) + \tfrac{1}{2} O_2(g) \rightleftharpoons SO_3(g) + 23 \text{ kcal.} \tag{15.14}$$

The rate of this reaction and the equilibrium yield of sulfur trioxide depend upon temperature and pressure. The principles involved here are the same as those discussed previously in connection with the Haber process. At low temperatures, the equilibrium constant for the formation of sulfur trioxide is large, but equilibrium is reached very slowly. As the temperature is raised, the rate increases, but since the reaction is exothermic, the yield of sulfur trioxide drops off. High pressures would tend to increase both the yield of sulfur trioxide and the rate of reaction.

TABLE 15.4 EFFECT OF TEMPERATURE ON THE EQUILIBRIUM:
$SO_2(g) + \tfrac{1}{2} O_2(g) \rightarrow SO_3(g)$

	$[SO_2] = 2\,[O_2]$,		$P = 1$ atm.			
Temperature, °C	200	300	400	500	600	700
K_c	5500	690	160	55	25	13
Mole % SO_3	98	91	75	61	46	31

In the so-called contact process for the manufacture of sulfuric acid, the equilibrium represented by equation 15.14 is reached rapidly by passing sulfur dioxide and oxygen, at atmospheric pressure, over a solid catalyst at a temperature of about 650°C. The equilibrium mixture is then recycled at a lower temperature, 400 to 500°C, to increase the yield of sulfur trioxide. The two catalysts which have proved most effective are vanadium pentoxide, V_2O_5, and finely divided platinum. The sulfur trioxide produced can be converted to sulfuric acid by reacting it with water.

$$SO_3(g) + H_2O(l) \longrightarrow H_2SO_4(l)$$

This reaction is ordinarily carried out in sulfuric acid solution; if sulfur trioxide is added directly to water, sulfuric acid is formed as a fog of tiny particles which are difficult to recover.

15.3 REACTIONS OF NONMETALS WITH METALS

Of the elementary substances whose chemical reactivities have been studied experimentally, approximately 20 might be classified as nonmetals and 70 more as metals. This means that if we were to present a detailed discussion of the reactions of metals with nonmetals, we should have to describe 1400 or more different reactions. Needless to say, we shall not attempt to do this. Instead, we shall present a brief survey of the reactions of metals with three nonmetallic elements; hydrogen, chlorine, and oxygen. Since these three elements are gaseous under ordinary conditions, the reactions studied will be ones occurring at a gas-solid interface.

The characteristics of reactions occurring at solid surfaces are quite different from those of gas phase reactions, which are commonly involved in the reactions of nonmetals with each other. In particular, the mechanism and consequently the kinetics of reaction are quite different. We might, for example, visualize the reaction of a diatomic gas such as chlorine with a metal such as sodium as occurring in several steps, the first of which involves the collision of a Cl_2 molecule with the metal surface. A loosely held electron is torn away from the metal and transferred to the nonmetal.

$$\text{Na} \cdot + \; :\!\overset{..}{\underset{..}{Cl}}\!:\!\overset{..}{\underset{..}{Cl}}\!: \; \longrightarrow \; \text{Na}^+ + (:\!\overset{..}{\underset{..}{Cl}}\!:)^- + \; :\!\overset{..}{\underset{.}{Cl}}\!: \qquad (15.15a)$$

This process, which probably passes through one or more intermediates, results in the formation of a reactive chlorine atom which quickly acquires an electron from another metal atom.

$$\text{Na} \cdot + \; :\!\overset{..}{\underset{.}{Cl}}\!: \; \longrightarrow \; \text{Na}^+ + (:\!\overset{..}{\underset{..}{Cl}}\!:)^- \qquad (15.15b)$$

The overall reaction is obtained by summing 15.15a and 15.15b:

$$2\,\text{Na} \cdot + \; :\!\overset{..}{\underset{..}{Cl}}\!:\!\overset{..}{\underset{..}{Cl}}\!: \; \longrightarrow \; 2\,\text{Na}^+ + 2\,(:\!\overset{..}{\underset{..}{Cl}}\!:)^-$$

or $\qquad\qquad\qquad 2\,\text{Na(s)} + Cl_2\text{(g)} \; \longrightarrow \; 2\,\text{NaCl(s)} \qquad\qquad (15.15)$

The immediate result of the process just described is the formation of a layer of reaction product on the surface of the metal. For reaction to continue, atoms in the interior of the metal must come in contact with gas molecules. This can occur in either of two quite different ways:

1. The surface film may form as a loose, porous coating which readily flakes off to expose the metal beneath. This ordinarily happens only if the volume of the compound produced by the reaction is less than that of the metal from which it is formed. Coatings of this type are commonly formed by metals of low density, in particular the alkali and alkaline earth metals. In the reaction of potassium with chlorine, for example, the potassium chloride formed has a smaller molar volume (37 cc.) than that of potassium itself (45 cc.), and so is unable to protect the metal from further attack by chlorine.

2. If the surface film adheres to the metal, as is ordinarily the case with the transition metals, which have comparatively high densities, further reaction must occur by diffusion. Either metal or nonmetal atoms must diffuse through the surface layer so as to come in contact with each other. Such a process is ordinarily quite slow at low temperatures and is dependent upon the existence of imperfections within the crystals of the reaction product formed at the surface of the metal (cf. Chapter 12). At high temperatures, both the rate of diffusion and the concentration of crystal defects increase and the rate of reaction goes up accordingly.

Reactions of Metals with Hydrogen

Saline (Saltlike) Hydrides. Hydrogen reacts readily with the 1A metals and the higher members of the 2A group (Ca, Sr, Ba) to form compounds referred to as saltlike or **saline** hydrides because of their resemblance to the halides of these metals. Lithium hydride, empirical formula LiH, can be formed by passing hydrogen over molten lithium at 600°C:

$$2 \text{ Li(l)} + \text{H}_2(\text{g}) \longrightarrow 2 \text{ LiH(s)} \qquad (15.16)$$

The crystal structure of this compound is entirely analogous to that of lithium chloride. At temperatures slightly above the melting point, lithium hydride conducts an electric current; upon electrolysis, lithium metal is formed at the negative electrode and hydrogen gas at the positive electrode. These observations indicate that the solid is made up of alternating Li^+ and H^- ions.

TABLE 15.5 PROPERTIES OF THE SALINE HYDRIDES

Property	LiH	NaH	KH	RbH	CsH	CaH$_2$	SrH$_2$	BaH$_2$
Hf(kcal./mole)	−21.6	−13.8	−14.5	−12	−19.9	−23.3	−21.2	−20.5
Melting point (°C)	680	d. 700	d.	d. 200	—	d. 1000	—	~1200
Color	white	white	white	white	white	white	white	white
Density (g./ml.)	0.8	1.40	1.43	2.59	3.42	1.90	3.27	4.15

Of the alkali metal hydrides, lithium hydride is by far the most stable with respect to decomposition into the elements, reflecting its higher heat of formation (Table 15.5). All of the saline hydrides decompose if exposed to oxygen or water; the reactions with lithium hydride are typical.

$$2 \text{ LiH(s)} + \tfrac{1}{2} \text{O}_2(\text{g}) \longrightarrow \text{Li}_2\text{O(s)} + \text{H}_2(\text{g}) + 98.1 \text{ kcal.}$$

$$\text{LiH(s)} + \text{H}_2\text{O(l)} \longrightarrow \text{LiOH(s)} + \text{H}_2(\text{g}) + 26.7 \text{ kcal.}$$

Metallic (Interstitial) Hydrides. The behavior of hydrogen towards certain of the transition metals is quite different from that described above with the 1A and 2A metals. Many of the heavy metals, notably platinum and palladium, take up large quantities of hydrogen when exposed to the gas at room temperature and atmospheric pressure. For many years, it was supposed that only a physical interaction was involved; hydrogen was believed to form a solid solution in the metal. It is indeed difficult to explain the wide deviations from stoichiometry observed in these hydrides in terms of a chemical reaction between metal and hydrogen. Formulas such as $\text{PdH}_{0.7}$ and $\text{ZrH}_{1.9}$ are difficult to rationalize in terms of definite compounds.

Nevertheless, a great deal of evidence accumulated over the past two decades suggests that hydrogen interacts chemically with the transition metals. For one thing, the heat effects observed are much greater than one would expect if only a solid solution were involved. When 1 mole of hydrogen is taken up by palladium, 17.1 kcal. of heat are evolved; the heat of solution of hydrogen in various liquid solvents is of the order of 0.2 kcal. Moreover, x-ray studies reveal that the interaction of hydrogen with a transition metal almost always leads to a distortion or rearrangement of the crystal structure of the metal. This is hard to reconcile with the simple picture of hydrogen molecules entering randomly into holes in the metal lattice to form a solid solution. Even more significant is the fact that introduction of hydrogen frequently alters the magnetic properties of the transition metal. Certain metals with unpaired electrons lose their paramagnetism when they take up hydrogen. This suggests an electronic interaction and hence, by definition, a reaction between hydrogen and the transition metal.

The particle structure of the transition metal hydrides is not definitely established. It has been suggested that hydrogen enters the metal lattice as individual atoms, each with an unpaired electron. If this is the case, one might visualize a transition metal hydride as a network of close-packed metal atoms with a variable number of hydrogen atoms located at interstitial positions within the metal lattice.

Reaction of Metals with Chlorine

Elementary chlorine is a powerful enough oxidizing agent to react with all the metals to form binary compounds. The alkali and alkaline earth metals are oxidized to the $+1$ and $+2$ oxidation states respectively.

$$Na(s) + \tfrac{1}{2} Cl_2(g) \longrightarrow NaCl(s) \tag{15.17}$$

$$Ca(s) + Cl_2(g) \longrightarrow CaCl_2(s) \tag{15.18}$$

TABLE 15.6 CHLORIDES OF THE FIRST SERIES TRANSISTION ELEMENTS

	3B	4B	5B	6B	7B	8B	1B	2B
$+1$							CuCl	
$+2$		$TiCl_2$	VCl_2	$CrCl_2$	$MnCl_2$	$FeCl_2, CoCl_2, NiCl_2$	$CuCl_2$	$ZnCl_2$
$+3$	$ScCl_3$	$TiCl_3$	VCl_3	$CrCl_3$	$MnCl_3$	$FeCl_3, CoCl_3$		
$+4$		$TiCl_4$	VCl_4					

The metals in the first transition series rarely reach oxidation states higher than $+3$ in their reactions with chlorine (Table 15.6). Compounds of higher oxidation state are more frequently formed by elements in the second and third transition series. Thus, while chromium, in group 6B, gives the $+3$ chloride when heated in chlorine

$$2 Cr(s) + 3 Cl_2(g) \longrightarrow 2 CrCl_3(s) \tag{15.19}$$

the higher members of this group, molybdenum and tungsten, under similar conditions give the $+5$ and $+6$ chlorides respectively.

$$2 Mo(s) + 5 Cl_2(g) \longrightarrow 2 MoCl_5(s) \tag{15.20}$$

$$W(s) + 3 Cl_2(g) \longrightarrow WCl_6(s) \tag{15.21}$$

Among the binary compounds formed by chlorine with the metals, four different crystal structures may be distinguished.

1. **Molecular crystals.** This type of structure is restricted for the most part to chlorides of the transition and post-transition metals in their highest oxidation state. Included in this category are WCl_6 (m.p. $= 275°C$, b.p. $= 347°C$), $SnCl_4$ (m.p. $= -30°C$, b.p. $= 114°C$) and $HgCl_2$ (m.p. $= 277°C$, b.p. $= 304°C$). Gallium(III) chloride is a particularly interesting case; x-ray studies on the solid confirm the existence of dimeric molecules of formula Ga_2Cl_6, with a structure

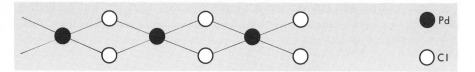

FIGURE 15.3 Crystal structure of palladium chloride.

similar to that of Al_2Br_6 (cf. Chapter 10). The $+3$ chlorides of aluminum and iron are known to form similar molecules (Al_2Cl_6, Fe_2Cl_6) in the vapor state, but there is no evidence for these in the solid (see below).

2. **Linear chains,** in which the atoms are arranged in the threadlike pattern shown in Figure 15.3. Palladium chloride, $PdCl_2$, and anhydrous copper(II) chloride, $CuCl_2$, crystallize in this pattern.

3. **Layer structures,** analogous to graphite, in which metal and nonmetal atoms are strongly bonded in two dimensions. The structure of one such compound, $CdCl_2$, is shown schematically in Figure 15.4. The layer actually consists of a plane of cadmium atoms sandwiched between two planes of chlorine atoms; there are no bonds between adjacent layers. Many of the $+2$ chlorides of the transition metals ($MnCl_2$, $FeCl_2$, $CoCl_2$, $NiCl_2$, $ZnCl_2$) have a similar structure. Several $+3$ chlorides, including $CrCl_3$, $AlCl_3$, and $FeCl_3$ have layer structures resembling that shown in Figure 15.4, except that every third metal atom is missing.

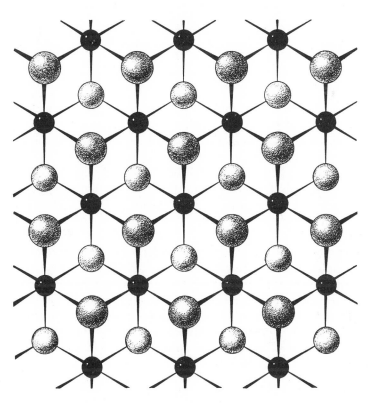

FIGURE 15.4 Crystal structure of cadmium chloride. (Sisler, H. H., *Electronic Structure, Properties and the Periodic Law*, Reinhold Publishing Corporation, New York, 1963.)

4. **Three-dimensional network structures,** in which all the particles are held together by strong bonds. Such a structure is typical of the chlorides of the 1A and 2A metals in which the bonding is predominantly ionic. A simple crystal structure of this type, typical of the alkali halides, is shown in Figure 9.1. Several of the transition metal chlorides in which the metal is in the $+1$ oxidation state, including AgCl and CuCl, crystallize in this simple pattern.

Reactions of Oxygen with Metals

Stability of Metal Oxides. The reactions of oxygen with metals are invariably exothermic. The amount of heat evolved per gram atomic weight of

TABLE 15.7 ΔH OF FORMATION, (kcal.) PER MOLE OXYGEN

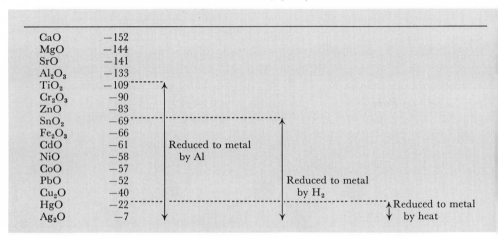

CaO	-152	
MgO	-144	
SrO	-141	
Al_2O_3	-133	
TiO_2	-109	
Cr_2O_3	-90	
ZnO	-83	
SnO_2	-69	
Fe_2O_3	-66	
CdO	-61	Reduced to metal
NiO	-58	by Al
CoO	-57	
PbO	-52	Reduced to metal
Cu_2O	-40	by H_2
HgO	-22	Reduced to metal
Ag_2O	-7	by heat

oxygen is a direct measure of the thermal stability of the oxide formed. Referring to Table 15.7, we find that the oxides which decompose most readily to the elements upon heating are those whose formation from the elements evolves the least amount of heat. Silver oxide, Ag_2O, can be decomposed by heating to 190°C; mercury(II) oxide, HgO, gives off oxygen readily at 450°C. Oxides of the elements above mercury in the table are progressively more resistant to thermal decomposition. For example, copper(I) oxide, Cu_2O, decomposes to the elements at 2000°C, Fe_2O_3 at 2800°C. The oxides located near the top of the table (CaO, MgO, and so on) cannot be broken down by heat alone.

Many metal oxides which are not readily decomposed by heat can be reduced to the corresponding metals by reacting with an element which has a strong affinity for oxygen such as hydrogen, carbon, or aluminum. As one might expect, the extent to which such reactions occur is related to the position of the metal oxide in Table 15.7. The oxides at the bottom of the table react so readily that heating these compounds with hydrogen frequently results in explosions. Tin(IV) oxide must be heated to a relatively high temperature, approximately 600°C before it will react with hydrogen.

$$SnO_2(s) + 2\ H_2(g) \longrightarrow Sn(s) + 2\ H_2O(g)$$

Even at temperatures as high as 1600°C, the reduction of zinc oxide by hydrogen is incomplete.

Commercially, the reduction of metal oxides is most often accomplished by heating with carbon, usually in the form of coke. Iron and tin are prepared from their ores, Fe_2O_3 (hematite) and SnO_2 (cassiterite) by this process. The actual reducing agent appears to be the carbon monoxide produced by the incomplete combustion of carbon.

$$3\ CO(g) + Fe_2O_3(s) \longrightarrow 3\ CO_2(g) + 2\ Fe(l)$$

From the position of aluminum oxide in Table 15.7, one can deduce that aluminum metal should be an effective agent for the reduction of metal oxides. Powdered aluminum is capable of reducing all of the oxides listed up to and including TiO_2. The reaction of aluminum with oxides of elements such as chromium and iron is highly exothermic. A mixture of aluminum powder and finely divided iron(III) oxide, ignited by means of a fuse, produces a temperature above 3000°C. The iron formed is readily separated from the aluminum oxide slag that adheres loosely to its surface. At one time, this reaction, known as the Thermit process, was used to weld steel rails and repair broken machinery.

$$2\ Al(s) + Fe_2O_3(s) \longrightarrow Al_2O_3(s) + 2\ Fe(l)$$

Elements Forming More than One Oxide.   Most of the transition and post-transition metals form more than one stable oxide (Table 15.8). Among the oxides of a given metal, the metal-to-oxygen bond becomes more covalent as the oxidation state of the metal increases. Consider, for example, the oxides of manganese. The $+2$ oxide, MnO, appears to be a typical, high-melting, (m.p. $= 1650°C$) ionic solid. Manganese(IV) oxide, MnO_2, is a high-melting, macromolecular solid similar in structure to silicon dioxide. The highest oxide of manganese, Mn_2O_7, is a reddish liquid freezing below $-20°C$, indicating a molecular structure.

TABLE 15.8 OXIDES OF THE METALS OF THE FIRST TRANSITION SERIES

Oxidation	3B	4B	5B	6B	7B		8B		1B	2B
No. Metal	Sc	Ti	V	Cr	Mn	Fe	Co	Ni	Cu	Zn
7					Mn_2O_7					
6				CrO_3						
5			V_2O_5							
4		TiO_2	VO_2		MnO_2					
3	Sc_2O_3	Ti_2O_3	V_2O_3	Cr_2O_3	Mn_2O_3	Fe_2O_3	Co_2O_3			
*8/3					Mn_3O_4	Fe_3O_4	Co_3O_4			
2		TiO	VO	CrO	MnO	FeO	CoO	NiO	CuO	ZnO
1									Cu_2O	

* Two $+ 3$ ions, one $+ 2$.

Where a metal forms more than one oxide, it is found that low temperatures and excess oxygen favor the formation of the higher oxide. Powdered copper, exposed to air at room temperature, is slowly converted to black copper(II) oxide:

$$Cu(s) + \tfrac{1}{2} O_2(g) \longrightarrow CuO(s) \quad \text{at} \quad 25°C \qquad (15.22)$$

Lower oxides such as red copper(I) oxide can be formed by heating the higher oxide to a high temperature in air:

$$2\ CuO(s) \longrightarrow Cu_2O(s) + \tfrac{1}{2} O_2(g) \quad \text{at} \quad 900°C$$

or, more readily, by heating the higher oxide with an equivalent amount of metal in the absence of oxygen.

$$CuO(s) + Cu(s) \longrightarrow Cu_2O(s) \quad \ll 900°C$$

Peroxides, Superoxides. The alkali metals react readily with oxygen, even at room temperature and atmospheric pressure. In the case of lithium, the product is, as one might expect, Li_2O. However, sodium, on exposure to dry oxygen, gives a product which can be shown by analysis to have the empirical formula NaO. X-ray studies show that the oxygen in this compound is present as a diatomic ion with a -2 charge, i.e., O_2^{-2}. This anion, called the **peroxide ion,** has the electronic structure:

$$(: \overset{..}{O}—\overset{..}{\underset{..}{O}} :)^{-2} \qquad \text{oxidation no. oxygen} = -1$$

The formula of sodium peroxide is ordinarily written as Na_2O_2 to indicate that there are two Na^+ ions present for every O_2^{-2} ion. The reaction between sodium and oxygen can be represented by the equation:

$$2 \, Na \cdot + \; : \overset{..}{\underset{.}{O}}—\overset{..}{\underset{.}{O}} : \; \longrightarrow 2 \, Na^+ + (: \overset{..}{O}—\overset{..}{\underset{..}{O}} :)^{-2}$$

$$2 \, Na(s) + O_2(g) \longrightarrow Na_2O_2(s) \tag{15.23}$$

Peroxides are known for several of the 1A and 2A metals (Table 15.9). Of these, only the peroxides of sodium and barium are readily prepared by direct reaction of the metal with oxygen.

When potassium burns in oxygen, the principal product is a compound of empirical formula KO_2. The potassium in this compound is present as K^+ ions; the oxygen is tied up in the form of a diatomic ion with a -1 charge. This ion, called the **superoxide ion,** has the electronic structure:

$$(: \overset{..}{O}—\overset{..}{\underset{..}{\underset{.}{O}}} :)^{-} \qquad \text{oxidation no. oxygen} = -\tfrac{1}{2}$$

It is formed by the transfer of an electron from a potassium atom to an oxygen molecule:

$$K \cdot + \; : \overset{..}{\underset{.}{O}}—\overset{..}{\underset{.}{O}} : \; \longrightarrow K^+ + (: \overset{..}{O}—\overset{..}{\underset{..}{O}} :)^{-}$$

$$K(s) + O_2(g) \longrightarrow KO_2(s) \tag{15.24}$$

The higher members of the 1A group, rubidium and cesium, also form superoxides as the principal product when they react with oxygen.

TABLE 15.9 OXYGEN COMPOUNDS OF THE 1A AND 2A METALS*

	Li	Na	K	Rb	Cs	Be	Mg	Ca	Sr	Ba
Oxide	Li_2O	Na_2O	K_2O	Rb_2O	Cs_2O	BeO	MgO	CaO	SrO	BaO
Peroxide	Li_2O_2	Na_2O_2	K_2O_2	Rb_2O_2	Cs_2O_2			CaO_2	SrO_2	BaO_2
Superoxide		NaO_2	KO_2	RbO_2	CsO_2					

* The compounds underlined represent the principal product of the direct reaction of the metal with oxygen.

Metal peroxides decompose on heating to give off oxygen and form the normal oxide. Barium peroxide, for example, begins to give off oxygen at 700°C.

$$BaO_2(s) \longrightarrow BaO(s) + \tfrac{1}{2} O_2(g)$$

Superoxides decompose to give first the peroxide and finally, at higher temperatures the normal oxide.

$$2 KO_2(s) \longrightarrow K_2O_2(s) + O_2(g)$$
$$K_2O_2(s) \longrightarrow K_2O(s) + \tfrac{1}{2} O_2(g)$$

All the binary oxygen compounds of the 1A and 2A metals except BeO react exothermically with water to give hydroxides. With the peroxides, a second product, hydrogen peroxide, H_2O_2, is formed. The superoxides yield elementary oxygen as well.

oxides: $Li_2O(s) + H_2O(l) \longrightarrow 2 LiOH(s)$

$CaO(s) + H_2O(l) \longrightarrow Ca(OH)_2(s)$

peroxides: $Na_2O_2(s) + 2 H_2O(l) \longrightarrow 2NaOH(s) + H_2O_2(l)$

$BaO_2(s) + 2 H_2O(l) \longrightarrow Ba(OH)_2(s) + H_2O_2(l)$

superoxide: $2 KO_2(s) + 2 H_2O(l) \longrightarrow 2 KOH(s) + H_2O_2(l) + O_2(g)$

PROBLEMS

15.1   Give the oxidation number of each atom in:
  a. La_2O_3 b. K_2CO_3 c. N_2H_4 d. Na_2MnO_4 e. $Cr_2O_7^{-2}$ f. BaO_2

15.2   Indicate, for each of the following reactions:

$$W(s) + 3 Cl_2(g) \longrightarrow WCl_6(s)$$
$$SnO_2(s) + 2 CO(g) \longrightarrow Sn(s) + 2 CO_2(g)$$
$$LiH(s) + H_2O(l) \longrightarrow LiOH(s) + H_2(g)$$

  a. The element that is oxidized.
  b. The element that is reduced.
  c. The substance that acts as an oxidizing agent.
  d. The substance that acts as a reducing agent.

15.3   The following compounds are either extremely unstable or have never been prepared. Suggest an explanation in terms of oxidation number.
  a. $HClO_5$ b. H_3Se c. BiF_5 d. HFO e. $NiCl_4$

15.4   From the data in Table 15.1, estimate the energy changes for each of the following reactions.
  a. $I_2(g) + Cl_2(g) \rightarrow 2 ICl(g)$ c. $C_2H_2(g) + 2 HCl(g) \rightarrow C_2H_4Cl_2(g)$
  b. $C_2H_4(g) + H_2(g) \rightarrow C_2H_6(g)$ d. $Cl_2(g) + 2 HF(g) \rightarrow 2 HCl(g) + F_2(g)$

15.5   Which one of the three compounds, CH_4, SnH_4, or GeH_4 would you expect to be most readily decomposed to the elements? Explain your reasoning.

15.6   For each of the following reactions:

$$N_2(g) + 3 H_2(g) \longrightarrow 2 NH_3(g) + 22.0 \text{ kcal.}$$
$$N_2(g) + O_2(g) + 43.2 \text{ kcal.} \longrightarrow 2 NO(g)$$

discuss the effect of pressure, temperature, and the addition of a catalyst upon the position of the equilibrium and the rate of reaching equilibrium.

15.7   Consider the data in Table 15.2.
   a. From the table, determine the number of moles of NH_3, H_2, and N_2 in an equilibrium mixture containing a total of one mole of gas at 300°C and 100 atm. Note that $[H_2] = 3[N_2]$.
   b. Calculate, using the Ideal Gas Law, the volume occupied by one mole of gas under these conditions.
   c. Combining your answers to a and b, calculate the equilibrium concentrations, in moles/l., of NH_3, H_2, and N_2.
   d. From your answer to c, calculate K_c at 300°C and 100 atm. and compare to the value given in the table.

15.8   Consider the following mechanism for a chain reaction between hydrogen and iodine.

$$I_2 \longrightarrow 2\ I \qquad\qquad \text{(Step 1)}$$

$$I + H_2 \longrightarrow HI + H \qquad\qquad \text{(Step 2)}$$

$$H + I_2 \longrightarrow HI + I \qquad\qquad \text{(Step 3)}$$

   a. From the data in Table 15.1, estimate the energy change for each step.
   b. Would this reaction be more, or less, difficult to *initiate* than that between hydrogen and chlorine?
   c. The overall energy change for the reaction can be found by summing the energy changes for Steps 2 and 3. Why is Step 1 not included in taking this sum?
   d. Suggest several different processes which could break the chain of reaction.

15.9   Consider the data in Table 15.3. Suggest an explanation for the fact that:
   a. At any given temperature, the percentage dissociation of HI is greater than that of HBr.
   b. The percentage of dissociation of HI increases more slowly with temperature than does the percentage dissociation of HBr. (Consider the relative heat changes involved.)

15.10 A student wishes to prepare each of the following compounds by reacting the elements with each other. What (helpful) advice can you give him?
   a. HF   b. HBr   c. CH_4 d. PH_3 e. NH_3 f. H_2S

15.11 Suggest how one might accomplish the following conversions. Be as specific as possible.
   a. $CO \rightarrow CO_2$ c. $NO \rightarrow NO_2$ e. $NH_3 \rightarrow HNO_3$
   b. $SO_2 \rightarrow SO_3$ d. $SO_3 \rightarrow H_2SO_4$ f. $N_2 \rightarrow NO$

15.12 Consider the preparation of SO_3 from SO_2 (equation 15.14). By increasing the pressure, it should be possible to increase both the yield of SO_3 and the rate of reaching equilibrium. Commercially, this reaction is carried out at atmospheric pressure. Can you suggest a reason for this?

15.13 Write balanced equations for the reactions of the following elements with hydrogen, chlorine, and oxygen:
   a. Lithium   b. Sodium   c. Potassium   d. Strontium

15.14 What are the coordination numbers of aluminum and chlorine in gaseous aluminum chloride? Solid aluminum chloride?

15.15 Show how the structures in Figures 15.3 and 15.4 both lead to the empirical formula MCl_2. (M = metal.)

15.16 Of the following metal oxides, CoO, CaO, TiO_2, Fe_2O_3, HgO:
   a. How many could be reduced to the metal by heat alone?
   b. How many could be reduced to the metal by heating with hydrogen?
   c. How many could be reduced to the metal by heating with chromium?

15.17 For each of the following pairs of compounds, state which one you would expect to show the greatest degree of ionic character in the bonds linking metal to nonmetal.
   a. CrO_3 or Cr_2O_3 b. Li_2O or Cs_2O c. Li_2O or LiH

15.18 Describe in some detail how you would carry out the following conversions.
   a. $PbO_2 \rightarrow PbO$ c. $Na_2O_2 \rightarrow Na_2O$ e. $MnO \rightarrow MnO_2$
   b. $SnO_2 \rightarrow Sn$ d. $KO_2 \rightarrow K_2O_2$ f. $BaO_2 \rightarrow H_2O_2$

15.19 State in words how each of the following compounds can be prepared from the elements (more than one step may be required).
   a. K_2O b. CaH_2 c. H_2O_2 d. $LiOH$

15.20 Write balanced equations for each of the reactions involved in Problem 15.19.

15.21 Give the formulas and electronic structures of seven different compounds containing no elements other than potassium, hydrogen, and oxygen.

15.22 Explain in terms of bonding and/or crystal structure why:
   a. Copper(I) chloride is much higher melting than gallium(III) chloride.
   b. The "adsorption" of hydrogen by palladium is exothermic.
   c. Bromine reacts more slowly with hydrogen than does chlorine.
   d. Nitrogen is a much less reactive element than fluorine.

*15.23 When 0.100 g. of a certain metal is heated with an excess of chlorine, it reacts to form 0.290 g. of a volatile metal chloride. When the same amount of this metal is added to an excess of dilute hydrochloric acid, it goes into solution with the evolution of hydrogen; evaporation of this solution at 100°C gives 0.227 g. of a deliquescent metal chloride. Identify the metal.

*15.24 Using the data in Table 15.2, calculate the mole percentage of NH_3 in an equilibrium mixture at 600°C and 500 atm. Take $[H_2] = 3[N_2]$.

*15.25 A chemist heats cesium superoxide in air to produce a material which analysis shows to contain 10.74 per cent O and 89.26 per cent Cs. On this basis, he reports the preparation of cesium peroxide, Cs_2O_2. What other possible reaction might explain his results? How would you distinguish chemically between the two possibilities?

*15.26 Using an appropriate reference source, look up the formulas of the known oxides of the metals in the second and third transition series. Use this information to test the principle that as one moves down in a given group, higher oxidation states tend to become more stable. Note particularly any exceptions to this rule.

16 | PRECIPITATION REACTIONS

Almost all of the reactions considered up to this point have involved pure substances as reactants and products. While such reactions are of great importance to the layman and chemist alike, reactions taking place in solution are of perhaps even greater significance and are certainly more widespread. Life itself depends upon the intricate processes occurring in solution within our bodies in the blood, in the digestive fluids, and in glandular secretions. Indeed, life originates as the result of an interaction taking place in solution.

Having considered some of the properties of solutions in Chapter 13, we are now in a position to study reactions taking place between particles in solution. Such a study will occupy our attention for the next several chapters. We shall be concerned primarily with reactions occurring in water solution, since water is by far the most common solvent. The majority of the reactions considered will be those taking place between dissolved ions.

In this chapter, we shall consider what is perhaps the simplest type of reaction that can occur between ions in water solution, that of precipitation. When certain pairs of solutions such as nickel chloride and sodium hydroxide or barium bromide and aluminum sulfate are mixed, ions combine to form an insoluble solid. We shall develop principles to predict when such reactions will occur, what their products will be and how they can be represented by chemical equations.

16.1 NET IONIC EQUATIONS

If one takes a 0.1 M solution of nickel chloride, $NiCl_2$, and adds to it a 0.1 M solution of sodium hydroxide, $NaOH$, a chemical reaction is observed to take place. A gelatinous green precipitate starts to form at the instant the solutions are mixed. When this precipitate stops forming, the green color of the nickel chloride solution has faded. Let us now attempt to deduce in a logical fashion the identity of the precipitate, the nature of the reaction and the form of the equation which best describes the reaction.

Clearly, the green, insoluble solid must have resulted from the interaction of a species present in the nickel chloride solution with a particle contained in the solution of sodium hydroxide. Each solution contains two different ions; in the nickel chloride solution, there are Ni^{+2} and Cl^- ions, while in the sodium hydroxide

374

solution, Na^+ and OH^- ions are present. It is reasonable to suppose that the precipitate came from the reaction of the positive ion of one solution with the negative ion of the other. In principle, the green precipitate might be either sodium chloride, NaCl, resulting from the interaction of Na^+ ions of the NaOH solution with Cl^- ions of the $NiCl_2$ solution, or nickel hydroxide, $Ni(OH)_2$, formed when Ni^{+2} ions of the $NiCl_2$ solution come in contact with OH^- ions of the NaOH solution. Experience enables us to make a choice between these two possibilities: we know that sodium chloride, ordinary table salt, is neither green nor insoluble. By elimination, we deduce that nickel hydroxide, $Ni(OH)_2$, must be the product of the reaction. To confirm this reasoning, we might filter off the precipitate and conduct various tests upon it, all of which would give the results to be expected for this particular compound. The green color of the precipitate can be ascribed to the presence of the Ni^{+2} ion, which is also responsible for the green color of the original $NiCl_2$ solution.

Having deduced the nature of the reaction, it is now possible to write an equation for it. The product is solid nickel hydroxide, $Ni(OH)_2$; the reactants are Ni^{+2} and OH^-. Consequently, the balanced equation must be:

$$Ni^{+2} + 2\ OH^- \longrightarrow Ni(OH)_2(s) \qquad (16.1)$$

Such an equation, representing a reaction between ions in water solution, is often referred to as a net ionic equation. Many such equations will be encountered throughout the remainder of this text. We shall use them to describe many types of reactions other than precipitation reactions. It is important to keep in mind that whenever a formula such as Ni^{+2} or OH^- appears alone in a chemical equation, *it is understood that the corresponding species is in aqueous solution.* This is sometimes emphasized by writing (aq) after the formula. Thus, one might write:

$$Ni^{+2}(aq) + 2\ OH^-(aq) \longrightarrow Ni(OH)_2(s) \qquad (16.1')$$

In writing net ionic equations, the same conventions are followed as in writing any equation. Only those species which actually take part in the reaction are included in the equation. In equation 16.1, neither the Na^+ nor the Cl^- ions are included since they do not take part in the reaction. By the same token, an equation for the combustion of aluminum in air does not involve the N_2 molecules present in the reaction mixture, since they do not enter into the reaction.

To further illustrate how net ionic equations can be deduced from experimental observations, let us consider what happens when dilute solutions of aluminum sulfate, $Al_2(SO_4)_3$ and barium bromide, $BaBr_2$, are mixed. In this case, a white, granular precipitate forms. To decide upon the nature of this precipitate, we note that the ions originally present are:

$$Al_2(SO_4)_3 \text{ solution:} \quad Al^{+3},\ SO_4^{-2}$$

$$BaBr_2 \text{ solution:} \quad Ba^{+2},\ Br^-$$

Logically, one could obtain either barium sulfate, $BaSO_4$, or aluminum bromide, $AlBr_3$, as a precipitate. In order to choose between these possibilities, one could obtain bottles of the two solids from the storeroom and test their solubilities. Alternatively, the identity of the precipitate could be decided upon by testing other pairs of solutions. Suppose, for example, solutions of $Al_2(SO_4)_3$ and NaBr are mixed. If this is done, it is found that no precipitate forms, indicating that aluminum bromide is soluble in water. On the other hand, mixing solutions of $Ba(NO_3)_2$ and $Al_2(SO_4)_3$ gives a precipitate. Indeed, whenever two solutions, one containing Ba^{+2} ions, the other SO_4^{-2} ions, are mixed, a white precipitate, identical in its properties to that resulting from the reaction under study, is formed. We therefore deduce that the process occurring when solutions of $Al_2(SO_4)_3$ and $BaBr_2$ are mixed must be the reaction of Ba^{+2} ions with SO_4^{-2} ions to form solid barium sulfate, $BaSO_4$. Hence, the net ionic equation must be:

$$Ba^{+2} + SO_4^{-2} \longrightarrow BaSO_4(s) \tag{16.2}$$

In certain cases, two precipitation reactions occur when a pair of solutions is mixed. Suppose, for example, a solution of barium hydroxide, $Ba(OH)_2$, is added to a solution of nickel sulfate, $NiSO_4$. It has been pointed out that both of the possible products, $Ni(OH)_2$ and $BaSO_4$, are insoluble in water. Hence, we would predict that both of these compounds should precipitate. Experiment confirms this deduction; if one examines the precipitate under a microscope, it is possible to distinguish white crystals of $BaSO_4$ from green particles of $Ni(OH)_2$. In representing this double precipitation reaction, we write two net ionic equations, since two entirely different reactions are taking place:

$$Ba^{+2} + SO_4^{-2} \longrightarrow BaSO_4(s)$$

and:

$$Ni^{+2} + 2\ OH^- \longrightarrow Ni(OH)_2(s)$$

Net ionic equations such as these can be given a quantitative meaning in precisely the manner outlined in Chapter 4 for reactions between pure substances. Examples 16.1 and 16.2 illustrate how this is done.

Example 16.1. A 0.20 M solution of NaOH is added to 100 ml. of 0.50 M $NiCl_2$ solution until precipitation is complete.

    a. What volume of 0.20 M NaOH is required?
    b. How many grams of $Ni(OH)_2$ are formed?

Solution

    a. Let us first calculate the number of moles of OH^- required and then the volume of 0.20 M NaOH required to produce that quantity.
        In 100 ml. of 0.50 M $NiCl_2$ solution, there are:

$$0.100\ l. \times 0.50\ \frac{mole\ Ni^{+2}}{l.} = 0.050\ mole\ Ni^{+2}$$

Equation 16.1 reveals that 2 moles of OH^- is required for every mole of Ni^{+2}; consequently, the quantity of OH^- needed here must be:

$$2 \times 0.050\ mole = 0.10\ mole\ OH^-$$

To calculate the volume of 0.20 M NaOH required:

$$(V\ of\ NaOH\ solution)\ (0.20\ \frac{mole}{l.}\ OH^-) = 0.10\ mole\ OH^-$$

Solving:

$$V\ of\ NaOH\ solution = \frac{0.10\ mole\ OH^-}{0.20\ \frac{mole}{l.}\ OH^-} = 0.50\ l. = 500\ ml.$$

    b. We note from (a) that 0.050 mole of Ni^{+2} reacted; equation 16.1 tells us that 1 mole of Ni^{+2} gives 1 mole of $Ni(OH)_2$. It follows that *0.050* mole of $Ni(OH)_2$ must have precipitated. The calculated formula weight of $Ni(OH)_2$ is 92.7; therefore:

$$no.\ grams\ Ni(OH)_2 = 0.050\ mole\ Ni(OH)_2 \times \frac{92.7\ g.\ Ni(OH)_2}{1\ mole\ Ni(OH)_2} = 4.6\ g.\ Ni(OH)_2$$

Example 16.2.   400 ml. of 0.30 M $Al_2(SO_4)_3$ is added to 300 ml. of 0.50 M $BaBr_2$ solution. Calculate:

    a. The number of moles of $BaSO_4$ precipitated.

    b. The number of moles and concentration of each ion remaining in solution after precipitation.

Solution.   Before making any calculations of this type, one must determine the number of moles of each ion originally present:

$$\text{no. moles } Al_2(SO_4)_3 = 0.400 \text{ l.} \times 0.30 \, \frac{\text{mole}}{\text{l.}} \, Al_2(SO_4)_3 = 0.12 \text{ mole } Al_2(SO_4)_3$$

$$\text{no. moles } BaBr_2 = 0.300 \text{ l.} \times 0.50 \, \frac{\text{mole}}{\text{l.}} \, BaBr_2 = 0.15 \text{ mole } BaBr_2$$

Noting that *1* mole of $Al_2(SO_4)_3$ gives *2* moles of Al^{+3} and *3* moles of SO_4^{-2}, while *1* mole of $BaBr_2$ yields *1* mole of Ba^{+2} and *2* moles of Br^-, we have:

    no. moles $Al^{+3} = 2 \times 0.12 = 0.24$ no. moles $Ba^{+2} = 1 \times 0.15 = 0.15$

    no. moles $SO_4^{-2} = 3 \times 0.12 = 0.36$ no. moles $Br^- = 2 \times 0.15 = 0.30$

    a. It may be noted from equation 16.2 that *one* mole of Ba^{+2} is required to react with *one* mole of SO_4^{-2}, producing *one* mole of $BaSO_4$. The limiting factor here is clearly the number of moles of Ba^{+2} available:

$$0.15 \text{ mole } Ba^{+2} + 0.15 \text{ mole } SO_4^{-2} \longrightarrow 0.15 \text{ mole } BaSO_4$$

    b. Subtracting the 0.15 mole of Ba^{+2} and 0.15 mole of SO_4^{-2} reacting from the number of moles originally present gives:

        no. moles Ba^{+2} = 0.15 mole − 0.15 mole = 0.00 mole

        no. moles SO_4^{-2} = 0.36 mole − 0.15 mole = 0.21 mole

        no. moles Al^{+3} = 0.24 mole − 0   = 0.24 mole

        no. moles Br^- = 0.30 mole − 0   = 0.30 mole

To obtain the concentrations of these ions in moles per liter, we need only divide by the total volume of the final solution. Assuming no volume change or mixing, the total volume must be 0.400 l. + 0.300 l. = 0.700 l.

$$\text{conc. } Ba^{+2} = \frac{0.00 \text{ mole}}{0.70 \text{ l.}} = 0.00 \text{ M} \qquad \text{conc. } SO_4^{-2} = \frac{0.21 \text{ mole}}{0.70 \text{ l.}} = 0.30 \text{ M}$$

$$\text{conc. } Al^{+3} = \frac{0.24 \text{ mole}}{0.70 \text{ l.}} = 0.34 \text{ M} \qquad \text{conc. } Br^- = \frac{0.30 \text{ mole}}{0.70 \text{ l.}} = 0.43 \text{ M}$$

Summarizing:

	orig.	−	reacted	=	final	final
		Number of Moles				Concentration (M)
Al^{+3}	0.24	−	0.00	=	0.24	0.34 M
SO_4^{-2}	0.36	−	0.15	=	0.21	0.30 M
Ba^{+2}	0.15	−	0.15	=	0.00	0.00 M
Br^-	0.30	−	0.00	=	0.30	0.43 M

16.2 SOLUBILITIES OF IONIC COMPOUNDS

It is always possible to decide by direct experimental observation whether or not a precipitate forms when two solutions are mixed. More conveniently, solubility data obtained from a limited number of precipitation reactions can be used to predict the results of a great many other reactions. For example, having established the fact that nickel hydroxide is insoluble in water, one can predict that mixing solutions of

$Ni(NO_3)_2$ and NaOH, $NiSO_4$ and KOH, or $NiBr_2$ and $Ca(OH)_2$ will result in the formation of a precipitate of $Ni(OH)_2$ according to equation 16.1. Again, if it is established through experiment that sodium chloride and potassium nitrate are both soluble in water, it follows that no precipitation reaction will occur when solutions of $NaNO_3$ and KCl are mixed. It might then appear that all one needs to predict the results of possible precipitation reactions is a table of solubilities in which every ionic solid is neatly classified as soluble or insoluble. Unfortunately, there are difficulties associated with any attempt to set up such a simple classification scheme.

In the first place, ionic solids do not fall clearly into the two categories, soluble and insoluble, with a sharp dividing line between them. Instead, they cover an enormous range of solubility. One of the most soluble salts known is lithium chlorate, $LiClO_3$, which dissolves to the extent of 35 moles/l. at room temperature. One can safely predict that this compound will not be the product of a precipitation reaction. At the other extreme is mercury(II) sulfide, HgS; one can calculate that a saturated solution should contain only about 10^{-26} mole/l. of Hg^{+2} and S^{-2} ions. Quite clearly, we can expect to get a precipitate of mercuric sulfide whenever water solutions containing Hg^{+2} and S^{-2} ions, however dilute, are mixed. Lead chloride, $PbCl_2$, is an example of a compound of intermediate solubility. One can calculate that if equal volumes of 0.1 M $Pb(NO_3)_2$ and 0.1 M NaCl are mixed, the solubility of $PbCl_2$ will be exceeded and it will precipitate. If, on the other hand, the solutions mixed are somewhat more dilute, say 0.04 M, no precipitate is formed. Compounds such as lead chloride are difficult to classify as soluble or insoluble; it is perhaps begging the question to classify them as slightly soluble.

In attempting to decide whether or not a precipitate will form when two solutions are mixed, one must always consider the effect of temperature on solubility. This factor is particularly important when the compound in question is in the slightly soluble class. Consider, for example, lead chloride: its solubility in boiling water is about four times as great as at room temperature. As a result, although lead chloride precipitates when equal volumes of solutions 0.1 M in Pb^{+2} and Cl^- are mixed at room temperature, no precipitate forms when the same reaction is attempted at 100°C. Because of this behavior, lead chloride is sometimes described as being soluble in hot water and insoluble in cold water.

TABLE 16.1 SOLUBILITY RULES

NO_3^-, ClO_3^-	All nitrates and chlorates are soluble.
Cl^-, Br^-, I^-	All chlorides are soluble except AgCl, Hg_2Cl_2 and $PbCl_2$*. The same rule applies to bromides and iodides except that $HgBr_2$* and HgI_2 are also insoluble.
F^-	All fluorides are soluble, except those of the 2A elements, FeF_3, and PbF_2.
SO_4^{-2}	All sulfates are soluble except $CaSO_4$*, $SrSO_4$, $BaSO_4$, Hg_2SO_4, $HgSO_4$, $PbSO_4$, and Ag_2SO_4.
CO_3^{-2}, PO_4^{-3}	All carbonates are insoluble except those of the 1A elements and NH_4^+. The same rule applies to phosphates except that Li_3PO_4 is also insoluble.
OH^-	All hydroxides are insoluble except those of the 1A elements, $Sr(OH)_2$ and $Ba(OH)_2$. ($Ca(OH)_2$ is slightly soluble.)
S^{-2}	All sulfides except those of the 1A and 2A elements and NH_4^+ are insoluble.

* Insoluble compounds are those which precipitate upon mixing equal volumes of solutions 0.1 M in the corresponding ions. Compounds which fail to precipitate at concentrations slightly below 0.1 M are starred.

Bearing these qualifications in mind, one can classify the more common ionic solids on the basis of their solubility behavior according to the rules outlined in Table 16.1

The use of solubility rules to predict the results of precipitation reactions is illustrated by Example 16.3.

Example 16.3. Write balanced equations for the reactions, if any, that occur when equal volumes of 0.1 M solutions of the following compounds are mixed.

    a. $Hg(NO_3)_2$ and $AlBr_3$ b. Na_2SO_4 and KOH c. $CuSO_4$ and $Ba(OH)_2$

Solution. In each case, we first deduce the formulas of the two possible precipitates and then, on the basis of the solubility rules, decide whether one or both of these compounds will precipitate. Having made this decision, the net ionic equation for the precipitation reaction is readily derived.

    a. Possible precipitates: $HgBr_2$, $Al(NO_3)_3$. Table 16.1 indicates that $HgBr_2$ is insoluble, while $Al(NO_3)_3$ is soluble (all nitrates are soluble). Consequently, we have:

$$Hg^{+2} + 2\ Br^- \longrightarrow HgBr_2(s)$$

    b. Possible precipitates: $NaOH$, K_2SO_4. From the solubility rules, it is clear that both of these compounds are soluble. No precipitation reaction occurs.

    c. Possible precipitates: $Cu(OH)_2$, $BaSO_4$. Of these compounds, $BaSO_4$ is specifically listed as insoluble; it can be deduced that $Cu(OH)_2$ is also insoluble. Two precipitation reactions occur simultaneously:

$$Ba^{+2} + SO_4^{-2} \longrightarrow BaSO_4(s) \text{ and } Cu^{+2} + 2\ OH^- \longrightarrow Cu(OH)_2(s)$$

16.3   SOLUBILITY AND STRUCTURE

It may perhaps be inferred from the amount of space devoted to empirical solubility rules that there is no simple theory for predicting the solubility of a given ionic compound in water. However, by considering certain structural features, it is possible to develop principles to explain trends in solubility. That this is by no means a simple task may be deduced from such solubility data as that given in Table 16.2.

TABLE 16.2 SOLUBILITIES (moles/l. at 20°C)
OF COMPOUNDS OF THE 2A METALS

	SO_4^{-2}	OH^-	F^-
Mg^{+2}	2.0	0.00014	0.0012
Ca^{+2}	0.012	0.022	0.0003
Sr^{+2}	0.0006	0.034	0.0009
Ba^{+2}	0.00003	0.12	0.0091

The solubilities of the 2A sulfates steadily decrease from magnesium to barium, while the hydroxides follow exactly the opposite trend. In the case of the fluorides, the solubility passes through a minimum with CaF_2. One can hardly hope to discover a single, simple explanation for these diverse solubility trends.

The difficulties involved in predicting relative solubilities of ionic compounds are inherent in the nature of the solution process. When an ionic solute is added to water, a balance is achieved between the attractive forces of the ions for each other, which tend to hold them in the solid state, and the attractive forces of the ions for water, which tend to bring the compound into solution. These two attractive forces are essentially similar in origin. The ions are held together in the crystal lattice by electrostatic attraction; the attraction of a polar water molecule for ions is also largely electrostatic. As a result, the factors which tend to increase the attractive forces between ions simultaneously increase the attraction of these ions for water molecules.

Four of the most important factors that affect the solubility of ionic compounds are the charge density of ions, the radius ratio, covalent bonding, and hydrogen bonding. While each of these factors is considered separately in the following discussion, it must be kept in mind that in comparing solubilities of a series of ionic compounds, more than one factor will ordinarily be applicable.

Charge Density of Ions

It was pointed out in Chapter 9 that the ratio of the charge of an ion to its size, or its charge density, determines its attraction for an ion of opposite charge. In magnesium oxide, in which the ions have high charges ($+2$ and -2) and are relatively small (radius $Mg^{+2} = 0.65$ Å, $O^{-2} = 1.40$ Å), the electrostatic forces are stronger than in sodium chloride, in which the ions have smaller charges ($+1$ and -1) and are somewhat larger (radius $Na^+ = 0.95$ Å, $Cl^- = 1.81$ Å). As a result magnesium oxide has a melting point, 2800°C, considerably higher than that of sodium chloride, 800°C.

The charge density of ions affects not only their attraction for each other but also their attraction for water molecules. A magnesium ion, Mg^{+2}, attracts the negative pole of a water molecule more strongly than does a Na^+ ion: in a similar manner, the attraction of the positive pole of a water molecule for an O^{-2} ion will exceed that for the Cl^- ion with its lower charge density.

Here we have an illustration of the situation mentioned earlier; an increase in the charge density of ions enhances both the stability of the ionic lattice and the tendency for the lattice to break down when placed in contact with water. Nevertheless, it is possible to make a generalization applicable to the great majority of cases. The effect of charge density on interionic attractive forces ordinarily predominates over its effect on the attraction of ions for water. Other factors being equal, an increase in charge density results in decreased solubility. This general principle is reflected in :

1. The fact that the common salts of the 1A metals, almost without exception, are quite soluble in water, while those of the 2A metals and the transition elements are often insoluble. Compare, for example, the high solubilities of the alkali metal halides such as NaCl to the low solubilities of the alkaline earth carbonates such as $CaCO_3$. In calcium carbonate, the $+2$ and -2 ions have considerably higher charge densities than the $+1$ and -1 ions in NaCl.

2. The generally high solubility of nitrates (-1 ion) as compared to sulfates or carbonates (-2 ions).

3. The low solubilities of the 2A fluorides (radius $F^- = 1.36$ Å) as compared to the chlorides, bromides, and iodides (radius $Cl^- = 1.81$ Å, $Br^- = 1.95$ Å, $I^- = 2.16$ Å) of these metals, all of which are extremely soluble in water.

Although the charge density effect is perhaps the most important single factor in determining solubilities of ionic compounds, it is by no means sufficient to explain all the observed trends in solubility. For example, one would predict from this effect alone that the solubilities of the salts of the 2A metals should invariably increase as one moves from the small Mg^{+2} ion to the larger Ba^{+2} ion. Table 16.2 reveal precisely the opposite trend with the sulfates of these metals. To explain this and similar anomalies, one must consider the following additional factors.

Radius Ratio

The stability of an ionic crystal and consequently its solubility in water depend not only upon the charge density of its ions but also upon their relative sizes, that is, upon the ratio of their radii. Whenever the two types of ions making up a compound differ markedly in size, the compound can be expected to have an anomalously high solubility. To understand why this happens, consider the crystal structure of lithium iodide (Figure 9.2). The lithium ion, with a radius less than $\frac{1}{3}$ that of the iodide ion (0.60 Å vs. 2.16 Å), is too small to effectively separate the iodide ions from each other. Contact between ions of like charge results in an electrostatic repulsion which lowers the stability of the lattice and makes the salt more vulnerable to attack by water molecules. For this reason, lithium iodide is considerably more soluble than rubidium iodide, in which the ionic radii are more nearly equal ($Rb^+ = 1.48$ Å). This effect is precisely the opposite of that to be expected on the basis of charge density alone; the higher charge density of the Li^+ ion as compared to Rb^+ might be expected to make lithium iodide the less soluble of the two compounds. Along this line, it is interesting that the melting point of lithium iodide is some 200°C lower than that of rubidium iodide; here again the trend is opposite in direction to that predicted on the basis of charge density alone.

The radius ratio effect can be used to explain the abnormal trend previously noted in the solubilities of the 2A sulfates. In $MgSO_4$, the relatively small Mg^{+2} ions (radius = 0.65 Å) do not occupy enough space to insulate the larger SO_4^{-2} ions (S—O distance = 1.44 Å) from each other. In $CaSO_4$ (radius $Ca^{+2} = 0.99$ Å) and $SrSO_4$ (radius $Sr^{+2} = 1.13$ Å), the sulfate ions are forced further apart, the stability of the ionic lattice is increased, and the compounds become less soluble. In $BaSO_4$ (radius $Ba^{+2} = 1.35$ Å), in which the two ions are of comparable size, the solubility reaches a minimum.

In considering the crystal structures of the 2A sulfates, it is interesting to note that magnesium sulfate crystallizes from water solution as the heptahydrate, $MgSO_4 \cdot 7\,H_2O$, in which water molecules are packed around the small Mg^{+2} ions so as to separate the larger SO_4^{-2} ions from each other. Calcium sulfate precipitates as the dihydrate, $CaSO_4 \cdot 2\,H_2O$, in which the water molecules perform the same structural function. Neither $SrSO_4$ nor $BaSO_4$ form hydrates.

Covalent Bonding

Up to this point, the solubilities of salts have been interpreted in terms of a balance between the electrostatic forces attracting ions to each other and to water molecules. Such a treatment works quite well for compounds of the 1A and 2A metals in which the bonding is predominantly ionic. However, in considering the solubilities of salts of the transition metals, one must take into account the effect of covalent bonding, both in the solid state and in water solution.

Covalent Bonding in the Solid. The insolubility of the transition metal sulfides can be explained in terms of covalent bonding in the solid state. Such compounds as CuS and HgS, in which the elements differ only slightly in electronegativity, have macromolecular structures; these sulfides resemble in physical appearance such covalently bonded crystals as graphite. The soluble sulfides are those of the 1A and 2A metals, in which the bonding is predominantly ionic.

Covalent Bonding in Solution. In certain cases, it is found that the transition metal salts are more soluble than their 1A or 2A counterparts. Copper sulfate, $CuSO_4$, is about twice as soluble in water as potassium sulfate. The high solubility of many of the compounds of copper and other transition metals can be ascribed in large part to the very stable hydrated species these metal ions form in water solution.

The fact that white, anhydrous $CuSO_4$ on dissolving in water gives a blue solution indicates that a new chemical species has been formed. Experimental evidence indicates the presence of a hydrated ion in which four water molecules are

$$
\begin{bmatrix}
H \quad\quad H \\
\diagdown \quad\diagup \\
H \quad O \quad\quad H \\
\diagdown \quad | \quad\diagup \\
O-Cu-O \\
\diagup \quad | \quad\diagdown \\
H \quad O \quad\quad H \\
\diagup \quad\diagdown \\
H \quad\quad H
\end{bmatrix}^{+2}
$$

joined to the Cu^{+2} ion by strong, coordinate covalent bonds. The bonding electrons are furnished by the oxygen atoms of the water molecules. The electronic structure of this ion may be represented as:

Its formula is written as $Cu(H_2O)_4^{+2}$.

Some idea of the stability of the hydrated Cu^{+2} ion may be obtained by noting that when a mole of anhydrous copper sulfate is dissolved in a large amount of water, 16 kcal. of heat is evolved. In contrast, the formation of an aqueous solution of potassium sulfate is an endothermic process; about 6 kcal. is absorbed for every mole of K_2SO_4 dissolved.

When salts of the transition metals dissolve in water, **aquo complex ions,** analogous in structure to the hydrated Cu^{+2} ion, are commonly formed. Some of these ions are listed in Table 16.3. The number of water molecules coordinated to the metal ion may be 2, 4, or 6. Frequently, the water is retained when the salt crystallizes from solution. In the solid hydrates $CdSO_4 \cdot 4\ H_2O$ and $Fe(NO_3)_3 \cdot 6\ H_2O$, the water molecules are bonded to the metal ion to form the species $Cd(H_2O)_4^{+2}$ and $Fe(H_2O)_6^{+3}$ respectively. In copper sulfate pentahydrate, $CuSO_4 \cdot 5\ H_2O$, four of the water molecules are coordinated to the copper while the fifth is associated with the SO_4^{-2} ion.

TABLE 16.3 HYDRATED IONS

$Al(H_2O)_6^{+3}$	$Mn(H_2O)_6^{+2}$	$Cu(H_2O)_4^{+2}$	$Ag(H_2O)_2^{+}$
$Cr(H_2O)_6^{+3}$	$Fe(H_2O)_6^{+2}$	$Zn(H_2O)_4^{+2}$	
$Fe(H_2O)_6^{+3}$	$Co(H_2O)_6^{+2}$		
$Co(H_2O)_6^{+3}$			

The aquo complex ions listed in Table 16.3 are examples of a general type of polyatomic ion known simply as a *complex ion* in which a metal ion is joined to nonmetal atoms by coordinate covalent bonds. We shall postpone a general discussion of such ions to Chapter 19. At the moment, our interest in aquo complex ions lies in the increased stability which they impart to water solutions of transition metal salts. This effect accounts for the high solubility of many of the salts of the transition metals.

Hydrogen Bonding

Hydrogen bonding can be expected to have an effect on solubility similar to that of covalent bonding. When there is extensive hydrogen bonding in the solid, the stability of the crystal lattice is enhanced and solubility is lowered. Conversely, hydrogen bonding in solution results in increased solubility.

An important example of hydrogen bonding in the solid state occurs in the metal hydroxides. In a compound such as $Mg(OH)_2$, the cation is too small (radius $Mg^{+2} = 0.65$ Å) to effectively separate the hydroxide ions (O—H bond distance $= 0.96$ Å) from each other. The OH^- ions in the lattice are held together by a network of hydrogen bonds joining the hydrogen atom of one anion to the oxygen of the next. The stability which hydrogen bonding lends to the magnesium hydroxide lattice is in large measure responsible for the low solubility of the compound. As the size of the cation increases in $Ca(OH)_2$, $Sr(OH)_2$, and $Ba(OH)_2$, the OH^- ions are forced farther apart, the effect of hydrogen bonding diminishes, and the compounds become more soluble. The 1A hydroxides, in which the positive ion is large enough to virtually eliminate hydrogen bonding between adjacent OH^- ions, are all extremely soluble.

An example of hydrogen bonding in solution occurs with salts containing the ammonium ion, NH_4^+. The four hydrogen atoms of this polyatomic cation form hydrogen bonds with adjacent water molecules. As one might expect, ammonium salts, almost without exception, are extremely soluble in water.

16.4 SOLUBILITY EQUILIBRIA

Qualitative Aspects: Common Ion Effect

When a solid such as silver acetate is dissolved in pure water to form a saturated solution, an equilibrium is established between the solid and its ions in solution.

$$AgC_2H_3O_2(s) \rightleftharpoons Ag^+ + C_2H_3O_2^- \tag{16.3}$$

The concentrations of Ag^+ and $C_2H_3O_2^-$ ions under these conditions will, of course, be equal to each other and will have a fixed value independent of the amount of silver acetate or water used in preparing the saturated solution. At 20°C, the equilibrium concentrations of Ag^+ and $C_2H_3O_2^-$ in a solution prepared by dissolving silver acetate in pure water are found experimentally to be 0.045 mole/l.

It is possible to change the relative concentrations of Ag^+ and $C_2H_3O_2^-$ ions in equilibrium with solid silver acetate in any of various ways. Specifically, one might accomplish this by adding to the solution:

1. *An electrolyte containing a common ion, Ag^+ or $C_2H_3O_2^-$.* Suppose, for example, one adds a concentrated solution of a more soluble silver salt, such as silver nitrate. Some of the added Ag^+ ions will combine with the $C_2H_3O_2^-$ ions in solution to precipitate silver acetate. This behavior is often referred to as the **common ion** effect; addition of a common ion, Ag^+, to a saturated solution of an electrolyte, $AgC_2H_3O_2$, disturbs the solubility equilibrium so as to bring about precipitation.

to a gIA turated sol add a soluble salt which have anion of the saturated sol giving the sol a common ion effect which disturbs the solubility equil + brings about a ppt

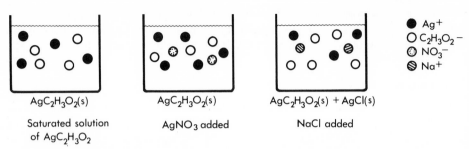

AgC₂H₃O₂(s)   AgC₂H₃O₂(s)   AgC₂H₃O₂(s) + AgCl(s)

Saturated solution   AgNO₃ added   NaCl added
of AgC₂H₃O₂

FIGURE 16.1   Effect of added substances on silver acetate equilibria in solution.

When equilibrium is re-established, it is found that the concentration of $C_2H_3O_2^-$ ion is reduced from its original value while that of Ag^+ ion is increased (Figure 16.1).

2. *An electrolyte which forms a precipitate with one of the ions.* If one adds sodium chloride to a saturated solution of silver acetate, it is observed that the very insoluble salt, silver chloride, precipitates. As Ag^+ ions are removed from solution as AgCl, more silver acetate dissolves to restore equilibrium between Ag^+ and $C_2H_3O_2^-$ ions. The net effect is to increase the concentration of $C_2H_3O_2^-$ ions in solution and simultaneously decrease the concentration of Ag^+ ions (Figure 16.1).

Quantitative Treatment: Solubility Product

As the foregoing discussion implies, there is an inverse relationship between the equilibrium concentrations of ions in contact with the electrolyte from which they are derived. Any process which shifts the equilibrium so as to increase the concentration of one of these ions simultaneously decreases the concentration of the other. The quantitative relationship between these concentrations can be derived in a manner entirely analogous to that used in Chapter 14 in dealing with gaseous equilibria. This derivation, outlined as follows, is strictly applicable only in very dilute solution in which ionic interactions of the type described in Chapter 13, Section 13.7, may be neglected.

Let us consider a slightly soluble 1:1 electrolyte of general formula MX in equilibrium with its ions, M^+ and X^-, in aqueous solution.

$$MX(s) \rightleftharpoons M^+ + X^-$$

For this equilibrium, we can write the general expression:

$$K = \frac{[M^+] \times [X^-]}{[MX(s)]}$$

or: $$K \times [MX(s)] = [M^+] \times [X^-] \qquad (16.4)$$

in which the square brackets are used to denote equilibrium concentrations in moles per liter and K is an equilibrium constant analogous to those written for gaseous equilibria in Chapter 14.

This expression can be simplified by noting that the concentration of solid is uniquely determined by its density and is not affected by changing the concentrations of ions. In other words, the term $[MX(s)]$, like the equilibrium constant, K, is independent of $[M^+]$ and $[X^-]$. Consequently, the entire left-hand side of equation

16.4 can be treated as a constant and we can write:

$$\text{constant} = [M^+] \times [X^-]$$

The constant in this equation is a particular type of equilibrium constant, referred to as the solubility product of the electrolyte, and given the symbol Ksp.

$$\text{Ksp of MX(s)} = [M^+] \times [X^-] \tag{16.5}$$

For any given electrolyte at a particular temperature, Ksp should have a fixed value, independent of the concentrations of the individual ions in equilibrium with the solid. In principle, at least, the numerical value of the solubility product can be calculated from the measured solubility, as illustrated by Example 16.4. In practice, values of Ksp, particularly for electrolytes of very low solubility, are ordinarily calculated by less direct methods, one of which is described in Chapter 21 in connection with voltage measurements on electrical cells.

Example 16.4.   The measured solubility of silver acetate, $AgC_2H_3O_2$, at 20°C is 0.045 mole/l. Calculate the solubility product of silver acetate.

Solution.   From the equation:

$$AgC_2H_3O_2(s) \rightleftharpoons Ag^+ + C_2H_3O_2^-$$

it is evident that for every mole of silver acetate that dissolves, a mole of Ag^+ ions and a mole of $C_2H_3O_2^-$ ions enter the solution. It follows that if 0.045 mole of solid dissolves per liter of solution, the equilibrium concentrations of Ag^+ and $C_2H_3O_2^-$ must be 0.045 M.

$$\begin{aligned} \text{Ksp} &= [Ag^+] \times [C_2H_3O_2^-] \\ &= (0.045)(0.045) = 2.0 \times 10^{-3} \end{aligned}$$

The concept of solubility product is readily extended to electrolytes of any valence type. For an electrolyte MX_2, for which the solubility equilibrium may be expressed by the equation:

$$MX_2(s) \rightleftharpoons M^{+2} + 2 X^- \tag{16.6}$$

we can write:

$$\text{Ksp} = [M^{+2}] \times [X^-]^2$$

Thus, we have, for example,

$$\text{Ksp of PbCl}_2 = [Pb^{+2}] \times [Cl^-]^2 = 1.7 \times 10^{-5}$$

Again, for a compound such as arsenic(III) sulfide, As_2S_3:

$$As_2S_3(s) \rightleftharpoons 2 As^{+3} + 3 S^{-2} \tag{16.7}$$

$$\text{Ksp} = [As^{+3}]^2 \times [S^{-2}]^3 = 5 \times 10^{-27}$$

In general, the solubility product principle may be stated as follows: **In any water solution in equilibrium with a slightly soluble ionic compound, the product of the ion concentrations, each raised to a power equal to the coefficient of the ion in the solubility equation, has a constant value.**

The solubility product principle, in the form just stated, is strictly applicable only in very dilute solutions. The value of Ksp for a given electrolyte depends to some extent upon the total concentration of ions in solution. It may be seen from the data in Table 16.4 that the solubility product of AgCl, which has the limiting value of 1.6×10^{-10} in pure water, is increased above this number in the presence of potassium nitrate. This behavior is typical of most slightly soluble salts and can be attributed qualitatively to the increased effect of inter-ionic attractive forces in more concentrated solutions. A quantitative treatment of this subject, involving ionic activities, is beyond the scope of an elementary text.

TABLE 16.4   Ksp OF AgCl IN KNO$_3$ SOLUTIONS

Concentration KNO$_3$	Solubility AgCl	$[Ag^+] \times [Cl^-]$
0	1.28×10^{-5}	1.64×10^{-10}
0.0010	1.33×10^{-5}	1.77×10^{-10}
0.0050	1.38×10^{-5}	1.90×10^{-10}
0.010	1.43×10^{-5}	2.04×10^{-10}
0.020	1.49×10^{-5}	2.22×10^{-10}
0.040	1.55×10^{-5}	2.40×10^{-10}

The solubility products of a representative number of slightly soluble electrolytes are given in Table 16.5. It will be noted that, for the most part, they are given to only one significant figure, in several cases, only to the nearest power of 10. Fortunately, calculations involving Ksp do not ordinarily require an accuracy greater than this.

TABLE 16.5   SOLUBILITY PRODUCTS

Acetate	AgC$_2$H$_3$O$_2$	2×10^{-3}	Iodides	AgI	1×10^{-16}
				PbI$_2$	1×10^{-8}
Bromides	AgBr	1×10^{-13}			
	PbBr$_2$	5×10^{-6}	Sulfates	BaSO$_4$	1.5×10^{-9}
				CaSO$_4$	3×10^{-5}
Carbonates	BaCO$_3$	1×10^{-9}		PbSO$_4$	1×10^{-8}
	CaCO$_3$	5×10^{-9}			
	MgCO$_3$	2×10^{-8}	Sulfides	Ag$_2$S	1×10^{-49}
	PbCO$_3$	1×10^{-13}		CdS	1×10^{-26}
				CoS	1×10^{-21}
Chlorides	AgCl	1.6×10^{-10}		CuS	1×10^{-25}
	Hg$_2$Cl$_2$	1×10^{-18}		FeS	2×10^{-17}
	PbCl$_2$	1.7×10^{-5}		HgS	1×10^{-52}
				MnS	1×10^{-13}
Chromates	Ag$_2$CrO$_4$	1×10^{-12}		NiS	1×10^{-22}
	BaCrO$_4$	2×10^{-10}		PbS	1×10^{-27}
	PbCrO$_4$	2×10^{-14}		ZnS	1×10^{-23}
Fluorides	BaF$_2$	2×10^{-6}			
	CaF$_2$	2×10^{-10}			
	PbF$_2$	4×10^{-8}			
Hydroxides	Al(OH)$_3$	5×10^{-33}			
	Cr(OH)$_3$	1×10^{-30}			
	Fe(OH)$_2$	1×10^{-15}			
	Fe(OH)$_3$	5×10^{-38}			
	Mg(OH)$_2$	1×10^{-11}			
	Zn(OH)$_2$	5×10^{-17}			

We shall be primarily interested in using solubility products to determine: (1) whether or not a precipitate will form under a given set of conditions (Example 16.5), and (2) the extent to which a precipitation reaction occurs (Example 16.6).

Example 16.5.   If AgNO$_3$ is slowly added to a 0.020 M solution of NaC$_2$H$_3$O$_2$:
   a. Will a precipitate of AgC$_2$H$_3$O$_2$ form when conc. Ag$^+$ $= 1 \times 10^{-2}$ M?
   b. At approximately what $[Ag^+]$ will a precipitate start to form?

Solution
   a. Let us calculate the product of the concentrations of Ag$^+$ and C$_2$H$_3$O$_2^-$ and compare to Ksp (2×10^{-3}).

$$\text{conc. Ag}^+ \times \text{conc. C}_2\text{H}_3\text{O}_2^- = (1 \times 10^{-2})(2 \times 10^{-2}) = 2 \times 10^{-4}$$

Since the concentration product is *less* than Ksp ($2 \times 10^{-4} < 2 \times 10^{-3}$) equilibrium is *not* established, and no silver acetate forms.

b. At the instant a precipitate starts to form, the concentration product, conc. $Ag^+ \times$ conc. $C_2H_3O_2^-$, must equal the equilibrium value, 2×10^{-3}. Neglecting dilution effects, the concentration of $C_2H_3O_2^-$ at that point must be 0.020 M. Therefore:

$$[Ag^+] \times (0.020) = 2 \times 10^{-3} \qquad [Ag^+] = 0.10 \text{ M}$$

This is the minimum concentration of Ag^+ at which a precipitate will form. At higher Ag^+ ion concentrations, precipitation will occur and sufficient $C_2H_3O_2^-$ ions will be removed from solution to maintain the concentration product at 2×10^{-3}.

Example 16.6. Sufficient CrO_4^{-2} ion is added to a solution originally 0.010 M in Ag^+ to make the equilibrium concentration of CrO_4^{-2} 2×10^{-3} M.

   a. What is the equilibrium concentration of Ag^+ at this point?
   b. What percentage of the Ag^+ originally present remains in solution?

Solution

a. From the equation:

$$Ag_2CrO_4(s) \rightleftharpoons 2\,Ag^+ + CrO_4^{-2}$$
$$Ksp = [Ag^+]^2 \times [CrO_4^{-2}] = 1 \times 10^{-12}$$

But, $[CrO_4^{-2}]$ is given as 2×10^{-3} M.
So:

$$[Ag^+]^2 \,(2 \times 10^{-3}) = 1 \times 10^{-12}$$

$$[Ag^+]^2 = \frac{1 \times 10^{-12}}{2 \times 10^{-3}} = 5 \times 10^{-10}$$

$$[Ag^+] = (5 \times 10^{-10})^{\frac{1}{2}} = 2 \times 10^{-5} \text{ M (1 significant figure)}$$

b. Originally, the concentration of Ag^+ was 1×10^{-2} M; it is now 2×10^{-5} M.

$$\% \ Ag^+ \text{ remaining} = \frac{2 \times 10^{-5}}{1 \times 10^{-2}} \times 100 = 0.2\%$$

In other words, 99.8 per cent of the Ag^+ has been precipitated as Ag_2CrO_4.

16.5 PRECIPITATION REACTIONS IN ANALYTICAL CHEMISTRY

Quantitative Analysis

In Chapter 3, precipitation reactions were cited as a method of elementary analysis. One can, for example, find the percentage of chloride in a solid mixture by determining the weight of sliver chloride produced when excess silver nitrate is added to a weighed sample of the mixture. Similarly, it is possible to analyze for barium by adding sulfate ions to precipitate barium sulfate. Analyses of this type, based on weights of products and reactants, constitute a branch of quantitative analysis known as gravimetric analysis. The calculations involved in analyses of this type are illustrated in Example 16.7.

Example 16.7. A sample consisting of a mixture of Na_2SO_4 and NaCl is analyzed by adding an excess of Ba^{+2} ions to precipitate $BaSO_4$. A 1.000 g. sample of the mixture yields 0.846 g. of $BaSO_4$. Calculate the percentage of Na_2SO_4 in the mixture.

Solution. From the net ionic equation for the precipitation reaction:

$$Ba^{+2} + SO_4^{-2} \longrightarrow BaSO_4(s)$$

it should be obvious that 1 mole of Na_2SO_4, containing 1 mole of SO_4^{-2} ions, yields 1 mole of $BaSO_4$.

$$1 \text{ mole } Na_2SO_4 \longrightarrow 1 \text{ mole } BaSO_4$$

But, since the gram formula weights of Na_2SO_4 and $BaSO_4$ are respectively 142.1 g. and 233.4 g., it follows that:

$$142.1 \text{ g. } Na_2SO_4 \longrightarrow 233.4 \text{ g. } BaSO_4$$

Consequently, the weight of Na_2SO_4 required to produce 0.846 g. of $BaSO_4$ must be:

$$0.846 \text{ g. } BaSO_4 \times \frac{142.1 \text{ g. } Na_2SO_4}{233.4 \text{ g. } BaSO_4} = 0.515 \text{ g. } Na_2SO_4$$

The percentage of Na_2SO_4 in the one-gram sample must then be:

$$\frac{0.515 \text{ g.}}{1.000 \text{ g.}} \times 100 = 51.5\%$$

The composition of a mixture can also be determined by measuring the volume of a reagent of known concentration required to react exactly with one of the components of the mixture. Analyses based on volume measurements of this type fall in the general area of volumetric analysis. The principles involved are illustrated by Example 16.8.

Example 16.8. A chloride sample weighing 0.208 g. is found to require 15.0 ml. of 0.184 M $AgNO_3$ for complete reaction. Calculate the percentage of Cl^- in the mixture.

Solution. To obtain the percentage of Cl^-, the weight of Cl^- in the sample must be known. This is readily determined from the number of moles of Cl^- present, which can be calculated directly from the data:

$$\text{no. moles } Cl^- = \text{no. moles } Ag^+ \text{ (1 mole } Cl^- \text{ reacts with 1 mole } Ag^+)$$

$$= 0.184 \frac{\text{mole}}{\text{l.}} \times 0.0150 \text{ l.} = 0.00276 \text{ mole } Cl^-$$

$$\text{no. g. } Cl^- = 0.00276 \text{ mole } Cl^- \times \frac{35.45 \text{ g. } Cl^-}{1 \text{ mole } Cl^-} = 0.0978 \text{ g. } Cl^-$$

$$\% \ Cl^- = \frac{\text{g. } Cl^-}{\text{g. sample}} \times 100 = \frac{0.0979}{0.208} \times 100 = 47.0\% \ Cl^-$$

In this method for the determination of chloride, as in all volumetric analyses, it is essential to know the exact point at which reaction is complete. In principle, this could be done by noting the point at which the precipitate of silver chloride stops forming. In practice, it is more convenient to add a substance known as an *indicator* which changes color when the equivalence point is reached, that is, when chemically equivalent quantities of precipitating agent and sample are present. A few drops of potassium chromate solution added to a chloride sample serves as a suitable indicator for titration with silver ions. At the equivalence point, when essentially all of the chloride ion has been removed as silver chloride, a dark red precipitate of silver chromate, Ag_2CrO_4, forms. This compound, being somewhat more soluble than silver chloride, does not precipitate so long as there is any appreciable amount of chloride ion remaining (see Problem 16.11).

The experimental setup for the quantitative determination of Cl^- ion by this method, referred to as a Mohr titration, is shown in Figure 16.2. Silver nitrate solution of accurately known molarity is added from a buret until a permanent red color develops. Many other ions can be determined in a similar manner. Bromides and iodides as well as chlorides can be determined by titrating with Ag^+. Soluble samples containing Ag^+ ions are often analyzed by titrating with thiocyanate ions SCN^-, which form a white precipitate, $AgSCN$. In this titration, a small amount of

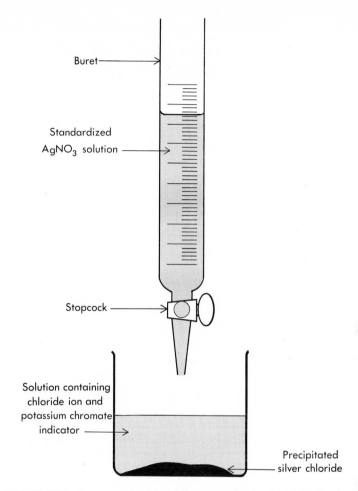

Buret

Standardized
AgNO$_3$ solution

Stopcock

Solution containing
chloride ion and
potassium chromate
indicator

Precipitated
silver chloride

FIGURE 16.2 Apparatus for chloride ion determination by Mohr titration.

an iron(III) salt serves as an indicator; after all of the Ag$^+$ is gone, a small excess of SCN$^-$ reacts with Fe^{+3} to give a blood-red complex.

Qualitative Analysis

The qualitative detection of ions in a mixture is commonly accomplished by a scheme of analysis in which precipitation reactions play a major role. The general objectives of such a scheme are illustrated by Example 16.9.

Example 16.9.   Develop a scheme, based on the information given in Table 16.1, to separate and identify, in a water solution, the ions Ag$^+$, Ca^{+2} and Ni^{+2}. It may be assumed that no other cations are present in the solution.

Solution.   To carry out this analysis, we look first for a reagent which will precipitate one ion, leaving the other two in solution. Clearly the Cl$^-$ ion is such a species, since it precipitates Ag$^+$ but not Ca^{+2} or Ni^{+2}. The first step in the analysis might then be the addition of a solution of sodium chloride or hydrochloric acid. Formation of a precipitate would indicate the presence of Ag$^+$; if no precipitate forms, Ag$^+$ must be absent.

Having removed any Ag$^+$ ions present, we next choose a reagent which will distinguish between Ca^{+2} and Ni^{+2}. Table 16.1 reveals that this can be done by adding sulfide ions (for example, a solution of sodium sulfide). This precipitates any Ni^{+2} present in the solution but has no effect on the Ca^{+2} ions.

At this point, the solution remaining need only be tested for Ca^{+2}. A convenient method of accomplishing this is to add a solution of sodium carbonate, which will precipitate Ca^{+2} as $CaCO_3$. Failure to obtain a precipitate at this point would show Ca^{+2} to be absent. In summary:

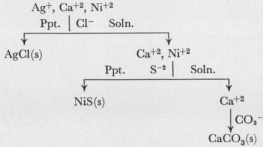

Obviously, this is not the only scheme that could be used to test for these ions. It does, however, illustrate two important points concerning precipitation analyses:

1. The order in which precipitating agents are added is crucial. It would have been useless to have added CO_3^{-2} to the original solution, since it gives a precipitate with all three cations.

2. All precipitations must be quantitative. Any Ag^+ left after the first step would interfere with the tests for Ni^{+2} and Ca^{+2}, since both Ag_2S and Ag_2CO_3 are insoluble.

Several different analytical schemes have been devised to separate and identify the 25 or more ions commonly included in a laboratory course in qualitative analysis. Needless to say, these schemes are a great deal more complex than that outlined in Example 16.9. Many other types of reactions in addition to precipitation are used. We shall consider later how acid-base reactions (Chapter 18), complex-ion formation (Chapter 19) and oxidation-reduction reactions (Chapter 22) are utilized in qualitative analysis. At this stage, it may be useful to indicate the scope of qualitative analysis by giving a brief outline of one of the simpler schemes of cation analysis. The experimental procedures pertinent to this and other such schemes are described in various laboratory manuals dealing with qualitative analysis.

The cations are first separated into five major groups on the basis of the solubilities of their compounds.

Group 1. (Ag^+, Pb^{+2}, Hg_2^{+2}) Separated as the insoluble chlorides, usually by the addition of dilute hydrochloric acid. All other cations remain in solution, since their chlorides are soluble.

Group 2. (Cu^{+2}, Bi^{+3}, Cd^{+2}, Hg^{+2}, As^{+3}, Sb^{+3}, Sn^{+2}) These ions, which form extremely insoluble sulfides, are precipitated by adding S^{-2} in low concentration. This can be done by saturating with hydrogen sulfide the acidic solution remaining after precipitation of group 1.*

Group 3. (Al^{+3}, Cr^{+3}, Fe^{+3}, Zn^{+2}, Ni^{+2}, Co^{+2}, Mn^{+2}) The sulfides of these metals are somewhat more soluble than those in group 2; the ions may be precipitated by adding H_2S in basic solution.* Al^{+3} and Cr^{+3} come down as the hydroxides, the other ions as the sulfides.

Group 4. (Mg^{+2}, Ca^{+2}, Sr^{+2}, Ba^{+2}) May be precipitated as the carbonates.

Group 5. (Na^+, K^+, NH_4^+) Since neither the chlorides, sulfides, hydroxides, nor carbonates of these ions are insoluble, they remain in solution after the first

---

* The concentration of S^{-2} in an H_2S solution depends upon the acidity, as may be deduced from the equation:
$$H_2S \rightleftharpoons 2 H^+ + S^{-2}$$

See Chapter 18 for a further discussion of this effect.

four groups have been separated. Special reagents are ordinarily used to identify these ions. In the case of K^+, the violet color imparted to a flame by potassium salts is a useful test.

Once the cations have been separated into groups, the problem becomes one of further subdividing the groups. We shall not attempt at this point to describe the chemistry involved in these separations. A single example may, however, be instructive. Lead can be separated from the other Group 1 ions by heating the chloride precipitate with boiling water and testing the hot solution with CrO_4^{-2}. The formation of a yellow precipitate of lead chromate, $PbCrO_4$, which is much less soluble than $PbCl_2$, indicates the presence of lead.

$$PbCl_2(s) \longrightarrow Pb^{+2} + 2\ Cl^-$$

$$Pb^{+2} + CrO_4^{-2} \longrightarrow PbCrO_4(s)$$

$$PbCl_2(s) + CrO_4^{-2} \longrightarrow 2\ Cl^- + PbCrO_4(s) \tag{16.8}$$

16.6 PRECIPITATION REACTIONS IN INORGANIC PREPARATIONS

Precipitation reactions serve as a convenient source of insoluble ionic compounds. Barium sulfate, for example, is readily prepared by adding a slight excess of a solution containing sulfate ions, SO_4^{-2}, to a solution of a barium salt. The precipitate is filtered, washed to remove foreign ions, and dried at $100°C$ to give a product of high purity. Similar techniques can be used to convert silver nitrate to any one of the insoluble halides of silver, $AgCl$, $AgBr$, or AgI.

In addition to their use in preparing insoluble inorganic compounds, precipitation reactions form the basis of a general method of converting one type of soluble ionic compound to another. Let us suppose, for example, that it is desired to convert a soluble metal chloride to the corresponding nitrate. If one adds silver nitrate to a solution of the chloride, a precipitate of $AgCl$ will form; Cl^- ions in solution will be replaced by NO_3^- ions. If just enough Ag^+ ions are added to react with all the Cl^- ions originally present, the solution remaining after the $AgCl$ is filtered off will contain only two kinds of ions; the metal ions originally present and the NO_3^- ions introduced with the silver nitrate.

$$M^+ + Cl^- + Ag^+ + NO_3^- \longrightarrow AgCl(s) + M^+ + NO_3^- \tag{16.9}*$$

Evaporation of this solution gives the pure metal nitrate:

$$M^+ + NO_3^- \longrightarrow MNO_3(s) \tag{16.10}$$

Quite clearly, the quantities of reagents used in preparations of this type are critical. If too little silver nitrate is added as a precipitant, some of the chloride ions will remain in solution; evaporation will give a mixture of the metal nitrate and chloride. If too much precipitant is added, the product will be contaminated with the excess silver nitrate. Only if exactly equivalent quantities of the two solutions are mixed will a pure product be obtained on evaporation.

---

* Note that these are not net ionic equations. The extra ions (M^+, NO_3^- in equation 16.9; Cs^+, Cl^- in 16.11) are included to explain the formation of the solids MNO_3 and $CsCl$ in equations 16.10 and 16.12 respectively.

The method of preparation just described is applicable to a wide variety of inorganic syntheses. Metal bromides and iodides as well as chlorides are readily converted to the corresponding nitrates, since AgBr and AgI, like AgCl, are insoluble in water. Soluble sulfates can be converted to other salts by taking advantage of the insolubility of $BaSO_4$. For example, cesium chloride, CsCl, can be prepared from cesium sulfate by adding an equivalent amount of barium chloride, filtering off the precipitated $BaSO_4$, and evaporating:

precipitation:

$$2\ Cs^+ + SO_4^{-2} + Ba^{+2} + 2\ Cl^- \longrightarrow BaSO_4(s) + 2\ Cs^+ + 2\ Cl^- \quad (16.11)*$$

evaporation: $$2\ Cs^+ + 2\ Cl^- \longrightarrow 2\ CsCl(s) \quad (16.12)$$

16.7 WATER SOFTENING

A great many important industrial processes involve a precipitation reaction as an essential step. One of these is the "softening" of water. "Hardness" in water is brought about by certain cations, notably Ca^{+2} and Mg^{+2}. Hard water has many undesirable characteristics. Among these is its tendency to form a precipitate with soap, which we recognize as a slimy bathtub deposit. The most common type of soap has as its major ingredient sodium stearate, $NaC_{18}H_{35}O_2$, the sodium salt of an organic acid. The calcium and magnesium salts of this acid are insoluble in water; the reaction taking place when soap is used in hard water may be represented as:

$$M^{+2} + 2\ C_{18}H_{35}O_2^- \longrightarrow M(C_{18}H_{35}O_2)_2(s) \qquad M = Mg \quad or \quad Ca \quad (16.13)$$

This reaction continues until nearly all the Ca^{+2} or Mg^{+2} ions are removed from the water; only then does the soap become effective as a cleansing agent.

If the only disadvantage of hard water were its tendency to form a precipitate with soap, hardness would be a relatively minor problem. Detergents do not form a precipitate with Ca^{+2} and Mg^{+2} ions and hence are more effective sudsing agents in hard water. From an industrial standpoint, a more serious disadvantage of hard water is its tendency to form precipitates when heated or partially evaporated, as in a boiler. The nature of the precipitate depends upon the anions present in the hard water. One of the most common anions in surface water is the HCO_3^- ion, formed by the reaction of atmospheric carbon dioxide with water. When a solution containing Ca^{+2} and HCO_3^- ions is heated, a precipitate of calcium carbonate forms as a result of the reaction sequence:

$$2\ HCO_3^- + heat \longrightarrow CO_3^{-2} + CO_2(g) + H_2O$$
$$Ca^{+2} + CO_3^{-2} \longrightarrow CaCO_3(s)$$

$$\overline{2\ HCO_3^- + Ca^{+2} \longrightarrow CaCO_3(s) + CO_2(g) + H_2O \quad (16.14)}$$

The scale formed on tea kettles in the home is frequently of this type: it can be removed without too much trouble by treating with a weakly acidic solution such as vinegar.

---

* Note that these are not net ionic equations. The extra ions (M^+, NO_3^- in equation 16.9; Cs^+, Cl^- in 16.11) are included to explain the formation of the solids MNO_3 and CsCl in equations 16.10 and 16.12 respectively.

More serious problems arise if significant quantities of sulfate ion are present in hard water. In this case, heating may produce a precipitate of calcium sulfate, which, curiously enough, is less soluble at high than at low temperatures:

$$Ca^{+2} + SO_4^{-2} \longrightarrow CaSO_4(s) \tag{16.15}$$

Crystals of calcium sulfate are particularly likely to form in a steam boiler where water is constantly being vaporized, thereby increasing the concentrations of Ca^{+2} and SO_4^{-2} ions. The calcium sulfate deposits as a tightly adherent scale which lowers the heat conductivity of the boiler. Eventually, the deposition of calcium sulfate in boiler tubes may block the flow of water and lead to rupture of the pipes.

The various methods used to soften water have as their common objective the removal of Ca^{+2} and, to a lesser extent, Mg^{+2} ions. We shall consider two methods of water softening, both of which involve precipitation reactions.

Lime-Soda Method

One of the oldest methods of softening water, still used in a great many localities, involves the addition of two chemicals: slaked lime, $Ca(OH)_2$, and soda ash, Na_2CO_3. The purpose of adding the sodium carbonate is rather obvious; it acts as a source of carbonate ions for the removal of Ca^{+2} ions through the reaction:

$$Ca^{+2} + CO_3^{-2} \longrightarrow CaCO_3(s) \tag{16.16}$$

The function served by the lime is less apparent. Indeed, it might seem that the addition of $Ca(OH)_2$ to water in an attempt to remove Ca^{+2} ions would be a step in the wrong direction. As a matter of fact, lime is an effective water softener only when there are HCO_3^- ions in the hard water. To understand why this is the case, consider what happens when 1 mole of $Ca(OH)_2$ is added to water containing 2 moles of HCO_3^- ions:

dissolving of $Ca(OH)_2$: $Ca(OH)_2(s) \longrightarrow Ca^{+2} + 2 OH^-$

conversion of $HCO_3^- \longrightarrow CO_3^{-2}$: $2 HCO_3^- + 2 OH^- \longrightarrow 2 CO_3^{-2} + 2 H_2O$

precipitation of Ca^{+2} added: $Ca^{+2} + CO_3^{-2} \longrightarrow CaCO_3(s)$

overall reaction: $Ca(OH)_2(s) + 2 HCO_3^- \longrightarrow CaCO_3(s) + CO_3^{-2} + 2 H_2O$

$$\tag{16.17}$$

It may be noted from this reaction sequence that the lime furnishes the OH^- ions required to convert HCO_3^- ions in the water to CO_3^{-2} ions. The net effect of the addition of the lime, as represented by equation 16.17, is to form an extra mole of free CO_3^{-2} ions. These ions are then capable of removing a mole of Ca^{+2} ions originally present in the hard water. Thus, for every mole of $Ca(OH)_2$ added, a mole of Ca^{+2} ions is removed from the hard water. It is, of course, extremely important not to add too much $Ca(OH)_2$ to the water; any excess over that required for reaction 16.17 will tend to increase the Ca^{+2} ion concentration in the water.

The procedure used in softening hard water may be summarized as follows:
1. The water is first analyzed for Ca^{+2} and HCO_3^- ions.
2. Sufficient lime is added to give 1 mole of $Ca(OH)_2$ for every 2 moles of HCO_3^-. Every mole of $Ca(OH)_2$ added removes 1 mole of Ca^{+2} from the water.
3. Any Ca^{+2} ions remaining in the hard water are removed by adding soda ash, Na_2CO_3, in a 1:1 mole ratio.

Example 16.10. A sample of water is found on analysis to contain 0.0030 mole/l. of Ca^{+2}, 0.0040 mole/l. of HCO_3^- and 0.0010 mole/l. of SO_4^{-2}. Calculate the number of moles of $Ca(OH)_2$ and Na_2CO_3 that should be added to one liter of this water to soften it.

Solution. The first step is to add 1 mole of $Ca(OH)_2$ for every 2 moles of HCO_3^- present:

$$\text{no. moles } Ca(OH)_2 = 0.0040/2 = 0.0020 \text{ mole } Ca(OH)_2$$

This removes an equal amount, 0.0020 mole, of Ca^{+2} from the water, leaving in one liter of the water:

$$(0.0030 - 0.0020) \text{ mole} = 0.0010 \text{ mole of } Ca^{+2}$$

Consequently, it is necessary to add 0.0010 mole of Na_2CO_3 to the water.

Ion Exchange

The lime-soda method of water softening has gradually lost favor because of its many economic disadvantages. The water, before treatment, must be analyzed for Ca^{+2} and HCO_3^- ions; the amounts of lime and soda added must be carefully controlled, and the calcium carbonate formed must be removed from the water by filtration or settling. All of these processes are time-consuming and expensive.

The so-called *ion exchange* method of water softening suffers from none of these drawbacks. The water need not be analyzed, reagents need not be added in specified amounts, and there is no precipitate to be removed. Moreover, the method is applicable to large or small-scale operations; ion exchangers can be used to treat the water supply of a home, a factory, or an entire city.

The ion-exchange process makes use of a class of substances known collectively as zeolites. A typical zeolite particle, which looks much like a grain of sand, contains the four elements sodium, silicon, aluminum, and oxygen. The atoms of aluminum, silicon, and oxygen are bonded into a vast anionic network similar in structure to such macromolecular solids as quartz. The negative charge of the network is compensated for by a large number of Na^+ ions, located in "corridors" or "cages" within the anionic lattice. Many zeolites of different and rather complicated empirical formulas ($NaAlSi_3O_8$, $NaAlSi_2O_6$, and so on) occur in nature; others have been synthesized in the laboratory.

If pure water is passed through a zeolite column, nothing spectacular happens. The crystals themselves contain far too many atoms to dissolve in water; the small Na^+ ions cannot dissolve since this would leave behind an unstable anionic network carrying a large negative charge. However, if the water coming in contact with the zeolite contains ions, the situation is quite different. Some of the positive ions in the water change positions with the sodium ions in the lattice. With Ca^{+2} ions, the exchange that takes place may be represented by the equation:

$$Ca^{+2} + 2 NaZ(s) \longrightarrow CaZ_2(s) + 2 Na^+ \qquad (16.18)$$

in which Z represents a small portion of the anionic lattice. The net effect of this process is the replacement of Ca^{+2} ions responsible for hardness with unobjectionable Na^+ ions. This, of course, is precisely what happens in the lime-soda process when Na_2CO_3 is added to hard water; the difference is that in the ion-exchange process there is no precipitate to filter off since the Ca^{+2} ions are incorporated into the zeolite lattice.

An ion-exchange column slowly loses its effectiveness as the Na^+ ions in the lattice are replaced by Ca^{+2} ions. To rejuvenate the column, it is necessary to reverse

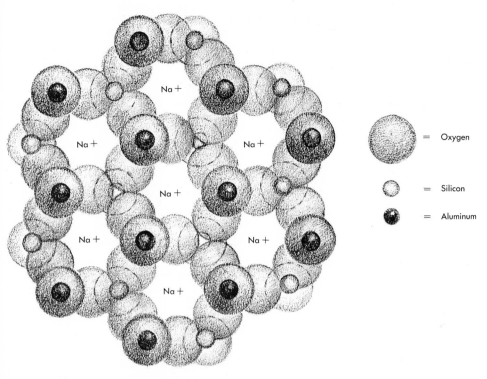

FIGURE 16.3 Structure of zeolite, $NaAlSiO_4$.

reaction 16.18, replacing Ca^{+2} ions with Na^+ ions:

$$2 \, Na^+ + CaZ_2(s) \longrightarrow Ca^{+2} + 2 \, NaZ(s)$$

The simplest way to do this is to pass a concentrated solution of sodium chloride through the column. With a properly designed column, this is the only type of maintenance required—an occasional flushing with a concentrated brine solution.

The type of ion-exchange column we have described, which replaces positive ions in water with Na^+ ions, is referred to as a cation exchanger. Zeolites can be developed to replace positive ions with any desired cation. For example, if the zeolite framework contains K^+ ions, these ions will be substituted for the cations in the water passed through the column. By the proper use of cation-exchangers, it is possible to convert salts of one metal to the corresponding salts of a different metal. If one runs a solution of NaCl through a zeolite containing K^+ ions, a solution of KCl results. By reversing the procedure, i.e., running a KCl solution through a sodium ion exchanger, potassium chloride can be converted to sodium chloride.

Synthetic zeolites have been developed for anion exchange. A column packed with particles in which Cl^- ions are trapped in a cationic network can be used to substitute Cl^- ions for the anions originally present in a water solution. Suppose, for example, that a solution containing nitrate ions is passed through a chloride exchanger. As a result of the reaction:

$$NO_3^- + RCl(s) \longrightarrow RNO_3(s) + Cl^- \quad (R = \text{portion of cationic network.}) \quad (16.19)$$

Cl^- ions are substituted for NO_3^- ions and a metal nitrate is transformed into the corresponding chloride.

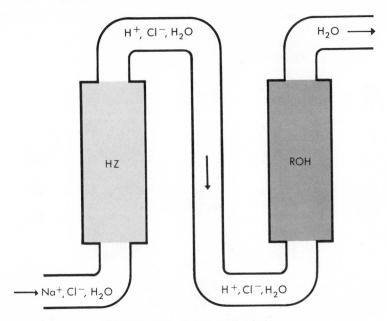

FIGURE 16.4 A deionizing column.

By combining a cationic with an anionic exchanger, it is possible to develop an apparatus known as a **deionizer** which completely removes the ions from a sample of water. The water is first passed through a cation exchanger which replaces cations with H^+ ions. The water leaving this column is then passed through an anion exchange column in which OH^- ions are substituted for the negative ions present. The hydroxide ions produced by the anion exchanger react with the hydrogen ions formed in the first column to give water. If a solution of sodium chloride is passed through a two-stage exchanger of this type, the reactions taking place may be represented as:

cation exchange: $Na^+ + HZ(s) \longrightarrow NaZ(s) + H^+$

anion exchange: $Cl^- + ROH(s) \longrightarrow RCl(s) + OH^-$

$$H^+ + OH^- \longrightarrow H_2O$$

overall reaction: $Na^+ + Cl^- + HZ(s) + ROH(s) \longrightarrow NaZ(s) + RCl(s) + H_2O$

$$(16.20)$$

Such a combination of ion-exchange columns produces water comparable in purity to distilled water. Indeed, such deionizers have replaced stills in a great many teaching and industrial laboratories.

16.8 SUMMARY

One of the simplest reactions that can occur when solutions of two different electrolytes are mixed is that of precipitation, in which a cation from one solution combines with an anion of the other solution to give a water-insoluble product. A typical reaction of this type is that which takes place when a solution of $Ba(NO_3)_2$ is added to a solution of K_2SO_4; a white precipitate of $BaSO_4$ forms. In writing an equation to represent this reaction, only the participating ions are included:

$$Ba^{+2} + SO_4^{-2} \longrightarrow BaSO_4(s)$$

In order to decide whether or not a precipitation reaction will occur under a particular set of conditions, one must know something about the relative solubilities of the compounds involved. The solubilities of ionic compounds are difficult to predict from first principles. While it is true that compounds formed between ions of high charge density, such as HgS and $NiCO_3$, tend to be among the least soluble, there are a great many other structural factors which influence solubility. Some of these factors are outlined in Section 16.2; the fact that they frequently operate in opposite directions makes it particularly difficult to estimate solubilities of ionic compounds. For this reason, empirical solubility rules (Table 16.1) are extremely helpful in predicting the results of precipitation reactions.

Quantitative predictions concerning the direction and extent of precipitation reactions are based on the use of a particular type of equilibrium constant known as the solubility product. Consider, for example, the case of calcium carbonate, for which $Ksp = 5 \times 10^{-9}$. If one mixes very dilute solutions containing Ca^{+2} and CO_3^{-2} at such concentrations that (conc. Ca^{+2}) $\times$ (conc. CO_3^{-2}) $< 5 \times 10^{-9}$, no reaction occurs. If, on the other hand, the concentration product exceeds 5×10^{-9}, a precipitate forms, removing enough ions from solution to reach the equilibrium condition: $[Ca^{+2}] \times [CO_3^{-2}] = 5 \times 10^{-9}$. By adding a sufficient excess of one ion, it is often possible to reduce the concentration of the other ion to an extremely low value. One can, for example, by adding 1 M $CaCl_2$ to a solution of K_2CO_3, reduce the CO_3^{-2} ion concentration to 5×10^{-9} M.

Precipitation reactions are particularly useful in analytical chemistry. They may be employed in qualitative analysis to separate one ion from another. One might, for example, separate Cl^- ions from NO_3^- ions in solution by adding Ag^+ to obtain a precipitate of AgCl. In quantitative analysis, one can often determine the amount of a particular ion in solution by a titration involving a precipitation reaction. The amount of Cl^- ion in a water solution or a water-soluble solid can be determined by measuring the volume of a solution of $AgNO_3$ of known concentration required to react exactly with it.

The inorganic chemist makes frequent use of precipitation reactions in preparing compounds. This method can be applied to the preparation of soluble as well as insoluble compounds; $Ni(NO_3)_2$, for example, can be made by treating $NiCl_2$ with an equivalent amount of $AgNO_3$, filtering off the AgCl, and evaporating the remaining solution.

Of the many industrial applications of precipitation reactions, only one has been discussed in this chapter; the softening of water by the removal of Ca^{+2} and Mg^{+2} ions. The classical lime-soda treatment achieves this by precipitating these ions as $CaCO_3$ and $Mg(OH)_2$. A simpler way to obtain the same result is to pass the water through an ion-exchange column, which substitutes less objectionable Na^+ ions for the cations in the hard water.

PROBLEMS

16.1   Write net ionic equations for the reactions, if any, that occur when 0.1 M solutions of the following ionic compounds are mixed.

a. $AgNO_3$ and KCl

b. $Pb(NO_3)_2$ and Na_2SO_4

f. $SbCl_3$ and Na_2S

g. $CuSO_4$ and KOH

   c. KNO_3 and $NaClO_3$
   d. NH_4Cl and $Hg_2(NO_3)_2$
   e. $FeCl_3$ and NaF

   h. Na_2CO_3 and $Ba(NO_3)_2$
   i. $ZnSO_4$ and BaS
   j. $Pb(NO_3)_2$ and KI

16.2 Calculate the total number of moles of each ion in the following solutions.
   a. 520 ml. of 3.0 M NaI
   b. 2.00 ml. of 0.15 M $BaCl_2$
   c. 1.30 l. of 0.960 M Li_2SO_4
   d. 160 ml. of 0.220 M $Al_2(SO_4)_3$

16.3 Calculate the number of moles of $Fe(OH)_2$ formed and the number of moles of each ion remaining in solution when 1.20 l. of 0.380 M $FeCl_2$ is added to 1.50 l. of 0.460 M $NaOH$.

16.4 Calculate the number of moles and concentration of each ion remaining in solution when 212 cc. of 0.352 M KOH is mixed with 616 cc. of 0.219 M $NaCl$ solution.

16.5 Why is it so difficult to predict from first principles whether or not a given electrolyte will be soluble in water?

16.6 Suggest an explanation for the fact that:
   a. High-melting ionic compounds tend to be less soluble in water than low-melting compounds of similar structure.
   b. Phosphates are generally less soluble in water than nitrates.
   c. $BaSO_4$ is less soluble in water than $MgSO_4$.
   d. CuS is less soluble in water than CaS.
   e. Ammonium salts are generally soluble in water.

16.7 Given the following solubilities, calculate the corresponding values of Ksp.
   a. $BaCO_3$: 3×10^{-5} mole/l. b. $BaSO_4$: 7×10^{-3} g./l. c. SrF_2: 1.0×10^{-3} mole/l.

16.8 From the Ksp values given in Table 16.5, calculate:
   a. The solubility of $Mg(OH)_2$, in moles per liter.
   b. The solubility of $PbCO_3$, in grams per liter.
      $AgCrO_4$
16.9 State whether or not precipitates will form under the following conditions.
   a. 0.10 M $AgNO_3$ is added to tap water in which the concentration of Cl^- is 1.0×10^{-5} M.
   b. Enough $AgNO_3$ is added to a 0.10 M solution of Na_2CrO_4 to make $[Ag^+] = 1 \times 10^{-3}$ M.
   c. 100 ml. of 0.10 M $Pb(NO_3)_2$ is added to 900 ml. of 0.010 M $NaCl$.
   d. 10 ml. of 0.010 M $Ca(NO_3)_2$ is added to 40 ml. of 0.010 M Na_2SO_4.

16.10 If Ag^+ is slowly added to a solution 0.10 M in Na_2CrO_4:
   a. At what concentration of Ag^+ does a precipitate start to form?
   b. When $[Ag^+] = 1 \times 10^{-4}$ M, what percentage of the CrO_4^{-2} is left in solution?
   c. What concentration of Ag^+ will be required to precipitate 99 per cent of the CrO_4^{-2}?

16.11 A solution is 0.10 M in Cl^- and 0.010 M in CrO_4^{-2}. If Ag^+ ions are slowly added:
   a. What is the precipitate which forms first?
   b. What is the concentration of the first ion when the second ion starts to precipitate? On the basis of your answers to (a) and (b), suggest why CrO_4^{-2} ion might serve as a suitable indicator for the titration of Cl^- with Ag^+.

16.12 How many moles of $AgBr$ will dissolve in 5 l. of 0.02 M KBr solution?

16.13 What would you observe when the following experiments are carried out in the laboratory?
   a. A 1.0 M solution of $NaCl$ is added to a saturated solution of $PbCl_2$.
   b. Concentrated HCl (12 M) is added to a saturated solution of $NaCl$ (solubility = 5.3 M).
   c. A 4.0 M solution of $NaOH$ is added to a saturated solution of $NaCl$.
   d. A 0.10 M solution of KBr is added to a saturated solution of $AgBr$.

16.14 Neither of the following statements is entirely valid in the form given. Explain why this is the case and rephrase the statements to make them correct.
  a. Of two slightly soluble electrolytes, the one with the larger Ksp value is the more soluble in water.
  b. In dilute solution, the product (conc. Ag^+) × (conc. Cl^-) is approximately equal to 1.6×10^{-10}.

16.15 A student analyzes a solid mixture for S^{-2} ions by adding excess $Cu(NO_3)_2$ solution and weighing the precipitated CuS. He finds that a 0.500 g. sample yields 0.618 g. of CuS. Calculate the percentage of S^{-2} in the mixture.

16.16 A student determines the percentage of Br^- in a mixture by weighing out 0.582 g., dissolving in 15 cc. of water, and titrating with 0.154 M $AgNO_3$ solution. 32.0 ml. of this solution are required. What is the percentage of Br^- in the mixture?

16.17 Develop a scheme, based on Table 16.1, to analyze qualitatively for the following ions (cf. Example 16.9).
  a. Ag^+, Ca^{+2}, Na^+ b. Pb^{+2}, Ni^{+2}, Mg^{+2} c. Cl^-, SO_4^{-2}

16.18 Explain why, in the scheme of cation analysis described in Section 16.5, Pb^{+2} often precipitates in group 2, even though an excess of HCl has been added to precipitate the group 1 ions.

16.19 A student, before analyzing a group 1 unknown, runs through the separation scheme on a solution prepared by mixing equal volumes of 0.10 M $AgNO_3$, $Pb(NO_3)_2$, and $Hg_2(NO_3)_2$. To precipitate the group 1 cations, he adds enough HCl to give a Cl^- ion concentration of 0.02 M. Later on in the analysis, he obtains positive tests for Ag^+ and Hg_2^{+2} but not for Pb^{+2}. Explain what happened, using the Ksp values for AgCl, $PbCl_2$, and Hg_2Cl_2.

16.20 Describe, in some detail, how the following conversions could be accomplished by means of precipitation reactions.
  a. $RbCl \rightarrow RbNO_3$ b. $CuSO_4 \rightarrow CuCl_2$ c. $LiCl \rightarrow LiClO_3$ d. $RaI_2 \rightarrow RaCl_2$

16.21 Water softening consists essentially of the removal of Ca^{+2} and Mg^{+2}. Yet, in the lime-soda process, more Ca^{+2} ions are added to the water in the form of $Ca(OH)_2$. Explain why this is done.

16.22 Write balanced equations for:
  a. The removal of Mg^{+2} salts from water, using the zeolite NaZ.
  b. The removal of dissolved $CaCl_2$ by passing water through successive columns containing an anion exchanger (ROH) and a cation exchanger (HZ).
  c. The regeneration of a cation exchange column packed with a resin of formula HZ which has been used to remove K^+ salts from water.

16.23 A municipal water supply contains the following ions in the indicated concentrations. Calculate the number of moles of Na_2CO_3 and $Ca(OH)_2$ that must be added to one liter of the water to soften it most economically.
  a. 1.0×10^{-3} M Ca^{+2} and 2.0×10^{-3} M HCO_3^-
  b. 1.0×10^{-3} M Ca^{+2}, 1.0×10^{-3} M HCO_3^-, 1.0×10^{-3} M Cl^-
  c. 2.0×10^{-4} M Ca^{+2}, 2.0×10^{-4} M SO_4^{-2}

*16.24 A certain zeolite column is designed to remove 10 per cent of the Ca^{+2} ions in hard water per foot length of column. If the water originally contains a Ca^{+2} concentration of 1.0×10^{-3} M, through how long a column must it pass to lower the $[Ca^{+2}]$ to 5.0×10^{-4} M?

*16.25 A student, in testing for group 1 cations, works with a precipitate containing approximately one tenth of a gram of $PbCl_2$.
  a. How much water must be added to this precipitate if it is to be completely dissolved by heating to 100°C (solubility $PbCl_2$ at 100°C = 33 g./l.)?
  b. What volume of 0.10 M Na_2CrO_4 solution must be added to the solution formed in (a) to precipitate 99 per cent of the Pb^{+2}?

*16.26 Referring to a laboratory manual on qualitative analysis, work out flow sheets similar to that shown in Example 16.9 for the separation of:
   a. Ag^+, Cu^{+2}, and Al^{+3} c. Hg_2^{+2}, Fe^{+3}, and Ca^{+2}
   b. Cu^{+2}, Bi^{+3}, and Sb^{+3} d. Cl^-, I^-, and SCN^-

*16.27 According to the Debye-Hückel theory (Chapter 13), the solubility of AgCl(s) in a solution of a 1 : 1 electrolyte of concentration c should be related to its solubility in pure water (S_0) by the expression:

$$S = S_0/f$$

in which f, known as the activity coefficient, is given by the relation:

$$\log_{10} f = -0.50 \ (c)^{1/2}$$

Using these equations, calculate the ratio S/S_0 for AgCl in KNO_3 solutions of concentrations 0.0010, 0.0050, 0.010, 0.020, and 0.040 M and compare to the values listed in Table 16.4.

17 | ACIDS AND BASES

In earlier chapters, we have, on occasion, referred to the properties and structures of acids and bases. In Chapter 13, for example, the electrical conductivities of water solutions of acids and bases were touched on briefly.

We shall now expand the discussion of acids and bases, paying particular attention to the properties of acidic and basic water solutions, the nature of the ions responsible for these properties and the methods by which such solutions are formed. We shall find that a quantitative study of the equilibria involved in acidic and basic water solutions enables one to distinguish between strong and weak acids or bases. Furthermore, one can, from structural considerations, predict the relative acidic or basic strengths of different compounds.

17.1 PROPERTIES OF ACIDIC AND BASIC WATER SOLUTIONS

Acidic solutions may be identified in various ways. Their characteristic sour taste reveals itself in vinegar, lemon juice, and rhubarb pie. It has been reliably reported that solutions of nitric, sulfuric, and hydrochloric acids also have a sour taste. A safer way to determine whether or not a solution is acidic is to test its behavior with zinc or magnesium; these metals, when added to acidic water solutions, evolve hydrogen. A more sensitive test involves the addition of carbonate ions to the solution; sodium carbonate or calcium carbonate, in the presence of an acid, react to give off bubbles of carbon dioxide.

Perhaps the simplest experimental test for acidity utilizes the fact that certain organic dyes change color when placed in acidic solution. One of the most familiar of these so-called acid-base indicators is litmus, which turns red in acidic solution. Interestingly enough, acidic solutions bring about the same color change in grape juice. For various reasons, litmus is more widely used than grape juice to test for acidity in the general chemistry laboratory.

Basic water solutions, like acidic solutions, possess certain characteristic properties. Anyone who uses liquid detergents or household ammonia in cleaning is aware of the soapy feeling of these solutions. This property of basic solutions, which depends upon dissolving a surface layer of skin, is possessed to an even greater extent by a solution of lye. A more satisfactory way of finding out whether or not a water solution is basic is to add to it a small amount of a solution of a magnesium salt such as $MgCl_2$. The formation of a white precipitate of magnesium hydroxide indicates the presence of a base.

The color of indicators is affected by basic as well as acidic solutions; litmus turns blue in a basic solution. The organic dye phenolphthalein, which is colorless in acid or neutral solution, takes on a bright red color in the presence of a base.

17.2   IONS PRESENT IN ACIDIC AND BASIC WATER SOLUTIONS

Basic Solution: OH⁻

The characteristic properties of basic water solutions are those of a specific ion, common to all such solutions, the hydroxide ion, OH^-. It is this particle which is responsible for the soapy feeling, the effect on indicators, and the formation of a precipitate with magnesium salts.

$$Mg^{+2} + 2\ OH^- \longrightarrow Mg(OH)_2(s) \tag{17.1}$$

Acidic Solution: the Hydrated Proton or Hydronium Ion

The ion responsible for the properties common to acidic solutions may be described most simply as a proton or H^+ ion. It is this ion which accounts for the reaction of acidic water solutions with zinc or with carbonate ions:

$$Zn(s) + 2\ H^+ \longrightarrow Zn^{+2} + H_2(g) \tag{17.2}$$

$$CO_3^{-2} + 2\ H^+ \longrightarrow CO_2(g) + H_2O \tag{17.3}$$

The sour taste of acidic solutions and their effect on the color of indicators can also be attributed to the presence of protons.

The proton, like all other positive ions of high charge density, is hydrated in water solution. Although the exact number of water molecules associated with a proton is difficult to determine, it is generally supposed that the principal species present is the hydronium ion, H_3O^+. This ion consists of a proton joined by a coordinate covalent bond to the oxygen atom of a water molecule:

$$\left[\begin{array}{c} H \\ | \\ H\!-\!\overset{..}{O}\!-\!H \end{array}\right]^+$$

The hydronium ion bears a close resemblance to the ammonium ion, NH_4^+, previously discussed; both are derived from a neutral molecule (H_2O, NH_3) by the addition of a proton. The existence of the hydronium ion has been demonstrated in the solid $HClO_4 \cdot H_2O$, which has a structure (H_3O^+, ClO_4^- ions) entirely analogous to that of ammonium perchlorate, NH_4ClO_4.

In discussing acidic water solutions, we shall often find it convenient to ignore the hydration of the proton and write it as the simple, unhydrated ion, H^+. In writing mathematical expressions or chemical equations to explain the properties of acidic water solutions, the use of the H_3O^+ ion seldom contributes to understanding. Compare, for example, equations 17.2 and 17.3 to the corresponding equations written with H_3O^+ as a reactant:

$$Zn(s) + 2\ H_3O^+ \longrightarrow Zn^{+2} + H_2(g) + 2\ H_2O \qquad (17.2')$$
$$CO_3^{-2} + 2\ H_3O^+ \longrightarrow CO_2(g) + 3\ H_2O \qquad (17.3')$$

On the other hand, in writing equations to describe the way in which acidic solutions are formed, we shall often find it helpful to use the H_3O^+ ion.

Equilibrium Between H+ and OH−: Concept of Kw

In any water solution, regardless of what other species may be present, there will always be an equilibrium between H_2O molecules, H^+ ions and OH^- ions, expressed most simply as:

$$H_2O \rightleftharpoons H^+ + OH^- \qquad (17.4)$$

The corresponding equilibrium constant takes the form:

$$K = \frac{[H^+] \times [OH^-]}{[H_2O]} \quad \text{or} \quad K \times [H_2O] = [H^+] \times [OH^-] \qquad (17.5)$$

Equation 17.5 may be simplified by taking account of the fact that in any dilute water solution, the concentration of water molecules greatly exceeds that of any other species and hence remains nearly constant. In other words, the entire left-hand side of equation 17.5 is a constant, independent of the concentration of H^+ or OH^- ions, and we may write:

$$Kw = [H^+] \times [OH^-]$$

in which Kw, referred to as the ionization constant of water, is written in place of the expression $K \times [H_2O]$ in equation 17.5.

The numerical value of the ionization constant of water may be determined experimentally in any of several ways. At 25°C, it has the value 1.0×10^{-14}; that is:

$$Kw = [H^+] \times [OH^-] = 1.0 \times 10^{-14} \qquad (17.6)$$

Equation 17.6 indicates that in any water solution the concentrations of H^+ and OH^- are inversely proportional to each other. Accordingly, a 100-fold increase in the concentration of one of these ions produces a 100-fold decrease in the concentration of the other (Table 17.1).

It is possible to distinguish between neutral, basic, and acidic solutions on the basis of the relative concentrations of H^+ and OH^-. A *neutral solution* may be defined as one in which the concentrations of these two ions are equal:

$$[H^+] = [OH^-] = (10^{-14})^{1/2} = 10^{-7}\ M$$

Chemically pure water is, of course, exactly neutral.

An *acidic solution* may be defined as one in which the concentration of H^+ ions exceeds that of OH^- ions:

$$[H^+] > [OH^-], \qquad [H^+] > 10^{-7}\ M, \qquad [OH^-] < 10^{-7}\ M$$

The three solutions listed at the left of Table 17.1 are acidic; in each of these solutions, litmus takes on a red color.

TABLE 17.1

Solution	No. 1	No. 2	No. 3	No. 4	No. 5	No. 6	No. 7
H^+	10^{-1}	10^{-3}	10^{-5}	10^{-7}	10^{-9}	10^{-11}	10^{-13}
OH^-	10^{-13}	10^{-11}	10^{-9}	10^{-7}	10^{-5}	10^{-3}	10^{-1}
pH	1	3	5	7	9	11	13

In *basic solutions*, there are more OH^- ions than H^+ ions:

$$[OH^-] > [H^+], \qquad [OH^-] > 10^{-7} \text{ M}, \qquad [H^+] < 10^{-7} \text{ M}$$

Solutions 5 to 7 in Table 17.1 are basic; they show to a steadily increasing extent the properties characteristic of basic water solutions.

17.3   pH

We have seen that it is possible, by specifying the concentration of H^+ ion, to describe quantitatively the acidity or basicity of a solution. Sörenson, in 1909, proposed an alternative method of accomplishing this purpose, making use of a term known as pH, defined as follows:

$$pH \equiv -\log [H^+] = \log 1/[H^+] \tag{17.7}$$

The pH of a great many common solutions (Table 17.2) ranges from 1 to 14, corresponding to a variation in hydrogen ion concentration of 10^{-1} to 10^{-14} M. For such solutions, it is perhaps more convenient to express acidity in terms of pH rather than H^+ ion concentration, thereby avoiding the use of either small fractions or negative exponents.

It follows from the definition that the lower the pH, the more acidic a solution is. A solution of pH 1 has a H^+ ion concentration 100 times greater than one of pH 3. Conversely, a solution of pH 13 has an OH^- ion concentration 100 times greater than one of pH 11 (Table 17.1). Just as it is possible to differentiate between neutral, basic, and acidic solutions on the basis of the concentrations of H^+ or OH^- ions, so one can make this distinction in terms of pH:

Know {
neutral solution: $[H^+] = 10^{-7}$ M,   pH $= 7.0$
acidic solution: $[H^+] > 10^{-7}$ M,   pH < 7.0
basic solution: $[H^+] < 10^{-7}$ M,   pH > 7.0
}

TABLE 17.2 pH OF COMMON MATERIALS

Vinegar	2.2	Human urine	7.4
Apples	3	Sea water	8.3
Sauerkraut	3.5	0.1 M $NaHCO_3$	8.4
Tomatoes	4.2	Satd $Mg(OH)_2$	10.5
Carrots	5	0.1 M NH_3	11.2
Saliva	5.7–7.1	0.1 M Na_2CO_3	11.6
Milk	6.6	Satd $Ca(OH)_2$	12.1

Example 17.1 illustrates the calculation of the pH of water solutions and the inter-relationships between pH, [H⁺], and [OH⁻].

Example 17.1. Calculate:
   a. The pH of a solution 0.020 M in H^+.
   b. The pH of a solution 0.0025 M in OH^-.
   c. The [H^+] and [OH^-] in sea water, pH = 8.3.

Solution
   a. $[H^+] = 0.020$ M $= 2.0 \times 10^{-2}$ M
      By definition,

$$pH = -\log [H^+] = -\log (2.0 \times 10^{-2}) = -(0.3 - 2.0) = -(-1.7) = 1.7$$

   b. $[OH^-] = 0.0025$ M $= 2.5 \times 10^{-3}$ M
      To calculate [H^+], we make use of the relation:

$$[H^+] \times [OH^-] = 1.0 \times 10^{-14}$$

$$[H^+] = \frac{1.0 \times 10^{-14}}{[OH^-]}$$

   Hence, $[H^+] = \dfrac{1.0 \times 10^{-14}}{2.5 \times 10^{-3}} = 0.40 \times 10^{-11} = 4.0 \times 10^{-12}$ M

   In this case, for illustrative purposes, let us use the relation:

$$pH = \log 1/[H^+]$$

$$pH = \log \frac{1}{4 \times 10^{-12}} = \log (0.25 \times 10^{12}) = \log (2.5 \times 10^{11}) = (0.4 + 11.0) = 11.4$$

   c. Using the relation pH = $\log 1/[H^+]$, we have:

$$\log 1/[H^+] = 8.3$$

   Taking antilogs of both sides:

   $1/[H^+] = 2.0 \times 10^8,$ or $[H^+] = \dfrac{1}{2.0 \times 10^8} = 0.5 \times 10^{-8} = 5.0 \times 10^{-9}$ M

   To obtain the concentration of OH^-, we again make use of the relation:

$$[H^+] \times [OH^-] = 1.0 \times 10^{-14}$$
$$(5.0 \times 10^{-9}) \times [OH^-] = 1.0 \times 10^{-14}$$

   Solving: $[OH^-] = \dfrac{1.0 \times 10^{-14}}{5.0 \times 10^{-9}} = 0.20 \times 10^{-5} = 2.0 \times 10^{-6}$ M

The pH, [H^+] or [OH^-] of a water solution may be determined experimentally in a number of different ways, one of which involves the use of acid-base indicators, which undergo a color change over a rather narrow pH range. By the judicious use of one or more of the indicators listed in Table 17.3, it is possible to bracket quite accurately the pH or [H^+] of a solution. For example, if one finds that a solution gives a red (basic) color with phenolphthalein but a yellow (acidic) color with alizarine yellow, its pH must be approximately 10.

A universal indicator made by combining several acid-base indicators, may be used to determine, within about one unit, the pH of any water solution. This mixture of indicators shows an entire spectrum of colors ranging from deep red in strongly acidic solution to deep blue in strongly basic solution. A similar principle is used to prepare pH paper, widely used to test the acidity of biological fluids. Strips of paper impregnated with a mixture of indicators can be designed to give gradations of color over a wide or narrow pH range.

TABLE 17.3   COLOR CHANGE INTERVALS OF INDICATORS

Name	pH Interval	Acid color	Base color
Methyl violet	0–2	yellow	violet
Methyl yellow	2.9–4.0	red	yellow
Methyl orange	3.1–4.4	red	yellow
Methyl red	4.4–6.2	red	yellow
Bromthymol blue	6.0–8.0	yellow	blue
Thymol blue	8.0–9.6	yellow	blue
Phenolphthalein	8.5–10.0	colorless	red
Alizarine yellow	10.1–12.0	yellow	red

In discussing the relative basicities of different water solutions, the term pOH, analogous to pH, is sometimes used.

$$pOH \equiv -\log\,[OH^-]$$

Thus, the pOH of a solution 0.10 M in OH^- is 1.0; a solution 10^{-4} M in OH^- has a pOH of 4, and so on. Since, for any water solution:

$$[H^+] \times [OH^-] = 1.0 \times 10^{-14}$$

$$-\log\,[H^+] - \log\,[OH^-] = 14$$

or, $$pH + pOH = 14$$

17.4   FORMATION OF ACIDIC WATER SOLUTIONS

The formation of an acidic water solution results from the *transfer of a proton from a solute particle to a water molecule.* The hydronium ion, H_3O^+, formed by such a transfer, gives the solution its characteristic acidic properties. The proton donor may be a neutral molecule, a negative ion, or a positive ion. We shall now consider examples of each of these three types of proton transfer.

Transfer of a Proton from a Neutral Solute Molecule

The molecular compounds which react with water to produce acidic solutions can be subdivided into three major categories:

1. The binary hydrogen compounds of the 6A and 7A elements. The reaction of gaseous hydrogen chloride with water is representative:

$$HCl(g) + H_2O \longrightarrow Cl^- + H_3O^+ \qquad (17.8)$$

In electron dot notation, this equation takes the form

$$H:\overset{\cdot\cdot}{\underset{\cdot\cdot}{Cl}}: \; + \; H:\overset{\cdot\cdot}{O}:H \longrightarrow (:\overset{\cdot\cdot}{\underset{\cdot\cdot}{Cl}}:)^- + \left[H:\overset{\cdot\cdot}{\underset{H}{O}}:H \right]^+$$

from which it can be seen that a proton has been transferred from the chlorine atom of an HCl molecule to the oxygen atom of a water molecule. Although this transfer probably takes place directly, it may be easier to visualize if one imagines that the reaction occurs in two steps: (a) The rupture of the covalent bond in the HCl molecule to form a proton and a Cl^- ion:

$$H:\overset{..}{\underset{..}{Cl}}: \longrightarrow H^+ + (:\overset{..}{\underset{..}{Cl}}:)^-$$

and (b) The acceptance of the proton by one of the unshared electron pairs of the oxygen atom of a water molecule to form the hydronium ion.

$$H^+ + H:\overset{..}{\underset{..}{O}}:H \longrightarrow \left[H:\overset{..}{\underset{\overset{\displaystyle |}{H}}{O}}:H \right]^+$$

2. Certain molecular compounds in which a hydrogen atom is joined by a covalent bond to an oxygen atom which is in turn bonded to a nonmetal atom. The electronic structures of several such compounds, known collectively as oxyacids, are shown in Table 17.4. Three of the most important oxyacids are perchloric acid, $HClO_4$, nitric acid, HNO_3, and sulfuric acid, H_2SO_4. The reactions of these compounds with water are entirely analogous to that of HCl (cf. equations 17.9 to 17.11 with equation 17.8).

$$HClO_4(l) + H_2O \longrightarrow ClO_4^- + H_3O^+ \qquad (17.9)$$

$$HNO_3(l) + H_2O \longrightarrow NO_3^- + H_3O^+ \qquad (17.10)$$

$$H_2SO_4(l) + H_2O \longrightarrow HSO_4^- + H_3O^+ \qquad (17.11)$$

In each case, a proton is transferred from an oxygen atom of the oxyacid molecule to the oxygen atom of a water molecule. The products are an oxyanion (ClO_4^-, NO_3^-, HSO_4^-) and a hydronium ion.

TABLE 17.4 ELECTRONIC STRUCTURES OF SOME OXYACIDS

Acid	Formula	Structure	Acid	Formula	Structure
Perchloric acid	$HClO_4$	$H-O-Cl-O$ (with :O: above and :O: below)	Nitric acid	HNO_3	$H-O-N=O$ (with :O: above)
Hypochlorous acid	$HClO$	$H-O-Cl-O$	Phosphoric acid	H_3PO_4	$H-O-P-O-H$ (with :O: above and :O: below, H at bottom)
Sulfuric acid	H_2SO_4	$H-O-S-O-H$ (with :O: above and :O: below)	Acetic acid	$HC_2H_3O_2$	$H-O-C-CH_3$ (with :O: below)
Sulfurous acid	H_2SO_3	$H-O-S-O-H$ (with :O: below)			

3. Certain nonmetal oxides, which react with water to form oxyacids. Typical of these compounds is sulfur trioxide, which reacts with water to form sulfuric acid:

$$SO_3(g) + H_2O(l) \longrightarrow H_2SO_4(l) \tag{17.12}$$

The sulfuric acid produced by this process reacts further with water to form an acidic solution according to equation 17.11.

Nonmetal oxides which react with water to form oxyacids are often referred to as **acid anhydrides**. Several such compounds are listed in Table 17.5, along with the corresponding oxyacids and oxyanions which they form in water solution. It may be noted that in each set of related species (acid anhydride, oxyacid, and oxyanion), the central, nonmetal atom is in the same oxidation state. For example, sulfur has an oxidation number of $+6$ in SO_3, H_2SO_4, and HSO_4^-; chlorine has an oxidation number of $+7$ in Cl_2O_7, $HClO_4$, and ClO_4^-.

TABLE 17.5   ACID ANHYDRIDES,
OXYACIDS, AND OXYANIONS

Acid Anhydride	Oxyacid	Oxyanion
Cl_2O_7	$HClO_4$	ClO_4^-
Cl_2O	$(HClO)$*	ClO^-
SO_3	H_2SO_4	HSO_4^-
SO_2	(H_2SO_3)	HSO_3^-
N_2O_5	HNO_3	NO_3^-
P_2O_5	H_3PO_4	$H_2PO_4^-$
CO_2	(H_2CO_3)	HCO_3^-

* The oxyacids enclosed in parentheses can not be isolated from water solution as pure compounds. Indeed, in the case of carbonic acid, H_2CO_3, the evidence for its existence is fragmentary at best.

Transfer of a Proton from a Negative Ion (HSO_4^-, HSO_3^-, $H_2PO_4^-$)

The hydrogen sulfate ion, HSO_4^-, produced by the reaction of sulfuric acid with water, retains a hydrogen atom attached to oxygen which can be transferred to a water molecule.

$$HSO_4^- + H_2O \longrightarrow SO_4^{-2} + H_3O^+ \tag{17.13}$$

As a result of this reaction, solutions containing the HSO_4^- ion are acidic. A solution of $NaHSO_4$, for example, gives an acidic test with litmus. Solutions of sodium hydrogen sulfite, $NaHSO_3$, and sodium dihydrogen phosphate, NaH_2PO_4, are also acidic.

$$HSO_3^- + H_2O \longrightarrow SO_3^{-2} + H_3O^+ \tag{17.14}$$

$$H_2PO_4^- + H_2O \longrightarrow HPO_4^{-2} + H_3O^+ \tag{17.15}$$

It should be pointed out that many negative ions of this type, in which a hydrogen atom is joined to oxygen, do *not* react with water to give an acidic solution. A solution of sodium hydrogen carbonate, $NaHCO_3$, is actually basic to litmus, for reasons which we shall discuss later in this chapter.

Transfer of a Proton from a Positive Ion (NH_4^+, Al^{+3}, Transition Metal Ions)

It is experimentally observed that concentrated solutions of NH_4Cl, $ZnCl_2$ and $Al_2(SO_4)_3$ are acidic. Solutions of these salts, for example, give a red color with methyl red, indicating a pH of 5 or lower. Clearly, the negative ion in these solutions (Cl^-, SO_4^{-2}) is incapable of accounting for their acidity. By elimination, it must be the positive ion (NH_4^+, Zn^{+2}, Al^{+3}) which is responsible for the acidic properties. The question arises how a positive ion is able to react with water to form a H_3O^+ ion and thereby produce an acidic solution.

Proton transfer from a positive ion to a water molecule is most readily visualized with the ammonium ion, NH_4^+, in which a proton originally bonded to nitrogen can shift to the more strongly electronegative oxygen atom:

$$NH_4^+ + H_2O \longrightarrow NH_3 + H_3O^+ \tag{17.16}$$

This reaction accounts for the acidic properties of water solutions of such ammonium salts as NH_4Cl, NH_4NO_3, and $(NH_4)_2SO_4$.

In order to explain why a solution of zinc chloride is acidic, it must be realized that the cationic species in this solution is not a bare Zn^{+2} ion but rather a hydrated ion, $Zn(H_2O)_4^{+2}$, in which four water molecules are joined to the central ion by coordinate covalent bonds. Proton transfer can occur from one of the water molecules in the complex ion to a solvent water molecule:

$$Zn(H_2O)_4^{+2} + H_2O \longrightarrow Zn(H_2O)_3(OH)^+ + H_3O^+ \tag{17.17}$$

It may be noted that one result of the proton transfer is the conversion of a water molecule bound up in the hydrated zinc ion to a hydroxide ion, OH^-.

The acidity of a water solution of aluminum sulfate may be explained similarly:

$$Al(H_2O)_6^{+3} + H_2O \longrightarrow Al(H_2O)_5(OH)^{+2} + H_3O^+ \tag{17.18}$$

The reaction of a cation such as Al^{+3} or Zn^{+2} with water is probably best represented as a proton transfer from the hydrated ion $(Zn(H_2O)_4^{+2}, Al(H_2O)_6^{+3})$ to a solvent water molecule (equations 17.17, 17.18). It is possible, however, to look at these reactions from a somewhat different viewpoint which, although less exact, may be easier to visualize. Let us consider the effect of the cation upon the position of the equilibrium:

$$H_2O \rightleftharpoons H^+ + OH^-$$

A positive ion such as Zn^{+2} can be expected to strongly attract an OH^- ion, leading to the formation of an associated species most simply represented as $Zn(OH)^+$.

$$Zn^{+2} + OH^- \longrightarrow Zn(OH)^+$$

Such a process, by consuming OH^- ions, shifts the equilibrium to produce an excess of H^+ ions, making the solution acidic. The overall process may be summarized by adding the two equations to give

$$Zn^{+2} + H_2O \longrightarrow Zn(OH)^+ + H^+ \tag{17.17'}$$

Comparison of equations 17.17 and 17.17' reveals their essential similarity. In both cases, the ion responsible for acidic properties, H_3O^+ or H^+, is a product of the reaction. The only difference between the two equations is in the formulas written for the metal ion species $(Zn(H_2O)_4^{+2}$ vs. Zn^{+2}, $Zn(H_2O)_3(OH)^+$ vs. $Zn(OH)^+)$.

The reaction of the Al^{+3} ion with water may be represented similarly (cf. equation 17.18):

$$Al^{+3} + H_2O \longrightarrow Al(OH)^{+2} + H^+ \tag{17.18'}$$

17.5 STRONG AND WEAK ACIDS: Ka

Many of the reactions which we have been considering are reversible; that is, the proton transfer to a water molecule is incomplete. Consider, for example, the reaction of hydrogen fluoride with water:

$$HF + H_2O \rightleftharpoons F^- + H_3O^+ \tag{17.19}$$

It is found experimentally that only a comparatively small fraction of the HF molecules react; the concentrations of H_3O^+ and F^- ions are low compared to that of undissociated HF molecules. One can calculate (Example 17.4) that in a 0.10 M solution of hydrogen fluoride, the concentration of F^- or H_3O^+ ions is only about 0.008 mole/l., corresponding to 8 per cent ionization.

Species such as HF, which react reversibly with water to form H_3O^+ ions are referred to as **weak acids.** Substances which undergo complete proton transfer upon addition to water are known as **strong acids.** Relatively few strong acids are known; the common acids in this category include three hydrogen halides (HCl, HBr, HI) and three oxyacids $(HClO_4, HNO_3, H_2SO_4)$. In contrast, there are a large number of weak acids, including many molecular species (HF, HClO, H_3PO_4, $HC_2H_3O_2$), all the acidic anions $(HSO_4^-, HSO_3^-, H_2PO_4^-)$ and all the acidic cations $(NH_4^+, Al^{+3}, Zn^{+2})$.

Experimentally, one can distinguish between strong and weak acids by measuring:

1. The conductivities of their water solutions. Strong acids behave as strong electrolytes; solutions of weak molecular acids such as hydrofluoric acid or acetic acid are relatively poor electrical conductors.

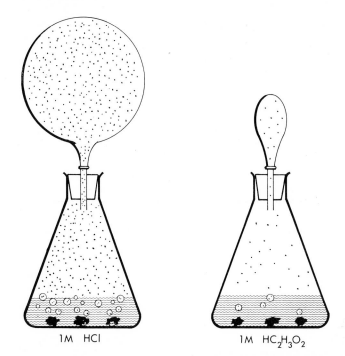

1M HCl   1M HC₂H₃O₂

FIGURE 17.1   Reaction of zinc with acids. Rate of reaction depends upon concentration of H⁺, and hence, at a given molarity, on the strength of the acid.

2. The colligative properties of their water solutions. The freezing point of a 0.10 M solution of HCl is almost exactly the same as that of 0.10 M NaCl. In contrast, the freezing point of a 0.10 M solution of acetic acid is comparable to that of 0.10 M solutions of nonelectrolytes such as sugar or urea.

3. The pH of their water solutions. A 0.10 M solution of perchloric acid has a pH of 1, indicating complete dissociation. The pH of a 0.10 M solution of HF is about 2.1, indicating that relatively few of the HF molecules are ionized.

4. The rate of reaction with metals such as zinc or magnesium (Figure 17.1).

The equilibria between species in solutions of weak acids can be handled quantitatively in a manner entirely analogous to that developed previously in connection with gases (Chapter 14) and slightly soluble salts (Chapter 16). In particular, it is possible to derive an expression for the equilibrium constant, or the ionization constant, of a weak acid in water. We shall now consider how this equilibrium constant, symbol Ka, is expressed; how it is determined experimentally; and how it is used in practical calculations.

Expression for Ka

Consider a weak acid reacting with water as follows:

$$HX + H_2O \rightleftharpoons H_3O^+ + X^-$$

For this equilibrium, one can write:

$$K = \frac{[H_3O^+] \times [X^-]}{[HX] \times [H_2O]} \quad \text{or} \quad K \times [H_2O] = \frac{[H_3O^+] \times [X^-]}{[HX]}$$

It has been pointed out previously that the term $[H_2O]$ is itself a constant. For simplicity, $[H_3O^+]$ can be replaced by $[H^+]$. Consequently, the foregoing equation can be written:

$$Ka = \frac{[H^+] \times [X^-]}{[HX]} \tag{17.20}$$

in which Ka, known as the ionization constant of the weak acid, is independent of the concentrations of H^+, X^-, or HX. Equation 17.20 is, of course, the expression one would arrive at directly by starting with the simplified equation for the dissociation of HX:

$$HX \rightleftharpoons H^+ + X^-$$

To illustrate the form taken by Ka for various weak acids, consider the three particles HF, HSO_4^-, and NH_4^+:

$$HF \rightleftharpoons H^+ + F^- \qquad Ka = \frac{[H^+] \times [F^-]}{[HF]}$$

$$HSO_4^- \rightleftharpoons H^+ + SO_4^{-2} \qquad Ka = \frac{[H^+] \times [SO_4^{-2}]}{[HSO_4^-]}$$

$$NH_4^+ \rightleftharpoons H^+ + NH_3 \qquad Ka = \frac{[H^+] \times [NH_3]}{[NH_4^+]}$$

Experimental Determination of Ka

One approach to the experimental determination of the ionization constant of a weak acid is illustrated by Example 17.2.

Example 17.2. When 1.00 mole of HF is dissolved to give one liter of solution, the equilibrium concentration of H^+ is found, through the use of indicators, to be 2.6×10^{-2} M. Calculate the ionization constant of HF.

Solution. The expression for Ka is:

$$HF \rightleftharpoons H^+ + F^- \qquad Ka = \frac{[H^+] \times F^-]}{[HF]}$$

To obtain the numerical value of Ka, the equilibrium concentrations of H^+, F^-, and HF must be known. That of H^+ has been determined to be 2.6×10^{-2} M. From the expression for the dissociation of HF, it is evident that 1 mole of F^- is formed for every mole of H^+. In a solution of HF, in which the only source of H^+ and F^- ions is the HF molecule (the $[H^+]$ produced by the dissociation of water is so small in comparison that it may be neglected), the concentrations of F^- and H^+ must be equal:

$$[H^+] = [F^-] = 2.6 \times 10^{-2} \text{ M}$$

To obtain the equilibrium concentration of HF, we note that for every mole of H^+ formed, a mole of HF is consumed. The concentration of HF remaining at equilibrium can be obtained by subtracting the concentration of H^+ formed, 2.6×10^{-2} M, from the original concentration of HF, 1.00 M:

$$[HF] = 1.00 \text{ M} - 2.6 \times 10^{-2} \text{ M} = 1.00 \text{ M} - 0.026 \text{ M} = 0.97 \text{ M}$$

Substituting:

$$Ka = \frac{[H^+] \times [F^-]}{[HF]} = \frac{(2.6 \times 10^{-2}) \times (2.6 \times 10^{-2})}{(0.97)} = 7.0 \times 10^{-4}$$

The procedure illustrated by Example 17.2 can be applied to any weak acid. Two quantities must be measured: the original concentration of the weak acid and the equilibrium concentration of H^+.

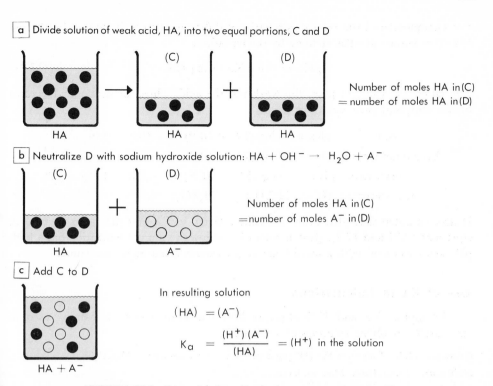

FIGURE 17.2 Determination of ionization constant of weak acid.

A somewhat simpler method of measuring the ionization constant of a weak acid HX:

$$Ka = \frac{[H^+] \times [X^-]}{[HX]}$$

makes use of the fact that in a solution in which $[X^-] = [HX]$, $Ka = [H^+]$. What is done is to design an experiment in such a way that this condition is realized, measure the concentration of H^+ and equate it to Ka. The way in which the solution containing equal quantities of HX and X^- is produced is shown schematically in Figure 17.2. This method, in contrast to the one just described, does not require a knowledge of the original concentration of weak acid. Furthermore, it is far less sensitive to the presence of acidic or basic impurities in the reagents used to prepare the solutions (see Chapter 18, Section 18.6).

Interpretation of Ka

The numerical value of the ionization constant of an acid gives a quantitative measure of its strength. The stronger the acid, the larger will be the value of Ka. From Table 17.6, p. 419, it can be deduced that acetic acid, $HC_2H_3O_2$ (Ka = 1.8×10^{-5}) is weaker than hydrofluoric acid (Ka = 7.0×10^{-4}), but stronger than boric acid (Ka = 5.8×10^{-10}). In equimolar solutions of two different acids, the concentration of H^+ or the fraction of the weak acid dissociated will be greater for the acid of larger ionization constant.

Comparison of the relative strengths of different acids is facilitated by the use of a term known as pKa, defined by the equation:

$$pKa \equiv -\log Ka = \log 1/Ka \qquad (17.21)$$

The larger the value of pKa, the weaker is the acid. Thus, for acetic acid, hydrofluoric acid, and boric acid. We have:

$$\text{acetic acid: } pKa = -\log (1.8 \times 10^{-5}) = -(0.3 - 5.0) = 4.7$$
$$\text{hydrofluoric acid: } pKa = -\log (7.0 \times 10^{-4}) = -(0.8 - 4.0) = 3.2$$
$$\text{boric acid: } pKa = -\log (5.8 \times 10^{-10}) = -(0.8 - 10.0) = 9.2$$
$$\text{acid strength: } HF > HC_2H_3O_2 > H_3BO_3$$

It may be noted that pKa bears the same relation to Ka that pH bears to H^+ (cf. equations 17.21 and 17.7). Just as a solution of low H^+ ion concentration has a high pH, so a weak acid with a small ionization constant has a high pKa value.

Use of Ka in Calculations

Examples 17.3 and 17.4 illustrate how ionization constants can be used in calculations involving solutions of weak acids.

Example 17.3. Calculate the $[H^+]$ and pH of a 1.0 M solution of $HC_2H_3O_2$.
Solution. From Table 17.6, we have:

$$HC_2H_3O_2 \rightleftharpoons H^+ + C_2H_3O_2^- \qquad Ka = \frac{[H^+] \times [C_2H_3O_2^-]}{[HC_2H_3O_2]} = 1.8 \times 10^{-5}$$

Let us represent by x the unknown equilibrium concentration of H^+. It is evident from the equation for the dissociation of acetic acid that a mole of acetate ions is produced for every mole of H^+ formed; neglecting the small amount of H^+ produced from the water, the concentration of $C_2H_3O_2^-$ must also be x. The formation of x moles of H^+ consumes an equal number of moles of acetic acid; the equilibrium concentration of $HC_2H_3O_2$ must then be $1.0 - x$. Substituting:

$$\frac{(x)(x)}{1.0 - x} = 1.8 \times 10^{-5}$$

This equation could be rearranged to the form: $x^2 + bx + c = 0$ and solved for x, using the quadratic formula. Such a procedure is tedious and, in this case, unnecessary. Since $HC_2H_3O_2$ is a weak acid, only slightly dissociated in water, the equilibrium concentration of $HC_2H_3O_2$, $1.0 - x$, must be very nearly equal to its original concentration before dissociation, 1.0 M. Making this approximation, we obtain:

$$\frac{x^2}{1.0} = 1.8 \times 10^{-5} \qquad x^2 = 1.8 \times 10^{-5} = 18 \times 10^{-6}$$

Solving for x by extracting the square root of both sides:

$$x = [H^+] = 4.2 \times 10^{-3}$$

To find the pH: $pH = -\log H^+ = -\log (4.2 \times 10^{-3}) = -(0.6 - 3.0) = 2.4$
The fact that the concentration of H^+, 0.0042, is so much less than the original concentration of $HC_2H_3O_2$, justifies the approximation made earlier, i.e., $1.0 - x = 1.0$. In general, the expression for Ka is rarely valid to better than ± 5 per cent. Consequently, in the expression:

$$Ka = \frac{x^2}{a - x}$$

Ka = large : strong acid

Ka = small : weak

pKa = "

in which $x = [H^+]$, a = concentration of weak acid prior to dissociation, one is justified in setting (a − x) equal to a, provided this approximation does not introduce an error of more than about 5 per cent. In practice, it is ordinarily simplest to make the approximation, calculate x, and compare to a. If the value of x thus obtained is less than 5 per cent of a (in this problem, x is 0.42 per cent of a), the approximation is valid. If x is greater than about 5 per cent of a, one can go back to the original equation and solve by means of the quadratic formula or, alternatively, the method of successive approximations can be used (Example 17.4).

Example 17.4. Calculate the $[H^+]$ of a 0.100 M HF solution.

Solution. Proceeding as in Example 17.3, we have:

$$HF \rightleftharpoons H^+ + F^-$$

$$Ka = \frac{[H^+] \times [F^-]}{[HF]} = 7.0 \times 10^{-4}$$

Letting $[H^+] = x$:

$$\frac{(x)(x)}{0.100 - x} = 7.0 \times 10^{-4}$$

If we make the same approximation as before, i.e., $0.10 - x \approx 0.10$:

$$x^2 = 7.0 \times 10^{-5} = 70 \times 10^{-6}$$

$$x = [H^+] = 8.4 \times 10^{-3}$$

We note that, in this case, the calculated concentration of H^+ is greater than 5 per cent of the original concentration of undissociated acid:

$$\frac{8.4 \times 10^{-3}}{1.0 \times 10^{-1}} = 0.084 = 8.4\%$$

To refine our calculation, we can make a second approximation, more nearly valid than the first. Let us use the value of $[H^+]$ just calculated to obtain a better approximation to the true value of $[HF]$.

If $[H^+] = 8.4 \times 10^{-3}$, then $[HF] = 0.100 - 8.4 \times 10^{-3}$
$$= 0.100 - 0.0084 = 0.092 \text{ M}$$

Substituting this value for $[HF]$ into the expression for Ka, we have:

$$\frac{x^2}{0.092} = 7.0 \times 10^{-4}$$

$$x^2 = 6.4 \times 10^{-5} = 64 \times 10^{-6}$$

$$x = [H^+] = 8.0 \times 10^{-3}$$

This value is, of course, more nearly equal to the true $[H^+]$ in the solution, since 0.092 M is a better approximation to the equilibrium concentration of HF than was 0.100 M. If we are still not satisfied, we can attempt a further refinement, using the value of $[H^+]$ just calculated to obtain a still more accurate value for $[HF]$. If we do, we find that $[HF]$ remains unchanged at 0.092 M, i.e.:

if $[H^+] = 8.0 \times 10^{-3}$,   then $[HF] = 0.100 - 0.0080 = 0.092$ M

This means that if we were to solve again for $[H^+]$ we would get the same answer. In other words, we "have gone about as far as we can go."

The method of successive approximations just described is a very useful one for working problems of this type involving the dissociation of weak acids. In the vast majority of cases, it will be found that a first approximation (i.e., (a − x) ≈ a) will be sufficient. Occasionally, it will be necessary, as it appeared to be in this example, to make one further refinement. Very seldom does one need to go beyond this.

17.6   FORMATION OF BASIC WATER SOLUTIONS

We have seen that it is the hydroxide ion which is responsible for the basic properties of water solutions. When the concentration of OH^- ions exceeds 10^{-7} M, the solution is basic. Such a situation can arise in two quite different ways. The hydroxides of the 1A and 2A metals, produce hydroxide ions directly when added to water. These compounds contain hydroxide ions in the solid state; when they dissolve in water, the OH^- ions are liberated to form a strongly basic solution.

$$NaOH(s) \longrightarrow Na^+ + OH^- \tag{17.22}$$

$$Ca(OH)_2(s) \longrightarrow Ca^{+2} + 2\ OH^- \tag{17.23}$$

Magnesium hydroxide, unlike calcium hydroxide, is quite insoluble in water. A water solution or suspension of $Mg(OH)_2$, known as milk of magnesia, is only slightly basic because of the low concentration of OH^- ions. Consequently, milk of magnesia is effective in "neutralizing excess stomach acidity." Sodium hydroxide, lye, is even more effective but has the undesirable side effect of dissolving the stomach lining and other parts of the digestive tract. The hydroxides of aluminum and the transition metals, like magnesium hydroxide, are too insoluble to give high concentrations of OH^- ions in solution.

The oxides of the 1A and 2A metals react with water to form the corresponding hydroxides. Consequently, the addition of such compounds as CaO or Li_2O to excess water yields a basic solution. The reaction of calcium oxide may be represented as:

$$CaO(s) + H_2O \longrightarrow Ca(OH)_2(s)$$
$$\underline{Ca(OH)_2(s) \longrightarrow Ca^{+2} + 2\ OH^-}$$
$$CaO(s) + H_2O \longrightarrow Ca^{+2} + 2\ OH^- \tag{17.24}$$

With lithium oxide, the net reaction is:

$$\tfrac{1}{2}\ Li_2O(s) + \tfrac{1}{2}\ H_2O \longrightarrow Li^+ + OH^- \tag{17.25}$$

In electron dot notation, these reactions may be represented in terms of a proton transfer from a water molecule to an oxide ion.

$$(:\overset{..}{\underset{..}{O}}:)^{-2} + H:\overset{..}{\underset{..}{O}}:H \longrightarrow 2\ (:\overset{..}{\underset{..}{O}}:H)^-$$

(Metal oxides such as CaO and Li_2O which react with water to give metal hydroxides are often referred to as **basic anhydrides.**)

A somewhat different way of forming hydroxide ions in solution is illustrated by the reaction of ammonia with water. The basicity of an aqueous solution of ammonia results from the following reversible reaction:

$$H\!-\!\overset{..}{N}\!-\!H + H\!-\!\overset{..}{\underset{..}{O}}\!-\!H \rightleftharpoons \left[H\!-\!\overset{H}{\underset{H}{N}}\!-\!H \right]^+ + (:\overset{..}{\underset{..}{O}}\!-\!H)^-$$

$$NH_3 + H_2O \rightleftharpoons NH_4^+ + OH^- \tag{17.26}$$

The weak base, ammonia, abstracts a proton from a water molecule, forming the weak acid, NH_4^+, and liberating an OH^- ion, which makes the solution basic.

Certain negative ions are also capable of abstracting a proton from a water molecule. A water solution of sodium fluoride is weakly basic because of the reversible reaction of the fluoride ion with water:

$$(:\ddot{F}:)^- + H—\ddot{O}—H \rightleftharpoons H—\ddot{F}: + (:\ddot{O}—H)^-$$

$$F^- + H_2O \rightleftharpoons HF + OH^- \qquad (17.27)$$

As equation 17.27 indicates, a molecule of the weak acid HF is formed as a by-product of the reaction. The reaction of the carbonate ion with water follows a similar path:

$$CO_3^{-2} + H_2O \rightleftharpoons HCO_3^- + OH^- \qquad (17.28)$$

accounting for the fact that a water solution of sodium carbonate is basic.

The reaction of the HCO_3^- ion with water is particularly interesting. Here, we have two competing processes, one the transfer of a proton from a water molecule to the HCO_3^- ion, which tends to make the solution basic

$$HCO_3^- + H_2O \longrightarrow H_2CO_3 + OH^- \qquad (17.29)$$

and the other the transfer of a proton from the HCO_3^- ion to the water molecule, which tends to make the solution acidic

$$HCO_3^- + H_2O \longrightarrow CO_3^{-2} + H_3O^+ \qquad (17.30)$$

It is found experimentally that reaction 17.29 occurs to a somewhat greater extent than reaction 17.30; a water solution of $NaHCO_3$ is slightly basic.

Competing reactions analogous to 17.29 and 17.30 can, of course, occur with any negative ion which has an ionizable hydrogen. In some cases (HCO_3^-, HS^-, $H_2BO_3^-$, HPO_4^{-2}, and so on), the net effect is to produce a basic solution; in others (HSO_4^-, HSO_3^-, $H_2PO_4^-$) proton transfer occurs predominantly in the opposite direction, from anion to water molecule, and the solution is acidic.

17.7 WEAK BASE EQUILIBRIA: Kb

Equilibria in water solutions of weak bases may be treated in a manner entirely analogous to that used with weak acids. Consider, for example, the ionization of ammonia:

$$NH_3 + H_2O \rightleftharpoons NH_4^+ + OH^- \qquad (17.31)$$

Following the argument outlined previously, one can arrive at the expression:

$$Kb = \frac{[NH_4^+] \times [OH^-]}{[NH_3]}$$

in which Kb represents the ionization constant of the weak base, ammonia. In a similar manner, for the equilibrium:

$$F^- + H_2O \rightleftharpoons HF + OH^- \qquad (17.32)$$

$$Kb = \frac{[HF] \times [OH^-]}{[F^-]}$$

The numerical value of Kb for reaction 17.32 can be determined experimentally in a manner entirely analogous to that used to determine Ka for the reaction of the weak acid HF with water.

$$Ka = \frac{[H^+] \times [F^-]}{[HF]}$$

In practice, if one of these quantities, Ka or Kb, is known, it is unnecessary to measure the other. If we multiply Ka by Kb

$$Ka \times Kb = \frac{[H^+] \times [F^-]}{[HF]} \times \frac{[HF] \times [OH^-]}{[F^-]}$$

we see that

$$Ka \times Kb = [H^+] \times [OH^-] = Kw = 1.0 \times 10^{-14} \qquad (17.33)$$

Thus, having established that Ka for HF is 7.0×10^{-4}, it follows that

$$Kb \text{ for } F^- = \frac{1.0 \times 10^{-14}}{7.0 \times 10^{-4}} = 0.14 \times 10^{-10} = 1.4 \times 10^{-11}$$

Equation 17.33 applies, of course, for any weak-acid, weak-base pair such as HF—F^- or NH_4^+—NH_3. The species F^- and NH_3 are sometimes referred to as the **conjugate bases** of the weak acids HF and NH_4^+; alternatively, HF and NH_4^+ may be regarded as the **conjugate acids** corresponding to the bases F^- and NH_3.

Just as it is convenient to define a quantity pKa by the equation:

$$pKa \equiv -\log Ka$$

so one can define the quantity pKb:

$$pKb \equiv -\log Kb$$

Here again, we find that the value of pKb is inversely related to the strength of the base; the higher the pKb value, the weaker the base.
Since:

$$Ka \times Kb = 1.0 \times 10^{-14}$$

it follows that:

$$pKa + pKb = 14$$

In other words, the sum of the pK values for a weak acid and its conjugate base is always equal to 14, just as the sum of the pH and pOH of a water solution is always exactly 14.

Calculations involving weak-base equilibria can be handled in a manner entirely analogous to that used with weak acids (cf. Examples 17.5 to 17.3).

Example 17.5. For a 0.10 M solution of NH_3 ($Kb = 1.8 \times 10^{-5}$), calculate:
    a. $[OH^-]$ b. $[H^+]$ c. Per cent of ionization.

Solution

    a. To determine $[OH^-]$, we first set up the expression for Kb:

$$NH_3 + H_2O \rightleftharpoons NH_4^+ + OH^- \qquad Kb = \frac{[NH_4^+] \times [OH^-]}{[NH_3]} = 1.8 \times 10^{-5}$$

If we let the equilibrium concentration of OH^- be x, it follows, using the approximations introduced in Example 17.3 that:

$$[OH^-] = [NH_4^+] = x \qquad [NH_3] = 0.10 - x \approx 0.10$$

Substituting in the expression for Kb:

$$\frac{(x)(x)}{0.10} = 1.8 \times 10^{-5}$$

Rearranging and solving, we obtain:

$$x^2 = 1.8 \times 10^{-6}; x = [OH^-] = 1.3 \times 10^{-3} \text{ M}$$

b. Since $[H^+] \times [OH^-] = 1.0 \times 10^{-14}$, we have:

$$[H^+] = \frac{1.0 \times 10^{-14}}{1.3 \times 10^{-3}} = 0.8 \times 10^{-11} = 8 \times 10^{-12} \text{ M}$$

c. Per cent of ionization $= \dfrac{[OH^-]}{\text{orig. conc. NH}_3} \times 100 = \dfrac{1.3 \times 10^{-3}}{0.10} \times 100 = 1.3\%$

Note that since the per cent of ionization is considerably less than 5 per cent, the approximation $0.10 - x = 0.10$ is justified.

TABLE 17.6 IONIZATION CONSTANTS OF WEAK ACIDS AND BASES

	Acid	Ka	pKa	Base	Kb	pKb
Acetic acid	$HC_2H_3O_2$	1.8×10^{-5}	4.7	$C_2H_3O_2^-$	5.6×10^{-10}	9.3
Ammonium ion	NH_4^+	5.6×10^{-10}	9.3	NH_3	1.8×10^{-5}	4.7
Benzoic acid	$HC_7H_5O_2$	6.6×10^{-5}	4.2	$C_7H_5O_2^-$	1.5×10^{-10}	9.8
Boric acid	H_3BO_3	5.8×10^{-10}	9.2	$H_2BO_3^-$	1.7×10^{-5}	4.8
Carbonic acid	H_2CO_3	4.2×10^{-7}	6.4	HCO_3^-	2.4×10^{-8}	7.6
	HCO_3^-	4.8×10^{-11}	10.3	CO_3^{-2}	2.1×10^{-4}	3.7
Formic acid	$HCHO_2$	2.1×10^{-4}	3.7	CHO_2^-	4.8×10^{-11}	10.3
Hydrocyanic acid	HCN	4.0×10^{-10}	9.4	CN^-	2.5×10^{-5}	4.6
Hydrofluoric acid	HF	7.0×10^{-4}	3.2	F^-	1.4×10^{-11}	10.8
Hydrogen sulfide	H_2S	1×10^{-7}	7	HS^-	1×10^{-7}	7
	HS^-	1×10^{-15}	15	S^{-2}	1×10^1	-1
Hypochlorous acid	$HClO$	3.2×10^{-8}	7.5	ClO^-	3.1×10^{-7}	6.5
Nitrous acid	HNO_2	4.5×10^{-4}	3.3	NO_2^-	2.2×10^{-11}	10.7
Phosphoric acid	H_3PO_4	7.5×10^{-3}	2.1	$H_2PO_4^-$	1.3×10^{-12}	11.9
	$H_2PO_4^-$	6.2×10^{-8}	7.2	HPO_4^{-2}	1.6×10^{-7}	6.8
	HPO_4^{-2}	1.7×10^{-12}	11.8	PO_4^{-3}	5.9×10^{-3}	2.2
Propionic acid	$HC_3H_5O_2$	1.4×10^{-5}	4.9	$C_3H_5O_2^-$	7.1×10^{-10}	9.1
Sulfurous acid	H_2SO_3	1.7×10^{-2}	1.8	HSO_3^-	5.9×10^{-13}	12.2
	HSO_3^-	5.6×10^{-8}	7.3	SO_3^{-2}	1.8×10^{-7}	6.7

17.8 RELATIVE STRENGTHS OF ACIDS AND BASES

Up to this point in our study of acids and bases, we have been concerned with the questions "how?" and "how many?". We have considered how acidic and basic water solutions are formed and how many H^+ or OH^- ions are produced from a given amount of reactant. We shall now turn our attention to the question "why?", i.e., why do certain substances act as acids in water solution while other substances behave as bases? We shall attempt to develop principles which will make it possible to predict the relative acid or base strengths of compounds of similar structure. Three different classes of substances will be considered: nonmetal hydrides, compounds containing O—H groups, and inorganic salts. Within each category, we shall be interested in relating basic or acidic properties to structure and bond type.

Hydrides of the 7A, 6A, and 5A Elements

The hydrides of the 7A elements (HF, HCl, HBr, HI) form acidic water solutions. All these compounds, with the exception of hydrogen fluoride, are completely ionized in water solution. To understand why hydrogen fluoride is a much weaker acid than the other hydrogen halides, it is convenient to imagine the reaction with water as being broken up into three steps:

(Step 1) Rupture of the covalent bond in the HX molecule to form hydrogen and halogen atoms

$$H:\ddot{X}: \longrightarrow H\cdot + \cdot\ddot{X}:$$

(Step 2) Electron transfer from a hydrogen to a halogen atom

$$H\cdot + :\ddot{X}: \longrightarrow H^+ + (:\ddot{X}:)^-$$

(Step 3) Proton transfer to a water molecule

$$H^+ + H:\ddot{O}:H \longrightarrow \left[H:\ddot{O}:H\atop \quad\ \ \ H\right]^+$$

The third step is, of course, the same for all of the hydrogen halides; Steps 1 and 2 differ depending upon the nature of X. We see then that the relative acid strengths of the hydrogen halides should depend upon two factors: (a) the ease with which the covalent bond in the HX molecule is broken, and (b) the attraction of the halogen atom for electrons.

It happens that in this series of compounds, it is the first factor which predominates. Hydrogen fluoride is a weak acid because of the large amount of energy (135 kcal./mole) required to break the HF bond. The bonds in HCl (103 kcal./mole), HBr (88 kcal./mole) and HI (71 kcal./mole) are considerably weaker.

The hydrogen compounds of the 6A elements (H_2S, H_2Se, H_2Te) are all weak acids in water solution. Acid strength in this series, as measured by the first ionization constant, increases from H_2S to H_2Te. This trend may be attributed to the decrease in the strength of the bond formed with hydrogen as one passes from sulfur to tellurium.

TABLE 17.7   ACID STRENGTHS OF 6A
HYDRIDES

	K_1	Bond Energy (kcal./mole)
H_2S	1×10^{-7}	H—S $= 81$
H_2Se	1.7×10^{-4}	H—Se $= 66$
H_2Te	2.3×10^{-3}	H—Te $= 59$

None of the binary hydrogen compounds of the elements to the left of the 6A elements in the periodic table acts as an acid in water solution. The 5A hydrides tend to accept protons from water molecules rather than donating them. The tendency to act as a base is greatest for the first member of the series, ammonia:

$$NH_3 + H_2O \rightleftharpoons NH_4^+ + OH^-$$

The hydrides of the other 5A elements are much less basic; phosphine (PH_3), arsine (AsH_3), and stibine (SbH_3) show little or no tendency to accept a proton from a water molecule. The phosphonium ion, PH_4^+, can be formed by reacting phosphine with a strong proton donor such as hydrogen iodide:

$$PH_3(g) + HI(g) \longrightarrow PH_4I(s) \qquad (17.34)$$

In water solution, the phosphonium ion acts as a strong acid, decomposing quantitatively to phosphine:

$$PH_4I(s) + H_2O \longrightarrow PH_3(g) + H_3O^+ + I^- \qquad (17.35)$$

Compounds Containing an O—H Group

When a compound of general formula MOH is added to water, the resulting solution may be either basic or acidic. If the bond joining the central atom to oxygen breaks, OH^- ions are produced:

$$MOH \longrightarrow M^+ + OH^- \qquad (17.36)$$

This process occurs with ionic compounds in which the bond between the central atom and oxygen is more ionic than that between oxygen and hydrogen. In particular, it is observed with the hydroxides of the strongly electropositive 1A and 2A metals.

If the bond joining oxygen to the central atom is less polar than that between oxygen and hydrogen, ionization of a quite different sort occurs. Here, it is the O—H bond that breaks, producing an acidic solution:

$$MOH \longrightarrow MO^- + H^+ \qquad (17.37)$$

The hydroxy compounds of the nonmetals, in which the central atom is more electronegative than hydrogen, ionize in this manner. These compounds, the oxyacids, include hypochlorous acid ($HOCl = ClOH$), nitric acid ($HNO_3 = NO_2OH$), and sulfuric acid ($H_2SO_4 = SO_2(OH)_2$).

Among the oxyacids ionizing via equation 17.37, it is found that:

1. In a series of acids containing the same central atom ($HClO$, $HClO_2$, $HClO_3$, $HClO_4$) acid strength increases with the oxidation number of the central atom.

2. In a series of acids of different elements, each of which is in the same oxidation state, acid strength increases with the electronegativity of the central atom.

TABLE 17.8 STRENGTH OF OXYACIDS

Variation with Oxidation Number					
Acid	Ka	Acid	Ka	Acid	Ka
$HClO_4$	10^7	H_2SO_4	very large	HNO_3	very large
$HClO_3$	large	H_2SO_3	1.7×10^{-2}	HNO_2	4.5×10^{-4}
$HClO_2$	1×10^{-2}			$H_2N_2O_2$	9×10^{-8}
$HClO$	3.2×10^{-8}				
Variation with Electronegativity					
Acid	Ka	Acid	Ka	Acid	Ka
$HClO$	3.2×10^{-8}	H_2SO_3	1.7×10^{-2}	HNO_3	very large
$HBrO$	2×10^{-9}	H_2SeO_3	3×10^{-3}	H_3PO_4	7.5×10^{-3}
HIO	5×10^{-13}	H_2TeO_3	6×10^{-6}	H_3AsO_4	5×10^{-3}

These two effects can be given a simple structural interpretation. As the central atom becomes more electronegative, the bonding electrons joining it to oxygen are withdrawn from the oxygen. The reduced electron density around the oxygen makes it easier for a positively charged particle, the proton, to break away. In a similar manner, an increase in the oxidation number of the central atom tends to withdraw electrons from the oxygen and weaken the O—H bond.

The first of the rules just quoted may be expanded to a general relationship applicable to a wide variety of oxyacids of quite different structures: **Acid strength increases with the number of unprotonated oxygen atoms in the molecule.**

The strong oxyacids are all ones in which there are three ($HClO_4$) or two (HNO_3, H_2SO_4, etc.) oxygens bonded to the central atom but not to hydrogen. Where this number is 1 as in H_3PO_4, HNO_2, or H_2SO_3, the acid is moderately weak, with an ionization constant in the vicinity of 10^{-2} to 10^{-6}. The weakest oxyacids are those such as $HClO$, $H_2N_2O_2$, or H_3BO_3, in which all the oxygen atoms are bonded to hydrogen.

It should be emphasized that the rule just stated applies only to *molecular* oxyacids. Oxyanions such as HSO_4^- and $H_2PO_4^-$ are much weaker acids than the molecules (H_2SO_4, H_3PO_4) from which they are derived. It is, as one would expect, more difficult to remove a proton from a negative ion than from a neutral molecule. The successive ionization constants of such acids as H_2SO_4 and H_3PO_4 which contain more than one ionizable hydrogen decrease in the approximate ratio $1:10^{-5}:10^{-10}$.

Hydrolysis of Salts

We have seen that the anions of weak acids (F^-, CO_3^{-2}, etc.) react with water to form OH^- ions; certain cations (such as NH_4^+, Al^{+3}, Zn^{+2}) react with water to form H^+ ions. The term **hydrolysis** is often used to describe these reactions. Depending upon the relative extents of hydrolysis of anion and cation, a given salt solution may be acidic, basic, or neutral.

Anions.   The extent to which a negative ion hydrolyzes is inversely related to the strength of its conjugate acid. The chloride ion, derived from the strong acid HCl, does not undergo hydrolysis and hence does not affect the pH of a water solution. On the other hand, the fluoride ion reacts with water to form the weak acid HF and liberate OH^- ions, thereby producing a basic solution. One of the most strongly hydrolyzed ions is the sulfide ion, derived from the extremely weak acid, HS^-. A water solution of sodium sulfide has about the same pH as a solution of sodium hydroxide of the same concentration.

$$Cl^- + H_2O \longleftarrow HCl + OH^- \qquad Kb = 0$$
$$F^- + H_2O \rightleftharpoons HF + OH^- \qquad Kb = 1.4 \times 10^{-11}$$
$$S^{-2} + H_2O \longrightarrow HS^- + OH^- \qquad Kb = 1 \times 10^1$$

Cations.   The extent of hydrolysis of a metal ion is directly related to its charge density. The Al^{+3} ion (charge $= +3$, r $= 0.50$ Å) is strongly hydrolyzed to give an acidic solution. The Na^+ ion (charge $= +1$, r $= 0.95$ Å) has no detectable effect on the pH of water. The influence of charge density can be explained in terms of the attraction of a positive ion for OH^- ions. The higher the charge density of the cation, the greater will be this attraction and hence the greater the extent of hydrolysis.

Salts. The effect of a given salt upon the pH of water can be deduced if the relative extents of hydrolysis of the two ions involved are known. Four categories may be distinguished:

1. *Neither ion hydrolyzes.* Solution is *neutral*. NaCl, K_2SO_4, $Ba(NO_3)_2$.
2. *Only the cation hydrolyzes.* Solution is *acidic*. NH_4Cl, $ZnSO_4$, $Al(NO_3)_3$.
3. *Only the anion hydrolyzes.* Solution in *basic*. NaF, K_2CO_3, BaS.
4. *Both ions hydrolyze.* Solution may be acidic, neutral, or basic, depending upon the relative extents of hydrolysis of cation and anion. In the case of NH_4F, the NH_4^+ ion ($Ka = 5.6 \times 10^{-10}$) is more strongly hydrolyzed than the F^- ion ($Kb = 1.4 \times 10^{-11}$), and the solution is acidic. A solution of $NH_4C_2H_3O_2$ is neutral,

TABLE 17.9 HYDROLYSIS OF IONS

Anions		Cations	
Negligible	Appreciable	Negligible	Appreciable
ClO_4^-	F^-	K^+	NH_4^+
I^-	Ac^-	Na^+	Al^{+3}
Br^-	CN^-	Li^+	
Cl^-	PO_4^{-3}	Ba^{+2}	
NO_3^-	CO_3^{-2}	Ca^{+2}	transition metal ions
SO_4^{-2}	S^{-2}	Sr^{+2}	
	etc.		

since the NH_4^+ ion ($Ka = 5.6 \times 10^{-10}$) and the $C_2H_3O_2^-$ ion ($Kb = 5.6 \times 10^{-10}$) are hydrolyzed to the same extent. A solution of $(NH_4)_2S$ is distinctly basic; the S^{-2} ion ($Kb = 1 \times 10^1$) is much more strongly hydrolyzed than the NH_4^+ ion.

17.9 GENERAL CONCEPTS OF ACIDS AND BASES

Throughout this chapter, our discussion of acids and bases has centered around water solutions. We have considered an acid to be a substance which upon addition to water forms hydrated protons (H_3O^+). A substance which produces hydroxide ions in water solution has been referred to as a base. Although most of the reactions dealt with in general chemistry take place in water solution, it will be instructive to consider two acid-base concepts which are applicable to nonaqueous systems as well. One of these was proposed independently in 1923 by Brönsted in Denmark and Lowry in England. The other was suggested that same year by the American physical chemist, G. N. Lewis.

Brönsted-Lowry Concept

According to the Brönsted-Lowry picture, any process in which there is a proton transfer from one species to another is classified as an acid-base reaction. The species which gives up (*donates*) a *proton* is referred to as an *acid*; the molecule or ion which *accepts* a *proton* is called a *base*. To illustrate, consider the reactions which occur when hydrogen chloride is added to water (17.38), ammonia (17.39), or a solution of sodium acetate (17.40).

$$HCl + H_2O \longrightarrow Cl^- + H_3O^+ \tag{17.38}$$

$$HCl + NH_3 \longrightarrow Cl^- + NH_4^+ \tag{17.39}$$

$$HCl + C_2H_3O_2^- \longrightarrow Cl^- + HC_2H_3O_2 \tag{17.40}$$

In each of these reactions, the HCl molecule is acting as an acid; it is giving up a proton to form a chloride ion. The water molecule in reaction 17.38, the ammonia molecule in 17.39, and the acetate ion in 17.40 are all acting as bases, accepting protons to yield a hydronium ion (H_3O^+), an ammonium ion (NH_4^+), and an acetic acid molecule ($HC_2H_3O_2$) respectively.

In principle, any molecule or ion which contains a covalently-bonded hydrogen atom can act as a Brönsted acid. For example, the NH_4^+ ion, which is capable of giving up a proton to form an NH_3 molecule, acts as an acid in reacting with water or OH^- ions:

$$NH_4^+ + H_2O \rightleftharpoons NH_3 + H_3O^+ \tag{17.41}$$

$$NH_4^+ + OH^- \rightleftharpoons NH_3 + H_2O \tag{17.42}$$

Similarly, the hydrated zinc ion, $Zn(H_2O)_4^{+2}$, in contact with these same species, acts as a Brönsted acid:

$$Zn(H_2O)_4^{+2} + H_2O \rightleftharpoons Zn(H_2O)_3(OH)^+ + H_3O^+ \tag{17.43}$$

$$Zn(H_2O)_4^{+2} + OH^- \rightleftharpoons Zn(H_2O)_3(OH)^+ + H_2O \tag{17.44}$$

In the Brönsted-Lowry sense, it is entirely possible for a substance to act as a base in one reaction and an acid in another. The only requirement is that the substance be capable of either donating or accepting a proton. By far the most important species in this category is the water molecule, which can either accept a proton to yield a H_3O^+ ion or donate a proton to form an OH^- ion. In reactions 17.38, 17.41, and 17.43, water is acting as a Brönsted base in accepting a proton. In reactions 17.45 and 17.46, in which the other species present is an avid proton acceptor (NH_3, CN^-), the water molecule behaves as an acid:

$$H_2O + NH_3 \rightleftharpoons OH^- + NH_4^+ \tag{17.45}$$

$$H_2O + CN^- \rightleftharpoons OH^- + HCN \tag{17.46}$$

Another species showing this behavior is the HCO_3^- ion, which can either give up a proton to form the CO_3^{-2} ion or accept a proton to form the H_2CO_3 molecule. (cf. equations 17.29, 17.30).

By studying acid-base equilibria in water solution, it is possible to establish the relative abilities of different species to donate or accept protons. The results of such a study are summarized in Table 17.10. The acids, listed in the left-hand column, are arranged in order of decreasing tendency to give up protons. Conversely, the ability of their conjugate bases to accept protons increases as one moves down the table.

The first six compounds listed in Table 17.10 ($HClO_4$, HI, HBr, HCl, HNO_3, and H_2SO_4) are strong acids in the conventional sense. They react quatitatively via proton transfer with water or any stronger base such as the NH_3 molecule or the OH^- ion. Their conjugate bases (ClO_4^-, I^-, Br^-, Cl^-, NO_3^-, HSO_4^-) show no tendency to accept protons from any of the acids listed. The species listed below the H_3O^+ ion are weak acids. As pointed out previously, such species as HSO_4^-, HF, and NH_4^+ react reversibly with water to produce a relatively low concentration of H_3O^+ ions:

$$HSO_4^- + H_2O \rightleftharpoons SO_4^{-2} + H_3O^+ \tag{17.47}$$

$$HF + H_2O \rightleftharpoons F^- + H_3O^+ \tag{17.48}$$

$$NH_4^+ + H_2O \rightleftharpoons NH_3 + H_3O^+ \tag{17.49}$$

TABLE 17.10 BRÖNSTED-LOWRY
ACIDS AND BASES

Acid	Conjugate Base
$HClO_4$	ClO_4^-
HI	I^-
HBr	Br^-
HCl	Cl^-
HNO_3	NO_3^-
H_2SO_4	HSO_4^-
H_3O^+	H_2O
HSO_4^-	SO_4^{-2}
H_2SO_3	HSO_3^-
HF	F^-
HNO_2	NO_2^-
$HC_2H_3O_2$	$C_2H_3O_2^-$
H_2S	HS^-
HSO_3^-	SO_3^{-2}
HOCl	OCl^-
HCN	CN^-
NH_4^+	NH_3
H_2O_2	HO_2^-
HPO_4^{-2}	PO_4^{-3}
HS^-	S^{-2}
H_2O	OH^-

In the presence of a strong base such as the OH^- ion, proton transfer is more nearly quantitative. It can be calculated, for example, that the addition to a 1 M hydrogen fluoride solution of an equivalent amount of sodium hydroxide increases the fluoride ion concentration from 0.027 M to 0.999996 M as a result of the nearly quantitative reaction:

$$HF + OH^- \longrightarrow F^- + H_2O \tag{17.50}$$

Even with the extremely weak acid HCN ($Ka = 4 \times 10^{-10}$), the equilibrium with OH^- ions lies rather far to the right:

$$HCN + OH^- \xrightleftharpoons{} CN^- + H_2O \tag{17.51}$$

The weakest acid listed in Table 17.10 is the water molecule. It will be recalled, however, that the H_2O molecule shows sufficient tendency to donate protons to bases such as NH_3 and $C_2H_3O_2^-$.

$$H_2O + NH_3 \rightleftharpoons NH_4^+ + OH^-$$

$$H_2O + C_2H_3O_2^- \rightleftharpoons HC_2H_3O_2^- + OH^-$$

to make water solutions of ammonia or sodium acetate weakly basic.

Many substances which show no tendency to donate protons to water behave as acids in the presence of a strong base such as the hydroxide ion. One such species is the organic compound methyl alcohol, CH_3OH. Although a water solution of methyl alcohol is neutral, addition of sodium hydroxide to this solution results in a reversible extraction of a proton from a CH_3OH molecule:

$$\begin{matrix} \text{H} \\ | \\ \text{H}-\text{C}-\text{O}-\text{H} + \text{OH}^- \\ | \\ \text{H} \end{matrix} \longrightarrow \left[\begin{matrix} \text{H} \\ | \\ \text{H}-\text{C}-\text{O} \\ | \\ \text{H} \end{matrix} \right]^- + \text{H}_2\text{O} \qquad (17.52)$$

The fact that the equilibrium constant for this reaction is rather small ($\sim$0.5) indicates that if methyl alcohol were to be added to Table 17.10, it should be placed below water as an extremely weak acid.

In water solution, it is impossible to distinguish between the acid strengths of such compounds as $HClO_4$ and HNO_3, both of which ionize completely in water. This situation is sometimes described by saying that water, because of its basic properties, exerts a leveling effect on various strong acids, making them appear to be of the same strength. A distinction between the acid strengths of nitric and perchloric acids can be made by using a solvent which is a weaker base than water. One such solvent is diethyl ether, $(C_2H_5)_2O$. Accurate freezing point measurements show that an ether solution of perchloric acid contains a higher concentration of ions than an ether solution containing an equivalent amount of nitric acid.

$$\text{HClO}_4 + \text{C}_2\text{H}_5-\overset{..}{\underset{..}{\text{O}}}-\text{C}_2\text{H}_5 \rightleftharpoons \text{ClO}_4^- + \left[\text{C}_2\text{H}_5-\overset{..}{\underset{|}{\text{O}}}-\text{C}_2\text{H}_5 \right]^+ \quad (17.53)$$
$$\phantom{\text{HClO}_4 + \text{C}_2\text{H}_5-\text{O}-\text{C}_2\text{H}_5 \rightleftharpoons \text{ClO}_4^- + [\text{C}_2\text{H}_5-\text{O}-\text{C}_2\text{H}_5}_{\text{H}}$$

$$\text{HNO}_3 + \text{C}_2\text{H}_5-\overset{..}{\underset{..}{\text{O}}}-\text{C}_2\text{H}_5 \rightleftharpoons \text{NO}_3^- + \left[\text{C}_2\text{H}_5-\overset{..}{\underset{|}{\text{O}}}-\text{C}_2\text{H}_5 \right]^+ \quad (17.54)$$

Lewis Concept

Although the Brönsted-Lowry picture extends the concept of acids and bases beyond processes occurring in water solution, it remains tied to proton-transfer reactions. The Lewis concept, in which an acid-base reaction is defined as one in which *a pair of electrons is donated by a base to an acid* to form a coordinate covalent bond, removes this restriction.

In the Lewis sense, a proton acts as an acid when it combines with a molecule such as H_2O or NH_3, which contains an unshared pair of electrons:

$$\text{H}^+ + :\text{O} \begin{matrix} \nearrow \text{H} \\ \searrow \text{H} \end{matrix} \longrightarrow \left[\text{H}-\text{O} \begin{matrix} \nearrow \text{H} \\ \searrow \text{H} \end{matrix} \right]^+ \qquad (17.55)$$

$$\text{H}^+ + :\text{N} \begin{matrix} \text{H} \\ \diagup \\ \diagdown \\ \text{H} \end{matrix} \text{H} \longrightarrow \left[\begin{matrix} \text{H} \\ | \\ \text{H}-\text{N}-\text{H} \\ | \\ \text{H} \end{matrix} \right]^+ \qquad (17.56)$$

Recall that in the Brönsted-Lowry system, the acid is considered to be the substance which donates the proton rather than the proton itself.

A great many cations besides the proton are capable of acting as Lewis acids. Consider, for example, the reaction of the Cu^{+2} ion with water:

$$Cu^{+2} + 4 \ :\overset{\displaystyle H}{\underset{\displaystyle H}{O}} \longrightarrow Cu(H_2O)_4^{+2} \tag{17.57}$$

Here, the Cu^{+2} ion is acting as a Lewis acid in accepting pairs of electrons from the four water molecules. Note in particular that although this reaction is analogous to reaction 17.55, there is no proton transfer involved. The reaction of the Cu^{+2} ion or other transition metal cation with water could not be classified as an acid-base reaction on the basis of the Brönsted-Lowry definitions.

An important example of a Lewis acid-base reaction in which neither reactant contains hydrogen atoms is that between a nonmetal oxide and a metal oxide. Consider, for example, the reaction between carbon dioxide and calcium oxide to form calcium carbonate:

$$CaO(s) + CO_2(g) \longrightarrow CaCO_3(s) \tag{17.58}$$

Here, the oxide ion acts as a base, supplying a pair of electrons to the carbon dioxide molecule to form a carbonate ion.

$$(:\overset{..}{\underset{..}{O}}:)^{-2} + \ :\overset{..}{O}{=}C{=}\overset{..}{O}: \ \longrightarrow \left[:\overset{..}{O}{-}C\overset{..}{=}O: \atop \quad \ :\overset{..}{\underset{..}{O}}: \right]^{-2}$$

The reaction of sulfur trioxide with lithium oxide may be given a similar interpretation.

$$Li_2O(s) + SO_3(g) \longrightarrow Li_2SO_4(s) \tag{17.59}$$

$$(:\overset{..}{\underset{..}{O}}:)^{-2} + \ :\overset{\displaystyle :\overset{..}{O}:}{\underset{..}{O}}{-}\overset{..}{S}{=}\overset{..}{O}: \ \longrightarrow \left[:\overset{..}{O}{-}\overset{\displaystyle :\overset{..}{O}:}{\underset{\displaystyle :\overset{..}{O}:}{S}}{-}\overset{..}{O}: \right]^{-2}$$

17.10 SUMMARY

An acidic water solution is one in which there is an excess of hydrated protons (hydronium ions). Mathematically: $[H^+] > 10^{-7}$ M, $[H^+] > [OH^-]$, pH < 7. Acidic solutions arise through the transfer of a proton from a substance called an acid to a water molecule. The types of substances which react with water to produce an acidic solution include:

1. Hydrides of 6A, 7A elements. $HCl(g) + H_2O \rightarrow Cl^- + H_3O^+$

2. Hydroxy compounds of nonmetals. $HClO_4(l) + H_2O \rightarrow ClO_4^- + H_3O^+$

3. Oxides of nonmetals. $SO_3(g) + H_2O \rightarrow H_2SO_4(l)$
                                    $H_2SO_4(l) + H_2O \rightarrow HSO_4^- + H_3O^+$

4. Perchlorates, iodides, bromides, chlorides, sulfates, and nitrates of NH_4^+, Be^{+2}, Mg^{+2}, transition metal ions. $NH_4^+ + H_2O \rightleftharpoons NH_3 + H_3O^+$

5. Salts containing the anions HSO_4^-, $\qquad HSO_4^- + H_2O \rightleftharpoons SO_4^{-2} + H_3O^+$
HSO_3^- or $H_2PO_4^-$.

When proton transfer to water is nearly 100 per cent complete in moderately concentrated solution, the substance which gives up the proton is said to be a strong acid. The common strong acids are $HClO_4$, HI, HBr, HCl, HNO_3, and H_2SO_4. With weak acids, proton transfer is reversible. With a species such as HF or NH_4^+, an equilibrium is set up in which the concentration of undissociated acid is ordinarily much greater than that of its dissociation products. The relative strengths of different acids can be estimated from their ionization constants, which also make possible the calculation of the concentration of H^+ in a water solution of a weak acid.

The acid strengths of a series of compounds of similar structure can be correlated with the bonding involved. In general, it is found that:

1. For the binary hydrogen compounds, acid strength increases as one moves down and to the right in the periodic table ($H_2Se < H_2Te < HI$).

2. The strength of oxyacids increases with the oxidation number and electronegativity of the central atom. ($HNO_3 > HNO_2$; $H_2SO_4 > H_2SeO_4$.)

3. The acid strength of a metal cation increases with its charge density ($Al^{+3} > Mg^{+2} \gg Na^+$).

Basic water solutions contain an excess of hydroxide ions: $[OH^-] > 10^{-7}$ M, $[OH^-] > [H^+]$, pH > 7. Basic solutions are formed by adding to water:

1. Hydroxides or oxides of the 1A $\qquad CaO(s) + H_2O \rightarrow Ca(OH)_2(s)$
or 2A metals. $\qquad\qquad\qquad\qquad Ca(OH)_2(s) \rightarrow Ca^{+2} + 2\ OH^-$

2. Weak acid salts of Ca^{+2}, Sr^{+2}, $\qquad C_2H_3O_2^- + H_2O \leftrightharpoons HC_2H_3O_2 + OH^-$
Ba^{+2}, and the 1A metals.

3. Ammonia. $\qquad\qquad\qquad\qquad NH_3 + H_2O \rightleftharpoons NH_4^+ + OH^-$

The ionization constants of weak bases such as $C_2H_3O_2^-$ or' NH_3 may be calculated from the ionization constants of their conjugate acids ($HC_2H_3O_2$, NH_4^+)

$$Ka \times Kb = 1.0 \times 10^{-14}$$

A neutral water solution is one in which H^+ and OH^- ions are present in exactly equivalent amounts: $[H^+] = [OH^-] = 10^{-7}$ M; pH $= 7$. Solutions of salts such as $NaNO_3$ and KCl, in which neither ion hydrolyzes, are neutral.

The concept of acids and bases may be extended beyond water solutions by making use of the Brönsted-Lowry (acid = proton donor, base = proton acceptor) or G. N. Lewis (acid = electron pair acceptor, base = electron pair donor) definitions. The Brönsted-Lowry picture is particularly useful in interpreting acid-base reactions in water solutions, a topic which we shall discuss in Chapter 18.

PROBLEMS

17.1 Explain exactly what is meant by each of the following terms.
   a. pH   e. Conjugate acid   i. Lewis acid
   b. Strong acid   f. Conjugate base   j. Lewis base
   c. Weak base   g. Brönsted acid
   d. Acid anhydride h. Brönsted base

17.2 Calculate the pH of solutions with the following $[H^+]$:
   a. 10^{-7} b. 10^{-2} c. 10^1 d. 2.5×10^{-6} e. 1.6×10^{-9} f. 2.0×10^{-15}

17.3 Calculate the $[H^+]$ in solutions of the following pH.
    a. 6   b. 12   c. 1.5   d. 9.6   e. -1.5 f. 13.9

17.4 Calculate the $[H^+]$, $[OH^-]$ and pH of each of the following (assume complete ionization).
    a. 0.010 M HNO_3
    b. 0.090 M KOH
    c. A solution made by diluting 20 ml. of 0.1 M HCl to one liter.
    d. A solution made by dissolving 32.0 g. of KOH in enough water to make 200 ml. of solution.
    e. A solution made by mixing 20 cc. of 0.2 M HCl with 60 cc. of 0.1 M $Ca(OH)_2$.

17.5 If you were given 10 cc. of 1.0 M HCl, how would you prepare from it solutions of the following pH?
    a. 1.0   b. 2.0   c. 3.0   d. 7.0   e. 13.0

17.6 Complete the following table.

Acid Anhydride	Oxyacid	Oxyanion
Cl_2O_7	—	—
SeO_3	—	—
—	H_3PO_4	—
—	H_2TeO_3	—
—	—	NO_2^-

17.7 Write balanced net ionic equations to explain why solutions prepared by adding the following species to water are acidic.
    a. HBr   b. H_2S c. $HClO_4$ d. HSO_4^- e. NH_4^+

17.8 Write balanced net ionic equations to explain why solutions prepared by adding the following species to water are basic.
    a. $Ca(OH)_2$ b. BaO   c. NH_3 d. CH_3NH_2

17.9 Write balanced net ionic equations for the reactions, if any, of the following ions with water
    a. Na^+ c. CO_3^{-2} e. $Cu(H_2O)_4^{+2}$ g. HCO_3^-
    b. $Cr(H_2O)_6^{+3}$ d. F^- f. Cl^-

17.10 A student dissolves 105 g. of an acid of formula HN_3 to form one liter of solution. The pH of this solution is 2.2. Calculate the ionization constant of HN_3.

17.11 A student measures the ionization constant of an acid of unknown molecular weight by the following procedure. He dissolves 1.0 g. of the acid in 50 ml. of water and splits the resulting solution into two exactly equal parts. One of these portions is neutralized with NaOH and added to the other portion. The pH of the resulting solution is found to be 5.7. Calculate Ka.

17.12 Calculate the pH of a solution made by dissolving 12.0 g. of $HC_2H_3O_2$ to form 2.0 1. of solution.

17.13 Calculate the pH, percentage of ionization, $[H^+]$, and $[OH^-]$ of the following solutions:
    a. 0.12 M $HC_2H_3O_2$ c. 0.20 M HF
    b. 1.0 M HCN   d. Pure water

17.14 Calculate the $[OH^-]$ and pH of:
    a. 1.0 M NaOH   b. 0.50 M NH_3 c. 0.20 M $NaC_2H_3O_2$

17.15 Calculate the $[OH^-]$ in a 0.10 M solution of a salt NaY, given that Ka for HY is 1.0×10^{-7}.

17.16 In each of the following series, state which species is the strongest acid.
   a. HF, HCl, H_2S.
   b. PH_4^+, NH_4^+, AsH_4^+
   c. $HClO_4$, $HClO$, $HClO_3$
   d. H_2SO_3, H_2SeO_3, H_2TeO_3
   e. HNO_3, HNO_2, $H_2N_2O_2$.
   f. Na^+, Mg^{+2}, Al^{+3}
   g. Ca^{+2}, Zn^{+2}, Cu^+
   h. NH_4^+, NH_3, NH_2^-

17.17 Write net ionic equations for reactions in which:
   a. HF acts as a Brönsted acid.
   b. HCO_3^- acts as a Brönsted acid.
   c. HCO_3^- acts as a Brönsted base.
   d. H_2O acts as a Brönsted acid.
   e. H_2O acts as a Brönsted base.
   f. $C_2H_3O_2^-$ acts as a Brönsted base.

17.18 For each of the following reversible reactions, underline the Brönsted acids and bases.

$$NH_4^+ + H_2O \rightleftharpoons NH_3 + H_3O^+$$
$$HCO_3^- + HF \rightleftharpoons H_2CO_3 + F^-$$
$$CH_3OH + OH^- \rightleftharpoons CH_3O^- + H_2O$$

17.19 Suggest how one might determine experimentally the relative positions of HCl and HBr in Table 17.10.

17.20 Write an equation for a reaction, other than those listed in the text, which would be considered an acid-base reaction by the Lewis but not by the Brönsted-Lowry definition.

17.21 Show that for an acid H_2X, which ionizes in two steps,

$$\frac{[H^+]^2 \times [X^{-2}]}{[H_2X]} = K_1K_2$$

in which K_1 and K_2 are the first and second ionization constants respectively.

*17.22 List, in order of decreasing concentration, all of the species (molecules and ions) present in a 0.1 M solution of H_2S. Calculate the approximate concentration of each species.

*17.23 It is desired to make up a solution of acetic acid with a pH of 3.0. If one starts with glacial acetic acid (d = 1.050 g./ml., 100 per cent by weight $HC_2H_3O_2$), state precisely how this should be done.

*17.24 It is found that 0.1 M solutions of three sodium salts NaX, NaY, and NaZ have pH's of 7.0, 9.0, and 11.0 respectively. Arrange the acids HX, HY, and HZ in order of increasing strength. Where possible, calculate the ionization constants of the acids.

*17.25 When a certain solution of acetic acid is made 1.0 M in Ag^+, a precipitate of $AgC_2H_3O_2$ just starts to form. What is the concentration of $HC_2H_3O_2$ in this solution?

18 | ACID-BASE REACTIONS

In Chapter 17, the properties of acids and bases were considered. In this chapter, we shall turn our attention to the reactions that take place when an acid and a base are mixed with each other. Here, as before, emphasis will be placed on reactions occurring in water solution. We shall be interested in the nature of acid-base reactions, including the mass and energy relations involved. The greater part of the chapter will be devoted to applications of acid-base reactions to analytical chemistry, synthetic inorganic chemistry, and industrial processes.

18.1 CLASSIFICATION OF ACID-BASE REACTIONS

The reactions that occur when acidic water solutions are mixed with solutions containing a base can be conveniently classified into three general categories:
1. The reaction of a solution of a strong acid with a solution of a strong base.
2. The reaction of a solution of a weak acid with a solution of a strong base.
3. The reaction of a solution of a strong acid with a solution of a weak base.

These reactions, in contrast to many of those discussed in Chapter 17, go virtually to completion. A fourth type of acid-base reaction, that between a weak acid and a weak base, ordinarily gives an equilibrium mixture of products and reactants and so is of less practical value.

Strong Acid + Strong Base

A great deal of evidence indicates that when a water solution of a strong acid is added to a solution of a strong base, a simple reaction involving only the two ions, H^+* and OH^-, occurs:

$$H^+ + OH^- \longrightarrow H_2O + 13.4 \text{ kcal.} \tag{18.1}$$

This reaction, commonly referred to as **neutralization,** occurs when solutions of NaOH and HCl, $Ca(OH)_2$ and $HClO_4$, or any other strong acid–strong base combination are mixed. The other ions present in these solutions (Na^+, Cl^-, Ca^{+2}, ClO_4^-) take no part in the reaction. Perhaps the best proof of this statement lies in

---

* As was pointed out in Chapter 17, it is ordinarily more convenient in discussing reactions of acidic water solutions to use the H^+ ion rather than the H_3O^+ ion. This practice will be followed throughout this chapter.

431

the experimental observation that the amount of heat evolved per mole of H^+ or OH^- reacting is the same, 13.4 kcal., regardless of the identity of the strong acid or strong base.

Since the equilibrium constant for reaction 18.1 is a very large number (note that this reaction is the reverse of 17.4, for which $Kw = 10^{-14}$), the neutralization process goes essentially to completion. If, for example, one neutralizes a solution of hydrochloric acid with sodium hydroxide, a solution of pure sodium chloride is produced. This solution is, of course, neutral; i.e., $[H^+] = [OH^-] = 1 \times 10^{-7}$ M.

Weak Acid + Strong Base

The reaction of a weak acid such as HCN with a strong base differs from that of a strong acid such as HCl in several important respects. Since the principal species present in a water solution of hydrogen cyanide is the undissociated HCN molecule, the reaction with OH^- ions is best represented by the equation:

$$HCN + OH^- \longrightarrow H_2O + CN^- + 2.5 \text{ kcal.} \tag{18.2}$$

It will be noted that the amount of heat evolved in this reaction, 2.5 kcal., is considerably less than that given off in neutralization (reaction 18.1). This is readily explained if one breaks up reaction 18.2 into two steps, the first of which is the dissociation process:

$$HCN + 10.9 \text{ kcal.} \longrightarrow H + CN^- \tag{18.2a}$$

which is endothermic, followed by neutralization:

$$H + OH^- \longrightarrow H_2O + 13.4 \text{ kcal.} \tag{18.2b}$$

Reaction 18.2, like 18.1, is virtually quantitative; one can calculate that the equilibrium constant for the reaction of HCN with OH^- ions is 4×10^4. At the **equivalence point,** i.e., when equivalent quantities of HCN and OH^- ions have been added, one has a solution of a pure metal cyanide. If, for example, the base used is sodium hydroxide, the product is a dilute solution of sodium cyanide. As pointed out in Chapter 17, such a solution is basic. Indeed, whenever a weak acid is reacted with a strong base, a basic solution is produced at the equivalence point.

With weak acids containing more than one acidic hydrogen, reaction with OH^- ions can occur stepwise. An important example is the reaction of carbonic acid (a water solution of carbon dioxide) with a solution of a strong base such as sodium hydroxide:

$$H_2CO_3 + OH^- \longrightarrow H_2O + HCO_3^- \tag{18.3}$$

$$HCO_3^- + OH^- \longrightarrow H_2O + CO_3^{-2} \tag{18.4}$$

The ultimate product depends upon the relative quantities of acid and base used. If one mole of OH^- ions is added per mole of H_2CO_3, the product is the HCO_3^- ion. Addition of another mole of OH^- removes the second proton to give the carbonate ion, CO_3^{-2}. Reaction 18.4 can be brought about directly by adding a strong base to a solution prepared by dissolving sodium hydrogen carbonate, $NaHCO_3$, in water.

Strong Acid + Weak Base

When a strong acid is added to a solution of a weak base such as ammonia, an acid-base reaction occurs which may be represented most simply as:

$$H^+ + NH_3 \longrightarrow NH_4^+ \tag{18.5}$$

It may be noted that this reaction is the reverse of that which occurs when ammonium salts are added to water (reaction 17.16). The equilibrium constant for reaction 18.5 is once again a very large number, approximately 1.8×10^9, indicating that ammonia reacts quantitatively with a strong acid to produce a solution of an ammonium salt.

A reaction entirely analogous to 18.5 occurs when a strong acid is added to a solution containing an anion which is a weak base. The reaction with the acetate ion is typical:

$$H^+ + C_2H_3O_2^- \longrightarrow HC_2H_3O_2 \tag{18.6}$$

If the anion is capable of acquiring two protons, a two-step reaction takes place.

$$H^+ + CO_3^{-2} \longrightarrow HCO_3^- \tag{18.7}$$

$$H^+ + HCO_3^- \longrightarrow H_2CO_3 \longrightarrow CO_2(g) + H_2O \tag{18.8}$$

Addition of excess acid to a solution containing the CO_3^{-2} ion leads to the formation of CO_2 via reactions 18.7 and 18.8. Carbon dioxide may also be formed by adding sodium hydrogen carbonate to a strongly acidic solution. This is, of course, what happens in the stomach when bicarbonate of soda, $NaHCO_3$, is taken to relieve acid indigestion.

It will be noted that in each of the foregoing reactions, the species produced is a weak acid (NH_4^+, $HC_2H_3O_2$, HCO_3^-, H_2CO_3). The reaction of a strong acid with a weak base ordinarily gives, at the equivalence point, a solution which is slightly acidic.

TABLE 18.1   CHARACTERISTICS OF ACID-BASE REACTIONS

Type	Example	Equilibrium Constant	Equivalence Point
Strong acid + strong base	$H^+ + OH^- \rightarrow H_2O$	1×10^{14}	neutral: pH = 7.0
Weak acid + strong base	$HCN + OH^- \rightarrow H_2O + CN^-$	4×10^4	basic: pH $\approx$ 11.7
Strong acid + weak base	$H^+ + NH_3 \rightarrow NH_4^+$	1.8×10^9	acidic: pH $\approx$ 4.6

18.2 ACID-BASE TITRATIONS

Acid-base reactions are commonly used in quantitative analysis to determine the concentration or amount of an acidic or basic constituent of a mixture. The experimental setup resembles that shown in Figure 16.2. The calculations involved are illustrated by Examples 18.1 and 18.2.

Example 18.1.   It is found that 22.3 ml. of 0.240 M NaOH is required to react with a 50.0 ml. sample of vinegar, a solution of acetic acid in water. Calculate the concentration of acetic acid in the vinegar.

Solution. From the equation for the reaction of OH^- ions with acetic acid:

$$HC_2H_3O_2 + OH^- \longrightarrow C_2H_3O_2^- + H_2O$$

it is evident that the reactants are consumed in a 1:1 mole ratio. That is:

$$\text{no. moles } OH^- = \text{no. moles } HC_2H_3O_2$$

But: no. moles of $OH^- = (M\ NaOH)(\text{volume } NaOH)$

no. moles $HC_2H_3O_2 = (M\ HC_2H_3O_2)(\text{volume } HC_2H_3O_2 \text{ solution})$

Hence: $(M\ NaOH)(\text{volume } NaOH) = (M\ HC_2H_3O_2)(\text{volume } HC_2H_3O_2 \text{ solution})$

$$\left(0.240\ \frac{\text{mole}}{\text{l.}}\right)(0.0223\ \text{l.}) = (M\ HC_2H_3O_2)(0.0500\ \text{l.})$$

Solving: $M\ HC_2H_3O_2 = 0.240\ \dfrac{\text{mole}}{\text{l.}} \times \dfrac{0.0223}{0.0500} = 0.107\ M$

Example 18.2. A solid mixture of $Ca(OH)_2$ and $CaCl_2$ is analyzed by titration with HCl. It is found that a sample weighing 0.500 g. requires 24.0 ml. of 0.200 M HCl. Determine the percentage of $Ca(OH)_2$ in the mixture.

Solution. We shall first calculate the number of moles of HCl used in the titration and equate this to the number of moles of OH^- ion in the sample. From the latter quantity, we can determine the number of moles of $Ca(OH)_2$, convert this to grams and finally to percentage by weight.

$$\text{no. moles } HCl = 0.200\ \frac{\text{mole}}{\text{l.}} \times 0.0240\ \text{l.} = 0.00480$$

Since 1 mole of HCl reacts with 1 mole of OH^-:

$$\text{no. moles } OH^- = 0.00480$$

Since 1 mole $Ca(OH)_2$ contains 2 moles of OH^-:

$$\text{no. moles } Ca(OH)_2 = \tfrac{1}{2} \times 0.00480 = 0.00240$$

Since 1 mole of $Ca(OH)_2$ weighs 74.0 g.:

$$\text{no. g. } Ca(OH)_2 = 0.00240\ \text{mole} \times \frac{74.0\ \text{g.}}{1\ \text{mole}} = 0.178\ \text{g.}$$

$$\%\ Ca(OH)_2 = \frac{\text{wt. } Ca(OH)_2}{\text{wt. sample}} \times 100 = \frac{0.178\ \text{g.}}{0.500\ \text{g.}} \times 100 = 35.6\%$$

Acid-Base Indicators

Essential to any acid-base titration is the presence in small amount of an indicator. To understand how an indicator works, consider a specific example, bromthymol blue. This organic dye is a weak acid in which the undissociated molecule, which we shall represent simply as HIn, has a color (yellow) different from that of its conjugate base, In^- (blue). For the equilibrium involved, we can write:

$$\underset{\text{yellow}}{HIn} \rightleftharpoons H^+ + \underset{\text{blue}}{In^-} \qquad\qquad Ka = \frac{[H^+] \times [In^-]}{[HIn]} = 1 \times 10^{-7}$$

The color of a solution of bromthymol blue depends upon the relative concentrations of the two colored species, HIn and In^-. When these concentrations are equal, the indicator has a green color intermediate between the yellow of the HIn molecule and the blue of the In^- ion. It is evident from the foregoing equation that this condition is fulfilled, that is [HIn] = [In⁻] when:

$$[H^+] = Ka = 1 \times 10^{-7} \text{ M}$$

In other words, if bromthymol blue is used in an acid-base titration, the **end point** (the point at which a color change occurs) is reached at a H^+ ion concentration of about 10^{-7} M or a pH of 7. In more strongly acidic solution (pH < 7), bromthymol blue will exist primarily in the form of the yellow HIn molecule; above a pH of 7, the blue color of the In⁻ ion predominates.

In practice, an acid-base indicator such as bromthymol blue does not undergo an abrupt color change at a particular pH. Instead, it shows a gradual color change over a range of about 2 pH units. If a strongly acidic solution containing a drop of bromthymol blue is slowly neutralized, one can begin to detect a color change when the concentration of In⁻ is about one tenth that of HIn, that is, at a pH of 6. Not until the concentration of In⁻ is 10 times that of HIn (pH = 8) is the yellow color of the latter species completely obscured by the blue of the In⁻ ion.

It should be evident from this discussion that the end point observed with a particular indicator depends upon the magnitude of its ionization constant, Ka. Methyl red (Ka = 1×10^{-5}) shows a color change from yellow to red at pH 5; phenolphthalein (Ka = 1×10^{-9}) turns red at pH 9. In general, the stronger the acid used as an indicator, the lower the pH at which a color change occurs. The choice of indicator for a particular acid-base titration depends primarily upon the relative strengths of the acid and base involved.

1. Titration of a Strong Acid with a Strong Base (pH at Equivalence Point = 7). In this case, the pH changes very rapidly near the equivalence point. The addition of less than a drop of reagent at that point can change the pH by as much as six units (e.g., from 4 to 10; Example 18.3). Consequently, almost any indicator can be used; methyl red (end point at pH 5) or phenolphthalein (end point at pH 9) work as well as an indicator such as bromthymol blue (end point at pH 7) where the color change coincides exactly with the equivalence point.

Example 18.3. 50.00 ml. of 1.00 M HCl is titrated with 1.00 M NaOH. Calculate the pH:
 a. After 49.99 ml. of 1.00 M NaOH has been added.
 b. After 50.00 ml. of 1.00 M NaOH has been added.
 c. After 50.01 ml. of 1.00 M NaOH has been added.

Solution
 a. At this point, 0.01 ml. of HCl remains unreacted in a total volume of almost exactly 100 ml. Consequently:

$$\text{conc. HCl} = \text{conc. } H^+ = 1.00 \text{ M} \times \frac{0.01}{100} = 1 \times 10^{-4} \text{ M}$$

$$pH = -\log [H^+] = 4$$

 b. At the equivalence point, we have a neutral solution of sodium chloride

$$pH = 7$$

 c. We now have an excess of 0.01 ml. of NaOH in a total volume of 100 ml.

$$\text{conc. NaOH} = \text{conc. OH}^- = 1.00 \text{ M} \times \frac{0.01}{100} = 1 \times 10^{-4} \text{ M}$$

$$\text{conc. } H^+ = \frac{1 \times 10^{-14}}{1 \times 10^{-4}} = 1 \times 10^{-10} \text{ M}$$

$$pH = 10$$

We see that the addition of only 0.02 ml. of base ($\approx \frac{1}{2}$ drop) near the equivalence point changes the pH by six units. If the acid and base are more dilute, the change is slightly less abrupt, but the general conclusions remain valid.

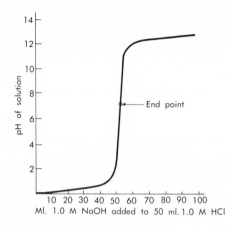

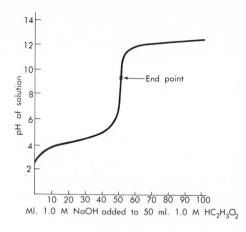

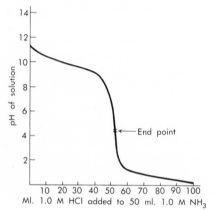

FIGURE 18.1   Titration curves for acids and bases.

2. Titration of a Weak Acid with a Strong Base (*pH at Equivalence Point > 7*).   Here, the choice of indicator is more critical, since the pH changes more slowly in the vicinity of the equivalence point (Figure 18.1). One must use an indicator which changes color in the basic region. Phenolphthalein (end point at pH 9) is frequently used in titrations of this type.

3. Titration of a Weak Base with a Strong Acid (*pH at Equivalence Point < 7*).   Here again, the pH changes rather slowly near the equivalence point, so one must use an indicator whose end point coincides approximately with the equivalence point. Methyl orange (end point at pH 4) or methyl red (end point at pH 5) are often used.

Normality: Gram Equivalent Weights of Acids and Bases

The concentrations of solutions used in acid-base titrations are frequently expressed in terms of normality (cf. Chapter 13, Section 13.3).

$$\text{Normality} = \frac{\text{no. of G.E.W. solute}}{\text{no. l. solution}} \qquad (18.9)$$

In acid-base reactions, the gram equivalent weight of an acid is defined as the weight that reacts with one mole of OH^- ions; the gram equivalent weight of a base is defined as the weight that reacts with one mole of H^+ ions. Since OH^- and H^+ ions react in a $1:1$ mole ratio, it follows that one gram equivalent weight of any acid must react exactly with one gram equivalent weight of any base. Stated another way, in any acid-base reaction:

$$\text{no. of G.E.W. acid} = \text{no. of G.E.W. base} \qquad (18.10)$$

Combining equations 18.9 and 18.10, we conclude that in any acid-base titration:

$$(\text{N acid}) \, (\text{V acid}) = (\text{N base}) \, (\text{V base}) \qquad (18.11)$$

in which the symbols N and V stand for normality and volume respectively.

The simplicity and general validity of equation 18.11 explains the usefulness of normality as a concentration unit in analytical chemistry. It tells us, for example, that acidic and basic solutions of equal normality will react in a $1:1$ volume ratio, regardless of the particular acid or base involved. Furthermore, it makes it possible to determine the normality of an acidic or basic solution directly from an acid-base titration. If it is found, for example, that 20 cc. of 0.40 N NaOH are required to titrate 30 cc. of a solution of a certain acid, it can be established immediately from equation 18.11 that:

$$\text{N acid} = \text{N base} \times \frac{\text{V base}}{\text{V acid}} = 0.40 \text{ N} \times \frac{20}{30} = 0.27 \text{ N}$$

The normality of an acidic or basic solution is readily calculated from the molarity by the equation:

$$\text{N} = \text{x M} \qquad (18.12)$$

in which x is the number of gram equivalent weights furnished by one mole. For an acid such as HCl, one mole of which always neutralizes one mole of OH^- ions, the gram equivalent weight is identical with the mole, x in equation 18.12 is one, and the normality is equal to the molarity.

For acids such as H_2SO_4 or H_3PO_4 which are capable of reacting with more than 1 mole of OH^- ions, x can be greater than one and consequently the normality can be a whole-number multiple of the molarity. When a solution of sulfuric acid is completely neutralized by base, 1 mole of H_2SO_4 reacts with 2 moles of OH^- ions, x in equation 18.12 is 2 and the normality is exactly twice the molarity. By a similar line of reasoning, one can deduce that in an acid-base reaction in which phosphoric acid is completely neutralized, $x = 3$, $N = 3$ M.

Although equations 18.9 to 18.12 have been applied to acid-base reactions, they are valid for any reaction. The gram equivalent weights of substances participating in a reaction are always defined in such a way that the fundamental relation 18.10 holds. For this reason, normality is widely used as a concentration unit in volumetric analyses, including those based on precipitation reactions (Chapter 16) and oxidation-reduction reactions (Chapter 22) as well as acid-base reactions.

18.3 APPLICATION OF ACID-BASE REACTIONS IN INORGANIC SYNTHESIS

Acid-base reactions are frequently used to prepare inorganic compounds. They may be adapted to the preparation of almost any salt; in addition, acid-base reactions may be used to prepare certain volatile acids and bases.

Preparation of Salts

Let us suppose that it is desired to prepare a sample of pure cesium nitrate, $CsNO_3$, from cesium hydroxide, $CsOH$. This may be done by a two-step process, in which the hydroxide is first neutralized by nitric acid:

$$Cs^+ + OH^- + H^+ + NO_3^- \longrightarrow Cs^+ + NO_3^- + H_2O \qquad (18.13a)$$

and the resulting solution, which should contain only Cs^+ and NO_3^- ions, is then evaporated:

$$Cs^+ + NO_3^- \longrightarrow CsNO_3(s) \qquad (18.13b)$$

In an entirely analogous manner, it is possible to convert ammonia to ammonium salts by reacting with an equivalent amount of acid and evaporating:

$$NH_3 + H^+ + Cl^- \longrightarrow NH_4^+ + Cl^- \qquad (18.14a)$$
$$NH_4^+ + Cl^- \longrightarrow NH_4Cl(s) \qquad (18.14b)$$

Acids such as HF are readily converted to their salts in the same manner:

$$Rb^+ + OH^- + HF \longrightarrow Rb^+ + F^- + H_2O \qquad (18.15a)$$
$$Rb^+ + F^- \longrightarrow RbF(s) \qquad (18.15b)$$

When acid-base reactions such as 18.13a, 18.14a, and 18.15a are to be used to prepare pure inorganic salts, it is highly desirable that one use exactly equivalent quantities of acid and base. Suppose, for example, that in reaction 18.13a, one were to use an excess of cesium hydroxide; upon evaporation the cesium nitrate would be contaminated with unreacted cesium hydroxide.

When an acid contains more than one ionizable hydrogen, the product obtained depends upon the relative quantities of acid and base used. An example of particular commercial interest is carbonic acid, H_2CO_3. Either $NaHCO_3$ or Na_2CO_3 can be prepared by bubbling carbon dioxide through a solution of sodium hydroxide and evaporating. To make $NaHCO_3$, 1 mole of H_2CO_3 is needed for every mole of $NaOH$:

$$H_2CO_3 + Na^+ + OH^- \longrightarrow Na^+ + HCO_3^- + H_2O \qquad (18.16a)$$
$$Na^+ + HCO_3^- \longrightarrow NaHCO_3(s) \qquad (18.16b)$$

If the desired product is Na_2CO_3, 2 moles of $NaOH$ should be used:

$$H_2CO_3 + 2\,Na^+ + 2\,OH^- \longrightarrow 2\,Na^+ + CO_3^{-2} + 2\,H_2O \qquad (18.17a)$$
$$2\,Na^+ + CO_3^{-2} \longrightarrow Na_2CO_3(s) \qquad (18.17b)$$

In practice, it is extremely difficult to add carbon dioxide to a solution of sodium hydroxide in a fixed ratio. To prepare $NaHCO_3$, all one has to do is to bubble carbon dioxide through a sodium hydroxide solution until saturation is reached; $NaHCO_3$ crystallizes on evaporation or cooling. The preparation of Na_2CO_3 is more difficult, since one must avoid adding an excess of carbon dioxide. One way of solving this problem is to add an indicator which changes color when reaction 18.17a is complete, that is, when a water solution of Na_2CO_3 is formed.

Preparation of Volatile Acids or Bases

A convenient way to prepare small quantities of anhydrous ammonia is to heat a solution containing NH_4^+ ions with a strong base such as sodium hydroxide.

$$NH_4^+ + OH^- \longrightarrow NH_3(g) + H_2O \qquad (18.18)$$

By passing the gas evolved over a drying agent, it is possible to remove any water present and thereby obtain relatively pure ammonia.

Several volatile weak acids are readily prepared by treating a solution of one of their salts with a strong, nonvolatile acid such as sulfuric acid. Thus, carbon dioxide is produced by adding sulfuric acid to sodium carbonate or sodium hydrogen carbonate.

$$CO_3^{-2} + 2\ H^+ \longrightarrow (H_2CO_3) \longrightarrow CO_2(g) + H_2O \qquad (18.19)$$

$$HCO_3^- + H^+ \longrightarrow (H_2CO_3) \longrightarrow CO_2(g) + H_2O \qquad (18.20)$$

In a similar manner, hydrogen sulfide can be prepared from a soluble sulfide.

$$S^{-2} + 2\ H^+ \longrightarrow H_2S(g) \qquad (18.21)$$

TABLE 18.2 VOLATILITY OF ACIDS FROM WATER SOLUTION

Acid	Boiling Point (°C)	
Hydrogen sulfide	100	H_2S escapes on warming
Carbonic acid	100	CO_2 escapes on warming
Sulfurous acid	100	SO_2 escapes on warming
Hydrochloric acid	110	constant boiling mixture (20% HCl)
Hydrofluoric acid	120	constant boiling mixture (35% HF)
Nitric acid	121	constant boiling mixture (68% HNO_3)
Hydrobromic acid	126	constant boiling mixture (47% HBr)
Hydriodic acid	127	constant boiling mixture (57% HI)
Phosphoric acid	213	$2\ H_3PO_4 \rightarrow H_4P_2O_7 + H_2O$
Sulfuric acid	330	$H_2SO_4 \rightarrow SO_3 + H_2O$

The usefulness of the type of reaction illustrated by equations 18.19 to 18.21 depends upon the weak acid formed being volatile. Indeed, one can prepare volatile strong acids by reactions entirely analogous to these. For example, hydrogen chloride can be formed by heating a concentrated solution of sodium chloride with sulfuric acid:

$$H^+ + Cl^- \longrightarrow HCl(g)$$

To prepare hydrogen bromide or hydrogen iodide, phosphoric acid is ordinarily used rather than sulfuric acid to avoid oxidation of the hydrogen halide to the free halogen (cf. Chapter 22, Section 22.5).

18.4 APPLICATION OF ACID-BASE REACTIONS IN QUALITATIVE ANALYSIS

Acid-base reactions are widely used in qualitative analysis for either of two different purposes. An acid-base reaction may be used to test for a specific ion by converting that ion into a volatile, easily detectable product. Alternatively, such a reaction may be used to separate one ion from another. In this case, advantage is taken of the ability of acidic solutions to dissolve certain water-insoluble salts while leaving others unaffected.

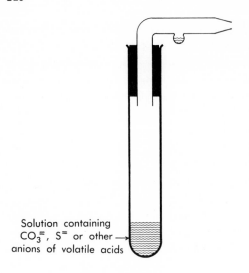

FIGURE 18.2 Qualitative detection of anions. Solution is acidified and heated. Volatile constituents (H_2S, CO_2, etc.) pass through the exit tube where they may be trapped and detected. (Williams, T., and Stock, J., *Journal of Chemical Education, 36*: 384, 1959.)

Solution containing $CO_3^=$, $S^=$ or other → anions of volatile acids

Tests for Specific Ions

The reaction that occurs when an ammonium salt is heated with a strong base (equation 18.18) is frequently used as a qualitative test for the NH_4^+ ion. The ammonia formed may be detected either by its odor or its effect on litmus; of all the gases commonly encountered in the analytical laboratory, ammonia is the only one which is basic to litmus.

The reactions represented by equations 18.19 to 18.21 are useful for the qualitative detection of CO_3^{-2}, HCO_3^-, or S^{-2} ions. Carbon dioxide, formed by reaction 18.19 or 18.20, is detected by passing it through a solution of calcium hydroxide to give a white precipitate of calcium carbonate:

$$Ca^{+2} + 2\ OH^- + H_2CO_3 \longrightarrow CaCO_3(s) + 2\ H_2O \qquad (18.22)$$

Hydrogen sulfide, produced by reaction 18.21, may be recognized either by its foul odor or its ability to form a black precipitate with Pb^{+2} ions. A piece of filter paper moistened with lead nitrate solution turns black if exposed to a gas mixture containing hydrogen sulfide:

$$Pb^{+2} + H_2S(g) \longrightarrow PbS(s) + 2\ H^+ \qquad (18.23)$$

Separation of Ions

The use of an acid-base reaction to separate one ion from another is illustrated by a procedure commonly used in anion analysis to distinguish between CO_3^{-2} and SO_4^{-2}. These ions are first precipitated as the barium salts. The mixed precipitate of $BaCO_3$ and $BaSO_4$ is then treated with hydrochloric acid. The carbonate is brought into solution by reaction 18.19, while the sulfate is unaffected.

$$CO_3^{-2},\ SO_4^{-2}$$
$$\downarrow Ba^{+2}$$
$$BaCO_3,\ BaSO_4$$
$$\downarrow H^+$$

$$Ba^{+2},\ CO_2(g) \qquad\qquad BaSO_4(s)$$

A more subtle application of this same principle is involved in the reaction of hydrochloric acid with a mixed precipitate of CuS and CoS. The cobalt sulfide dissolves in acid while copper sulfide does not. This separation is more commonly carried out in reverse. That is, by adding hydrogen sulfide in acidic solution to a mixture of Co^{+2} and Cu^{+2} ions, CuS is precipitated while Co^{+2} remains in solution:

$$Co^{+2}, Cu^{+2}$$

$$\boxed{H_2S, H^+(.3\ M)}$$

$$Co^{+2} \qquad\qquad CuS(s)$$

As noted in Chapter 16, ions which form water-insoluble sulfides can be separated into two groups in this manner. The ions which form extremely insoluble sulfides (group $2 = Cu^{+2}$, Bi^{+3}, As^{+3}, Sb^{+3}, Sn^{+2}, Sn^{+4}, Cd^{+2}) are precipitated by hydrogen sulfide in acidic solution, while those sulfides which are somewhat more soluble (Co^{+2}, Fe^{+2}, Fe^{+3}, Ni^{+2}, Zn^{+2}, Mn^{+2} in group 3) are precipitated only after the solution is made basic.

To understand the principles behind these separations, one must consider the factors that influence the solubility of a solid in a dilute, nonoxidizing acid. These factors may be deduced by studying the equilibria involved. Consider, for example, the process by which a metal sulfide, general formula MS, dissolves in acid:

$$MS(s) \rightleftharpoons M^{+2} + S^{-2} \qquad\qquad (18.24a)$$

$$S^{-2} + 2\ H^+ \rightleftharpoons H_2S(g) \qquad\qquad (18.24b)$$

$$MS(s) + 2\ H^+ \rightleftharpoons M^{+2} + H_2S(g) \qquad\qquad (18.24)$$

The solubility of a metal sulfide in hydrochloric acid depends upon the position of the equilibrium in 18.24 which is determined by:

1. *The solubility of the solid in water.* The greater the solubility in water, the farther to the right equilibrium (18.24a) will be displaced and consequently the greater will be the solubility of the solid in acid. Cobalt sulfide ($Ksp = 1 \times 10^{-21}$) is more soluble in water than is copper sulfide ($Ksp = 1 \times 10^{-25}$); this same order of solubility is maintained in acid. It so happens that in a solution 0.3 M in H^+, the solubility range is such that CuS precipitates while CoS remains in solution (Example 18.4).

2. *The concentration of the acid.* Since H^+ ions appear on the left side of equation (18.24b), it is clear that an increase in their concentration shifts the solubility equilibrium to the right, thereby bringing more of the solid into solution. Conversely, if the concentration of acid is lowered, the solid shows less tendency to dissolve. When an acidic solution containing Co^{+2} and S^{-2} ions is partially neutralized with base, cobalt sulfide precipitates.

3. *The strength of the weak acid formed.* The weaker the acid (H_2S, H_2CO_3, and so on) formed, the more soluble the solid is in acid. All water-insoluble carbonates are readily dissolved by dilute acid to form the very weak acid H_2CO_3 ($K_1 = 4 \times 10^{-7}$, $K_2 = 5 \times 10^{-11}$). In contrast, water-insoluble fluorides (Ka HF $= 7 \times 10^{-4}$) can be brought into solution only by using concentrated acid. The comparison is particularly striking for the two compounds $BaCO_3$ and BaF_2. Even though $BaCO_3$ is considerably less soluble in water than BaF_2 (Ksp $BaCO_3 = 1 \times 10^{-9}$, Ksp $BaF_2 = 2 \times 10^{-6}$), it dissolves readily in very dilute acid, while BaF_2 can be brought into solution only at high acid concentrations. Water-insoluble salts of strong acids, such as $BaSO_4$, PbI_2, and AgCl, show no tendency to dissolve in acid.

The quantitative applications of these principles are illustrated in Example 18.4.

Example 18.4. A solution 0.1 M in Cu^{+2} and Co^{+2} and 0.3 M in H^+ is saturated with H_2S so as to make $[H_2S] = 0.1$ M.
  a. Show that under these conditions CuS but not CoS precipitates.
  b. To what value must $[H^+]$ be reduced to start to precipitate CoS?

Solution
  a. In order to determine whether or not a precipitate is formed under these conditions, we must first find out how the concentration products, conc. $Cu^{+2} \times$ conc. S^{-2}, and conc. $Co^{+2} \times$ conc. S^{-2}, compare to the solubility products of these salts (Ksp CuS $= 1 \times 10^{-25}$, Ksp CoS $= 1 \times 10^{-21}$). The concentrations of Cu^{+2} and Co^{+2} are given as 0.1 M; the concentration of S^{-2} must be calculated from that of H^+ and H_2S. To do this, we multiply the first and second ionization constants of H_2S together to give:

$$\frac{[H^+] \times [HS^-]}{[H_2S]} \times \frac{[H^+] \times [S^{-2}]}{[HS^-]} = \frac{[H^+]^2 \times [S^{-2}]}{[H_2S]} = (1 \times 10^{-7})(1 \times 10^{-15})$$

or
$$\frac{[H^+]^2 \times [S^{-2}]}{[H_2S]} = 1 \times 10^{-22}$$

Substituting: $[H^+] = 0.3$ M, $[H_2S] = 0.1$ M, and solving gives:

$$[S^{-2}] = 1 \times 10^{-22} \times \frac{0.1}{0.09} = 1 \times 10^{-22} \qquad \text{(1 significant figure)}$$

Therefore:

$$\text{conc. } Cu^{+2} \times \text{conc. } S^{-2} = (10^{-1})(10^{-22}) = 10^{-23} > \text{Ksp CuS } (1 \times 10^{-25})$$
CuS precipitates.

$$\text{conc. } Co^{+2} \times \text{conc. } S^{-2} = (10^{-1})(10^{-22}) = 10^{-23} < \text{Ksp CoS } (1 \times 10^{-21})$$
CoS does not precipitate.

  b. A precipitate of CoS will form when: $[Co^{+2}] \times [S^{-2}] = \text{Ksp CoS} = 10^{-21}$
  Since $[Co^{+2}] = 10^{-1}$ M, this requires that $[S^{-2}] = 10^{-20}$ M.
  We must now calculate what concentration of H^+ will give this value for $[S^{-2}]$ in a solution 0.1 M in H_2S:

$$\frac{[H^+]^2 \times [S^{-2}]}{[H_2S]} = 1 \times 10^{-22}$$

$$[H^+]^2 = \frac{1 \times 10^{-22} \times 0.1}{10^{-20}} = 1 \times 10^{-3} = 10 \times 10^{-4}; \quad [H^+] = 3 \times 10^{-2} \text{ M}$$

In other words, if the concentration of H^+ is reduced from 0.3 M to 0.03 M by adding base, a precipitate of CoS will start to form.

18.5 AN INDUSTRIAL APPLICATION OF ACID-BASE REACTIONS: THE SOLVAY PROCESS

A commercially important process in which acid-base reactions play an important part is the so-called Solvay Process for the manufacture of sodium hydrogen carbonate, $NaHCO_3$, and sodium carbonate, Na_2CO_3. This process is competitive with the method described earlier for the preparation of these compounds, i.e., the reaction of carbon dioxide with a solution of sodium hydroxide. The principal economic advantage of the Solvay Process is that it uses as a raw material sodium chloride, which is considerably less expensive than sodium hydroxide.

Preparation of $NaHCO_3$

The first product formed in the Solvay Process is sodium hydrogen carbonate, $NaHCO_3$. To prepare this compound, advantage is taken of its comparatively low solubility at temperatures near the freezing point of water. Carbon dioxide is bubbled through a concentrated brine solution saturated with ammonia and maintained at a temperature of approximately $0°C$. Under these conditions, finely-divided crystals of sodium hydrogen carbonate precipitate. The equation for the overall reaction may be written:

$$CO_2(g) + H_2O + NH_3(g) + Na^+ + Cl^- \longrightarrow NaHCO_3(s) + NH_4^+ + Cl^-$$
$$(18.25)$$

The sodium hydrogen carbonate may be filtered from the solution of ammonium chloride. It is possible to prepare $NaHCO_3$ in this manner because its solubility at $0°C$ (0.82 mole/l.) is considerably less than that of any of the other possible products, NH_4Cl (5.5 moles/l.), $NaCl$ (6.1 moles/l.) or NH_4HCO_3 (1.5 moles/l.).

A reaction such as 18.25 involving as it does a large number of particles, can best be understood by breaking it down into a series of relatively simple steps. In this case, three such steps may be considered:

(Step 1) Bubbling carbon dioxide through water establishes the equilibrium:

$$CO_2(g) + H_2O \rightleftharpoons H_2CO_3 \rightleftharpoons H^+ + HCO_3^- \qquad (18.25a)$$

The concentration of HCO_3^- ion produced by this reaction (0.00018 M) is far lower than that required to precipitate $NaHCO_3$ (about 0.10 M).

(Step 2) To increase the concentration of HCO_3^- ions in solution, it is necessary to add a reagent which will shift the equilibrium in (18.25a) to the right. This may be accomplished by adding ammonia, which removes H^+ ions by converting them to NH_4^+ ions:

$$NH_3(g) + H^+ \longrightarrow NH_4^+ \qquad (18.25b)$$

Adding: $$CO_2(g) + NH_3(g) + H_2O \longrightarrow NH_4^+ + HCO_3^- \qquad (18.25a + b)$$

(Step 3) Under these conditions, the HCO_3^- ions are present at a sufficiently high concentration to be precipitated by the sodium ions of the sodium chloride solution:

$$Na^+ + Cl^- + HCO_3^- \longrightarrow NaHCO_3(s) + Cl^- \qquad (18.25c)$$

Adding:

$$CO_2(g) + H_2O + NH_3(g) + Na^+ + Cl^- \longrightarrow NaHCO_3(s) + NH_4^+ + Cl^-$$
$$(18.25a + b + c)$$

Preparation of Na_2CO_3 from $NaHCO_3$

The greater part of the sodium hydrogen carbonate prepared by the Solvay Process is converted to the more widely used salt, sodium carbonate. This conversion is accomplished by heating $NaHCO_3$ to about $300°C$; at this temperature carbon dioxide and water vapor are given off and a white residue of sodium carbonate remains:

$$2\ NaHCO_3(s) + heat \longrightarrow Na_2CO_3(s) + CO_2(g) + H_2O(g) \qquad (18.26)$$

The carbon dioxide formed is recycled to prepare more $NaHCO_3$ by reaction 18.25.

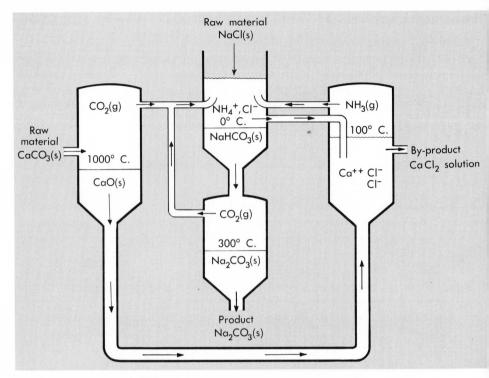

FIGURE 18.3   Schematic diagram of Solvay Process.

Preparation of CO_2 and Recovery of NH_3

For every mole of $NaHCO_3$ or Na_2CO_3 produced by the Solvay Process, one mole of CO_2 is consumed. The carbon dioxide is produced by heating limestone:

$$CaCO_3(s) \longrightarrow CaO(s) + CO_2(g) \qquad (18.27)$$

The economics of the Solvay Process, like that of all industrial operations, depends upon the effective use of all the products. In particular, it is important that the calcium oxide produced by reaction 18.27 be utilized. Furthermore, the solution of ammonium chloride remaining after the precipitation of sodium hydrogen carbonate is far too valuable to be discarded. Indeed, if the ammonia consumed in reaction 18.25 were not recovered, the Solvay Process would be economically impossible, since the sodium hydrogen carbonate produced by this reaction sells for less than the ammonia consumed. Fortunately, these two problems, the utilization of the CaO produced in reaction 18.27 and the recovery of the NH_3 used in 18.25, can be solved simultaneously. It was pointed out earlier that ammonia can be formed from ammonium salts by heating with a base:

$$2\ NH_4^+ + 2\ OH^- \longrightarrow 2\ NH_3(g) + 2\ H_2O$$

Calcium oxide upon addition to water gives a strongly basic solution:

$$CaO(s) + H_2O \longrightarrow Ca^{+2} + 2\ OH^-$$

Consequently, if the solution of NH_4Cl remaining after the precipitation of $NaHCO_3$ is heated with CaO, the reaction:

$$CaO(s) + 2\ NH_4^+ + 2\ Cl^- \longrightarrow Ca^{+2} + 2\ Cl^- + 2\ NH_3(g) + H_2O \quad (18.28)$$

occurs, liberating ammonia and leaving, as a final by-product, a solution of calcium chloride.

Summary of the Solvay Process

The raw materials used in the Solvay Process are sodium chloride, water, and limestone. The first product formed is sodium hydrogen carbonate, $NaHCO_3$, which precipitates at $0°C$ from a sodium chloride solution saturated with CO_2 (produced by the thermal decomposition of $CaCO_3$) and NH_3 (recovered by heating the solution remaining with CaO). The $NaHCO_3$ may be sold for use in medicine, baking powder, and so on, or it may be converted by heating to Na_2CO_3. More than six million tons of sodium carbonate are used annually in this country in the manufacture of glass, paper, soap, and other chemicals. Calcium chloride, formed as a by-product, is used as a drying agent and in ice removal from highways.

18.6 BUFFER ACTION

It is a well-known fact that the pH of blood and many other body fluids is relatively insensitive to the addition of acid or base. If one adds as much as 0.01 mole of HCl or NaOH to 1 l. of blood, its pH changes by less than 0.1 of a unit from its normal value of 7.4. In contrast, the addition of these same quantities of acid or base to pure water changes its pH by about 5 units (from 7 to 2 with 0.01 mole of HCl, from 7 to 12 with 0.01 mole of NaOH).

Solutions whose pH remains virtually unchanged upon the addition of small quantities of strong acid or base are said to be **buffered.** Buffer action ordinarily requires that the solution contain two different components, one capable of reacting with H^+ ions, the other with OH^- ions. A simple example of a buffer system is one prepared by adding acetic acid to a solution of sodium acetate. If a strong base such as sodium hydroxide is added to the system, the OH^- ions react with acetic acid molecules.

$$OH^- + HC_2H_3O_2 \longrightarrow H_2O + C_2H_3O_2^- \quad (18.29)$$

Since the equilibrium constant for this reaction is large, the OH^- ions are almost completely removed.

Addition of a strong acid to the buffer results in a reaction of the H^+ ions of the acid with the acetate ions of the sodium acetate.

$$H^+ + C_2H_3O_2^- \longrightarrow HC_2H_3O_2 \quad (18.30)$$

In either case, the OH^- ions or H^+ ions added are consumed and hence fail to produce the drastic pH change observed when a strong acid or base is added to pure water or an unbuffered solution.

The addition of acid or base to a buffered solution such as the $HC_2H_3O_2$—$C_2H_3O_2^-$ system does result in a small pH change whose magnitude can be calculated as illustrated in Example 18.5.

Example 18.5. A buffer system contains 0.10 mole of $HC_2H_3O_2$ and 0.10 mole of $C_2H_3O_2^-$ per liter. Calculate:

    a. The pH of the buffer.

    b. The pH after addition of 0.01 mole/l. of HCl.

    c. The pH after addition of 0.01 mole/l. of NaOH.

Solution

    a. To obtain the pH for the buffer system, we set up the expression for the ionization constant of acetic acid.

$$Ka = 1.8 \times 10^{-5} = \frac{[H^+] \times [C_2H_3O_2^-]}{[HC_2H_3O_2]}$$

Substituting $[HC_2H_3O_2] = [C_2H_3O_2^-] = 0.10$ M, and solving gives $[H^+] = 1.8 \times 10^{-5}$

$$pH = -\log[H^+] = -\log(1.8 \times 10^{-5}) = -(0.26 - 5.00) = 4.74$$

    b. When 0.01 mole of H^+ is added, reaction 18.30 occurs, thereby consuming 0.01 mole of $C_2H_3O_2^-$ and forming 0.01 mole of $HC_2H_3O_2$. This means that $(0.10 - 0.01)$ 0.09 mole of $C_2H_3O_2^-$ and $(0.10 + 0.01) = 0.11$ mole of $HC_2H_3O_2$ remain. Therefore:

$$[H^+] = 1.8 \times 10^{-5} \times \frac{[HC_2H_3O_2]}{[C_2H_3O_2^-]} = 1.8 \times 10^{-5}\frac{(0.11)}{(0.09)} = 2.2 \times 10^{-5} \quad pH = 4.66$$

In other words, the addition of 0.01 mole of HCl to this buffer system reduces the pH by only 0.08 unit.

    c. Here, reaction 18.29 takes place, consuming 0.01 mole of $HC_2H_3O_2$ and producing 0.01 mole of $C_2H_3O_2^=$.

$$\text{no. moles } HC_2H_3O_2 = 0.10 - 0.01 = 0.09$$

$$\text{no. moles } C_2H_3O_2^- = 0.10 + 0.01 = 0.11$$

$$[H^+] = 1.8 \times 10^{-5} \times \frac{[HC_2H_3O_2]}{[C_2H_3O_2^-]} = 1.8 \times 10^{-5}\frac{(0.09)}{(0.11)} = 1.5 \times 10^{-5}$$

$$pH = 4.82$$

Again, we find that the pH changes by less than 0.1 unit.

Two principles concerning the quantitative aspects of buffer action are worthy of note:

1. The capacity of a buffer to absorb H^+ or OH^- ions without an appreciable change in pH is directly related to the concentrations of the two species making up the buffer. One can calculate that the pH change produced by adding 0.01 mole of HCl or NaOH to an $HC_2H_3O_2$ - $C_2H_3O_2^-$ buffer containing only 0.02 mole of these species would be about 0.47 units, nearly five times that observed when the concentrations of $HC_2H_3O_2$ and $C_2H_3O_2^-$ are 0.10 M.

2. A buffer system such as $HC_2H_3O_2$ - $C_2H_3O_2^-$ is capable of maintaining a relatively constant pH in only a rather narrow pH range of about 2 pH units. An acetic acid–sodium acetate buffer is useful in the range from pH 3.7 to 5.7. To maintain a pH outside this region would require that the concentration of either $HC_2H_3O_2$ or $C_2H_3O_2^-$ be so low as to make the capacity of the buffer approach the vanishing point.

Any system containing both a weak acid and its conjugate base can serve as a buffer. *Phosphate buffers*, widely used in biological work, are made by neutralizing phosphoric acid, H_3PO_4, with a strong base such as sodium hydroxide. Three different buffers combinations are possible: H_3PO_4 - $H_2PO_4^-$, $H_2PO_4^-$ - HPO_4^{-2}, and HPO_4^{-2} - PO_4^{-3}, effective at pH 2, 7, and 12 respectively.

Buffered solutions are used whenever it is important to maintain constant pH throughout a physical or chemical change. They are particularly useful in studying rates of chemical reactions in which H^+ ions are produced or consumed. Suppose, for example, one wishes to study the rate of oxidation of iodide ions with hydrogen peroxide:

$$2 \ I^- + H_2O_2 + 2 \ H^+ \longrightarrow I_2 + 2 \ H_2O \qquad (18.31)$$

Since this reaction involves H^+ ions, its rate may be expected to be strongly influenced by pH. If the pH is maintained at a constant value, it becomes possible to eliminate this variable and determine more accurately the effect of such factors as the concentration of I^-, the temperature, or the presence of a catalyst upon the reaction rate. Almost all biochemical reactions, particularly those involving enzymes, are pH dependent. Buffers are an invaluable tool in the study of such reactions.

Buffered solutions have many applications in analytical and physical chemistry. In particular, it may be recalled that one of the methods described in Chapter 17 for the determination of the ionization constant of a weak acid involves its partial neutralization with base. Since the resulting solution is buffered, its pH can be determined quite accurately even in the presence of basic or acidic impurities. This feature is perhaps the outstanding advantage of this particular method of determining ionization constants.

PROBLEMS

18.1   In what way(s) do the reactions of strong and weak acids with a strong base resemble each other? In what way(s) do they differ?

18.2   Write balanced net ionic equations for the reactions that occur when solutions of the following compounds are mixed.
   a. HCl and $NaOH$ c. HNO_3 and NH_3 e. HF and $Ca(OH)_2$
   b. $HC_2H_3O_2$ and $NaOH$ d. $HClO_4$ and $Ca(OH)_2$ f. HCl and $NaC_2H_3O_2$

18.3   Write balanced net ionic equations for the reactions that occur when:
   a. Solutions of $NaHCO_3$ and HBr are mixed.
   b. An excess of a strong acid is added to a solution of sodium carbonate.
   c. Solid calcium carbonate is treated with an excess of hydrochloric acid.
   d. Carbon dioxide is bubbled through a water solution of $NaOH$ until no further reaction occurs.
   e. Solutions containing equimolar quantities of $NaOH$ and CO_2 are mixed.

18.4   250 ml. of 0.300 M HCl is added to 150 ml. of 0.400 M $Ca(OH)_2$. Calculate the number of moles and the concentration of each ion remaining in solution after neutralization.

18.5   What volume of 0.22 M HCl will be required to neutralize 26 ml. of 0.18 M $Ba(OH)_2$?

18.6   A solid mixture contains only Na_2CO_3 and $NaCl$. It is found that 20.0 ml. of 0.180 M HCl is required to react completely with a 0.324 g. sample of the mixture. Calculate the percentage of Na_2CO_3.

18.7   Explain why equation 18.11 is valid for all acid-base reactions. If, in this equation, normality were replaced by molarity, would the equation remain generally valid? Explain, citing examples.

18.8   The gram equivalent weight of an acid is defined as the weight which reacts with one mole of OH^- ion. It is found that 0.466 g. of a solid acid requires 22.6 ml. of 0.254 M $NaOH$ to neutralize it. Calculate the gram equivalent weight of the acid.

18.9   What is the ratio of normality to molarity for each of the underlined reagents in the following acid-base reactions?
    a. $HC_2H_3O_2 + OH^- \rightarrow C_2H_3O_2^- + H_2O$
    b. $\underline{H_3PO_4} + 3\ OH^- \rightarrow PO_4^{-3} + 3\ H_2O$
    c. $\underline{H_3PO_4} + OH^- \rightarrow H_2PO_4^- + H_2O$
    d. $\underline{2\ H^+} + Zn(OH)_2(s) \rightarrow Zn^{+2} + 2\ H_2O$

18.10 The ionization constant of a certain weak acid is 1×10^{-9}. The undissociated acid is colored yellow; the anion derived from it has a blue color. What will be the color of this compound in a solution of pH 7? pH 8? pH 9? pH 10?

18.11 Fifty ml. of 0.10 M HCl is titrated with 0.10 M NaOH. Calculate the pH of the solution after the following volumes of NaOH are added.
    a. 49.00 ml.   c. 49.99 ml.   e. 50.01 ml.   g. 51.00 ml.
    b. 49.90 ml.   d. 50.00 ml.   f. 50.10 ml.
    From your data, construct a titration curve similar to that shown in Figure 18.1.

18.12 Explain why the choice of indicator in the titration of a weak acid with a strong base is much more critical than is the case when both acid and base are strong.

18.13 Of the three indicators, methyl red (end point at pH 5), bromthymol blue (end point at pH 7), or phenolphthalein (end point at pH 9), which would you suggest for the titration of:
    a. HCl with KOH?   b. $HC_2H_3O_2$ with KOH?   c. $NaC_2H_3O_2$ with HCl?
    Explain your choices.

18.14 Describe in some detail how you could prepare:
    a. $CaBr_2$ from $Ca(OH)_2$ e. NH_3 from NH_4Cl
    b. $NaHCO_3$ from NaOH   f. HCl from KCl
    c. NH_4Cl from NH_3 g. HBr from KBr
    d. H_2S from $FeS(s)$ h. HI from KI

18.15 Describe how the following conversions might be accomplished.
    a. $NaCl \rightarrow NaHCO_3$ e. $HF \rightarrow KF$
    b. $NaHCO_3 \rightarrow Na_2CO_3$ f. $KF \rightarrow HF$
    c. $CoCl_2 \rightarrow CoBr_2$ g. $Na_2CO_3 \rightarrow NaF$
    d. $NaCl \rightarrow NaHSO_4$ h. $Na_2S \rightarrow NaCl$

18.16 Suggest ways of separating the following series of ions, using acid-base and/or precipitation reactions.
    a. CO_3^{-2}, SO_4^{-2}, Cl^- c. F^-, SO_4^{-2} e. Ag^+, Cu^{+2}
    b. HCO_3^-, NO_3^- d. Cu^{+2}, Zn^{+2}, Ca^{+2}

18.17 Indicate briefly how you would distinguish between the following, all of which are white solids.
    a. Na_2CO_3 and NaOH   e. $BaCl_2$ and $CaCl_2$
    b. NaOH, $NaCHO_3$, and Na_2SO_4 f. $Ca(OH)_2$ and CaO
    c. NaCl and $NaNO_3$ g. KNO_3 and $Ca(OH)_2$
    d. $CaCl_2$ and $CaSO_4$ h. $CaCO_3$ and K_2CO_3

18.18 A solution is 0.10 M in H_2S and Co^{+2} and 0.01 M in Pb^{+2}.
    a. At what $[H^+]$ will CoS start to precipitate?
    b. At what $[H^+]$ will PbS start to precipitate?
    c. In view of your answers to (a) and (b), suggest a procedure for separating Co^{+2} and Pb^{+2}

18.19 A solution 0.01 M in Ni^{+2} and Zn^{+2} and 1.0 M in H^+ is saturated with H_2S so as to make $[H_2S] = 0.10$ M.
    a. Will a precipitate form under these conditions?
    b. How much base must be added to a liter of such solution to start to precipitate one of these ions?

18.20 State whether or not a precipitate will form in each of the following cases.
   a. Enough OH^- is added to 0.01 M $ZnCl_2$ to make the pH = 8.
   b. Enough OH^- is added to a solution 0.10 M in Zn^{+2} and in H_2S to make the pH = 8.
   c. Equal volumes of 0.10 M solutions of $AgNO_3$ and $HC_2H_3O_2$ are mixed.

18.21 The solubility product of $Fe(OH)_2$ is 1×10^{-15}. What must be the maximum pH of a solution in which $[Fe^{+2}] = 0.1$ M? Would you expect $Fe(OH)_2$ to be soluble in strongly acidic solution?

18.22 Explain the principle of buffer action, using an example other than that given in the text.

18.23 A buffer solution is made up by adding one mole of NH_4Cl to one l. of a 1.00 M solution of ammonia.
   a. What is the pH of this solution?
   b. What is the pH when 0.20 mole of HCl is added?
   c. What is the pH when 0.20 mole of NaOH is added?

*18.24 Using the Ka values given in Table 17.6, and the fact that Kw = 1×10^{-14}, calculate equilibrium constants for the following reactions:
   a. Strong acid—strong base $H^+ + OH^- \rightarrow H_2O$
   b. Weak acid—strong base $HCN + OH^- \rightarrow H_2O + CN^-$
   c. Strong acid—weak base $H^+ + NH_3 \rightarrow NH_4^+$
   d. Weak acid—weak base $HCN + NH_3 \rightarrow NH_4^+ + CN^-$
   Explain how your answers illustrate the statement made in Section 18.1 that acid-base reactions go essentially to completion unless both the acid and base are weak.

*18.25 In general, one can say that a compound is soluble in acid if 0.1 mole dissolves in 1 l. of 1 M acid. What is the smallest value that Ksp for a +2 hydroxide, $M(OH)_2$, can have if it is to be soluble in acid? A +3 hydroxide, $M(OH)_3$? Referring to the Ksp values of the various hydroxides given in Table 16.5, explain why one can make the general statement that, "All hydroxides are soluble in acid."

*18.26 Consider the titration of the weak acid $HC_2H_3O_2$ with NaOH. Suppose one starts with 50.0 ml. of 1.00 M $HC_2H_3O_2$ and adds the following volumes of 1.00 M NaOH. Calculate the pH in each case.
   a. 40.0 ml.   b. 49.0 ml.   c. 50.0 ml.   d. 51.0 ml.   e. 60.0 ml.
      In part (c) note that you are calculating the pH of a 0.50 M solution of $NaC_2H_3O_2$. In parts (a) and (b) calculate the ratio of $C_2H_3O_2^-$ to $HC_2H_3O_2$ and use Ka for acetic acid to obtain the pH.
      From your results, construct a titration curve for the reaction. Note particularly how such a curve differs from that for the titration of a strong acid with NaOH.

*18.27 A buffer solution is made up by adding 0.10 mole of $NaC_2H_3O_2$ to one l. of 0.10 M $HC_2H_3O_2$. What is the maximum amount of HCl that can be added to the solution without changing the pH by more than 0.5 unit?

*18.28 The overall reaction in the Solvay Process for the preparation of Na_2CO_3 is:

$$2 \ Na^+ + CaCO_3(s) \longrightarrow Na_2CO_3(s) + Ca^{+2}$$

Write balanced equations for the various steps of the process and add them to give this equation as the net result.

19 | COMPLEX IONS

If a powdered sample of white, anhydrous copper(II) sulfate is exposed to ammonia gas, a deep blue crystalline product is formed. Analysis reveals that this product contains four moles of ammonia for every mole of copper sulfate. X-ray studies indicate that the positive ion in this compound consists of a Cu^{+2} ion bonded to four ammonia molecules, i.e., $Cu(NH_3)_4^{+2}$. The reaction between the Cu^{+2} ion and the NH_3 molecules is represented in electron dot notation as:

$$Cu^{+2} + 4 : N{-}H \longrightarrow \left[\begin{array}{c} H{-}N{-}Cu{-}N{-}H \end{array} \right]^{+2}$$

$$Cu^{+2} + 4\,NH_3 \longrightarrow Cu(NH_3)_4^{+2} \qquad (19.1)$$

colorless   deep blue

The nitrogen atom of each ammonia molecule contributes a pair of unshared electrons to form a coordinate covalent bond between the Cu^{+2} ion and an NH_3 molecule.

It may be noted that in this reaction the ammonia is acting as a Lewis base, the Cu^{+2} ion as a Lewis acid. In this sense, reaction 19.1 resembles that between an ammonia molecule and a proton, which combine with each other to form an ammonium ion.

Addition of aqueous ammonia to a water solution of copper sulfate gives the same deep blue color. If the solution is carefully evaporated, blue crystals of hydrated $Cu(NH_3)_4SO_4$ can be obtained. From these observations it would appear that the $Cu(NH_3)_4^{+2}$ ion may exist in aqueous solution as well as in the solid state. Indeed, whenever Cu^{+2} ions and NH_3 molecules are brought into contact with each other, they show a strong tendency to combine in this manner.

The $Cu(NH_3)_4^{+2}$ ion is an example of a type of particle commonly referred to as a **complex ion.** In the broadest sense, a complex ion may be considered to be a charged particle consisting of more than one atom. Strictly speaking, such oxyanions as nitrate (NO_3^-) and sulfate (SO_4^{-2}) can be classified as complex ions. However, we shall use the term in a more restricted sense to refer to a *charged particle in which a* *metal atom is joined by coordinate covalent bonds to neutral. molecule(s) and/or negative ions.* Species such as $Cu(H_2O)_4^{+2}$ and $Zn(H_2O)_3(OH)^+$, encountered in previous chapters, are properly considered to be complex ions.

The metal atom in a complex ion (Cu, Zn, Al, and so on) is often referred to as the **central atom.** The molecules (such as NH_3, H_2O) or anions (such as OH^-, Cl^-) attached to the central atom by coordinate covalent bonds are known as **coordinating groups** or **ligands.** In order to act as a coordinating group, a molecule or ion must ordinarily have a pair of unshared electrons which can be shared with the central atom to form a covalent bond. The number of bonds (2, 4, 6, and so on) formed by the central atom is called its **coordination number.** The nomenclature of complex ions and their salts is discussed in Appendix 2.

The complex ions encountered in previous chapters have been ones in which the coordinating groups were either water molecules or hydroxide ions. In this chapter, we shall study a much wider variety of complex ions. We shall be interested in the charge, composition, geometry, and electronic structure of such ions. A knowledge of the properties of complex ions is essential to an understanding of the solution chemistry of the transition metals.

19.1 CHARGES OF COMPLEX IONS: NEUTRAL COMPLEXES

The charge of a complex ion can be obtained in a formal way by taking the algebraic sum of the oxidation number of the central atom and the charges of the ligands. The application of this simple rule is shown in Table 19.1 for certain complex ions of Pt(II).

TABLE 19.1 CHARGES OF COMPLEX IONS

Complex Ion	Oxidation No. Pt	Coordinating Groups	Charge of Ion
$Pt(NH_3)_4^{+2}$	+2	4 NH_3	$+2 + 4(0) = +2$
$Pt(NH_3)_3Cl^+$	+2	3 NH_3, 1 Cl^-	$+2 + 3(0) - 1 = +1$
$Pt(NH_3)Cl_3^-$	+2	1 NH_3, 3 Cl^-	$+2 + 0 - 3 = -1$
$PtCl_4^{-2}$	+2	4 Cl^-	$+2 + 4(-1) = -2$

As Table 19.1 indicates, a complex ion may carry either a positive or a negative charge. When a water solution of $[Pt(NH_3)_4]Cl_2$ is electrolyzed, the platinum, in the form of the $Pt(NH_3)_4^{+2}$ ion, migrates to the negative electrode. If the compound used is $K_2[PtCl_4]$, the platinum, present as the $PtCl_4^{-2}$ anion, moves to the positive electrode. The chlorine atoms in these two compounds also behave quite differently. In $[Pt(NH_3)_4]Cl_2$, chlorine is present as monatomic Cl^- ions which are immediately precipitated as AgCl by addition of silver nitrate. Addition of Ag^+ ions to a solution of $K_2[PtCl_4]$, in which the chlorine is covalently bonded to platinum, fails to give a precipitate.

Species such as $[Pt(NH_3)_2Cl_2]$ or $[Zn(H_2O)_2(OH)_2]$ in which the oxidation number of the central atom (+2) is exactly balanced by the total charge of the ligands (−2) are examples of neutral complexes. Compounds of this type are usually quite insoluble in polar solvents such as water. If sufficient base is added to a solution of a zinc salt to give an appreciable concentration of the neutral species [$Zn(H_2O)_2(OH)_2$], a precipitate of zinc hydroxide is obtained.

Among the most interesting of the neutral complexes are the *metal carbonyls*, in which a transition metal atom in the zero oxidation state is bonded to molecules of carbon monoxide. One of the most stable of these compounds is nickel carbonyl, [$Ni(CO)_4$], formed by passing carbon monoxide over elementary nickel at 60°C:

$$Ni(s) + 4\ CO(g) \rightleftharpoons Ni(CO)_4(l) + heat \qquad (19.2)$$

Nickel carbonyl, a colorless liquid boiling at 43°C, has the properties characteristic of molecular compounds. It is insoluble in water but soluble in organic solvents such as ether. Reaction 19.2 is reversed by heating to 200°C. The Mond process for the refining of nickel takes advantage of this reversible complex formation to remove impurities such as cobalt and iron.

19.2 COMPOSITION OF COMPLEX IONS

The determination of the exact composition of complex ions is by no means a simple task. If a complex ion can be isolated in the solid state in the form of a salt, chemical analysis can often be used to suggest its composition. For example, when we find that the compound formed by reacting ammonia with copper(II) sulfate contains the elements copper, nitrogen, hydrogen, sulfur, and oxygen in the atom ratio

1 Cu:4 N:12 H:1 S:4 O

we have reason to believe that the solid consists of equal numbers of SO_4^{-2} and $Cu(NH_3)_4^{+2}$ ions. The existence in this compound of the $Cu(NH_3)_4^{+2}$ ion is confirmed by a great deal of other evidence, in particular by x-ray diffraction data which shows that each copper atom is surrounded by four nitrogen atoms.

The formulas of complex ions in water solution are much more difficult to establish experimentally. What is frequently done is to assume the existence of species in solution which are known to exist in the solid state. Knowing, for example, that evaporation of an ammoniacal solution of copper(II) sulfate gives the compound [$Cu(NH_3)_4$]SO_4, we may assume the presence in the solution of the $Cu(NH_3)_4^{+2}$ ion. Going one step further, one might postulate that in a solution prepared by dissolving a copper(II) salt in pure water, the species $Cu(H_2O)_4^{+2}$, analogous to $Cu(NH_3)_4^{+2}$, should be present. Such a process of extrapolation can and often does lead to erroneous conclusions. In particular, one can seldom be certain of the exact number of water molecules present as ligands in an aquo-complex ion in solution.

Central Atom

The metals which show the greatest tendency to form stable complex ions are the transition metals falling in groups 6B through 2B of the periodic table (e.g., in the first transition series, the elements from chromium through zinc). The cations of these metals are ordinarily complexed both in water solution and in the solid state. Elements in other regions of the periodic table, notably aluminum in group 3A and tin and lead in 4A, form a more limited number of stable complex ions.

The metals which are most active in complex-ion formation are those which have small atomic and ionic radii. In the first transition series, for example, the atomic radii of the elements from chromium through zinc fall in the range 1.25 to 1.33 Å, significantly smaller than the radii of the first three elements of this period, potassium (2.31 Å), calcium (1.97 Å), and scandium (1.60 Å), all of which are poor complex formers. The correlation of atomic size with complexing tendency is understandable if one considers the driving force behind complex-ion formation to be the electrostatic attraction of a metal ion for the unshared electron pair of a ligand. The smaller the cation, the greater should be its attraction for electrons.

Many metals exhibit a variety of oxidation states in the complex ions that they form. Iron forms the neutral complex $[Fe(CO)_5]$, in which its oxidation number is zero, the $Fe(CN)_6^{-4}$ ion (oxid. no. Fe $= +2$) and the $Fe(CN)_6^{-3}$ ion (oxid. no. Fe $= +3$). Platinum forms a large number of complexes in both the $+4$ and the $+2$ oxidation states. Metals which form more than one cation frequently show a greater tendency toward complex-ion formation in the higher oxidation state. The complex ions of Cr^{+3}, Fe^{+3}, and Co^{+3} are both more stable and more numerous than those of Cr^{+2}, Fe^{+2}, and Co^{+2}. This effect can be explained in terms of the effect of oxidation number upon the electrostatic attraction between cation and ligand. The higher the oxidation number or charge of the central atom, the greater should be its attraction for a negative ion or a polar molecule.

TABLE 19.2 A FEW COMPLEX IONS OF THE TRANSITION METALS

H_2O	NH_3	OH^-	Cl^-	CN^-
$Cu(H_2O)_4^{+2}$	$Ag(NH_3)_2^+$	$Zn(OH)_4^{-2}$	$AgCl_2^-$	$Ag(CN)_2^-$
$Zn(H_2O)_4^{+2}$	$Cu(NH_3)_4^{+2}$	$Cr(OH)_6^{-3}$	$CuCl_4^{-2}$	$Zn(CN)_4^{-2}$
$Ni(H_2O)_6^{+2}$	$Zn(NH_3)_4^{+2}$		$HgCl_4^{-2}$	$Ni(CN)_4^{-2}$
$Co(H_2O)_6^{+3}$	$Ni(NH_3)_6^{+2}$		$PtCl_4^{-2}$	$Au(CN)_4^-$
$Cr(H_2O)_6^{+3}$	$Co(NH_3)_6^{+3}$		$AuCl_4^-$	$Fe(CN)_6^{-3}$
			$PtCl_6^{-2}$	$Fe(CN)_6^{-4}$

Coordinating Group: Chelating Agents

In principle, any molecule or anion possessing an unshared pair of electrons can donate them to a metal to form a complex ion. In practice, the atom within the ligand which furnishes these electrons is ordinarily derived from one of the more electronegative elements (C, N, O, S, F, Cl, Br, I). Hundreds of different ligands containing one or more of these atoms are known. Among those most frequently encountered in general chemistry are the NH_3 and H_2O molecules and the OH^-, Cl^- and CN^- ions (Table 19.2).

The relative abilities of different ligands to coordinate with metal ions depend upon a great many factors. One of the most important of these is the basicity of the ligand. It is perhaps not too surprising to find that molecules or ions which have a strong attraction for a proton are the best coordinating agents. The species NH_3, OH^- and CN^-, all of which are strong bases in the Brönsted-Lowry or G. N. Lewis sense form stable complexes with a wide variety of transition metal ions. The ClO_4^- ion, which shows no tendency to acquire a proton in water solution, is a notoriously poor coordinating agent; the NO_3^- and HSO_4^- ions, both derived from strong acids, form relatively few stable complexes. It should be pointed out, however, that the Cl^- ion, which does not act as a base in water, forms stable complexes with many transition metal ions. (cf. Table 19.2.)

One of the first coordinating groups to be studied extensively was the ethylene-diamine molecule:

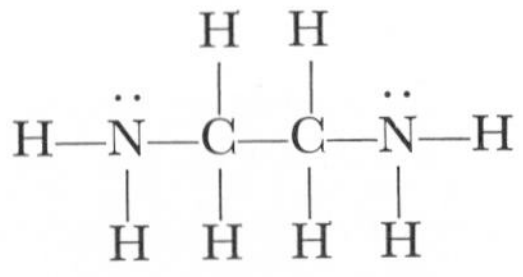

$$\begin{array}{c} \quad\;\; H\;\; H \\ \quad\quad |\;\; | \\ H-\overset{\cdot\cdot}{N}-C-C-\overset{\cdot\cdot}{N}-H \\ \quad\;\; |\;\; |\;\; |\;\; | \\ \quad\;\; H\; H\; H\; H \end{array}$$

This molecule, containing two nitrogen atoms, each with an unshared pair of electrons, forms two coordinate covalent bonds with metal atoms. These bonds are extremely stable, as shown by the fact that the addition of ethylenediamine to a solution containing the $Cu(NH_3)_4^{+2}$ ion results in the displacement of the four NH_3 molecules by two $H_2N—CH_2—CH_2—NH_2$ molecules.

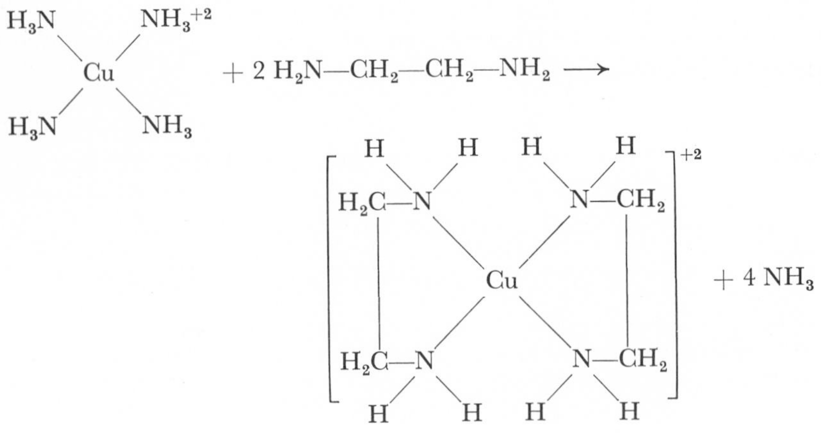

The fact that ethylenediamine is a powerful coordinating agent appears to be due at least in part to the high stability of the five-membered rings which it forms with metal ions.

A great many molecules and anions in addition to ethylenediamine form more than one coordinate covalent bond with a metal atom. Coordinating groups which behave in this manner are known as chelating agents; the complexes which they form are called **chelates.** Two important chelating agents are the oxalate ion, $C_2O_4^{-2}$, and the carbonate ion, CO_3^{-2}, both of which are capable of forming two oxygen-to-metal bonds. (The number 1 and 2 in the diagram indicate the atoms involved in chelate formation.)

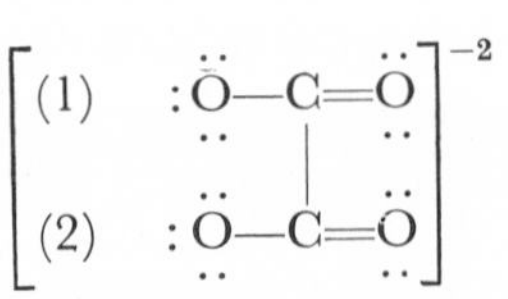

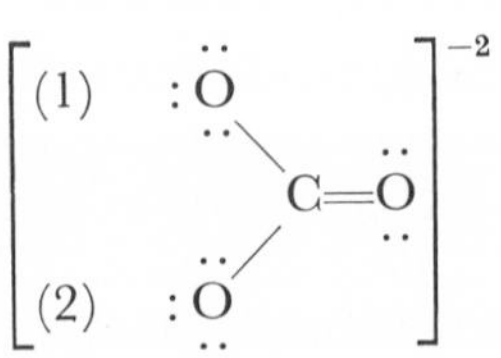

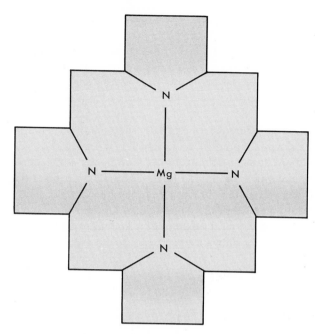

FIGURE 19.1   Ring structure in chlorophyll.

Chlorophyll, the green coloring matter of plants, and hemoglobin, the pigment responsible for the red color of blood, are both chelates. In each of these substances, metal atoms are coordinated to four nitrogen atoms which in turn form part of an intricate organic ring system. In chlorophyll, the central atom is magnesium: in hemoglobin, it is iron. The structure of the chlorophyll molecule is shown schematically in Figure 19.1.

In hemoglobin, it appears that the central iron atom is coordinated to six ligands rather than four. One of these "extra" ligands is a water molecule which can be replaced reversibly by a molecule of oxygen to give a derivative known as oxyhemoglobin.

$$\text{Hemoglobin} + O_2 \rightleftharpoons \text{Oxyhemoglobin} + H_2O$$

The position of this equilibrium is sensitive to the pressure of oxygen. In the lungs, where the blood is saturated with air (partial pressure $O_2 = 0.2$ atm.), the hemoglobin is almost completely converted to the oxidized form. In the tissues serviced by arterial blood, the partial pressure of oxygen drops and the oxyhemoglobin breaks down to release the elementary oxygen essential for the combustion of food. By this reversible process, hemoglobin acts as an oxygen carrier, absorbing oxygen in the lungs and liberating it to the tissues.

Unfortunately, hemoglobin forms a complex with carbon monoxide which is considerably more stable than oxyhemoglobin. The carbon monoxide complex is formed preferentially in the lungs even at CO concentrations as low as one part per thousand. When this happens, the flow of oxygen to the tissues is cut off, resulting eventually in muscular paralysis and death.

As has been pointed out previously, it is possible for a complex ion to contain more than one kind of ligand. The formation of the aquo-hydroxo complexes $Cu(H_2O)_3(OH)^+$, $Zn(H_3O)_3(OH)^+$ and $Al(H_2O)_5(OH)^{+2}$ was postulated earlier to explain the acidity of solutions of copper, zinc, and aluminum salts. The series of color changes observed when ammonia is added to a solution of a nickel salt can be attributed to the formation of a series of complex ions in which the water molecules in the $Ni(H_2O)_6^{+2}$ ion (green) are successively replaced by ammonia molecules to give $Ni(H_2O)_5(NH_3)^{+2}$, $Ni(H_2O)_4(NH_3)_2^{+2}$, $Ni(H_2O)_3(NH_3)_3^{+2}$, $Ni(H_2O)_2(NH_3)_4^{+2}$ (deep blue), $Ni(H_2O)(NH_3)_5^{+2}$, and $Ni(NH_3)_6^{+2}$ (purple).

Coordination Number

As may be seen from Table 19.3, the most common coordination numbers shown by metal atoms in complex ions are 6 and 4. A coordination number of 2 occurs less frequently, being restricted for the most part to the complex ions formed by the 1B metals in the $+1$ oxidation state. Odd coordination numbers (1, 3, 5 and so on) occur very rarely.

A metal in a given oxidation state usually shows only one coordination number, regardless of the particular complex ion in which it is present. For example, platinum in the $+2$ oxidation state invariably forms four bonds with coordinating groups, giving complex ions such as $Pt(H_2O)_4^{+2}$, $Pt(NH_3)_4^{+2}$, and $PtCl_4^{-2}$. Similarly, chromium (III) and cobalt (III) in their complex ions always show a coordination number of 6. Certain metals can show more than one coordination number in a given oxidation state. The Ni^{+2} ion, for example, is known to have two different coordination numbers, 4 and 6, shown respectively in the complex ions $Ni(CN)_4^{-2}$ and $Ni(H_2O)_6^{+2}$. Aluminum also shows coordination numbers of 4 or 6 depending upon the nature of the attached ligands.

TABLE 19.3 COORDINATION NUMBER AND GEOMETRY OF COMPLEX IONS

Coordination No.	Geometry	Examples
2	linear	Cu^+, Ag^+, Au^+
4	square planar	Cu^{+2}, Ni^{+2}, Pd^{+2}, Pt^{+2}, Au^{+3}
4	tetrahedral	Cu^+, Zn^{+2}, Cd^{+2}, Hg^{+2}, Al^{+3}
6	octahedral	Co^{+3}, Cr^{+3}, Fe^{+2}, Fe^{+3}, Pt^{+4}, Cd^{+2}, Al^{+3}, Ni^{+2}

19.3 GEOMETRY OF COMPLEX IONS

Coordination Number = 2

In principle, it should be possible for a complex ion in which the central atom has a coordination number of 2 to be linear as in CO_2 or bent as in the H_2O molecule. In practice, all the complex ions of this type which have been investigated have been shown to be linear. The structures of the $Ag(NH_3)_2^+$, $Ag(CN)_2^-$ and $Au(CN)_2^-$ ions may be represented as follows:

$$(H_3N—Ag—NH_3)^+, \quad (N\equiv C—Ag—C\equiv N)^-, \quad (N\equiv C—Au—C\equiv N)^-$$

Coordination Number = 4

For a complex ion in which four ligands are arranged about the central atom, two symmetrical geometric arrangements are possible. The four coordinating groups may be located at the corners of a square, giving what is known as a **square planar complex,** or at the corners of a regular tetrahedron **(tetrahedral complex).** Both arrangements are known; x-ray studies show that the complexes of platinum(II)

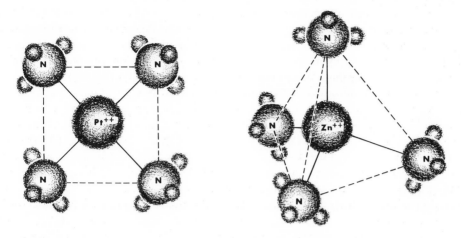

FIGURE 19.2 Geometry of ammonia complex ions formed by platinum(II) and zinc(II).

are of the square planar type while the four-coordinated complexes of zinc(II) are tetrahedral. As we shall see later, the electronic structure of the central metal atom plays a major role in determining which of these two structures a particular metal forms.

It has been found experimentally that certain square complexes can exist in two different forms with quite different properties. Consider, for example, the neutral complex, $[Pt(NH_3)_2Cl_2]$. Two forms of this compound, differing in color, water solubility, and chemical reactivity have been prepared. One of these, made by reacting ammonia with the $PtCl_4^{-2}$ ion, has a structure in which the two ammonia molecules are located at adjacent corners of a square. In the other form, prepared by reacting the $Pt(NH_3)_4^{+2}$ ion with hydrochloric acid, the two ammonia molecules are located at opposite corners of the square:

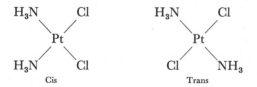

The two forms of $Pt(NH_3)_2Cl_2$ are called **geometrical isomers.** From a structural standpoint, they differ only in the spatial arrangement of the groups coordinated about the central atom. The form in which like groups are as close together as possible is called the **cis** isomer; the form in which like groups are far apart is referred to as the **trans** isomer. Geometrical isomerism can occur with any square, planar complex of general formula Ma_2b_2 or Ma_2bc, in which M refers to the central atom and a, b, c represent ligands. Geometrical isomers cannot exist for tetrahedral complexes, since each ligand is equidistant from the other three.

The assignment of a cis or trans configuration to a particular isomer of a co-ordination compound is by no means a simple experimental problem. X-ray diffraction studies have been used successfully in a few cases, but are generally difficult to apply. One method that has been used with a few neutral molecules involves dipole moment measurements in a suitable nonpolar solvent. The symmetrical trans isomer of a compound such as $[Pt(NH_3)_2Cl_2]$ can be expected to have a dipole moment of zero; the cis isomer, in which the ligands are unsymmetrically located about the central atom, will have a positive dipole moment. Another approach involves studying the reactivity of the coordination compound towards certain chelating agents. When the cis isomer of $[Pt(NH_3)_2Cl_2]$ is reacted with oxalate ions in solution, two Cl^- ions are displaced by an $C_2O_4^{-2}$ ion:

$$\begin{array}{c} H_3N \\ \diagdown \; \diagup \\ Pt \\ \diagup \; \diagdown \\ H_3N \quad Cl \end{array} \; Cl \; + \; \begin{bmatrix} O-C=O \\ | \\ O-C=O \end{bmatrix}^{-2} \longrightarrow \begin{array}{c} H_3N \quad O-C=O \\ \diagdown \; \diagup \\ Pt \qquad | \\ \diagup \; \diagdown \\ H_3N \quad O-C=O \end{array} \; + \; 2\,Cl^- \quad (19.4)$$

The trans isomer does not react readily since the oxalate ion cannot be sufficiently distorted to become attached to platinum at two points trans to each other.

Coordination Number = 6

The six groups surrounding the central atom in such complexes as $Fe(CN)_6^{-3}$ and $Co(NH_3)_6^{+3}$ are located at the corners of a regular octahedron, a geometric figure with eight sides, all of which are equilateral triangles, and six apices (Figure 19.3). The metal atom is located at the center of the octahedron. The spatial arrangement of ligands in octahedral complexes is often shown by skeleton structures such as that shown at the right of Figure 19.3.

Geometrical isomerism can occur in octahedral as well as square complexes. It may be noted from Figure 19.3 that for any given position of a ligand in an octahedral complex, there are four equivalent positions equidistant from the first and one at a greater distance. If, for example, we choose position 1 as a point of reference, groups located at 2, 3, 4, and 5 will be equidistant from it, while a group at position 6 will be farther away. We may refer to positions 1 and 2, 1 and 3, 1 and 4, or 1 and 5 as being cis to each other while positions 1 and 6 are trans. Consequently, an ion

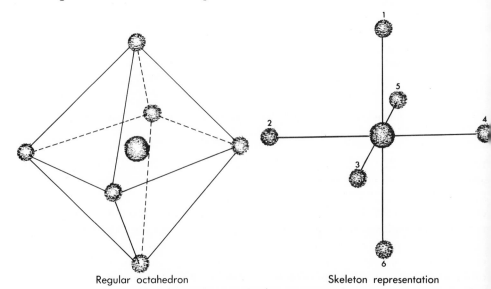

Regular octahedron   Skeleton representation
FIGURE 19.3 The octahedral configuration.

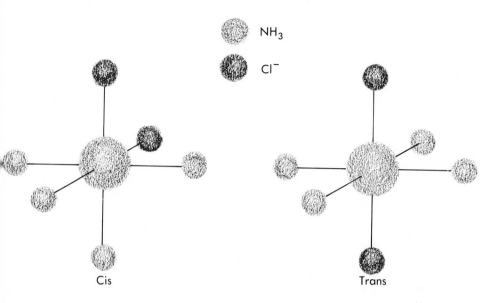

NH$_3$

Cl$^-$

Cis

Trans

FIGURE 19.4 Isomers of Co(NH$_3$)$_4$Cl$_2$$^+$.

such as Co(NH$_3$)$_4$Cl$_2$$^+$ can exist in two isomeric forms, one in which the two chloride ions are in a cis relationship to each other and another in which they are in a trans configuration (Figure 19.4).

The complexes formed by cobalt(III) with ammonia and chloride ions played an important part in the development of the structural theory of coordination compounds. By the end of the nineteenth century, five different compounds containing trivalent cobalt, chloride ions and ammonia were known:

1. CoCl$_3$·6 NH$_3$ orange-yellow
2. CoCl$_3$·5 NH$_3$ violet
3. CoCl$_3$·4 NH$_3$ green
4. CoCl$_3$·4 NH$_3$ violet
5. CoCl$_3$·3 NH$_3$ green

Treatment of any of these salts with hydrochloric acid fails to remove the ammonia, indicating that the NH$_3$ molecules must be strongly bonded to cobalt. When silver nitrate is added to a water solution of 1, all the chlorine is precipitated immediately as AgCl. With compound 2, on the other hand, only two thirds of the chlorine is precipitated by Ag$^+$ at room temperature, while compounds 3 and 4 give up only one third of their chlorine under these conditions. Compounds 3 and 4 differ from each other in chemical reactivity as well as color. Compound 5 fails to react with Ag$^+$.

Alfred Werner, in 1893, reflecting on the properties of these and analogous compounds of chromium, platinum, and palladium, proposed the basic structural theory of coordination complexes which is accepted today and has been presented in the foregoing discussion. His ideas, reputed to have come to him in a dream, were revolutionary at the time, opening up a whole new area of inorganic chemistry. Following Werner, the compounds just listed may be assigned the structures:

1. [Co(NH$_3$)$_6$] Cl$_3$
2. [Co(NH$_3$)$_5$Cl] Cl$_2$
3. [Co(NH$_3$)$_4$Cl$_2$] Cl   (trans)
4. [Co(NH$_3$)$_4$Cl$_2$] Cl   (cis)
5. [Co(NH$_3$)$_3$Cl$_3$]

Only those chlorides which are outside the coordination sphere are precipitated by silver nitrate.

On the basis of his theory, Werner predicted the existence of geometrical isomers for certain square, planar complexes. Many years later, he was able to isolate cis and trans isomers of $[Pt(NH_3)_2Cl_2]$ and analogous platinum complexes. In recognition of his outstanding contributions to inorganic chemistry, Werner, in 1913, received the Nobel prize in chemistry.

19.4 ELECTRONIC STRUCTURE OF COMPLEX IONS

One of the first attempts to explain the stability of complex ions in terms of the electronic structure of the central metal atom was that of Sidgwick, who suggested in 1927 that metal atoms tend to achieve a noble-gas structure by accepting electron pairs from ligands. This approach, which proved so successful in explaining the formulas and properties of the molecular compounds formed by the nonmetals of the first and second periods of the periodic table, can be applied to many complex ions.

Among the complex ions in which the central metal atom has a noble-gas structure are those in which four ligands are attached to a Zn^{+2} ion, e.g., $Zn(H_2O)_4^{+2}$, $Zn(NH_3)_4^{+2}$, and so on. To show that this is the case, let us count the electrons surrounding the zinc nucleus. A Zn^{+2} ion has 28 electrons, two less than a zinc atom (at. no. = 30). Each ligand donates two electrons; four ligands must then contribute a total of eight electrons. Adding these eight electrons to the 28 associated with the bare Zn^{+2} ion gives a total of 36, which is the number of electrons in an atom of the noble gas krypton.

Several other complex ions are known in which the central metal has a noble-gas

TABLE 19.4 NUMBER OF ELECTRONS SURROUNDING CENTRAL ATOM IN COMPLEXES OF FIRST SERIES OF TRANSITION METAL

Atom	No. e⁻	Monatomic Ion	No. e⁻	Complex Ion	No. e⁻
Cr	24	Cr^{+3}	21	$Cr(H_2O)_6^{+3}$	$21 + 12 = 33$
Mn	25	Mn^{+2}	23	$Mn(H_2O)_6^{+2}$	$23 + 12 = 35$
Fe	26	Fe^{+3}	23	$Fe(CN)_6^{-3}$	$23 + 12 = 35$
		Fe^{+2}	24	$Fe(CN)_6^{-4}$	$24 + 12 = 36*$
Co	27	Co^{+3}	24	$Co(NH_3)_6^{+3}$	$24 + 12 = 36*$
		Co^{+2}	25	$Co(NH_3)_6^{+2}$	$25 + 12 = 37$
Ni	28	Ni^{+2}	26	$Ni(CN)_4^{-2}$	$26 + 8 = 34$
				$Ni(NH_3)_6^{+2}$	$26 + 12 = 38$
Cu	29	Cu^{+2}	27	$Cu(NH_3)_4^{+2}$	$27 + 8 = 25$
		Cu^+	28	$Cu(CN)_4^{-3}$	$28 + 8 = 36*$
Zn	30	Zn^{+2}	28	$Zn(NH_3)_4^{+2}$	$28 + 8 = 36*$

* Complexes in which the central atom has a noble-gas structure.

structure (Table 19.4). However, exceptions to this rule are far more common than examples. Among these exceptions are all of the complex ions formed by chromium (III), manganese(II), iron(III), cobalt(II), nickel(II), and copper(II). Quite clearly, any attempt to predict the stoichiometry of complex ions based on the tendency of the central atom to acquire a noble-gas structure is doomed to failure. In the case of nickel(II) complexes, for example, one would predict a coordination number of 5, since this would put $26 + 10 = 36$ electrons around the nickel. In practice nickel(II) shows a coordination number of 4 or 6 rather than 5.

For one particular series of complex compounds, the metal carbonyls, predictions based on the tendency to achieve a noble-gas electronic configuration agree remarkably well with the observed stoichiometry. Considering the first transition series, we find that the metals of even atomic number, $_{24}Cr$, $_{26}Fe$, and $_{28}Ni$, form stable carbonyl complexes $Cr(CO)_6$, $Fe(CO)_5$, and $Ni(CO)_4$, in each of which the central atom has a noble-gas electronic configuration. Single atoms of the elements of odd atomic number, $_{25}Mn$, $_{27}Co$, and $_{29}Cu$ cannot, by accepting pairs of electrons from CO molecules, reach a noble-gas structure. Experimentally, no carbonyl complex of copper(0) has ever been isolated; the carbonyls of cobalt and manganese are polymeric materials of rather complicated structures.

In the past three decades, several more sophisticated models of bonding in complex ions have been developed. One of these, the *atomic orbital* or *valence bond* approach, was introduced in Chapter 10 to explain the bonding in relatively simple molecules of the nonmetals. The application of this theory to coordination compounds, due in large measure to Professor Pauling, has proved sufficiently useful to warrant centering our discussion around it. Rather recently, a quite different approach, known as the **crystal field** theory, has been developed to explain certain of the chemical and physical properties of coordination compounds which were difficult to understand in terms of the valence bond theory. We shall present a brief introduction to this theory, which is still going through an evolutionary development.

Valence Bond (Atomic Orbital) Approach

The valence bond treatment presented in Chapter 10 is readily extended to explain the electronic structures of complex ions in which various ligands are bonded to a central metal atom. It is assumed that the electron pairs donated by the ligands enter hybrid orbitals associated with the metal atom. You will recall that hybrid orbitals are formed by combining the individual orbitals of the isolated atoms in a particular manner. For example, a set of four completely equivalent sp^3 orbitals is formed by hybridizing one s and three p orbitals.

In discussing the hybrid orbitals occupied by bonding electrons in complex ions, it will be convenient to organize our discussion according to the coordination number shown by the central metal atom (2, 4, or 6).

Coordination Number = 2: sp hybridization. Complex ions in which the central metal atom has a coordination number of two can be assigned electronic structures analogous to that postulated for the BeF_2 molecule (p. 225). The two pairs of bonding electrons are assumed to occupy two hybrid orbitals formed by combining an s and a p orbital. These hybrid orbitals should be oriented at angles of 180° to each other, in agreement with the experimental observation that complex ions of this type have a linear structure.

To illustrate the formation of sp hybrid bonds, consider the electronic structure of the complex ions of silver (I). (All levels below 5s are completely filled.)

	5s	5p		
Ag	(·)	( )	( )	( )
Ag⁺	( )	( )	( )	( )
Ag(NH₃)₂⁺	(··)	(··)	( )	( ) (Bonding orbitals enclosed by rectangle.)

Coordination Number = 4: sp³ hybridization. Complexes in which zinc or aluminum have a coordination number of 4 show the tetrahedral geometry characteristic of such compounds as CH_4 and CCl_4. In the $Zn(NH_3)_4^{+2}$ ion as in the CH_4 molecule, the four pairs of bonding electrons can be accommodated in four sp³ hybrid orbitals.

	4s	4p		
Zn	(· ·)	( )	( )	( )
Zn^{+2}	( )	( )	( )	( )
$Zn(NH_3)_4^{+2}$	(· ·)	(· ·)	(· ·)	(· ·)

Coordination Number = 4: dsp² hybridization. The square planar complexes formed, for example, by platinum(II), differ in electronic structure as well as geometry from the tetrahedral complexes of zinc. In the valence bond approach the four bonding orbitals occupied in square, planar complexes are described as dsp² hybrids, formed by combining a d, an s, and two p orbitals.

	5d					6s	6p		
Pt	(· ·) (· ·) (· ·) (· ·) (·)					(·)	( ) ( ) ( )		
Pt⁺²(valence state)	(· ·) (· ·) (· ·) (· ·) ( )					( )	( ) ( ) ( )		
$Pt(NH_3)_4^{+2}$	(· ·) (· ·) (· ·) (· ·) (· ·)					(· ·)	(· ·) (· ·)		( )

This type of bonding is shown in many other types of complex ions, including those formed by copper(II). In this case, the formation of dsp² hybrid bonds requires that an electron be promoted to the 4p level in order to make a 3d orbital available for bonding.

	3d					4s	4p		
Cu	(· ·) (· ·) (· ·) (· ·) (· ·)					(·)	( ) ( ) ( )		
Cu^{+2}	(· ·) (· ·) (· ·) (· ·) (·)					( )	( ) ( ) ( )		
Cu^{+2} (valence state)	(· ·) (· ·) (· ·) (· ·) ( )					( )	( ) ( ) (·)		
$Cu(NH_3)_4^{+2}$	(· ·) (· ·) (· ·) (· ·) (· ·)					(· ·)	(· ·) (· ·)		(·)

Coordination Number = 6: d²sp³ hybridization and Inner and Outer Complexes. In the octahedral complex ion $Fe(CN)_6^{-4}$, the six pairs of electrons contributed by the ligands can be located in six hybrid d²sp³ bonding orbitals, formed by combining two 3d, one 4s and three 4p orbitals.

	3d					4s	4p		
Fe	(· ·) (·) (·) (·) (·)					(· ·)	( ) ( ) ( )		
Fe^{+2}	(· ·) (·) (·) (·) (·)					( )	( ) ( ) ( )		
Fe^{+2} (valence state)	(· ·) (· ·) (· ·) ( ) ( )					( )	( ) ( ) ( )		
$Fe(CN)_6^{-4}$	(· ·) (· ·) (· ·) (· ·) (· ·)					(· ·)	(· ·) (· ·) (· ·)		

The fact that compounds such as $K_4Fe(CN)_6$ are diamagnetic tends to confirm a structure such as this in which there are no unpaired electrons.

Certain octahdedral complexes of iron(II) are known to be paramagnetic; the $Fe(H_2O)_6^{+2}$ ion, for example, has been shown from magnetic studies to have four unpaired electrons. One way to explain this in terms of the valence bond picture is to postulate that the d orbitals involved in bonding are those in the fourth principal energy level rather than the third.

Bonds of this type are sometimes referred to as sp^3d^2 hybrids (recall the discussion of the bonding in SF_6, p. 226), to distinguish them from the d^2sp^3 hybrid bonds found in the $Fe(CN)_6^{-4}$ ion. Perhaps more frequently, the terms **outer complex** and **inner complex** are used to distinguish between these two types of octahedral complexes. In general, it is found that ligands, such as the CN^- ion, which are strong bases tend to form inner complexes. Ligands such as H_2O and, in particular, the F^- ion, which are weaker bases tend to form outer complexes. Among the complex ions of cobalt (III), for example, the only ones which appear to be outer complexes are those such as CoF_6^{-3}, in which several fluoride ions are bonded to cobalt.

Crystal Field Theory

Although the valence bond approach has proved extremely useful in explaining and correlating the geometries, electronic structures, and many of the properties of complex ions, it is deficient in certain important respects. For example, it cannot explain the wide variety of brilliant colors characteristic of so many coordination compounds. Again, although the valence bond model can rationalize the existence of two different kinds of octahedral complexes of iron(II), it cannot explain why the CN^- ion forms one type of complex and the H_2O molecule another.

It has long been recognized that many of the properties of complex ions can best be explained in terms of an electrostatic rather than a covalent type of bonding between metal and ligand. The fact that the ability of a metal ion to form complexes seems to be directly related to its charge density implies that it forms ionic or ion-dipole bonds with anions or molecules acting as ligands. In many cases, the strength of the metal-ligand bonds follows this same trend and lends itself to the same simple explanation. For these reasons, among others, electrostatic models of the bonding in complex ions have become increasingly popular in recent years.

The crystal field model starts with the assumption that the attractive forces holding a complex ion together are primarily electrostatic rather than covalent. The major part of the stabilization energy holding metal to ligand is attributed to coulombic interactions between the positively charged metal ion and the electrons associated with the ligand. While the valence bond model assumes that electrons donated by the ligand enter the orbitals of the central metal ion to form covalent bonds, the crystal field theory considers that the modification of the electronic structure of the metal ion is due only to coulombic interactions between the ligands and the d electrons of the metal. The physical and chemical properties of the complex are explained largely in terms of these modifications.

To illustrate the changes which ligands can produce in the electronic structure of a metal ion, let us consider a specific example, the formation of the $Fe(CN)_6^{-4}$ complex ion.

$$Fe^{+2} + 6\ CN^- \longrightarrow Fe(CN)_6^{-4} \tag{19.5}$$

In the uncomplexed Fe^{+2} ion, there are six electrons distributed among five 3d orbitals, all of which have the same energy. However, when CN^- ions approach the Fe^{+2} ion to form an octahedral complex, geometric considerations suggest that these orbitals should no longer have the same energy. It happens that two of the five 3d orbitals are oriented in such a way that they lie along the direction of approach of the CN^- ions coming in at octahedral angles. Electrons in these orbitals are repelled more strongly than those in the other three orbitals.

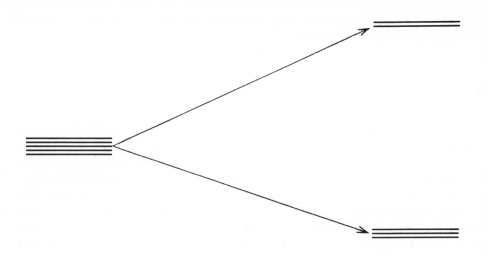

FIGURE 19.5 Splitting of d orbitals in octahedral field.

In other words, as the result of the formation of an octahedral complex, the five 3d orbitals which are originally equivalent to each other are split into two groups of different energies. Schematically, we have the situation shown in Figure 19.5. As a result, one might expect to find a rearrangement of the electronic structure of the Fe^{+2} ion; the six 3d electrons will tend to pair in the three lower energy levels. In other words, as a result of the formation of the $Fe(CN)_6^{-4}$ ion, the electronic structure of the Fe^{+2} ion changes from

3d

Fe^{+2} (free ion) $(\cdot\,\cdot)$ $(\cdot\ )$ $(\cdot\ )$ $(\cdot\ )$ $(\cdot\ )$

to

Fe^{+2} (in $Fe(CN)_6^{-4}$ complex) $(\cdot\,\cdot)$ $(\cdot\,\cdot)$ $(\cdot\,\cdot)$ $(\ )$ $(\ )$

The extent to which the energies of the d orbitals are modified by complex ion formation will depend upon how strongly the ligands interact with the electrons within these orbitals. The H_2O molecule, which is a weaker Lewis base than the CN^- ion, will repel electrons in the d orbitals to a lesser extent, resulting in a smaller energy separation. It is not unreasonable to suppose that in the weaker crystal field exerted by the water molecules, the electron distribution of the uncomplexed Fe^{+2} ion, in which there are a maximum number of unpaired electrons, will be retained. In other words water molecules do not interact strongly enough with the d electrons of the Fe^{+2} ion to overcome their tendency to remain unpaired insofar as possible.

Fe^{+2} (in $Fe(H_2O)_6^{+2}$) $(\cdot\,\cdot)$ $(\cdot\ )$ $(\cdot\ )$ $(\cdot\ )$ $(\cdot\ )$

Looking at the structures just written for the Fe^{+2} ion in the $Fe(CN)_6^{-4}$ and $Fe(H_2O)_6^{+2}$ complex ions, we see that the crystal field theory explains why the first complex is diamagnetic (no unpaired electrons) while the second is paramagnetic, with four unpaired electrons. To be sure, the valence bond theory also explains these observations, in terms of inner and outer complexes. The advantage of the crystal field theory is that it suggests *why* the CN^- ion should form one type of complex and the H_2O molecule another. In general, the crystal field theory predicts that ligands which are weak bases (H_2O, F^-) tend to form complexes in which there are a maximum number of unpaired electrons, while strongly basic ligands (CN^-) tend to produce complexes in which the d electrons are paired.

The crystal field theory also offers a rational explanation for the fact that most complexes in which the metal ion has unfilled d orbitals available are colored. The splitting of the d orbitals by ligand interactions creates a situation in which electrons can move into higher energy levels by absorbing light. The extent to which the d orbitals are split will determine the amount of energy required to promote an electron from a lower to a higher orbital and hence the wavelength of the light which is absorbed. In some cases, it is possible to predict quite accurately from the crystal field theory the wavelengths at which absorption will occur.

Lest it be supposed that the crystal field theory can explain all the properties of complex ions, it may be advisable to point out at least one of its deficiencies. If one thinks of the bonding in complex ions as being primarily electrostatic, it is hard to explain why certain molecules which have very small dipole moments such as CO can be effective coordinating agents. In order to explain this, it is necessary to modify the crystal field theory to take into account covalent as well as ionic bonding. A more sophisticated version of the electrostatic approach, known as the **ligand field** theory, has recently been developed with this in mind.

19.5   RATE OF COMPLEX-ION FORMATION: LABILE AND INERT COMPLEXES

One of the most common reactions shown by complex ions in solution is that of substitution, in which a new complex is formed through an exchange of ligands. When a solution of a copper(II) salt is treated with ammonia, the light blue color characteristic of the $Cu(H_2O)_4^{+2}$ complex ion is replaced by the deep blue color of the $Cu(NH_3)_4^{+2}$ ion.

$$Cu(H_2O)_4^{+2} + 4\ NH_3 \longrightarrow Cu(NH_3)_4^{+2} + 4\ H_2O \qquad (19.6)$$

Addition of concentrated hydrochloric acid to a solution of a copper(II) salt causes a color change from blue to green, reflecting the formation of species such as $CuCl_4^{-2}$, in which Cl^- ions rather than H_2O molecules are bonded to copper.

$$Cu(H_2O)_4^{+2} + 4\ Cl^- \longrightarrow CuCl_4^{-2} + 4\ H_2O \qquad (19.7)$$

Reactions such as 19.6 and 19.7 are, of course, reversible. One obtains an equilibrium mixture of products whose relative concentrations depend upon the relative (thermodynamic) stabilities of the various complex ions. We shall consider some of the equilibrium relations involved in such reactions later in this chapter. At the moment, we are concerned with the *rate* at which equilibrium is established in substitution reactions involving complex ions

In the case of copper(II) complexes, the establishment of equilibria involving species such as $Cu(H_2O)_4^{+2}$ and $Cu(NH_3)_4^{+2}$ is virtually instantaneous. If one adds ammonia to a water solution of a copper(II) salt, the deep blue color of the $Cu(NH_3)_4^{+2}$ ion appears immediately. The color quickly changes to green if hydrochloric acid is added to replace ammonia molecules in the complex by chloride ions. Complexes such as these in which the rate of ligand exchange is too rapid to be measured by ordinary techniques are said to be **labile.** Species in this category include, in addition to copper(II) complexes, all of the known complexes of silver(I) and zinc(II), most of those of nickel(II), and all of the outer (sp^3d^2) octahedral complexes of the transition metals.

Complexes which undergo substitution reactions in solution at a measurable rate are said to be nonlabile or inert. If the purple compound $[Co(NH_3)_5Cl]Cl_2$ is added to water, a slow reaction occurs in which the chloride ion inside the complex is replaced by a water molecule:

$$Co(NH_3)_5Cl^{+2} + H_2O \longrightarrow Co(NH_3)_5H_2O^{+3} + Cl^- \qquad (19.8)$$

The rate of this reaction can be determined by following the color change or measuring the increase in conductivity brought about by the formation of free chloride ions. It is found that at room temperature only about six out of every 1000 $Co(NH_3)_5Cl^{+2}$ ions have reacted with water in an hour's time. Even after a day has passed, better than 85 per cent of the starting material remains unreacted. This is true despite the fact that the aquo-complex, $Co(NH_3)_5H_2O^{+3}$ is inherently the more stable species under these conditions. That is, the equilibrium constant for reaction 19.8 is so large that, given sufficient time, virtually all of the cobalt(III) is converted to the $Co(NH_3)_5H_2O^{+3}$ complex. Here we see again the importance of distinguishing between kinetic considerations, as described in the terms *lability* or *inertness*, and thermodynamic factors which can predict only the ultimate state of a system in terms of the *stabilities* of the species involved.

Almost all the complex ions formed by cobalt(III), chromium(III) and platinum(II and IV) can be classified as inert. These ions vary greatly, however, in the rate at which they participate in substitution reactions. The rate of substitution depends not only upon the nature of the central atom but also upon the ligands bonded to it. For example, if one adds the complex compound $[Co(NH_3)_5I]Cl_2$ to water, a reaction analogous to 19.8

$$Co(NH_3)_5I^{+2} + H_2O \longrightarrow Co(NH_3)_5H_2O^{+3} + I^-$$

occurs at a rate such that about 3 per cent of the $Co(NH_3)_5I^{+2}$ ions are consumed in one hour. On the other hand, the $[Co(NH_3)_5NO_2]^{+2}$ complex ion is so inert that no detectable reaction with water takes place within a week.

19.6 COMPLEX-ION EQUILIBRIA

In the preceding section, we compared the (kinetic) labilities of different complex ions. It is, of course, equally important to be able to compare their (thermodynamic) stabilities. One way to do this is to formulate and measure the equilibrium constant for the reaction that occurs when a compound containing a particular complex ion is added to water. In doing this, it is customary to treat the reaction as if it were a simple dissociation, ignoring the water molecules involved. Thus for the equilibrium which is set up when a compound containing $Ag(NH_3)_2^+$ ions is added to water, we write:

$$Ag(NH_3)_2^+ \rightleftharpoons Ag^+ + 2 NH_3 \qquad K_c = \frac{[Ag^+] \times [NH_3]^2}{[Ag(NH_3)_2^+]}$$

The fact that the equilibrium constant for this reaction is a very small number, 4×10^{-8}, means that the $Ag(NH_3)_2^+$ ion dissociates to only a very slight extent when added to water. Looking at it another way, the addition of ammonia in low concentrations to a solution containing Ag^+ ions should convert most of them to the $Ag(NH_3)_2^+$ ion (Example 19.1).

Example 19.1. Using the value of 4×10^{-8} for the dissociation constant of the $Ag(NH_3)_2^+$ ion, calculate:

    a. The ratio of the concentrations of Ag^+ and $Ag(NH_3)_2^+$ in a solution 1 M in NH_3.

    b. The equilibrium concentration of NH_3 necessary to produce a 50 per cent conversion of Ag^+ to $Ag(NH_3)_2^+$.

Solution

a. All that is required is to substitute for the concentration of NH_3 in the equilibrium expression:

$$K_c = \frac{[Ag^+] \times [NH_3]^2}{[Ag(NH_3)_2^+]} = 4 \times 10^{-8} \qquad \frac{[Ag^+] \, (1)^2}{[Ag(NH_3)_2^+]} = 4 \times 10^{-8}$$

$$\frac{[Ag^+]}{[Ag(NH_3)_2^+]} = 4 \times 10^{-8}$$

The fact that this ratio is extremely small means that in a solution 1 M in ammonia, nearly all the silver is in the form of the $Ag(NH_3)_2^+$ complex. If, for example, the concentration of $Ag(NH_3)_2^+$ is 1 M, that of uncomplexed Ag^+ is only 4×10^{-8} M.

b. The conditions of part b, 50 per cent conversion of Ag^+ to $Ag(NH_3)_2^+$, require that the equilibrium concentrations of these two ions be equal to each other:

$$\frac{[Ag^+] \times [NH_3]^2}{[Ag(NH_3)_2^+]} = 4 \times 10^{-8} \qquad [NH_3]^2 = 4 \times 10^{-8} \qquad [NH_3] = 2 \times 10^{-4}$$

It is evident that a very low concentration of NH_3 is sufficient to convert half the Ag^+ ions to the ammine complex. At concentrations of NH_3 above 2×10^{-4}, better than half the silver ions will be complexed.

The relative stabilities of different complex ions of silver can be estimated from a knowledge of their dissociation constants. For example, when we find that the equilibrium constant for the reaction:

$$Ag(CN)_2^- \rightleftharpoons Ag^+ + 2 \, CN^- \qquad K_c = \frac{[Ag^+] \times [CN^-]^2}{[Ag(CN)_2^-]}$$

is only about 1×10^{-21}, we deduce that the $Ag(CN)_2^-$ complex is even more stable than $Ag(NH_3)_2^+$. We would expect that in a solution containing equal concentrations of CN^- ions and NH_3 molecules, any silver(I) ions present would be tied up almost exclusively in the form of the $Ag(CN)_2^-$ ion (Example 19.2).

Example 19.2. Calculate the ratio of the concentrations of $Ag(CN)_2^-$ and $Ag(NH_3)_2^+$ in a solution in which $[NH_3] = [CN^-]$.

Solution. Starting with the expression:

$$\frac{[Ag^+] \times [NH_3]^2}{[Ag(NH_3)_2^+]} = 4 \times 10^{-8} \tag{a}$$

and

$$\frac{[Ag^+] \times [CN^-]^2}{[Ag(CN)_2^-]} = 1 \times 10^{-21} \tag{b}$$

we divide equation *a* by *b* to get rid of $[Ag^+]$:

$$\frac{[NH_3]^2 \times [Ag(CN)_2^-]}{[CN^-]^2 \times [Ag(NH_3)_2^+]} = 4 \times 10^{13}$$

Noting that in the statement of the problem, $[NH_3] = [CN^-]$, we can simplify this expression to give the required information:

$$\frac{[Ag(CN)_2^-]}{[Ag(NH_3)_2^+]} = 4 \times 10^{13}$$

We deduce that virtually all the Ag^+ ions under these conditions are present in the form of $Ag(CN)_2^-$; for every $Ag(NH_3)_2^+$ ion, there will be 40,000,000,000,000 $Ag(CN)_2^-$ ions.

The experimental determination of the dissociation constants of complex ions is a very tricky problem. Complex ions which are relatively nonlabile may take a long time to reach equilibrium. In such cases, one can either find a catalyst for the reaction, raise the temperature, or be very, very patient. A more serious obstacle to the direct determination of dissociation constants of complex ions is the fact that these dissociations seldom occur in a single step. In studying the equilibrium:

$$Cu(NH_3)_4^{+2} \rightleftharpoons Cu^{+2} + 4\ NH_3$$

we can expect to find, in addition to $Cu(NH_3)_4^{+2}$ and (aquated) Cu^{+2} ions, several intermediate species containing three, two, and one NH_3 molecules as ligands. The presence of such species makes it difficult to determine the concentrations of $Cu(NH_3)_4^{+2}$ and Cu^{+2}, which we need to know to calculate the equilibrium constant. For this reason among others, dissociation constants of complex ions are usually obtained indirectly by observing the effect of a complexing agent on the solubility of a metal salt (Section 19.7) or on the voltage of an electrical cell (Chapter 21).

TABLE 19.5 DISSOCIATION CONSTANTS OF COMPLEX IONS

MA_2		MA_4		MA_6	
$AgCl_2^-$	1×10^{-6}	$CdCl_4^{-2}$	4×10^{-3}	$Cr(OH)_6^{-3}$	1×10^{-38}
$Ag(NH_3)_2^+$	4×10^{-8}	$Cd(NH_3)_4^{+2}$	1×10^{-7}	$Co(NH_3)_6^{+3}$	1×10^{-35}
$Ag(SCN)_2^-$	1×10^{-10}	$Cd(CN)_4^{-2}$	1×10^{-19}	$Co(CN)_6^{-3}$	1×10^{-64}
$Ag(S_2O_3)_2^{-3}$	1×10^{-13}	$Cu(NH_3)_4^{+2}$	2×10^{-13}	$Fe(CN)_6^{-3}$	1×10^{-31}
$Ag(CN)_2^-$	1×10^{-21}	$Cu(CN)_4^{-2}$	1×10^{-25}	$Ni(NH_3)_6^{+2}$	2×10^{-9}
$CuCl_2^-$	3×10^{-6}	$Ni(CN)_4^{-2}$	1×10^{-14}		
$Cu(NH_3)_2^+$	1×10^{-7}	$PdCl_4^{-2}$	1×10^{-13}		
		$Zn(NH_3)_4^{+2}$	3×10^{-10}		
		$Zn(OH)_4^{-2}$	3×10^{-16}		
		$Zn(CN)_4^{-2}$	1×10^{-17}		

19.7 COMPLEX IONS IN ANALYTICAL CHEMISTRY

Qualitative Analysis

Reactions involving the formation of complex ions are widely used in qualitative analysis for either of two purposes. The ability of a metal ion to form a colored complex or a precipitate with a particular complexing agent may be used as a specific test for that ion. Alternatively, two ions may be separated from each other by adding a complexing agent which forms a complex with only one of them. Not infrequently, these two purposes are achieved simultaneously by adding the proper complexing agent at a particular stage in an analysis.

Tests for Specific Ions. An extremely sensitive test for the Cu^{+2} ion in water solution involves its ability to form a deep blue complex with ammonia. The color of the $Cu(NH_3)_4^{+2}$ ion is much more intense than that of the light blue $Cu(H_2O)_4^{+2}$ ion; it can be detected at concentrations of Cu^{+2} as low as 10^{-4} M. Certain other ions interfere with this test; nickel, for example, also forms a deep blue complex ion with ammonia.

Ferric (Fe^{+3}) ions are readily detected by adding a solution of potassium thiocyanate, KSCN. A blood-red color develops due to the formation of a complex ion whose exact composition is difficult to determine; the formula of the complex is often written simply as $Fe(SCN)^{+2}$. Ferric ions also give a precipitate known as Prussian blue upon addition of a solution of potassium ferrocyanide:

$$Fe^{+3} + K^+ + Fe(CN)_6^{-4} \longrightarrow KFe[Fe(CN)_6](s) \qquad (19.9)$$

This same precipitate is obtained when solutions of iron(II) chloride, $FeCl_2$, and potassium ferricyanide, $K_3[Fe(CN)_6]$ are mixed.

Chelating agents, because of their strong complexing ability, are widely used in qualitative analysis. Dimethyl glyoxime:

$$\begin{array}{c} H_3C-C-C-CH_3 \\ \parallel \quad \parallel \\ HO-\underset{\cdot\cdot}{N} \quad \underset{\cdot\cdot}{N}-OH \end{array}$$

in one such chelating agent. It uses the unshared pairs of electrons on the two nitrogen atoms to form chelates with many metal ions. The complexes formed with nickel(II) (red) and palladium(II) (yellow) are both insoluble in water.

Separation of Ions. Metal ions are often separated from each other by taking advantage of differences in their tendencies to form complex ions with a particular coordinating agent. To illustrate the method, consider the separation of the two ions Fe^{+3} and Al^{+3}, which are ordinarily precipitated in the same group in cation analysis. If one adds sodium hydroxide to a solution containing these ions, they both precipitate as the hydroxides.

$$Al^{+3} + 3\ OH^- \longrightarrow Al(OH)_3(s) \qquad (19.10)$$

$$Fe^{+3} + 3\ OH^- \longrightarrow Fe(OH)_3(s) \qquad (19.11)$$

However, as more sodium hydroxide is added to increase the OH^- concentration, it is found that the aluminum hydroxide dissolves to form a complex ion which may be represented most simply as $Al(OH)_4^-$

$$Al(OH)_3(s) + OH^- \longrightarrow Al(OH)_4^- \qquad (19.12)$$

Iron(III) hydroxide fails to dissolve and is thus separated from the aluminum.

$$Al^{+3},\ Fe^{+3}$$
$$\downarrow\ OH^-\ \text{(dilute)}$$
$$Al(OH)_3(s),\ Fe(OH)_3(s)$$
$$\mid\ OH^-\ \text{(conc.)}$$
$$Al(OH)_4^- \qquad\qquad Fe(OH)_3(s)$$

Many of the transition metals, like aluminum, form sufficiently stable complex ions with OH^- to bring their hydroxides into solutions in concentrated sodium hydroxide. Among the hydroxides which dissolve in strong base are $Zn(OH)_2$, $Cr(OH)_3$ and, to a lesser extent, $Cu(OH)_2$. Compounds such as these, which are capable of reacting with OH^- ions as well as H^+ ions are said to be **amphoteric.**

Another complexing agent which is frequently used to separate metal ions is the ammonia molecule, NH_3. In the analysis of the group 1 cations, advantage is taken of the stability of the $Ag(NH_3)_2{}^+$ complex to separate silver from mercury. Treatment of a precipitate containing AgCl with dilute ammonia leads to the reaction:

$$AgCl(s) + 2\ NH_3 \longrightarrow Ag(NH_3)_2{}^+ + Cl^- \qquad (19.13)$$

bringing the silver into solution in the form of the complex ion. To confirm the presence of Ag^+, one can add nitric acid to the solution. The hydrogen ions from the acid destroy the complex by converting NH_3 molecules to $NH_4{}^+$ ions.

$$Ag(NH_3)_2{}^+ + Cl^- + 2\ H^+ \longrightarrow AgCl(s) + 2\ NH_4{}^+ \qquad (19.14)$$

The ability of silver (I) salts to form a complex ion with ammonia may be used in a more subtle way to separate the three anions Cl^-, Br^-, and I^- from each other. Addition of silver nitrate to a solution containing these three ions gives a mixed precipitate of silver chloride, silver bromide, and silver iodide. Silver chloride dissolves in dilute ammonia to give the $Ag(NH_3)_2{}^+$ complex. Silver bromide goes into solution only in concentrated ammonia while silver iodide remains insoluble even at very high ammonia concentrations. Consequently, the addition of silver nitrate, followed first by dilute and then by concentrated ammonia, serves to separate Cl^-, Br^-, and I^- ions from each other.

$$Cl^-,\ Br^-,\ I^-$$
$$\downarrow Ag^+$$
$$AgCl(s),\ AgBr(s),\ AgI(s)$$
$$\big|\ \text{dilute } NH_3\ (6\ M)$$

$Ag(NH_3)_2{}^+,\ Cl^- \qquad\qquad\qquad AgBr(s),\ AgI(s)$
$$\big|\ \text{conc. } NH_3\ (15\ M)$$

$Ag(NH_3)_2{}^+,\ Br^- \qquad\qquad\qquad AgI(s)$

To understand the principles underlying the separation of metal ions by complex formation, one must consider the factors which determine the solubility of a solid in a complexing agent. These factors are very similar to those enumerated in Chapter 18 in discussing the solubility of solids in strong acids. They may be deduced from a consideration of the equilibria involved. Take, for example, the process by which a silver halide, AgX, dissolves in ammonia:

$$AgX(s) \rightleftharpoons Ag^+ + X^- \qquad (19.15a)$$
$$Ag^+ + 2\ NH_3 \rightleftharpoons Ag(NH_3)_2{}^+ \qquad (19.15b)$$
$$\overline{AgX(s) + 2\ NH_3 \rightleftharpoons Ag(NH_3)_2{}^+ + X^-} \qquad (19.15)$$

The solubility of a silver halide in ammonia or indeed, the solubility of any solid in a complexing agent will depend upon:

1. *The solubility of the solid in water (equilibrium 19.15a).* The greater the solubility in water, the greater will be the solubility in a complexing agent. The three silver halides, AgCl, AgBr, and AgI, are successively less soluble in water as shown by their solubility products (Ksp $AgCl = 1.6 \times 10^{-10}$, $AgBr = 1 \times 10^{-13}$, $AgI = 1 \times 10^{-16}$). Consequently, one can predict that the solubility of these three compounds in ammonia or in any complexing agent will decrease in the same order: AgCl > AgBr > AgI. It so happens that the solubilities of the three silver halides in ammonia cover a convenient range insofar as their separation is concerned.

2. *The concentration of complexing agent (equilibrium* 19.15b). The greater the concentration of complexing agent, the greater will be the tendency of the solid to dissolve to form a complex ion. As pointed out earlier, silver bromide is soluble in concentrated ammonia but insoluble in dilute ammonia. An increase in the concentration of ammonia from 6 M to 15 M exerts a sufficient influence on the equilibrium in reaction 19.15b to bring a significant amount of silver bromide into solution.

Another example of the effect of concentration of complexing agent on solubility is furnished by the reaction with ammonia of solutions of copper(II) salts. Addition of a small amount of ammonia gives a precipitate of $Cu(OH)_2$. As more ammonia is added to increase the concentration of NH_3 molecules relative to OH^- ions, the hydroxide dissolves to form the $Cu(NH_3)_4^{+2}$ complex ion.

3. *The stability of the complex ion formed.* In many cases, a solid which does not dissolve in one complexing agent can be brought into solution by using a reagent which forms a more stable complex. Silver iodide, which is insoluble in ammonia $(K_c\ Ag(NH_3)_2^+ = 4 \times 10^{-8})$, dissolves readily in potassium cyanide solution to form the $Ag(CN)_2^-$ complex $(K_c\ Ag(CN)_2^- = 1 \times 10^{-21})$ or in sodium thiosulfate to form the $Ag(S_2O_3)_2^{-3}$ complex $(K_c\ Ag(S_2O_3)_2^{-3} = 1 \times 10^{-13})$.

Solubility in a complexing agent may be treated quantitatively by using the solubility product principle in combination with the dissociation constant of the complex ion involved. Example 19.3 illustrates how this is done.

Example 19.3. Calculate the minimum concentration of NH_3 necessary to dissolve:
   a. 0.01 mole/l. of AgCl.   b. 0.01 mole/l. of AgBr.   c. 0.01 mole/l. of AgI.

Solution

   a. We note from the expression:

$$K_c = \frac{[Ag^+] \times [NH_3]^2}{[Ag(NH_3)_2^+]} = 4.0 \times 10^{-8}$$

that in order to calculate the concentration of NH_3, the concentrations of Ag^+ and $Ag(NH_3)_2^+$ must first be determined. From the equation:

$$AgCl(s) + 2\ NH_3 \longrightarrow Ag(NH_3)_2^+ + Cl^-$$

it is evident that in a solution formed by dissolving 0.01 mole/l. of silver chloride, the concentrations of both $Ag(NH_3)_2^+$ and Cl^- must be 0.01 M. But, the concentrations of Cl^- and Ag^+ are related by the expression:

$$Ksp\ AgCl = [Ag^+] \times [Cl^-] = 1.6 \times 10^{-10}$$

Consequently: $[Ag^+] \times 0.01 = 1.6 \times 10^{-10}$ $[Ag^+] = 1.6 \times 10^{-8}$

Substituting these values for the concentrations of $Ag(NH_3)_2^+$ and Ag^+ in the expression for the dissociation constant of the $Ag(NH_3)_2^+$ complex, we have:

$$\frac{(1.6 \times 10^{-8}) \times [NH_3]^2}{10^{-2}} = 4.0 \times 10^{-8}$$

Solving: $[NH_3]^2 = \dfrac{4.0 \times 10^{-10}}{1.6 \times 10^{-8}} = 0.025$ $[NH_3] = 0.16$ M

   b. Following the same reasoning process, we arrive at a value of 0.01 M for the concentration of $Ag(NH_3)_2^+$ and, for the concentration of Ag^+:

$$[Ag^+] = \frac{Ksp\ AgBr}{[Br^-]} = \frac{1 \times 10^{-13}}{10^{-2}} = 1 \times 10^{-11}$$

Substituting and solving as before:

$$\frac{(1 \times 10^{-11}) \times [NH_3]^2}{10^{-2}} = 4 \times 10^{-8} \qquad [NH_3]^2 = \frac{4 \times 10^{-10}}{1 \times 10^{-11}} = 40$$

$$[NH_3] = 6 \text{ M}$$

c. Following the procedure outlined in b, using 1×10^{-16} for Ksp of AgI, one can calculate:

$$[NH_3] = 200 \text{ M}$$

In summary, to dissolve 0.01 mole/l. of AgCl, the concentration of ammonia need only be 0.16 M, while to accomplish the same result with AgBr, an NH_3 concentration of about 6 M is required. The answer obtained with AgI, an impossibly high value of 200 M, means that it is not possible to dissolve significant quantities of AgI even at high ammonia concentrations.

Quantitative Analysis

The reaction of a metal ion with a complexing agent bears at least a superficial resemblance to the reaction of a H^+ ion with an OH^- ion. Comparing the two equations:

$$Cu^{+2} + 4 \text{ NH}_3 \longrightarrow Cu(NH_3)_4{}^{+2}$$

$$H^+ + OH^- \longrightarrow H_2O$$

we note that in both cases a positive ion is converted to an extremely stable, covalently bonded species (K $H_2O = 1 \times 10^{-14}$, K $Cu(NH_3)_4{}^{+2} = 2 \times 10^{-13}$). One might suppose, then, that one could determine the concentration of a metal ion by titrating with a complexing agent in much the same way that an acid is titrated with a base.

In practice, it is seldom possible to use ordinary complexing agents to analyze quantitatively for metal ions in solution. The difficulty is that, as previously noted, the formation of a metal complex is a stepwise process. If one adds ammonia to a solution of a copper(II) salt, the hydrated Cu^{+2} ion is not converted directly to the $Cu(NH_3)_4{}^{+2}$ ion. Instead, intermediate species containing one, two, or three ammonia molecules are formed. As the concentration of ammonia increases, the various equilibria gradually shift to lower the Cu^{+2} ion concentration. There is no sharp change in "free" Cu^{+2} ion concentration, analogous to the abrupt change in H^+ ion concentration that one observes at the equivalence point of an acid-base titration. The end point, instead of being sharp and precise, is drawn out and diffuse.

Within the past few years, analytical chemists have developed a series of reagents which react with metal ions to give extremely stable 1:1 complexes and hence are suitable for metal-ion titrations. These substances are chelating agents; the best known is the sodium salt of ethylenediaminetetracetic acid, commonly called **EDTA**. The anion of this salt has the following structure:

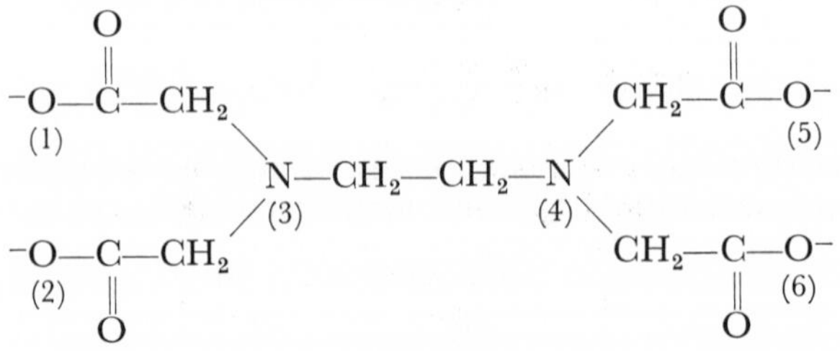

A single EDTA anion can attach itself to a metal ion through as many as six different atoms (numbered 1 to 6 in the foregoing structural formula), filling all of its coordination requirements. Difficulties inherent in stepwise complex formation are thereby avoided; EDTA titrations yield a sharp, easily observed end point.

EDTA is among the most effective complexing agents known; it forms stable 1:1 chelates with a wide variety of metals. One of its earliest applications was in the determination of the alkaline-earth metals calcium and magnesium found in hard water. Several hundred papers, appearing over the past 20 years, have described the use of EDTA titrations in the determination of over 60 different elements.

To illustrate how an EDTA titration may be carried out, let us consider the use of this chelating agent in the determination of iron(III) salts. The reaction that occurs may be represented as follows:

$$Fe^{+3} + EDTA^{-4} \longrightarrow Fe(EDTA)^- \qquad (19.16)$$

The SCN^- ion, which forms a blood-red complex with Fe^{+3}, can be used as an indicator. As EDTA is added, the thiocyanate complex of iron(III) is converted to the more stable EDTA complex. At the equivalence point, the SCN^- ions attached to iron are quantitatively displaced. The color change from deep red to yellow yields a sharp end point. Knowing the concentration of the EDTA solution and the volume which must be added to reach the end point, one can readily calculate the amount of Fe^{+3} present.

19.8 SUMMARY

In this chapter, we have considered the preparation, properties, and structures of complex ions in which there are coordinate covalent bonds between metal and nonmetal atoms. Such species may be regarded as consisting of:

1. A *central atom*, which is ordinarily a transition metal ion. The transition metals falling in groups 6B through 2B of the periodic table are particularly active in complex ion formation. Water solutions of compounds of these metals invariably contain complex ions.

2. Two or more *ligands* joined to the central atom by coordinate covalent bonds. Ligand species ordinarily contain an unshared pair of electrons; they may be molecules (such as NH_3, H_2O) or anions (F^-, Cl^-, OH^-, and so on). The ligands in a particular complex ion may be the same, as in $Ag(CN)_2^-$, $Cu(NH_3)_4^{+2}$ and $CoCl_6^{-3}$, or different as in $Cu(H_2O)_3(OH)^+$, $Co(NH_3)_5Cl^{+2}$, and so on. Ligands capable of forming more than one bond with the central atom are particularly effective complexing agents; the resulting compounds, known as chelates, are often extremely stable.

The coordination number of the central atom is most commonly 2, 4, or 6. Complex ions in which the central atom is surrounded by two ligands are found to be linear; according to the valence bond model, the bonding electrons occupy two hybrid sp orbitals. Complex ions with a coordination number of 4 may show tetrahedral, sp^3 bonding as in $Zn(NH_3)_4^{+2}$, or a square planar, dsp^2 configuration as in $Cu(NH_3)_4^{+2}$ and $Pt(NH_3)_4^{+2}$. Octahedral complexes, corresponding to a coordination number of 6, are perhaps the most common; they show d^2sp^3 bonding ($Co(NH_3)_6^{+3}$, $Fe(CN)_6^{-4}$, and so on) or sp^2d^3 bonding ($Fe(H_2O)_6^{+2}$). Certain square and octahedral complexes can be isolated in two different forms known as geometrical (cis-trans) isomers.

In discussing reactions involving complex ions, one must distinguish carefully between their thermodynamic stability on the one hand and kinetic lability on the other. Stability is measured in terms of the equilibrium constant for the dissociation of the complex; stable complex ions are ones whose dissociation constants are very small (e.g., $Ag(CN)_2^-$: $K_c = 1 \times 10^{-21}$). Certain complex ions which are thermodynamically unstable are, at the same time, relatively nonlabile. For example, the $Co(NH_3)_5Cl^{+2}$ reacts very slowly with water to yield the more stable species $Co(NH_3)_5H_2O^{+3}$.

Complexing agents are widely used in qualitative analysis to test for specific ions or to separate mixtures of ions. They are particularly useful in separating precipitates by bringing one of the solids into solution as a complex ion. Chelating agents such as EDTA which form an extremely stable 1:1 complex with metal ions are useful in quantitative analysis.

PROBLEMS

19.1   Explain what is meant by the following terms.
   a. Ligand
   b. Coordination number
   c. Chelate
   d. Square, planar complex
   e. Cis-trans isomerism
   f. dsp² hybridization
   g. Outer complex
   h. Labile complex
   i. Inert complex
   j. Amphoteric hydroxide
   k. EDTA

19.2   Determine the charges of chromium(III) complexes in which the ligands are:
   a. 6 NH_3 molecules.
   b. 3 NH_3 molecules, 3 Cl^- ions.
   c. 2 NH_3 molecules, 4 Cl^- ions.
   d. 3 ethylenediamine molecules.
   e. 5 H_2O molecules, 1 OH^- ion.

19.3   Explain why:
   a. Zn^{+2} is a better complex former than Ca^{+2}.
   b. CN^- is a better coordinating agent than ClO_4^-.
   c. NH_3 is a better coordinating agent than CH_4.
   d. Two ethylenediamine molecules can replace four ammonia molecules in a complex.

19.4   Write structural formulas to indicate the geometry of
   a. $AgCl_2^-$
   b. $Cu(NH_3)_4^{+2}$
   c. $Zn(NH_3)_4^{+2}$
   d. $Zn(H_2O)_3(OH)^+$
   e. $Pt(NH_3)_2Br_2$ (two forms)

19.5   Show by diagrams the structures of the following octahedral complexes.
   a. $Cr(H_2O)_6^{+3}$
   b. $Fe(CN)_6^{-4}$
   c. $Co(NH_3)_4(NO_2)_2^+$
   d. $Co(NH_3)_3(NO_2)_3$

19.6   Write structural formulas for the following ions (en = ethylenediamine).
   a. $Co(en)_2NH_3Cl^{+2}$
   b. $Co(NH_3)_4CO_3^+$
   c. $Cr(C_2O_4)_3^{-3}$
   d. $Cu(en)_2^{+2}$

19.7   Write structural formulas for all of the compounds having the empirical formula $CrN_4H_{12}Cl_2Br$. Suggest how one might distinguish experimentally between these various compounds.

19.8   Calculate the total number of electrons associated with the central metal atom in
   a. $Zn(OH)_4^{-2}$
   b. $Au(CN)_2^-$
   c. $Fe(CN)_6^{-4}$
   d. $Fe(CN)_6^{-3}$
   e. $Ni(H_2O)_6^{+2}$
   f. $PdCl_4^{-2}$
   g. $Cd(en)_2^{+2}$
   h. $Co(en)_3^{+3}$

19.9   Explain why metals of odd atomic number (23, 25, 27, and so on) do not form stable complexes with CO in which there is one metal atom per molecule.

19.10 Indicate the type of hybridization to be expected in each of the following complex ions.
       a. $Cr(NH_3)_6^{+3}$ c. $Au(CN)_2^-$ e. $PtCl_4^{-2}$
       b. $Fe(CN)_6^{-4}$ d. $Cu(H_2O)_4^{+2}$ f. $Ni(CN)_4^{-2}$

19.11 Consider the $AuCl_4^-$ complex ion.
       a. Give the electronic structure of the gold atom in this complex, assuming it to be square planar.
       b. Repeat (a), assuming the ion to be tetrahedral.
       c. How could you determine experimentally whether this ion is square planar or tetrahedral?

19.12 Give the electronic structures of the following complex ions, using the valence bond model.
       a. $Ag(CN)_2^-$ c. $Al(H_2O)_6^{+3}$ e. $Ni(CN)_4^{-2}$
       b. $Pt(NH_3)_4^{+2}$ d. $Cd(NH_3)_4^{+2}$ f. $PtCl_6^{-2}$

19.13 Indicate how one might determine experimentally whether $Fe(NH_3)_6^{+2}$ is an inner or an outer complex.

19.14 Consider the two complex ions $[Co(NH_3)_5NO_3]^{+2}$ and $[Co(NH_3)_5SCN]^{+2}$. How could one determine experimentally which of these complexes is the more labile? The more stable?

19.15 Of the several complexes of Ag^+ listed in Table 19.5, which one is the most stable?

19.16 Using the value of 1×10^{-17} for the dissociation constant of the $Zn(CN)_4^{-2}$ ion, calculate:
       a. The ratio of the concentrations of Zn^{+2} and $Zn(CN)_4^{-2}$ in a solution 0.01 M in CN^-.
       b. The concentration of CN^- necessary to produce a 10 per cent conversion of Zn^{+2} to $Zn(CN)_4^{-2}$.

19.17 Enough ammonia is added to a solution containing Cu^{+2} and Zn^{+2} ions to produce approximately equal concentrations of $Cu(NH_3)_4^{+2}$ and $Zn(NH_3)_4^{+2}$. What is the ratio of $[Cu^{+2}]$ to $[Zn^{+2}]$ in this solution?

19.18 Outline a separation scheme for:
       a. Ag^+, Ni^{+2}, Al^{+3} b. Cl^-, Br^-, SO_4^{-2} c. Br^-, I^-, CO_3^{-2}

19.19 Suggest at least two reagents, including, perhaps, a complexing agent, which could be used to bring each of the following compounds into solution.
       a. $CaCO_3$ b. $AgCl$ c. AgI d. $Fe(OH)_3$ e. $Al(OH)_3$ f. $Zn(OH)_2$

19.20 Calculate the minimum concentration of $S_2O_3^{-2}$ necessary to dissolve 0.1 mole/l. of $AgBr$; 0.1 mole/l. of AgI.

19.21 In what ways does the reaction of Cu^{+2} with NH_3 resemble the reaction of H^+ with NH_3? In what respects do the two reactions differ?

19.22 Kidney stones consist of an isoluble calcium compound, usually either calcium carbonate or calcium oxalate. EDTA forms a very stable chelate with Ca^{+2}. One could, in principle, prevent the formation of kidney stones or remove them once they are formed, by taking EDTA internally. Suggest some reasons why such a treatment might be highly undesirable.

19.23 Write balanced net ionic equations for the reactions that occur when:
       a. Excess sodium hydroxide is added to a solution of zinc chloride.
       b. Aluminum hydroxide dissolves in concentrated potassium hydroxide.
       c. Excess ammonia is added to a solution of copper(II) nitrate.
       d. Nitric acid is added to a solution prepared by dissolving silver chloride in ammonia.
       e. Cis $Pd(NH_3)_2Cl_2$ is treated with a solution of sodium oxalate.

*19.24 A solution containing Ni^{+2} and Al^{+3} ions is treated with aqueous ammonia. A bluish precipitate forms at first; as more ammonia is added, part of the precipitate dissolves to form a deep blue solution. The precipitate that remains is white. The solution is separated and treated with dimethylglyoxime to form a red precipitate. The white precipitate previously referred to, upon treatment with excess OH^-, forms a clear solution. If acid is slowly added to this solution, a white precipitate forms which dissolves as more acid is added. Write balanced net ionic equations for each reaction that took place.

*19.25 A sample of 1 g. of silver chloride is shaken with 1 M NH_3. Assuming equilibrium is reached when half of the precipitate has dissolved, calculate the concentrations of Ag^+, $Ag(NH_3)_2^+$, Cl^-, H^+ and OH^- in this solution. (Assume the concentration of NH_3 does not change.)

*19.26 It is generally observed that d^2sp^3 inner complexes tend to be labile if they contain a vacant inner d orbital. Can you suggest an explanation for this? You may wish to consult a reference text on coordination chemistry.

*19.27 A certain coordination compound analyzes as follows:

$$23.4\% \ Co, \quad 22.3\% \ N, \quad 5.6\% \ H, \quad 6.4\% \ O, \quad 42.3\% \ Cl$$

It is found that the conductivity of a water solution of this compound corresponds to that of a 1:1 electrolyte such as NaCl. Write a structural formula for the compound consistent with this information. Suggest at least two further experiments which one might perform to check this structural formula.

20

ELECTROLYTIC CELLS: BALANCING OXIDATION-REDUCTION EQUATIONS

An electrolytic cell is a device for converting electrical energy into chemical energy. The process going on within such a cell, known as electrolysis, employs a direct electric current to bring about an oxidation-reduction reaction. To understand how an electrolytic cell operates, consider the generalized cell diagram shown in Figure 20.1.

The portion of the circuit labeled B at the top of the diagram represents a battery. The short vertical line stands for the negative terminal of the battery, the long line for the positive terminal. The battery is connected by means of two wires to the electrolytic cell, which consists of two electrodes, A and C, dipping into a liquid in which ions, M^+ and X^-, are free to move.

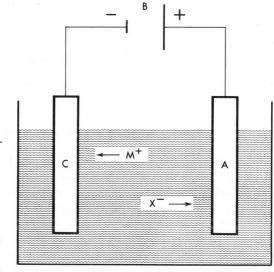

FIGURE 20.1 Diagram of electrolytic cell.

By a mechanism which will be considered in Chapter 21, the battery acts as an electron pump, pushing electrons into the electrode shown at the left in Figure 20.1 and withdrawing them from the electrode at the right. In order to maintain electrical neutrality, some process must take place within the cell so as to consume electrons at C and produce them at A. This process is an oxidation-reduction reaction. At electrode C, known as the **cathode,** an ion or molecule undergoes **reduction** by accepting electrons. At the **anode,** A, electrons are produced by the **oxidation** of an ion or molecule. The overall cell reaction is the sum of the two half-reactions occurring at the electrodes. While electrolysis is proceeding, there is a steady flow of ions to the two electrodes. Positive ions (*cations*) move towards the *cathode*; negative ions (*anions*) move toward the *anode*.

Electrolyses may be carried out either by passing a direct current through a water solution of an electrolyte or through a molten salt or oxide. The cell reactions are somewhat easier to visualize in the latter case.

20.1   ELECTROLYSIS OF MOLTEN IONIC COMPOUNDS

In principle, any ionic compound can be decomposed to the elements by melting and electrolyzing it. To illustrate the principles involved, we shall consider three electrolyses of this type. These involve the production of elementary sodium from sodium chloride, aluminum from aluminum oxide, and fluorine from a potassium fluoride–hydrogen fluoride mixture.

Na from NaCl

The so-called Downs cell used commercially to electrolyze molten sodium chloride is shown in Figure 20.2. The half-reactions occurring in this cell are particularly simple. At the circular iron *cathode*, sodium ions are reduced to metallic sodium:

$$Na^+ + e^- \longrightarrow Na(1) \qquad (20.1a)$$

For every sodium ion reduced at the cathode, a chloride ion is oxidized to chlorine gas at the graphite *anode*:

$$Cl^- \longrightarrow \tfrac{1}{2} Cl_2(g) + e^- \qquad (20.1b)$$

The total cell reaction, obtained by summing 20.1a and 20.1b is.

$$Na^+ + Cl^- \longrightarrow Na(1) + \tfrac{1}{2} Cl_2(g)$$

or: $$NaCl(1) \longrightarrow Na(1) + \tfrac{1}{2} Cl_2(g) \qquad (20.1)$$

Reaction 20.1 is nonspontaneous; one can calculate, for example, that at the operating temperature, 600°C, the free energy change for the reaction as written is +77,200 cal. This quantity of energy, in the form of electrical work, must be supplied to make the reaction go. If the products of the cell reaction, elementary sodium and chlorine, are allowed to come in contact with each other, they will combine spontaneously to give the starting material, sodium chloride. To prevent this, the electrodes in the Downs cell are separated by a circular iron screen which allows for the migration of ions but prevents direct contact between the products of electrolysis.

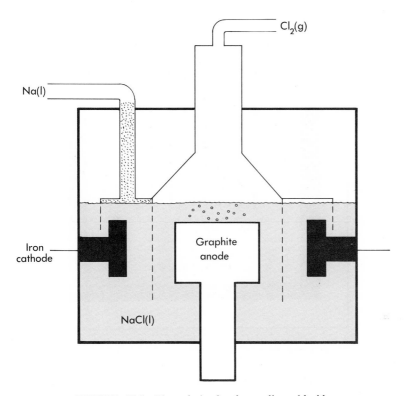

FIGURE 20.2 Electrolysis of molten sodium chloride.

Some 10,000 tons of sodium are made annually in the United States by the electrolysis of molten sodium chloride. The chlorine formed simultaneously is a valuable by-product; there is, however, a cheaper way of producing chlorine electrolytically (Section 20.2). The relatively high cost of the sodium produced by the Downs process (20 cents a pound) reflects the large amount of energy that must be expended to carry out the electrolysis and maintain the sodium chloride in the liquid state. In practice, the cell is operated at a temperature of about 600°C, some 200°C, below the melting point of pure sodium chloride. The lower temperature is made possible by adding a small amount of calcium chloride, thereby forming an ionic solution with a melting point lower than that of the pure "solvent," sodium chloride.

Al from Al_2O_3

Aluminum is the third most abundant element in the earth's crust. Its importance as a structural material is indicated by the fact that about 2,000,000 tons of aluminum are produced annually in the United States, an amount greater than that of any other metal except copper and iron. Yet, from 1828, when aluminum was first isolated by Wöhler until 1886, when the Hall electrolytic process for its manufacture was developed, the metal remained little more than a scientific curiosity. In this 58-year period, the price of aluminum never fell below $8 a pound; today it sells for about 30 cents a pound.

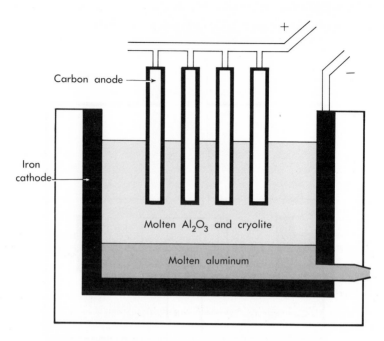

Carbon anode

Iron cathode

Molten Al_2O_3 and cryolite

Molten aluminum

FIGURE 20.3   Electrolytic preparation of aluminum.

The long time lag between the isolation of aluminum and its commercial utilization reflected the difficulties of extracting the metal from its ores. Aluminum occurs in such common minerals as feldspar, granite, and clay, but unfortunately, the aluminum in these materials is tightly bound in a network of silicon and oxygen atoms from which its extraction is extremely difficult. The principal source of aluminum has always been bauxite ore, in which the element occurs as the hydrated oxide. Prior to 1886, it was necessary to first convert the oxide to the chloride and then reduce the latter with sodium. The high cost of the sodium in this two-step process made the aluminum prohibitively expensive.

The electrolytic process by which aluminum is produced today from aluminum oxide was worked out by Charles Hall, a graduate student at Oberlin College. After experimenting with a great many materials, he found a solvent known as cryolite, empirical formula Na_3AlF_6, in which aluminum oxide is soluble at high temperatures to give an electrically conducting solution. The use of cryolite makes it possible to reduce the temperature of electrolysis from 2000°C, the melting point of pure Al_2O_3, to about 1000°C. Curiously enough, within a few weeks of the time that Hall produced his first aluminum, a young Frenchman, Heroult, independently worked out an almost identical process for its manufacture.

The cell used to produce aluminum from aluminum oxide is shown schematically in Figure 20.3. The purified bauxite ore is placed in the electrically heated cell, mixed with cryolite,* and melted. The iron wall of the cell serves as the cathode at which Al^{+3} ions are reduced to form molten aluminum. The anodes, retractable

---

* A mixture of the fluorides of aluminum, sodium, and calcium is commonly used today in place of cryolite. This mixture gives a solution with aluminum oxide which has a lower melting point and density than that obtained with cryolite. The lower density facilitates the separation of the molten aluminum, which sinks to the bottom of the cell.

carbon rods, are attacked by the oxygen produced in the cell to form a mixture of carbon dioxide and carbon monoxide. The two half-reactions occurring at the electrodes may be represented most simply as:

cathode: $2 \; Al^{+3} + 6 \; e^- \longrightarrow 2 \; Al(1)$ (20.2a)

anode: $3 \; O^{-2} \longrightarrow \frac{3}{2} \; O_2(g) + 6 \; e^-$ (20.2b)

$$2 \; Al^{+3} + 3 \; O^{-2} \longrightarrow 2 \; Al(s) + \tfrac{3}{2} \; O_2(g) \qquad (20.2)$$

The production of 1 lb. of aluminum consumes about 2 lb. of aluminum oxide, 0.6 lb. of anodic carbon, 0.1 lb. of cryolite and 10 kilowatt-hours (kwhr.) of electrical energy.

F_2 from KF–HF Mixture

The fluoride ion has such a strong attraction for electrons that it cannot be oxidized to fluorine chemically. However, it is possible to oxidize F^- ions in an electrolytic cell at a sufficiently high voltage. Commercially, fluorine is prepared by electrolysis of a solution of anhydrous hydrogen fluoride in molten potassium fluoride. Graphite electrodes are used; the cell itself is made of copper, one of the few metals that withstands attack by fluorine. The products are two gases, hydrogen and fluorine.

cathode: $2 \; H^+ + 2 \; e^- \longrightarrow H_2(g)$ (20.3a)

anode: $2 \; F^- \longrightarrow F_2(g) + 2 \; e^-$ (20.3b)

$$2 \; H^+ + 2 \; F^- \longrightarrow H_2(g) + F_2(g) \qquad (20.3)$$

The electrode reactions are actually somewhat more complex than those indicated by equations 20.3a and b. In a solution of hydrogen fluoride in potassium fluoride, the principal anionic species is the HF_2^- ion, formed by the interaction of an HF molecule with a fluoride ion:

$$\left(: \!\overset{..}{\underset{..}{F}} : \right)^- + H : \overset{..}{\underset{..}{F}} : \longrightarrow \left(: \overset{..}{\underset{..}{F}} : H : \overset{..}{\underset{..}{F}} : \right)^-$$

This hydrogen-bonded species is reduced to elementary hydrogen at the cathode and oxidized to elementary fluorine at the anode.

20.2 ELECTROLYSIS OF WATER SOLUTIONS

It is ordinarily less expensive and more convenient to carry out electrolyses in water solution rather than in the molten state. However, the presence of water multiplies the number of possible reactions that can take place in an electrolytic cell. It is entirely possible for water molecules to participate in the reactions at the anode or cathode. Water can be oxidized to elementary oxygen (oxid. no.: $-2 \rightarrow 0$) or reduced to hydrogen (oxid. no.: $+1 \rightarrow 0$). We shall consider four different types of electrolysis reactions in water solution: (1) metal ion reduced at cathode, nonmetal ion oxidized at anode; (2) water molecule reduced at cathode, nonmetal ion oxidized at anode; (3) metal ion reduced at cathode, water molecule oxidized at anode; and (4) water molecule reduced at cathode, water molecule oxidized at anode.

Metal Ion Reduced at Cathode: Nonmetal Ion Oxidized at Anode

The electrolysis of a water solution of copper(II) chloride follows a path entirely analogous to that described for molten sodium chloride. At the cathode, which may be a platinum or copper wire, Cu^{+2} ions are reduced to copper metal. Chloride ions are oxidized to chlorine at the anode, which is usually made of graphite or some other inert material.

cathode: $\qquad\qquad\qquad Cu^{+2} + 2\ e^- \longrightarrow Cu(s)$ $\qquad\qquad\qquad$ (20.4a)

anode: $\qquad\qquad\qquad\quad 2\ Cl^- \longrightarrow Cl_2(g) + 2\ e^-$ $\qquad\qquad\qquad$ (20.4b)

$$Cu^{+2} + 2\ Cl^- \longrightarrow Cu(s) + Cl_2(g) \qquad\qquad (20.4)$$

Electrolysis of solutions of many of the transition metal halides including $CoCl_2$, $NiBr_2$, and ZnI_2 follows this simple path. Water molecules take no part in the electrode reactions.

Water Molecule Reduced at Cathode: Nonmetal Ion Oxidized at Anode

The electrolysis of solutions of the chlorides, bromides, or iodides of the 1A and 2A metals proceeds in a manner quite different from that of $CuCl_2$. Consider, for example, the electrolysis of a water solution of sodium chloride, perhaps the most important of all industrial electrolytic processes. At the anode, the product is, as one might expect, chlorine gas:

anode: $\qquad\qquad\qquad 2\ Cl^- \longrightarrow Cl_2(g) + 2\ e^-$ $\qquad\qquad\qquad$ (20.5a)

Bubbles of hydrogen form at the cathode; the solution immediately surrounding this electrode becomes strongly basic. This evidence indicates that a water molecule rather than a sodium ion is being reduced:

cathode: $\qquad\qquad\quad 2\ H_2O + 2\ e^- \longrightarrow H_2(g) + 2\ OH^-$ $\qquad\quad$ (20.5b)*

It appears that the water molecule is more readily reduced than the Na^+ ion. This seems entirely reasonable when one recalls that the addition of sodium metal to water results in the highly spontaneous reaction:

$$2\ Na(s) + 2\ H_2O \longrightarrow 2\ Na^+ + H_2(g) + 2\ OH^-$$

One can then argue that any sodium atoms produced by electrolysis would immediately react with water to produce H_2 molecules and OH^- ions, giving 20.5b as the net reaction at the cathode.

To obtain the overall cell reaction for the electrolysis of a water solution of sodium chloride, equations 20.5a and 20.5b are added to give:

$$2\ Cl^- + 2\ H_2O \longrightarrow Cl_2(g) + H_2(g) + 2\ OH^- \qquad\qquad (20.5)$$

---

* This equation is applicable in neutral or basic solution. In acidic solution, in which the concentration of H^+ is high, the simpler equation:

$$2\ H^+ + 2\ e^- \longrightarrow H_2(g)$$

is more appropriate. This equation would, for example, be used to describe the cathode reaction in the electrolysis of hydrochloric acid.

It may be noted that one effect of this cell reaction is the replacement of the chloride ions originally present by an equal number of hydroxide ions. Consequently, evaporation of the solution remaining after electrolysis yields a residue of sodium hydroxide:

electrolysis: $2\ Cl^- + 2\ H_2O \longrightarrow Cl_2(g) + H_2(g) + 2\ OH^-$

evaporation: $2\ Na^+ + 2\ OH^- \longrightarrow 2\ NaOH(s)$

$$2\ Na^+ + 2\ Cl^- + 2\ H_2O \longrightarrow 2\ NaOH(s) + Cl_2(g) + H_2(g) \quad (20.6)$$

The greater part of the sodium hydroxide and almost all the chlorine made in the United States is prepared by the electrolysis of aqueous sodium chloride; hydrogen is an important by-product.

Electrolysis of water solutions of the chlorides of other 1A and 2A metals proceeds along a path entirely similar to that already described for sodium chloride. Potassium hydroxide is prepared commercially by evaporating the solution remaining after electrolysis of potassium chloride. Electrolysis of a solution of a 1A or 2A bromide yields bromine at the anode:

anode: $2\ Br^- \longrightarrow Br_2 + 2\ e^-$ (20.7a)

cathode: $2\ H_2O + 2\ e^- \longrightarrow H_2(g) + 2\ OH^-$ (20.7b)

$$2\ Br^- + 2\ H_2O \longrightarrow Br_2 + H_2(g) + 2\ OH^- \qquad (20.7)$$

If the salt used is an iodide, iodine is the oxidation product.

Metal Ion Reduced at Cathode: Water Molecule Oxidized at Anode

Chlorine, bromine, and iodine are among the few nonmetals which can be prepared by the electrolytic oxidation of anions in water solution. When the anion present is one which has an extremely strong attraction for electrons, the anode reaction yields oxygen via the oxidation of water molecules. This occurs, for example, in the electrolysis of a water solution of copper (II) fluoride:

anode: $H_2O \longrightarrow \frac{1}{2} O_2(g) + 2\ H^+ + 2\ e^-$ (20.8a)

The product formed at the cathode is elementary copper (cf. equation 20.4a):

cathode: $Cu^{+2} + 2\ e^- \longrightarrow Cu(s)$ (20.8b)

giving, for the total cell reaction:

$$Cu^{+2} + H_2O \longrightarrow Cu(s) + \frac{1}{2} O_2(g) + 2\ H^+ \qquad (20.8)$$

As electrolysis proceeds, Cu^{+2} ions are replaced by H^+ ions, giving, ultimately, a solution of hydrofluoric acid.

Reaction 20.8, written for the electrolysis of a CuF_2 solution, applies equally well to $CuSO_4$ or $Cu(NO_3)_2$. The SO_4^{-2} and NO_3^- ions, like the F^- ion, are more difficult to oxidize than the H_2O molecule. Analogous cell reactions occur with the sulfates, nitrates, and fluorides of other transition metals such as nickel, cobalt, and zinc.

Water Molecule Reduced at Cathode: Water Molecule Oxidized at Anode

In the electrolysis of certain salt solutions, neither the cation nor the anion of the salt is involved in the cell reaction. Sodium fluoride is a typical example; both the cathodic and anodic reactions involve water molecules:

cathode: $$2 H_2O + 2 e^- \longrightarrow H_2(g) + 2 OH^- \qquad (20.9a)$$

anode: $$H_2O \longrightarrow \tfrac{1}{2} O_2(g) + 2 H^+ + 2 e^- \qquad (20.9b)$$

It is evident from equations 20.9a and 20.9b that the electrolysis of a water solution of sodium fluoride yields two gases, hydrogen and oxygen, in a $2:1$ mole ratio. This is, of course, precisely what happens when water itself is electrolyzed. Indeed, if a solution of sodium fluoride is continuously stirred during electrolysis so that the H^+ and OH^- ions produced at anode and cathode respectively neutralize each other, the overall reaction, obtained by combining equations 20.9a and 20.9b, becomes simply:

$$H_2O \longrightarrow H_2(g) + \tfrac{1}{2} O_2(g) \qquad (20.9)$$

This type of cell reaction can be expected to occur with electrolytes in which the anion is difficult to oxidize and the cation difficult to reduce. Solutions of $NaNO_3$, KF, and Li_2SO_4 behave in this manner.

In practice, the electrolysis of a sufficiently dilute solution of any salt proceeds according to equation 20.9. Hydrogen and oxygen are produced, for example, in the electrolysis of a very dilute solution of sodium chloride. The chloride ion is only slightly easier to oxidize than the water molecule; when the concentration of Cl^- ions is very small compared to that of H_2O molecules, it is the latter species which is oxidized.

The four types of reactions just described by no means exhaust the possibilities

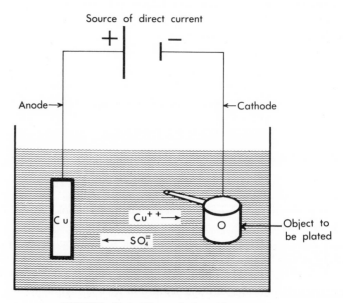

FIGURE 20.4 Electroplating with copper.

for electrolyses carried out in water solution. Frequently, the cell is designed so that one of the electrodes participates in the cell reaction. For example, in the commercial electroplating of copper, a bar of copper is used as the anode. When a direct current is applied across the cell, copper atoms at the anode are oxidized to Cu^{+2} ions. The plating bath is a solution of copper sulfate; Cu^{+2} ions from the solution are reduced to copper atoms at the cathode, which becomes coated with copper metal (Figure 20.4). The reactions at the two electrodes are precisely the reverse of each other.

cathode: $Cu^{+2} + 2 e^- \longrightarrow Cu(s)$ (20.10a)

anode: $Cu(s) \longrightarrow Cu^{+2} + 2 e^-$ (20.10b)

It may be seen from equations 20.10a and 20.10b that the net result of the cell reaction is simply the transfer of copper atoms from anode to cathode; the concentration of Cu^{+2} ions in solution remains constant.

20.3   FARADAY'S LAW OF ELECTROLYSIS

From an economic standpoint, one of the most important aspects of an electrochemical process is the relationship between the quantity of electricity passed through the cell and the amounts of substances produced by oxidation and reduction at the electrodes. Before discussing this relationship, it may be helpful to review the units used to express it.

In electrochemistry, one of the most convenient units for expressing amount of electrical charge is the mole of electrons (6.02×10^{23} electrons). This quantity is so important that it is given a special name—the **faraday.** Another widely used unit is the **coulomb.** It can be shown experimentally that one faraday, to three significant figures, is equal to 96,500 coulombs:

$$1 \text{ mole of electrons} = 1 \text{ faraday} = 96,500 \text{ coulombs}$$

We shall also have occasion to refer to a unit of current flow, the **ampere;** an ampere (amp.) is a rate of flow of electricity of such magnitude that one coulomb passes a given point in the circuit in one second. The number of coulombs flowing through a cell can be calculated from the amperage and time using the relation:

$$\text{no. of coulombs} = \text{no. of amperes} \times \text{no. of seconds}$$

Of the three units of mass that we shall use in electrochemistry, the gram, the mole and the gram equivalent weight, only the third requires comment. It will be recalled that in Chapter 2, the gram equivalent weight of an element was defined as the weight that reacts with or is otherwise equivalent to eight grams of oxygen. This definition is useful for a particular type of oxidation-reduction reaction, that between elements. We are now in a position to frame a more general definition of gram equivalent weight valid for any oxidation-reduction reaction. The *gram equivalent weight* of a substance is the weight in grams which reacts with, is produced by, or is otherwise equivalent to *one mole of electrons (one faraday)*. The use of this definition to calculate the gram equivalent weights of species taking part in oxidation-reduction reactions is illustrated by Example 20.1.

Example 20.1. Calculate the gram equivalent weights of:
   a. Aluminum and oxygen in the electrolysis of Al_2O_3 (reaction 20.2).
   b. Zinc and Ag^+ in the reaction: $Zn(s) + 2\ Ag^+ \rightarrow Zn^{+2} + 2\ Ag(s)$

Solution
   a. Breaking the overall reactions into two half-reactions, we have:

cathode: $2\ Al^{+3} + 6\ e^- \longrightarrow 2\ Al(l)$
anode: $3\ O^{-2} \longrightarrow 3\ O + 6\ e^-$

Clearly, 6 moles of electrons (6 faradays) produces 2 moles of aluminum and 3 moles of (monatomic) oxygen. It follows that 1 mole of electrons (1 faraday) will yield $\frac{2}{6}$ or $\frac{1}{3}$ of a mole of Al and $\frac{3}{6}$ or $\frac{1}{2}$ of a mole of O:

$$6 \text{ moles } e^- \simeq 2 \text{ moles Al} \simeq 3 \text{ moles O}$$
$$1 \text{ mole } e^- \simeq \tfrac{1}{3} \text{ mole Al} \simeq \tfrac{1}{2} \text{ mole O}$$

Hence, from the definition:

$$\text{G.E.W. O} = \tfrac{1}{2} \text{ mole O} = \tfrac{1}{2} \times 16.00 \text{ g. O} = 8.00 \text{ g. O}$$
$$\text{G.E.W. Al} = \tfrac{1}{3} \text{ mole Al} = \tfrac{1}{3} \times 26.97 \text{ g. Al} = 8.99 \text{ g. Al}$$

(Compare the values in Table 2.2, Chapter 2.)

   b. Proceeding exactly as in (a):

$$Zn(s) \longrightarrow Zn^{+2} + 2\ e^- \qquad\qquad 2\ Ag^+ + 2\ e^- \longrightarrow 2\ Ag(s)$$
$$2 \text{ moles } e^- \simeq 1 \text{ mole Zn} \simeq 2 \text{ moles } Ag^+$$
$$1 \text{ mole } e^- \simeq \tfrac{1}{2} \text{ mole Zn} \simeq 1 \text{ mole } Ag^+$$
$$\text{G.E.W. Zn} = \tfrac{1}{2} \text{ mole Zn} = \tfrac{1}{2} \times 65.4 \text{ g. Zn} = 32.7 \text{ g. Zn}$$
$$\text{G.E.W. Ag} = 1 \text{ mole } Ag^+ = 1 \times 107.9 \text{ g. } Ag^+ = 107.9 \text{ g. } Ag^+$$

Going back to the overall equation, it may be noted that 2 G.E.W. of Ag^+ (2 moles Ag^+) react exactly with 2 G.E.W. of Zn (1 mole Zn). In any oxidation-reduction reaction, the number of gram equivalent weights of oxidizing agent (Ag^+, and so on) will always be exactly equal to the number of gram equivalent weights of reducing agent (Zn, and so on). This is, of course, a necessary consequence of the way in which gram equivalent weight is defined (cf. the definitions of G.E.W. for acid-base reactions, Chapter 18).

The foregoing definition of gram equivalent weight leads immediately to the fundamental law of electrolysis which was first discovered by Michael Faraday more than a century ago. This law can be stated as follows: **The number of faradays of electricity (moles of electrons) passed through an electrical cell is exactly equal to the number of gram equivalent weights of the substances produced at each of the two electrodes.**

$$\text{no. of faradays} = \text{no. of G.E.W.} \qquad (20.11)$$

The basic equation 20.11, expressing the relationship between quantity of electricity and quantity of matter produced by electrolysis, can be applied to a great many practical problems that arise in the laboratory. Example 20.2 illustrates the general approach involved.

Example 20.2. Calculate:
   a. The number of grams of aluminum produced when 7200 coulombs of electricity pass through molten aluminum oxide.
   b. The time required to plate a spoon 14.0 cm.² in area to a depth of 0.010 cm. with silver, using an $Ag(CN)_2^-$ plating bath with a current of 0.0120 amp.

Solution

a. We start with the fundamental relationship:

$$\text{no. of faradays} = \text{no. of G.E.W.}$$

The number of faradays in 7200 coulombs is readily calculated, knowing that 1 faraday = 96,500 coulombs:

$$\text{no. of faradays} = 7200 \text{ coulombs} \times \frac{1 \text{ faraday}}{96,500 \text{ coulombs}} = 0.0746$$

The number of gram equivalent weights of aluminum must then be 0.0746. But since one gram equivalent weight of aluminum is 8.99 g. (Example 20.1):

$$\text{no. of g. Al} = 0.0746 \text{ G.E.W. Al} \times \frac{8.99 \text{ g. Al}}{1 \text{ G.E.W. Al}} = 0.671 \text{ g. Al}$$

b. Here, we shall proceed along a well-defined path. We shall first calculate the volume of silver to be plated; then, using the density of silver, the weight required can be obtained. We shall then find the number of gram equivalent weights and hence the number of faradays required, from which the number of coulombs and finally the time can be calculated.

$$\text{Vol. Ag} \rightarrow \text{wt. Ag} \rightarrow \text{no. G.E.W. Ag} \rightarrow \text{no. faradays} \rightarrow \text{no. coulombs} \rightarrow \text{no. secs.}$$

(1)   (2)   (3)   (4)   (5)   (6)

(1) Volume Ag = 14.0 cm.^{2} × 0.0100 cm. = 0.140 cm.^{3}
(2) no. g. Ag = 0.140 cm.^{3} × 10.5 g./cm.^{3} = 1.47 g. Ag
(3) To calculate the number of G.E.W. of Ag, we note from the equation:

$$Ag(CN)_2^- + e^- \longrightarrow Ag(s) + 2 CN^-$$

that one mole of electrons gives one mole of Ag and hence:

$$\text{G.E.W. Ag} = \text{G.A.W. Ag} = 108 \text{ g.}$$

$$\text{no. of G.E.W. Ag} = 1.47 \text{ g. Ag} \times \frac{1 \text{ G.E.W. Ag}}{108 \text{ g.}} = 0.0136 \text{ G.E.W. Ag}$$

(4) no. faradays = no. G.E.W. = 0.0136

(5) no. coulombs = 0.0136 faradays × 96500 $\dfrac{\text{coulombs}}{\text{faraday}}$ = 1310 coulombs

(6) no. sec. = $\dfrac{\text{no. coulombs}}{\text{no. amp.}} = \dfrac{1310 \text{ coulombs}}{0.0120 \text{ amp.}}$ = 109000 sec. (30.3 hrs)

In working these problems, it has been tacitly assumed that all the electrons passing into the cell are used in forming the products, aluminum and silver. In practice, this is never exactly true of any electrolytic process. There are always side reactions which consume at least a small fraction of the current. In the Hall process for the preparation of aluminum, the **current efficiency,** that is, the fraction of the current used to produce aluminum, is only about 80 per cent. We calculated that 7200 coulombs should yield 0.671 g. of aluminum, assuming 100 per cent current efficiency. The amount of aluminum actually formed is closer to 80 per cent of this amount, or about 0.54 g. In silver plating, with a properly designed cell and a plating bath free of impurities, it is possible to approach very closely a current efficiency of 100 per cent.

Faraday's Law offers a convenient experimental means of determining the gram equivalent weight of a substance involved in an oxidation-reduction reaction. All that one has to do is to determine the weight of the substance produced or consumed when 1 faraday of electricity passes through a cell. Going one step further, it is possible to combine the gram equivalent weight, as determined by electrolysis, with the gram formula weight to calculate the number of moles of electrons involved in the oxidation-reduction reaction. In the simplest case, in which the product is an elementary substance formed by oxidation or reduction of a monatomic ion, this information serves to establish the charge of that ion. Example 20.3 illustrates the calculations involved.

Example 20.3. A sample of gadolinium metal (at. wt. = 157) is dissolved in hydrochloric acid and the resulting solution is electrolyzed. It is found that when 3216 coulombs pass through the cell, 1.74 g. of gadolinium is formed at the cathode. Calculate the charge on the gadolinium ion.

Solution. Let us first calculate the gram equivalent weight of gadolinium. Noting that 3216 coulombs pass through the cell, the number of faradays must be:

$$\text{no. faradays} = 3216 \text{ coulombs} \times \frac{1 \text{ faraday}}{96500 \text{ coulombs}} = 0.0333 \text{ faradays} = 0.0333 \text{ G.E.W. Gd}$$

It follows that 1.74 g. of gadolinium must represent 0.0333 G.E.W.

$$1.74 \text{ g. Gd} \simeq 0.0333 \text{ G.E.W. Gd}$$

$$\text{no. of g./G.E.W.} = 1 \text{ G.E.W. Gd} \times \frac{1.74 \text{ g. Gd}}{0.0333 \text{ G.E.W.}} = 52.3\text{g.}$$

Since the gram equivalent weight of gadolinium (52.3 g.) is one third of its gram atomic weight (157 g.), it is clear that three moles of electrons are required to form one mole of the element. This means that the gadolinium cation must carry a charge of $+3$; the equation for the reduction half-reaction is:

$$Gd^{+3} + 3 \text{ e}^- \longrightarrow Gd(s)$$

The electrolytic method illustrated by Example 20.3 was one of the first employed to determine the charges of ions in solution. It has the advantage that the compound used for electrolysis need not be highly pure, provided the impurities present do not take part in the electrode reaction.

20.4 BALANCING OXIDATION-REDUCTION EQUATIONS

Throughout this chapter, we have had frequent occasion to represent the overall reaction going on in an electrolytic cell by means of a balanced equation. We have arrived at such an equation by first writing balanced half-equations for the half-reactions of oxidation and reduction occurring at the electrodes. These two half-equations are then combined into one equation representing the entire electrolysis reaction. To recall one example, in arriving at the balanced equation for the electrolysis of a water solution of sodium chloride, we first wrote an equation for the oxidation reaction at the anode (20.5a) and the reduction reaction at the cathode (20.5b). Combining these in such a way that there was no net loss or gain of electrons, we arrived at the final equation, 20.5.

This method of analyzing an oxidation-reduction reaction and the corresponding equation helps one to understand what is taking place within an electrolytic cell. We shall find it equally applicable when we consider voltaic cells in Chapter 21. Indeed, whenever one is faced with the problem of arriving at an equation for an oxidation-reduction reaction, whether it is occurring in an electrical cell, a test tube, or elsewhere, it is convenient to first break the equation down into two half-equations, balance these separately, and then combine them so as to arrive at an overall equation involving no net loss or gain of electrons.

To illustrate the application of this method to the balancing of a simple oxidation-reduction equation, consider the reaction that occurs when a water solution of ferric chloride is electrolyzed. The products are observed to be metallic iron and chlorine gas. The unbalanced equation may be written:

$$Fe^{+3} + Cl^- \longrightarrow Fe(s) + Cl_2(g)$$

To balance this equation, we proceed as follows:

1. Split the equation into two half-equations, one oxidation and one reduction:

reduction: $\hspace{4cm} Fe^{+3} \longrightarrow Fe(s) \hspace{4cm}$ (1a)

oxidation: $\hspace{4cm} Cl^- \longrightarrow Cl_2(g) \hspace{4cm}$ (1b)

2. Balance these half-equations, first with respect to mass and then with respect to charge:

Equation 1a is balanced insofar as mass is concerned, since there is one atom of Fe on both sides. The charges, however, are unbalanced; the Fe atom on the right has 0 charge while the Fe^{+3} ion on the left has a charge of $+3$. To correct this, we add three electrons to the left of 1a, arriving at:

$$Fe^{+3} + 3\ e^- \longrightarrow Fe(s) \hspace{3cm} (2a)$$

Equation 1b must first be balanced with respect to mass by providing two Cl^- ions to give one molecule of Cl_2:

$$2\ Cl^- \longrightarrow Cl_2(g)$$

To balance charges, two electrons must be added to the right, giving a charge of -2 on both sides:

$$2\ Cl^- \longrightarrow Cl_2(g) + 2\ e^- \hspace{3cm} (2b)$$

3. Having arrived at two balanced half-equations, combine them so as to make the number of electrons gained in reduction equal to the number lost in oxidation.

In equation 2a, three electrons are gained; in 2b, two electrons are given off. To arrive at a final equation in which no electrons appear, multiply 2a by 2, 2b by 3 and add:

$2 \times 2a$: $\hspace{2cm} 2\ Fe^{+3} + 6\ e^- \longrightarrow 2\ Fe(s) \hspace{2.5cm}$ (3a)

$3 \times 2b$: $\hspace{3.5cm} 6\ Cl^- \longrightarrow 3\ Cl_2(g) + 6\ e^- \hspace{1.5cm}$ (3b)

$$\overline{2\ Fe^{+3} + 6\ Cl^- \longrightarrow 2\ Fe(s) + 3\ Cl_2(g)} \hspace{2cm} (3)$$

The equation just balanced corresponds to the simplest type of oxidation-reduction reaction in which only two elements are involved. One of these elements (chlorine, in the form of Cl^- ions) underwent oxidation, the other (iron, in the form of Fe^{+3} ions) was reduced. Equations for such reactions can ordinarily be balanced by inspection. The reaction itself becomes more complicated, the equation more difficult to balance, and the method just outlined more pertinent when atoms of elements other than those being oxidized or reduced are involved in the overall reaction. Regardless of the number of elements participating in the reaction or the complexity of the resulting equation, the method we have outlined, with minor modifications, can be applied.

For oxidation-reduction reactions in water solution, the two most common "extra" elements (elements whose atoms undergo no change in oxidation number) are hydrogen and oxygen. Both of these elements occur in the water molecule, which frequently participates in aqueous oxidation-reduction reactions. Hydrogen may also be present as the H^+ ion (acidic solution) or the OH^- ion (basic solution). Oxygen is found in such oxyanions as SO_4^{-2}, NO_3^-, MnO_4^-, and OH^- and in neutral molecules such as SO_2, NO_2, or CO_2, any of which may appear as a reactant or product in oxidation-reduction reactions. In all these species, oxygen ordinarily retains throughout the reaction an oxidation number of -2, hydrogen an oxidation number of $+1$.

To illustrate the balancing of an oxidation-reduction equation in which oxygen and hydrogen appear along with the elements being oxidized or reduced, consider the reaction that occurs between chloride and permanganate ions in acidic solution. Experimental evidence indicates that this reaction can best be represented by the equation:

$$MnO_4^- + H^+ + Cl^- \longrightarrow Mn^{+2} + Cl_2(g) + H_2O$$

Note that the two elements that undergo a change in oxidation number are manganese $(+7 \to +2)$ and chlorine $(-1 \to 0)$. Neither hydrogen nor oxygen change oxidation number, yet atoms of these elements participate in the reaction. The oxygen atoms tied up originally in the MnO_4^- ion end up as H_2O molecules; the H^+ ions meet the same fate.

To balance this equation, we proceed as follows:

1. Separate into two half-equations:

oxidation: $\qquad\qquad\qquad\qquad\qquad\qquad Cl^- \longrightarrow Cl_2(g)$ (1a)

reduction: $\qquad\qquad\qquad\qquad MnO_4^- + H^+ \longrightarrow Mn^{+2} + H_2O$ (1b)

2. Half-equation 1a is readily balanced as before, arriving at:

$$2\ Cl^- \longrightarrow Cl_2(g) + 2\ e^- \qquad\qquad\text{(2a)}$$

To balance 1b, we first make sure that there are the same number of Mn atoms on both sides, one. Next, the oxygen is balanced by writing a coefficient of 4 in front of the H_2O on the right to account for the four oxygens in the MnO_4^- ion:

$$MnO_4^- + H^+ \longrightarrow Mn^{+2} + 4\ H_2O$$

To complete the mass balance, the number of hydrogen atoms on the two sides must be equalized. The four H_2O molecules on the right contain eight hydrogen atoms; there must then be eight H^+ ions on the left:

$$MnO_4^- + 8\ H^+ \longrightarrow Mn^{+2} + 4\ H_2O$$

Finally, the charges must be balanced; at the moment there is a charge of $+2$ on the right and $+7$ on the left $(-1 + 8)$. To balance, five electrons are added to the left:

$$MnO_4^- + 8\ H^+ + 5\ e^- \longrightarrow Mn^{+2} + 4\ H_2O \qquad\qquad\text{(2b)}$$

It may be seen from this discussion that balancing a half-equation containing hydrogen and oxygen in addition to the elements undergoing oxidation or reduction involves, as one would expect, two extra steps. In obtaining the mass balance for the half-equation, it is ordinarily simplest to deal first with the element being oxidized or reduced, then with the oxygen and finally the hydrogen.

3. Half-equations 2a and 2b are now combined as usual so as to eliminate electrons from the final equation. To do this, multiply 2a by 5 and 2b by 2, producing 10 e^- on both sides:

$5 \times 2a$: $10 \ Cl^- \longrightarrow 5 \ Cl_2(g) + 10 \ e^-$ (3a)

$2 \times 2b$: $2 \ MnO_4^- + 16 \ H^+ + 10 \ e^- \longrightarrow 2 \ Mn^{+2} + 8 \ H_2O$ (3b)

$$2 \ MnO_4^- + 16 \ H^+ + 10 \ Cl^- \longrightarrow 2 \ Mn^{+2} + 8 \ H_2O + 5 \ Cl_2(g) \qquad (3)$$

Frequently, we have occasion to write balanced equations for oxidation-reduction reactions taking place in basic solution. For such reactions, it would be inappropriate to write equations in which H^+ ions appear, since this ion is present in only very small concentrations in basic solution. Instead, the equations should contain hydrogen in the form of OH^- ions or H_2O molecules. A simple way to accomplish this is to eliminate any H^+ ions appearing in the half-equations, "neutralizing" them by adding an equal number of OH^- ions to both sides. To illustrate, consider the oxidation, in basic solution, of odide by permanganate ions:

$$I^- + MnO_4^- \longrightarrow I_2 + MnO_2(s) \ \text{(basic solution)}$$

One can proceed, exactly as in the foregoing example, to obtain the half-equations:

oxidation: $2 \ I^- \longrightarrow I_2 + 2 \ e^-$ (2a)

reduction: $MnO_4^- + 4 \ H^+ + 3 \ e^- \longrightarrow MnO_2(s) + 2 \ H_2O$ (2b)

The H^+ ions appearing in the reduction half-equation must now be removed to obtain an equation valid in basic solution. To do this, four OH^- ions are added to both sides:

$$MnO_4^- + 4 \ H^+ + 3 \ e^- \longrightarrow MnO_2(s) + 2 \ H_2O$$
$$+ 4 \ OH^- \qquad \longrightarrow \qquad\qquad + 4 \ OH^-$$

$$MnO_4^- + 4 \ H_2O + 3 \ e^- \longrightarrow MnO_2(s) + 2 \ H_2O + 4 \ OH^-$$

Eliminating two water molecules from each side, we arrive at:

$$MnO_4^- + 2 \ H_2O + 3 \ e^- \longrightarrow MnO_2(s) + 4 \ OH^- \qquad (2b')$$

for the reduction half-reaction in basic solution. To obtain the overall equation, we proceed as before, combining 2a and 2b' in such a way as to make the electron gain equal the electron loss:

$3 \times 2a$: $6 \ I^- \longrightarrow 3 \ I_2 + 6 \ e^-$

$2 \times 2b$: $2 \ MnO_4^- + 4 \ H_2O + 6 \ e^- \longrightarrow 2 \ MnO_2(s) + 8 \ OH^-$

$$6 \ I^- + 2 \ MnO_4^- + 4 \ H_2O \longrightarrow 3 \ I_2 + 2 \ MnO_2(s) + 8 \ OH^- \qquad (3)$$

Oxidation Number Method of Balancing Equations

The *half-equation* method just described is by no means the only, or even the simplest method of balancing oxidation-reduction equations. We have stressed this particular method because it involves techniques which are valuable in studying other aspects of oxidation-reduction reactions. Of the various other methods which can be used to balance redox equations, we shall discuss only one: the *oxidation number* method.

To illustrate the application of this method, consider the equation referred to earlier:

$$MnO_4^- + Cl^- + H^+ \longrightarrow Mn^{+2} + Cl_2(g) + H_2O$$

To balance this equation by the oxidation number method, we proceed as follows:

1. Determine the oxidation number of each element on both sides of the equation, thereby determining which elements have undergone oxidation and reduction:

	Oxid. No Reactants	Oxid. No. Products	
Mn	+7	+2	reduced
O	−2	−2	
Cl	−1	0	oxidized
H	+1	+1	

2. By adjusting the coefficients of the species being oxidized and reduced, make the total increase in oxidation number equal to the total decrease.

In this case, each Mn atom undergoes a decrease in oxidation number of five units; each Cl atom increases in oxidation number by one unit. To make the increase in oxidation number equal to the decrease, there must be five Cl atoms oxidized for every Mn reduced. Thus:

$$MnO_4^- + 5\ Cl^- \longrightarrow Mn^{+2} + \tfrac{5}{2}\ Cl_2(g)$$

or, multiplying through by two to eliminate fractional coefficients:

$$2\ MnO_4^- + 10\ Cl^- \longrightarrow 2\ Mn^{+2} + 5\ Cl_2(g) \tag{a}$$

Note that for equation a, the total increase in oxidation number of Cl is $10 \times 1 = 10$, the total decrease in oxidation number of Mn $= 2 \times 5 = 10$.

3. Having determined the coefficients of the species being oxidized and reduced, balance the number of atoms of the remaining elements in the usual manner.

Here, starting with equation a, the oxygen is balanced first. The presence of 2 MnO_4^- ions on the left, containing a total of eight oxygen atoms, requires that there be eight H_2O molecules, each with one oxygen atom, on the right:

$$2\ MnO_4^- + 10\ Cl^- \longrightarrow 2\ Mn^{+2} + 5\ Cl_2(g) + 8\ H_2O \tag{b}$$

Finally, to balance the hydrogen, 16 H^+ ions must be added to the left:

$$2\ MnO_4^- + 10\ Cl^- + 16\ H^+ \longrightarrow 2\ Mn^{+2} + 5\ Cl_2(g) + 8\ H_2O \tag{c}$$

The final balanced equation is, of course, identical to that previously derived by the half-equation method.

Oxidation-Reduction Equations Which Cannot be Balanced Formally

In each of the examples we have just worked, there has been only one oxidation and one reduction. The situation is more complicated if multiple oxidations or reductions occur. Suppose, for example, that in the reaction of MnO_4^- with Cl^-, MnO_2 as well as Mn^{+2} were to be among the reaction products. Two reductions would then be taking place simultaneously, part of the manganese in the MnO_4^- ion ending up as MnO_2 and part as Mn^{+2}. Without recourse to experiment, it would be impossible to decide what fraction of the MnO_4^- was reduced to MnO_2 and what fraction to Mn^{+2}. Consequently, one could not properly balance the equation:

$$MnO_4^- + Cl^- + H^+ \longrightarrow MnO_2(s) + Mn^{+2} + Cl_2(g) + H_2O$$

Situations such as that just described frequently arise in redox reactions carried out in the laboratory. For example, when nitric acid, HNO_3, is used as an oxidizing agent, it is ordinarily reduced to give a mixture of products including NO, NO_2, and, occasionally, N_2, NH_4^+, or NO_2^-. The proportions of these species found among the products depend not only on the substance being oxidized but also upon the reaction conditions, particularly the concentration of nitric acid. Sulfuric acid, H_2SO_4, behaves similarly; on reduction it may yield SO_2, S, H_2S, or a mixture of these products. Indeed, whenever we write and balance an oxidation-reduction equation involving only one oxidation and one reduction, we are indulging in oversimplification.

In a few cases, it is possible to balance an equation involving more than one oxidation or reduction without recourse to experiment to determine the relative amounts of products. Consider, for example, the oxidation of Cu_2S, an insoluble compound, by nitric acid. The unbalanced equation may be written:

$$Cu_2S(s) + H^+ + NO_3^- \longrightarrow Cu^{+2} + SO_2(g) + H_2O + NO_2(g)$$

Here, both copper (oxid. no $+1 \rightarrow +2$) and sulfur (oxid. no $-2 \rightarrow +4$) undergo oxidation. However, since the two elements are present in a fixed $2:1$ ratio in Cu_2S, it is possible to determine immediately what the relative coefficients of the products Cu^{+2} and SO_2 must be ($2 Cu^{+2}$ for every SO_2) and hence one can eventually arrive at the balanced equation:

$$Cu_2S(s) + 12 H^+ + 8 NO_3^- \longrightarrow 2 Cu^{+2} + SO_2(g) + 6 H_2O + 8 NO_2(g)$$

20.5 SUMMARY

An electrolytic cell is one in which electrical energy is used to cause an oxidation-reduction to occur. Oxidation takes place at the anode, reduction at the cathode. Current is carried through the cell by the migration of ions, cations moving toward the cathode, anions toward the anode.

Electrolyses may be carried out either in the molten state or in water solution. Many elements, including sodium, aluminum, and fluorine, which are difficult or impossible to obtain by conventional chemical means, can be produced by electrolysis of their molten ionic compounds. Nonreactive solutes are often added to the cell to lower the operating temperature and thereby reduce the cost of electrolysis.

When a salt is electrolyzed in water solution, several different electrode reactions are possible. Reduction at the cathode may involve either the cation of the salt ($Cu^{+2} + 2 e^- \rightarrow Cu(s)$) or a water molecule ($H_2O + e^- \rightarrow \frac{1}{2} H_2(g) + OH^-$). At the anode, an anion ($Cl^- \rightarrow \frac{1}{2} Cl_2(g) + e^-$) or a water molecule ($H_2O \rightarrow \frac{1}{2} O_2(g) + 2 H^+ + 2 e^-$) may be oxidized. With the salts of the transition metals, it is ordinarily the cation which is reduced; salts of the 1A and 2A metals, whose cations are difficult to reduce, yield H_2 and OH^- at the cathode. Electrolysis of a water solution containing Cl^-, Br^- or I^- ions forms the corresponding halogen at the anode; with anions which are more difficult to oxidize such as SO_4^{-2}, NO_3^- or F^-, oxygen is produced instead.

The quantity of electricity passing through a cell is directly proportional to the quantity of matter produced by oxidation and reduction at the electrodes. One faraday (96,500 coulombs) forms one gram equivalent weight of a substance at each electrode. In other words:

no. of faradays passed through cell = no. of G.E.W. produced at electrodes

This simple relationship makes it possible to calculate the amount of a substance produced in a given electrolysis or the time required to produce a given amount of material (Example 20.2). Even more important, it forms the basis of an experimental method of determining the gram equivalent weight of an element or the charge of its ions. (Example 20.3).

A reaction going on in an electrolytic cell may be regarded as the sum of two half-reactions occurring at the electrodes. By writing balanced half-equations for these reactions and adding them in such a way as to produce electrical neutrality, it is possible to arrive at the balanced equation for the overall process. A general method of balancing oxidation-reduction equations based on this principle was developed in Section 20.4.

PROBLEMS

20.1 Explain precisely what is meant by each of the following terms.
   a. Electrolysis   e. Faraday
   b. Cathode   f. Coulomb
   c. Anode   g. Ampere
   d. Gram equivalent weight (in electrolysis)

20.2 Explain why:
   a. In the electrolysis of molten sodium chloride, the electrodes are separated by a screen.
   b. It is cheaper to produce chlorine by the electrolysis of a water solution of sodium chloride than by electrolyzing molten sodium chloride.
   c. Cryolite is used in the electrolysis of aluminum oxide.
   d. The carbon electrodes used in the Hall process have to be replaced frequently.
   e. Fluorine is produced by the electrolysis of a molten KL-HF mixture rather than by electrolyzing a water solution of KF.

20.3 Describe in some detail the commercial preparations of the following elements.
   a. Sodium   b. Aluminum   c. Chlorine   d. Fluorine

20.4 A paper company located in Maine is producing Cl_2 by the electrolysis of NaCl. In order to make use of the H_2 obtained as by-product, the company buys land in South Carolina and raises peanuts on it. They intend to crush the peanuts and hydrogenate the resulting peanut oil. Where would you advise them to build the hydrogenation plant?

20.5 Write balanced net ionic equations for the reactions that occur when the following water solutions are electrolyzed.
   a. NaCl   b. $CuBr_2$ c. KF   d. HCl   e. $Cu(NO_3)_2$ f. K_2SO_4

20.6 Describe in some detail how one might prepare:
   a. I_2 from KI   d. H_2 from H_2O
   b. Cu from $CuSO_4$ e. KOH from KBr
   c. Pure Cu from impure Cu

20.7 Describe how the following transformations might be carried out with the aid of electrolytic reactions.
   a. NaCl $\rightarrow$ NaBr   b. NaBr $\rightarrow$ Br_2 c. $Cu(NO_3)_2 \rightarrow HNO_3$

20.8 When a solution of $ZnBr_2$ is electrolyzed, the products are Zn and Br_2. If 20,200 coulombs are passed through the solution:
   a. How many gram equivalent weights of Zn and Br_2 are produced?
   b. How many gram atomic weights of Zn and Br are produced?
   c. How many grams of Zn and Br_2 are produced?

20.9 In the electrolysis of Al_2O_3, using a current of 25.0 amp.:
   a. What is the rate of production of Al in grams per hour?
   b. The O_2 liberated at the positive carbon electrode reacts with it to form CO_2. How many grams of CO_2 are produced per hour?

20.10 In the electrolysis of a solution of $CuSO_4$, what weight of Cu is plated in 4.0 hours by a current of 1.2 amp.?

20.11 A sample of brass weighing 12.02 g. and containing 62.3 per cent Cu is dissolved in concentrated nitric acid, converting the copper to Cu^{+2} ions. The resulting solution is electrolyzed. If it is desired to plate out all of the copper using a current of 0.542 amp., how long will it take?

20.12 A dry cell has an outer coating of zinc which weighs 55 g. If the cell fails when 20 per cent of the zinc is consumed, how long can it be used to supply a current of 2.0 amp.?

20.13 A student finds that 16.8 g. of a certain metal is plated in the same time as 12.9 g. of copper, using the same current. What is the gram equivalent weight of the metal?

20.14 Complete and balance the following half-equations and calculate the gram equivalent weights of the products.
a. $PtCl_6^{-2} \rightarrow Pt(s)$ b. $MnO_2(s) \rightarrow MnO_4^-$ (basic solution)   c. $Fe^{+3} \rightarrow Fe^{+2}$

20.15 In the electrolysis of a potassium dichromate solution, it is found that 0.90×10^{-4} g. of chromium are produced per coulomb.
a. How many electrons are required to produce one atom of chromium?
b. How many electrons are required to reduce one $Cr_2O_7^{-2}$ ion?
c. Write a balanced half-equation for the reduction of $Cr_2O_7^{-2}$ to $Cr(s)$.

20.16 Balance the following oxidation-reduction equations.
a. $Cu(s) + H^+ + NO_3^- \rightarrow Cu^{+2} + NO_2(g) + H_2O$
b. $SO_2(g) + NO_3^- + H_2O \rightarrow SO_4^{-2} + NO(g) + H^+$
c. $MnO_2(s) + H^+ + Cl^- \rightarrow Cl_2(g) + Mn^{+2} + H_2O$
d. $Cu(s) + H^+ + SO_4^{-2} \rightarrow Cu^{+2} + SO_2(g) + H_2O$

20.17 Balance the following equations, all of which correspond to reactions occurring in acidic solution.
a. $Cr_2O_7^{-2} + Fe^{+2} \rightarrow Cr^{+3} + Fe^{+3}$
b. $CuS(s) + NO_3^- \rightarrow Cu^{+2} + SO_4^{-2} + NO(g)$
c. $PbO_2(s) + Mn^{+2} \rightarrow MnO_4^- + Pb^{+2}$
d. $NH_4^+ + NO_3^- \rightarrow N_2O(g)$

20.18 Balance the following equations for reactions occurring in basic solution.
a. $Cr(OH)_3(s) + ClO^- \rightarrow CrO_4^{-2} + Cl^-$
b. $Fe(OH)_2(s) + O_2(g) \rightarrow Fe(OH)_3(s)$
c. $Cl_2(g) \rightarrow Cl^- + ClO_3^-$

20.19 Write balanced equations to correspond to the following reactions.
a. A solution of nitric acid and hydrochloric acid is heated to give nitric oxide and chlorine.
b. Permanganate ions (MnO_4^-) and sulfide ions in acidic solution react to give Mn^{+2} and sulfur.
c. Mn^{+2} ions are oxidized to manganate ions (MnO_4^{-2}) by nitrate ions in basic solution (NO_2^- ions are also produced).

20.20 What weight of copper can be oxidized to Cu^{+2} ions by 1.20 l. of 0.500 M H_2SO_4 (cf. Problem 20.16d)?

20.21 What volume of chlorine at 25°C and 750 mm. Hg can be produced by the reaction of 20.0 g. of MnO_2 with excess hydrochloric acid (cf. Problem 20.16c)?

*20.22 Explain how Avogadro's number might be determined by an electrolysis experiment. What assumptions would have to be made in the calculations? How could these assumptions be checked experimentally?

*20.23 In commercial electroplating processes, complexing agents are frequently used to reduce the concentrations of metal ions. Can you suggest an explanation for this? You may wish to consult a textbook on electrochemistry.

*20.24 It is desired to plate a brass cylinder open at the top only with silver. The cylinder is 12.0 cm. high and its circular base is 2.56 cm. in diameter.

    a. What weight of silver is required to plate the cylinder (inside and outside) to a thickness of 0.10 mm.? (The density of silver is 10.54 g./cc.)

    b. If the plating is carried out from $Ag(CN)_2^-$, using a current of 0.15 amp., how much time is required to give a coating this thick?

*20.25 Write a balanced equation for the reaction of sulfuric acid with sodium iodide. All of the iodide ions are oxidized to iodine. Of the SO_4^{-2} ions, it is found that 50 per cent are reduced to SO_3^{-2} ions, 30 per cent to elementary sulfur and the remainder to H_2S.

*20.26 A mixture of $CuCl_2$, NaCl, and $NaNO_3$ is analyzed. It is found that a 1.000 g. sample, on treatment with excess silver nitrate gives 1.628 g. of AgCl. An electrolysis of a 1.000 g. sample gives 0.148 g. of copper. Calculate the percentages of the three constituents of the mixture.

21

VOLTAIC CELLS: SPONTANEITY OF OXIDATION-REDUCTION REACTIONS

Electrolytic cells, to which Chapter 20 was devoted, use a direct electric current to bring about an oxidation-reduction reaction. Voltaic cells, which will be discussed in this chapter, perform the reverse function; a spontaneous oxidation-reduction reaction taking place within the cell generates a direct electric current. Voltaic cells have long been used for such mundane purposes as starting an automobile or operating a flashlight. More recently, they have served as a source of power for hearing aids and satellite communications systems. In both the industrial and teaching laboratory, voltaic cells are commonly used to provide electrical energy to operate electrolytic cells of the type discussed in Chapter 20.

To the chemist, the most important application of voltaic cells is their use in determining the spontaneity of oxidation-reduction reactions. By measuring cell voltages, it is possible to predict whether a given reaction will take place in the laboratory and, if so, the extent to which it will occur.

21.1 A SIMPLE VOLTAIC CELL: THE Zn–Cu CELL

If a piece of zinc is added to a solution of copper sulfate, the following, spontaneous oxidation-reduction reaction takes place:

$$Zn(s) + Cu^{+2} \longrightarrow Zn^{+2} + Cu(s) \tag{21.1}$$

Electron transfer from Zn atoms to Cu^{+2} ions takes place directly at the surface of the zinc. A spongy, reddish-brown deposit of copper forms on the surface of the zinc; the blue color of the solution fades as Cu^{+2} ions are replaced by Zn^{+2} ions. Energy is liberated as heat; the temperature of the solution rises several degrees. The spontaneity of the reaction is commonly explained by saying that zinc loses electrons more readily than copper or, alternatively, that Cu^{+2} ions gain electrons more readily than Zn^{+2} ions.

497

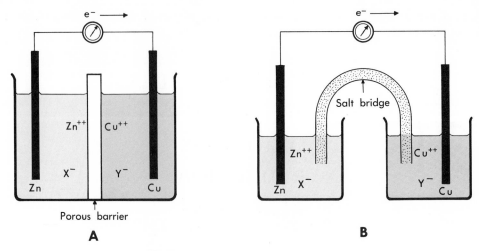

FIGURE 21.1 Zinc-copper voltaic cells.

To design a cell using reaction 21.1 as a source of electrical energy, the electron transfer must be made to occur indirectly. That is, the electrons given up by the zinc atoms must pass through an electrical circuit before they reduce Cu^{+2} ions to copper atoms. A schematic diagram of a cell in which this is achieved is shown in Figure 21.1a.

It will be instructive to trace the path of electrical current through this cell.

1. At the zinc *anode*, electrons are produced by the oxidation half-reaction:

$$\text{anode:} \qquad \qquad Zn(s) \longrightarrow Zn^{+2} + 2\ e^- \qquad \qquad (21.1a)$$

This electrode, which "pushes" electrons into the external circuit, is ordinarily considered to be the negative pole of the cell.

2. The electrons generated by reaction 21.1a move through the external circuit, which may be a simple resistance wire, a motor, or an electrolytic cell.

3. Electrons pass through the external circuit into the copper *cathode*, where they are consumed in *reducing* Cu^{+2} ions in the solution to copper atoms:

$$\text{cathode:} \qquad \qquad Cu^{+2} + 2\ e^- \longrightarrow Cu(s) \qquad \qquad (21.1b)$$

The copper electrode, which "pulls" electrons out of the external circuit is considered to be the positive pole of the cell.

4. The circuit is completed by the passage of ions through the cell. As reactions 21.1a and 21.1b proceed, a surplus of positive ions (Zn^{+2}) is created around the zinc electrode. The region around the copper electrode becomes deficient in positive ions due to the discharge of Cu^{+2} ions. To maintain electrical neutrality, cations must move into the region around the copper cathode or, alternatively, anions must flow towards the zinc anode. In practice, both of these migrations occur.

The net result of the half-reactions occurring within the Zn-Cu cell is, of course, reaction 21.1. The cell is so designed that electron transfer from Zn atoms to Cu^{+2} ions occurs indirectly through an external circuit. In this way, the energy liberated by the reaction is used to do electrical work rather than being dissipated as heat.

Two essential points concerning the design of a zinc-copper cell are implied by equation 21.1:

1. The only species which need be present in the cell initially are the reactants, zinc atoms and Cu^{+2} ions. In other words, the anode of the cell must be made of zinc

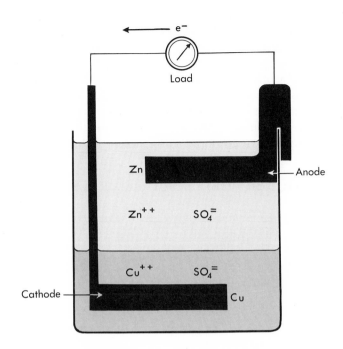

FIGURE 21.2 Gravity (Daniell) cell.

and the solution surrounding the cathode must contain Cu^{+2} ions. On the other hand, the products of the reaction, copper atoms and Zn^{+2} ions, need not be present when the cell is set up. A platinum wire can be substituted for the strip of copper shown in Figure 21.1a; Cu^{+2} ions plate out as readily on platinum as on copper. Any positive ion which does not react with zinc can replace the Zn^{+2} ions surrounding the zinc electrode. A solution of Na_2SO_4, or KNO_3 works as well as a solution of $ZnSO_4$.

2. It is imperative that Cu^{+2} ions not come in contact with the zinc electrode. If this happens, reaction 21.1 will occur directly at the surface of the zinc, thereby short-circuiting the cell. One way of preventing the Cu^{+2} ions formed at the cathode from diffusing over to the zinc anode is to interpose a porous partition between the two halves of the cell (Figure 21.1a). The partition permits the migration of ions while the cell is in use but minimizes the random diffusion of ions that otherwise takes place when the cell is not connected.* Another way of accomplishing this same purpose is to connect the two halves of the cell by means of a U-shaped tube referred to as a salt bridge (Figure 21.1b). The tube is filled with a solution of an electrolyte such as potassium nitrate to which gelatin or agar-agar has been added to give a semisolid paste. When current is drawn from the cell, ions move slowly through the salt bridge to complete the circuit. When the cell is not in use, diffusion of ions through the bridge is so slow that it may take several days for the Cu^{+2} ions to reach the zinc electrode.

---

* It will be recalled that when the zinc-copper cell is operating, Cu^{+2} ions move away from the zinc electrode. This means that so long as current is being drawn from the cell, there is no tendency for Cu^{+2} ions to come in contact with the zinc electrode. For this reason, it is common practice, with cells of this type which are used intermittently, to set up an auxiliary circuit to draw a small amount of current when the cell is not in use. This procedure is followed in the commercial model of the zinc-copper cell (Figure 21.2).

Still another way of preventing Cu^{+2} ions from coming in contact with the zinc electrode is illustrated in the gravity cell shown in Figure 21.2. To form this cell, enough copper sulfate solution is added to the jar to cover the copper electrode. A more dilute, less dense solution of zinc sulfate is then carefully poured over the copper sulfate. So long as the cell is not subjected to vibrations, the boundary between the layers may be maintained over long periods of time. Cells of this design were once used extensively to operate telegraph relays, doorbells, and other stationary electrical apparatus. Since their internal resistance is much lower than that of porous-partition or salt-bridge cells, much larger currents can be drawn from them.

21.2   OTHER VOLTAIC CELLS: COMMERCIAL CELLS

A great many simple voltaic cells can be set up in a manner entirely analogous to the zinc-copper cell shown in Figure 21.1. One can, for example, devise cells (Figure 21.3) in which the following spontaneous oxidation-reduction reactions serve as a source of electrical energy:

$$Ni(s) + Cu^{+2} \longrightarrow Ni^{+2} + Cu(s) \tag{21.2}$$

$$Zn(s) + 2\ H^+ \longrightarrow Zn^{+2} + H_2(g) \tag{21.3}$$

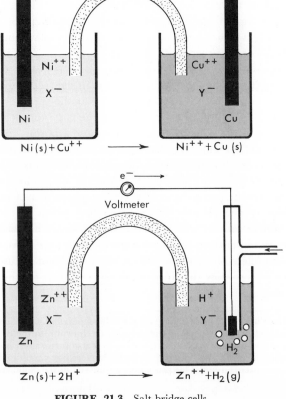

FIGURE 21.3 Salt-bridge cells.

In each case, the apparatus consists of two half-cells, each containing an electrode dipping into a solution of an appropriate electrolyte, separated by a salt bridge or similar device. Atoms of the element having the greatest tendency to lose electrons (Ni, Zn) are oxidized at the anode, giving up electrons which travel through the external circuit to the cathode, where they combine with the cation (Cu^{+2}, H^+) which is most readily reduced.

All the cells discussed to this point, with the single exception of the gravity cell shown in Figure 21.2, are unsuitable for commercial use because of their high internal resistance. There are on the market today several dozen different cells, all of which are capable of supplying a comparatively large current, at least for a short time. Two of these, the dry cell and the lead storage battery, were as familiar to our grandparents as they are to us. Another type of voltaic cell, now in the development stage, gives promise of becoming a major source of electrical energy, perhaps within this decade. This is the so-called fuel cell, which has received so much attention during the past few years.

Dry Cell (Leclanché Cell)

The composition of the ordinary dry cell used in flashlights, portable radios, and similar appliances is shown in Figure 21.4. The zinc wall of the cell serves as the anode; the graphite rod passing through the center of the cell is the cathode. The space between the electrodes is filled with a moist paste containing manganese dioxide, carbon black, and ammonium chloride. When the cell is being used to generate energy, the half-reaction at the anode is:

anode: $\qquad$ $Zn(s) \longrightarrow Zn^{+2} + 2\ e^-$ $\qquad$ (21.4a)

The exact nature of the cathode reaction has never been established. It is known that the manganese dioxide is reduced; a plausible half-equation for its reduction is:

cathode: $\qquad$ $MnO_2(s) + 4\ NH_4^+ + 2\ e^- \longrightarrow Mn^{+2} + 2\ H_2O + 4\ NH_3$ (21.4b)

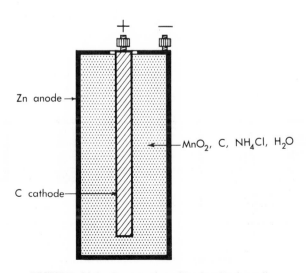

FIGURE 21.4 Cross section of Leclanché dry cell.

This gives, for the overall reaction:

$$\text{Zn(s)} + \text{MnO}_2\text{(s)} + 4 \text{ NH}_4^+ \longrightarrow \text{Zn}^{+2} + \text{Mn}^{+2} + 4 \text{ NH}_3 + 2 \text{ H}_2\text{O} \quad (21.4)$$

If too large a current is drawn from the cell, the ammonia formed by reaction 21.4b forms a gaseous, insulating layer around the carbon electrode. In normal operation, this condition is prevented by the migration of Zn^{+2} ions to the cathode where they react with ammonia molecules to form complex ions such as $\text{Zn(NH}_3)_4^{+2}$, $\text{Zn(NH}_3)_2(\text{H}_2\text{O})_2^{+2}$, and so on. An apparently "dead" dry cell can sometimes be revived by careful heating, which increases the rate of diffusion of Zn^{+2} ions across the cell.

Lead Storage Battery

The 12-volt storage battery commonly used in automobiles consists of six voltaic cells of the type shown in Figure 21.5 connected in series. A group of lead plates, the grids of which are filled with spongy, gray lead, forms the anode of the cell. The multiple cathode consists of a group of plates of similar design filled with lead dioxide. These two series of plates, alternating with each other throughout the cell, are immersed in a water solution of sulfuric acid, which acts as the electrolyte.

When a lead storage battery is supplying current, the lead in the anode grids is oxidized to Pb^{+2} ions, which immediately precipitate on the plates as lead sulfate, PbSO_4. At the cathode, the lead dioxide is reduced to Pb^{+2} ions, which also precipitate as PbSO_4.

anode : $\text{Pb(s)} + \text{SO}_4^{-2} \longrightarrow \text{PbSO}_4\text{(s)} + 2 \text{ e}^-$ (21.5a)

cathode : $\text{PbO}_2\text{(s)} + 4 \text{ H}^+ + \text{SO}_4^{-2} + 2 \text{ e}^- \longrightarrow \text{PbSO}_4\text{(s)} + 2 \text{ H}_2\text{O}$ (21.5b)

$$\text{Pb(s)} + \text{PbO}_2\text{(s)} + 4 \text{ H}^+ + 2 \text{ SO}_4^{-2} \longrightarrow 2 \text{ PbSO}_4\text{(s)} + 2 \text{ H}_2\text{O} \quad (21.5)$$

Deposits of lead sulfate formed by reactions 21.5a and 21.5b slowly build up on the plates, partially covering and replacing the lead and lead dioxide. As the cell discharges, the concentration of sulfuric acid decreases; for every mole of lead reacting,

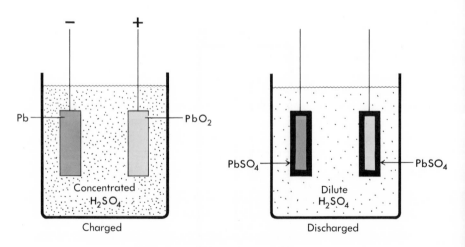

FIGURE 21.5 Lead storage battery.

2 moles of H_2SO_4 (4 H^+, 2 SO_4^{-2}) are replaced by 2 moles of water, The state of charge of a storage battery can be checked by measuring the density of the electrolyte. A low density indicates a low sulfuric acid concentration and hence a partially discharged cell.

A lead storage battery, unlike an ordinary dry cell, can be restored to its original condition by passing a direct current through it. While a storage battery is being charged, it acts as an electrolytic cell; the half-reactions represented by equations 21.5a and 21.5b are reversed:

$$2 \text{ PbSO}_4(s) + 2 \text{ H}_2\text{O} \longrightarrow \text{Pb}(s) + \text{PbO}_2(s) + 4 \text{ H}^+ + 2 \text{ SO}_4^{-2} \quad (21.6)$$

The electrical energy required to bring about reaction 21.6 may be furnished by a direct-current generator or an auxiliary battery.

Fuel Cells

By far the major portion of our electrical energy is obtained indirectly from the combustion of fuels. The thermal energy produced by burning coal, oil or natural gas is converted to mechanical energy which in turn is used to run electrical generators. Although this method of producing electrical energy is more economical than a conventional voltaic cell, it is relatively inefficient. A steam power plant using coal as a fuel converts only about 35 per cent of the available chemical energy of the coal into electrical energy.

Scientists for generations have speculated on the possibility of converting the chemical energy of fuels directly to electrical energy in a type of voltaic cell known as a fuel cell. In principle, there is no reason why this cannot be done. The combustion of a fuel is a spontaneous oxidation-reduction reaction and hence should serve as the basis for a voltaic cell. In practice, it turns out to be extremely difficult to design cells in which such apparently simple reactions as:

$$C(s) + O_2(g) \longrightarrow CO_2(g)$$

and:
$$H_2(g) + \tfrac{1}{2} O_2(g) \longrightarrow H_2O(l)$$

will occur. Recently, however, fuel cells have been built which convert up to 80 per cent of the energy available from combustion reactions to electrical energy.

A prototype of the modern fuel cell, built in Germany in 1937, is shown in Figure 21.6A. The anode consists of a layer of carbon granules packed around a central, inert electrode. Air or oxygen is blown through magnetite (Fe_3O_4) particles which surround the cathode. The electrolyte consists of a molten mixture of several different metal oxides; oxide ions (O^{-2}) carry the current through the cell. The reaction taking place may be represented most simply as:

anode:	$C(s) + 2 O^{-2} \longrightarrow CO_2(g) + 4 e^-$	(21.7a)
cathode:	$O_2(g) + 4 e^- \longrightarrow 2 O^{-2}$	(21.7b)

$$C(s) + O_2(g) \longrightarrow CO_2(g) \quad (21.7)$$

An inherent disadvantage of this cell is the high operating temperature, approximately 1000°C, required to maintain the electrolyte in the molten state.

A modern fuel cell with attractive commercial possibilities is sketched in

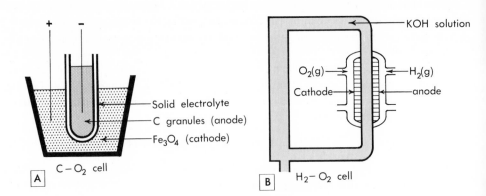

FIGURE 21.6 Fuel cells.

Figure 21.6B. This cell uses the spontaneous reaction between hydrogen and oxygen to produce electrical energy. The operating temperature of the cell is about 250°C under a pressure of 50 atm. A water solution of sodium or potassium hydroxide serves as the electrolyte. In the presence of certain catalysts, the reactions:

anode :
$$H_2(g) + 2 \ OH^- \longrightarrow 2 \ H_2O + 2 \ e^- \qquad (21.8a)$$

cathode :
$$\tfrac{1}{2} O_2(g) + H_2O + 2 \ e^- \longrightarrow 2 \ OH^- \qquad (21.8b)$$

$$\overline{\rule{0pt}{1.5ex}\hspace{1em} H_2(g) + \tfrac{1}{2} O_2(g) \longrightarrow H_2O \hspace{1em}} \qquad (21.8)$$

occur at graphite electrodes to give a maximum voltage of about 1 v. Either air or pure oxygen can be used at the cathode. At present, pure hydrogen appears to be required for the anode reaction. Current research on this cell is directed towards using impure hydrogen; if water gas, a mixture of carbon monoxide and hydrogen, could be used, the cost of the electrical energy produced might be cut in half.

21.3 STANDARD ELECTRODE POTENTIALS

It was stated earlier that the principal interest of the chemist in voltaic cells lies in the information which they provide concerning the spontaneity of oxidation-reduction reactions. This information can be deduced from a measurement of cell voltages. With a properly designed cell, it is found that the voltage at a given temperature, let us say 25°C, depends upon two factors: the nature of the cell reaction and the concentrations of the various species (atoms, ions, or molecules) participating in the cell reaction. The *standard* voltage corresponding to a given cell reaction is that obtained when all such species have an activity of one. This condition is approximately fulfilled when all ions or molecules in solution are at a concentration of 1 M and all gases at a partial pressure of 1 atm. To illustrate, consider the Zn-H$_2$ cell shown in Figure 21.3; it is found experimentally that when the pressure of hydrogen is 1 atm. and the concentrations of both Zn^{+2} and H$^+$ are 1 M, the cell voltage is $+0.76$ v. This quantity, $+0.76$ v., is referred to as the standard cell voltage, corresponding to the cell reaction represented by equation 21.3.

Just as one can split a cell reaction such as 21.3 into two half-reactions of oxidation and reduction, so it is possible to divide a standard cell voltage into two parts, one corresponding to the oxidation half-reaction, the other to the reduction half-reaction. The quantities thus obtained are referred to as **standard electrode potentials.** The potential corresponding to the oxidation half-reaction is referred to as a **standard oxidation potential:** associated with the reduction half-reaction is a **standard reduction potential.** For reaction 21.3, we have:

$$Zn(s) \longrightarrow Zn^{+2}(1\ M) + 2\ e^- \qquad \text{S.O.P. Zn} = x$$
$$2\ H^+(1\ M) + 2\ e^- \longrightarrow H_2(g,\ 1\ atm.) \qquad \text{S.R.P. } H^+ = y$$

$$\overline{Zn(s) + 2\ H^+(1\ M) \longrightarrow Zn^{+2}(1\ M) + H_2(g,\ 1\ atm.)\ \text{std. voltage} = x + y =}$$
$$+0.76\ \text{v.}$$

By methods which we shall now consider, it is possible to establish a table of standard electrode potentials corresponding to a wide variety of oxidation and reduction half-reactions. We shall find such a table to be of value in predicting the results of reactions occurring in voltaic or electrolytic cells and, even more important, the spontaneity and extent of oxidation-reduction reactions in general, wherever they take place.

Assignment of Potentials

To illustrate how standard electrode potentials can be established, let us consider once again the Zn-H_2 cell. It has been pointed out that, at standard concentrations, the voltage of this cell is +0.76 v. and further, that this quantity is the sum of the two standard potentials involved. That is:

$$+0.76\ \text{v.} = \text{S.O.P. Zn} + \text{S.R.P. } H^+ \qquad (21.9)$$

It is experimentally impossible to determine the absolute value of either of the two quantitites on the right-hand side of equation 21.9. To establish a value for the standard oxidation potential of zinc, one must arbitrarily assign a value to the standard reduction potential of the H^+ ion. It was agreed many years ago to take this value to be 0.00 v. That is:

$$2\ H^+(1\ M) + 2\ e^- \longrightarrow H_2(g,\ 1\ atm.) \qquad \text{S.R.P. } H^+ = 0.00\ \text{v.} \quad (21.10)$$

Substituting in equation 21.9, it is clear that, on the basis of this convention, the standard oxidation potential of zinc must be +0.76 v.

As soon as one or two standard electrode potentials have been established, it becomes relatively easy to determine others. Suppose, for example, we wish to determine the standard oxidation potential of nickel. This can be done by setting up a cell, similar in design to those shown in Figure 21.3, in which the reaction:

$$Ni(s) + 2\ H^+(1\ M) \longrightarrow Ni^{+2}(1\ M) + H_2(g) \qquad (21.11)$$

occurs. When it is found that this cell produces a voltage of +0.25 v., it follows immediately that the standard oxidation potential of nickel must be +0.25 v. That is:

$$+0.25\ \text{v.} = \text{S.O.P. Ni} + \text{S.R.P. } H^+$$
$$+0.25\ \text{v.} = \text{S.O.P. Ni} + 0.00 \qquad \text{S.O.P. Ni} = +0.25\ \text{v.}$$

As another example, let us suppose that it is desired to evaluate the standard reduction potential of the Ni^{+2} ion. To do this, one might set up a cell consisting of a Zn-Zn^{+2} (1 M) half cell and a Ni-Ni^{+2} (1 M) half-cell. If this is done, it is found that the reaction:

$$Zn(s) + Ni^{+2}(1 M) \longrightarrow Zn^{+2}(1 M) + Ni(s) \qquad (21.12)$$

occurs and that the voltage is $+0.51$ v. It follows that:

$$+0.51 \text{ v.} = \text{S.O.P. Zn} + \text{S.R.P. Ni}^{+2}$$

Knowing that the standard oxidation potential of zinc is $+0.76$ v.:

$$+0.51 \text{ v.} = +0.76 \text{ v.} + \text{S.R.P. Ni}^{+2} \qquad\qquad \text{S.R.P. Ni}^{+2} = -0.25 \text{ v.}$$

It will be noted that the standard reduction potential of the Ni^{+2} ion (-0.25 v.) could have been obtained from the standard oxidation potential of Ni ($+0.25$ v.) by reversing the sign. Indeed, one might have anticipated such a relationship. A cell constructed of two identical Ni-Ni^{+2} half cells would be expected to have zero voltage. The tendency of nickel atoms to be oxidized in one half cell would be just balanced by the tendency of Ni^{+2} ions to be reduced in the other. Mathematically:

$$0.00 \text{ v.} = \text{S.O.P. Ni} + \text{S.R.P. Ni}^{+2} \qquad\qquad \text{S.R.P. Ni}^{+2} = -\text{S.O.P. Ni}$$

This relationship applies to any oxidation-reduction couple. That is: *The standard potentials for the forward and reverse half-reactions (oxidation and reduction) are always equal in magnitude but opposite in sign.*

The validity of this rule simplifies the experimental determination of electrode potentials, since it means that only one potential need be measured for a given couple.

TABLE 21.1   STANDARD ELECTRODE POTENTIALS

Standard Oxidation Potential (volts)			Standard Reduction Potential (volts)
3.05	Li$^+$ + e$^-$	= Li(s)	-3.05
2.93	K$^+$ + e$^-$	= K(s)	-2.93
2.90	Ba^{+2} + 2 e$^-$	= Ba(s)	-2.90
2.87	Ca^{+2} + 2 e$^-$	= Ca(s)	-2.87
2.71	Na$^+$ + e$^-$	= Na(s)	-2.71
2.37	Mg^{+2} + 2 e$^-$	= Mg(s)	-2.37
1.66	Al^{+3} + 3 e$^-$	= Al(s)	-1.66
1.18	Mn^{+2} + 2 e$^-$	= Mn(s)	-1.18
0.76	Zn^{+2} + 2 e$^-$	= Zn(s)	-0.76
0.74	Cr^{+3} + 3 e$^-$	= Cr(s)	-0.74
0.44	Fe^{+2} + 2 e$^-$	= Fe(s)	-0.44
0.41	Cr^{+3} + e$^-$	= Cr^{+2}	-0.41
0.40	Cd^{+2} + 2 e$^-$	= Cd(s)	-0.40
0.36	PbSO$_4$(s) + 2 e$^-$	= Pb(s) + SO$_4^{-2}$	-0.36
0.34	Tl$^+$ + e$^-$	= Tl(s)	-0.34
0.28	Co^{+2} + 2 e$^-$	= Co(s)	-0.28
0.25	Ni^{+2} + 2 e$^-$	= Ni(s)	-0.25
0.15	AgI(s) + e$^-$	= Ag(s) + I$^-$	-0.15
0.14	Sn^{+2} + 2 e$^-$	= Sn(s)	-0.14
0.13	Pb^{+2} + 2 e$^-$	= Pb(s)	-0.13
0.00	2 H$^+$ + 2 e$^-$	= H$_2$(g)	0.00
-0.10	AgBr(s) + e$^-$	= Ag(s) + Br$^-$	0.10
-0.14	S(s) + 2 H$^+$ + 2 e$^-$	= H$_2$S	0.14
-0.15	Sn^{+4} + 2 e$^-$	= Sn^{+2}	0.15
-0.15	Cu^{+2} + e$^-$	= Cu$^+$	0.15

TABLE 21.1 (Contd.)

Standard Oxidation Potential (volts)			Standard Reduction Potential (volts)
−0.20	$SO_4^{-2} + 4 H^+ + 2 e^-$	$= SO_2(g) + 2 H_2O$	0.20
−0.34	$Cu^{+2} + 2 e^-$	$= Cu(s)$	0.34
−0.52	$Cu^+ + e^-$	$= Cu(s)$	0.52
−0.53	$I_2(s) + 2 e^-$	$= 2 I^-$	0.53
−0.77	$Fe^{+3} + e^-$	$= Fe^{+2}$	0.77
−0.79	$Hg_2^{+2} + 2 e^-$	$= 2 Hg(l)$	0.79
−0.80	$Ag^+ + e^-$	$= Ag(s)$	0.80
−0.92	$2 Hg^{+2} + 2 e^-$	$= Hg_2^{+2}$	0.92
−0.96	$NO_3^- + 4 H^+ + 3 e^-$	$= NO(g) + 2 H_2O$	0.96
−1.00	$AuCl_4^- + 3 e^-$	$= Au(s) + 4 Cl^-$	1.00
−1.07	$Br_2(l) + 2 e^-$	$= 2 Br^-$	1.07
−1.23	$O_2(g) + 4 H^+ + 4 e^-$	$= 2 H_2O$	1.23
−1.23	$MnO_2(s) + 4 H^+ + 2 e^-$	$= Mn^{+2} + 2 H_2O$	1.23
−1.33	$Cr_2O_7^{-2} + 14 H^+ + 6 e^-$	$= 2 Cr^{+3} + 7 H_2O$	1.33
−1.36	$Cl_2(g) + 2 e^-$	$= 2 Cl^-$	1.36
−1.47	$ClO_3^- + 6 H^+ + 5 e^-$	$= \frac{1}{2} Cl_2(g) + 3 H_2O$	1.47
−1.50	$Au^{+3} + 3 e^-$	$= Au(s)$	1.50
−1.52	$MnO_4^- + 8 H^+ + 5 e^-$	$= Mn^{+2} + 4 H_2O$	1.52
−1.77	$H_2O_2 + 2 H^+ + 2 e^-$	$= 2 H_2O$	1.77
−1.82	$Co^{+3} + e^-$	$= Co^{+2}$	1.82
−2.87	$F_2(g) + 2 e^-$	$= 2 F^-$	2.87
		Basic Solution	
1.22	$Zn(OH)_4^{-2} + 2 e^-$	$= Zn(s) + 4 OH^-$	−1.22
0.88	$Fe(OH)_2(s) + 2 e^-$	$= Fe(s) + 2 OH^-$	−0.88
0.83	$2 H_2O + 2 e^-$	$= H_2(g) + 2 OH^-$	−0.83
0.56	$Fe(OH)_3(s) + e^-$	$= Fe(OH)_2(s) + OH^-$	−0.56
0.48	$S(s) + 2 e^-$	$= S^{-2}$	−0.48
0.36	$Cu(OH)_2(s) + 2 e^-$	$= Cu(s) + 2 OH^-$	−0.36
0.12	$CrO_4^{-2} + 4 H_2O + 3 e^-$	$= Cr(OH)_3(s) + 5 OH^-$	−0.12
−0.01	$NO_3^- + H_2O + 2 e^-$	$= NO_2^- + 2 OH^-$	0.01
−0.34	$Ag_2O(s) + H_2O + 2 e^-$	$= 2 Ag(s) + 2 OH^-$	0.34
−0.36	$ClO_4^- + H_2O + 2 e^-$	$= ClO_3^- + 2 OH^-$	0.36
−0.40	$O_2(g) + 2 H_2O + 4 e^-$	$= 4 OH^-$	0.40
−0.62	$ClO_3^- + 3 H_2O + 6 e^-$	$= Cl^- + 6 OH^-$	0.62
−0.89	$ClO^- + H_2O + 2 e^-$	$= Cl^- + 2 OH^-$	0.89

Calculation of Cell Voltages from Standard Potentials

As the foregoing discussion implies, the *standard voltage of any cell (symbol* $E°$*) is the algebraic sum of the standard oxidation potential of the species being oxidized in the cell reaction and the standard reduction potential of the species being reduced.* This simple relationship makes it possible, using Table 21.1, to calculate the standard voltages of more than 3000 different voltaic cells. Example 21.1 illustrates how this may be done for three specific cases.

Example 21.1. Calculate the voltages of cells in which the following reactions occur:
  a. $Cl_2(g, 1 \text{ atm.}) + 2 I^-(1 M) \rightarrow 2 Cl^-(1 M) + I_2(s)$
  b. $MnO_4^-(1 M) + 8 H^+(1 M) + 5 Cl^-(1 M) \rightarrow Mn^{+2}(1 M) + 4 H_2O + \frac{5}{2} Cl_2(g, 1 \text{ atm.})$
  c. $Sn^{+2}(1 M) + 2 Ag(s) \rightarrow Sn(s) + 2 Ag^+(1 M)$

Solution.   In each case, we shall split the reaction into two half-reactions, tabulate the proper electrode potentials and add to obtain the cell voltage.

a. oxidation: $2 \ I^-(1 \ M) \rightarrow I_2(s) + 2 \ e^-$ S.O.P. = -0.53 v.
   reduction: $Cl_2(g) + 2 \ e^- \rightarrow 2 \ Cl^-$ S.R.P. = $+1.36$ v.

$$E^\circ = \overline{+0.83 \text{ v.}}$$

b. oxidation: $2 \ Cl^-(1 \ M) \rightarrow Cl_2(g) + 2 \ e^-$ S.O.P. = -1.36 v.
   reduction: $MnO_4^-(1 \ M) + 8 \ H^+(1 \ M) + 5e^- \rightarrow$ S.R.P. = $+1.52$ v.
   $Mn^{+2}(1 \ M) + 4 \ H_2O$

$$E^\circ = \overline{+0.16 \text{ v.}}$$

c. oxidation: $Ag(s) \rightarrow Ag^+(1 \ M) + e^-$ S.O.P. = -0.80 v.
   reduction: $Sn^{+2}(1 \ M) + 2 \ e^- \rightarrow Sn(s)$ S.R.P. = -0.14 v.

$$E^\circ = \overline{-0.94 \text{ v.}}$$

The negative voltage means that the reaction as written is not spontaneous and cannot occur in a voltaic cell. If Ag-Ag$^+$ and Sn-Sn^{+2} half cells are connected, the reverse reaction:

$$2 \ Ag^+(1 \ M) + Sn(s) \longrightarrow 2 \ Ag(s) + Sn^{+2}$$

occurs, producing a voltage of $+0.94$ v.

Standard electrode potentials can be used in connection with electrolytic as well as voltaic cells. By adding the proper electrode potentials, one can calculate the minimum applied voltage necessary, at standard concentrations, to bring about a nonspontaneous oxidation-reduction reaction in an electrolytic cell. Consider, for example, the electrolysis of a water solution of copper(II) chloride, discussed in Chapter 20. Adding the standard potentials for the two half-reactions, we have:

$$Cu^{+2} + 2 \ e^- \longrightarrow Cu(s) \qquad \text{S.R.P. } Cu^{+2} = -0.34 \text{ v.}$$
$$\underline{2 \ Cl^- \qquad\qquad \longrightarrow Cl_2(g) + 2 \ e^- \qquad \text{S.O.P. } Cl^- = -1.36 \text{ v.}}$$
$$Cu^{+2} + 2 \ Cl^- \longrightarrow Cu(s) + Cl_2(g) \qquad\qquad\qquad\qquad -1.70 \text{ v.}$$

We deduce that in order to operate the cell, a potential of at least 1.70 v. must be applied across the electrodes. A similar calculation for the electrolysis of a sodium chloride solution shows that, at standard concentrations, a potential of at least 2.19 v. must be applied to bring about the nonspontaneous reaction:

$$2 \ Cl^- + 2 \ H_2O \longrightarrow Cl_2(g) + 2 \ OH^- + H_2(g)$$

In practice, it is ordinarily found that the voltage required to operate an electrolytic cell is somewhat higher than that calculated from electrode potentials. The excess voltage, referred to as **overvoltage,** may be 1 v. or more; it is particularly large when one of the products of the cell reaction is a gas such as hydrogen or oxygen. In the evolution of hydrogen, the magnitude of the overvoltage is found to vary greatly with the metal used as a cathode. Zinc, tin, or cadmium electrodes give hydrogen overvoltages in the neighborhood of 1 v. On the other hand, at platinum or palladium cathodes, hydrogen can be generated with zero overvoltage.

Although the exact mechanism of overvoltage is poorly understood, it is known to arise from kinetic effects. Electrode processes, involving the transfer of electrons between a metal electrode and ions in solutions, are inherently slow. By using a voltage higher than that theoretically required, one supplies the activation energy necessary to make the reaction proceed at a finite rate.

In the evolution of hydrogen, it appears that the most difficult step is the combination of hydrogen atoms to give H_2 molecules. This process occurs on the surface of the metal electrode. It is significant that the two metals, platinum and palladium, which show the lowest hydrogen overvoltages, are precisely the metals which adsorb hydrogen atoms most strongly. They provide an effective catalytic surface for the formation of diatomic molecules. Traces of impurities can poison the electrode surfaces; 0.001 cc. of carbon monoxide spread out over an electrode 1 cm.^{2} in area can raise the hydrogen overvoltage by as much as half a volt.

Qualitative Interpretation of Electrode Potentials

The standard potentials listed in Table 21.1 may be regarded as a measure of the relative tendencies of the different species to be oxidized or reduced. The more positive the potential, the more readily the corresponding half-reaction occurs. A large negative potential signifies a half-reaction which is difficult to accomplish.

Of all the species listed in the right-hand column of Table 21.1, elementary lithium (S.O.P. = +3.05 v.) is most readily oxidized. Moving down the column, we encounter species which are successively more difficult to oxidize. At the bottom of the right-hand column is the fluoride ion (S.O.P. = −2.87 v.) whose attraction for electrons is so great that it cannot be oxidized chemically. Species which are capable of reduction are listed in the left-hand column in increasing order of ease of reduction. The most readily reduced species is the fluorine molecule (S.R.P. = +2.87 v.) located at the bottom of the column. The cations of the 1A and 2A metals, situated at the top of the left-hand column, cannot be reduced in water solution. It will be recalled from Chapter 20 that in the electrolysis of water solutions of salts of these metals, it is the water molecule (S.R.P. = −0.83 v.) rather than the cation (S.R.P. Na^+ = −2.71 v., Ca^{+2} = −2.87 v., and so on) which is reduced.

From a slightly different point of view, Table 21.1 can be regarded as an arrangement of atoms, molecules, and ions in order of their relative strengths as oxidizing or reducing agents. The strongest reducing agents are the 1A and 2A metals located at the upper right of the table. Passing down the right-hand column, we come to elements such as tin and hydrogen which are relatively weak reducing agents, arriving finally at metals such as silver and gold which have so little tendency to give up electrons that they are quite ineffective as reducing agents. Of the oxidizing agents listed in the left-hand column, the strongest are those listed at the bottom: the F_2 molecule, the MnO_4^- ion, and so on. The halogens above fluorine in the table (chlorine, bromine, and iodine) are successively less effective oxidizing agents. At the top of the column are the cations of the 1A and 2A metals which show little tendency to acquire electrons and hence are rarely if ever used as chemical oxidizing agents.

21.4 SPONTANEITY AND EXTENT OF OXIDATION-REDUCTION REACTIONS

It was pointed out in the first paragraph of this chapter that a voltaic cell is one in which a spontaneous oxidation-reduction reaction occurs. The converse of this statement is also true; any reaction which can occur in a voltaic cell to produce a positive voltage must be spontaneous. To decide whether a given reaction is capable of taking place under a particular set of conditions, all one has to do is to calculate the voltage associated with it. If the calculated voltage is positive, the reaction must be spontaneous. If the voltage is negative, the reaction cannot go by itself; the reverse reaction will be spontaneous.

These criteria can readily be applied to determine whether or not an oxidation-reduction reaction can occur at standard concentrations. All one has to do is add the appropriate standard electrode potentials to obtain the $E°$ values corresponding to the reaction and note whether this quantity is positive or negative. Referring to Example 21.1, we recall that the $E°$ values associated with the reactions:

$$Cl_2(g, 1 \text{ atm.}) + 2 \ I^-(1 \ M) \longrightarrow 2 \ Cl^-(1 \ M) + I_2(s) \qquad (21.13)$$

$$MnO_4^-(1 \ M) + 8 \ H^+(1 \ M) + 5 \ Cl^-(1 \ M) \longrightarrow$$
$$Mn^{+2}(1M) + 4 \ H_2O + \tfrac{5}{2} \ Cl_2(g, 1 \text{ atm.}) \qquad (21.14)$$

$$Sn^{+2}(1 \ M) + 2 \ Ag(s) \longrightarrow Sn(s) + 2 \ Ag^+(1 \ M) \qquad (21.15)$$

are $+0.83$ v., $+0.16$ v., and -0.94 v. respectively. We deduce that reactions 21.13 and 21.14 will occur spontaneously in the laboratory, while reaction 21.15 will not. In other words, at standard concentrations, chlorine gas will oxidize iodide ions to elementary iodine, and permanganate ions will oxidize hydrochloric acid to chlorine. Under the same conditions, Sn^{+2} ions will not react with silver metal; instead, the reverse reaction will be spontaneous.

Example 21.2 illustrates the application of this simple principle to a somewhat more complex situation.

Example 21.2.   Assuming standard concentrations, will a reaction occur between nitric acid and a solution of iron(II) chloride?

Solution.   Before we can answer this question, we must decide what the possible reactions are; only then can we calculate whether or not a reaction will occur. To be sure that we do not neglect any possibilities, let us list separately, using Table 21.1, every possible half-reaction. Noting that the species present are H^+, NO_3^-, Fe^{+2} and Cl^- ions, we have:

possible oxidations:
O_1 $Fe^{+2}(1 \ M) \longrightarrow Fe^{+3}(1 \ M) + e^-$ S.O.P. $= -0.77$ v.
O_2 $2 \ Cl^-(1 \ M) \longrightarrow Cl_2(g, 1 \text{ atm.}) + 2 \ e^-$ S.O.P. $= -1.36$ v.

possible reductions:
R_1 $2 \ H^+(1 \ M) + 2 \ e^- \longrightarrow H_2 (g, 1 \text{ atm.})$ S.R.P. $= \ \ 0.00$ v.
R_2 $NO_3^-(1 \ M) + 4 \ H^+(1 \ M) + 3e^- \longrightarrow$
      $NO \ (g, 1 \text{ atm.}) + 2 \ H_2O$ S.R.P. $= +0.96$ v.
R_3 $Fe^{+2}(1 \ M) + 2 \ e^- \longrightarrow Fe(s)$ S.R.P. $= -0.44$ v.

In principle, the two possible oxidations, O_1 and O_2, taken in combination with the three possible reductions, R_1, R_2, and R_3, could lead to six different overall reactions ($O_1 + R_1$, $O_1 + R_2$, $O_1 + R_3$; $O_2 + R_1$, $O_2 + R_2$, $O_2 + R_3$). In practice, it is readily seen that only one of these combinations, $O_1 + R_2$, will give a positive voltage. We deduce that the spontaneous reaction is:

oxidation: $3 \ Fe^{+2}(1 \ M) \longrightarrow 3 \ Fe^{+3}(1 \ M) + 3 \ e^-$ -0.77 v.

reduction:

$NO_3^-(1 \ M) + 4 \ H^+(1 \ M) + 3 \ e^- \longrightarrow NO \ (g, 1 \text{ atm.}) + 2 \ H_2O$ $+0.96$ v.

$\overline{3 \ Fe^{+2}(1 \ M) + NO_3^-(1 \ M) + 4 \ H^+(1 \ M) \longrightarrow 3 \ Fe^{+3}(1 \ M) + NO \ (g, 1 \text{ atm.})}$
                                    $+ \ 2 \ H_2O$ $+0.19$ v.

In other words, nitric acid, at standard concentrations, will oxidize a solution of iron(II) chloride to a solution of iron(III) chloride, forming NO as a reduction product.

While it is, of course, important to know whether or not an oxidation-reduction reaction will occur at standard concentrations, this information alone is hardly sufficient for the chemist who is interested in carrying out the reaction in the laboratory.

In the first place, it is highly unlikely that he will wish to run the reaction under such conditions that all reactants and products are at standard concentrations.

Moreover, he would like to know, not only whether a particular reaction will take place, but also the *extent* to which it will occur.

In order to decide whether a reaction will take place under a particular set of conditions and, if so, the extent to which it will occur, one must know the numerical value of the equilibrium constant for the reaction. Fortunately, it is possible to calculate the equilibrium constant for an oxidation-reduction reaction from standard electrode potentials.

Relation Between E° and K

We shall not attempt to derive in any formal way the relationship between the E° value for a redox reaction and the equilibrium constant for that reaction. It may, however, be helpful to rationalize the existence and perhaps the form of such a relationship by relating these two quantities, E° and K, to the free energy change for the reaction.

It will be recalled from Chapter 5 that a spontaneous reaction is characterized by a *negative* free energy change. We have seen in this chapter that a spontaneous oxidation-reduction reaction is always associated with a *positive* voltage. These two statements, taken together, imply a direct relationship between the free energy decrease $(-\Delta G)$ and the voltage (E). It can be shown that this relationship is of the form:

$$\Delta G = -nFE$$

in which ΔG is the free energy change (in volt-coulombs or joules); n is the number of moles of electrons transferred in the reaction; F, the so-called faraday constant, is the number of coulombs in one faraday (96,500); and E is the voltage. At standard concentrations, we can write:

$$\Delta G° = -nFE° \tag{21.16}$$

in which $\Delta G°$ is the standard free energy change for the reaction and E° is the voltage calculated from standard electrode potentials.

Now, it was pointed out in Chapter 14 that the standard free energy change, $\Delta G°$, is related to the equilibrium constant K by the equation:

$$\Delta G° = -2.303 \text{ RT log } K \tag{21.17}$$

in which R is the gas constant and T the absolute temperature. Combining equations 21.16 and 21.17, we obtain:

$$nFE° = 2.303 \text{ RT log } K$$

Solving for E°:
$$E° = 2.303 \frac{RT}{nF} \text{ log } K$$

Substituting for the constants R and F their values in the proper units and taking T to be 298°K (25°C), we finally obtain:

$$E° = \frac{0.059}{n} \text{ log } K. \tag{21.18}$$

or
$$\text{log } K = \frac{n \, E°}{0.059} \tag{21.19}$$

Equation 21.19 enables us to determine the equilibrium constant K* for an oxidation-reduction reaction from the value of E° as calculated from standard electrode potentials. To illustrate the procedure involved, let us consider three different reactions with quite different E° values.

(1) $$Zn(s) + Cu^{+2} \longrightarrow Zn^{+2} + Cu(s)$$

$$E° = S.O.P.\ Zn + S.R.P.\ Cu^{+2} = 0.76\ v. + 0.34\ v. = 1.10\ v.$$

$$n = 2\ (2\ \text{moles of } e^-\ \text{required to reduce 1 mole of } Cu^{+2}\ \text{ions})$$

$$\log K = \frac{2(1.10)}{0.059} = 37 \qquad K = \frac{[Zn^{+2}]}{[Cu^{+2}]} = 10^{37}$$

The fact that the equilibrium constant for this reaction is such a large number, 10^{37}, means that at ordinary concentrations, the reaction between zinc and Cu^{+2} ions goes to completion. If excess zinc is added to a 1 M solution of $CuSO_4$, nearly all the Cu^{+2} ions will be replaced by Zn^{+2} ions; the equilibrium concentration of Zn^{+2} will be 1 M, while that of Cu^{+2} will be 10^{-37} M.

(2) $$Sn(s) + Pb^{+2} \longrightarrow Sn^{+2} + Pb(s)$$

$$E° = +0.14\ v. - 0.13\ v. = 0.01\ v. \quad n = 2$$

$$\log K = \frac{(2)(0.01)}{0.059} = 0.3 \qquad K = \frac{[Sn^{+2}]}{[Pb^{+2}]} = 2$$

Here, the situation is quite different from that in (1). Since the equilibrium constant is relatively small (K = 2), we can expect to find both products and reactants present at equilibrium in significant amounts (see Example 21.3). This situation will arise whenever the E° value for a reaction is small. The direction in which such reactions will proceed is particularly sensitive to changes in concentrations of reactants or products (Example 21.4).

(3) $$Ag(s) + Tl^+ \longrightarrow Ag^+ + Tl(s)$$

$$E° = -0.80\ v. - 0.34\ v. = -1.14\ v. \qquad n = 1.$$

$$\log K = \frac{(1)(-1.14)}{0.059} = -19 \qquad K = \frac{[Ag^+]}{[Tl^+]} = 10^{-19}$$

The equilibrium constant for this reaction is so small (K = 10^{-19}) that it is impossible to form significant amounts of Ag^+ by reacting elementary silver with Tl^+ ions. Conversely, one can predict that the reverse reaction, that of thallium metal with Ag^+ ions, will proceed almost to completion.

Calculations Involving K

The equilibrium constant for a redox reaction can be used to calculate the extent to which that reaction will occur if one starts with pure reactants at known concentrations (Example 21.3).

---

* In the expression for K, concentrations of species in water solution are expressed in moles per liter. For gases participating in the reaction, partial pressures in atmospheres are used. Concentrations of solids or solvent water molecules do not appear in the equilibrium expression.

Example 21.3. Calculate the equilibrium concentrations of Sn^{+2} and Pb^{+2} if excess tin is added to a solution originally 4.5 M in Pb^{+2}.

Solution. The reaction involved is: $Sn(s) + Pb^{+2} \rightarrow Sn^{+2} + Pb(s)$ for which we have shown that:

$$K = \frac{[Sn^{+2}]}{[Pb^{+2}]} = 2$$

If we let $[Sn^{+2}] = x$, then $[Pb^{+2}] = 4.5 - x$, since 1 mole of Pb^{+2} reacts for every mole of Sn^{+2} formed. Substituting in the expression for K:

$$\frac{x}{4.5 - x} = 2$$

Solving: $\qquad x = [Sn^{+2}] = 3 \qquad 4.5 - x = [Pb^{+2}] = 1.5$

We see that the reaction gives an equilibrium mixture in which there are two Sn^{+2} ions for every Pb^{+2} ion.

The equilibrium constant K can also be used to predict the direction in which a redox reaction will occur spontaneously under specified conditions (Example 21.4).

Example 21.4. Will the following reaction occur in the direction indicated?

$$Ni(s) + Co^{+2}(1\ M) \longrightarrow Ni^{+2}(0.01\ M) + Co(s)$$

Solution. To answer this question, let us first calculate K and then determine which "side" of the equilibrium we are on.

$$E° = 0.25\ v. - 0.28\ v. = -0.03\ v. \qquad n = 2$$

$$\log K = \frac{2(-0.03)}{0.059} = -1 \qquad K = \frac{[Ni^{+2}]}{[Co^{+2}]} = 0.1$$

We see that, at equilibrium, the concentration of Ni^{+2} ions must be $\frac{1}{10}$ that of Co^{+2}. Under the conditions stated, the concentration of Ni^{+2} is only $\frac{1}{100}$ that of Co^{+2}. Clearly, in order to reach equilibrium, Ni^{+2} ions will have to be produced at the expense of Co^{+2} ions. This means that the reaction will proceed from left to right; i.e., the reaction will be spontaneous under the conditions specified.

It is worth pointing out that this reaction will not take place at standard concentrations, i.e., conc. $Ni^{+2} = $ conc. $Co^{+2} = 1$. This is immediately obvious from the fact that E° is negative. From a different point of view, one can say that the ratio, conc. Ni^{+2}: conc. Co^{+2} is too high $(1 > 0.1)$; the reaction must proceed in the reverse direction to reach equilibrium. Finally, if we were to add nickel metal to a solution 1 M in Co^{+2} and 0.1 M in Ni^{+2}, no net change would occur; we would already be at equilibrium and there would be no tendency for the reaction to proceed in either direction. In summary, if:

$$\frac{\text{conc. } Ni^{+2}}{\text{conc. } Co^{+2}} < K, \text{ reaction} \longrightarrow$$

$$\frac{\text{conc. } Ni^{+2}}{\text{conc. } Co^{+2}} > K, \text{ reaction} \longleftarrow$$

$$\frac{\text{conc. } Ni^{+2}}{\text{conc. } Co^{+2}} = K, \text{ reaction is at equilibrium}$$

21.5 EFFECT OF CONCENTRATION ON VOLTAGE: THE NERNST EQUATION

Our discussion of cell voltages up to this point has been limited to cases in which all species participating in the cell reaction are at standard concentrations (more precisely, unit activities). We shall now consider how, for a given reaction, the voltage is affected by changes in the concentrations of reactants and products. We shall proceed from a qualitative discussion of the direction of this effect to a quantitative treatment of its magnitude.

Direction of Effect

If the voltage of a cell is taken to be a measure of the spontaneity of the reaction occurring, it follows that any change in conditions which makes that reaction take place more readily should increase the voltage. We know from equilibrium considerations that a reaction becomes more spontaneous when the concentrations of *reactants* are *increased* or those of the *products* are *decreased*. Concentration changes in this direction should then *increase* the cell voltage. Conversely, the reaction should become less spontaneous and the voltage less positive if the concentrations of reactants are decreased or those of the products increased. To illustrate, consider the familiar reaction:

$$Zn(s) + Cu^{+2} \longrightarrow Zn^{+2} + Cu(s)$$

At standard concentrations, this reaction, going on in a cell such as that shown in Figure 21.1, produces a voltage of 1.10 v. From the argument just outlined, one would expect the cell voltage to rise above 1.10 v. if the concentration of Cu^{+2} ions were increased above 1 M or if that of the Zn^{+2} ions, produced by the reaction, were decreased below 1 M. A decrease in the concentration of Cu^{+2} ions or an increase in the concentration of Zn^{+2} ions would be expected to have the opposite effect, decreasing the cell voltage below 1.10 v. The data in Table 21.2 indicates that this reasoning is in accord with experiment.

TABLE 21.2 EFFECT OF
CHANGE IN CONCENTRATION
ON VOLTAGE OF Zn-Cu
CELL

$[Cu^{+2}]$	$[Zn^{+2}]$	Volts
10	0.10	1.16
10	1.0	1.13
1.0	0.10	1.13
1.0	1.0	1.10
0.10	0.10	1.10
0.10	1.0	1.07
1.0	10	1.07
0.10	10	1.04

It may be noted from Table 21.2 that a change of as much as a power of 10 in the concentration of a reactant or product produces only a small change in the cell voltage—about 0.03 v. with this particular cell. It follows that so long as the concentrations of the ions used in setting up voltaic cells do not differ too greatly from 1 M, the cell voltage will be very nearly that calculated from standard electrode potentials. In practice, with simple metal-metal ion cells, great voltage changes are observed only when the concentration of one of the species is drastically lowered by adding a complexing or precipitating agent. Suppose, for example, one were to add

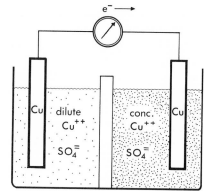

FIGURE 21.7 A concentration cell.

a large excess of ammonia or sulfide ions to the Cu-Cu^{+2} half cell of Figure 21.1. This would remove all but a tiny fraction of the free Cu^{+2} ions from solution and hence would materially reduce the cell voltage. If sufficient sulfide ions were added to make [S^{-2}] = 1 M, then since Ksp of CuS = 1 × 10^{-25}, the concentration of Cu^{+2} would be reduced to 1 × 10^{-25}. One can calculate the under these conditions, the cell voltage would be only 0.01 v.

It is possible to design voltaic cells whose driving force depends solely on concentration differences of the type just discussed. An example of such a *concentration cell* is shown in Figure 21.7. Each of the half cells consists of a copper electrode dipping into a solution of copper sulfate. They differ only in the concentration of CuSO$_4$; one solution is more dilute than the other. The cell produces a small but measurable voltage whose magnitude depends on the ratio of the concentrations of Cu^{+2} ions in the two solutions.

When current is drawn from the cell, it is found that the copper electrode dipping into the more dilute solution decreases in weight. At the same time, the blue color of this solution intensifies, indicating an increase in Cu^{+2} ion concentration. Exactly the reverse process takes place in the half cell containing the more concentrated CuSO$_4$ solution; copper plates out on the electrode, while the concentration of Cu^{+2} ions decreases. Clearly, the half-reactions must be:

anode :$\qquad\qquad\qquad\qquad$ Cu(s) $\longrightarrow$ Cu^{+2}(dilute) + 2 e$^-$

cathode:$\qquad\qquad$ Cu^{+2}(conc.) + 2 e$^-$ $\longrightarrow$ Cu(s)

The net effect of this process is to cause the two solutions to approach each other in concentration. The cell produces a voltage because this process is spontaneous; matter always tends to go from a region of high concentration to one of low concentration. If the cell is operated long enough, the concentrations of copper sulfate in the two half cells become equal, equilibrium is reached, and the voltage drops to zero.

Magnitude of Effect

A quantitative study of the effect of the concentrations on the voltage of the Zn-Cu cell leads to the following equation:

$$E = 1.10 \text{ v.} - 0.030 \log \frac{\text{conc. Zn}^{+2}}{\text{conc. Cu}^{+2}} \qquad\qquad (21.20)$$

It is easily shown that this equation is in agreement with the observations made earlier. For example, if the concentration of Zn^{+2} ions is increased above that of Cu^{+2}, the second term on the right of equation 21.20 is negative and the voltage drops below 1.10 v. This same effect can be achieved by reducing the concentration of Cu^{+2} ions. Conversely, an increase in the ratio of Cu^{+2} ions to Zn^{+2} ions makes the concentration term in the equation positive and therefore increases the voltage. Finally, it may be seen that a change of a power of 10 in the concentration ratio changes the voltage by 0.03 v., as pointed out earlier.

Equation 21.20 is a special form of a more general relation known as the **Nernst equation.** For the general oxidation-reduction reaction:

$$aA + bB \longrightarrow cC + dD$$

in which A, B, C, and D are species whose concentrations can be varied and a, b, c, and d are the corresponding coefficients of the balanced equation, the Nernst equation has the form:

$$E = E° - \frac{0.059}{n} \log \frac{(\text{conc. C})^c (\text{conc. D})^d}{(\text{conc. A})^a (\text{conc. B})^b} \qquad (21.21)$$

(E = cell voltage, E° = standard voltage, n = no. moles e^- transferred in reaction.)

Note the similarity between the form of the Nernst equation and the expression for the equilibrium constant for an oxidation-reduction reaction (equation 21.18). Indeed, one can readily derive equation 21.18 from equation 21.21 (see Problem 21.22). In the Nernst equation as in the expression for the equilibrium constant, concentrations of species in solution are expressed in moles per liter; partial pressures are used for gases.

Example 21.5 illustrates the calculations involved in using the Nernst equation.

Example 21.5. Calculate the voltage of a cell in which the following reaction occurs:

$$Zn(s) + 2 H^+(0.001 \text{ M}) \longrightarrow Zn^{+2}(1 \text{ M}) + H_2(g, 1 \text{ atm.})$$

Solution. For this reaction, n is 2 (2 moles of electrons are required to reduce 2 moles of H^+ ions). Hence, the Nernst equation becomes:

$$E = E° - \frac{0.059}{2} \log \frac{(\text{conc. } Zn^{+2})(p\,H_2)}{(\text{conc. } H^+)^2}$$

Substituting E° = +0.76 v., conc. Zn^{+2} = 1 M, $p\,H_2$ = 1 atm., conc. H^+ = 10^{-3} M, we have:

$$E = 0.76 \text{ v.} - \frac{0.059}{2} \log \frac{1}{(\text{conc. } H^+)^2} = +0.76 \text{ v.} - \frac{0.059}{2} \log \frac{1}{(10^{-3})^2}$$

$$E = 0.76 \text{ v.} - \frac{0.059}{2} (6) = +0.58 \text{ v.}$$

The Nernst equation can also be used to determine the effect of changes in concentration on the potential of an individual half cell (see Problem 21.25 and Example 22.1).

Use of the Nernst Equation to Determine Concentrations of Ions in Solution

One of the most important applications of the Nernst equation is in the experimental determination of concentrations of solutions from measured cell voltages. For example, the relation derived in Example 21.5

$$E = +0.76 \text{ v.} - \frac{0.059}{2} \log \frac{1}{(\text{conc. H}^+)^2}$$

enables one to determine the concentration of H^+ ions in a solution by measuring the voltage of a properly constructed Zn-H_2 cell. It is possible, from cell voltages to determine concentrations of ions present in amounts so small that more conventional analytical techniques are inapplicable. One could, for example, use a Zn-H_2 cell to determine the concentration of H^+ in a 0.01 M NaOH solution. Under these conditions, the measured cell voltage is 0.05 v., corresponding to a H^+ ion concentration of 10^{-12} M. That is:

$$+0.05 = +0.76 - \frac{0.059}{2} \log \frac{1}{(\text{conc. H}^+)^2}$$

$$\log \frac{1}{(\text{conc. H}^+)^2} = \frac{2(0.71)}{0.059} = 24$$

$$(\text{conc. H}^+)^2 = 10^{-24}, \text{ conc. H}^+ = 10^{-12} \text{ M}$$

The sensitivity of this method at very low ion concentrations makes it ideal for the measurement of ionic equilibrium constants. Electrochemical techniques are readily applicable to the measurement of ionization constants of weak acids, stability constants of complex ions or solubility products of slightly soluble salts. Example 21.6 illustrates the procedure and calculations involved.

Example 21.6. A student, in order to determine the solubility product of zinc sulfide, sets up a voltaic cell consisting of a standard Cu-Cu^{+2} half cell (conc. Cu^{+2} = 1 M) joined to a Zn-Zn^{+2} half cell. The concentration of Zn^{+2} is adjusted by adding enough sodium sulfide to precipitate almost all of the Zn^{+2} ions; the equilibrium concentration of S^{-2} is 1 M. Under these conditions, the measured cell voltage is +1.78 v. Calculate Ksp of ZnS.

Solution. The cell reaction is:

$$\text{Zn(s)} + \text{Cu}^{+2} \longrightarrow \text{Zn}^{+2} + \text{Cu(s)}$$

For this reaction, the Nernst equation takes the form:

$$E = E^\circ - \frac{0.059}{n} \log \frac{(\text{conc. Zn}^{+2})}{(\text{conc. Cu}^{+2})}$$

Or, since E° = 1.10 v., n = 2 and conc. Cu^{+2} = 1

$$E = 1.10 - \frac{0.059}{2} \log (\text{conc. Zn}^{+2})$$

Substituting the measured voltage, 1.78 v., and solving for the concentration of Zn^{+2}:

$$1.78 = 1.10 - \frac{0.059}{2} \log (\text{conc. Zn}^{+2})$$

$$\log (\text{conc. Zn}^{+2}) = \frac{0.68 \times 2}{-0.059} = -23 \qquad \text{conc. Zn}^{+2} = 10^{-23} \text{ M}$$

Knowing that the concentration of S^{-2} is 1 M:

$$\text{Ksp ZnS} = \text{conc. Zn}^{+2} \times \text{conc. S}^{-2} = 10^{-23} \times 1 = 1 \times 10^{-23}$$

One of the most useful of analytical instruments, the pH meter, shown in Figure 21.8 utilizes the dependence of cell voltage upon concentration to measure

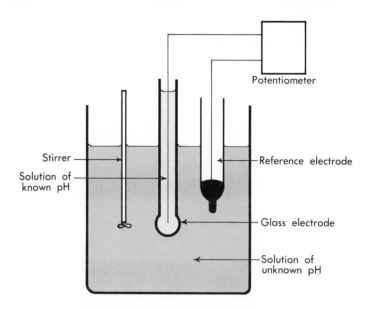

FIGURE 21.8 Schematic diagram of pH meter.

pH. The instrument incorporates three elements: a vacuum tube voltmeter for accurate potential measurements, a reference half cell of known potential, and another half cell whose potential depends upon the concentration of H⁺ ions. This half cell consists of a metal electrode dipping into a solution of known pH separated by a thin glass membrane from the solution whose pH is to be determined. The potential across this *glass electrode* and consequently the cell voltage itself is a linear function of the pH of the solution outside the membrane. The mechanism by which the glass electrode operates is poorly understood; it is commonly supposed that the glass acts as a sort of semipermeable membrane into which H⁺ ions can move.

Use of the Nernst Equation to Determine Reaction Spontaneity

It was pointed out in Section 21.4 that one can use the equilibrium constant for a redox reaction to determine whether or not the reaction will be spontaneous at specified concentrations. Alternatively, one can use the Nernst equation to calculate the voltage under these conditions. If the calculated voltage is positive, the reaction will be spontaneous; if it is negative, the reverse reaction will occur. If, perchance, E turns out to be zero, the reaction must be at equilibrium at the specified concentrations.

To illustrate this application of the Nernst equation, let us refer to the reaction considered in Example 21.4.

$$Ni(s) + Co^{+2}(1 \text{ M}) \longrightarrow Ni^{+2}(0.01 \text{ M}) + Co(s)$$

for which $E° = -0.03$ v., $n = 2$, and the Nernst equation takes the form:

$$E = -0.03 - \frac{0.059}{2} \log \frac{(\text{conc. Ni}^{+2})}{(\text{conc. Co}^{+2})}$$

Substituting for the concentrations of Ni^{+2} and Co^{+2}, we obtain:

$$E = -0.03 - \frac{0.059}{2} \log 0.01$$

$$= -0.03 + 0.059 = +0.03 \text{ v.}$$

and we come to the conclusion that at these concentrations, the reaction will be spontaneous. It will be recalled that we arrived at the same conclusion in Example 21.4 by comparing the ratio (conc. Ni^{+2}):(conc. Co^{+2}) to the equilibrium constant, K.

21.6 SUMMARY

In a voltaic cell such as the ordinary dry cell or the lead storage battery, a spontaneous oxidation-reduction reaction serves as a source of electrical energy. The manner in which a voltaic cell operates and the way in which it differs from an electrolytic cell can perhaps best be summarized by a schematic diagram such as that shown in Figure 21.9.

A cell in which a spontaneous redox reaction is taking place will produce a positive voltage. When the species participating in the cell reaction are at standard concentrations, the standard voltage (E°) can be calculated by adding together the standard oxidation potential of the species being oxidized and the standard reduction potential of the species being reduced. The Nernst equation (21.21) can be used to calculate the cell voltage E, corresponding to various concentrations of reactants and products.

If the calculated cell voltage for an oxidation-reduction reaction is positive, that reaction will proceed spontaneously in the laboratory. The extent to which the reaction goes can be estimated from its equilibrium constant, which in turn can be calculated from the E° value, using equation 21.19. One cannot, of course, by any calculations involving cell voltages, predict the rate at which a redox reaction will occur.

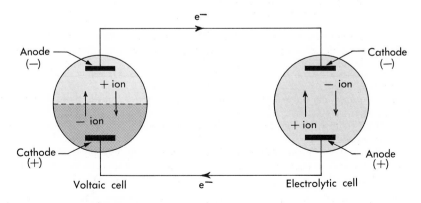

FIGURE 21.9 Voltaic cell vs. electrolytic cell.

PROBLEMS

21.1   A voltaic cell is made up of two half cells, one consisting of a silver electrode dipping into a solution of 1 M $AgNO_3$, the other a copper electrode in a solution 1 M in $Cu(NO_3)_2$.
a. Write a balanced equation for the cell reaction.
b. Draw a diagram of the cell. Label anode and cathode. Indicate the direction of electron flow through the external circuit and the direction in which ions move through the cell.
c. Calculate the voltage of the cell.

21.2   Consider a cell in which the following reaction occurs:

$$Zn(s) + 2 Ag^+ \longrightarrow Zn^{+2} + 2 Ag(s)$$

a. Could a platinum electrode be used as the anode in this cell? The cathode?
b. Could a copper electrode be used as the anode in this cell? The cathode?
c. Could Cl^- ions be present in the solution surrounding the anode? The cathode?
d. Could one use a solution of pure KNO_3 to surround the zinc electrode? The silver electrode?

21.3   Explain the purpose of the salt bridge used to separate the half cells in certain voltaic cells.

21.4   Consider cells in which the following reactions occur.
a. $Ni(s) + 2 H^+ (1 M) \rightarrow Ni^{+2} (1 M) + H_2 (g, 1 atm.)$
b. $3 Sn(s) + 2 Au^{+3} (1 M) \rightarrow 3 Sn^{+2} (1 M) + 2 Au(s)$
c. $Cl_2 (g, 1 atm.) + 2 I^- (1 M) \rightarrow 2 Cl^- (1 M) + I_2(s)$
In each case, draw a diagram of the cell, label the $+$ and $-$ electrodes and calculate the voltage.

21.5   Calculate the voltages of cells made up as follows:
a. Zn electrode in 1 M $ZnSO_4$; C electrode in solution 1 M in Cl^-, surrounded by Cl_2 at 1 atm.
b. Pt wire dipping into pool of Hg, surrounded by 1 M $Hg_2(NO_3)_2$ solution; Ag electrode in 1 M $AgNO_3$ solution.
c. Sn electrode in 1 M $SnCl_2$ solution; Au electrode in solution 1 M in $AuCl_4^-$ and Cl^-.

21.6   Write balanced equations for the reactions that occur when:
a. A dry cell is used to supply current.
b. A lead storage battery discharges.
c. A lead storage battery is charged.

21.7   A lead storage battery is to be charged by connecting it to another battery. To which terminal of the discharged battery should the negative terminal of the fresh battery be connected? Explain.

21.8   Explain why:
a. The ammonia liberated by reaction 21.4 does not ordinarily build up a gas pressure within a dry cell.
b. The density of the electrolyte in a lead storage battery decreases as it is discharged.
c. The fuel cell shown in Figure 21.6 is operated at a high pressure.
d. Fuel cells, at least in principle, are a cheaper source of energy than ordinary voltaic cells.

21.9   Calculate the minimum voltage necessary to electrolyze a solution of $NiCl_2$ so as to produce nickel at one electrode and chlorine gas at the other.

21.10 Referring to Table 21.1:
   a. Which is the stronger oxidizing agent, Ni^{+2} or I_2?
   b. Which is the stronger reducing agent, Ni or H_2S?
   c. Will oxygen react spontaneously, at standard concentrations, with a water solution of hydrogen iodide? Hydrogen chloride?

21.11 Exactly what is meant by the statement that, at standard concentrations, the following reaction is spontaneous?

$$Cl_2(g) + 2\ I^- \longrightarrow 2\ Cl^- + I_2(s)$$

How would you prove this statement experimentally?

21.12 From the table of standard potentials, decide whether or not each of the following reactions will go:
   a. $2\ Cr(s) + 3\ Ni^{+2}\ (1\ M) \rightarrow 2\ Cr^{+3}\ (1\ M) + 3\ Ni(s)$
   b. $Sn(s) + Cl_2\ (g, 1\ atm.) \rightarrow Sn^{+2}\ (1\ M) + 2\ Cl^-\ (1\ M)$
   c. $I_2(s) + 2\ Co^{+2}\ (1\ M) \rightarrow 2\ Co^{+3}\ (1\ M) + 2\ I^-\ (1\ M)$
   d. $MnO_4^-\ (1\ M) + 8\ H^+\ (1\ M) + 5\ F^-\ (1\ M) \rightarrow \frac{5}{2}\ F_2\ (g, 1\ atm.) + Mn^{+2}\ (1\ M) + 4\ H_2O$
   e. $Cl_2 + Cr_2O_7^{-2} \rightarrow ClO_3^- + Cr^{+3}$ (acidic soln., std. conc.)

21.13 Decide what reaction, if any, will occur when the following are mixed (standard concentrations).
   a. $H_2(g)$ and Ag^+
   b. $Cr_2O_7^{-2}$, H^+ and Fe^{+2}
   c. I^-, H^+, Fe^{+3}
   d. H_2S, Br^-, Mg^{+2}
   e. Cl_2, Br^-, and F^-
   f. NO_3^-, H^+, Fe^{+2}

21.14 Calculate equilibrium constants for the following reactions.
   a. $Cd(s) + Cu^{+2} \rightarrow Cd^{+2} + Cu(s)$
   b. $Fe^{+2} + Ag^+ \rightarrow Fe^{+3} + Ag(s)$
   c. $3\ Ag^+ + NO(g) + 2\ H_2O \rightarrow 3\ Ag(s) + NO_3^- + 4\ H^+$

21.15 Consider the reaction:

$$Cd(s) + Co^{+2} \longrightarrow Cd^{+2} + Co(s)$$

Calculate the equilibrium ratio of the concentrations of Cd^{+2} and Co^{+2}.

21.16 Consider the reaction:

$$Cd(s) + Fe^{+2} \longrightarrow Cd^{+2} + Fe(s)$$

If excess cadmium is added to a solution 1 M in Fe^{+2}, what will be the equilibrium concentration of Cd^{+2}?

21.17 Will the reaction cited in Problem 21.16 occur spontaneously if the ratio conc. Cd^{+2}/conc. Fe^{+2} is 1×10^{-4}?

21.18 Consider the reaction:

$$Cu(s) + 4\ H^+ + SO_4^{-2} \rightarrow Cu^{+2} + SO_2(g) + 2\ H_2O$$

Explain in words why the voltage corresponding to this reaction is increased by increasing the concentration of sulfuric acid.

21.19 Using the Nernst equation, calculate the voltages of the following cells:
   a. $Zn(s) + Cu^{+2}\ (1\ M) \rightarrow Zn^{+2}\ (10^{-5}\ M) + Cu(s)$
   b. $Cl_2\ (g, 1\ atm.) + 2\ I^-\ (0.01\ M) \rightarrow 2\ Cl^-\ (10^{-3}\ M) + I_2(s)$
   c. $MnO_2(s) + 4\ H^+\ (10\ M) + 2\ Cl^-\ (10\ M) \rightarrow Mn^{+2}\ (1\ M) + Cl_2\ (g, 1\ atm.) + 2\ H_2O$

21.20 Explain how the zinc-hydrogen cell shown in Figure 21.3 could be used to determine:
   a. The pH of a certain water solution.
   b. The ionization constant of water.
   c. The solubility product of $Zn(OH)_2$.

21.21 A voltaic cell consists of two half cells. One contains a zinc electrode dipping into a solution 1 M in $Zn(NO_3)_2$. The other is made up of a lead electrode dipping into a solution 1 M in Cl^- and saturated with lead chloride. The observed voltage of the cell under these conditions is 0.49 v. Estimate the solubility product of $PbCl_2$.

*21.22 Starting with the Nernst equation (21.21) and noting that the voltage of a cell is zero when all species are at their equilibrium concentrations, derive equation 21.19, relating log K to E°.

*21.23 Calculate $\Delta G°$ in *kilocalories* at 25°C for the reaction:

$$Zn(s) + 2 H^+ \longrightarrow Zn^{+2} + H_2(g)$$

What would be the value of ΔG in kilocalories for this reaction when conc. $H^+ = 10^{-3}$ M, conc. $Zn^{+2} = 1$ M?

*21.24 Excess MnO_2 is added to one liter of a solution originally 2 M in HCl. Assuming chlorine gas is produced at 1 atm. pressure, calculate:
a. The equilibrium concentrations of H^+, Cl^- and Mn^{+2}.
b. The volume of Cl_2 produced at 1 atm. and 25°C.

*21.25 By applying the Nernst equation to the half-reaction:

$$H_2(g) \longrightarrow 2 H^+ + 2 e^-$$

show that the standard oxidation potential for hydrogen in basic solution, i.e., the voltage corresponding to the half-reaction:

$$H_2(g) + 2 OH^-(1 M) \longrightarrow 2 H_2O + 2 e^-$$

is +0.83 v.

*21.26 From the values given in Table 21.1 for the standard reduction potentials of $PbSO_4$ and Pb^{+2}, calculate the solubility product for this salt and compare to the value given in Table 16.5.

22 | OXIDIZING AGENTS IN WATER SOLUTION

In Chapter 21, we considered how standard electrode potentials can be used to determine whether a given redox reaction will occur and, if so, the extent to which it will take place. In this chapter, we shall apply the principles that we have developed to a descriptive study of some of the more common oxidation-reduction reactions occurring in water solution. It is convenient to organize this material according to the oxidizing agents which participate in the reaction.

An oxidizing agent is, by definition, an atom, ion, or molecule which is capable of accepting electrons in an oxidation-reduction reaction. In principle, any species in which an element is in an oxidation state above its minimum value can serve as an oxidizing agent. For example, the ClO_3^- ion, the ClO^- ion, and the Cl_2 molecule are all potential oxidizing agents, since, in each of these species, chlorine is in an oxidation state $(+5, +1, 0)$ higher than the minimum shown by the element, -1. We shall consider only a limited number of oxidizing agents which commonly participate in aqueous reactions. These species can be classified for convenience into four major categories:

1. The H^+ *ion* which, in acting as an oxidizing agent, is reduced to hydrogen gas.

2. *Metal cations*, such as Ag^+, Cu^{+2}, and Fe^{+3}. These ions may be reduced to the free metal or, in certain cases, to another cation in a lower oxidation state.

3. *Molecules* of *nonmetals*: O_2, Cl_2, and so on.

4. *Oxyanions* such as NO_3^-, SO_4^{-2}, $Cr_2O_7^{-2}$, and MnO_4^- in which the central atom is in its highest oxidation state $(+5$ for N, $+6$ for S, $+6$ for Cr, $+7$ for Mn).

The species which is oxidized (i.e., the reducing agent) in an oxidation-reduction reaction must contain an element in a state of oxidation below its maximum. The NH_4^+ ion, the N_2 molecule, and the NO_2^- ion can all be oxidized; the nitrogen atom in these particles is in an oxidation state $(-3, 0, +3)$ lower than its maximum value of $+5$. In our study of oxidizing agents, we shall deal primarily with their action on three different types of reducing agents:

1. *Metals*, which can be oxidized to metal cations.

2. *Metal cations* such as Fe^{+2} and Cu^+ which can be oxidized to a higher state (Fe^{+3}, Cu^{+2}).

3. *Anions*, such as I^- and S^{-2}, which are readily oxidized to the corresponding nonmetals.

22.1 H⁺ ION

$$2 \text{ H}^+ + 2 \text{ e}^- \longrightarrow \text{H}_2(\text{g}) \quad \text{S.R.P.} = 0.00 \text{ v.}$$

Reaction of Metals with Acids

A very important type of reaction in which the H^+ ion participates as an oxidizing agent is that which occurs when a metal above hydrogen in the activity series is added to an acidic solution. The metal atom is oxidized to the corresponding cation; the H^+ ion is reduced to elementary hydrogen.

$$\text{Na}(\text{s}) + \text{H}^+ \longrightarrow \text{Na}^+ + \tfrac{1}{2} \text{H}_2(\text{g}) \text{ (1A metals)} \tag{22.1}$$

$$\text{Mg}(\text{s}) + 2 \text{ H}^+ \longrightarrow \text{Mg}^{+2} + \text{H}_2(\text{g}) \text{ (2A metals, Mn, Fe, Co, Ni, Zn, Cd, Sn)} \tag{22.2}$$

$$\text{Al}(\text{s}) + 3 \text{ H}^+ \longrightarrow \text{Al}^{+3} + \tfrac{3}{2} \text{H}_2(\text{g}) \text{ (Al, Cr)} \tag{22.3}$$

With many active metals such as sodium (S.O.P. $= +2.71$ v.) and calcium (S.O.P. $= +2.87$ v.), this reaction is violently exothermic; the hydrogen formed often ignites or explodes. Reaction proceeds more smoothly with less active metals such as magnesium, zinc, and aluminum, which are often used with dilute hydrochloric or sulfuric acid to produce small quantities of hydrogen in the general chemistry laboratory. Even in the case of tin (S.O.P. $= +0.14$ v.), the equilibrium constant for reaction 22.2 is sufficiently large (6×10^4) to ensure virtually complete reaction under ordinary conditions. Metals such as copper and silver which have negative standard oxidation potentials (Cu $= -0.34$ v., Ag $= -0.80$ v.) do not react with dilute acids to produce hydrogen.

In principle, any strong acid can serve as a source of H^+ ions for the oxidation of a metal. Hydrochloric acid is frequently used; evaporation of the solution remaining after reaction with excess metal gives the corresponding metal chloride. It is possible, for example, to convert nickel to nickel chloride* by the two-step process:

reaction with HCl: $\text{Ni}(\text{s}) + 2 \text{ H}^+ + 2 \text{ Cl}^- \longrightarrow \text{Ni}^{+2} + \text{H}_2(\text{g}) + 2 \text{ Cl}^-$

evaporation: $\text{Ni}^{+2} + 2 \text{ Cl}^- \longrightarrow \text{NiCl}_2(\text{s})$

$$\text{Ni}(\text{s}) + 2 \text{ H}^+ + 2 \text{ Cl}^- \longrightarrow \text{NiCl}_2(\text{s}) + \text{H}_2(\text{g}) \tag{22.4}$$

Bromides and iodides may also be prepared by this method. To obtain cobalt(II) iodide, CoI_2, from cobalt, one can react the metal with hydriodic acid, HI, and evaporate the resulting solution. Dilute sulfuric acid reacts smoothly with metals above hydrogen in the activity series to give solutions of metal sulfates. With concentrated sulfuric acid, the SO_4^{-2} ion rather than the H^+ ion may act as the oxidizing agent, forming sulfur dioxide as a reduction product rather than hydrogen. Dilute perchloric acid in the cold reacts with active metals to evolve hydrogen. In hot or concentrated solution, perchloric acid is such a powerful oxidizing agent that it reacts with metals with explosive violence. The reaction of metals with nitric acid, unless carried out in very dilute solution, does not evolve hydrogen; the NO_3^- ion rather than the H^+ ion is reduced (Section 22.5).

---

* At room temperature, evaporation gives crystals of the hydrated salt, $\text{NiCl}_2 \cdot 6 \text{ H}_2\text{O}$.

The reaction of metals with weak acids is both less spontaneous and slower than with strong acids. A 1 N solution of acetic acid ($[H^+] = 0.004$ M) reacts much more slowly with zinc or magnesium than does a 1 N solution of HCl or H_2SO_4. Solutions of extremely weak acids such as H_3BO_3 ($Ka = 6 \times 10^{-10}$) or HCN ($Ka = 4 \times 10^{-10}$) fail to react with such metals as zinc or magnesium.

Reaction of Metals with Water

The metals above magnesium in the activity series (Na, Ca, Ba, K, Li) are so readily oxidized by H^+ ions that they react even at extremely low H^+ ion concentrations. In particular, these metals react with pure water ($[H^+] = 10^{-7}$ M) to evolve hydrogen. One may consider the reaction of water with a metal such as sodium to occur in two steps:

$$H_2O \longrightarrow H^+ + OH^-$$
$$Na(s) + H^+ \longrightarrow Na^+ + \tfrac{1}{2} H_2(g)$$

$$Na(s) + H_2O \longrightarrow Na^+ + OH^- + \tfrac{1}{2} H_2(g) \qquad (22.5)$$

Calcium reacts similarly, forming a solution of calcium hydroxide:

$$Ca(s) + 2 H_2O \longrightarrow Ca^{+2} + 2 OH^- + H_2(g) \qquad (22.6)$$

With sodium, the exothermic reaction generates heat so rapidly that the hydrogen ignites; with calcium, the reaction is less vigorous.

It might be supposed that aluminum, which has a standard oxidation potential ($+1.66$ v.) nearly as great as those of the 1A and 2A metals, would react with water in a similar manner:

$$Al(s) + 3 H_2O \longrightarrow Al^{+3} + 3 OH^- + \tfrac{3}{2} H_2(g) \qquad (22.7)$$

In practice, no reaction can be detected when aluminum is added to pure water, presumably because the Al^{+3} and OH^- ions formed combine to give an insoluble product, $Al(OH)_3$ (more exactly, hydrated aluminum oxide, $Al_2O_3 \cdot x\,H_2O$), which adheres tightly to the metal surface. However, reaction does occur if a piece of aluminum foil coated with mercury is exposed to water. Here, the aluminum hydroxide is unable to adhere to the surface of the metal; rapid oxidation occurs as shown by the evolution of bubbles of hydrogen and a considerable amount of heat. Aluminum can also be oxidized in strongly basic solution; $Al(OH)_3$, being amphoteric, does not precipitate in the presence of excess OH^- ions:

$$Al(s) + 3 H_2O \longrightarrow Al^{+3} + 3 OH^- + \tfrac{3}{2} H_2(g)$$
$$Al^{+3} + 4 OH^- \longrightarrow Al(OH)_4{}^-$$

$$Al(s) + 3 H_2O + OH^- \longrightarrow Al(OH)_4{}^- + \tfrac{3}{2} H_2(g) \qquad (22.8)$$

22.2 METAL CATIONS

Any metal cation, in undergoing reduction to the corresponding metal, can serve as an oxidizing agent. The oxidizing power of the cation depends upon:

The magnitude of its standard reduction potential. Ions such as Al^{+3} (S.R.P. = -1.66 v.) or Zn^{+2} (S.R.P. = -0.76 v.) are extremely weak oxidizing agents. The

Ag^+ ion (S.R.P. $= +0.80$ v.), on the other hand, is a quite powerful oxidizing agent, considerably more effective than the H^+ ion. A piece of copper added to a solution of silver nitrate is oxidized to Cu^{+2} ions as a result of the spontaneous reaction:

$$2\ Ag^+ + Cu(s) \longrightarrow 2\ Ag(s) + Cu^{+2} \tag{22.9}$$

$$E° = \text{S.R.P. } Ag^+ + \text{S.O.P. } Cu = +0.80\text{ v.} - 0.34\text{ v.} = +0.46\text{ v.}$$

This reaction, carried out with a copper wire bent into an appropriate shape, leads to the formation of a "chemical Christmas tree"; shiny needles of metallic silver appear to grow out of the surface of the wire.

The concentration of "free" (hydrated) cation. If the concentration of a metal cation is reduced below the standard value of 1 M, its reduction potential drops and it becomes a less effective oxidizing agent. This effect is ordinarily small unless one adds a precipitant or complexing agent so as to drastically lower the concentration of free metal ions. Addition of excess CN^- ions to a solution of a silver salt, resulting in the formation of the very stable $Ag(CN)_2^-$ complex, reduces the concentration of Ag^+ to the point where it becomes a very weak oxidizing agent (Example 22.1).

Example 22.1. Enough sodium cyanide is added to a solution of silver nitrate to make $[CN^-] = [Ag(CN)_2^-] = 1$ M. Calculate the reduction potential of Ag^+ under these conditions.

Solution. Let us first calculate the concentration of Ag^+ in this solution, using the fact that the dissociation constant for the $Ag(CN)_2^-$ ion is 1×10^{-21} (Table 19.5). We can then use the Nernst equation to determine the reduction potential of Ag^+ at this concentration.

$$Ag(CN)_2^- \rightleftharpoons Ag^+ + 2\ CN^- \qquad K_c = \frac{[Ag^+] \times [CN^-]^2}{[Ag(CN)_2^-]} = 1 \times 10^{-21}$$

Substituting $[CN^-] = [Ag(CN)_2^-] = 1$, we obtain:

$$[Ag]^+ = 1 \times 10^{-21}$$

For the half-reaction $Ag^+ + e^- \rightarrow Ag(s)$, the Nernst equation has the form:

$$\text{R.P.} = \text{S.R.P.} - \frac{0.059}{n} \log \frac{1}{[Ag^+]}$$

But,

$$\text{S.R.P. } Ag^+ = +0.80 \text{ v.}, n = 1, [Ag]^+ = 1 \times 10^{-21}$$

$$\text{R.P.} = +0.80 \text{ v.} - 0.059 \log \frac{1}{10^{-21}}$$

$$= +0.80 \text{ v.} - 0.059(21) \text{ v.} = -0.44 \text{ v.}$$

The information obtained in Example 22.1 is sometimes expressed by saying that the standard reduction potential of the $Ag(CN)_2^-$ ion, i.e., the reduction potential corresponding to the half-reaction:

$$Ag(CN)_2^-(1 \text{ M}) + e^- \longrightarrow Ag(s) + 2\ CN^-(1 \text{ M})$$

is -0.44 v. The fact that this potential is so much less positive than the standard reduction potential of Ag^+ explains, at least in part, why silver plating is ordinarily conducted from a cyanide bath. The presence of excess CN^- ions prevents the spontaneous formation of a rough, porous coating of silver which is obtained at high Ag^+ ion concentrations.

When the Ag^+ ion acts as an oxidizing agent, it must, of course, be reduced to the metal. However, with many transition and posttransition metal ions of higher charge such as Fe^{+3} or Cu^{+2}, another possibility arises. Instead of being reduced to the metal (Fe, Cu), they may be reduced to an ion in a lower oxidation state (Fe^{+2}, Cu^+). The path which the reduction takes will depend upon several factors. If we limit ourselves to situations in which there is an excess of oxidizing agent (Fe^{+3}, Cu^{+2}) available, it is a relatively simple task to decide between the two possibilities. To illustrate the principle involved, let us consider a redox reaction involving excess Fe^{+3} ions. Let us suppose, for the moment, that this reaction were to produce elementary iron. If this happened, one can calculate that the iron would be re-oxidized to the Fe^{+2} state by the excess Fe^{+3} ions, since the reaction

$$2\ Fe^{+3} + Fe(s) \longrightarrow 3\ Fe^{+2} \tag{22.10}$$

$$E° = \text{S.R.P.}\ (Fe^{+3} \longrightarrow Fe^{+2}) + \text{S.O.P.}\ (Fe \longrightarrow Fe^{+2})$$

$$= +0.77\ \text{v.} + 0.44\ \text{v.} = 1.21\ \text{v.}$$

is spontaneous. We deduce then that the product must be Fe^{+2}. Regardless of what the reducing agent may be, so long as excess Fe^{+3} ions are available, the product will be Fe^{+2} ions rather than Fe atoms.

When the Cu^{+2} ion acts as an oxidizing agent, the situation is quite different. The reaction, analogous to 22.10,

$$Cu^{+2} + Cu(s) \longrightarrow 2\ Cu^+$$

$$E° = \text{S.R.P.}\ (Cu^{+2} \longrightarrow Cu^+) + \text{S.O.P.}\ (Cu \longrightarrow Cu^+)$$

$$= +0.15\ \text{v.} - 0.52\ \text{v.} = -0.37\ \text{v.}$$

is nonspontaneous. Any Cu^+ ions formed by the reduction of Cu^{+2} undergo a reaction known as **disproportionation** (simultaneous oxidation and reduction), precisely the reverse of that just stated.

$$2\ Cu^+ \longrightarrow Cu^{+2} + Cu(s) \qquad E° = +0.37\ \text{v.} \tag{22.11}$$

The spontaneity of this reaction explains why such salts as copper(I) sulfate, Cu_2SO_4, are unstable in water solution; they decompose to copper metal and the corresponding copper(II) salt. The only copper(I) compounds which are stable in contact with water are those which are only very slightly soluble such as CuI (Ksp $= 5 \times 10^{-12}$).

22.3   OXYGEN

Of all oxidizing agents, elementary oxygen is the most abundant and, in many ways, the most important. Its presence in air insures that all water supplies will contain dissolved oxygen. Water solutions used in the laboratory are ordinarily saturated with atmospheric oxygen. Finally, and most important, whenever we carry out a reaction in an open container, we must consider the possibility of elementary oxygen entering into the reaction.

As implied by its standard reduction potential,

$$\tfrac{1}{2}\ O_2(g) + 2\ H^+ + 2\ e^- \longrightarrow H_2O \qquad \text{S.R.P.} = +1.23\ \text{v.}$$

oxygen is a comparatively powerful oxidizing agent, at least in acidic solution. Since H^+ ions are involved as a reactant in this half-reaction, the reduction potential and consequently the oxidizing strength of elementary oxygen decreases as one moves from acidic to neutral to basic solution (Example 22.2). In basic solution, the half-equation for the reduction of oxygen is more properly written as:

$$\tfrac{1}{2} O_2(g) + H_2O + 2\ e^- \longrightarrow 2\ OH^-   \text{S.R.P.} = +0.40\ v.$$

Example 22.2.   Calculate the reduction potential of oxygen, at 1 atm. pressure, in
a. Neutral solution, i.e., $[H^+] = 10^{-7}$ M
b. A solution 1 M in OH^-, $[H^+] = 10^{-14}$ M

Solution.   Here, as in Example 22.1, we can apply the Nernst equation to determine the effect of the concentration of H^+ on the potential for the half-reaction:

$$\tfrac{1}{2} O_2(g) + 2\ H^+ + 2\ e^- \longrightarrow H_2O   \text{S.R.P.} = +1.23\ v.$$

$$\text{R.P.} = +1.23\ v. - \frac{0.059}{n} \log \frac{1}{[H^+]^2 (p\ O_2)^{\frac{1}{2}}}$$

Noting that n = 2, pO_2 = 1 atm. we have:

$$\text{R.P.} = +1.23\ v. - \frac{0.059}{2} \log \frac{1}{[H^+]^2}$$

Simplifying: $$\text{R.P.} = +1.23\ v. + 0.059 \log [H^+]$$

a. $[H^+] = 10^{-7}$ M   R.P. = +1.23 v. + 0.059(−7) v. = +0.82 v.
b. $[H^+] = 10^{-14}$ M   R.P. = +1.23 v. + 0.059(−14) v. = +0.40 v.

Note that the potential just calculated is the standard reduction potential for oxygen in basic solution, i.e., for the half-reaction:

$$\tfrac{1}{2} O_2\ (g, 1\ atm.) + H_2O + 2\ e^- \longrightarrow 2\ OH^-\ (1\ M)   \text{S.R.P.} = +0.40\ v.$$

Oxidation of Anions by Oxygen

Halide Ions.   When a solution of hydriodic acid is exposed to air, it slowly takes on a yellow and finally a brown color as a consequence of the oxidation of I^- ions to elementary iodine by dissolved oxygen:

oxidation: $2\ I^- \longrightarrow I_2 + 2\ e^-$ S.O.P. = −0.53 v.
reduction: $\tfrac{1}{2} O_2(g) + 2\ H^+ + 2\ e^- \longrightarrow H_2O$ S.R.P. = +1.23 v.

$\tfrac{1}{2} O_2(g) + 2\ H^+ + 2\ I^- \longrightarrow H_2O + I_2$ +0.70 v.   (22.12)

Oxygen is also capable of reacting with a water solution of hydrogen bromide (S.O.P. Br^- = −1.07 v.). The reaction of oxygen with hydrochloric acid is less spontaneous, as indicated by the fact that the E° value for the reaction is negative.

$$\tfrac{1}{2} O_2(g) + 2\ H^+ + 2\ Cl^- \longrightarrow H_2O + Cl_2(g)   (22.13)$$
$$E° = \text{S.R.P.}\ O_2 + \text{S.O.P.}\ Cl^-$$
$$= +1.23\ v. - 1.36\ v. = -0.13\ v.$$

It is, however, possible to prepare chlorine gas, in rather poor yield, by bubbling oxygen through concentrated hydrochloric acid. The gas phase reaction between oxygen and hydrogen chloride was at one time used commercially to prepare chlorine by the so-called Deacon process.

Sulfide Ion.   A solution of sodium sulfide in contact with air turns cloudy due to the oxidation of sulfide ions to colloidal sulfur. Since the sodium sulfide solution is strongly basic because of hydrolysis, the equations for its oxidation are best written:

oxidation: $S^{-2} \longrightarrow S(s) + 2 e^-$ S.O.P. $= +0.48$ v.

reduction: $\frac{1}{2} O_2(g) + H_2O + 2 e^- \longrightarrow 2 OH^-$ S.R.P. $= +0.40$ v.

$$\frac{1}{2} O_2(g) + H_2O + S^{-2} \longrightarrow 2 OH^- + S(s) \qquad +0.88 \text{ v.} \quad (22.14)$$

Solutions of hydrogen sulfide undergo a similar reaction, taking on a milky appearance.

Oxyanions. Many oxyanions in which the central atom is in an intermediate oxidation state are susceptible to air oxidation. Typical of these are the sulfite and nitrite ions:

$$SO_3^{-2} + \tfrac{1}{2} O_2(g) \longrightarrow SO_4^{-2} \tag{22.15}$$

$$NO_2^- + \tfrac{1}{2} O_2(g) \longrightarrow NO_3^- \tag{22.16}$$

Analytical tests for SO_3^{-2} and NO_2^- invariably reveal the presence of sulfate and nitrate ions produced by these reactions.

Oxidation of Cations by Oxygen

Many transition metal cations in intermediate oxidation states are oxidized by oxygen of the air. Typical of these is the Fe^{+2} ion. Green, hydrated crystals of iron(II) sulfate, $FeSO_4$, gradually acquire a brownish coating on exposure to air, due to the formation of Fe^{+3} ions. If one adds OH^- ions to a solution of an iron(II) salt, the $Fe(OH)_2$ formed at first slowly turns brown as a result of its oxidation to $Fe(OH)_3$.

$$Fe(OH)_2(s) + \tfrac{1}{2} O_2(g) + H_2O \longrightarrow Fe(OH)_3(s) \tag{22.17}$$

Solutions of iron(II) salts are sometimes protected from air oxidation by adding finely divided iron metal. So long as any elementary iron is present, it will react with Fe^{+3} ions according to equation 22.10, converting them back to Fe^{+2} ions.

Reaction with Metals: Corrosion

Reaction with oxygen can take place at room temperature if a metal is exposed to a water solution containing dissolved air. The "water solution" may be a body of fresh or salt water or a thin film of water on the surface of a metal exposed to the atmosphere. Attack by oxygen under these conditions is referred to as corrosion.

The susceptibility of a metal to corrosion depends to a certain extent upon the magnitude of its oxidation potential. Such easily oxidized metals as sodium (S.O.P. $= +2.71$ v.) and calcium (S.O.P. $= +2.87$ v.) are quantitatively converted to their oxides or hydroxides by exposure to air. Inert metals such as gold and platinum resist corrosion under all circumstances. With metals of intermediate reactivity, there is little correlation between oxidation potential and extent of corrosion. The corrosion of magnesium and aluminum is negligible under ordinary conditions since the oxides formed adhere tightly to the metal surface; iron, a less active metal, corrodes readily because its oxidation product, rust, fails to adhere to the metal. Copper (S.O.P. $= -0.34$ v.) is attacked by oxygen and carbon dioxide of the air to form an insoluble, green corrosion product with the approximate composition $CuCO_3 \cdot Cu(OH)_2$.

Corrosion of Iron and Steel: Electrochemical Mechanism

The corrosion of iron is a particularly serious problem. It has been estimated that the annual cost to this country of the corrosion of iron and steel exceeds five billion dollars.

In order to understand the mechanism by which iron corrodes, let us consider what happens when a sheet of iron is exposed to a neutral water solution containing an electrolyte such as sodium chloride (Figure 22.1). The iron tends to oxidize according to the half-reaction:

$$Fe(s) \longrightarrow Fe^{+2} + 2\ e^- \quad \text{S.O.P.} = +0.44 \text{ v.} \qquad (22.18a)$$

For this reaction to take place, some other species must simultaneously be reduced. Quite clearly, the sodium ion cannot pick up electrons (S.R.P. $Na^+ = -2.71$ v.). A more reasonable possibility would be the reduction of H^+ ions to elementary hydrogen (S.R.P. $H^+ = 0.00$ v.). This does occur in strongly acidic solution, but cannot take place in neutral solution in which the concentration of H^+ ions is only 10^{-7} M. Instead, oxygen molecules dissolved in the solution are reduced:

$$\tfrac{1}{2} O_2(g) + H_2O + 2\ e^- \longrightarrow 2\ OH^- \quad \text{S.R.P.} = +0.40 \text{ v.} \qquad (22.18b)$$

Adding these two half-equations and noting that iron(II) hydroxide is insoluble in water, we obtain for the primary corrosion reaction:

$$Fe(s) + \tfrac{1}{2} O_2(g) + H_2O \longrightarrow Fe(OH)_2(s) \qquad (22.18)$$

There is a great deal of evidence to indicate that reaction 22.18 represents the first and most important step in the corrosion of iron or steel. However, as pointed out earlier, iron(II) hydroxide, exposed to air or dissolved oxygen, is further oxidized to iron(III) hydroxide, $Fe(OH)_3$. The overall reaction for the corrosion process, obtained by combining 22.18 (oxidation of iron to $Fe(OH)_2$), and 22.17 (oxidation of $Fe(OH)_2$ to $Fe(OH)_3$) is:

$$2\ Fe(s) + \tfrac{3}{2} O_2(g) + 3\ H_2O \longrightarrow 2\ Fe(OH)_3(s) \qquad (22.19)$$

The final product, the loose, flaky deposit that we call rust, has the reddish-brown color of iron(III) hydroxide.

One of the most significant clues to the mechanism of the corrosion of iron emerges from the experimental observation that the oxidation half-reaction (22.18a) and the reduction half-reaction (22.18b) do not occur at the same location. If one examines a sheet of iron in the early stages of corrosion, the surface is found to be pitted by individual rust spots with areas of uncorroded metal in between. It appears that the oxidation half-reaction takes place at particular locations on the surface corresponding to the rust deposits; in surrounding areas, where the iron is unaffected, the reduction reaction occurs.

The observation that the oxidation and reduction half-reactions take place at separate locations suggests that corrosion occurs by an electrochemical mechanism. The surface of a piece of corroding iron may be visualized as consisting of a series of tiny voltaic cells. At the anode of each of these cells (anodic area), iron is oxidized to Fe^{+2} ions; at the neighboring cathode (cathodic area), elementary oxygen is reduced to OH^- ions. Electrons are transferred through the iron, which acts like the external conductor of an ordinary voltaic cell. The electrical circuit is completed by the

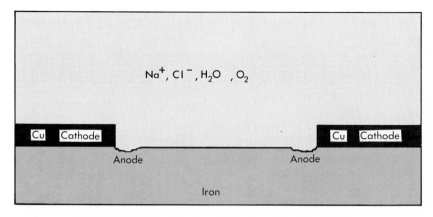

FIGURE 22.1 Corrosion of iron in contact with copper.

movement of ions through the water solution surrounding the electrodes of the corrosion cells. Under special conditions, it is possible to measure a corrosion current, which may run to several amperes.

Many of the characteristics of corrosion are most readily explained in terms of an electrochemical mechanism. A perfectly dry metal surface is not attacked by oxygen; iron exposed to dry air does not corrode. This seems plausible if corrosion occurs through a voltaic cell, which requires a water solution through which ions can move to complete the circuit. The fact that corrosion occurs more readily in sea water than in fresh water has a similar explanation.* The dissolved salts in sea water supply the ions necessary for the conduction of current.

The existence of discrete cathodic and anodic areas on a piece of corroding iron implies that adjacent surface areas differ chemically from each other. There are several ways in which one small area on a piece of iron or steel can become anodic or cathodic with respect to an adjacent area. Two of the most important are:

1. *The presence of impurities at scattered locations along the metal surface.* A tiny crystal of a less active metal such as copper or tin embedded in the surface of the iron acts as a cathode at which oxygen molecules are reduced. The iron atoms in the vicinity of these impurities are anodic and undergo oxidation to Fe^{+2} ions. This effect can be demonstrated on a large scale by immersing in water an iron plate which has been partially copper plated (Figure 22.1). At the interface between the two metals, a voltaic cell is set up in which the iron is anodic and the copper cathodic. A thick deposit of rust forms at the interface. The formation of rust inside an automobile bumper where the chromium plate stops is another example of this phenomenon.

2. *Differences in oxygen concentration along the metal surface.* To illustrate this effect, consider what happens when a drop of water adheres to the surface of a piece of iron exposed to the air (Figure 22.2). The metal around the edges of the drop is in contact with water containing a high concentration of dissolved oxygen. The water touching the metal beneath the center of the drop is depleted in oxygen, since it is cut off from

---

* Certain salts, unlike sodium chloride, inhibit corrosion rather than enhancing it. An example is zinc sulfate, $ZnSO_4$. The Zn^{+2} ions react with the OH^- ions produced by reaction 22.18b to form an adherent, protective film of $Zn(OH)_2$. Calcium salts react similarly to form $Ca(OH)_2$, which combines with dissolved carbon dioxide to give a final product of $CaCO_3$. Two other effective corrosion inhibitors are potassium chromate, K_2CrO_4, and sodium benzoate, $NaC_7H_5O_2$.

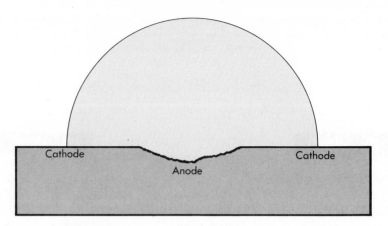

FIGURE 22.2 Corrosion of iron covered by water drop.

contact with air. As a result, a small oxygen-concentration cell is set up. The area around the edge of the drop, where the oxygen concentration is high, becomes cathodic; oxygen molecules are reduced there. Directly beneath the drop is an anodic area where the iron is oxidized. A particle of dirt on the surface of an iron object can act in much the same way as a drop of water to cut off the supply of oxygen to the area beneath it and thereby establish anodic and cathodic areas. This explains why garden tools left covered with soil are particularly susceptible to corrosion.

Iron or steel objects may be protected from corrosion in either of two ways:

1. The surface may be covered with a protective coating. This may be a layer of paint which cuts off access to moisture and oxygen. Under more severe conditions, it may be desirable to cover the surface of the iron or steel object with a layer of

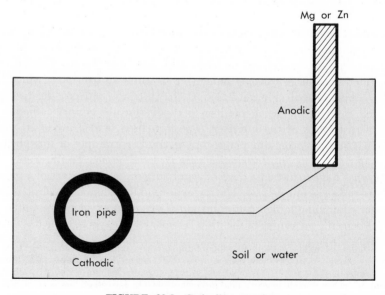

FIGURE 22.3 Cathodic protection.

another metal. Metallic plates, applied electrically (Cr, Ni, Cu, Ag, Zn, Sn) or by immersion at high temperatures (Zn, Sn) are ordinarily more resistant to heat and chemical attack than the organic coating left when paint dries. However, if the plating metal is less active than iron, there is a danger that cracks in its surface may enhance the corrosion of the iron or steel. This problem can arise with "tin cans," which are made by applying a layer of tin over a steel base. If the food in the can contains citric acid, some of the tin plate may dissolve, exposing the steel beneath.* When the can is opened, exposing the interior to the air, rust forms spontaneously on the iron surrounding the breaks in the tin surface. A thin coating of lacquer is ordinarily applied over the tin to prevent corrosive effects of this type.

2. The object may be brought into electrical contact with a bar of a more active metal such as magnesium or zinc. The iron becomes cathodic and hence is protected against rusting; the more active metal serves as a sacrificial anode in a large-scale corrosion cell. This method of combating corrosion, known as *cathodic protection* is particularly useful for steel objects such as cables or pipelines which are buried under soil or water. (Figure 22.3.)

22.4 CHLORINE

$$Cl_2(g) + 2\ e^- \longrightarrow 2\ Cl^- \quad S.R.P. = +1.36\ v.$$

Elementary chlorine is a somewhat more powerful oxidizing agent than oxygen, as judged by the magnitude of its standard reduction potential. Perhaps the most familiar redox reactions in which chlorine acts as an oxidizing agent are those involving bromide and iodide ions.

$$Cl_2(g) + 2\ Br^- \longrightarrow 2\ Cl^- + Br_2 \quad E° = +1.36\ v. - 1.07\ v. = +0.29\ v. \quad (22.20)$$

$$Cl_2(g) + 2\ I^- \longrightarrow 2\ Cl^- + I_2 \quad E° = +1.36\ v. - 0.53\ v. = +0.83\ v. \quad (22.21)$$

These reactions are frequently used to test for the presence of Br^- or I^- ions. Addition of chlorine to a solution containing either of these ions gives the free halogens Br_2 or I_2. If the water solution is then shaken with a small amount of a nonpolar organic solvent such as carbon disulfide or carbon tetrachloride, the halogens enter the organic layer, to which they impart their characteristic colors: reddish-brown (bromine) or violet (iodine).

Bromine is prepared commercially from sea water, in which it occurs as Br^- ions, by oxidation with chlorine (22.20). About 100,000 tons of bromine are produced annually in the United States by this method. The concentration of iodide ions in sea water is so low (conc. $I^- = 4 \times 10^{-7}$ M vs. conc. $Br^- = 8 \times 10^{-4}$ M) that it is not economically feasible to produce iodine in this way.

Chlorine, unlike oxygen, forms many compounds in which it has a positive oxidation number. These compounds are ordinarily formed by a disproportionation reaction in which elementary chlorine is simultaneously oxidized and reduced. An example of one such reaction is that which occurs when chlorine is added to water.

$$Cl_2(g) + H_2O \rightleftharpoons HOCl + H^+ + Cl^- \quad (22.22)$$

---

* Tin forms an extremely stable complex with citrate ion and hence is attacked more readily by citric acid than by many stronger inorganic acids.

The resulting solution, called *chlorine water*, contains equimolar amounts of the weak acid HOCl (hypochlorous acid) and the strong acid, HCl. Half of the chlorine (oxid. state = 0) is reduced to Cl⁻ ions (oxid. state = −1) while the remainder is oxidized to HOCl (oxid. state Cl = +1).

The hypochlorous acid formed by reaction 22.22 is stable in the dark but slowly decomposes on exposure to sunlight to give oxygen and a solution of hydrochloric acid:

$$HOCl \longrightarrow \tfrac{1}{2} O_2(g) + H^+ + Cl^- \tag{22.23}$$

To prevent this reaction, chlorine water is stored in bottles made of brown or amber-colored glass.

The position of the equilibrium in reaction 22.22 is strongly affected by the concentration of H⁺ ions. In basic solution, in which the concentration of H⁺ ions is low, chlorine is much more soluble than in pure water. The overall reaction that takes place when chlorine is bubbled through a solution of sodium hydroxide maintained at room temperature is:

$$Cl_2(g) + 2\ OH^- \longrightarrow ClO^- + Cl^- + H_2O \tag{22.24}$$

One may regard this as a two-step process:

oxidation-reduction: $Cl_2(g) + H_2O \rightleftharpoons HOCl + H^+ + Cl^-$

neutralization: $HOCl + H^+ + 2\ OH^- \longrightarrow ClO^- + 2\ H_2O$

$$\overline{Cl_2(g) + 2\ OH^- \longrightarrow ClO^- + Cl^- + H_2O}$$

The solution formed by reacting chlorine with sodium hydroxide via 22.24 is sold under various trade names as a household bleach and disinfectant. It is prepared commercially by electrolyzing a stirred water solution of sodium chloride. Recall that the electrolysis of an NaCl solution gives Cl₂ molecules and OH⁻ ions (Chapter 20); stirring ensures that these species react with each other. The active ingredient of the resulting solution is the hypochlorite ion, a relatively potent oxidizing agent:

$$ClO^- + H_2O + 2\ e^- \longrightarrow Cl^- + 2\ OH^- \qquad S.R.P. = +0.89\ v.$$

The reaction of chlorine with a hot, concentrated solution of sodium or potassium hydroxide is quite different from that observed at room temperature. Any ClO⁻ ions formed decompose on heating to ClO₃⁻ and Cl⁻ ions; the net reaction is:

$$3\ Cl_2(g) + 6\ OH^- \longrightarrow ClO_3^- + 5\ Cl^- + 3\ H_2O \tag{22.25}$$

Here, as in 22.24, chlorine acts as both an oxidizing and a reducing agent: $\tfrac{5}{6}$ of the chlorine atoms (oxid. state = 0) are reduced to Cl⁻ (oxid. state = −1) while $\tfrac{1}{6}$ of them are oxidized to ClO₃⁻ (oxid. state Cl = +5). Potassium chlorate, a powerful oxidizing agent is made commercially by reaction 22.25. The chlorine and potassium hydroxide required are made *in situ* by electrolyzing a hot, stirred solution of potassium chloride. On cooling, KClO₃ crystallizes out first, since it is less soluble than KCl (0.85 M vs. 5.0 M at 30°C). Sodium chlorate, NaClO₃, is more difficult to prepare in this manner, since its solubility exceeds that of sodium chloride.

If a hot, stirred solution of potassium chloride is electrolyzed for a long period of time, crystals of potassium perchlorate, KClO₄, separate out on cooling. The perchlorate ions are formed by the slow decomposition of ClO₃⁻ ions to ClO₄⁻ and

Cl⁻ ions. A more rapid method of preparing potassium perchlorate involves heating
the chlorate at a temperature slightly above its melting point, 307°C.

$$4 \text{ KClO}_3(s) \longrightarrow 3 \text{ KClO}_4(s) + \text{KCl}(s) \qquad\qquad (22.26)$$

Potassium perchlorate is readily separated from the potassium chloride by-product
by taking advantage of its relatively low solubility in water (0.05 M at 0°C).

22.5 OXYANIONS

Any oxyanion in which the central atom is in a positive oxidation state can, in
principle, serve as an oxidizing agent. The four oxyanions which we shall consider
(NO_3^-, SO_4^{-2}, $Cr_2O_7^{-2}$, and MnO_4^-) are ones in which the central atom is in its
highest oxidation state (N = +5, S = +6, Cr = +6, Mn = +7).

Although oxyanions differ greatly from one another in their oxidizing properties,
they have certain characteristics in common. In particular:

1. *Oxyanions are stronger oxidizing agents in acidic than in neutral or basic solution.*
Thus, we find that whereas concentrated nitric and sulfuric acids are relatively
powerful oxidizing agents, neutral salts containing NO_3^- or SO_4^{-2} ions such as
KNO_3 or K_2SO_4 are ineffective oxidizing agents in water solution. A solution prepared by adding sulfuric acid to potassium dichromate is frequently used to clean
laboratory glassware; it is particularly effective in oxidizing greases and oils which
are impervious to a solution containing only $K_2Cr_2O_7$. Finally, it may be mentioned
that a strongly acidic solution containing the MnO_4^- ion is a dangerously powerful
oxidizing agent; neutral or weakly acidic solutions of potassium permanganate are
much safer to work with.

One can readily explain the direct relationship between oxidizing strength and
acidity by examining the half-equation for the reduction of an oxyanion. Consider,
for example, the NO_3^- ion. The half-reaction for the reduction of NO_3^- to NO_2
involves H^+ as a reactant.

$$NO_3^- + 2 \text{ H}^+ + \text{e}^- \longrightarrow NO_2(g) + H_2O$$

An increase in the concentration of H^+ ions makes this reaction more spontaneous.
In terms of potentials, one can calculate that at a H^+ ion concentration of 1 M,
the reduction potential for the foregoing reaction is +0.78 v.; in neutral solution
($[H^+] = 10^{-7}$ M), it drops to −0.05 v., while in a solution 1 M in OH^- ($[H^+] =
10^{-14}$ M), it is a large negative number, −0.87 v.

The principle which we have used to explain the effect of H^+ ion concentration on
the oxidizing strength of the nitrate ion can be applied to other oxyanions as well.
Thus, we find that H^+ ions are involved as a reactant in the half-reactions:

$$SO_4^{-2} + 4 \text{ H}^+ + 2 \text{ e}^- \longrightarrow SO_2(g) + 2 H_2O$$
$$Cr_2O_7^{-2} + 14 \text{ H}^+ + 6 \text{ e}^- \longrightarrow 2 \text{ Cr}^{+3} + 7 H_2O$$
$$MnO_4^- + 8 \text{ H}^+ + 5 \text{ e}^- \longrightarrow \text{Mn}^{+2} + 4 H_2O$$

In general, whenever an oxyanion acts as an oxidizing agent, one or more of the
oxygen atoms bonded to the central atom is converted to a water molecule. This
means that at least two H^+ ions will be required for the reduction of an oxyanion,
causing the potential to increase with increasing H^+ ion concentration.

A corollary to this rule is that in preparing oxyanions such as NO_3^-, SO_4^{-2}, $Cr_2O_7^{-2}$, or MnO_4^- from species in which the central atom is in a lower oxidation state, it is ordinarily best to work in a strongly basic medium, in which half-reactions such as those just written are most easily reversed. This principle is applied in the commercial preparation of potassium permanganate from pyrolusite (MnO_2). The first step in the preparation involves fusing MnO_2 with potassium hydroxide in the presence of air:

$$2 \, MnO_2(s) + 4 \, OH^- + O_2(g) \longrightarrow 2 \, MnO_4^{-2} + 2 \, H_2O \qquad (22.27)$$

The product of this reaction is a green salt, potassium manganate, K_2MnO_4, which disproportionates in water to give a solution of potassium permanganate and a precipitate of MnO_2.

$$3 \, MnO_4^{-2} + 2 \, H_2O \longrightarrow 2 \, MnO_4^- + MnO_2(s) + 4 \, OH^- \qquad (22.28)$$

2. *Oxyanions can be reduced to a variety of species, depending upon the experimental conditions.* Table 22.1 indicates some of the species to which such ions as NO_3^-, SO_4^{-2}, $Cr_2O_7^{-2}$, and MnO_4^- can be reduced when they act as oxidizing agents.

TABLE 22.1   OXIDATION STATES OF N, S, Cr, Mn

| | Nitrogen | | | Sulfur | |
	Acidic Solution	Basic Solution		Acidic Solution	Basic Solution
+5	NO_3^-	NO_3^-	+6	SO_4^{-2}, HSO_4^-	SO_4^{-2}
+4	$NO_2(g)$	$NO_2(g)$	+4	$SO_2(g)$, H_2SO_3	SO_3^{-2}
+3	HNO_2	NO_2^-	+2	—	$S_2O_3^{-2}$
+2	$NO(g)$	$NO(g)$	0	$S(s)$	$S(s)$
+1	$N_2O(g)$	$N_2O(g)$	−2	$H_2S(g)$	S^{-2}
0	$N_2(g)$	$N_2(g)$			
−1	NH_3OH^+	NH_2OH			
−2	$N_2H_5^+$	N_2H_4			
−3	NH_4^+	NH_3			

| | Chromium | | | Manganese | |
	Acidic Solution	Basic Solution		Acid Solution	Basic Solution
+6	$Cr_2O_7^{-2}$	CrO_4^{-2}	+7	MnO_4^-	MnO_4^-
+3	$Cr(H_2O)_6^{+3}$	$Cr(H_2O)_2(OH)_4^-$	+6	—	MnO_4^{-2}
+2	$Cr(H_2O)_6^{+2}$	$Cr(OH)_2(s)$	+4	$MnO_2(s)$	$MnO_2(s)$
			+2	$Mn(H_2O)_6^{+2}$	$Mn(OH)_2(s)$

It may be noted from Table 22.1 that the stable species in a given oxidation state often depends upon the acidity or basicity of the solution. In the majority of cases, what is involved is an equilibrium between a weak base and its conjugate acid Consider, for example, the +3 state of nitrogen. The nitrite ion, NO_2^-, which is stable in basic solution, acquires a proton in strongly acidic solution to form a molecule of the weak acid HNO_2. An analogous situation applies to the −3, −2, and −1 states of nitrogen. Molecules of the weak bases ammonia (NH_3), hydrazine (N_2H_4), and hydroxylamine (NH_2OH) are capable of adding a proton in acidic solution to form the ions NH_4^+, $N_2H_5^+$, and NH_3OH^+ respectively.

The existence of different species in acidic and basic solutions of chromium(III) may be explained by the tendency for OH^- ions to replace H_2O molecules in the coordination sphere as the solution becomes more basic. What is actually involved here is a complex equilibrium with a series of species such as $Cr(H_2O)_6^{+3}$ (strongly acidic solution), $Cr(H_2O)_5(OH)^{+2}$ (weakly acidic solution), $Cr(H_2O)_3(OH)_3$ (weakly basic solution), and $Cr(H_2O)_2(OH)_4^-$ (strongly basic solution).

Chromium in the $+6$ oxidation state forms two different oxyanions, the chromate ion, CrO_4^{-2}, stable in basic solution, and the dichromate ion, $Cr_2O_7^{-2}$, stable in acidic solution. If a water solution of a metal chromate is acidified, the yellow color of the CrO_4^{-2} ion changes to the red color of the dichromate ion:

$$2\ CrO_4^{-2} + 2\ H^+ \rightleftharpoons Cr_2O_7^{-2} + H_2O \qquad (22.29)$$
$$\text{yellow} \qquad\qquad\qquad \text{red}$$

This reaction is readily reversed by adding base. At a pH lower than about 7, the $Cr_2O_7^{-2}$ ion is the principal species present; at a higher pH the CrO_4^{-2} ion predominates.

Of the oxidation states listed in Table 22.1, it will be noted that in two cases ($+6$ manganese, $+2$ sulfur) there is no stable species in acidic solution. In both instances, the ion which is stable in basic solution disproportionates in acid. The reaction of the manganate ion (MnO_4^{-2}) with water was mentioned earlier (equation 22.28). The thiosulfate ion ($S_2O_3^{-2}$) is considerably more stable; solutions prepared by dissolving in water such salts as sodium thiosulfate, $Na_2S_2O_3$, show little if any tendency to decompose. However, the addition of a strong acid to such solutions brings about the spontaneous redox reaction

$$S_2O_3^{-2} + 2\ H^+ \longrightarrow S(s) + SO_2(g) + H_2O \qquad E° = +0.10\ v. \quad (22.30)$$

in which half the sulfur atoms are reduced to elementary sulfur ($+2 \rightarrow 0$) and half are oxidized to sulfur dioxide ($+2 \rightarrow +4$). The small positive voltage associated with this reaction suggests that it should readily be reversed in basic solution. Indeed, sodium thiosulfate is prepared commercially by bubbling sulfur dioxide through a suspension of sulfur in concentrated sodium hydroxide.

In practice, the problem of deciding what species an oxyanion such as NO_3^- will be reduced to is not as difficult as the large number of possible reduction products might imply. The mechanisms by which redox reactions occur are poorly understood, but it is generally agreed that reduction and oxidation ordinarily take place in a series of one-electron steps. Consequently, it would be expected that as one moves down the oxidation scale, the first stable species formed would be the principal product. In the case of the NO_3^- ion (oxid. state N $= +5$), this would lead us to predict that the NO_2 molecule (oxid. state N $= +4$) would be a likely reduction product. This is indeed the case; brown fumes of nitrogen dioxide are almost invariably observed in reactions in which concentrated nitric acid is used as an oxidizing agent. In more dilute solutions (low H^+ ion concentrations), some of the NO_2 disproportionates to NO and HNO_3:

$$3\ NO_2(g) + H_2O \longrightarrow NO(g) + 2\ H^+ + 2\ NO_3^- \qquad (22.31)$$

and significant quantities of nitric oxide can be detected among the reduction products.

It is found experimentally that the species to which an oxyanion is reduced in a redox reaction depends to some extent upon the strength of the reducing agent used. Consider, for example, the reaction of concentrated sulfuric acid with bromide as opposed to iodide ions. If one allows sulfuric acid to drop on solid sodium bromide, the reaction

$$SO_4^{-2} + 4 H^+ + 2 Br^- \longrightarrow SO_2(g) + Br_2 + 2 H_2O \qquad (22.32)$$

occurs. Here, the only sulfur-containing species produced in significant amounts is sulfur dioxide (oxid. state S = +4). On the other hand, the addition of sulfuric acid to sodium iodide gives detectable quantities of sulfur (oxid. state S = 0) and hydrogen sulfide (oxid. state S = −2). One might explain this difference in behavior of Br^- and I^- ions in terms of the greater reducing strength of the iodide ion (S.O.P. = −0.53 v.) as compared to the bromide ion (S.O.P. = −1.07 v.); the I^- ion should be capable of reducing any SO_2 formed to lower oxidation states such as S and H_2S. It seems quite likely, however, that the difference between the two reactions should be ascribed to a difference in mechanism and that any argument involving electrode potentials may be of dubious validity.

Having considered some of the general principles governing the use of oxyanions as oxidizing agents, we shall now describe some of the more important redox reactions involving the NO_3^-, SO_4^{-2}, $Cr_2O_7^{-2}$, and MnO_4^- ions.

Reactions of Metals with Nitric and Sulfuric Acids

Nitric Acid. When a metal reacts with nitric acid, the products differ markedly from those obtained with dilute HCl or H_2SO_4. Unless the acid is very dilute, it is the NO_3^- ion rather than the H^+ ion which is reduced; no hydrogen is evolved. Since the nitrate ion in acidic solution is a much stronger oxidizing agent than the H^+ ion, many metals, including copper and silver, which do not react with dilute hydrochloric or sulfuric acids are brought into solution by nitric acid.

The species to which nitric acid is reduced by a metal depends on the concentration of the acid and the activity of the metal. With the very unreactive metal silver, nitrogen dioxide is the principal product:

$$Ag(s) + NO_3^- + 2 H^+ \longrightarrow Ag^+ + NO_2(g) + H_2O \qquad (22.33)$$

Copper reacts with concentrated nitric acid (16 M) to give nitrogen dioxide.

$$Cu(s) + 2 NO_3^- + 4 H^+ \longrightarrow Cu^{+2} + 2 NO_2(g) + 2 H_2O \qquad (22.34)$$

Dilute acid (6 M) gives nitric oxide as a principal product:

$$3 Cu(s) + 2 NO_3^- + 8 H^+ \longrightarrow 3 Cu^{+2} + 2 NO(g) + 4 H_2O \qquad (22.35)$$

Zinc, a strong reducing agent, may give any of a series of reduction products depending upon the concentration of the acid used:

$$Zn(s) + 2 NO_3^- + 4 H^+ \longrightarrow Zn^{+2} + 2 NO_2(g) + 2 H_2O$$
$$2 Zn(s) + 2 NO_3^- + 6 H^+ \longrightarrow 2 Zn^{+2} + 2 HNO_2 + 2 H_2O$$
$$3 Zn(s) + 2 NO_3^- + 8 H^+ \longrightarrow 3 Zn^{+2} + 2 NO(g) + 4 H_2O$$
$$4 Zn(s) + 2 NO_3^- + 10 H^+ \longrightarrow 4 Zn^{+2} + N_2O(g) + 5 H_2O$$
$$5 Zn(s) + 2 NO_3^- + 12 H^+ \longrightarrow 5 Zn^{+2} + N_2(g) + 6 H_2O$$
$$8 Zn(s) + 2 NO_3^- + 20 H^+ \longrightarrow 8 Zn^{+2} + 2 NH_4^+ + 6 H_2O$$

incr. conc. HNO_3

Curiously enough, concentrated nitric acid fails to react with certain active metals including aluminum and chromium which are readily attacked by dilute hydrochloric or sulfuric acid. The inertness of these metals towards nitric acid is poorly understood; it has been suggested that an insoluble oxide film forms on the metal surface thereby preventing further reaction. In support of this idea, it is found that the addition of a few drops of hydrofluoric acid, in which Al_2O_3 and Cr_2O_3 are soluble, enables the oxidation of aluminum or chromium by nitric acid to proceed smoothly.

A few very inactive metals including platinum and gold are not attacked by nitric acid. Both of these metals are dissolved by **aqua regia,** a mixture of concentrated nitric and hydrochloric acids. The oxidizing agent here is the nitrate ion; the hydrochloric acid serves as a source of chloride ions to form the stable complexes $AuCl_4^-$ and $PtCl_6^{-2}$:

$$Au(s) + 3\ NO_3^- + 6\ H^+ \longrightarrow Au^{+3} + 3\ NO_2(g) + 3\ H_2O$$
$$Au^{+3} + 4\ Cl^- \longrightarrow AuCl_4^-$$

$$Au(s) + 3\ NO_3^- + 6\ H^+ + 4\ Cl^- \longrightarrow AuCl_4^- + 3\ NO_2(g) + 3\ H_2O \qquad (22.36)$$

Sulfuric Acid. Sulfuric acid is a less powerful oxidizing agent than nitric acid, as may be seen by comparing the potential for the reduction of SO_4^{-2} to SO_2 with that for the reduction of NO_3^- to NO_2:

$$SO_4^{-2} + 4\ H^+ + 2\ e^- \longrightarrow SO_2(g) + 2\ H_2O \qquad \text{S.R.P.} = +0.20\ \text{v.}$$

$$NO_3^- + 2\ H^+ +\ \ e^- \longrightarrow NO_2(g) +\ \ H_2O \qquad \text{S.R.P.} = +0.81\ \text{v.}$$

The difference in oxidizing strengths of the NO_3^- and SO_4^{-2} ions is illustrated by comparing the reactions of HNO_3 and H_2SO_4 with metals. As pointed out earlier, when a metal reacts with nitric acid, it is ordinarily the NO_3^- ion rather than the H^+ ion which acts as the oxidizing agent. In contrast, dilute sulfuric acid reacts with many metals, including zinc and magnesium, to evolve hydrogen. Only when concentrated sulfuric acid is used are appreciable quantities of sulfur dioxide or other reduction products of the SO_4^{-2} ion formed.

Concentrated sulfuric acid is not a powerful enough oxidizing agent to react with very inactive metals such as silver (S.O.P. Ag = −0.80 v.). It will, however, react with copper (S.O.P. = −0.34 v.):

$$Cu(s) + SO_4^{-2} + 4\ H^+ \longrightarrow Cu^{+2} + SO_2(g) + 2\ H_2O$$
$$E° = -0.34 + 0.20 = -0.14\ \text{v.} \qquad (22.37)$$

The fact that the $E°$ value for this reaction is negative implies that it can proceed only if the acid is concentrated; dilute H_2SO_4 (3 M) does not react with copper.

Use of MnO_4^-, $Cr_2O_7^{-2}$ as Oxidizing Agents in Volumetric Analysis

A species which is readily oxidized can be determined quantitatively by titration with an oxidizing agent in much the same way that a base is titrated with an acid. Two oxidizing agents which are frequently used in redox titrations are potassium permanganate, $KMnO_4$, and potassium dichromate, $K_2Cr_2O_7$. One advantage of these compounds is that they are quite powerful oxidizing agents in acidic solution, as indicated by their standard reduction potentials.

$$MnO_4^- + 8\ H^+ + 5\ e^- \longrightarrow Mn^{+2} + 4\ H_2O \qquad \text{S.R.P.} = +1.52\ \text{v.}$$

$$Cr_2O_7^{-2} + 14\ H^+ + 6\ e^- \longrightarrow 2\ Cr^{+3} + 7\ H_2O \qquad \text{S.R.P.} = +1.33\ \text{v.}$$

To illustrate the use of MnO_4^- ion as an oxidizing agent in volumetric analysis, let us consider a specific redox titration, the determination of Fe^{+2} ions with MnO_4^-.

$$MnO_4^- + 8\ H^+ + 5\ Fe^{+2} \longrightarrow Mn^{+2} + 4\ H_2O + 5\ Fe^{+3} \qquad (22.38)$$

$$E° = \text{S.R.P. } MnO_4^- + \text{S.O.P. } Fe^{+2} = (+1.52 - 0.77)\ \text{v.} = 0.75\ \text{v.}$$

The large positive $E°$ value for this reaction means that the equilibrium constant is large enough ($K = 10^{64}$) to make the reaction go essentially to completion. What one does in the titration is to start with a known volume of an acidified solution containing Fe^{+2} ions and add from a buret a solution of potassium permanganate of known concentration. At the instant the MnO_4^- ions are added, the solution takes on the pink or purple color characteristic of that ion. As the MnO_4^- ions are used up by reaction 22.38, the color fades almost immediately. However, when all the Fe^{+2} ions have been titrated, i.e., at the equivalence point, the addition of one or two drops of excess MnO_4^- produces a permanent pink color. The volume of titrant necessary to reach this end point is recorded and the concentration of Fe^{+2} ions calculated as indicated in Example 22.3.

Example 22.3.   A 20.0 ml. sample containing Fe^{+2} ions requires 18.0 ml. of 0.100 M $KMnO_4$ solution for complete reaction. Calculate the concentration of Fe^{+2} ions in the solution.

Solution.   Let us first calculate the number of moles of MnO_4^- added. Then, using equation 22.38, we can calculate the number of moles of Fe^{+2} ion in the sample. Finally, knowing the volume of the sample, we can calculate the concentration of Fe^{+2}.

$$\text{no. moles } MnO_4^- = 0.100\ \frac{\text{mole}}{\text{l.}} \times 0.0180\ \text{l.} = 0.00180\ \text{mole}$$

According to equation 22.38,

$$1\ \text{mole } MnO_4^- \simeq 5\ \text{moles } Fe^{+2}$$

Hence,

$$\text{no. moles } Fe^{+2} = 0.00180\ \text{mole } MnO_4^- \times \frac{5\ \text{moles } Fe^{+2}}{1\ \text{mole } MnO_4^-} = 0.0900\ \text{mole } Fe^{+2}$$

$$\text{conc. } Fe^{+2} = \frac{0.00900\ \text{mole}}{0.0200\ \text{l.}} = 0.450\ \text{M}$$

The MnO_4^- ion is a powerful enough oxidizing agent to react with a wide variety of oxidizable substances. Thus, potassium permanganate can be used to titrate such species as I^-, NO_2^-, and $C_2O_4^{-2}$ ions.

$$MnO_4^- + 8\ H^+ + 5\ I^- \longrightarrow Mn^{+2} + 4\ H_2O + \tfrac{5}{2}\ I_2 \qquad E° = +0.99\ \text{v.}$$
$$(22.39)$$

$$2\ MnO_4^- + 6\ H^+ + 5\ NO_2^- \longrightarrow 2\ Mn^{+2} + 3\ H_2O + 5\ NO_3^- \qquad E° = +0.68\ \text{v.}$$
$$(22.40)$$

$$2\ MnO_4^- + 16\ H^+ + 5\ C_2O_4^{-2} \longrightarrow 2\ Mn^{+2} + 8\ H_2O + 10\ CO_2(g) \qquad E° = +2.15\ \text{v.}$$
$$(22.41)$$

Reaction 22.41 is particularly useful, since it can be adapted to the determination of metals which form insoluble oxalates. The concentration of Ca^{+2} ions in a solution can be determined by adding excess $C_2O_4^{-2}$ to precipitate calcium oxalate, CaC_2O_4, and then titrating this precipitate with a standard solution of $KMnO_4$.

Potassium dichromate has certain advantages over potassium permanganate as an oxidizing agent in redox titrations. Since it is not as powerful an oxidizing agent, standard solutions are easier to prepare and are stable for longer periods of time. On the other hand, the $Cr_2O_7^{-2}$ ion, unlike the MnO_4^- ion, cannot serve as its own indicator in a titration. If, for example, one attempts to titrate Fe^{+2} ions with $Cr_2O_7^{-2}$ directly

$$Cr_2O_7^{-2} + 14\ H^+ + 6\ Fe^{+2} \longrightarrow 2\ Cr^{+3} + 7\ H_2O + 6\ Fe^{+3} \qquad (22.42)$$
$$\text{orange} \qquad\qquad\qquad\qquad\qquad \text{green}$$

the end point is difficult to see because the green color of the Cr^{+3} ion obscures the orange color of excess $Cr_2O_7^{-2}$.

Redox titrations using $Cr_2O_7^{-2}$ ions are ordinarily carried out in the presence of an oxidation-reduction indicator. One such substance is diphenylamine, an organic compound which is colorless in the reduced form but can be oxidized to a species which has a deep violet color. Diphenylamine is oxidized by $Cr_2O_7^{-2}$ ions, but less readily than are Fe^{+2} ions. Consequently, if one adds a small amount of this indicator to a solution of Fe^{+2} ions being titrated with $Cr_2O_7^{-2}$, it remains colorless until virtually all of the Fe^{+2} ions are oxidized. At the equivalence point, the diphenyl-amine is oxidized by a slight excess of $Cr_2O_7^{-2}$ ions, giving a deep violet color which serves to indicate the end point.

Use of Oxidizing Agents in Qualitative Analysis

Many of the reactions involved in the standard schemes of cation and anion analysis are of the oxidation-reduction type. Oxidizing agents are commonly used in quantitative analysis for three different purposes.

1. *To bring a sample into solution so it can be analyzed.* Solid samples which are insoluble in both water and dilute, nonoxidizing acids can frequently be brought into solution by an oxidizing agent. Concentrated nitric acid is most often used for this purpose; it reacts with inactive metals such as silver or copper (equations 22.33, 22.34) or insoluble metal sulfides such as CuS.

$$CuS(s) + 2\ NO_3^- + 4\ H^+ \longrightarrow Cu^{+2} + S(s) + 2\ NO_2(g) + 2\ H_2O \qquad (22.43)$$

to form a solution containing the corresponding metal ion.

It should be emphasized that a solution prepared by treating a sample with concentrated nitric acid or other powerful oxidizing agent can hardly be expected to contain readily oxidizable ions such as Fe^{+2} or Sn^{+2}. In the presence of nitric acid, for example, Fe^{+2} ions are spontaneously oxidized to Fe^{+3}:

$$Fe^{+2} + NO_3^- + 2\ H^+ \longrightarrow Fe^{+3} + NO_2(g) + H_2O \quad E^\circ = +0.04\ v. \quad (22.44)$$

2. *To test for the presence of a particular ion.* Chromium(III) salts are ordinarily detected by oxidizing them to chromium(VI) compounds. One way to do this is to use sodium peroxide, Na_2O_2, as an oxidizing agent in basic solution.

$$Cr(OH)_3(s) + \tfrac{3}{2}\ O_2^{-2} \longrightarrow CrO_4^{-2} + OH^- + H_2O \qquad (22.45)$$

This reaction is often used in qualitative analysis to test for the presence of Cr^{+3}; the existence of CrO_4^{-2} ions in the final solution may be demonstrated either by acidifying to obtain the red color of the $Cr_2O_7^{-2}$ ion* or adding Ba^{+2} to give yellow, insoluble barium chromate, $BaCrO_4$.

3. *Separation of ions from one another.* Mercuric sulfide, because of its very low solubility in water, is not as readily oxidized by nitric acid as are the sulfides of the other ions in group 2 (Cu^{+2}, Bi^{+3}, Cd^{+2}, and so on). Advantage is taken of this difference in separating the Hg^{+2} ion from the other ions of this group. The sulfide precipitate obtained by saturating the solution of the unknown with H_2S is heated with moderately dilute nitric acid. All of the sulfides except HgS react under these conditions (cf. equation 22.43); the residue consists of a mixture of mercuric sulfide and sulfur.

22.6 THE PHOTOGRAPHIC PROCESS

A commercial process which involves, at a critical stage, an oxidation-reduction reaction in water solution, is that of photography. We shall consider the chemistry of the three steps by which a negative is produced on a photographic film: exposure, development, and fixing.

Exposure

The thin, light-sensitive layer which coats a photographic film or plate consists of an emulsion of a silver halide, usually AgBr, in gelatin. The silver bromide is dispersed in the gelatin as tiny crystals or **grains** which are clearly visible under the microscope. The grains range in diameter from 10^{-5} to 10^{-4} cm. (1000 to 10,000 Å); on the average, a silver bromide grain is made up of about 10^9 Ag^+ ions and an equal number of Br^- ions.

When a film is exposed momentarily to light, a few of the Ag^+ ions in each grain of silver bromide are reduced to Ag atoms. Aggregates of from 10 to 500 silver atoms form at various points within each grain. The number of aggregates produced depends upon the amount of light striking the film. Under ordinary conditions, the amount of silver constituting the so-called **latent image** is so small as to be invisible under a microscope. Long exposure to bright light reduces all the silver bromide to silver, darkening the entire film. Increasing the particle size of the grains facilitates the reaction; high-speed and x-ray film contain comparatively large crystals of silver bromide, approximately 10^{-4} cm. in diameter.

Despite a great deal of research devoted to the subject, the precise mechanism of latent image formation is not well-established. Several steps appear to be involved:

1. A photon of light ejects an electron from a bromide ion:

$$Br^- + h\nu \longrightarrow Br + e^-$$

---

* When an alkaline solution containing CrO_4^{-2} and O_2^{-2} ions is acidified, there is obtained a fleeting blue color which quickly changes to red. The blue color has been attributed to the triperoxy chromate ion, CrO_7^{-2}:

$$\begin{bmatrix} O-O & & O-O \\ & \diagdown \quad \diagup & \\ & Cr & \\ & \diagup \quad \diagdown & \\ O-O & & O \end{bmatrix}^{-2}$$

in which three of the four oxide ions of the CrO_4^{-2} anion have been replaced by peroxide ions.

2. Electrons produced in the first step migrate through the crystal until they encounter an **electron-trap.** The simplest type of trap is an anion vacancy, that is, a defect lattice position from which a Br^- ion is missing. Defects of this type are particularly abundant at the surface of the crystal or along the edges of dislocations within the crystal where tiny microcrystals intersect each other. High concentrations of vacant anion sites may also be found in the vicinity of impurities in the AgBr crystal. The substitution of a S^{-2} ion for a Br^- ion requires the simultaneous formation of a Br^- ion vacancy in order to maintain electroneutrality. The catalytic effect on latent image formation of small quantities of silver sulfide, Ag_2S, has been attributed to this phenomenon.

3. Trapped electrons, for reasons which are by no means obvious, tend to move close to one another so as to become concentrated within a small region of the silver bromide crystal.

4. These electrons in turn attract loosely held Ag^+ ions to their vicinity. These may be Ag^+ ions located at the crystal surface, along interior dislocations, or in interstitial positions within the AgBr lattice.

5. Ag^+ ions coming in contact with trapped electrons are reduced to silver:

$$Ag^+ + e^- \longrightarrow Ag$$

Clusters of silver atoms formed in this way constitute the latent image.

Development

After a film has been exposed briefly to light, it is treated, in the dark, with a solution of a weak reducing agent referred to as a developer. The silver bromide grains which have been sensitized by exposure are reduced to metallic silver. The development reaction may be represented as:

$$AgBr + e^- \longrightarrow Ag + Br^- \quad (e^- \text{ furnished by reducing agent})$$

The relatively small number of silver atoms constituting the latent image act as a catalyst for this reaction. They facilitate the electron transfer from reducing agent to Ag^+ ion, perhaps by adsorbing from solution the active ingredient of the developing solution.

In regions of the film which were not struck by light during exposure, no silver atoms are available and reaction occurs very slowly. If the film is left in the developing solution too long, the unexposed as well as the sensitized silver bromide is reduced to silver. The same undesirable effect can result from the use of a developer whose reducing strength is too great.

A wide variety of reducing agents may be used as developers. Iron(II) salts, often in the form of complexes, have been used successfully:

$$Fe^{+2} \longrightarrow Fe^{+3} + e^-$$

Hydroxylamine, in basic solution, is effective:

$$H_2NOH + OH^- \longrightarrow 2 H_2O + \tfrac{1}{2} N_2(g) + e^-$$

Most commercial developers employ organic reducing agents such as hydroquinone:

$$C_6H_6O_2 \longrightarrow C_6H_4O_2 + 2 H^+ + 2 e^-$$
$$\text{hydroquinone} \qquad \text{quinone}$$

Fixing

After development, a film shows dark areas of metallic silver where it was exposed to light and light areas of unchanged silver bromide in the regions where light did not reach the film. The remaining silver bromide must be removed so that the finished negative will not be light-sensitive. This is accomplished by dipping the negative into a **fixing bath,** a water solution of sodium thiosulfate, $Na_2S_2O_3$. The silver bromide is dissolved by complex formation:

$$AgBr(s) + 2\ S_2O_3^{-2} \longrightarrow Ag(S_2O_3)_2^{-3} + Br^- \qquad (22.46)$$

This reaction is, of course, reversible. Care must be taken not to allow the concentrations of products to rise to the point where they reprecipitate silver bromide on the film.

Preparation of the Positive

To prepare a positive print, the negative is superimposed over a piece of paper coated with a photographic emulsion. Light is then passed through the negative to the print. The amount of light reaching the print is inversely related to the thickness of the silver deposit on the negative. Subsequent development and fixing of the print gives a picture in which the light and dark areas of the negative are reversed, giving an accurate reproduction of the article being photographed.

One of the most interesting developments in photography in recent years has been an increased emphasis on processes for preparing a positive print directly without going through a negative. One method of doing this involves as a first step the over-exposure of the film. Curiously enough, if photographic film is exposed for somewhat longer than usual, a **reverse image** appears on development. The grains of silver bromide which have been overexposed are less readily reduced than those in the underexposed portions of the film. In development, the underexposed silver bromide is reduced to black, metallic silver while the overexposed portions remain white. This effect is enchanced by using special developers. In this way, a phenomenon once regarded as a nuisance has been converted into a commercially valuable technique of amateur photography. The mechanism of the reverse image effect is not well understood. It is believed, however, that overexposure liberates bromine which acts as an oxidizing agent to inhibit the reduction of silver bromide to silver.

22.7 SUMMARY

Throughout this chapter, the descriptive material concerning oxidation-reduction reactions in water solution has been organized around the properties of the oxidizing agents involved. In reviewing this material, it may be helpful to take the opposite point of view and consider the reducing agents taking part in these reactions. These include: (1) metals which are oxidized to metal cations, (2) metal cations in intermediate oxidation states, and (3) anions.

Metals Which Are Oxidized to Metal Cations

This may be accomplished by:

1. *H^+ ions.* All metals with standard oxidation potentials greater than zero are oxidized by dilute acids to give hydrogen and a solution of the metal salt. Metals

above magnesium in activity are oxidized by water $([H^+] = 10^{-7} M)$, to give hydrogen and a solution of the metal hydroxide.

Cations of metals lower in the activity series. For example, zinc is oxidized by Cu^{+2} ions, giving Zn^{+2} ions and copper metal.

2. O_2. Many metals, of which iron is the most important example, are oxidized on exposure to moist air or immersion in a water solution containing dissolved oxygen. The overall equation for the corrosion of iron is:

$$Fe(s) + \tfrac{1}{2} O_2(g) + H_2O \longrightarrow Fe(OH)_2(s)$$

The iron(II) hydroxide formed is further oxidized to iron(III) hydroxide, $Fe(OH)_3$, on continued exposure to air. The corrosion process ordinarily occurs as two separate half-reactions at different locations on the metal surface. Any factor which tends to create a chemical distinction between adjacent surface areas enhances corrosion. Such factors include differences in dissolved oxygen concentration or contact with a less active metal such as tin or copper.

3. NO_3^- *ions*. Nitric acid oxidizes copper and silver, neither of which react with dilute HCl or H_2SO_4. When a metal reacts with nitric acid, it is the NO_3^- ion which is reduced. The nature of the reduction product depends upon the concentration of the acid and the reduction potential of the metal. Certain active metals such as aluminum and chromium, which are oxidized by dilute HCl or H_2SO_4, are passive to nitric acid.

4. SO_4^{-2} *ions*. Concentrated sulfuric acid reacts with copper to form Cu^{+2} ions and sulfur dioxide. Less active metals such as silver and mercury fail to react.

Metal Cations in Intermediate Oxidation States

These may be classified into two categories:

1. Ions such as Cu^+ which are unstable in solution, undergoing disproportionation:

$$2 Cu^+ \longrightarrow Cu^+ + Cu(s)$$

2. Ions such as Cr^{+2}, Sn^{+2}, and Fe^{+2} which, while stable towards disproportionation, are oxidized by dissolved oxygen, concentrated nitric acid, MnO_4^-, $Cr_2O_7^{-2}$, and so on, to higher oxidation states (Cr^{+3}, Sn^{+4}, Fe^{+3}). Ease of oxidation decreases in the order Cr^{+2} (S.O.P. $= +0.41$ v.) $> Sn^{+2}$ (S.O.P. $= -0.15$ v.) $>$ Fe^{+2} (S.O.P. $= -0.77$ v.).

Anions

1. The halide ions Cl^-, Br^-, I^-; ease of oxidation increases in the order listed. Powerful oxidizing agents such as NO_3^-, $Cr_2O_7^{-2}$, MnO_4^-, or MnO_2 in acidic solution are required to oxidize Cl^- to Cl_2. Iodine is produced from iodide ions by weaker oxidizing agents, including dissolved oxygen, bromine, and Fe^{+3} ions.

2. S^{-2} ions, which are readily oxidized to sulfur (S.O.P. $= +0.48$ v.). Water solutions of hydrogen sulfide are oxidized slowly by air, rapidly by nitric acid. Sulfides of very low solubility, such as CuS, are oxidized by heating with concentrated HNO_3.

3. Certain oxyanions in which the central atom is in an intermediate oxidation state. Two examples are the SO_3^{-2} and NO_2^- ions, which are readily oxidized to SO_4^{-2} and NO_3^- respectively.

A few species do not fit readily into any of these categories. Consider, for example, the NH_4^+ ion, the H_2O_2 molecule and the SO_2 molecule. Each of these can serve as a reducing agent since it contains an atom (N, O, S) in an oxidation state $(-3, -1, +4)$ lower than the maximum for that element $(N = +5, O = 0, S = +6)$. This is the criterion which must be satisfied by any reducing agent, just as any oxidizing agent must contain an atom in an oxidation state higher than the minimum.

PROBLEMS

In answering these problems, use Table 21.1 for the necessary potentials.

22.1　State whether the following species, when taking part in a redox reaction, are capable of acting *only* as oxidizing agents, *only* as reducing agents, or can act as either oxidizing or reducing agents depending upon the circumstances.
　　a. Cl_2　　b. Cl^-　　c. ClO_4^-　　d. N_2　　e. NO_3^-　　f. NH_3

22.2　Give an example of:
　　a. A metal cation which can act only as an oxidizing agent in a redox reaction.
　　b. A metal cation which can act as either an oxidizing or reducing agent.
　　c. An oxyanion which can act only as an oxidizing agent in a redox reaction.
　　d. A nonmetal which can act only as an oxidizing agent in a redox reaction.

22.3　Indicate which of the following metals will react with dilute HCl, and which will react directly with water.
　　a. Mg　　　b. Au　　　c. Zn　　　d. Ba　　　e. Cu

22.4　Describe, in some detail, a suitable method of preparation of the following compounds, starting with the corresponding metals.
　　a. $ZnCl_2$　　b. $Co(NO_3)_2$　　c. $MgBr_2$　　d. $Ca(OH)_2$　　e. $Zn(OH)_2$

22.5　List three metals with which Cu^{+2} ions will react spontaneously.

22.6　In the reaction of excess Sn^{+4} with Cr^{+2}:
　　a. Would you expect to find $Cr_2O_7^{-2}$ among the reaction products?
　　b. Would you expect to find Sn(s) among the products?
　　c. Would your answer to (a) or (b) differ if Cr^{+2} were in excess?

22.7　Solutions containing Sn^{+2}, on exposure to air, slowly form a precipitate of SnO_2.
　　a. Write a balanced equation for the redox reaction involved.
　　b. Explain why this reaction is inhibited by adding tin to the solution.

22.8　Which of the following species would you expect to have a pronounced effect on the oxidizing power of the Ag^+ ion? Explain your answers.
　　a. CN^-　　b. NH_3　　c. NO_3^-　　d. $S_2O_3^{-2}$　　e. H_2O

22.9　Calculate the reduction potential of the Ag^+ ion in a solution 1 M in NH_3 and $Ag(NH_3)_2^+$.

22.10　Explain why:
　　a. Oxygen is a more powerful oxidizing agent in acidic than in neutral solution.
　　b. Solutions of hydrogen sulfide become cloudy on standing.
　　c. Solutions of sodium iodide exposed to air slowly develop a yellow color.
　　d. Solutions of sodium sulfite frequently give a positive test for sulfate ion.

22.11　Write balanced equations to describe the observations of Problem 22.10.

22.12　Explain the following observations regarding corrosion:
　　a. Corrosion occurs more readily in acidic than in neutral solution.
　　b. The presence of dissolved salts increases the rate of corrosion.
　　c. The presence of dissolved air makes corrosion occur more readily.
　　d. A tin can rusts rapidly when punctured while a piece of galvanized zinc does not.
　　e. A piece of steel in contact with a piece of nickel plated steel rusts rapidly at the point of contact.

f. Aluminum, although more active chemically than iron, does not corrode as rapidly.

g. Corrosion of a cast iron pipe passing through acid soil can be prevented by giving it a slight negative charge.

h. A steel bridge support rusts more rapidly at the water line than at any other point.

22.13 Describe, with the aid of balanced equations, how the following compounds can be made from potassium chloride.

a. Cl_2 b. KOH c. $HOCl$ d. $KClO_3$ e. $KClO_4$

22.14 Calculate the change in reduction potential caused by increasing the pH by one unit in the following half-reactions.

a. $\frac{1}{2} O_2(g) + 2 H^+ + 2 e^- \rightarrow H_2O$

b. $NO_3^- + 6 H^+ + 5 e^- \rightarrow \frac{1}{2} N_2(g) + 3 H_2O$

c. $SO_4^{-2} + 8 H^+ + 6 e^- \rightarrow S(s) + 4 H_2O$

d. $MnO_4^- + 8 H^+ + 5 e^- \rightarrow Mn^{+2} + 4 H_2O$

22.15 Balance the following redox equations.

a. $NO_3^- + Ag(s) \rightarrow NO_2(g) + Ag^+$	(acidic solution)
b. $Cr_2O_7^{-2} + I^- \rightarrow Cr^{+3} + I_2$	(acidic solution)
c. $SO_4^{-2} + Br^- \rightarrow SO_2(g) + Br_2$	(acidic solution)
d. $MnO_4^- + Br^- \rightarrow Mn^{+2} + Br_2$	(acidic solution)
e. $MnO_4^- + Fe^{+2} \rightarrow MnO_2(s) + Fe(OH)_3(s)$	(basic solution)

22.16 Explain what is meant by disproportionation. Give examples of reactions in which the species which disproportionates is:

a. A cation   b. An anion   c. A molecule

22.17 Explain why:

a. A color change occurs when an acidic solution of MnO_4^- is treated with Fe^{+2}.

b. A color change occurs when a solution of K_2CrO_4 is acidified.

c. Silver reacts with nitric but not with sulfuric acid.

d. Sodium thiosulfate decomposes in acidic solution.

Write balanced equations to represent the reactions involved in (a) through (d).

22.18 Suppose you wished to prepare $K_2Cr_2O_7$ from $CrCl_3$:

a. Suggest a reason for carrying out this oxidation in basic rather than in acidic solution.

b. Referring to the table of oxidation potentials, what would you select as a suitable oxidizing agent?

c. What would be the product of the oxidation in basic solution? How would you convert this to $K_2Cr_2O_7$?

d. On the basis of your answers to (a), (b), and (c), write balanced net ionic equations for each step involved in the preparation of $K_2Cr_2O_7$ from $CrCl_3$.

22.19 A sample containing Fe^{+2} ions is titrated with $KMnO_4$. It is found that a 2.000 g. sample requires 16.4 ml. of 0.100 M $KMnO_4$ for complete reaction. Calculate the percentage of Fe^{+2} in the sample.

22.20 A solution containing $C_2O_4^{-2}$ ions is titrated with $KMnO_4$. It is found that 12.0 ml. of 0.124 M $KMnO_4$ is required to react with 26.2 ml. of this solution. Calculate the concentration of $C_2O_4^{-2}$ in the solution.

22.21 Explain how an oxidation-reduction indicator works.

22.22 Suggest how the following pairs of ions might be separated with the aid of an oxidizing agent.

a. I^-, Cl^- b. Hg^{+2}, Cu^{+2} c. Cr^{+3}, Fe^{+3}

22.23 Write balanced equations to represent:

a. The reaction which occurs when silver bromide which has been exposed to light is treated with a solution of hydroquinone.

b. The reaction that occurs when silver bromide is treated with a solution of sodium thiosulfate.

*22.24 The gram equivalent weight of an oxidizing agent is defined as the weight that reacts with 1 mole of electrons. Calculate the normality of:

    a. 0.100 M $K_2Cr_2O_7$ when it is reduced to $Cr(III)$.

    b. 0.100 M $KMnO_4$ when it is reduced to Mn^{+2}

    c. 0.100 M $KMnO_4$ when it is reduced to MnO_2.

*22.25 Calculate $E°$ for the reaction represented by equation 22.18 and compare it to the $E°$ value for the same reaction in acidic solution.

*22.26 Consider the following ions: Ag^+, Fe^{+2}, Sn^{+4}, I^-, MnO_4^-. Which of these ions could not be present simultaneously, at ordinary concentrations, in acidic solution?

*22.27 It turns out that an oxidation-reduction indicator should have a standard reduction potential about halfway between that of the oxidizing agent and that of the oxidized form of the reducing agent used in the titration. For example, in the titration of Fe^{+2} with $Cr_2O_7^{-2}$, one should use an indicator with a standard reduction potential midway between that of $Cr_2O_7^{-2}$ and Fe^{+3}, or about 1.05 v. Can you suggest an explanation for this rule? You may wish to consult a textbook on quantitative analysis.

23 | NUCLEAR REACTIONS

23.1 INTRODUCTION

Throughout this text, we have dealt with what might be called "ordinary" chemical reactions, which involve changes in the outer electronic structures of atoms. In this chapter, we shall turn our attention to a quite different type of reaction which produces changes in the nuclear structures of atoms. Before discussing such reactions, it may be helpful to review briefly what we have learned concerning the particle structure of atomic nuclei (cf. Chapter 8).

Nuclear Structure

From a chemical standpoint, the composition of atomic nuclei can be described in terms of two fundamental particles: the proton and the neutron. The proton carries a unit positive charge; the neutron has zero charge. Both particles have a mass of approximately one on the atomic weight scale.

TABLE 23.1 NUCLEAR PARTICLES

Particle	Charge	Mass No.
Proton	+1	1
Neutron	0	1

The simplest nucleus, that of the "light" hydrogen atom, consists of a single proton. All other nuclei contain both protons and neutrons. A "heavy" hydrogen (deuterium) nucleus, for example, contains one proton and one neutron. The number of protons in the nucleus is referred to as the **atomic number**; the **mass number** of a nucleus is found by adding the number of protons and neutrons (Table 23.2). Species having the same atomic number but different mass numbers are referred to as isotopes. Examples include $_1H^1$ and $_1H^2$ or $_{17}Cl^{35}$ and $_{17}Cl^{37}$.

Types of Nuclear Reactions

A nuclear reaction is, by definition, one which results in a change in nuclear composition, i.e., a change in the number of protons and/or neutrons. Nuclear reactions are conveniently classified into four main categories:

TABLE 23.2 COMPOSITION OF NUCLEI

Nuclear Symbol*	Atomic No.	Mass No.	Protons	Neutrons
$_1H^1$	1	1	1	0
$_1H^2$	1	2	1	1
$_2He^4$	2	4	2	2
$_{11}Na^{23}$	11	23	11	12
$_{92}U^{238}$	92	238	92	146

* Recently, nuclear chemists have adopted the convention of showing the mass number as a superscript at the upper left (e.g., $_1^2H$). Throughout this text, the older convention (e.g., $_1H^2$) is followed.

1. **Radioactivity,** in which a nucleus spontaneously disintegrates or **decays** to give a product nucleus of different composition. All the naturally occurring isotopes of the elements beyond bismuth in the periodic table are radioactive, decaying ultimately to a stable isotope of lead. A few radioactive isotopes of the lighter elements, notably $_6C^{14}$, are found in nature. We now have available hundreds of different radioactive isotopes produced artificially in the laboratory; at least one such isotope has been made for every known element.

2. **Bombardment reactions,** in which a small, high-energy particle brings about the decomposition of a nucleus.

3. **Nuclear fission,** in which a heavy nucleus such as $_{92}U^{235}$ or $_{94}Pu^{239}$ interacts with a neutron in such a way as to split into two large fragments of comparable size.

4. **Nuclear fusion,** in which two small nuclei combine to give a heavier nucleus. An example is the fusion of two deuterium nuclei ($_1H^2$) to yield a helium nucleus ($_2He^4$).

Characteristics of Nuclear Reactions

Nuclear reactions differ from ordinary chemical reactions in several respects. Some of the more important differences are listed as follows.

1. In ordinary reactions, the different isotopes of an element show virtually identical chemical properties; in nuclear reactions, they behave quite differently. Consider, for example, two isotopes, $_6C^{12}$ and $_6C^{14}$. Although atoms of these isotopes have the same chemical properties, $_6C^{14}$ is radioactive while $_6C^{12}$ is not.

This difference between nuclear and chemical reactivity is the basis of the use of radioactive isotopes in tracing the path of an element through a series of chemical or physical changes. By incorporating a small amount of $_6C^{14}$ as a tracer into ordinary carbon dioxide, it becomes possible to follow the path of carbon atoms through the complex chain of reactions involved in the photosynthesis process.

2. The ability of an element to take part in a nuclear reaction is essentially independent of its state of chemical combination. For example, in the nuclear chemistry of radium, it makes little difference whether we deal with the element itself or one of its compounds. The radium atom in elementary radium and the Ra^{+2} ion in radium chloride behave similarly from a nuclear standpoint, since their nuclei are identical.

In discussing nuclear reactions or writing equations to represent them, we shall not ordinarily be concerned with what is happening to the electrons outside the nucleus. Even though the particles participating in these reactions may be atomic rather than nuclear species, the reactions themselves take place within the nucleus.

3. Nuclear reactions commonly involve the conversion of one element to another. Whenever a nuclear reaction results in a change in the number of protons in the nucleus, a new element of different atomic number is formed. In contrast, elements taking part in ordinary chemical reactions retain their identity.

Bombardment reactions have proved particularly useful in synthesizing isotopes of elements which do not occur in nature. Thirty years ago, the periodic table ended with uranium (at. no. 92). Below uranium, there were four gaps in the table, corresponding to elements 43, 61, 85, and 87. To be sure, various groups of scientists had reported the discovery of these elements and assigned names to them, but none of these claims had been substantiated. Within a period of about five years, between 1937 and 1942, radioactive isotopes of these elements (technetium, at. no. 43; promethium, at. no. 61; astatine, at. no. 85; francium, at. no. 87) were synthesized in the laboratory. The past quarter century has seen the preparation by Glenn Seaborg and his colleagues at the University of California of a series of transuranium elements (actinides) extending from neptunium (at. no. 93) to lawrencium (at. no. 103).

4. Nuclear reactions as a class are accompanied by energy changes which exceed, by several orders of magnitude, those observed in ordinary chemical reactions. For example, the amount of energy evolved when a gram of radium undergoes radioactive decay is about 500,000 times as great as that given off when an equal amount of radium reacts with chlorine to form radium chloride. Still larger amounts of energy are given off in nuclear fission (Section 23.5) and fusion (Section 23.7).

The high-energy radiation given off by radium has long been used in the treatment of cancer to burn and retard the growth of malignant tissue. More recently, a radioactive isotope of cobalt, $_{29}Co^{60}$, which gives off radiation even more powerful than that of radium, has been used for this purpose. The vast quantities of energy available from nuclear fission and fusion have been utilized in the atomic and hydrogen bombs. On a more hopeful note, we have seen within the past few years the development of nuclear engines and power plants capable of converting the energy of controlled nuclear fission into electrical and mechanical energy.

23.2 NATURAL RADIOACTIVITY

Discovery

The phenomenon of radioactivity was discovered by a French scientist, Henri Becquerel, as a result of some anomalous observations encountered in a study of the fluorescence of uranium salts. Becquerel thought that by exposing these salts to sunlight, he might be able to produce high-energy radiation similar to x-rays. In February of 1896, he wrapped several photographic plates with black paper, covered the paper with a thin layer of potassium uranyl sulfate, $K_2UO_2(SO_4)_2$, and exposed the setups to sunlight for a few hours. Upon developing the plates, he found them to be blackened, exactly as he had expected. However, Becquerel soon discovered to his surprise that plates exposed on cloudy days when there was very little sunlight gave images just as intense as those exposed for an equal amount of time to bright sunlight. Further experiments showed that plates covered with uranium salts were darkened even when they were sealed within an opaque cardboard box put away in a closed locker. From these observations, Becquerel concluded that uranium must spontaneously emit a powerful type of radiation whose existence had not previously been observed or even suspected.

Becquerel, in further studies on the radioactivity of uranium salts, was able to show that the rate at which radiation was emitted from a sample was directly proportional to the amount of uranium present. There was one apparent exception to this rule; a certain uranium ore known as pitchblende gave off radiation at a rate nearly four times as great as one would calculate on the basis of its uranium content. In July of 1898, Marie and Pierre Curie, colleagues of Becquerel at the Sorbonne, were able to isolate from a ton of pitchblende ore a fraction of a gram of a new element which was much more intensely radioactive than uranium. They named this element polonium, after Marie Curie's native country. Six months later, the Curies isolated still another, intensely radioactive, previously unknown element, radium. The Nobel Prize for physics in 1903 was awarded jointly to Henri Becquerel and Marie and Pierre Curie; eight years later, Madame Curie received an unprecedented second Nobel Prize, this time in chemistry.

Properties and Nature of Radiation

The rays given off during radioactive decay possess a high enough energy to interact with matter in several different ways. One of their most important properties

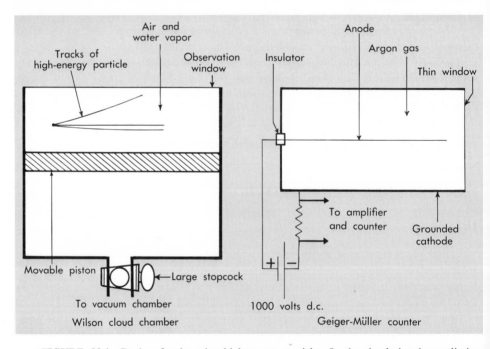

FIGURE 23.1 Devices for detecting high-energy particles. In the cloud chamber radiation ionizes air molecules upon which supersaturated water vapor can condense, producing fog tracks. Supersaturated vapor is produced by suddenly lowering pressure in lower chamber, causing movable piston to fall rapidly. In the Geiger-Müller counter, high-energy particles entering counter through thin window ionize gas molecules, causing an electrical discharge in tube. Successive discharges are counted on automatic recording device.

was discovered by Becquerel, who found that an electroscope could be discharged by bringing it near a radioactive sample. This behavior he correctly attributed to the ability of the radiation to ionize gas molecules with which it comes in contact. The energy associated with the radiation is sufficient to knock electrons out of these molecules, leaving behind a trail of positively charged ions. This property can be demonstrated dramatically in the Wilson cloud chamber (Figure 23.1), where the ions produced serve as nuclei upon which tiny water droplets condense. The instrument which is perhaps most widely used today to measure radiation, the Geiger-Müller counter (Figure 23.1), utilizes this same property.

The radiation emitted by naturally radioactive elements can be split by an electrical or magnetic field into three distinct parts (Figure 23.2):

1. **Alpha rays,** which consist of a stream of positively charged particles (alpha particles) which carry a charge of $+2$ and have a mass of 4 on the atomic weight scale. These particles are, of course, identical with the nuclei of ordinary helium atoms (at. no. 2, mass no. 4). Alpha particles, picking up electrons to form gaseous helium atoms, are readily absorbed by matter; a piece of paper or a sheet of aluminum foil is capable of stopping alpha radiation.

When an alpha particle is ejected from the nucleus, there is a decrease of two units in atomic number and a decrease of four in mass number. For example, the loss of an alpha particle by the nucleus of an ordinary uranium atom (at. no. 92, mass no. 238) gives an isotope of thorium with an atomic number of 90 and a mass number of 234. This nuclear reaction may be represented by the equation:

$$_{92}U^{238} \longrightarrow {}_2He^4 + {}_{90}Th^{234} \tag{23.1}$$

Note that here, as in all nuclear equations, there is a balance of both atomic number $(90 + 2 = 92)$ and mass number $(4 + 234 = 238)$ on the two sides.

2. **Beta rays,** which are made up of a stream of negatively charged particles (beta particles) which have all the properties of electrons. The penetrating power of beta radiation is considerably greater than that of alpha rays; a sheet of aluminum at least 1 cm. thick is required to ensure protection from beta rays.

The ejection of a beta particle (mass $= 0$, charge $= -1$) from a nucleus corresponds to the transformation of a neutron (mass $= 1$, charge $= 0$) into a proton (mass $= 1$, charge $= +1$). Consequently, the emission of a beta particle leaves the

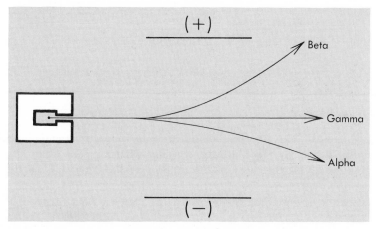

FIGURE 23.2 Deflection in an electric field of rays emitted by naturally radioactive materials.

mass number unchanged but increases the atomic number by one unit. An example of beta-emission is the spontaneous radioactive decay of thorium-234 (90 protons, 144 neutrons) to protactinium-234 (91 protons, 143 neutrons):

$$_{90}\text{Th}^{234} \longrightarrow {}_{-1}\text{e}^{0} + {}_{91}\text{Pa}^{234} \tag{23.2}$$

The symbol $_{-1}\text{e}^{0}$ is written to represent a beta particle (electron).

3. **Gamma rays,** which consist of high-frequency electromagnetic radiation, i.e., high-energy photons (cf. Chapter 5). Gamma rays are much more penetrating than either alpha or beta radiation; they readily pass through a block of concrete several inches thick. Metals of high atomic number are most effective in absorbing gamma radiation; a sheet of lead two inches thick has a stopping power equivalent to a foot of steel.

The emission of gamma rays accompanies virtually all nuclear reactions. It results from an energy change within the nucleus, whereby an unstable, excited nucleus resulting from alpha- or beta-emission gives off a photon and drops to a lower, more stable energy state. Since gamma-emission changes neither the atomic number nor the mass number, we shall frequently neglect it in writing nuclear equations.

TABLE 23.3 URANIUM-238 RADIOACTIVE SERIES*

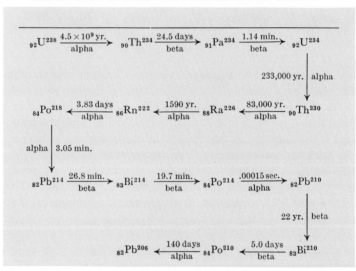

* The times listed in this table are half-lives, discussed in Section 23.3.

Radioactive Series

Natural radioactivity produces many isotopes which are themselves unstable, undergoing further decay. To illustrate, consider what happens when uranium-238 decays (equation 23.1); the thorium-234 isotope produced by this reaction is itself radioactive, decaying via equation 23.2 to protactinium-234. This isotope, like those which preceded it, is unstable, spontaneously decaying by beta-emission:

$$_{91}\text{Pa}^{234} \longrightarrow {}_{-1}\text{e}^{0} + {}_{92}\text{U}^{234} \tag{23.3}$$

The product of this reaction, $_{92}U^{234}$, again decomposes, this time by alpha-emission:

$$_{92}U^{234} \longrightarrow {_2}He^4 + {_{90}}Th^{230} \tag{23.4}$$

The successive decompositions represented by equations 23.1 to 23.4 continue until one finally arrives at a stable isotope, $_{82}Pb^{206}$. A total of 14 separate steps is involved in this series of reactions; eight of those occur by alpha-emission, six by beta-emission. The isotopes in this chain (Table 23.3) compose what is known as a **radioactive series.** For the overall process, one can write the net nuclear equation:

$$_{92}U^{238} \longrightarrow {_{82}}Pb^{206} + 8\ {_2}He^4 + 6\ {_{-1}}e^0 \tag{23.5}$$

The natural radioactive series just described was the first to be discovered; two other series were later found. One of these starts with the less abundant isotope of uranium, $_{92}U^{235}$, and ends with another stable lead isotope, $_{82}Pb^{207}$. The other starts with $_{90}Th^{232}$ and ends with $_{82}Pb^{208}$.

23.3 RATE OF RADIOACTIVE DECAY

The rate at which a radioactive sample decays can be measured by counting the number of particles emitted in a given time. Modern measuring instruments perform this counting automatically. In determining the rate at which a particular isotope decays, one must, of course, be careful not to include counts arising from radio-active "daughter" isotopes produced from the parent. Fortunately, it is usually possible to surmount this problem, either by cleverly designing the experiment so that the daughter isotope is removed as it is formed or by modifying the counting device so that it becomes sensitive to only one of the emitted particles.

One of the most striking generalizations that emerges from rate studies with radioactive isotopes is that the rate of decay is completely independent of temperature. From an experimental standpoint, this eliminates any need for temperature control in rate studies. From a theoretical point of view, it implies that the activation energy for radioactive decay is zero.

Algebraic Rate Law

It was pointed out earlier that the rate at which a radioactive isotope decays is directly proportional to the amount of that isotope present. Putting this statement in the form of an algebraic equation, we have:

$$\frac{\Delta x}{\Delta t} = -cx \tag{23.6}$$

in which x may represent the number of atoms of the radioactive isotope and Δx the number of atoms decaying in time Δt. The c in this equation is a positive number characteristic of the particular isotope but independent of x or t. The minus sign emphasizes that the number of radioactive atoms decreases with time.

Equation 23.6 can be interpreted quite simply in terms of a statistical model of radioactive decay. Let us suppose that there is a fixed probability that an atom of a particular isotope will decompose in a given period of time. Specifically, suppose there is exactly one chance in a thousand that an atom will decompose in one second. In a sample containing, let us say, 300,000 atoms, an average of 300 atoms will decompose per second.

$$300{,}000 \times \frac{1}{1000} = 300 \text{ atoms/sec.}$$

With a sample containing twice as many atoms, 600,000, we would expect twice as many, 600, to decompose in a second.

$$600{,}000 \times \frac{1}{1000} = 600 \text{ atoms/sec.}$$

In general, the number of atoms decaying per second should be directly proportional to the number of atoms in the sample, as predicted by equation 23.6.

Concept of Half-Life

One can look at the rate expression for radioactive decay from a somewhat different but equally important point of view. Equation 23.6 can be rearranged to read:

$$\frac{\Delta x}{x} = -c\Delta t \qquad (23.7)$$

The quantity $\Delta x/x$ clearly represents the fraction of the radioactive sample ($\frac{1}{1000}$, $\frac{1}{100}$, and so on) which decomposes. Equation 23.7 says that this fraction is directly proportional to the time, Δt. Moreover, the equation suggests that the time required for a given fraction of a particular isotope to decay should be a constant. Experimentally, this is found to be the case. In particular, the time required for one half of the radioactivity associated with a particular sample to disappear is found to be independent of the amount of sample. This quantity of time, known as the **half life,** is a fundamental property of a particular isotope.

It may be helpful to consider precisely what is meant when we say that an isotope has a particular half-life. Consider, for example, bismuth-210, with a half-life of five days. If one starts with, let us say, 1 g. of this isotope, $\frac{1}{2}$ g. will be left after 5 days, $\frac{1}{4}$ g. after 10 days, $\frac{1}{8}$ g. after 15 days, and so on (Table 23.4).

TABLE 23.4   RATE OF DECAY OF $_{83}Bi^{210}$ (HALF-LIFE $= 5$ DAYS)

Time (days)	Mass Left (g.)	Mass Decayed (g.)	Fraction Left	Fraction Decayed
0	1.0000	0.0000	1	0
5	0.5000	0.5000	1/2	1/2
10	0.2500	0.7500	1/4	3/4
15	0.1250	0.8750	1/8	7/8
20	0.0625	0.9375	1/16	15/16

Example 23.1.   The half-life of $_{84}Po^{210}$ is 140 days. It decomposes, by alpha-emission, to $_{82}Pb^{206}$:

$$_{84}Po^{210} \rightarrow {}_{82}Pb^{206} + {}_2He^4$$

If one starts with 0.480 g. of $_{84}Po^{210}$:

    a. How many grams of $_{84}Po^{210}$ will be left after 420 days?
    b. How many alpha particles will be emitted in 420 days?
    c. How long will it take to reduce the amount of $_{84}Po^{210}$ to 0.120 g.?

Solution

a. Since the half-life of this isotope is 140 days, 420 days represents three half-lives. Thus, the fraction of $_{84}Po^{210}$ left must be:

$$\tfrac{1}{2} \times \tfrac{1}{2} \times \tfrac{1}{2} = \tfrac{1}{8}$$

Since we started with 0.480 g.: grams left $= \tfrac{1}{8} \times 0.480$ g. $= 0.060$ g.

b. Let us first calculate the number of atoms of polonium decomposed. Then, knowing from the equation that an alpha particle is emitted for every polonium atom that decomposes, we can immediately calculate the number of alpha particles formed.

No. of g. Po decomposed $= 0.480$ g. $- 0.060$ g. $= 0.420$ g.

Since 1 mole Po $= 210$ g., 6.023×10^{23} atoms $= 210$ g.
Hence,

$$\text{no. atoms Po decomposed} = 0.420 \text{ g.} \times \frac{6.023 \times 10^{23} \text{ atoms}}{210 \text{ g.}} = 1.20 \times 10^{21}$$

$$\text{no. alpha particles} = \text{no. atoms Po decomposed} = 1.20 \times 10^{21}$$

c. The fraction of $_{84}Po^{210}$ left is: $0.120/0.480 = 1/4$
Consequently, two half-lives or 280 days must have passed.

Logarithmic Rate Law

In working Example 23.1, we were careful to restrict ourselves to periods of time which represent a whole number of half-lives. Thus, 420 days is exactly three half-lives for $_{84}Po^{210}$; 280 days is exactly two half-lives. The question naturally arises as to how one calculates the amount of a radioactive isotope left in the more general case when the elapsed time is not an integral number of half-lives. How, for example, could one calculate the amount of $_{84}Po^{210}$ left after 100 days? One year?

To make calculations of this type, we need a more general expression for the rate of radioactive decay. Such a relationship can be deduced from data such as that given in Table 23.4. Suppose, out of curiosity perhaps, that we calculate the logarithm of the fraction of bismuth-210 left as a function of time.

TABLE 23.5　LOGARITHMIC DECAY RATE FOR $_{83}Bi^{210}$

Time (in days)	Fraction Left	log (fraction left)
0	1	0.000
5	1/2	−0.301
10	1/4	−0.602
15	1/8	−0.903
20	1/16	−1.204

It should be obvious from Table 23.5 that the logarithm of the fraction of $_{83}Bi^{210}$ left decreases by a constant amount (0.301) in a given time (5 days). Stated another way, the *logarithm of the fraction left is directly proportional to time*:

$$\log(\text{fraction left}) = -kt \qquad (23.8)$$

The minus sign is included in this equation to emphasize that the logarithm of the fraction left decreases with time; the proportionality constant, k, is a positive number whose magnitude depends upon the isotope involved.

Equation 23.8 is most frequently written in the form:

$$\log \frac{x}{x_0} = -kt$$

in which x is the amount left after time t and x_0 the amount originally present at time zero. One can get rid of the minus sign in this expression by making use of the fact that:

$$\log \frac{x_0}{x} = -\log \frac{x}{x_0}$$

Consequently:

$$\log \frac{x_0}{x} = kt \qquad (23.9)$$

Equation 23.9 is the fundamental rate law governing the decay of radioactive isotopes. In order to use it, one must, of course, know the value of k, which is a characteristic of the particular isotope. If the half-life of the isotope is known, k is readily calculated as illustrated by Example 23.2.

Example 23.2. If one starts with 1.000 g. of $_{83}Bi^{210}$ (half-life = five days):
    a. How long will it be before only 0.200 g. of bismuth-210 is left?
    b. After 12 days, how many grams of bismuth-210 will be left?

Solution. In order to use equation 23.9 to solve this problem, we must first evaluate k. This can be done by making use of the fact that after 5 days, one half of the sample remains. In other words, when t = 5 days, $x/x_0 = \frac{1}{2}$ or $x_0/x = 2$. Consequently:

$$\log 2 = k \, (5 \text{ days}) \qquad k = \frac{\log 2}{5 \text{ days}} = \frac{0.301}{5 \text{ days}} = 0.0602/\text{day}$$

Having calculated k, we are now in a position to solve the problem.
    a. Here, $x_0 = 1.000$ g., x = 0.200 g., so we have:

$$\log \frac{1.000}{0.200} = \frac{0.0602}{\text{day}} t$$

$$\text{But } \log \frac{1.000}{0.200} = \log 5.00 = 0.699, \text{ so:}$$

$$0.699 = \frac{0.0602}{\text{day}} t \qquad t = \frac{0.699}{0.0602} \text{ day} = 11.6 \text{ day}$$

    b. In this case,

$$x_0 = 1.000 \text{ g., } t = 12.0 \text{ days}$$

$$\log \frac{1.000 \text{ g.}}{x} = \frac{0.0602}{\text{day}} (12.0 \text{ days}) = 0.722$$

Taking antilogs:

$$\frac{1.000 \text{ g.}}{x} = 5.27 \qquad x = 0.190 \text{ g.}$$

You may well wonder what impulse led us to calculate the logarithm of the amount left, compare it to the time elapsed, and thereby happen upon the logarithmic rate law expressed in equation 23.9. As you may have suspected, it was not done in quite that way. One can start with the rate expression given algebraically by equation 23.7, express it in derivative notation, and apply simple calculus to arrive at equation 23.9. That is

$$\frac{dx}{x} = -c \, dt$$

where dx and dt represent infinitesimal changes in x and t. Integrating between the limits x_0 (the value of x when $t = 0$) and x, we have:

$$\ln \frac{x}{x_0} = -ct \qquad \text{or} \qquad \log \frac{x_0}{x} = \frac{(c)(t)}{2.303}$$

which obviously becomes equivalent to equation 23.9 when $c/2.303 = k$. Those of you who are taking a course in calculus probably wondered all along why we followed such a tortuous path to arrive at the logarithmic rate law.

Age of Rocks

A knowledge of the rate of decay of certain radioactive isotopes makes it possible to estimate the time at which various rock deposits solidified, or, in other words, to estimate their age. To understand how this can be done, consider a uranium-bearing rock, formed billions of years ago at time "zero." The uranium present immediately started to decay, establishing the uranium-238, lead-206 radioactive series. Since the half-lives of all of the intermediate members of that series are very short compared to that of uranium-238 (4.5×10^9 years), virtually all the uranium decaying over a long period of time was converted to the stable, end product of the series, lead-206. It should then be possible, by comparing the quantity of lead-206 produced to that of uranium-238 remaining, to estimate the age of the rock. If, for example, analysis shows that equal numbers of atoms of these two isotopes are present, it follows that one half-life must have passed and that the rock must be 4.5×10^9 (4.5 billion) years old.

This method of estimating the age of mineral deposits assumes, among other things, that none of the $_{82}Pb^{206}$ has become separated from its parent, $_{92}U^{238}$. If atmospheric weathering or some other natural process were to remove one or the other of these elements preferentially, the $_{92}U^{238}:_{82}Pb^{206}$ ratio would, of course, be misleading. One way to correct for such effects is to measure simultaneously the $_{92}U^{235}:_{82}Pb^{207}$ ratio; you may recall that these two isotopes form the beginning and end products of a second radioactive series, with a half-life of 7.1×10^8 years. Although the results of these two methods are not in complete agreement, both indicate the age of the oldest rocks to be in the vicinity of 3.5 billion years. This period of time is often taken as an approximation to the age of the earth.

Age of Organic Material

During the 1950's, Professor W. F. Libby and others worked out a method based on the decay rate of a naturally occurring isotope, carbon-14, to determine the age of organic matter. This method can be applied to objects from a few hundred up to 50,000 years old. It has been used, for example, to check the authenticity of canvases of Renaissance painters and to determine the age of relics left by prehistoric cavemen.

Carbon-14 is produced in the atmosphere by the interaction of neutrons from cosmic radiation with ordinary nitrogen atoms:

$$_7N^{14} + _0n^1 \longrightarrow _6C^{14} + _1H^1 \tag{23.10}$$

The carbon-14 produced by this nuclear reaction is eventually incorporated into the carbon dioxide of the air. A steady-state concentration, amounting to about one atom of carbon-14 for every 10^{12} atoms of carbon-12, is established in atmospheric

CO_2. A living plant, taking in carbon dioxide, has this same $C^{14}:C^{12}$ ratio in the organic compounds that make up its tissues. By the same token, the $C^{14}:C^{12}$ ratio in plant-eating animals or human beings has this same equilibrium value of about $1:10^{12}$.

When a plant or animal dies, the intake of radioactive carbon stops. Consequently, the radioactive decay of carbon-14:

$$_6C^{14} \longrightarrow {}_7N^{14} + {}_{-1}e^0 \text{ (half-life} = 5760 \text{ years)} \qquad (23.11)$$

takes over and the ratio of $C^{14}:C^{12}$ drops. By measuring this ratio and comparing it to that in living plants, one can estimate the time at which the plant or animal died (Example 23.3).

Example 23.3. A piece of wood, believed to be taken from the cross of Christ, is found to have a $C^{14}:C^{12}$ ratio 0.785 times that in a living plant. Estimate the age of the wood.

Solution. To obtain an accurate value for the elapsed time, let us use equation 23.9.

$$\log x_0/x = kt$$

The quantity x, which we may take to be the amount of $_6C^{14}$ now present, is 0.785 of x_0, the amount of $_6C^{14}$ present when the plant died.

$$\log \frac{1.000}{0.785} = 0.105 = kt \qquad \text{or } t = \frac{0.105}{k}$$

To obtain k, we proceed as in Example 23.2, using the fact that when $x = \frac{1}{2}x_0$, $t = 5760$ years, one half-life.

$$k = \frac{\log 2}{5760 \text{ yr.}} = \frac{0.301}{5760 \text{ yr.}} = 5.22 \times 10^{-5}/\text{yr.}$$

Consequently:
$$t = \frac{0.105}{k} = \frac{0.105}{5.22 \times 10^{-5}} \text{ yrs.} = 2010 \text{ yr.}$$

23.4 BOMBARDMENT REACTIONS: ARTIFICIAL RADIOACTIVITY

Prior to 1933, the study of radioactivity was limited to the relatively few radioisotopes which occur in nature. In that year Irene (daughter of Marie and Pierre) Curie and her husband, Frédéric Joliot, discovered the process of artificial radioactivity. By bombarding certain light isotopes with alpha particles, they produced several isotopes of low mass number which were unstable towards radioactive decay. One of the reactions they studied was:

$$_{13}Al^{27} + {}_2He^4 \longrightarrow {}_{15}P^{30} + {}_0n^1 \qquad (23.12)$$

The product of this nuclear reaction, phosphorus-30, is radioactive. It decays by emitting a particle called a *positron*, which has the same mass as the electron but the opposite charge:

$$_{15}P^{30} \longrightarrow {}_{14}Si^{30} + {}_1e^0 \qquad (23.13)$$

Hundreds of different radioactive isotopes have now been produced in the laboratory by bombardment reactions. At least one such isotope has been prepared of every element that occurs in nature; in addition, small quantities of isotopes of at least 15 previously unknown elements have been prepared.

Bombardment Reactions

A large number of different types of bombardment reactions have been carried out in the laboratory; examples of some of the more important types are listed in Table 23.6. It is very difficult to predict in advance exactly what will happen when a small, high-energy particle collides with a stable nucleus. Indeed, it is frequently observed that several different nuclear reactions occur simultaneously. For example, the excited nucleus produced when a deuteron ($_1H^2$) interacts with a copper-63 nucleus ($_{29}Cu^{63}$) may decompose in at least four different ways:

$$_{29}Cu^{63} + {}_1H^2 \begin{cases} {}_{30}Zn^{65} & (23.14) \\ {}_{30}Zn^{64} + {}_0n^1 & (23.15) \\ {}_{30}Zn^{63} + 2\,{}_0n^1 & (23.16) \\ {}_{29}Cu^{64} + {}_1H^1 & (23.17) \end{cases}$$

For obvious reasons, we shall not attempt to discuss the principles which govern the formation of products in bombardment reactions. Nevertheless, it may be helpful to list the particles which are most frequently used to initiate these reactions. They include:

Positively charged particles; protons ($_1H^1$), deuterons ($_1H^2$), alpha particles ($_2He^4$). For a positively charged particle to penetrate an atomic nucleus, which itself carries a positive charge, the particle must be moving at a very high velocity. One can calculate that if protons, deuterons, or alpha particles approaching a nucleus are to overcome the normal Coulombic repulsion, they must be accelerated to energies of several million electron-volts. (An electron-volt is the amount of energy acquired by a particle of unit charge passing through a potential gradient of one volt.) Nuclear physicists and engineers have built several different kinds of instruments for this purpose. One of these, the cyclotron, designed by E. O. Lawrence at the University of California, is shown schematically in Figure 23.3.

Photons (gamma or x-rays). The gamma radiation emitted by radioactive isotopes is too low in energy to initiate more than a handful of nuclear reactions. More effective photons can be produced by allowing high-energy electrons, accelerated in an instrument known as a betatron, to impinge on a tungsten target. In this manner, photons with energies as high as 300 million electron-volts can be produced.

Neutrons. Since a neutron experiences no Coulombic repulsion when it approaches a nucleus, it need have only a very small kinetic energy to initiate a nuclear reaction. So-called "slow" or "thermal" neutrons, with energies of the order of 0.03 to 0.04 ev., are most effective.

Our only source of neutrons is nuclear reactions (cf. equations 23.12, 23.15, 23.16). For many years, a mixture of radium and beryllium served as a standard neutron source; the alpha particles given off by radium brought about the nuclear reaction:

$$_4Be^9 + {}_2He^4 \longrightarrow {}_6C^{12} + {}_0n^1 \qquad (23.18)$$

More recently, nuclear chain reactions utilizing the fission process (Section 23.5) have become the leading source of neutrons.

The effectiveness of the neutron in initiating nuclear reactions may be judged from the fact that every known nucleus save one, the proton, is unstable toward

TABLE 23.6 TYPICAL BOMBARDMENT REACTIONS

Bombarding Particle	Expelled Particle	Example
Proton	$_0n^1$, $_2He^4$, γ	$_{15}P^{31} + {}_1H^1 \rightarrow {}_{16}S^{31} + {}_0n^1$
Deuteron	$_1H^1$, $_2He^4$, $_0n^1$, γ	$_{33}As^{75} + {}_1H^2 \rightarrow {}_{33}As^{76} + {}_1H^1$
Alpha	$_0n^1$, $_1H^1$, $_1H^2$	$_9F^{19} + {}_2He^4 \rightarrow {}_{11}Na^{22} + {}_0n^1$
Photon	$_0n^1$, $_1H^1$	$_{35}Br^{81} + \gamma \rightarrow {}_{35}Br^{80} + {}_0n^1$
Neutron	γ, $_2He^4$, $_1H^1$	$_{34}Se^{82} + {}_0n^1 \rightarrow {}_{34}Se^{83} + \gamma$

neutron bombardment. From a practical standpoint, the most important neutron-induced reaction is that of nuclear fission (Section 23.5), in which certain heavy nuclei, notably uranium-235, are split into two large fragments. Other heavy nuclei, of which uranium-238 is an example, are capable of absorbing low-energy neutrons:

$$_{92}U^{238} + {}_0n^1 \longrightarrow {}_{92}U^{239} + \gamma \qquad (23.19)$$

The product of this reaction, uranium-239, decays by beta-emission to give an isotope of the element of atomic number 93:

$$_{92}U^{239} \longrightarrow {}_{93}Np^{239} + {}_{-1}e^0 \qquad (23.20)$$

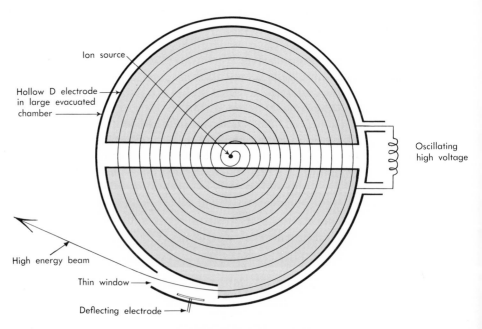

FIGURE 23.3 The cyclotron consists of two oppositely charged, evacuated "dees" placed between the poles of a powerful electromagnet. Positive ions, originating at the center, enter the upper dee, which is originally at a negative potential. They pass through this dee in a curved path. At the instant they reenter the central corridor, the polarity of the dees is reversed, and the particles enter the lower dee at an increased velocity. This procedure is repeated over and over; the particles move at higher and higher velocities in paths of greater and greater radius. Eventually they are deflected from the periphery of one of the dees to strike the target.

which in turn decomposes, again by beta-emission:

$$_{93}Np^{239} \longrightarrow {_{94}Pu^{239}} + {_{-1}e^0} \tag{23.21}$$

Elements 93 and 94, the first two transuranium elements, were discovered by McMillan and Seaborg at Berkeley in 1940. They were named neptunium and plutonium, after the two planets lying beyond Uranus in the solar system.

Decay of Artificially Produced Radioactive Isotopes

Over a thousand radioactive isotopes have been prepared by the various types of bombardment reactions just discussed. Each of these decays to one or another of the approximately 270 stable isotopes of elements ranging from hydrogen (at. no. 1) to bismuth (at. no. 83). The ratio of neutrons to protons required for stability varies with atomic number (Figure 23.4), but in any given region of the periodic table is restricted within very narrow limits. The way in which an artificially radioactive isotope decays depends upon whether its neutron-to-proton ratio is greater or less than that required for stability.

Neutron-to-proton ratio too high. An isotope whose nucleus has too many neutrons, i.e., a neutron-to-proton ratio above that required for stability, can become more stable if one of the neutrons in its nucleus is converted to a proton. Such a conversion results in the formation of an electron, which is ejected from the nucleus:

$$neutron \longrightarrow proton + electron$$

Beta-emission can be expected to occur whenever the neutron-to-proton ratio is too high; this is almost always the case when the *mass number of the radioactive isotope is greater than the average atomic weight of the element.* Examples include the beta-decay of

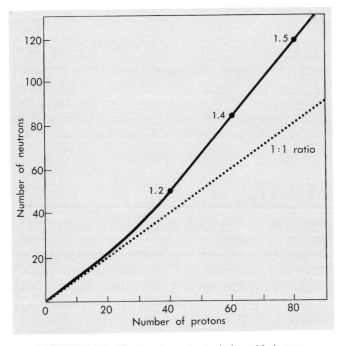

FIGURE 23.4 Neutron-to-proton ratio in stable isotopes.

$_9\text{F}^{20}$ (at. wt. F $= 19.0$) and $_6\text{C}^{14}$ (at. wt. C $= 12$):

$$_9\text{F}^{20} \longrightarrow {}_{10}\text{Ne}^{20} + {}_{-1}e^0 \tag{23.22}$$

$$_6\text{C}^{14} \longrightarrow {}_7\text{N}^{14} + {}_{-1}e^0 \tag{23.23}$$

In both these reactions, beta-emission from the nucleus converts a neutron into a proton, leaving the mass number unchanged but increasing the atomic number by one unit.

Neutron-to-proton ratio too low. A neutron-deficient nucleus tends to change in such a way that a proton is replaced by a neutron. This ordinarily happens with a radio-active isotope whose *mass number is less than the average atomic weight of the element.* It may come about in either of two ways: by emission of a positron or by orbital electron capture.

    1.   emission of a positron: proton $\longrightarrow$ neutron + positron

This mode of decay is prevalent with the light isotopes of elements of low atomic number. Examples include:

$$_7\text{N}^{13} \longrightarrow {}_6\text{C}^{13} + {}_1e^0 \tag{23.24}$$

$$_{16}\text{S}^{31} \longrightarrow {}_{15}\text{P}^{31} + {}_1e^0 \tag{23.25}$$

In both these reactions, a proton is converted to a neutron, leaving the mass number unchanged but decreasing the atomic number by one unit. The particle emitted, called a positron, has a charge opposite to that of an electron but the same mass.

    2.   orbital electron capture: proton + electron $\longrightarrow$ neutron

Nuclei of too light isotopes of elements of relatively high atomic number tend to decay by capturing orbital electrons. The electron which falls into the nucleus is ordinarily one in the K shell, closest to the nucleus, hence the name *K electron capture* to describe this type of reaction. Examples include:

$$_{37}\text{Rb}^{82} + {}_{-1}e^0 \longrightarrow {}_{36}\text{Kr}^{82} \tag{23.26}$$

$$_{47}\text{Ag}^{105} + {}_{-1}e^0 \longrightarrow {}_{46}\text{Pd}^{105} \tag{23.27}$$

The nuclear transformation resulting from K-capture is the same as that observed with positron emission; in both cases, a proton in the nucleus is converted to a neutron. In K-capture, as soon as a vacancy is created in the energy level closest to the nucleus, electrons move in from successively higher levels to fill this vacancy. The excess energy involved in this electronic transition is ordinarily given off in the form of x-rays.

23.5   NUCLEAR FISSION

Discovery

Shortly before World War II, several groups of scientists were studying the products obtained by bombarding uranium with neutrons, in hopes of discovering new elements. In 1938, two German chemists, Hahn and Strassman, isolated from the products a compound of a group 2A element, which they originally believed to be radium (at. no. 88). Subsequent work by a group led by Irene Joliot-Curie indicated that this element was really barium (at. no. 56). Hahn's first reaction to this discovery was one of disbelief; he later stated, in January of 1939, "$\cdots$ As chemists, we should replace the symbol Ra · · · by Ba · · · [but], as nuclear chemists, closely associated with physics, we cannot decide to take this step in contradiction to all previous experience in nuclear physics."

If Hahn was reluctant to admit the possibility of an entirely new type of nuclear reaction, a former colleague of his, Lisa Meitner, was not. In a letter published with O. R. Frisch in January of 1939, she stated: "At first sight, this result seems very hard to understand . . . . On the basis, however, of present ideas about the behavior of heavy nuclei, an entirely different picture of these new disintegration processes suggests itself. . . . It seems possible that the uranium nucleus . . . may, after neutron capture, divide itself into nuclei of roughly equal size." This revolutionary suggestion was quickly substantiated by experiments carried out in laboratories all over the world. The process by which uranium or other heavy elements split under neutron impact into smaller fragments was called **fission,** following a suggestion of Lisa Meitner.

Fissionable Isotopes

Several isotopes of the heavy elements, including platinum, gold, mercury, and lead, are capable of undergoing fission if bombarded by neutrons of sufficiently high energy. In practice, attention has centered upon two particular isotopes, $_{92}U^{235}$ and $_{94}Pu^{239}$, both of which can be split into fragments by low-energy neutrons. These are the two isotopes which have been used in the manufacture of atomic bombs. During World War II, several different processes were worked out for the separation of uranium-235 from the more abundant isotope, uranium-238, which makes up 99.3 per cent of naturally occurring uranium. The most successful separation technique was that of gaseous diffusion, described in Chapter 6. The element plutonium does not occur in nature; the 239-isotope is made from uranium-238 by the sequence of reactions described by equations 23.19 to 23.21.

Most of the available data on fission reactions has to do with uranium-235. For this reason, our discussion from this point on will concentrate upon the nuclear reactions that take place when a $_{92}U^{235}$ nucleus interacts with a neutron:

$$_{92}U^{235} + _{0}n^1 \longrightarrow \text{products} + \text{energy}$$

Fission Products

When a uranium-235 atom undergoes fission, it splits into two smaller fragments whose atomic numbers add up to 92. The fission process is complicated by the fact that different uranium-235 atoms split up in different ways. For example, while one atom of $_{92}U^{235}$ is splitting to give isotopes of rubidium (at. no. 37) and cesium (at. no. 55), another may break up to give isotopes of bromine (at. no. 35) and lanthanum (at. no. 57), while still another atom yields isotopes of zinc (at. no. 30) and samarium (at. no. 62). The fission of a macroscopic sample of uranium-235, containing billions of billions of atoms, gives a large number of products; at least 200 isotopes of 25 different elements have been identified among the fission products of uranium-235.

A rather curious fact emerges if one plots the relative amounts of various fission products as a function of mass number (Figure 23.5). Two distinct maxima show up in such a plot, one at a mass number of about 95, the other at mass 140. In other

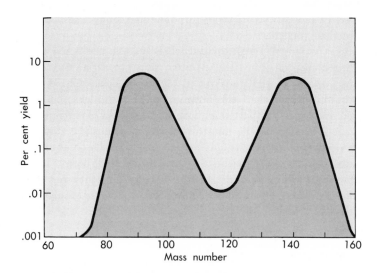

FIGURE 23.5 Distribution of fission products from uranium-235.

words, uranium-235 atoms tend to split into fragments one of which is roughly 50 per cent heavier than the other. Only about one out of every thousand atoms splits into fragments of equal mass (mass no. ≈ 117).

It will be recalled from our discussion of artificial radioactivity (Section 23.4) that the stable neutron-to-proton ratio near the middle of the periodic table, where the fission products are located, is considerably smaller (~ 1.2) than that for the very heavy elements such as uranium (~ 1.5). Consequently, the immediate products of the fission process, such as $_{37}Rb^{90}$ and $_{55}Cs^{144}$, contain too many neutrons for stability. These isotopes are radioactive, decaying by electron emission. In the case of rubidium-90, three steps are required to reach a stable nucleus:

$$_{37}Rb^{90} \longrightarrow {_{38}}Sr^{90} + {_{-1}}e^0 \text{ (very short half-life)} \tag{23.28}$$

$$_{38}Sr^{90} \longrightarrow {_{39}}Y^{90} + {_{-1}}e^0 \text{ (half-life = 25 yr.)} \tag{23.29}$$

$$_{39}Y^{90} \longrightarrow {_{40}}Zr^{90} + {_{-1}}e^0 \text{ (half-life = 65 yr.)} \tag{23.30}$$

The radiation hazard associated with nuclear testing arises from the formation of radioactive isotopes such as these. One of the most dangerous of these isotopes is strontium-90, which, in the form of strontium carbonate, is readily incorporated into the bones of animals and human beings.

Neutron Emission: Nuclear Chain Reactions

The early investigators showed that considerable numbers of neutrons were emitted in the fission process. Indeed, it is found that, on the average, about two to three neutrons are liberated for every neutron absorbed in bringing about fission. Two typical fission reactions might be represented as:

$$_{92}U^{235} + {_0}n^1 \begin{cases} \longrightarrow {_{37}}Rb^{90} + {_{55}}Cs^{144} + 2\,{_0}n^1 & \tag{23.31} \\ \\ \longrightarrow {_{35}}Br^{87} + {_{57}}La^{146} + 3\,{_0}n^1 & \tag{23.32} \end{cases}$$

The neutrons which are liberated as the result of fission are, of course, capable of causing other uranium-235 nuclei to undergo fission. Since two to three neutrons are evolved for every one absorbed, the necessary condition for a chain reaction exists. Once a few atoms of uranium-235 split up, the neutrons produced can bring about the fission of many more uranium-235 atoms, which in turn yield more neutrons, capable of splitting more uranium atoms, and so on. This is, of course, precisely what happens in the atomic bomb; the energy evolved in successive fissions escalates to give, within a few seconds, a tremendous explosion.

In order to ensure that nuclear fission will occur by a chain reaction, it is important that the uranium-235 sample be large enough so that most of the neutrons will be captured internally. If the sample is too small, too many of the neutrons produced by individual fissions will escape from the surface, thereby breaking the chain. The **critical mass** of uranium-235 required to maintain a nuclear chain reaction has been variously estimated at from 2 to 200 lb.; an educated guess would put it in the neighborhood of 20 lb. The problem in designing an atomic bomb is to bring together, at the time of explosion, two samples of subcritical size whose total mass exceeds the critical mass. One way to do this would be to use an ordinary explosive to fire one sample into the other.

Evolution of Energy: Nuclear Reactors

Some idea of the vast amount of energy available from nuclear fission may be obtained by comparing it to the energy evolved in ordinary chemical reactions. The fission of 1 g. of uranium-235 evolves about 20,000,000 kcal. of energy. The heat of combustion of coal is only about 8 kcal./g.; the energy given off when 1 g. of TNT explodes is still smaller, about 0.66 kcal. Putting it another way, the fission of 1 g. of uranium produces as much energy as the combustion of 5500 lb. of coal or the explosion of 33 tons of TNT. The enormous energy change accompanying nuclear fission is directly attributable to the change in mass that takes place in the fission process (Section 23.6).

Even before the first atomic bomb was exploded, scientists and politicians had begun to speculate on the use of nuclear fission as a source of energy for peaceful purposes. Many nuclear reactors, in which the fission reaction is made to occur at a controlled rate, have been designed to meet this need. The simplest type of reactor consists of lumps of uranium separated from each other by blocks of a neutron-moderating material such as graphite. To prevent the fission reaction from getting out of control, reactors are designed so that bars of graphite or cadmium, an excellent neutron absorber, can be inserted into the apparatus.

The energy produced by a nuclear reactor is given off primarily as heat. The construction of engines to convert this heat to mechanical or electrical energy poses special problems in engineering and metallurgy. The metals used in the engine must be immune to neutron attack and capable of withstanding high temperatures. Despite these difficulties, we have seen in the past decade the development of the nuclear submarine and the establishment of several nuclear power plants in various parts of the world.

From a long-range standpoint, it seems unlikely that uranium-235 will, by itself, make an important contribution to our future power needs. It has been estimated that the fission of all the uranium-235 that is known to exist in nature could fulfill our energy needs for one century at the most. A much more attractive possibility is to use uranium-235 as a neutron source to convert the more abundant isotope, uranium-238, to plutonium-239, which can then undergo fission. So-called breeder reactors based on this principle have been in existence for many years; the problem is to increase the yield of plutonium to the point at which the process becomes feasible on a large scale. Ultimately, the hope is to build breeder reactors capable of producing large quantities of fissionable isotopes from more abundant elements such as thorium, lead, and mercury.

23.6 MASS-ENERGY RELATIONS

The source of the energy evolved in a nuclear reaction is the mass change that occurs simultaneously. These two quantities are related by Einstein's equation:

$$\Delta E = \Delta mc^2$$

in which Δm is the change in mass,* ΔE the change in energy, and c the velocity of light. If one substitutes for c its value in cm./sec. (3.0×10^{10} cm./sec.) and for Δm the mass change in grams, the energy change, ΔE, is obtained in ergs since:

$$1 \text{ erg} = 1 \text{ g.} \times 1 \frac{\text{cm.}^2}{\text{sec.}^2}$$

Thus, if 1 g. of mass is "lost" in a reaction, 9.0×10^{20} ergs of energy are evolved.

In dealing with nuclear reactions, we are frequently interested in obtaining ΔE in units other than ergs. In particular, we may wish to calculate ΔE in kilocalories or in *millions of electron volts* (mev.). Again, it is often convenient to express the mass change in moles or in *atomic mass units* (amu.).† To facilitate calculations involving mass-energy conversions, it is useful to have available a series of conversion factors such as those given in Table 23.7.

TABLE 23.7 MASS-ENERGY CONVERSION FACTORS

Type of Conversion	To Convert From:	to	Multiply by
mass-mass	grams	amu.	6.02×10^{23}
	moles	grams	G.F.W.
energy-energy	ergs	kcal.	2.39×10^{-11}
	ergs	mev.	6.24×10^5
mass-energy	grams	ergs	9.00×10^{20}
	grams	kcal.	2.15×10^{10}
	amu.	mev.	9.31×10^2

* Specifically, Δm = mass products − mass reactants; ΔE = energy products − energy reactants. In most nuclear reactions, the products weigh less than the reactants (Δm negative); in this case, the energy of the products is less than that of the reactants (ΔE negative), and energy is evolved to the surroundings.

† An atomic mass unit is defined as exactly $\frac{1}{12}$ of the mass of a carbon-12 atom. This means that the mass of a particle in atomic mass units is numerically equal to its atomic weight on the carbon-12 scale. Thus, the proton (at. wt. = 1.00728) has a mass of 1.00728 amu.; the alpha particle (at. wt. = 4.00150) has a mass of 4.00150 amu., and so on.

Calculations Involving Mass-Energy Conversions

Using the appropriate conversion factors given in Table 23.7 in conjunction with the appropriate isotopic masses (Table 23.8), it is possible to calculate the energy change accompanying any nuclear reaction. Example 23.4 illustrates the calculations involved.

Example 23.4. For the nuclear reaction: $_{88}Ra^{226} \rightarrow {}_{86}Rn^{222} + {}_2He^4$
   a. Calculate ΔE, in mev., when one atom of radium decays.
   b. Calculate ΔE, in ergs, when one mole of radium decays.
   c. Calculate ΔE, in kcal. when one g. of radium decays.

Solution
   a. We shall first calculate Δm, in amu., and then convert this to energy in mev.

$$\Delta m = \text{mass } {}_2He^4 + \text{mass } {}_{86}Rn^{222} - \text{mass } {}_{88}Ra^{226}$$

$$= 4.0015 \text{ amu.} + 221.9703 \text{ amu.} - 225.9771 \text{ amu.}$$

$$= -0.0053 \text{ amu.}$$

(Note that Δm is extremely small; it is necessary to know the masses of the various particles very accurately to obtain an answer accurate to two significant figures.)

$$\Delta E = -0.0053 \text{ amu.} \times 931 \frac{\text{mev.}}{\text{amu.}} = -4.9 \text{ mev.}$$

i.e., 4.9 mev. of energy are *evolved* when an atom of radium decays.

   b. Here, we calculate the mass change in grams and convert to ergs:

$$\Delta m = \text{mass 1 mole } {}_2He^4 + \text{mass 1 mole } {}_{86}Rn^{222} - \text{mass 1 mole } {}_{88}Ra^{226}$$

$$= 4.0015 \text{ g.} + 221.9703 \text{ g.} - 225.9771 \text{ g.} = -0.0053 \text{ g.}$$

(Note that Δm in grams for the decay of a mole of radium is numerically equal to Δm in amu. for the decay of one atom of radium.)

$$\Delta E = -0.0053 \text{ g.} \times 9.0 \times 10^{20} \text{ ergs/g.} = -4.8 \times 10^{18} \text{ ergs}$$

i.e., 4.8×10^{18} ergs of energy are *evolved* when a mole of radium decays.

   c. Perhaps the simplest way to analyze this problem is to recall from b that the decay of 1 mole ($\sim$226 g.) of $_{88}Ra^{226}$ resulted in the loss of 0.0053 g. of mass; i.e., $\Delta m = -0.0053$ g. when 226 g. of Ra decays. Accordingly, when 1 g. of Ra decays:

$$\Delta m = \frac{-0.0053 \text{ g.}}{226} = -2.3 \times 10^{-5} \text{ g.}$$

$$\Delta E = -2.3 \times 10^{-5} \text{ g.} \times 2.15 \times 10^{10} \text{ kcal./g.} = -4.9 \times 10^5 \text{ kcal.}$$

(Note that while this amount of energy is vastly greater than that evolved in an ordinary chemical reaction, it is significantly less than the energy evolved in nuclear fission (about 2×10^7 kcal./g.).)

Nuclear Stability: Binding Energy

In Chapter 5, it was pointed out that the energy change in an ordinary chemical reaction reflects the difference in stability between products and reactants. If the products are more stable than the reactants, energy is evolved. If a reaction absorbs energy, we deduce that the products are less stable than the reactants. We can, of

TABLE 23.8 NUCLEAR MASSES IN ATOMIC MASS UNITS*

	At. No.	Mass No.	Mass		At. No.	Mass No.	Mass
n	0	1	1.00867	Br	35	79	78.8992
H	1	1	1.00728		35	81	80.8971
	1	2	2.01355	Kr	36	88	87.8944
	1	3	3.01550	Rb	37	89	88.8909
He	2	3	3.01493	Sr	38	90	89.8864
	2	4	4.00150	Mo	42	99	98.8849
Li	3	6	6.01348	Ru	44	106	105.8829
	3	7	7.01436	Ag	47	109	108.8789
Be	4	9	9.00999	Cd	48	109	108.8786
	4	10	10.01134		48	115	114.8793
B	5	10	10.01019	Sn	50	120	119.8747
	5	11	11.00656	I	53	130	129.8776
C	6	11	11.00814		53	136	135.8856
	6	12	11.99671	Pr	59	144	143.8807
	6	13	13.00006	Sm	62	152	151.8853
	6	14	13.99995	Eu	63	157	156.8914
O	8	16	15.99052	Er	68	168	167.8941
	8	17	16.99474	Hf	72	179	178.9048
	8	18	17.99477	W	74	186	185.9107
F	9	18	17.99601	Os	76	192	191.9187
	9	19	18.99346	Au	79	196	195.9231
Na	11	23	22.98373	Hg	80	196	195.9219
Mg	12	24	23.97845	Pb	82	206	205.9295
	12	25	24.97925		82	207	206.9309
	12	26	25.97600		82	208	207.9316
Al	13	26	25.97977	Po	84	210	209.9368
	13	27	26.97439		84	218	217.9628
	13	28	27.97477	Rn	86	222	221.9703
Si	14	28	27.96924	Ra	88	226	225.9771
S	16	32	31.96329	Th	90	230	229.9837
Cl	17	35	34.95952	Pa	91	234	233.9934
	17	37	36.95657	U	92	233	232.9890
Ar	18	40	39.95250		92	235	234.9934
K	19	39	38.95328		92	238	238.0003
	19	40	39.95358		92	239	239.0038
Ca	20	40	39.95162	Np	93	239	239.0019
Ti	22	48	47.93588	Pu	94	239	239.0006
Cr	24	52	51.92734		94	241	241.0051
Fe	26	56	55.92066	Am	95	241	241.0045
Co	27	59	58.91837	Cm	96	242	242.0061
Ni	28	59	58.91897	Bk	97	245	245.0129
Zn	30	64	63.91268	Cf	98	248	248.0186
	30	72	71.91128	Es	99	251	251.0255
Ge	32	76	75.90380	Fm	100	252	252.0278
As	33	79	78.90288		100	254	254.0331

* Note that these are *nuclear masses*. The masses of the corresponding atoms can be calculated by adding the mass of the extranuclear electrons (mass of electron = 0.000549 amu.). For example, the mass of an *atom* of $_2He^4$ is:

$$4.00150 \text{ amu.} + 2(0.000549) \text{ amu.} = 4.00260 \text{ amu.}$$

Similarly, the mass of an atom of $_6C^{12}$ is:

$$11.99671 \text{ amu.} + 6(0.000549) \text{ amu.} = 12.00000 \text{ amu.}$$

course, apply the same interpretation to nuclear reactions. Referring to Example 23.4, the evolution of energy in the nuclear reaction:

$$_{88}Ra^{226} \longrightarrow {}_{86}Rn^{222} + {}_{2}He^{4}$$

means that the products, an alpha particle and a radon-222 nucleus, are more stable than the reactants, a radium-226 nucleus.

It is of considerable interest to compare the relative stabilities of different nuclei. One of the most straightforward ways to do this is to compare the masses of nuclei to those of the individual protons and neutrons of which they are composed. It is found experimentally that the mass of every nucleus containing neutrons and protons is less than that of the isolated particles themselves. Consider, for example, the $_{2}He^{4}$ nucleus:

$$\text{mass 2 protons} = 2(1.00728) \text{ amu.} = 2.01456 \text{ amu.}$$
$$\text{mass 2 neutrons} = 2(1.00867) \text{ amu.} = 2.01734 \text{ amu.}$$
$$\overline{\; 4.03190 \text{ amu.}}$$

$$\text{mass } _{2}He^{4} = 4.00150 \text{ amu.}$$

In this case, there is a decrease in mass of $(4.03190 - 4.00150)$ amu. $= 0.03040$ amu. when a helium nucleus is formed from two protons and two neutrons. This decrease in mass, called the **mass decrement,** can be calculated for any isotope whose nuclear mass is known. A series of mass decrements, calculated for a few typical isotopes, is given in Table 23.9.

TABLE 23.9 BINDING ENERGIES OF VARIOUS NUCLEI

	Mass Decrement	Binding Energy (mev.)	Binding Energy per Nucleon (mev.)
$_{1}H^{2}$	0.00239	2.22	1.11
$_{2}He^{3}$	0.00829	7.72	2.57
$_{2}He^{4}$	0.0304	28.3	7.07
$_{3}Li^{7}$	0.0421	39.2	5.60
$_{5}B^{10}$	0.0695	64.7	6.47
$_{6}C^{12}$	0.0989	92.1	7.67
$_{13}Al^{27}$	0.2415	224.8	8.33
$_{27}Co^{59}$	0.5555	517.2	8.77
$_{42}Mo^{99}$	0.9146	851.6	8.60
$_{63}Eu^{157}$	1.3815	1286	8.19
$_{80}Hg^{196}$	1.6653	1550	7.91
$_{92}U^{238}$	1.9342	1801	7.57

The fact that the formation of a nucleus from protons and neutrons involves a decrease in mass means that any nucleus is stable toward decomposition into these particles. Consider, for example, the helium-4 nucleus; in order to break this up into two protons and two neutrons, one would have to add 0.03040 amu. of mass. This would, of course, require the absorption of a large amount of energy. The quantity of energy which would have to be absorbed to decompose a nucleus into protons and neutrons is referred to as the **binding energy** of the nucleus. The binding energy, in mev., is readily calculated from the mass decrement, making use of the conversion factor: 931 mev. = 1 amu. For the $_2\text{He}^4$ nucleus:

$$\text{binding energy (mev.)} = \text{mass decrement (amu.)} \times 931 \, \frac{\text{mev.}}{\text{amu.}}$$

$$= 0.0304 \text{ amu.} \times 931 \, \frac{\text{mev.}}{\text{amu.}} = 28.3 \text{ mev.}$$

We can interpret this binding energy to mean that the decomposition of a helium-4 nucleus (an alpha particle) into protons and neutrons would require the absorption of 28.3 mev. of energy. Conversely, 28.3 mev. would be evolved if an alpha particle were formed from two protons and two neutrons.

It will be noted from Table 23.9 that binding energy increases steadily as the number of protons and neutrons in the nucleus increases. One might indeed expect this to be the case; the more particles there are in the nucleus, the greater should be the total amount of energy required to break the nucleus apart. One can gain a better idea of the relative stabilities of different nuclei by calculating the binding energy per nuclear particle. For the $_2\text{He}^4$ nucleus, which contains a total of four nuclear particles (nucleons):

$$\text{binding energy per nucleon} = \frac{\text{binding energy}}{\text{no. nucleons}} = \frac{28.3 \text{ mev.}}{4} = 7.07 \text{ mev.}$$

Looking at the last column of Table 23.9, we note that the binding energy per nucleon is relatively small for very light isotopes such as $_1\text{H}^2$ and $_2\text{He}^3$. It rises to a maximum of about 9 mev. with isotopes of intermediate mass number such as cobalt-59 and copper-63. The binding energy per nucleon then falls off slowly to about 7.5 mev. for the very heavy elements such as uranium (Figure 23.6).

If we take the binding energy per nucleon to be a measure of the relative stability of a nucleus, it is obvious from Figure 23.6 that the most stable nuclei are those of intermediate mass such as $_{27}\text{Co}^{59}$, located near the broad maximum of the curve. Nuclei of very heavy elements such as uranium, which have comparatively low

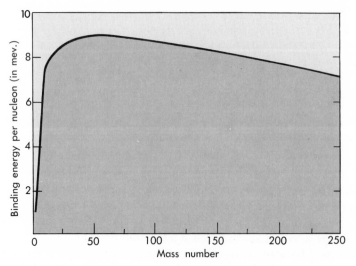

FIGURE 23.6   Relative stability of nuclei.

binding energies, should be unstable with respect to splitting into smaller nuclei. This conclusion, of course, is confirmed experimentally. The tremendous amount of energy evolved in the fission process is explained by the fact that the reactant atoms ($_{92}U^{235}$, for example) are less stable than the fragments ($_{37}Rb^{90}$, $_{55}Cs^{144}$, and so on) into which they split.

23.7   NUCLEAR FUSION

Referring again to Figure 23.6, let us concentrate our attention upon the early portion of the curve. It will be noted that the binding energy per nucleon rises very sharply from the isotopes of hydrogen to those of somewhat heavier elements such as helium, lithium, or boron. This suggests that it should be possible to obtain large amounts of energy by fusing hydrogen nuclei together to form heavier nuclei. Indeed, the energy available from nuclear fusion is considerably greater than that obtained from the fission of an equal mass of a very heavy element.

Some typical fusion reactions are:

$$_1H^2 + {}_1H^2 \longrightarrow {}_2He^4 \tag{23.33}$$

$$_1H^2 + {}_1H^3 \longrightarrow {}_2He^4 + {}_0n^1 \tag{23.34}$$

$$_1H^3 + {}_1H^3 \longrightarrow {}_2He^4 + 2\,{}_0n^1 \tag{23.35}$$

The energies evolved in these reactions, per gram of fusionable material, are respectively 14×10^7 kcal., 8.1×10^7 kcal., and 4.3×10^7 kcal. These compare favorably to the energy available from the fission of 1 g. of uranium-235, about 2×10^7 kcal.

It is believed that fusion reactions such as those represented by equations 23.33 to 23.35 take place on the sun at a temperature of several millions of degrees, serving as the ultimate source of solar energy. Within the past decade, man has learned how to use nuclear fusion in the hydrogen (thermonuclear) bomb. The technology of this super-bomb is quite different from that of the fission bomb. Since neutrons are not necessary to bring about fusion, there is no critical mass; hydrogen bombs may be of any size. On the other hand, extremely high temperatures must be attained before reactions such as 23.33 to 23.35 can occur rapidly; in other words, the fusion process has a very high activation energy. The fission reaction may be used to reach these temperatures; an atomic bomb can serve as a trigger to set off a thermonuclear explosion.

PROBLEMS

23.1   Explain what is meant by the following terms:
   a. Isotopes   f. Radioactive series   k. mev.
   b. Bombardment reaction   g. Half life   l. amu.
   c. Fission   h. Cyclotron   m. Mass decrement
   d. Fusion   i. Cloud chamber   n. Binding energy
   e. Beta ray   j. Critical mass   o. Tracer

23.2   Give the number of protons and the number of neutrons in the nucleus of:
   a. $_6C^{14}$ b. $_{29}Cu^{63}$ c. $_8O^{18}$

23.3   Explain why:
       a. $_6C^{14}$ shows the same chemical reactivity as $_6C^{12}$.
       b. So far as nuclear reactivity is concerned, radioactive Na^+ ions behave in the same
       way as radioactive Na atoms.
       c. A nuclear reaction frequently results in the conversion of one element to another.

23.4   Explain the principle of operation of the following instruments.
       a. Wilson cloud chamber   c. Cyclotron
       b. Geiger-Müller counter   d. Betatron

23.5   Write balanced nuclear equations for:
       a. The loss of an alpha particle by a $_{88}Ra^{224}$ nucleus.
       b. The loss of a beta particle by a $_5B^{12}$ nucleus.
       c. The emission of gamma radiation by $_{34}Se^{83}$.

23.6   A certain radioactive series starts with $_{92}U^{235}$ and ends with $_{82}Pb^{207}$. The particles
       given off are, in succession, $\alpha, \beta, \alpha, \alpha, \beta, \alpha, \alpha, \alpha, \beta, \beta, \alpha$. Write balanced nuclear equations
       for each step in the process.

23.7   A certain radioactive series starts with $_{94}Pu^{241}$ and ends with $_{83}Bi^{209}$. What are the total
       numbers of alpha and beta particles given off in this series?

23.8   The half-life of $_{33}As^{72}$ is 26 hours. If one starts with a sample of this isotope weighing
       0.100 g., how much will be left after 26 hours? 78 hours?

23.9   Referring to Problem 23.8, how much $_{33}As^{72}$ will be left after 12 hours? One day?
       Three days?

23.10 The half-life of $_{31}Ga^{70}$ is 20 minutes. How long will it take for $\frac{3}{4}$ of a sample of this
       isotope to decay? $\frac{7}{8}$?

23.11 Referring to Problem 23.10, how long will it take for 20 per cent of this sample to
       decay? 60 per cent? 90 per cent?

23.12 Explain the principle behind the radioactive method of determining the age of:
       a. Rocks or mineral deposits.   b. Organic material.

23.13 $_{92}U^{238}$ has a half-life of 4.5×10^9 years. A sample of uranium ore is found to contain
       11.9 g. of $_{92}U^{238}$ and 10.3 g. of $_{82}Pb^{207}$. How old is the ore? What weight of helium has
       escaped from the ore sample? How many alpha particles does this represent?

23.14 A certain painting attributed to Raphael (1483–1520) is studied by the $_6C^{14}$ method.
       It is found that the $_6C^{14}$ content of a tiny piece of the canvas is 0.96 of that in living
       plants. On the basis of this data, can you come to any conclusion as to whether or not
       the painting is a forgery?

23.15 Write balanced nuclear equations for the following reactions:

target nucleus	bombarding particle	expelled particle
$_{29}Cu^{63}$	$_1H^1$	$_0n^1$
$_{13}Al^{27}$	$_0n^1$	$_1H^1$
$_{12}Mg^{24}$	$_1H^2$	$_1H^1$

23.16 Explain why neutrons are able to initiate nuclear reactions at much lower energies
       than protons or alpha particles.

23.17 Predict whether the following unstable isotopes will decay by electron or by positron
       emission.
       a. $_5B^{12}$ b. $_6C^{11}$ c. $_6C^{14}$ d. $_8O^{14}$

23.18 Explain why the probability of decay by electron capture as compared to positron
       emission increases with atomic number.

23.19 Write balanced nuclear equations for the following:
       a. Loss of an alpha particle by $_{90}Th^{228}$.

  b. Loss of a positron by $_{49}In^{110}$.

  c. K electron capture by $_{49}In^{112}$.

  d. Bombardment of $_{48}Cd^{116}$ with a deuteron, resulting in the emission of 2 neutrons and another nucleus.

  e. Bombardment of $_{62}Sm^{154}$ with a proton, resulting in the emission of a neutron and another nucleus.

  f. Fission of $_{94}Pu^{239}$ to give $_{57}La^{145}$, 4 neutrons, and another nucleus.

23.20 Consider the reaction: $_6C^{11} \rightarrow {}_5B^{11} + {}_1e^0$. Using the data in Table 23.8,

  a. Calculate ΔE in mev. when one atom of $_6C^{11}$ decays.

  b. Calculate ΔE in ergs when 1 mole of $_6C^{11}$ decays.

  c. Calculate ΔE in kilocalories when 1 g. of $_6C^{11}$ decays.

23.21 Using the data in Table 23.8, calculate the mass decrement, the binding energy in mev. and the binding energy per nucleon for:

  a. $_2He^3$ b. $_6C^{12}$ c. $_{27}Co^{59}$ d. $_{92}U^{238}$

  Check your values by referring to Table 23.9. How can one interpret these results in terms of the relative stabilities of the four nuclei involved?

23.22 For the reaction: $_1H^2 + {}_1H^2 \rightarrow He^4$ calculate the energy evolved per gram of deuterium undergoing fusion and compare to the value given in the text (equation 23.33).

*23.23 Aluminum-28 decays by β-emission to silicon-28. Using the data in Table 23.8, calculate the energy of the β-particle in mev.

*23.24 Knowing the half-life of $_{92}U^{238}$, calculate the number of uranium atoms undergoing disintegration per second in a sample weighing 1 mg.

*23.25 One curie of a radioactive substance is the amount in which 3.7×10^{10} nuclei undergo radioactive decay during each second. Calculate the weight of 1 curie of radium (your answer should be 1 g.).

*23.26 The elements francium, technetium, promethium, and astatine were discovered as products of nuclear reactions in a five-year period between 1937 and 1942. Can you suggest how the names of these elements might have been derived? Consult: Samuel Glasstone, *Sourcebook on Atomic Energy*, D. Van Nostrand and Co., Princeton, N. J., 2nd edition, 1958.

24 | ORGANIC CHEMISTRY

The physical and chemical properties of elemental carbon are such that there are many more organic compounds than compounds of all other elements combined. The enormous number and variety of carbon-containing compounds have made the field of organic chemistry the most extensive of all areas of chemical science.

Organic compounds are important in our daily lives in many ways. The human body, for example, consists largely of tissues composed of organic molecules of a wide variety of sizes and structures. These molecules, many of which are synthesized by our bodies, are daily utilized as ingredients in complex reactions which produce additional new molecules, release energy, and, in general, carry on the life process. Similar molecules are found in all plant and animal systems, where they selectively participate in a myriad of reactions controlling growth, maturity, and reproduction.

Among the many chemical substances man has found useful, those of organic origin are notably numerous and valuable. From petroleum and coal we obtain our major fuels and the raw materials for the production of fabrics, paints, dyes, and the great variety of plastics. From plants we obtain such important substances as sugar, cotton, alcohol, quinine, turpentine, and rubber. From animals come leather, wool, and silk. Although the many products obtained from nature have been known and used for centuries, only recently has the chemist been able to determine the actual chemical composition of such natural materials as rubber, silk, petroleum, and leather. Our understanding of the nature of these and other materials has made possible great improvement in the quality of our synthetic rubbers, fabrics, coatings, and fuels.

One particularly important area of organic chemistry is concerned with the identification and development of medicinal products. Although man has for centuries recognized certain plant and animal products as valuable medicines, developments since 1940 have produced new chemicals that have truly revolutionized the practice of medicine. Sulfa drugs, cortisones, steroids, tranquilizers, and a variety of other medicinal agents, isolated or synthesized by researchers in the last two decades, have made it possible to deal with illness much more effectively than at any time in man's history. If one were to rate the scientific areas of progress in this century which have contributed most to the well-being of mankind, it would be only

576

fair to rank our ability to treat illness with medicines obtained through the knowledge of organic chemistry at the top of the list.

24.1 KINDS OF ORGANIC SUBSTANCES

We have acknowledged that organic chemistry owes its existence to unique properties of the carbon atom. You will recall that the electron configuration of carbon, $1s^2 2s^2 2p^2$, gives the atom four valence electrons. Through hybridization, or by the principle that electron pairs in a molecule occur at maximum distances from one another, the carbon atom can form four equivalent, strong, covalent bonds, located tetrahedrally about the carbon atom. Of special significance is the fact that bonds between carbon atoms are strong, making for the possibility of long carbon chains in organic molecules. Silicon and germanium, in the same family as carbon, can also form four bonds, but the relative weakness of the Si—Si and Ge—Ge bonds restricts the chemistry of those elements very severely. Because the electronegativity of carbon is near that of hydrogen and the other nonmetals such as oxygen, nitrogen, and sulfur that commonly occur in organic compounds, the bonding in organic compounds is typically covalent in character. Organic substances are, therefore, primarily molecular, with physical properties determined by molecular interactions due to Van der Waals forces, dipole forces, or hydrogen bonding.

Organic compounds can be classified into groups and subgroups, according to the nature of the covalent bonds and the kinds of atoms present. One very large group includes those substances whose molecules contain only carbon and hydrogen atoms. These substances are called **hydrocarbons,** and, depending on the kinds of carbon bonds present, can be further classified as paraffins, olefins, acetylenes, or aromatic substances. In this section we will first consider the hydrocarbons, then some compounds containing halogens, and finally oxygen-containing organic compounds.

Saturated Hydrocarbons: Paraffins and Cycloparaffins

One very large, and structurally simple, subgroup of the hydrocarbons includes those substances whose molecules contain only single carbon-carbon bonds. These substances are called **saturated** hydrocarbons or **paraffins.** In the paraffins the carbon atoms are bonded to each other in chains, which may be long or short, single or branched. In some cases the ends of the chain are bonded to each other, and **cycloparaffins** result.

The simplest paraffinic substances are methane, CH_4, and ethane, C_2H_6, whose molecules we used as models in the discussion of covalent bonding in Chapter 10.

$$
\begin{array}{ccc}
& H & \\
& | & \\
H- & C & -H \\
& | & \\
& H &
\end{array}
\qquad
\begin{array}{ccccc}
& H & & H & \\
& | & & | & \\
H- & C & - & C & -H \\
& | & & | & \\
& H & & H &
\end{array}
$$

Methane   Ethane

You will recall that in these molecules the bonding around each carbon atom is tetrahedral. Independent of the length of the carbon chain, the four bonds around each carbon atom in a saturated hydrocarbon will retain essentially tetrahedral geometry. The only exceptions occur in the small ring cycloparaffins, where the molecular structure restricts the bond angles.

Accepting the fact that carbon atoms in the paraffins occur in chains, which may or may not be branched or form rings, one can easily, and correctly, guess that the following higher paraffins exist:

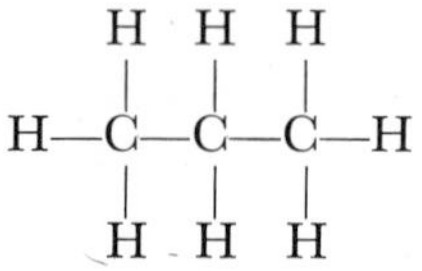

Propane

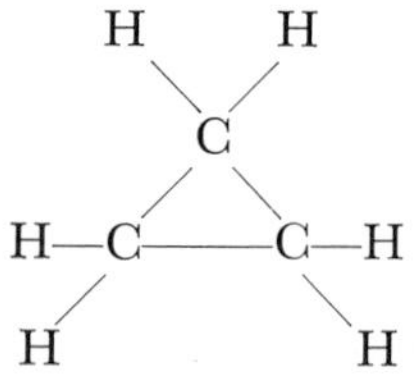

Cyclopropane

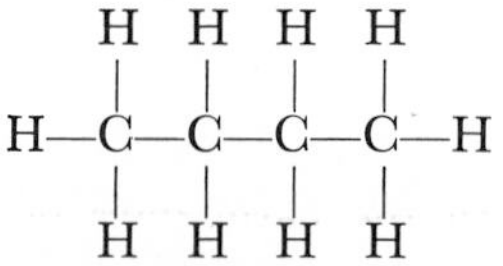

Butane (normal butane)

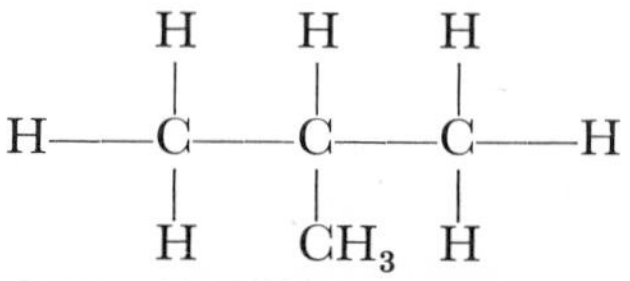

2-Methylpropane (isobutane)

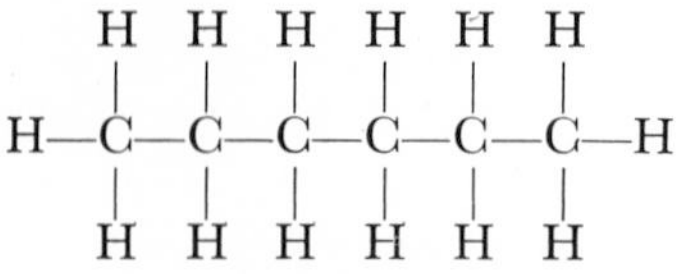

Hexane (normal hexane)

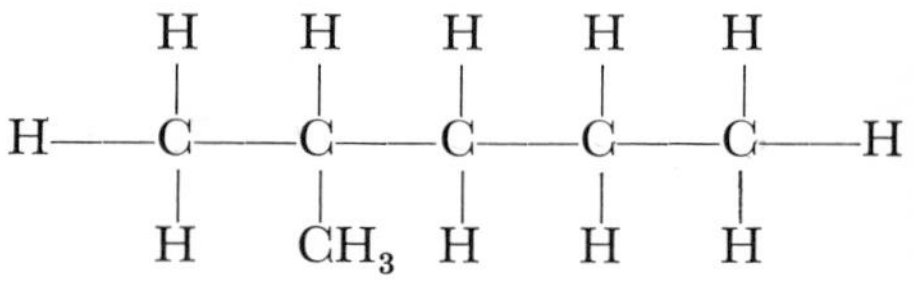

2-Methylpentane (isohexane)

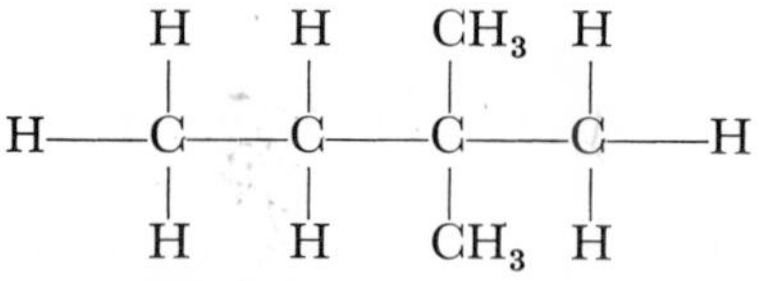

2,2-Dimethylbutane (neohexane)

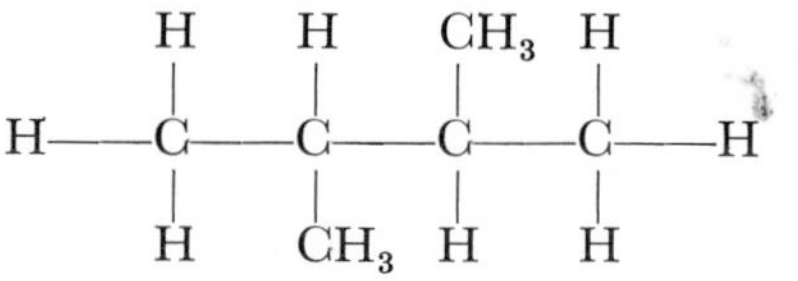

2,3-Dimethylbutane (diisopropyl)

In the paraffins, since the carbon chains are bent, the molecules are fairly compact, with less atom-atom repulsion than may seem apparent in the planar diagrams. In cyclopropane, where the 60° bond angle is much smaller than the energetically favored tetrahedral angle of 109°, there is considerable ring strain in the molecule and a marked decrease in stability.

The above molecules are typical of the paraffins. There are no well-defined positive and negative centers, so the molecules are relatively nonpolar. They are soluble in each other and in other nonpolar solvents, but are essentially insoluble in water. The paraffins are colorless and relatively odorless. Their melting and boiling points increase with molecular weight, reflecting the fact that intermolecular bonding in the compounds is due to Van der Waals forces. Methane and ethane are both gases (b.p. −161°C and −88°C respectively). Hexane is a liquid (b.p. 69°C), whereas eicosane, $C_{20}H_{42}$, a long-chain paraffin, is a solid (m.p. 38°C). The solids have the waxy properties of the common household paraffin used to seal jelly jars and make candles.

As a group the paraffins are relatively nonreactive chemically. The main reaction they ordinarily exhibit is burning in air. Their principal use is as fuels, both in home heating systems and internal combustion engines. Natural gas, fuel oil, and gasoline are for the most part mixtures of paraffins, selected to have the proper burning characteristics. The natural source of essentially all the paraffins is petroleum (see Section 24.3).

The molecular diagrams on the previous page illustrate the important general fact that in organic chemistry a given molecular formula frequently does not lead to a definite molecular structure. In the four-carbon paraffins the formula is C_4H_{10}, but the compound may be either butane or 2-methyl propane. For the six-carbon paraffins, formula C_6H_{14}, five structures are possible, of which we show four. Compounds such as these, with the same formula but different molecular structures, are called **isomers.** Isomerism of this kind and other kinds is very common in organic chemistry and increases the number of possible organic compounds enormously. Although many of the 75 possible isomers having the formula $C_{10}H_{22}$ will not be known, it is important that there be available a system of nomenclature by which one can denote unambiguously any given isomer.

As you might surmise, the problem of nomenclature has plagued organic chemists, and organic chemistry students, for many years. In the early days of chemistry each newly discovered organic compound was given a trivial name, describing its source, use, color, or possibly the name of its discoverer. By 1900 it became apparent that some system had to be established for denoting compounds in a manner that reflected structure rather than some one of many arbitrarily chosen characteristics. By 1930 the system of nomenclature now in general use was set up by international agreement; it enables the organic chemist to name a new compound, no matter how complex it may be, in such a way as to indicate its structure to other chemists. The only real difficulty for the novice chemist is that for the most common substances, which are the ones ordinarily first encountered in the laboratory, the old trivial names persist. Where the general population still speaks of muriatic acid instead of hydrochloric acid and blue vitriol instead of copper sulfate pentahydrate, the organic chemist still uses acetone instead of 2-propanone and will probably continue to do so for some time.

In this chapter we will make no attempt to discuss organic nomenclature in detail. We will name the compounds discussed in the manner of the practicing organic chemist, using the systematic notation where it is convenient and the trivial name where it is almost always employed. In some cases, as in the foregoing diagrams, both names will be given, with the common trivial name in parentheses.

Unsaturated Hydrocarbons: Olefins and Acetylenes

If one or more of the carbon-carbon bonds in a hydrocarbon is a double or triple bond, that substance is said to be **unsaturated.** If the multiple bond is double, the material is called an **olefin** (oil former). If the multiple bond is triple, it is an **acetylene,** after C_2H_2, the first member of that group of substances.

The olefins and acetylenes are similar to the paraffins in their number and variety. A typical paraffin, on being dehydrogenated or ruptured at a carbon-carbon bond, yields an olefin. This reaction, called *cracking*, is widely used in the petroleum industry to produce olefins from petroleum. Some cracking reactions which butane,

C_4H_{10}, would undergo follow:

$$C_4H_{10} \xrightarrow[435°C]{Fe}$$

$$H_2 + H-\overset{\overset{\displaystyle H}{|}}{\underset{\underset{\displaystyle H}{|}}{C}}-\overset{\overset{\displaystyle H}{|}}{\underset{\underset{\displaystyle H}{|}}{C}}-\overset{\overset{\displaystyle H}{|}}{C}=\overset{\overset{\displaystyle H}{|}}{C}-H$$

1-Butene (α-butylene)

$$H_2 + H-\overset{\overset{\displaystyle H}{|}}{\underset{\underset{\displaystyle H}{|}}{C}}-\overset{\overset{\displaystyle H}{|}}{C}=\overset{\overset{\displaystyle H}{|}}{C}-\overset{\overset{\displaystyle H}{|}}{\underset{\underset{\displaystyle H}{|}}{C}}-H$$

Trans-2-butene

$$CH_4 + H-\overset{\overset{\displaystyle H}{|}}{\underset{\underset{\displaystyle H}{|}}{C}}-\overset{\overset{\displaystyle H}{|}}{C}=\overset{\overset{\displaystyle H}{|}}{C}-H$$

Propene (propylene)

$$C_2H_6 + H-\overset{\overset{\displaystyle H}{|}}{C}=\overset{\overset{\displaystyle H}{|}}{C}-H$$

Ethene (ethylene)

1-Butene, propene, and ethene are the olefinic analogs of the paraffins butane, propane, and ethane. By virtue of these names, the olefins are sometimes called **alkenes,** and the paraffins called **alkanes.**

The geometry about a carbon atom that has a double bond is planar, with the three bonded atoms at about equal angles around the carbon. There is no free rotation around a double bond, so a molecule like 2-butene (see diagram) can exist in two isomeric forms, called **geometric** isomers, in which the two hydrogen atoms attached to the double bonded carbon atoms exist either on the same side (cis form) or on opposite sides (trans form) of the double bond. The nomenclature for such isomers is analogous to that used previously in denoting the geometry in inorganic complex ions.

Olefinic hydrocarbons are more reactive chemically than are the paraffins, due to the presence of the double bond. A reaction common to these hydrocarbons is one of addition, in which a molecule such as H_2, HCl, or Br_2 adds directly to the double bond; the resulting saturated compound may contain one or more halogen atoms. Another important reaction is that of polymerization, in which an olefinic molecule adds to itself to form a long chain:

$$n\left[H-\overset{\overset{\displaystyle H}{|}}{C}=\overset{\overset{\displaystyle H}{|}}{\underset{\underset{\displaystyle H}{|}}{C}}-H\right] \longrightarrow \left[-\overset{\overset{\displaystyle H}{|}}{\underset{\underset{\displaystyle H}{|}}{C}}-\overset{\overset{\displaystyle H}{|}}{\underset{\underset{\displaystyle H}{|}}{C}}-\right]_n$$

Ethylene   Polyethylene

Many modern plastics are polymers containing long-chain molecules of several thousand monomer units. Some well-known plastics produced by addition polymerization are polyvinyl chloride (CH_2=CHCl monomer), polypropylene

($CH_3CH{=}CH_2$ monomer), and polystyrene ($C_6H_5CH{=}CH_2$ monomer). These materials have the useful property of being thermoplastic, softening at about 150°C, at which temperature they can be readily molded or extruded.

If more than one double bond is present in a molecule, that molecule is called a **polyene,** and the properties of the substance may reflect the relative positions of the double bonds as well as their presence. Two double bonds on the same carbon atom in a chain always produce a very unstable, highly reactive molecule. If the double bonds are relatively far apart in the carbon chain they act as single isolated double bonds. In some molecules, in which the double bonds in the chain alternate with single bonds, the carbon bonds are said to be **conjugated.** The most common example of a conjugated system is 1,3-butadiene,

$$\underset{\displaystyle \text{1,3-Butadiene}}{H{-}\underset{\displaystyle |}{\underset{\displaystyle H}{C}}{=}\underset{\displaystyle |}{\underset{\displaystyle H}{C}}{-}\underset{\displaystyle |}{\underset{\displaystyle H}{C}}{=}\underset{\displaystyle |}{\underset{\displaystyle H}{C}}{-}H}$$

Substances like butadiene undergo rather different addition reactions than do ordinary olefins, and polymerize by addition reactions to produce polymers with one double bond per unit of monomer. This type of polymerization is typical of the process used to produce synthetic rubber (see Section 24.3).

Molecules containing a carbon-carbon triple bond are even more reactive than the olefins. Acetylene, the simplest of these substances, which are sometimes called **alkynes,** is typically unstable and chemically reactive. Its most commonly known use is in the oxyacetylene torch, where it is burned in oxygen to produce a very high-temperature flame useful for welding and cutting metals. It undergoes addition reactions with hydrogen or the halogens to produce olefins or saturated substituted hydrocarbons, many of which are very important industrially. Acetylene itself is a gas. It is manufactured by reacting calcium carbide, CaC_2, with water, or by the carefully controlled oxidation of methane.

$$CaC_2(s) + 2\ H_2O(l) \longrightarrow C_2H_2(g) + Ca(OH)_2(s)$$

The calcium carbide for this reaction is normally obtained by the direct reaction of limestone and coke in an electric furnace.

$$4\ CH_4(g) + 3\ O_2(g) \longrightarrow 2\ C_2H_2(g) + 6\ H_2O(g)$$

In the methane oxidation the gases are passed very quickly through an electric arc and the products quenched in water to prevent further oxidation of the acetylene to the much more stable carbon monoxide and carbon dioxide. This reaction is thermodynamically possible, $\Delta G° < 0$, since the relatively high stability of water more than compensates for very high instability of the acetylene produced simultaneously.

The geometric arrangement of atoms around a carbon atom on which there is a triple bond is linear. In acetylene all the atoms lie on the same straight line. This arrangement is reasonable if one remembers that in the alkynes the triple bond can be considered to result from the overlap of three of the four tetrahedrally oriented bonding orbitals around each of the participating carbon atoms (see Figure 10.11).

Aromatic Hydrocarbons

Relatively early in the history of organic chemistry some hydrocarbons were discovered which did not seem to behave chemically as one would have expected on the basis of their elementary composition. These substances all contained a relatively small amount of hydrogen and yet did not have the characteristic properties associated with unsaturation noted in the olefins and acetylenes. These hydrocarbons are members of a large group known as the aromatic substances.

The simplest aromatic substance, benzene, C_6H_6, was discovered by Michael Faraday in 1825. Benzene is a relatively stable liquid, that boils at about 80°C and has a characteristic odor. Though it has the same percentage by weight of hydrogen as does acetylene it does not readily add either hydrogen or the halogens; its reaction with bromine, which must be carried out in the presence of catalysts, is one of substitution rather than the expected addition. This behavior implies that the structure of benzene must differ considerably from that of other hydrocarbons of similar composition.

Kekulé, a German chemist, was the first to suggest the structure for benzene which is used at present. Using the rather sparse data then available, he was able to conclude that, when benzene was reacted with a halogen as in the following substitution reactions:

$$C_6H_6 + Br_2 \xrightarrow[50°]{Fe} C_6H_5Br + HBr$$

$$C_6H_5Br + Br_2 \xrightarrow[50°]{Fe} C_6H_4Br_2 + HBr$$

there was produced only one isomer of bromobenzene, C_6H_5Br, and three isomers of dibromobenzene, $C_6H_4Br_2$. Kekulé recognized that these facts require that benzene

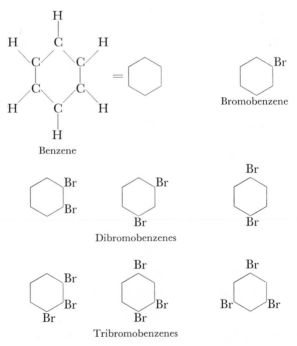

FIGURE 24.1   The geometry of benzene and some of its derivatives.

have a cyclic structure, with all hydrogens equivalent. In Figure 24.1 we have indicated the geometry Kekulé found necessary for the carbon skeleton and the structures of some of the substituted derivatives. Kekulé was able, on the basis of this structure, to predict that there would be three isomers of the trisubstituted halo-gen derivative of benzene. Later experiments verified this and other predictions which can be made from this structure, and soon established the validity of Kekulé's reasoning. More recent x-ray diffraction and vibrational spectra results confirm that in the benzene molecule the carbon atoms are at the corners of a regular plane hexagon and are bonded to the hydrogen atoms in such a way as to maintain perfect hexagonal symmetry. The carbon-carbon bond length is 1.39 Å, intermediate between that of 1.34 Å for the double-bonded carbon atoms in ethylene and 1.55 Å, the single carbon-carbon bond length in ethane.

If one attempts to draw valence bond structures for benzene, he finds that no one structure is adequate. Kekulé suggested that, in the molecule, single and double bonds alternated in the ring:

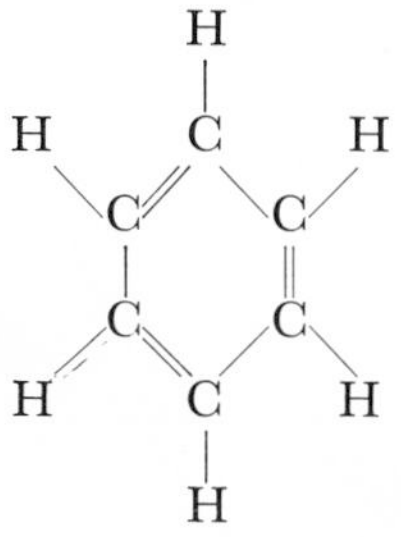

which is often drawn simply as

When it became clear that there were no disubstituted isomers of the form,

Kekulé proposed that the structure of the molecule continually oscillated between the following two forms:

If such an oscillation were very rapid, the atomic arrangement might well remain constant at some average configuration having the observed very high symmetry and equivalence of carbon-carbon bonds.

You may recognize the rather close similarity between the two Kekulé structures for benzene and the various resonance structures which were given for some in-organic molecules in Chapter 10. A common modern description of the structure of benzene is based on the resonance concept. The benzene molecule according to this idea has only *one* structure, intermediate between structures I and II, and is called a resonance hybrid of those structures. The high relative stability of the molecule is attributed to the fact that such resonance structures can be drawn. (As a matter of fact, several other resonance structures can be drawn for benzene, but I and II are thought to be the major contributors.)

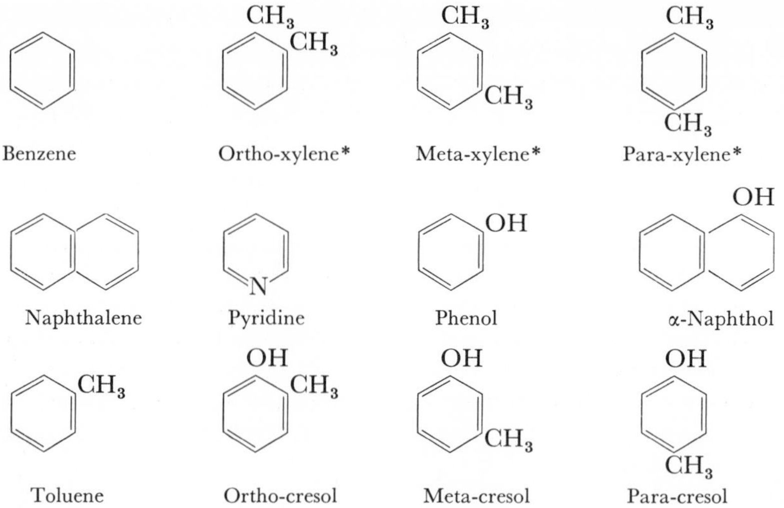

Benzene   Ortho-xylene*   Meta-xylene*   Para-xylene*

Naphthalene   Pyridine   Phenol   α-Naphthol

Toluene   Ortho-cresol   Meta-cresol   Para-cresol

* The terms ortho, meta, and para are used as prefixes on names of aromatic substances to indicate the relative positions of two substituted groups.

FIGURE 24.2   Some aromatic substances found in coal tar.

According to another form of the theory, 24 of the 30 valence electrons available for bonding in benzene are used in making up six carbon-carbon single bonds and the six carbon-hydrogen bonds. The remaining six electrons are considered to be relatively mobile and able to move around on the carbon-carbon ring, thereby furnishing the partial double bond character in equal amounts to the carbon-carbon bonds. In such a model the stability of benzene is the result of the added freedom of motion of the six electrons, a freedom which is presumably missing in ordinary molecules. As can be surmised, the story of the structure and properties of benzene is not yet complete and will probably continue to interest chemists and theorists for many years to come.

Many substances derived from or related to benzene contain the carbon ring that we have been discussing. These materials, all of which have chemical properties characteristic of the benzene ring, form the group of substances we call aromatic. Many of them are found in coal tar, which is evolved when soft coal is heated to about 1200°C in the absence of air. The main part of the coal is converted to coke, a much cleaner-burning fuel than soft coal. The coal tar, a gummy black residue which is produced in about 3 per cent yield, is refined by further distillation and chemical treatment, finally yielding a fairly large group of pure aromatic substances, some of which are indicated in Figure 24.2. Many of these materials are of commercial importance, and in recent years have also been produced synthetically to meet increased demand. Benzene has some use as a solvent, but its main application is as a raw material for the manufacture of styrene, $C_6H_5CH{=}CH_2$, which is polymerized to form polystyrene. Toluene and the xylenes are useful as components in motor fuel and as chemical intermediates. Naphthalene still has some use in mothballs and is also important in the production of dyes and agricultural chemicals. The cresols are the main components in the wood preservative known as creosote.

Halogen-Containing Organic Compounds

In discussing chemical reactions of hydrocarbons we have mentioned that a common product of addition reactions is a compound which can be thought of as a hydrocarbon in which one or more hydrogen atoms in the molecule have been replaced by halogen atoms. The halogen-containing derivatives of the hydrocarbons, though they rarely occur in nature, are very important to the synthetic organic chemist and also include some of the more common organic substances. Some of the typical reactions in which these substances are used will be discussed in the next section.

The geometries of the organic halogen derivatives are the same as those of the parent hydrocarbons. The bond angles within the substituted molecule are about the same as in the hydrocarbon. The C—X bond length is typically different from the C—H bond length and will vary with the halogen substituent. Since substitution on the hydrocarbon can usually occur at several nonequivalent positions, there are often several isomers of a halogen derivative with a given molecular formula. For instance, monochlorinated pentane could have any of the following isomeric structures:

| 1-Chloropentane | 2-Chloropentane | 3-Chloropentane |

Since pentane is only one of three isomers with the formula C_5H_{12}, it is clear that the number of possible isomers of a derivative with the formula $C_5H_{11}Cl$ is substantial.

Several of the relatively simple organic halides are well known because of their common uses. Carbon tetrachloride, CCl_4, is a solvent used in dry cleaning and since it is nonflammable, has had application as a fire extinguisher. This latter use is less frequent in recent years, since CCl_4 at high temperatures tends to partially oxidize to form phosgene, $COCl_2$, a poisonous gas used extensively in World War I. Chloroform, $CHCl_3$, is a low-boiling liquid, best known as an anesthetic. Since all the chlorinated hydrocarbons are toxic, chloroform has been essentially replaced in this application by other effective but less toxic materials. Freon, CCl_2F_2, which boils at $-28°C$, is chemically inert and used widely as a refrigerant in home refrigerators and freezers. Paradichlorobenzene, $C_6H_4Cl_2$, is a solid aromatic organic halide which is poisonous to insects, particularly moth larvae. The materials known as DDT and chlordane are somewhat more complex chlorinated derivatives of organic hydrocarbons and are very effective insecticides.

Dichlorodiphenyltrichloroethane (DDT)   Chlordane

Oxygen-Containing Organic Compounds

When one extends the discussion of organic compounds to include those which contain oxygen, the number and kinds of substances which can be prepared increases enormously. Whereas hydrogen and the halogen atoms form only one covalent bonds oxygen typically forms two, and so can be present in organic molecules in other than the substitutional role to which the halogens are limited.

If the bonds to the oxygen atom in an organic molecule are all single, the substance is either an **ether** or an **alcohol.** A typical representative of each of these classe, follows:

Diethyl ether   2-Butanol (sec-butyl alcohol)

These two substances are isomeric and differ in that in the ether the oxygen is between two carbon atoms and in the alcohol it is between a carbon atom and a hydrogen atom. Alcohols are hydroxy derivatives of hydrocarbons. (If the substitution of hydroxyl group for hydrogen occurs on an aromatic hydrogen, the product is called a phenol.)

Ethers are not highly reactive chemically, resembling the saturated hydrocarbon with the same number of atoms in the chain. They are mainly used as solvents, although diethyl ether is still used to some extent as an anesthetic. There is extensive industrial application of two cyclic ethers, ethylene oxide, which adds water to form ethylene glycol CH_2OHCH_2OH (permanent antifreeze), and tetrahydrofuran (made from corn cobs and oat hulls and used in nylon manufacture).

Ethylene oxide   Tetrahydrofuran

Alcohols and phenols are an important class of substances both from the synthetic and industrial viewpoints. The hydroxyl group, like the halogen group, affords a molecule a reactive center by which it can participate readily in chemical reactions. Some typical alcohol reactions will be considered in the next section.

Alcohols can be prepared from natural sources or by synthetic means. The most important alcohol is ethyl alcohol, or ethanol, C_2H_5OH, which is commonly made by fermentation of sugar or starch solutions in the presence of natural or prepared yeasts and the absence of air. The reaction may be schematically represented as

$$C_6H_{12}O_6 \longrightarrow 2\ C_2H_5OH + 2\ CO_2$$
A sugar   Ethanol (ethyl alcohol)

In addition to its use in intoxicating beverages, ethyl alcohol is an important solvent, a good antiseptic, and a reagent in many industrial processes. Methanol, CH_3OH, and isopropyl alcohol, $CH_3CHOHCH_3$, with physical and chemical properties similar to those of ethanol, are both prepared synthetically. Methanol is still used to some extent as an antifreeze and is the raw material for the manufacture of form-aldehyde. Isopropyl alcohol is an antiseptic and the main component of rubbing alcohol.

The most important phenol is the parent compound, C_6H_5OH, from which the class gets its name. Phenols in general are solids at room temperature, are weak acids, and have marked antiseptic properties. Phenol, carbolic acid, was one of the first antiseptics, but because of its irritant properties is no longer used to disinfect wounds. The main use of phenol at present is in the manufacture of Bakelite resins, which will be discussed later. Phenol is a component of coal tars, but must also be manufactured by various synthetic means to meet demand. One process by which it can be made is by hydrolysis of chlorobenzene in dilute alkaline solution at high temperature and pressure.

$$C_6H_5Cl \xrightarrow[300°C,\ 2500\ lb./in.^2]{Aq\ NaOH} C_6H_5ONa \xrightarrow{HCl} C_6H_5OH$$

Chlorobenzene   Sodium phenolate   Phenol

If the oxygen atom in an organic molecule is double bonded to carbon, the substance is called an **aldehyde** or a **ketone**. Aldehydes and ketones have the general structures:

$$\begin{array}{cc} R-C=O & R-C=O \\ | & | \\ H & R \end{array}$$

An aldehyde   A ketone

in which R is an aliphatic group like methyl, CH_3, or ethyl, C_2H_5, or an aromatic group like phenyl, C_6H_5. Since aldehydes and ketones are similar in their structures, they resemble each other in many of their physical and chemical properties. The carbonyl group, $C=O$, is unsaturated and undergoes many addition reactions in both aldehydes and ketones. The carbonyl group may be converted in both classes of compounds by reduction reactions to either the hydroxyl group, to form alcohols, or the methylene group, CH_2, to form saturated compounds. Aldehydes are readily oxidized to acids, whereas ketones are relatively oxidation resistant. This difference is responsible for a common test for aldehydes, carried out in alkaline solution:

$$R-C=O + 2\ Cu^{+2} + 5\ OH^- \longrightarrow (R-C=O)^- + Cu_2O(s) + 3\ H_2O$$

(with H below first C, and O below second C)

If an aldehyde is present, the cupric ion, on oxidizing the aldehyde, is itself reduced and precipitates as red cuprous oxide.

Most aldehydes and ketones are liquids at room temperature, with a solubility in water intermediate between that of the parent hydrocarbon and the related alcohol. Those of relatively high molecular weight have pleasant odors and are found in nature in flowers and spices. The lower members in both families have penetrating, rather sharp odors, and are prepared synthetically.

One of the common methods for the production of aldehydes is by the oxidation of alcohols. Formaldehyde, CH_2O, the first member of the aldehydes, is made commercially by the reaction of methanol vapor with air in the presence of a silver or copper catalyst.

$$2\ CH_3OH + O_2 \xrightarrow[250°C]{Ag} 2\ CH_2O + 2\ H_2O$$

The reaction is not carried to completion. The gaseous mixture is absorbed in water and marketed as formalin, a 40 per cent solution of formaldehyde containing some methanol, familiar to zoology students as a preservative. The main use of formaldehyde is in the manufacture of Bakelite resins. These are polymers made by reaction of phenol and formaldehyde. In the reaction, water is eliminated and the highly cross-linked, insoluble, infusible Bakelite is produced. Bakelite was one of the first commercially important polymers and was patented in 1909. It has good electrical insulating properties and is still one of the main substances used in electrical outlets, switches, and plugs. The molecular structure of Bakelite is still not certain, but it appears to be a three-dimensional polymer with benzene rings bonded as indicated in Figure 24.3.

Another important aldehyde is acetaldehyde, CH_3CHO, which is used mainly as a chemical intermediate. Acetaldehyde is produced commercially by an interesting reaction involving the hydration of acetylene:

$$H-C\equiv C-H + H_2O \xrightarrow[\text{HgSO}_4]{40\% \text{ H}_2\text{SO}_4} [CH_2=CHOH] \longrightarrow CH_3CHO$$

Vinyl alcohol   Acetaldehyde
(not isolable)

The reaction occurs because the vinyl alcohol that one would expect to be produced by the addition reaction is unstable and rearranges to the aldehyde. In aldehydes and ketones, hydrogen atoms attached to the carbon atom adjacent to the carbonyl group are relatively active and may be considered to participate in the following reaction:

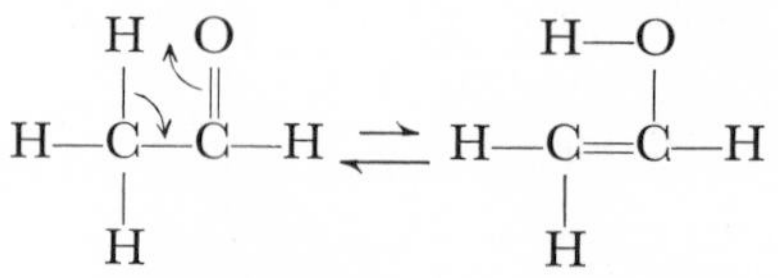

Keto form   Enol form

By shifting electrons as shown, the aldehyde or ketone is converted into an unsaturated alcohol. Ordinarily the carbonyl-containing, or keto, form is the more stable, but the reactions of some aldehydes and ketones are most easily understood if one accepts the existence of the unsaturated alcohol, or enol, form as a result of this equilibrium. The two forms are called **tautomers,** and the general phenomenon is known as **tautomerism.**

Among the ketones, acetone, CH_3COCH_3, is the simplest and best known. It is a volatile liquid widely used as a solvent in industrial and academic laboratories. It

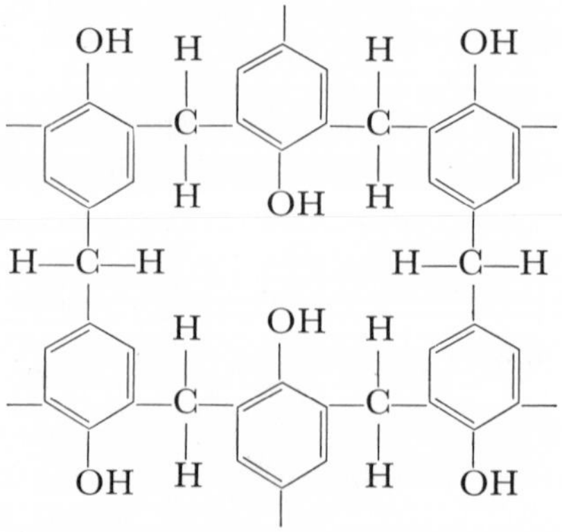

FIGURE 24.3 Schematic drawing of molecular structure of Bakelite (phenol-formaldehyde) resin.

is used as a raw material for the plastic substance known as Lucite or Plexiglas. It can be produced by fermentation of sugar or starch solutions by the proper choice of fermenting agents and is also made commercially by the oxidation of isopropyl alcohol.

Another class of oxygen-containing compounds is that of the **organic acids.** If a molecule contains both a carbonyl and a hydroxyl group on the same carbon atom, the compound will behave as a weak acid in water solution.

$$\begin{matrix} R{-}C{=}O \\ | \\ O{-}H \end{matrix} \rightleftharpoons \left(\begin{matrix} R{-}C{=}O \\ | \\ O^- \end{matrix} \right)^- + H^+$$

A carboxylic acid

The organic acids of molecular weight below about 150 are typically liquids at room temperature, with sharp, penetrating odors. Those with R groups containing up to three carbon atoms are, because of the presence of the polar carbonyl and hydroxyl groups, completely miscible with water.

The carboxylic acids are one of the most important classes of organic compounds. Animal fats and other natural products afford a source of a wide variety of acids, many of which are of considerable commercial importance. Unlike most of the substances we have already mentioned, some of the acids and their derivatives are nontoxic, at least in moderate amounts, to humans, and are present in many foods.

The carboxyl group, containing both the carbonyl and hydroxyl groups, possesses many of the chemical properties of ketones and alcohols as well as properties of its own. The fact that the carboxyl group acts as a weak acid allows for rapid reaction of organic acids with aqueous alkaline solutions to form salts.

$$\begin{matrix} R{-}C{=}O \\ | \\ O{-}H \end{matrix} + OH^- \longrightarrow \left(\begin{matrix} R{-}C{=}O \\ | \\ O \end{matrix} \right)^- + H_2O$$

The carbonyl group of organic acids undergoes several reactions. Probably the most important of these involves reaction with an alcohol:

$$\begin{matrix} R{-}C{=}O \\ | \\ O{-}H \end{matrix} + R'{-}O{-}H \rightleftharpoons \left[\begin{matrix} O{-}R' \\ | \\ R{-}C{-}O{-}H \\ | \\ O{-}H \end{matrix} \right] \rightleftharpoons \begin{matrix} O{-}R' \\ | \\ R{-}C{=}O \end{matrix} + H_2O$$

An acid   An alcohol   An ester

with water being eliminated from the unstable 1,1-dihydroxy intermediate, to form the class of substances called **esters.** The reaction is a very common one, and typically results in an equilibrium mixture. By removing water, the reaction can be driven to the right to produce the ester. If one starts with the ester, the hydrolysis reaction is favored in a basic solution, since under such conditions the organic acid concentration is kept very low.

Fats consist of the esters of long-chain carboxylic, or fatty, acids. The alcohol involved is usually glycerol, $HOCH_2CHOHCH_2OH$, while the acid may be one of many, depending on the natural source. The carbon chain may be saturated or unsaturated and is only rarely branched. A typical fatty acid is palmitic acid, $CH_3(CH_2)_{14}COOH$, found in palm oil. A very important industrial reaction of fats is that of hydrolysis, or saponification, carried out by boiling fats with sodium hydroxide solution to produce the substances known as **soaps:**

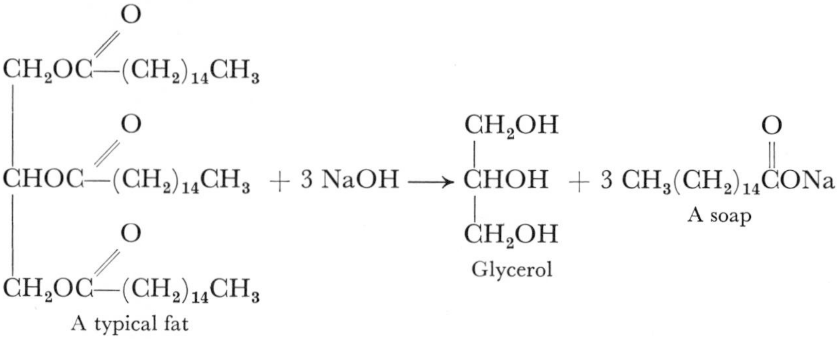

$$
\begin{array}{c}
\overset{\displaystyle O}{\underset{}{}} \\
CH_2OC{-}(CH_2)_{14}CH_3 \\
\overset{\displaystyle O}{} \\
CHOC{-}(CH_2)_{14}CH_3 \;+\; 3\,NaOH \;\longrightarrow\; CHOH \;+\; 3\,CH_3(CH_2)_{14}CONa \\
\overset{\displaystyle O}{} \\
CH_2OC{-}(CH_2)_{14}CH_3
\end{array}
$$

A typical fat

CH₂OH
CHOH
CH₂OH

Glycerol

A soap

A soap is the sodium salt of a fatty acid. It obtains its useful cleaning properties by combining a long-chain hydrocarbon, which has good solvent action on other hydrocarbons, with the polar carboxy group and its high water solubility. Other substances of similar structure also have good cleaning properties, and in recent years have replaced soaps to some extent. The difficulty with a soap is that in hard water, which typically contains calcium ions, the soap precipitates as a calcium salt. Much better solubility properties are obtained if one recovers the fatty acid from the above reaction, reduces it to the alcohol with hydrogen, and then forms an ester by reacting the alcohol with concentrated sulfuric acid, as in the following reaction:

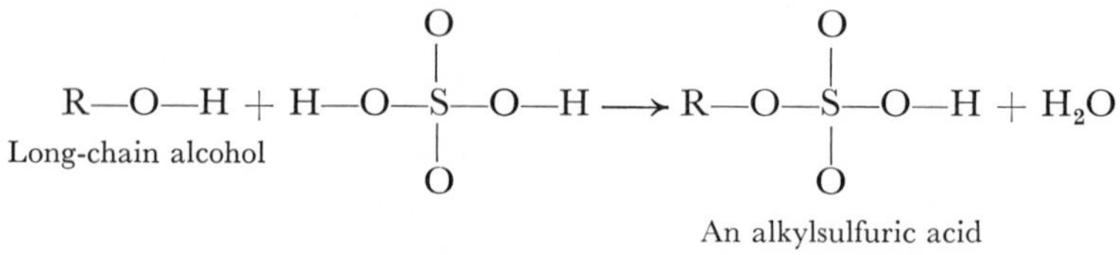

$$
\begin{array}{c}
\qquad\qquad\quad O \qquad\qquad\qquad\qquad O \\
\qquad\qquad\quad | \qquad\qquad\qquad\qquad | \\
R{-}O{-}H + H{-}O{-}S{-}O{-}H \longrightarrow R{-}O{-}S{-}O{-}H + H_2O \\
\qquad\qquad\quad | \qquad\qquad\qquad\qquad | \\
\qquad\qquad\quad O \qquad\qquad\qquad\qquad O
\end{array}
$$

Long-chain alcohol

An alkylsulfuric acid

By neutralizing the remaining acid hydrogen with sodium hydroxide, one obtains a substance which belongs to that class of materials commonly known as **detergents.** These materials, mainly because of their improved solubility characteristics, are now widely used for laundry purposes, particularly in hard-water areas.

Many of the fatty acids are produced by the saponification reaction just described. Those with low molecular weight are, however, not present in fats and are prepared either by synthetic means or from other natural sources. Acetic acid, CH_3COOH, is the most widely known of the carboxylic acids, and is the active component of vinegar, made for centuries by fermentation of apple or other ciders. Acetic acid is an important industrial chemical and is made synthetically by air oxidation of ethanol or by the oxidation of acetaldehyde.

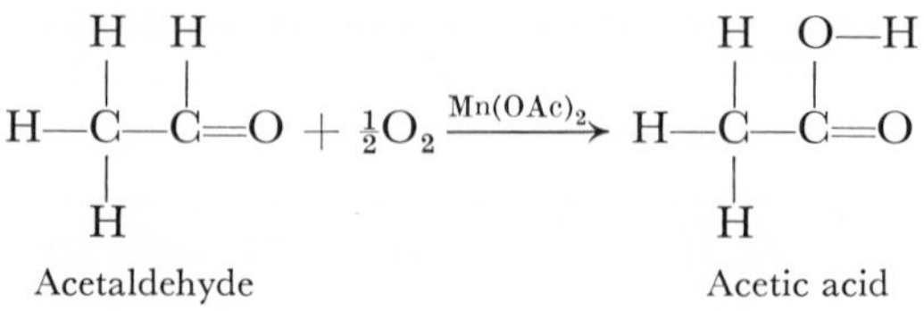

$$
\begin{array}{c}
H \; H \qquad\qquad\qquad\qquad\qquad H \; O{-}H \\
| \; | \qquad\qquad\qquad\qquad\qquad | \; | \\
H{-}C{-}C{=}O + \tfrac{1}{2}O_2 \;\xrightarrow{\text{Mn(OAc)}_2}\; H{-}C{-}C{=}O \\
| \qquad\qquad\qquad\qquad\qquad\qquad | \\
H \qquad\qquad\qquad\qquad\qquad\qquad H
\end{array}
$$

Acetaldehyde

Acetic acid

Acetic acid is an intermediate in many manufacturing processes, one of the more important of these being the production of cellulose acetate rayons.

24.2 SOME COMMON REACTIONS OF ORGANIC COMPOUNDS

Substitution Reactions

Perhaps the most important class of organic reactions is that involving substitution of one group for another in an organic molecule. Such reactions are extremely useful in organic synthesis, both in industry and in academic laboratories, and occur, by various mechanisms, in essentially all the different kinds of organic substances.

Nucleophilic Substitution Reactions. When the substitution reaction involves an electron-rich group displacing another electron-rich group from a saturated carbon atom, it is called a **nucleophilic substitution** reaction. An example of such a reaction is the following:

$$CH_3CH_2CH_2Cl + OH^- \longrightarrow CH_3CH_2CH_2OH + Cl^-$$

In this reaction, which occurs readily when propyl chloride is dissolved in a solution of sodium hydroxide in aqueous ethanol, the electron-rich hydroxide ion displaces an electron-rich chloride ion from the propyl chloride molecule. This kind of reaction typically occurs between alkyl halides and negative ions or other Lewis bases. It is reversible, and so is carried out under concentration conditions which favor the formation of the desired product; in the above example the presence of excess hydroxide ion tends to drive the reaction to the right. The substitution reaction can be carried out with many different anions and can be used to prepare a wide variety of organic substances. In Table 24.1 are listed some of the possible reactions of this type, first in general and then with specific examples.

Nucleophilic substitution reactions have been studied extensively from the kinetic and mechanistic viewpoints. Many of these reactions are first-order, depending only on the concentration of the alkyl halide; these are called S_N1 reactions (substitution, nucleophilic, first-order). In other cases these reactions are found to be second order overall, with rates which depend on both the concentration of the alkyl halide and that of the substituting group. Such reactions are described by the term S_N2 (substitution, nucleophilic, second-order). The mechanisms of the two kinds

TABLE 24.1 SOME TYPICAL NUCLEOPHILIC SUBSTITUTION REACTIONS*

$R—X + X'^- \rightarrow RX' + X^-$ an alkyl halide	$C_2H_5Cl + I^- \rightarrow C_2H_5I + Cl^-$ ethyl iodide
$R—X + OR'^- \rightarrow ROR' + X^-$ an ether	$CH_3CH_2CH_2Br + NaOCH_2CH_3$ $\rightarrow CH_3CH_2OCH_2CH_2CH_3 + NaBr$ ethyl n-propyl ether
$R—X + 2NH_3 \rightarrow RNH_2 + NH_4X$ an amine	$CH_3CH_2Br + 2\,NH_3 \rightarrow CH_3CH_2NH_2 + NH_4Br$ ethyl amine
$R—X + HC\equiv C^- \rightarrow RC\equiv CH + X^-$ a substituted acetylene	$CH_3I + HC\equiv CNa \rightarrow CH_3C\equiv CH + NaI$ methyl acetylene

* The sodium derivatives in these reactions are prepared by reaction of metallic sodium with either ethyl alcohol or acetylene, producing sodium ethoxide, $NaOCH_2CH_3$, or sodium acetylide, $NaCCH$, respectively.

of reactions necessarily differ. In an S_N1 reaction, the following mechanism seems likely:

(Step 1)

$$R_2-\underset{\underset{R_3}{|}}{\overset{\overset{R_1}{|}}{C}}-X \xrightarrow{\text{slow}} \left[R_2-\underset{R_3}{\overset{R_1}{C}} \right]^+ + X^-$$

(Step 2)

$$\left[R_2-\underset{R_3}{\overset{R_1}{C}} \right]^+ + Y^- \xrightarrow{\text{fast}} R_2-\underset{\underset{R_3}{|}}{\overset{\overset{R_1}{|}}{C}}-Y$$

The positive ion which is formed in the first step is called a **carbonium** ion. Since the carbon atom at the center of the carbonium ion has only six electrons, the ion will tend to be planar, with approximately equal angles between the bonds to the three R groups (sp^2 hybridization). The product is formed as fast as the carbonium ion is produced, and hence the reaction is first order. The electrons on the Y^- group are attracted to the positive carbon nucleus, which explains why the name nucleophilic is assigned to this reaction.

In S_N2 reactions, the attacking Y^- group is thought to form an activated complex with the alkyl halide, approaching the molecule from the side opposite the X group (you will remember that the bond geometry around the central carbon atom in the halide will be tetrahedral). The mechanism would be written as

$$Y^- + R_2-\underset{R_3}{\overset{R_1}{C}}-X \longrightarrow \left[Y-\underset{\underset{R_3}{|}}{\overset{R_1 \quad R_2}{C}}-X \right]^- + Y-\underset{R_3}{\overset{R_1}{C}}-R_2 + X^-$$

Activated complex

and would produce a second order reaction. In S_N2 reactions one would expect that the configuration of the substituted molecule would be, by virtue of the mechanism, the mirror image of the orginal halide. Experimentally, it can be shown that the inversion of the bonds around the central carbon atom actually occurs. The phenomenon is often called a Walden inversion and is characteristic of S_N2 reactions. In S_N1 reactions, since the carbonium ion is planar and equally subject to attack from both directions, the product includes molecules having the configurations of both the starting material and the mirror image.

Nucleophilic substitution reactions may be caused to vary in their mechanism by changing the reaction conditions. As one might expect, the S_N1 reaction is favored in very polar solvents, in which the ionization of the alkyl halide would tend to be greatest. It is also favored by relatively weak nucleophiles, which would not tend to form activated complexes readily.

If one attempts to extend the substitution reactions we have discussed to the aromatic halides he finds that essentially no reaction occurs under the mild conditions that are sufficient for nucleophilic substitutions. The halogen atoms on the benzene ring are more tightly bound to the molecule than is the case with the alkyl halides and so are not so readily replaced. It is thought that the C—X bonds in aromatic compounds are stabilized by interaction of the nonbonding electron pairs on the halogen atom with the mobile ring electrons, an interaction which results in some double bond character in the C—X bond.

Electrophilic Substitution Reactions. Substitution reactions with aromatic compounds typically result in the replacement of hydrogen atoms on the benzene ring by other groups. The reactions can occur with aromatic halides, but are most simply studied with the aromatic hydrocarbons. The following reactions are illustrative:

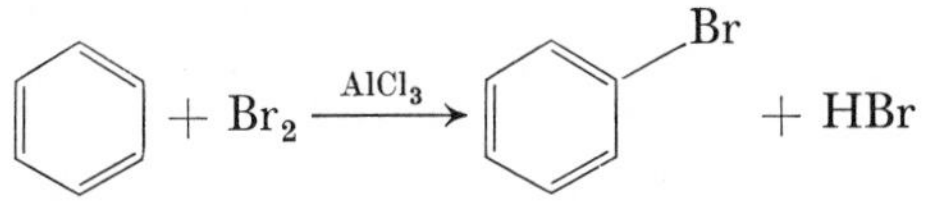

These reactions occur only in the presence of Lewis acid catalysts such as $AlCl_3$ or $FeCl_3$. It is thought that the species attacking benzene is a positive ion, produced by reaction of the substituting molecule with the catalyst. The mechanism proposed for the bromination of benzene follows:

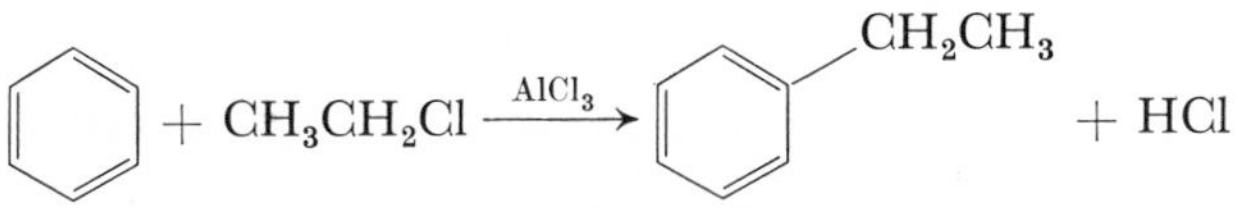

(Step 1) $Br_2 + AlCl_3 \longrightarrow Br^+ + AlCl_3Br^-$

(Step 2)

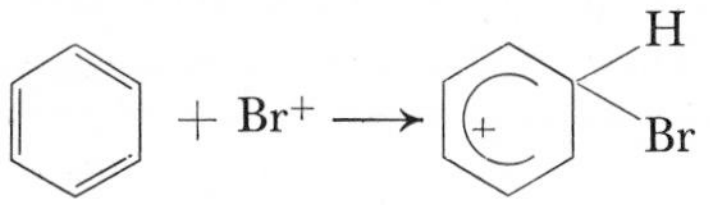

(Step 3)

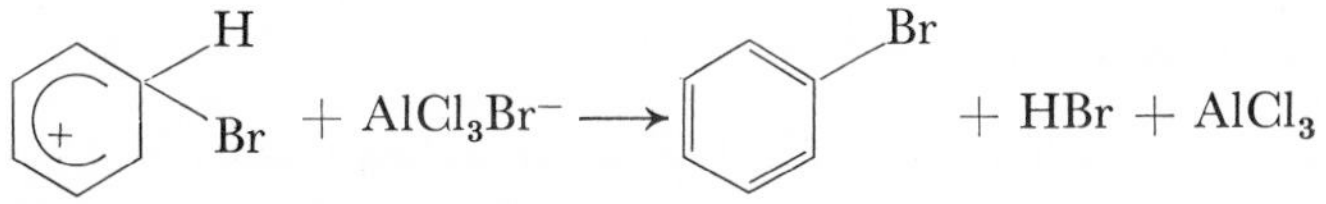

Since in these reactions the attacking positive ion is electron-seeking, they are called **electrophilic substitution** reactions. When the substitution reaction is carried out on an aromatic halide, a ring hydrogen atom is displaced, either from the ring position adjacent to or opposite to the position to which the halogen atom is bonded. It has been found in general that the positions at which substitution reactions occur in aromatic compounds which contain one substituted group are greatly influenced by the nature of that substituted group.

Substitution Reactions Involving Free Radicals. Substitution reactions of the saturated hydrocarbons proceed by a still different mechanism from those already mentioned. A mixture of a paraffinic hydrocarbon and chlorine shows no reaction if kept in the dark. On exposure to ultraviolet light the system reacts with explosive violence, producing molecules in which chlorine atoms have replaced hydrogen. The final product will in general be a complex mixture of halogenated hydrocarbons, which can be separated into its many components only with great difficulty. The reaction between propane and chlorine is illustrated schematically as follows:

$$CH_3CH_2CH_3 + n\ Cl_2 \longrightarrow \begin{array}{c} CH_3CH_2CH_2Cl + CH_3CHClCH_2Cl \\ + \qquad\qquad + \\ CH_3CHClCH_3 + CH_2ClCH_2CH_2Cl \\ + \qquad\qquad + \\ \text{Other polyhalogenated propanes} \end{array} + n\ HCl$$

The halogenation of saturated hydrocarbons, like the reaction between gaseous hydrogen and a halogen (see Chapter 14), is considered to proceed via a mechanism involving free radicals. Once the halogen molecule is dissociated by a photon of ultraviolet light, many many molecules of hydrocarbon can be halogenated before another halogen molecule need dissociate. Such a reaction, as you may recall, is described as a chain reaction. The mechanism for the reaction between methane and chlorine is as follows:

$$\text{initiation step:} \qquad Cl_2 \xrightarrow{\text{UV photon}} 2\ Cl\cdot$$

$$\text{chain propagation steps:} \qquad Cl\cdot + CH_4 \longrightarrow CH_3\cdot + HCl$$

$$CH_3\cdot + Cl_2 \longrightarrow CH_3Cl + Cl\cdot$$

$$\text{termination:} \qquad Cl\cdot + Cl\cdot \longrightarrow Cl_2$$

$$CH_3\cdot + CH_3\cdot \longrightarrow C_2H_6$$

$$CH_3\cdot + Cl\cdot \longrightarrow CH_3Cl$$

In the reaction mixture, the concentrations of the very reactive chlorine atom and the methyl free radical $CH_3\cdot$ are both very low, so that perhaps as many as a million methyl chloride molecules are produced before a chain is terminated. Here we have stopped the halogenation at CH_3Cl, but clearly it could continue, by the same kind of mechanism, to produce CH_2Cl_2, $CHCl_3$, and CCl_4.

Elimination Reactions

Sometimes, in nucleophilic substitution reactions, side reactions occur, producing other products. If, for instance, one is attempting to form an alcohol by the reaction

$$CH_3CH_2Br + OH^- \longrightarrow CH_3CH_2OH + Br^-$$

the following reaction, producing an olefin, may also occur:

$$CH_3CH_2Br + OH^- \longrightarrow CH_2{=}CH_2 + H_2O + Br^-$$

In this case the elements in hydrogen bromide are freed from the parent alkyl halide and react to form water and the halide ion. This kind of reaction, in which a small group is removed from a larger molecule, is called an **elimination** reaction. If the elements removed are hydrogen and a halogen, we speak of it as a **dehydrohalogenation** reaction. As you might expect, one can frequently adjust the reaction conditions to favor either the substitution or the elimination reaction. Ordinarily substitution will be more likely in an aqueous solution of potassium hydroxide; the elimination reaction is carried out in alcoholic KOH.

Alcohols can also be caused to undergo elimination reactions to form olefinic substances. In such reactions the elements in water are removed and the reaction is called a **dehydration**. The ease with which dehydration occurs depends on the number of carbon atoms attached to the carbon atom bonded to the hydroxyl group; the more carbon atoms, the easier is the dehydration reaction. A tertiary alcohol, like tertiary butyl alcohol, may dehydrate on being distilled, whereas a primary alcohol, like ethyl alcohol, may require much more drastic dehydrating conditions.

$$CH_3-\underset{\underset{CH_3}{|}}{\overset{\overset{CH_3}{|}}{C}}-OH \xrightarrow{\text{distillation}} CH_2=\underset{CH_3}{\overset{CH_3}{C}} + H_2O$$

Tertiary butyl alcohol   2-Methyl-propene (isobutylene)

$$CH_3CH_2OH \xrightarrow[160°C]{\text{conc. } H_2SO_4} CH_2=CH_2 + H_2O$$

(Carbon atoms are classified as being primary, secondary, or tertiary, depending on whether they are bonded to one, two, or three other carbon atoms, respectively. In a tertiary alcohol the hydroxyl group is bonded to a tertiary carbon atom; secondary and primary alcohols are analogously defined. This approach to naming compounds has been superseded by the modern system, but is still applied to given carbon atoms and to many commonly encountered organic substances.)

In dehydrohalogenation and dehydration reactions an interesting situation develops when highly substituted alcohols or halides are used. Consider the following dehydrohalogenation reaction:

$$CH_3-\underset{\underset{CH_3}{|}}{\overset{\overset{CH_3}{|}}{C}}-\underset{\underset{Br}{|}}{\overset{\overset{H}{|}}{C}}-CH_3 \xrightarrow[-(H_2O+Br^-)]{OH^-} CH_3-\underset{\underset{CH_3}{|}}{\overset{\overset{CH_3}{|}}{C}}-\overset{\overset{H}{|}}{C}=CH_2 \text{ and } CH_3-\underset{\underset{CH_3}{|}}{\overset{\overset{CH_3}{|}}{C}}=C-CH_3$$

(A)   (B)

In this reaction the halogen atom is removed from a carbon atom adjacent to a tertiary carbon atom; the product obtained includes A plus varying amounts of B, a molecule in which a methyl, CH_3, group has migrated from one carbon to the next. Such a product as B is said to result from a molecular **rearrangement** reaction. Rearrangements of this kind are reasonably common, and are attributed to the capacity of a reaction intermediate to undergo the group shift necessary for the structural change. In some cases the rearrangement reaction is the one of interest, and would be referred to as an isomerization reaction.

Elimination reactions, like nucleophilic substitution reactions, may follow first-order or second-order kinetics. The mechanism of the first-order elimination reaction, like the S_N1 reaction, is thought to involve the carbonium ion intermediate. This mechanism allows one to see a relation between nucleophilic substitution, elimination, and rearrangement reactions which is not at once apparent. For all of these reactions, when they are first-order, the first step in the accepted mechanism is the formation of the positively charged carbonium ion:

$$R_2-\underset{\underset{R_3}{|}}{\overset{\overset{R_1}{|}}{C}}-X \xrightarrow{\text{slow}} \left[R_2-\underset{R_3}{\overset{R_1}{C}}\right]^+ + X^-$$

As soon as the carbonium ion forms, the bonds to the central carbon atom assume a planar configuration with all bond angles equal. At that point there are several possible reactions which can occur:

1. Recombination of the carbonium ion with X^- to form the original halide.

2. Combination of the carbonium ion with a nucleophilic group present in the system, resulting in a nucleophilic substitution reaction.

3. Elimination of a hydrogen ion, H^+, from one of the carbon atoms adjacent to the central carbon atom, resulting in a dehydrohalogenation reaction. For example, assuming R_1 is a CH_3 group,

$$\left[CH_3-C\begin{smallmatrix} R_3 \\ \\ R_2 \end{smallmatrix} \right]^+ \longrightarrow CH_2{=}C\begin{smallmatrix} R_3 \\ \\ R_2 \end{smallmatrix} + H^+$$

4. Rearrangement of the carbonium ion to a more stable carbonium ion species, followed by elimination of a hydrogen ion; the net result would be a rearrangement reaction. If R_2 and R_3 were hydrogen groups and R_1 was a tertiary butyl group, a rearrangement to form a tertiary carbonium ion, which can be resonance stabilized, would be expected to occur.

$$\left[\begin{smallmatrix} & CH_3 & H \\ CH_3-C-C & \\ & CH_3 & H \end{smallmatrix} \right]^+ \longrightarrow \left[\begin{smallmatrix} CH_3 & H \\ CH_3-C---C-H \\ & CH_3 \end{smallmatrix} \right]^+ \longrightarrow \begin{smallmatrix} CH_3 & H \\ C{=}C \\ CH_3 & CH_3 \end{smallmatrix} + H^+$$

(It would also be possible for the rearranged carbonium ion to react with the nucleophilic group, yielding a product which was both substituted and rearranged.)

The reaction that is actually observed in a given case depends to some extent on the conditions in the reacting system. Since each of the possible reactions proceeds to an equilibrium state, and each has an equilibrium constant of roughly the same magnitude, it is often possible to obtain the product desired by proper choice of the reagent concentrations. Since dehydrohalogenation and dehydration reactions both produce a hydrogen ion, which reacts with hydroxide ion to form water, those reactions are favored in strongly alkaline alcoholic solutions, in which water concentration is kept low and hydroxide ion concentration is high. Nucleophilic substitution reactions would ordinarily be carried out in water solution in which there is a high concentration of the substituting negative ion. Molecular rearrangements will tend to occur if they are favored energywise, but can sometimes be controlled by using catalysts.

Reaction via the carbonium ion intermediate occurs most readily when the carbon atom bonded to the nucleophilic group X is tertiary; that is, it is attached to three other carbon atoms. Such substances form relatively stable carbonium ions and exhibit first-order kinetics in substitution and elimination reactions. On the other hand, substances in which X is bonded to a primary carbon atom, as in RCH_2X, follow second-order kinetics in such reactions. The mechanism for second-order elimination reactions, like that for S_N2 reactions, involves in the first step a collision between the nucleophilic group and the starting compound. No carbonium ion is formed and typically no molecular rearrangements occur.

Grignard Reagents

Some organic syntheses are accomplished by methods which at first seem unlikely. Empirical discoveries have furnished the organic chemist with special reagents which are extremely useful in particular cases, sometimes making possible syntheses which cannot be readily carried out by other means. One of the most important groups of special reagents comprises those materials known as **Grignard reagents.**

If a solution of an alkyl halide in anhydrous ethyl ether is mixed with magnesium shavings, a reaction takes place in which the magnesium dissolves and an ether soluble substance, an alkyl magnesium halide, is formed; this substance is called a Grignard reagent.

$$R—X + Mg \xrightarrow{\text{dry ether}} R—Mg—X$$

A Grignard reagent

Although the exact structure of the Grignard reagent is not known, it seems clear that the ether in the system serves both as a solvent and as a complexing agent with the Grignard reagent. The complex that results from the reaction is chemically very reactive and is typically used in the solution in which it was generated. Since there are many reactions in which Grignard reagents are employed, these substances rank among the most useful synthetic tools of the organic chemist. In 1912, Victor Grignard, a French chemist, was awarded the Nobel Prize for their discovery.

One of the very simple reactions of the Grignard reagents is that of hydrolysis, which occurs on addition of water or an alcohol to the ether solution, yielding a hydrocarbon.

$$R—Mg—X + R'OH \longrightarrow R—H + Mg\begin{smallmatrix} X \\ \\ OR' \end{smallmatrix}$$

If methylmagnesium bromide is used in this reaction, methane is produced and leaves the system as a gas. Higher-boiling hydrocarbons will dissolve in the ether layer and can be removed by distillation. The method is a very convenient one for the preparation of hydrocarbons from alkyl halides, and, since the reaction is quantitative, can be used for analysis of hydroxyl hydrogen in alcohols.

Another reaction of the Grignard reagents is that of addition to carbon dioxide, often carried out by simply pouring the ether solution over dry ice. Addition of water to the resulting mixture produces a carboxylic acid.

$$R—Mg—X + O{=}C{=}O \longrightarrow R—\overset{O}{\overset{\|}{C}}—O—Mg—X \xrightarrow{H_2O} R—C\overset{O}{\underset{OH}{\diagup}} + MgXOH$$

A carboxylic acid

Use of ethylmagnesium bromide ($R = CH_3CH_2$) in this reaction would produce propionic acid, CH_3CH_2COOH in about 70 per cent yield. Proper choice of the alkyl halide used to prepare the Grignard reagent allows the synthesis of a wide variety of carboxylic acids by this method.

Grignard reagents will add to the carbonyl groups in aldehydes, ketones, and esters to yield, on subsequent hydrolysis, alcohols. The reaction offers a very general method for the laboratory preparation of a wide variety of alcohols and is extensively used. Reaction with formaldehyde produces primary alcohols, containing the group —CH_2OH. Secondary alcohols, containing a —CRHOH group, result from reaction with higher aldehydes, and tertiary alcohols, with the —CRR'OH group, are formed when ketones and esters are the source of the carbonyl groups.

For primary alcohols:

$$R-Mg-X + O=C\begin{smallmatrix}H\\\\H\end{smallmatrix} \longrightarrow R-\overset{\overset{\displaystyle H}{|}}{\underset{\underset{\displaystyle H}{|}}{C}}-O-Mg-X \xrightarrow{H_2O} RCH_2OH$$

Ethylmagnesium bromide would yield 1-propanol, $CH_3CH_2CH_2OH$, in this reaction.
    For secondary alcohols:

$$R-Mg-X + O=C\begin{smallmatrix}R'\\\\H\end{smallmatrix} \longrightarrow R-\overset{\overset{\displaystyle R'}{|}}{\underset{\underset{\displaystyle H}{|}}{C}}-O-Mg-X \xrightarrow{H_2O} R-\overset{\overset{\displaystyle R'}{|}}{\underset{\underset{\displaystyle H}{|}}{C}}-OH$$

Ethylmagnesium bromide reacting with acetaldehyde $(R' = CH_3)$ would produce the secondary alcohol, 2-butanol, in the foregoing reaction.
    For tertiary alcohols:

$$R-Mg-X + O=C\begin{smallmatrix}R'\\\\R''\end{smallmatrix} \longrightarrow R-\overset{\overset{\displaystyle R'}{|}}{\underset{\underset{\displaystyle R''}{|}}{C}}-O-Mg-X \xrightarrow{H_2O} R-\overset{\overset{\displaystyle R'}{|}}{\underset{\underset{\displaystyle R''}{|}}{C}}-OH$$

Ethylmagnesium bromide added to acetone $(R' = R'' = CH_3)$ would yield, on hydrolysis, the tertiary alcohol 2-methyl-2-butanol.
    An ester, on being added to a Grignard reagent, produces an unstable intermediate that decomposes to a ketone, which then reacts with another molecule of the Grignard reagent to produce, on hydrolysis, a tertiary alcohol. The reactions are:

$$R-Mg-X + R'-\overset{\overset{\displaystyle O-R''}{|}}{C}=O \longrightarrow R-\overset{\overset{\displaystyle O-R''}{|}}{\underset{\underset{\displaystyle R'}{|}}{C}}-O-Mg-X \longrightarrow$$

$$R-\overset{}{\underset{\underset{\displaystyle R'}{|}}{C}}=O \xrightarrow{R-Mg-X} R-\overset{\overset{\displaystyle R}{|}}{\underset{\underset{\displaystyle R'}{|}}{C}}-O-Mg-X \xrightarrow{H_2O} R-\overset{\overset{\displaystyle R}{|}}{\underset{\underset{\displaystyle R'}{|}}{C}}-OH$$

Ethylmagnesium bromide in reaction with ethyl acetate $(R' = CH_3$ and $R'' = C_2H_5)$ would produce 3-methyl-3-pentanol.
    There are other reactions in which the Grignard reagents are used to good advantage, but the examples just given afford illustrations of their many possibilities in organic syntheses.

24.3 PETROLEUM AND RUBBER: TWO MATERIALS OF IMPORTANCE IN THE CHEMICAL INDUSTRY

Although chemists, like other people interested in research, often work simply to learn more about their science, a great deal of research is done for the purpose of financial profit. Attempts by the chemical industry to improve and develop products obtained from natural sources have resulted in increased knowledge, both applied and theoretical, and have been responsible in large measure for the enormous growth of the industry since 1940. One of the naturally occurring materials of greatest interest to the industrial chemist has been the substance known as petroleum.

Petroleum

Petroleum, or oil, is found in underground pools in many regions of the earth. Its origin lies in plants and animals which lived on the earth and in the sea many millions of years ago. The residues from these organisms accumulated in certain regions, possibly as a result of geologic conditions, became buried, and were subjected to high pressures and reducing conditions over long periods of time. The resulting material, petroleum, is a complex mixture of hydrocarbons, containing paraffinic chain and ring molecules, aromatic molecules, and small amounts of oxygen- and sulfur-containing substances.

Petroleum has been known for thousands of years, being observed as surface seepages, particularly as oil films on streams and ponds. It had no known use, except as "medicine oil," until about the mid-nineteenth century, when the first oil wells were drilled in this country and Rumania. Crude oil, on being distilled, yielded a fraction known as kerosene, which had immediate commercial importance as a lamp fuel; for many years kerosene was the main product of the petroleum industry.

With the development of the automobile a lower-boiling fraction obtained in the distillation of petroleum, straight-run gasoline, became of dominant value. Since a 50-gal. barrel of crude oil yielded only about 7 or 8 gal. of gasoline, it became a matter of great commercial significance to increase the size of the gasoline fraction. Chemical research on this problem has been very successful, and has resulted in: (1) more and better gasolines, (2) a knowledge of what substances make up petroleum, (3) a knowledge of what substances make a good gasoline, and (4) much basic knowledge in organic chemistry, including much of the material presented in the previous section of this chapter.

As a result of petroleum research, chemists now are able to manipulate almost at will the end products of the petroleum refining process to meet many different kinds of demands, from home heating gases to jet fuels to road asphalts, in the way which makes best use of the starting material. A by-product of this research has been the petrochemical industry, which is rapidly assuming a major role as a supplier of the many organic chemicals which can now be produced from petroleum.

Following a rough distillation of the crude oil into the fractions indicated in Table 24.2, the higher molecular weight fractions are carried through a controlled pyrolysis, or *cracking*, process, in which they are heated to about 500°C, often under catalytic conditions (see Section 24.1). In this process the molecules suffer a rupture of a carbon-carbon bond, yielding olefins and paraffins of lower molecular weight than the original fraction. The product contains a substantial fraction of substances which boil in the same range as gasoline, thus increasing significantly the yield of gasoline from crude oil. The lighter olefins, particularly ethylene and propylene, have in recent years found a market as raw materials in the plastics industry.

In order to further increase gasoline yield and quality, there are several other procedures used to treat both the original distillate fractions and the products from the cracking step. Since it has been found that branched-chain molecules perform better as motor fuels than do those containing straight chains, the middle distillation fractions are often subjected to a *reforming*, or isomerization process, in which the fraction is passed over a solid catalyst such as aluminum chloride, at about 200°C. The reactions which occur are very similar to the rearrangements discussed in the previous section. With normal pentane, for example, one would obtain on isomerization:

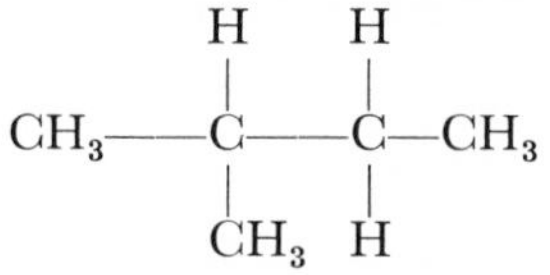

$$CH_3-\underset{\underset{CH_3}{|}}{\overset{\overset{H}{|}}{C}}-\underset{\underset{H}{|}}{\overset{\overset{H}{|}}{C}}-CH_3 \qquad\qquad CH_3-\underset{\underset{CH_3}{|}}{\overset{\overset{CH_3}{|}}{C}}-CH_3$$

2-Methylbutane 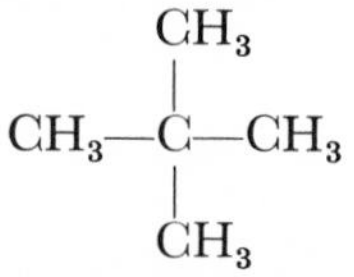 2,2-Dimethylpropane

Both these substances would be superior to the unbranched pentane as automobile fuel. Isomerization reactions also undoubtedly occur to some extent during cracking and so make an additional contribution in that step to the fuel quality of the product.

TABLE 24.2 FRACTIONS OBTAINED ON DISTILLATION OF PETROLEUM

Fraction	Boiling Range (°C)	Carbon Atom Content	Direct Use
Gas	below 20	C_1–C_4	gas heating
Petroleum ether	20–60	C_5–C_6	industrial solvent
Light naphtha	60–100	C_6–C_7	industrial solvent
Straight-run gasoline	40–200	C_5–C_{10}	motor vehicle fuel
Kerosene	175–325	C_{11}–C_{18}	jet fuel
Gas oil	275–500		diesel fuel
Lubricating oil	above 400	C_{15}–C_{40}	lubricant
Asphalt	nonvolatile		roofing and road construction

The light fractions, containing C_3 and C_4 hydrocarbons from the distillation and cracking operations, can be converted to useful gasolines by **polymerization** and **alkylation** processes, which are selective reversals of cracking. In polymerization reactions, gaseous olefins combine with each other to yield branched olefins, which can be used directly as fuel or hydrogenated to the saturated hydrocarbons:

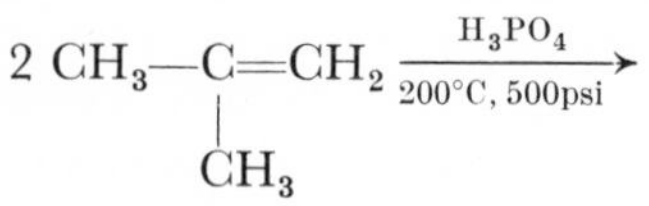

$$2\ CH_3-\underset{\underset{CH_3}{|}}{C}=CH_2 \xrightarrow[200°C,\ 500psi]{H_3PO_4}$$

Isobutene

$$CH_3-\underset{\underset{CH_3}{|}}{\overset{\overset{CH_3}{|}}{C}}-\underset{\underset{H}{|}}{\overset{\overset{H}{|}}{C}}-\underset{\underset{CH_3}{|}}{C}=CH_2 \xrightarrow{H_2} CH_3-\underset{\underset{CH_3}{|}}{\overset{\overset{CH_3}{|}}{C}}-\underset{\underset{H}{|}}{\overset{\overset{H}{|}}{C}}-\underset{\underset{CH_3}{|}}{\overset{\overset{H}{|}}{C}}-CH_3$$

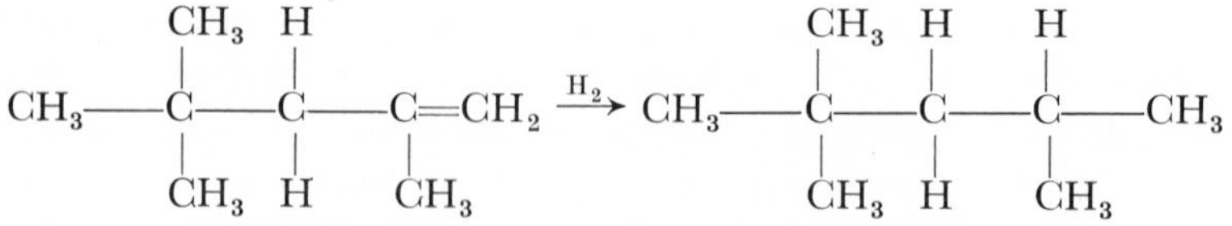

Isooctene Isooctane

In the alkylation reaction, a branched alkane is added to an olefin, producing another branched alkane of more suitable molecular weight. The following reaction is illustrative and commercially important:

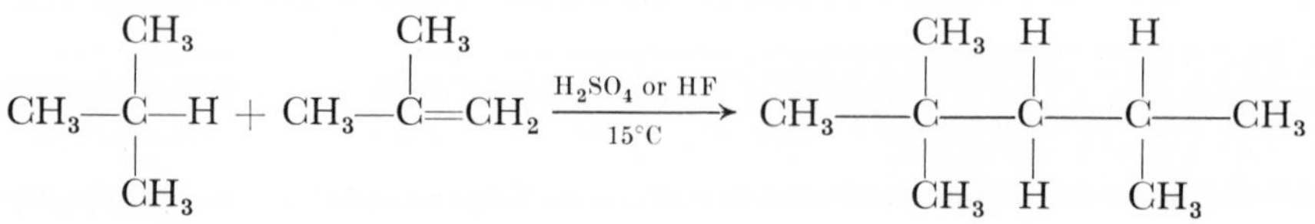

$$CH_3-\underset{\underset{CH_3}{|}}{\overset{\overset{CH_3}{|}}{C}}-H + CH_3-\underset{\underset{CH_3}{|}}{\overset{\overset{CH_3}{|}}{C}}=CH_2 \xrightarrow[15°C]{H_2SO_4\ or\ HF} CH_3-\underset{\underset{CH_3}{|}}{\overset{\overset{CH_3}{|}}{C}}-\underset{\underset{H}{|}}{\overset{\overset{H}{|}}{C}}-\underset{\underset{CH_3}{|}}{\overset{\overset{H}{|}}{C}}-CH_3$$

Isobutane Isobutene Isooctane

(Gasolines are rated in quality according to their resistance to "knock," or detonation, instead of smooth burning, in the automobile engine. Isooctane, produced in the foregoing reactions, is very resistant to knock, and has been assigned an *octane number* of 100. Normal heptane, a straight-chain hydrocarbon prone to knocking, is given an octane number of 0. Commercial gasolines are assigned octane numbers on the basis of their performances against mixtures of these two reference hydrocarbons.)

As a final process for the production and improvement of gasolines we should mention **aromatization.** In this process straight-chain hydrocarbons are cyclized and dehydrogenated to form aromatic substances. The reaction is carried out at about 500°C in the presence of molybdenum oxide catalyst on alumina. The reaction as applied to normal heptane is indicated schematically as follows:

n-Heptane   Methyl cyclohexane   Toluene

This process, which is called **hydroforming,** has become increasingly important as a source of aromatic substances in the chemical industry. The products, of which toluene is typical, may be blended into gasolines to upgrade quality, or may be sold as pure substances, depending on demand.

Rubber

Another naturally-occurring organic material of chemical importance is the substance we know as rubber. The source is a latex or sap, produced by the Hevea, or rubber tree, which is grown mainly in Ceylon and Indonesia. The latex is collected and treated with acetic acid to precipitate the raw rubber, which coagulates, is pressed dry, and rolled into sheets for shipment.

Raw rubber is a gummy, light-colored substance, which becomes sticky when warmed and brittle when cold. Charles Goodyear made the discovery in 1834 that if natural rubber is heated with sulfur a reaction occurs, which produces a new material with the properties we normally associate with rubber, namely elasticity, flexibility, and resistance to abrasion. Ordinarily commercial rubber is prepared by this process, which is called vulcanization; rubber also usually contains certain additives, particularly carbon blacks, which are both less expensive than rubber and also greatly improve its resistance to wear and tearing.

Soon after its discovery vulcanized rubber found significant uses in articles requiring good water resistance, such as raincoats and overshoes, and in tires for wagon wheels. With the development of the automobile, demand for tires resulted in an enormous increase in the rubber industry and provided great incentive for improving quality of tire rubber. Again, chemical research on the problem has resulted in rubbers with vastly improved properties as tire material and has also furnished us with knowledge of the chemical structure of rubber. This knowledge, applied to the production of synthetic rubbers, has led to a variety of rubbers tailored for special purposes.

It is now known that natural rubber is a polymeric substance, containing in its molecules many units of a monomer called isoprene, 2-methyl-1,3-butadiene, attached to one another in the following manner:

$$2n \left[\begin{array}{c} CH_3 \quad\quad H \\ \diagdown\quad\quad\diagup \\ C{-}C \\ \diagup\quad\quad\diagdown \\ CH_2 \quad\quad CH_2 \end{array} \right] \longrightarrow \left[\begin{array}{c} CH_3 \quad\quad H \\ \diagdown\quad\quad\diagup \\ C{=}C \\ \diagup\quad\quad\diagdown \\ {-}CH_2 \quad\quad CH_2{-}CH_2 \quad\quad CH_2{-} \\ \diagdown\quad\quad\diagup \\ C{=}C \\ \diagup\quad\quad\diagdown \\ CH_3 \quad\quad H \end{array} \right]_n$$

Isoprene unit   Natural rubber

Natural rubber polymer molecules contain long chains of isoprene units, linked as shown, with a molecular weight average of about 400,000. During the vulcanization process the long polymer chains are cross-linked by reaction with fairly short chains of sulfur atoms (one to about six atoms long); it appears that in the process H_2S is eliminated and relatively little of the unsaturation in the rubber is lost. Ordinary rubber is produced by vulcanization with about 3 per cent sulfur by weight; hard rubber results when the amount of sulfur is increased to about 30 per cent.

Recently it has become possible to carry out the polymerization of isoprene synthetically to produce a product essentially identical to natural rubber. There is now some commercial production of this synthetic "natural" rubber, which promises ultimately to make the rubber industry independent of the plantation-produced material. Though it only takes a moment to read these sentences, the determination of the true structure of natural rubber and its subsequent production by synthetic means was a problem that took many years and the work of many people for its solution.

Although the detailed evaluation of the structure of the rubber polymer was an extremely difficult problem, the nature of the monomer has been known for many years. It was found that isoprene could be polymerized to a rubberlike material even before 1900 (the substance produced was not natural rubber, since in natural rubber only the cis configuration shown in the foregoing diagram exists, whereas normal polymerization of isoprene yields chains with several different configurations). The knowledge of the nature of the monomer gave some incentive to production of synthetic rubbers, less expensive, or more available, than the natural product. In Germany during the first World War, since isoprene could not easily be produced, chemists turned to the following monomer,

$$\begin{array}{c} CH_3 \quad\quad CH_3 \\ \diagdown\quad\quad\diagup \\ C{-}C \\ \diagup\quad\quad\diagdown \\ CH_2 \quad\quad CH_2 \end{array}$$

2,3-Dimethylbutadiene

and, by its polymerization, produced significant amounts of the first synthetic rubber, called methyl rubber. By vulcanization they were able to manufacture a reasonably satisfactory hard rubber, but soft methyl rubber, such as that needed in tire tubes, was completely inadequate to its task.

Since about 1930 several synthetic rubbers have been produced commercially.

One of the most important of these is neoprene, a polymer of the monomer chloroprene,

$$
\begin{array}{ccc}
H & & Cl \\
\diagdown & & \diagup \\
& C\!-\!C & \\
\diagup & & \diagdown \\
CH_2 & & CH_2
\end{array}
$$

Chloroprene

This substance, when polymerized with due regard to the structure of the product,
yields a rubber which for many purposes is superior to natural rubber. It is highly
resistant to organic solvents, to water, and to oxidation. Although it is excellent as a
tire rubber, it is somewhat more expensive than other satisfactory synthetic rubbers.

During World War II supplies of natural rubber from Malaya and the East
Indies were cut off, making it imperative that the United States produce synthetic
rubber in large volume on short notice. A copolymer of 1,3-butadiene,

$$CH_2\!=\!CHCH\!=\!CH_2,$$

and styrene, $C_6H_5C\!=\!CH_2$, was found to perform satisfactorily, and in 1945 this synthetic rubber (Buna S, GRS, or SBR are some of its common names) was produced
in this country in the amount of 700,000 tons. This material is still used to some
extent as a tire rubber, but is usually mixed with natural rubber or other synthetic
rubbers to improve performance. Very recently, polymerized butadiene, having the
cis structure present in the polymer double bonds in natural rubber, has been manufactured commercially, and promises to become an important rubber either in its
own right or in blends with natural or styrene-butadiene rubbers.

24.4   NATURAL PRODUCTS

The organic substances we have so far considered contain relatively simple
molecules, which can, for the most part, be derived from petroleum or coal. Many,
perhaps most, organic compounds are obtained from the other natural source of such
substances, namely, living plants and animals. The organic compounds which are
found in living organisms are called *natural products*, and include some of the most
complex substances known. These substances have long been of interest to organic
and biochemists, who have studied their reactions both inside and outside the living
system and have expended great effort in determining their molecular structures.
In this section we shall be able to discuss but a few examples of this very important
area of research.

Glucose: A Typical Carbohydrate and Sugar

A very common natural product is the substance known as glucose. Glucose
is a member of that class of compounds known as sugars; it is present in syrup, in
some fruits, and is the sugar dissolved in blood. Glucose is obtained from the hydrolysis
of both starch and cellulose. Because of its very wide occurrence in both the free and
combined forms, it is perhaps the most abundant of all the organic substances.

Glucose also belongs to the **carbohydrate** family, which includes all the sugars.
The molecular formula of glucose is $C_6H_{12}O_6$, which, like the formulas of all the
carbohydrates, can be written as $C_x(H_2O)_y$. The carbohydrates are among the most
important of the foods of man, being used by the body as a source of energy and as

an intermediate in the formation of other substances. The chemical bonding in glucose is:

$$
O{=}\overset{\underset{|}{H}}{C}-\overset{\underset{|}{H}}{\underset{OH}{C}}-\overset{\underset{|}{H}}{\underset{OH}{C}}-\overset{\underset{|}{H}}{\underset{OH}{C}}-\overset{\underset{|}{H}}{\underset{OH}{C}}-\overset{\underset{|}{H}}{\underset{OH}{C}}-H
$$

The glucose molecule is typical of the simple sugars. It contains a carbon chain, with one carbonyl group and hydroxyl groups on each carbon atom except the one in the carbonyl group. Because of the tetrahedral symmetry about the saturated carbon atom, the carbon chain in glucose is bent; this means that, although there is free rotation around all the single C—C bonds, the relative positions of hydrogen atoms and hydroxyl groups on the chain are of significance, and that, for instance, the two structures below actually represent different substances:

Glucose	Mannose

(In these drawings, the large and small symbols denote atoms above and below the plane of the paper.) Both substances are simple sugars, but, without breaking bonds, cannot be converted one to the other. The two substances are called **stereoisomers** of the basic structure. Fischer recognized the existence of such isomers and was able to show that ordinary glucose was one of sixteen possible stereoisomers of the six-carbon sugars having an aldehyde end group (the aldohexoses).

The problem of finding which of the sixteen configurations of the stereoisomers of glucose actually belonged to naturally-occurring glucose was solved by the great German chemist, Emil Fischer, in the twenty-year period beginning about 1885. By degrading longer-chain sugars to shorter ones of known configurations, by synthesizing longer-chain sugars from shorter, and by studying the relations between various derivatives formed from his sugar products, Fischer was finally able to determine the actual configuration of glucose and the other naturally occurring aldohexoses. For this work Fischer was awarded the Nobel Prize in chemistry in 1902.

Glucose and most other sugars in solution have the rather remarkable property of being able to rotate the plane of a beam of polarized light as it passes through the solution. These substances are said to be **optically active.** Optical activity is found in any organic substance in which there are carbon atoms bonded to four different groups; such carbon atoms are said to be **asymmetric.** In the aldohexoses there are four asymmetric carbon atoms, atoms to which are attached four nonidentical groups. Since each of the stereoisomers of glucose has a characteristic ability to rotate the plane of polarized light, Fischer was able to make use of their optical activities in his identifications of the various isomers.

Natural glucose is dextrorotatory, meaning its solutions rotate the plane of polarized light in a clockwise direction as one looks at the oncoming beam. D-glucose, the naturally occurring isomer, will have a mirror image, L-glucose, one of the sixteen stereoisomers, which is levorotatory to the same degree that D-glucose is dextrorotatory. Like glucose, most naturally occurring optically active substances exist

in only one stereoisomeric configuration. (Natural glucose is given the prefix D-
because its configuration is related to that of D-glyceraldehyde, dextrorotary gly-
ceraldehyde, and *not* because it is itself dextrorotatory.)

Fischer's problem of the determinations of the structures of the sugars was
complicated by the fact that under ordinary circumstances sugars like glucose have
a cyclic structure. The most stable form of the D-glucose molecule is known to have
the following configuration:

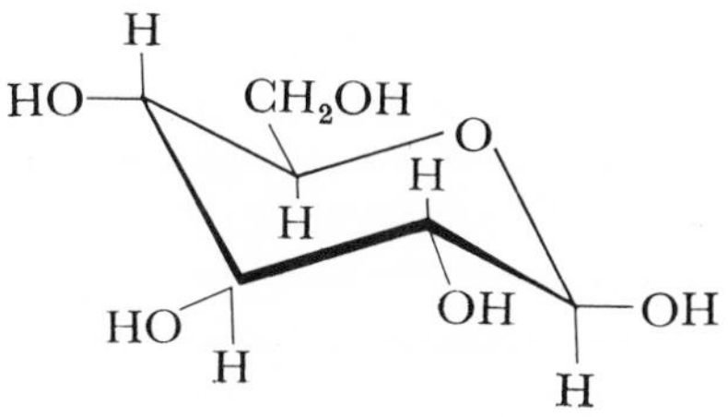

β-D-glucose

The ring is six-membered, containing one oxygen atom. From above it would appear
as a hexagon, with carbon ring atoms alternately up and down, in a so-called chair
configuration. The bulky OH and CH$_2$OH groups are oriented away from the
ring center, more or less in the plane of the molecule, whereas the H atoms are in
positions more directly above and below the ring; this structure, as might be expected,
minimizes intramolecular strains caused by large groups in close proximity. When the
ring is formed, the relative positions of the H and OH groups at the ring position
at the extreme right in the drawing are sometimes interchanged, giving rise to an
alternate, slightly less stable structure for the molecule, which is given the name
α-D-glucose. The aqueous solution of glucose actually contains mainly cyclic molecules, 64 per cent β and 36 per cent α forms, along with a small amount of the open-
chain form. In view of the enormous complexity of the properties of the aldohexoses,
the determination of the configurations of stereoisomers of glucose by Fischer must
even now be considered one of the major triumphs of the organic chemist.

Many sugars contain more than one simple sugar group per molecule. Ordinary
sucrose, cane sugar, is a **disaccharide,** and on acid hydrolysis yields two simple
sugars, of which one is D-glucose and the other, another common sugar, is called
D-fructose. The molecular structure of sucrose is as follows:

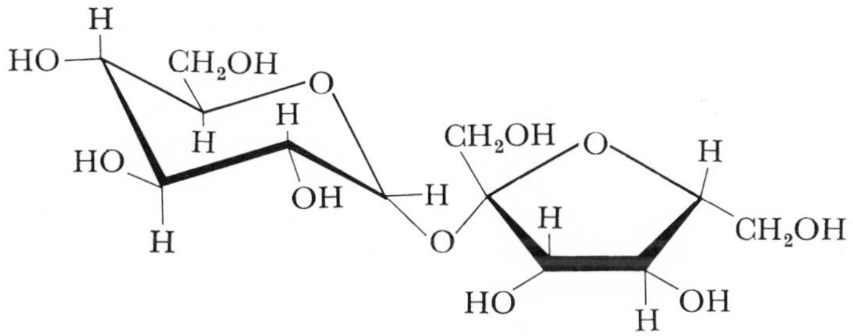

Sucrose

The substances known as starch and cellulose both yield only glucose when subjected to acid hydrolysis. Starch is found in many plants, in which it is the carbohydrate stored in roots and seeds. It is present in large amounts in corn, potatoes, and wheat, and is one of the main sources of energy in our foods. Cellulose is the substance which makes up the cell membranes of most plants. Ordinary wood is about 50 per cent cellulose; dry leaves, about 10 per cent. Cotton fiber, which contains about 98 per cent cellulose, is the best source of the pure material.

Both starch and cellulose are polymers of glucose, with molecular weights of about a million. The glucose units are linked through oxygen bridges, which may be considered to have formed in a condensation polymerization reaction in which one molecule of water is removed for each glucose molecule entering the chain. Cellulose molecules are unbranched; the chains are strongly hydrogen bonded, giving the material its high resistance to water and alcohols. Starch molecules are occasionally branched and cross-linked perhaps once in 25 glucose units. The structures of starch and cellulose are similar and are indicated in the following formulas:

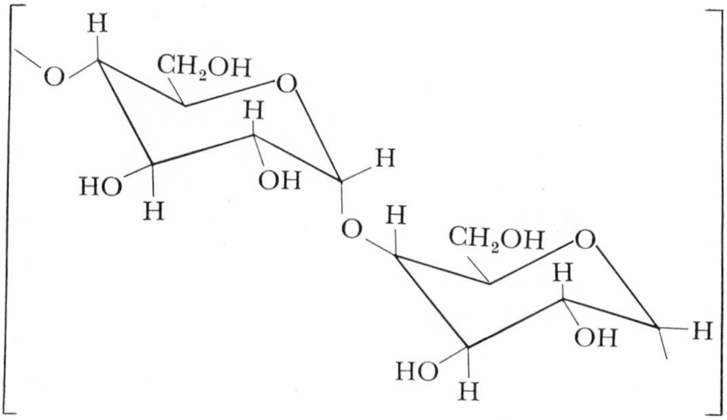

Starch

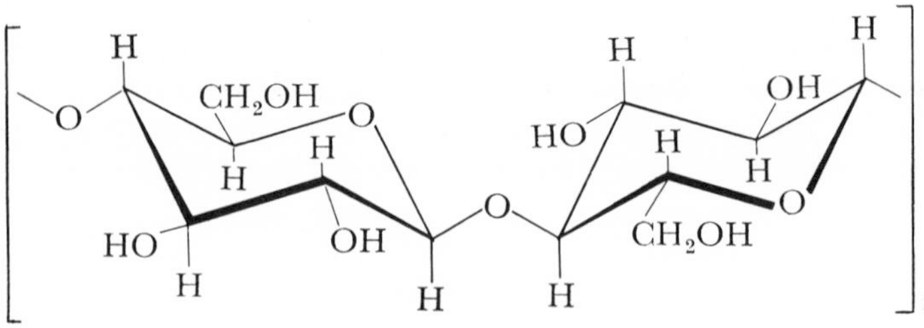

Cellulose

The essential difference between the cellulose and starch molecules appears to be that in the former the cyclic glucose units are in the β form, while in starch the α form exists. Starch can be readily hydrolyzed in the human body to the disaccharide called maltose by an enzyme called diastase. Cellulose, perhaps because of the more stable β configuration in its rings, is not affected by human enzymes and so is not useful as a food for man.

Amino Acids and Proteins

Although the structures of the carbohydrates are far from simple, some of the most complex substances belong to a different class of natural products, called the **proteins.** It is in this area that much of the recent structural work has been done, with results that are truly impressive.

Proteins, like the polysaccharides starch and cellulose, are polymeric substances derived from a fairly large group of monomer units, called **amino acids.** The amino acids which are obtained from proteins are all α-amino acids, meaning that the amino, NH_2, group is on the carbon atom adjacent to the carboxyl group. The general formula for an α-amino acid can be written as:

$$R—\underset{\underset{H}{|}}{\overset{\overset{NH_2}{|}}{C}}—C\overset{\displaystyle O}{\underset{\displaystyle OH}{}}$$

An α-amino acid

As you can see, unless R=H, the central carbon atom in the α-amino acid is asymmetric, making these substances optically active. As with the naturally occurring sugars, all the known α-amino acids derivable from proteins are of exactly the same symmetry, which turns out to be the L form, related to L-glyceraldehyde. These materials, however, may be dextro- or levorotatory, depending on the particular acid. The R group in the natural amino acids may be one of twenty-four groups. The names, abbreviations, and R groups present in these acids are given in Table 24.3.

Proteins constitute one of the major foods of man. They are present in most foods, but are more abundant in lean meats and vegetables such as beans and peas than in fats or starchy foods such as potatoes and corn. In the animal body the proteins are hydrolyzed to α-amino acids, which are used to synthesize the many kinds of body protein. The body cannot synthesize all these α-amino acids and must obtain about fourteen of them from the food which is eaten.

As we have noted, proteins are polymers of the α-amino acids. In a given protein, however, there are typically several amino acids, linked together in a specific order in a branched-chain structure. The linkage between amino acid molecules is from the acid carboxyl group on one molecule to the amino group on the next, with one water molecule being removed from the system per link formed; formally, then, the proteins may be considered to be condensation polymers of the amino acids. The bonding in the polymer chain is as indicated below:

$$—\underset{\underset{H}{|}}{\overset{\overset{}{|}}{N}}—\underset{}{\overset{\overset{R}{|}}{C}}—\overset{\overset{O}{||}}{C}—\underset{\underset{H}{|}}{\overset{\overset{}{|}}{N}}—\underset{}{\overset{\overset{R'}{|}}{C}}—\overset{\overset{O}{||}}{C}—\underset{\underset{H}{|}}{\overset{\overset{}{|}}{N}}—\underset{}{\overset{\overset{R''}{|}}{C}}—\overset{\overset{O}{||}}{C}—$$

Part of a protein chain

The bonds between acid units are sometimes called **peptide bonds,** and the protein itself may be called a polypeptide. In the chain just illustrated, R, R', and R″ would not ordinarily be the same groups. The molecular weights of proteins are similar to

TABLE 24.3 α-AMINO ACIDS OBTAINED FROM PROTEINS

Name	Abbreviation	R—	Name	Abbreviation	R
Glycine	Gly	H—	Tyrosine	Tyr	HO—C₆H₃—CH₂— (4-hydroxyphenyl)CH₂—
Alanine	Ala	CH_3-			
Valine	Val	$(CH_3)_2CH-$			
Leucine	Leu	$(CH_3)_2CHCH_2-$	Thyroxine	Thy	(see structure)
Isoleucine	Ileu	$CH_3CH_2CH(CH_3)-$			
Phenylalanine	Phe	$PhCH_2-$			
Serine	Ser	$HOCH_2-$	Tryptophan	Try	(indolyl)CH_2-
Threonine	Thr	CH_3CHOH-			
Cysteine	CySH	$HSCH_2-$			
Methionine	Met	$CH_3SCH_2CH_2-$			
Asparagine	Asp-NH₂	H_2NCOCH_2-			Acid Molecules
Glutamine	Glu-NH₂	$H_2NCOCH_2CH_2-$	Histidine	His	(imidazolyl)CH_2-
Lysine	Lys	$H_2NCH_2CH_2CH_2CH_2-$			
δ-Hydroxylysine	Lys-OH	$H_2NCH_2CH(OH)CH_2CH_2-$	Proline	Pro	(pyrrolidine-COOH)
Aspartic Acid	Asp	$HOOCCH_2-$			
Glutamic Acid	Glu	$HOOCCH_2CH_2-$			
Cystine	CySSCy	$-SCH_2-$ (an acid dimer)	Hydroxyproline	Hypro	(hydroxypyrrolidine-COOH)
Arginine	Arg	$H_2NCNHCH_2CH_2CH_2-$ (with $=NH$)			

those of many commercial polymers. Albumin from egg white has a molecular weight of about 44,000, whereas that of urease, obtained from soy beans, is about 450,000.

In view of the nature of proteins, it is clear that unambiguous structure determinations for these substances are extremely difficult. One must first obtain a sample of the pure protein. This is accomplished by precipitating the protein selectively at its pH of minimum solubility, removing residual salt by placing the protein in a semipermeable membrane and washing with water, thereby ultimately increasing the purity of the protein within the membrane to the point at which it can be crystallized. Some of the protein is then completely hydrolyzed and the resultant amino acids determined as to kind and amount. This can be accomplished by thin-layer or paper chromatography, by ion exchange resins, or by other means. The protein is then partially hydrolyzed, into fragments containing from two to about seven acid units. These are analyzed as were the amino acid units, as to type and relative amount, thereby establishing the sequences of acid units in the protein fragments. The final protein structure is obtained by noting how the fragments overlap one another, and how, therefore, the amino acid sequence must exist in the whole molecule. Several proteins have been analyzed by this method, one of the most complex being insulin, the structure of which was reported by F. Sanger in 1955 (Nobel Prize, 1958). The amino acid sequence in this substance is as follows:

$$
\begin{array}{l}
\text{NH}_2 \quad\quad\text{—S-S—} \quad\quad\quad\quad\quad\quad\quad \text{NH}_2 \quad\quad\quad\quad\quad\quad \text{AspNH}_2 \\
\;\;|\quad\; |\quad\quad\quad\quad\quad\quad\quad | \quad\quad\quad\quad\quad\quad\quad\quad\quad | \quad\quad\quad\quad\quad\quad\quad | \\
\text{Gly-Ileu-Val-Glu-Glu-Cy-Cy-Ala-Ser-Val-Cy-Ser-Leu-Tyr-Glu-Leu-Glu-Asp-Tyr-Cy}
\end{array}
$$

The insulin molecule

In addition to work on the problem of the amino acid sequence in proteins, there has been considerable research on the geometric arrangement of the protein chains in space. Within the protein chain there are many polar groups, some of which can interact through hydrogen bonding. It appears that in many proteins these interactions cause the chains to take on the form of a helix, like that of a coiled spring. In such a structure it is possible for hydrogen bonding to occur between a nitrogen atom at one point on the coil and an oxygen atom on a carbonyl group on the coil one turn down. In fibrous proteins such as hair and silk, several helices may intertwine, much in the manner in which the strands are twisted in a sisal rope, to give the fiber its strength and elasticity.

Some proteins, like insulin and egg albumin, yield only α-amino acids on hydrolysis. Other proteins are more complex, and can be resolved into two fractions, one containing a simple protein and the other a nonprotein group. Among the most interesting and challenging of the so-called *conjugated* proteins are the *nucleoproteins*, which can be resolved to produce a *nucleic acid* portion and a protein portion. Nucleoproteins are the main component of cell chromosomes; the nucleic acids are thought to be the substances which control cell reproduction and allow a species to reproduce its kind.

Nucleic acids are polymers with molecular weights of the order of one million. On complete hydrolysis they yield several kinds of substances, including one of two sugars, phosphoric acid, and a group of nitrogen ring compounds called nitrogen bases.

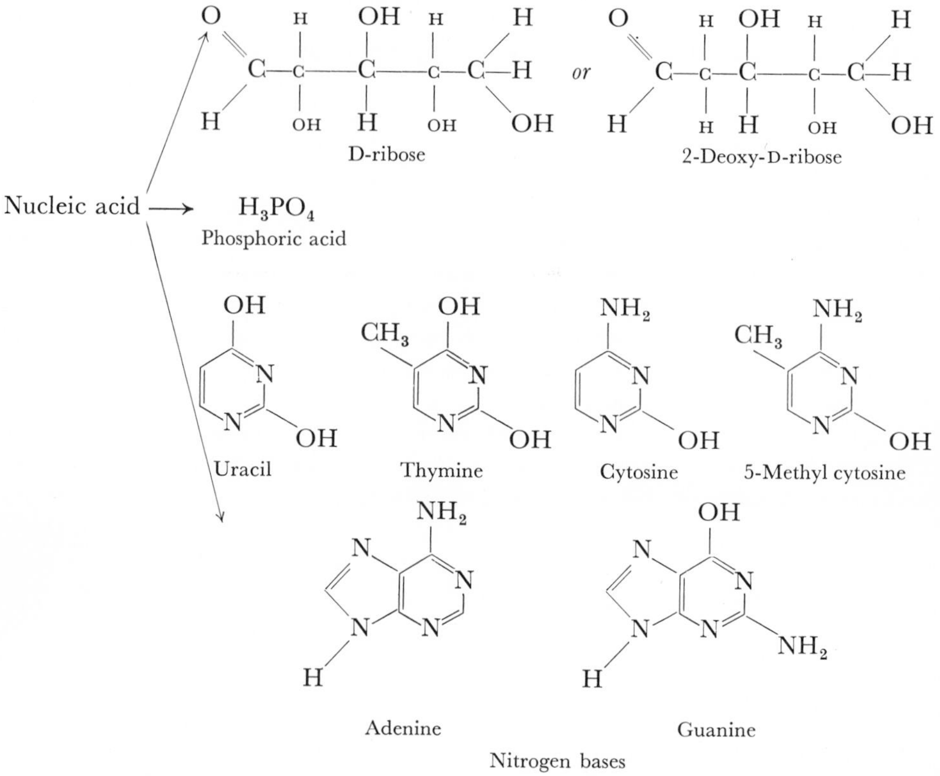

D-ribose

2-Deoxy-D-ribose

Nucleic acid $\longrightarrow$ H_3PO_4
Phosphoric acid

Uracil   Thymine   Cytosine   5-Methyl cytosine

Adenine   Guanine

Nitrogen bases

Partial hydrolysis of nucleic acids produces phosphoric acid plus fragments containing a sugar molecule bonded to a nitrogen base. This has led to the belief that the nucleic acid molecule consists of long chains of sugar–nitrogen base groups linked together by phosphate groups. When the sugar present is D-ribose, the nucleic

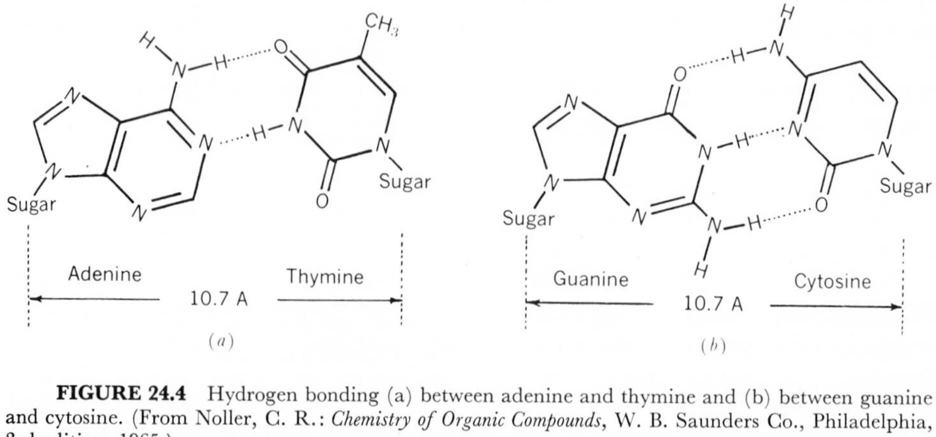

Adenine   Thymine   Guanine   Cytosine
|———— 10.7 A ————| |———— 10.7 A ————|
(a)   (b)

FIGURE 24.4   Hydrogen bonding (a) between adenine and thymine and (b) between guanine and cytosine. (From Noller, C. R.: *Chemistry of Organic Compounds*, W. B. Saunders Co., Philadelphia, 3rd edition, 1965.)

$\boxed{A}$ = Adenine $\boxed{T}$ = Thymine $\boxed{G}$ = Guanine $\boxed{C}$ = Cytosine

FIGURE 24.5 Representation of the double-stranded spiral structure of a hypothetical deoxy-ribonucleic acid. (From Noller, C. R.: *Chemistry of Organic Compounds*, W. B. Saunders Co., Philadelphia, 3rd edition, 1965.)

acid is called RNA (ribonucleic acid). When the sugar is 2-deoxy-D-ribose, the acid is given the name DNA (deoxyribonucleic acid). In a DNA molecule there are about 500 units. The arrangement of the units in RNA and DNA is thought to constitute the genetic code that defines species and individuals within the species. The overall composition of RNA and DNA within a given species appears to be fixed and to be different from that in other species. There are many, many different kinds of RNA and DNA molecules, presumably at least one for each species.

All DNA molecules produce on hydrolysis equal numbers of moles of adenine and thymine, and equal numbers of moles of guanine and cytosine plus methyl cytosine. This has led to the belief that in the molecule adenine and thymine groups are paired and so are guanine and cytosine groups. If one draws scale models of these substances, he finds that hydrogen bonding can readily occur between molecules in the same pair, but not between molecules in different pairs.

On the basis of this evidence and x-ray data on the DNA crystal, Watson and Crick (Nobel Prize, 1962) proposed that the DNA polymer consists of a two-stranded helix in which the two strands are held together by bonding between the pairs of substances. The sugar and phosphate units can be readily accommodated on the outside of the helix, producing a relatively compact molecule. The general structure is as indicated in Figure 24.5. The structure suggested by Watson and Crick has been examined by others and appears to be substantially correct. One important feature of the structure is that it leads to a rather simple explanation of the mechanism by which DNA can be reproduced by the organism. The double helix is thought to separate, and the individual strands to attract and bind to themselves in proper sequence the proper nitrogen base–sugar groups, creating in the process another strand essentially identical to the one which split off. The details of this process and of the actual arrangement of units in DNA and RNA molecules are not at present known, and are the subject of a great deal of research in that field of biochemistry which has come to be known as molecular biology.

PROBLEMS

24.1 Define each of the following terms. For each term give the formula of an organic substance which meets the definition and so would be included within the group of substances covered by the term:

Paraffin   Cycloparaffin
Hydrocarbon   Aromatic substance
Olefin   Alkene

24.2 Draw as many isomeric structures as you can for molecules with the formula C_5H_{12}.

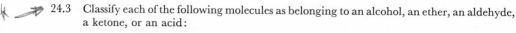

24.3 Classify each of the following molecules as belonging to an alcohol, an ether, an aldehyde, a ketone, or an acid:

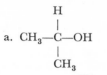

$$
\begin{array}{c}
\text{H} \\
| \\
\text{a. } CH_3—C—OH \\
| \\
CH_3
\end{array}
\qquad
\begin{array}{c}
\text{H} \\
| \\
\text{c. } CH_3—C—C—OH \\
| \quad \| \\
\text{H} \quad \text{O}
\end{array}
$$

$$
\begin{array}{c}
CH_3 \\
| \\
\text{b. } CH_3—C{=}O
\end{array}
\qquad\qquad
\text{d. } CH_3—CH_2—O—CH_3
$$

24.4 For each of the following molecular formulas, indicate whether the compound could be an <u>ether</u>, an <u>alcohol</u>, an <u>aldehyde</u>, a <u>ketone</u>, or an <u>acid</u>. Sketch the structures of the molecules which you believe to be consistent with your answers.

a. CH_4O b. C_2H_6O c. $C_2H_4O_2$ d. C_3H_6O e. CH_2O

24.5 Sketch the structure of the paradichlorobenzene molecule, $C_6H_4Cl_2$.

24.6 C_8H_8 is called cyclooctatetraene. Assuming the carbon skeleton of the molecule forms a regular plane octagon, how many dibromo derivatives of cyclooctatetraene would you expect to exist? (Actually cyclooctatetraene is not planar and it does not behave like a typical aromatic substance.)

24.7 How many isomers are there with the molecular formula C_4H_9Cl? Sketch each of the isomeric molecules.

24.8 Sketch the molecules of each of the following substances:
a. Methyl ethyl ether
b. Normal butyl alcohol
c. 2-Propanol
d. Acetaldehyde
e. Acetone
f. Glycerol
g. 1,2-Dichloroethane
h. 2-Methyl-3-ethylpentane

24.9 Define and give an example of a substance falling within each of the following classes of organic compounds:
a. Ketone
b. Ether
c. Carboxylic acid
d. Ester
e. Fat
f. Alkyl halide
g. Aldehyde
h. Phenol

24.10 What is the essential difference between soaps and the materials commonly called detergents?

24.11 Butane, C_4H_{10}, is a straight-chain saturated hydrocarbon. If each of the following substances contains a four-carbon unbranched chain, sketch its molecular structure:
Butyraldehyde
Butyric acid
2-Butanol
1-Butene
1-Butanol
2-Butanone (a ketone)

24.12 Consider the following possible reactions of 1-iodopropane:
a. $C_3H_7I + OH^- \rightarrow C_3H_7OH + I^-$
b. $C_3H_7I + OH^- \rightarrow C_3H_6 + H_2O + I^-$
What kind of reaction is reaction a? Reaction b? What reaction conditions would tend to favor reaction a? Reaction b?

24.13 What is a carbonium ion? Why is it useful when one is considering substitution, elimination, and rearrangement reactions?

24.14 Define and give an example for each of the following kinds of organic reactions:
Nucleophilic substitution   Electrophilic substitution
Elimination   Rearrangement

24.15 What is a polymer? Polypropylene is an addition polymer of propylene. Sketch a portion of the polypropylene molecule. What fraction by weight of polypropylene would be carbon?

24.16 What is a Grignard reagent? How would you prepare the Grignard reagent propyl magnesium bromide?

24.17 $CH_3—CH_2—CH_2—Mg—Br$ is the Grignard reagent propyl magnesium bromide. If each of the following substances, followed by water, is added to this Grignard reagent, what final product would be obtained? Indicate your answers by sketching the molecular structure of each product.
   a. Water
   b. Ethyl alcohol
   c. Carbon dioxide
   d. Formaldehyde
   e. Acetone

24.18 It is desired to prepare substances with the following molecular structures by using Grignard reagents. Show how you would prepare the proper Grignard reagent and then how you would proceed to obtain the desired substance.

$$\text{a. } CH_3—CH_2—C{\overset{\displaystyle O}{\underset{OH}{<}}}$$

$$\text{d. } CH_3—\overset{\displaystyle CH_3}{\underset{\displaystyle H}{\overset{|}{\underset{|}{C}}}}—CH_2—C{\overset{\displaystyle O}{\underset{OH}{<}}}$$

b. $CH_3—CH_2—CH_3$

$$\text{c. } CH_3—\overset{\displaystyle CH_3}{\underset{\displaystyle CH_3}{\overset{|}{\underset{|}{C}}}}—OH$$

$$\text{e. } C_2H_5—\overset{\displaystyle CH_3}{\underset{\displaystyle C_3H_7}{\overset{|}{\underset{|}{C}}}}—OH$$

24.19 Name four processes used in the petroleum industry to improve the amount and quality of gasoline produced. Give an example of a reaction which might occur in each process.

24.20 What does natural rubber consist of? Sketch a portion of a molecule which would be present in vulcanized natural rubber.

24.21 If neoprene has a molecular structure similar to that of natural rubber, sketch a portion of a neoprene molecule.

24.22 What does petroleum consist of? What problems must be solved if one is to obtain a maximum amount of usable gasoline from a given amount of petroleum?

24.23 Sketch a portion of the polybutadiene rubber recently produced with the molecular structure similar to that of natural rubber. Why would not simply polymerizing butadiene produce this material?

24.24 Define each of the following terms:
   Carbohydrate   Dextrorotatory
   Protein   Stereoisomer
   Asymmetric carbon atom   Optical activity

24.25 Sketch two stereoisomers of glucose not shown in the text. Use the open chain form.

24.26 Sketch the simplest optically active molecule you can think of.

24.27 How many asymmetric carbon atoms are there in each of the following α-amino acids:
   a. Glycine   c. Asparagine
   b. Valine   d. Arginine

24.28 Distinguish between a protein and a nucleic acid.

24.29 Sketch that portion of the insulin molecule containing the following chain of amino acid groups:

-Ser-Leu-Tyr-Glu-

|

NH$_2$

24.30 What are the components of the nucleic acids called DNA? Why are the nucleic acids of great biological interest?

*24.31 The general formula for a paraffin is C_nH_{2n+2}. Derive the general formula for an olefin. For an acetylene. What conditions must be satisfied if these formulas are to be valid?

*24.32 How many isomers would you expect for a paraffin with the molecular formula C_8H_{18}?

*24.33 Under what conditions would you expect the following reaction to proceed to the right:

$$C_2H_5OH + Br^- \longrightarrow C_2H_5Br + OH^-$$

*24.34 How many asymmetric carbon atoms are there in the D-ribose molecule? In the 2-deoxy-D-ribose molecule?

*24.35 Write equations for the reactions, including conditions, by which one could prepare the following from propyl chloride, $CH_3CH_2CH_2Cl$:

    a. An alcohol   b. An ether   c. An olefin   d. An amine

The following molecular formulas of substances named in the above problems may prove to be useful:

methyl ethyl ether: $CH_3OC_2H_5$
normal butyl alcohol:
  $CH_3CH_2CH_2CH_2OH$
2-propanol: $CH_3CHOHCH_3$
acetaldehyde: CH_3CHO
acetone: CH_3COCH_3

glycerol: $CH_2OHCH_2OHCH_2OH$
1,2-dichloroethane: CH_2ClCH_2Cl
2-methyl,3-ethylpentane:
  $CH_3CH(CH_3)CH(C_2H_5)CH_2CH_3$
propylene: $CH_3CH{=}CH_2$
methyl acetate: CH_3COOCH_3

Appendices

1 | MATHEMATICS

EXPONENTIAL NOTATION

Frequently in chemistry one has to deal with numbers which are either very large or very small. In a gram of lead metal there are about

$$2,910,000,000,000,000,000,000 \text{ atoms}$$

and each lead atom weighs about 0.000 000 000 000 000 000 000 344 gram. Rather than write out so many zeroes when such numbers arise, scientists employ a shorthand notation to express these numbers. The notation is easy to learn and very convenient to use.

To represent the number 100, one can write its equivalent, 10×10, and then abbreviate the product by the expression 10^2. Similarly, 1,000,000, which is equal to $10 \times 10 \times 10 \times 10 \times 10 \times 10$, can be written as 10^6. The numbers 2 and 6, the superscripts in 10^2 and 10^6, are called **exponentials** and indicate how many times 10 is multiplied by itself to obtain the desired number.

Any number greater than unity can be written as the product of a number between 1 and 10 times 10 raised to some positive integral exponential. For example,

$$1325 = 1.325 \times (10 \times 10 \times 10) = 1.325 \times 10^3$$

$$26 = 2.6 \times 10^1$$

$$2,910,000,000,000,000,000,000 = 2.91 \times 10^{21}$$

For numbers which are less than unity, the exponential notation can also be used.

$$0.01 = \frac{1}{100} = \frac{1}{10 \times 10} = \frac{1}{10^2} = 10^{-2}$$

The negative exponential indicates the number of times $\frac{1}{10}$, or 0.10, is to be multiplied by itself to obtain the desired number.

Any number less than unity can be expressed as the product of a number between 1 and 10, times 10 raised to some negative integral exponential. Some examples would be

$$0.0065 = 6.5 \times \frac{1}{10 \times 10 \times 10} = 6.5 \times 10^{-3}$$

$$0.1546 = 1.546 \times 10^{-1}$$

$$0.000\ 000\ 000\ 000\ 000\ 000\ 000\ 344 = 3.44 \times 10^{-22}$$

If it is necessary to multiply numbers written in exponential notation one can consider the product to be equal to the product of the number terms times the product of the exponential terms. The product of 10^x times 10^y equals 10^{x+y}, as one can readily prove. The following examples are illustrative:

$$(1.64 \times 10^2) \times (2.31 \times 10^8) = (1.64 \times 2.31) \times (10^2 \times 10^8) = 3.79 \times 10^{2+8}$$
$$= 3.79 \times 10^{10}$$

$$(3.1 \times 10^6) \times (4.2 \times 10^{-11}) = (3.1 \times 4.2) \times (10^6 \times 10^{-11}) = 13 \times 10^{-5}$$
$$= 1.3 \times 10^{-4}$$

The quotient of numbers written in exponential notation is equal to the quotient of the number terms times the quotient of the exponential terms. The quotient of 10^x divided by 10^y equals 10^{x-y}. Consider the following examples:

$$\frac{4.29 \times 10^5}{2.59 \times 10^2} = \frac{4.29}{2.59} \times \frac{10^5}{10^2} = 1.66 \times 10^{5-2} = 1.66 \times 10^3$$

$$\frac{(1.2 \times 10^{-3}) \times (4.7 \times 10^7)}{(6.0 \times 10^{15}) \times (3.1 \times 10^{-40})} = \frac{1.2 \times 4.7}{6.0 \times 3.1} \times \frac{10^{-3} \times 10^7}{10^{15} \times 10^{-40}} = 3.0 \times 10^{28}$$

To solve the last example without using exponential notation would be very tedious, and in all probability would result in a decimal error, at least.

It is, of course, not necessary to have the number multiplying the exponential term lie between 1 and 10, since clearly

$$1.65 \times 10^7 = 16.5 \times 10^6 = 165 \times 10^5$$

and in a given circumstance it might be most convenient to report the result by the last expression in the group.

Sometimes it is necessary to calculate the square, or cube, root of a number given in exponential notation. Since $(10^{2x})^{1/2}$ equals 10^x, it is most convenient to obtain a square root if the exponential is an even, rather than an odd, integer.

$$(72.4 \times 10^7)^{1/2} = (7.24)^{1/2} \times (10^8)^{1/2} = 2.69 \times 10^4$$

Similarly, a cube root is most easily obtained if the exponential is made a multiple of 3 by appropriate manipulation of the number.

$$(72.4 \times 10^7)^{1/3} = (724)^{1/3} \times (10^6)^{1/3} = 8.98 \times 10^2$$

COMMON AND NATURAL LOGARITHMS

In making calculations one frequently finds it convenient, or necessary, to employ logarithms. The ordinary, or common, logarithm of a number is equal to the exponential to which 10 must be raised to produce the number.

$$\log x = y \qquad \text{means } 10^y = x$$
$$\log 100 = 2 \qquad \text{means } 10^2 = 100$$
$$\log 0.001 = -3 \qquad \text{means } 10^{-3} = 0.001$$

Logarithms are useful for obtaining products of numbers, for taking their quotient, and for raising numbers to powers or extracting roots of numbers. The operations which must be carried out to accomplish such calculations are readily derived.

Multiplication: Division:

$$A \times B = C$$
$$A = 10^{\log A} \text{ and } B = 10^{\log B}$$
$$10^{\log A} \times 10^{\log B} = 10^{\log C}$$
$$10^{\log A + \log B} = 10^{\log C}$$
$$\therefore \log C = \log A + \log B$$

$$D \div E = F$$
$$10^{\log D} \div 10^{\log E} = 10^{\log F}$$
$$10^{\log D - \log E} = 10^{\log F}$$
$$\therefore \log F = \log D - \log E$$

The logarithm of the *product* of two numbers is equal to the *sum* of the logarithms of the two numbers. The logarithm of the *quotient* of two numbers is equal to the *difference* between the logarithms of the dividend and the divider.

Raising to a power or extracting a root:

$$G^n = H \text{ (in which n may be integral, nonintegral, positive, or negative)}$$
$$(10^{\log G})^n = 10^{\log H}$$
$$10^{n \log G} = 10^{\log H}$$
$$\therefore \log H = n \log G$$

The logarithm of a number *raised* to any *exponential* is equal to the *product* of the *exponential times* the logarithm of the number.

The logarithm of a number which doesn't happen to be equal to 10 raised to an integral power can be readily obtained from a table of logarithms or from the log, or L, scale on a slide rule. Since the logarithm table or slide rule will only furnish the logarithms of numbers between 1 and 10, the number whose logarithm is needed is first written in the exponential notation described in the previous section.

$$\log 640 = \log (6.40 \times 10^2) = \log 6.40 + \log 10^2$$
$$= 0.806 + 2 = 2.806$$
$$\log 0.00047 = \log (4.7 \times 10^{-4}) = \log 4.7 + \log 10^{-4}$$
$$= 0.67 + (-4) = -3.33$$

Given the logarithm of a number, one can find the number by the inverse of the procedure used in obtaining the logarithm.

$$\text{If } \log A = 3.24, \quad A = 10^{3.24} = 10^3 \times 10^{0.24}$$
$$= 1.7 \times 10^3$$
$$\text{If } \log B = -5.47, \quad B = 10^{-5.47} = 10^{-6} \times 10^{.53}$$
$$= 3.4 \times 10^{-6}$$

Ordinarily a final result is not expressed as being equal to 10 raised to a decimal exponential, but is modified as in the foregoing examples to the conventional exponential notation.

In chemical calculations one usually uses a slide rule rather than logarithms, since slide rule calculations can be carried out very rapidly and with a precision appropriate to most chemical data. The student must, however, be familiar with the properties of logarithms since they are involved in certain very common chemical expressions.

Calculations with logarithms are carried out in most cases with the kinds of logarithms we have been discussing, in which 10 is the base, or the number which is raised to an exponential. Logarithms to the base 10 are called **ordinary** or **common logarithms.** It is possible, however, to set up a system of logarithms based on any arbitrary number, by using rules completely analogous to those used for the base 10. Let us consider the relations obtaining in a system of logarithms based on an arbitrarily chosen number, which we shall call N:

$$\log_N x = y \qquad \text{means } N^y = x$$
$$\log_2 8 = 3 \qquad \text{means } 2^3 = 8$$
$$\log_2 0.25 = -2 \qquad \text{means } 2^{-2} = 0.25$$

in which the base of the logarithm is written as a subscript.

Many natural laws are found to be exponential in character. Radioactive decay, the temperature dependence of equilibrium constants and of reaction rate constants, and the distribution function for molecular speeds all involve equations which include exponential terms. The exponential terms in these equations are most conveniently expressed in terms of a number called e, raised to a power, rather than 10 raised to a power. The number e can be shown to have the value 2.71828 . . .. Sometimes the natural law will be expressed in logarithmic rather than exponential form, with the system of logarithms being based on e rather than 10. Such logarithms are called **natural logarithms,** because the relations from which logarithms can be calculated are most simply expressed in terms of the base e; natural logarithms are assigned the symbol ln, to distinguish them from common logarithms, usually written as log with no subscript.

$$P = C\, e^{-\Delta H/RT} \qquad \text{means} \qquad P = C \times 2.718^{-\Delta H/RT}$$
$$\ln P = \ln C - \Delta H/RT \text{ means } \log_e P = \log_e C - \Delta H/RT$$

Clearly the logarithm of an exponential of e is most easily determined as a natural logarithm, and since natural laws typically involve exponentials based on e, natural logarithms are often used in writing equations for such laws.

It is possible to convert very easily from natural logarithms to common logarithms, and this is frequently done to allow data to be reported in ordinary exponential form.

$$\log x = y \quad \text{means} \quad 10^y = x$$
$$\ln x = z \quad \text{means} \quad e^z = x$$
$$10^y = e^z$$
$$\log_{10}(10^y) = \log_{10}(e^z) = z \log_{10} e$$
$$y = z \times 0.43429 \ldots$$
$$\log_{10} x = 0.43429 \ldots \ln x$$

or
$$\ln x = 2.303 \ldots \log_{10} x$$

To convert from *common* logarithms to *natural* logarithms, one simply *multiplies* the *common* logarithm by 2.303.

If ln P = 0.46, in which the dimension of P is to be in atmospheres,

$$\log P = 0.46/2.303 = 0.20$$

$$P = 10^{0.20} = 1.6 \text{ atm.}$$

If n = $3.00 \times e^{-16.4}$,

$$n = 3.00 \times 10^{-16.4/2.303} = 3.00 \times 10^{-7.13} = 3.00 \times 10^{-8} \times 10^{0.87}$$

$$= 3.00 \times 10^{-8} \times 7.4 = 22 \times 10^{-8}$$

SIGNIFICANT FIGURES

Some numbers are, by their nature, exact. *Two* horses, *five* apples, or *sixteen* pennies indicate exactly how many items are described. Relations between dimensions in the same measuring system are also expressed in terms of exact numbers:

$$1 \text{ yard} = 3 \text{ feet} = 36 \text{ inches}$$

$$1000 \text{ millimeters} = 100 \text{ centimeters} = 1 \text{ meter}$$

These numbers arise by definition of the relationship between the various dimensional units and can all be considered to be perfectly exact.

When one relates dimensions in different measuring systems, the numbers involved are no longer all exact. Depending on the precision with which we wish to work, we can say

$$1 \text{ inch} = 2.540 \text{ centimeters}$$

or $\qquad\qquad 1 \text{ inch} = 2.54 \text{ centimeters}$

or $\qquad\qquad 1 \text{ inch} = 2.5 \text{ centimeters}$

In the foregoing equations the 1 may be taken to be exact. By stating that 1 in. equals 2.54 cm., we imply that 1 in. is closer in length to 2.54 cm. than it is to either 2.53 cm. or to 2.55 cm. To say that 1 in. equals 2.540 cm. means that it lies closer to 2.540 cm. than to either 2.539 cm. or to 2.541 cm. To use the first equation in a calculation means that we wish to work with a precision which is greater than that which is implied by the second or third equations. Somewhat loosely, we describe the precision of the numbers 2.540, 2.54, and 2.5, by saying that they contain four, three, and two **significant** figures respectively.

A similar situation arises when one obtains experimental data. Depending on the balance used, one might report that a sample of iron oxide weighed.

1.6459 g., or 1.646 g., or 1.65 g., or 1.6 g.,

and, depending on the circumstances in the experiment, any one of these masses might be the most appropriate to use in a subsequent calculation. The implied precision of the masses varies widely, however, and we could indicate their precision by stating the number of significant figures in each number; these would range from five for the first mass to two for the last.

Obtaining the number of significant figures in a number often simply involves counting the number of digits in that number, as in the examples just given. However, if a number contains zeroes which *only* serve to locate a decimal point, the zeroes *do not* contribute to the precision of the number and *are not* counted. For example, if the masses in the example were reported in kilograms, rather than in grams, they would be

$$0.0016549 \text{ kg., or } 0.001646 \text{ kg., or } 0.00165 \text{ kg., or } 0.0016 \text{ kg ,}$$

and those masses would clearly have the same precision as when reported in grams. The number of significant figures would remain, five, four, and so on, respectively, as before. The general rule in this regard is that the precision in the measurement of a quantity is not changed by the dimensions in which it is expressed.

An unambiguous method for determining number of significant figures is simply to express the number under consideration in exponential notation and count the digits in the number multiplying the exponential:

$$0.000000495 \text{ cm.} = 4.95 \times 10^{-7} \text{ cm. (3 significant figures)}$$
$$0.00006 \text{ amp.} = 6 \times 10^{-5} \text{ amp. (1 significant figure)}$$

Zeroes at the end of a number may either be significant or merely serve to fix a decimal point. Given the measurements

$$3100 \text{ cm. and } 16.500 \text{ g.}$$

the number of significant figures in 3100 is ambiguous and might be two, three, or four, depending on whether the zeroes serve to fix the decimal point or are experimentally meaningful. In 16.500 g. there are *five* significant figures, since the decimal point is present in the number, and the purpose of the zeroes *must* be to describe its precision. Again, if exponential notation were used, the decimal point would be of necessity present, and no ambiguity would arise.

The importance of significant figures lies in calculations based on experimental data. The precision of an experimental result depends on the precision of the data used to obtain it. The calculation operation cannot by itself improve the precision of an experimental result. An illustration might be helpful in revealing some of the common pitfalls which arise in calculations involving experimental data.

Let us assume a student is given the problem of measuring the density of an unknown liquid. He performs the experiment by weighing an empty graduated cylinder, pouring in the liquid and measuring its volume, and then weighing the cylinder with the liquid in it. He obtains the following data by reading the balance and the markings on the graduated cylinder as best he can:

mass of cylinder plus liquid	262.1 g.
mass of empty cylinder	128.4 g.
mass of liquid in cylinder	133.7 g.
volume of liquid	91.3 ml.

Since density of liquid $= \dfrac{\text{mass of liquid}}{\text{volume of liquid}}$, the student obtains, by long division,

$$\text{density} = \frac{133.7 \text{ g.}}{91.3 \text{ ml.}} = 1.46_{440...} \text{ g./ml.}$$

with as many digits in the quotient as he cares to determine. The obvious implication of the calculation is that, by using data of only moderate precision, one can find a density with very high precision. Any such implication is *incorrect*. The data used in the density calculation were found to *four* and *three* significant figures respectively, or, perhaps more meaningfully, the mass was measured with a precision of about 1 part in 1337 and the volume with a precision of about 1 part in 913. The calculated density *cannot* have a precision greater than that of the less precise of these numbers. This means that the liquid density found in the experiment should be reported as 1.46 g./ml., with an implied precision of 1 part in 146, rather than as 1.464 g./ml., which (improperly) has an implied precision of 1 part in 1464, greater than 1 part in 913 precision obtained in the measurement of the liquid volume.

As a general rule, in *multiplication* or *division* of experimentally obtained quantities we shall retain in the result a *number of significant figures equal to that in the least precise piece of data entering the calculation.* Since 91.3 ml. is the least precise quantity entering the density calculation in the example, the rule would require that the density be reported to three significant figures, the same result we obtained by more careful consideration of the precision in the experiment.

In addition or subtraction of experimental quantities we retain the general principle that the calculation operation cannot improve the precision of an experimental result. If, for example, we dissolve two substances, A and B, in some water, and wish to report the mass of the final solution, we might obtain the following data:

		Implied precision
mass of water	994.2 g.	$\pm$ 0.1 g.
mass of substance A	6.4545 g.	$\pm$ 0.0001 g.
mass of substance B	29. g.	$\pm$ 1 g.
sum of the masses	1029.$_{6545}$ g.	$\pm$ 1.1 g.
properly reported mass	1030 g.	($\pm$ 1.1 g.)

To the right of the measured masses we have indicated the implied precision of the measurement. The likely error in the sum of the masses is clearly equal to the sum of the likely errors in each individual mass. The likely error in the total mass is about ± 1 g., caused mainly by the poor precision in the measurement of the mass of substance B. The reported total mass should not have a precision greater than the likely error and would be best reported as 1030 g., since the implied precision of that result, ± 1 g., is about equal to the likely error. Carrying the result to eight significant figures would be nonsense in view of the likely error, and rounding off to three significant figures would imply a greater likely error than is actually present. Clearly it is *not true* that the number of significant figures in a sum must not be larger than the smallest number of significant figures in any element entering the sum; in the example, the number of significant figures in the sum is clearly equal to four, whereas the number of significant figures in the least precise element in the sum, 29 g., is only two.

In calculations from experimental data it is frequently necessary to round off a number to decrease the number of significant figures in a result. A rule which is often used in rounding off is to increase the last retained digit by 1 if the first dropped digit is greater than five, and kept the last retained digit if the first digit dropped is less than 5. If the first digit dropped happens to be a 5, the rule is to keep the first retained digit if it is odd and increase it by one if it is even. The following illustration follows these conventions:

16.4534629	9 significant figures	16.453	rounded off to 5
16.453463	rounded off to 8	16.45	rounded off to 4
16.45346	rounded off to 7	16.5	rounded off to 3
16.4535	rounded off to 6	17	rounded off to 2

PROBLEMS

1. Express the following numbers in exponential notation:
   a. 262.4   d. 0.000 000 4659   g. 2000
   b. 0.0039   e. 3294.5   h. 2000.0
   c. 42,000,000,000   f. 20010   i. 0.000 0400

   Ans.: b. 3.9×10^{-3} f. 2.0010×10^4
   g. 2×10^3

2. How many significant figures are there in each of the numbers in Problem 1?

   Ans.: b. Two   c. Probably two
   f. Probably five   i. Three

3. Carry out the indicated operations, using exponential notation where useful and observing rules on significant figures:
   a. 1594×0.0029 f. 16.2 g. + 39.65 g. + 2.4792 g.
   b. $1.40 \times 10.45 \div 16$ g. 155.4 g. + 19 g. + 245.2 g.
   c. 23.961 cm. $\times$ 10 mm./1 cm.   h. 16.54 g. + 208 g. $-$ 203.9 g.
   d. 52.6541 g. $\div$ 17.0 ml.   i. 3.69 m. $\times$ 100 cm./1 m. $\times$ 1 in./2.540 cm.
   e. 13.6 ft. $\times$ 12 in./1 ft.   j. 2325 ml. + 16.8 ml. $-$ 22.04 ml.

   Ans.: a. 46
   c. 2.3961×10^2 mm. or 239.61 mm.
   f. 58.3 g.
   h. 21 g.

4. Evaluate each of the following expressions, giving your result in exponential notation:
   a. log 435   e. ln 350   i. log x = 2.43; find x
   b. log 2.785   f. ln 0.004   j. log y = -5.6; find y
   c. log 0.022   g. ln 0.000 068   k. ln z = 4.60; find z
   d. ln 56.1   h. $\log_4 64$ l. ln q = -24.2; find q

   Ans.: a. 2.64   c. -1.66 e. 5.86
   i. 2.70×10^2 l. 3×10^{-11}

5. Evaluate each of the following expressions, giving the result in exponential notation:
   a. e^{16} d. $10^{-2.66}$ g. $85.1 \times e^{-8.3}$
   b. $e^{-2.88}$ e. $\log e^{4.4}$ h. 3.1 ln. 0.063
   c. $10^{4.3}$ f. $\ln(6.3 \times 10^4)$ i. $1.6 \times 10^3 \times e^{3.66}$

   Ans.: b. 5.6×10^{-2}
   f. 11

NOMENCLATURE OF INORGANIC COMPOUNDS

The composition of a compound may be specified by giving either its formula or its name. Throughout this text, we have discussed at some length how one can arrive at the chemical formulas of inorganic compounds. We now turn to a related problem, that of developing a system of nomenclature for these compounds. In the interest of clarity and simplicity, we shall restrict our discussion to a relatively small number of rules which will suffice to name the great majority of inorganic compounds encountered in an introductory course in chemistry.

IONIC COMPOUNDS

The names of ionic compounds are derived from those of the ions of which they are composed. We shall first consider the nomenclature of individual ions and then the names of the compounds they form.

Positive Ions

Monatomic positive ions take the names of the metal from which they are derived:

Na^+ sodium $\quad$ Ca^{+2} calcium $\quad$ Al^{+3} aluminum

When a metal forms more than one ion, it is necessary to distinguish between these ions. The accepted practice today is to indicate the oxidation number of the ion by a Roman numeral in parentheses immediately following the name of the metal:

Fe^{+2} iron(II) $\qquad$ Cu^+ copper(I) $\qquad$ Sn^{+2} tin(II)

Fe^{+3} iron(III) $\qquad$ Cu^{+2} copper(II) $\qquad$ Sn^{+4} tin(IV)

An earlier method, still widely used, adds to the stem of the Latin name of the metal the suffixes *-ous* or *-ic*, representing the lower and higher oxidation states respectively:

Fe^{+2} ferrous $\qquad$ Cu^+ cuprous $\qquad$ Sn^{+2} stannous

Fe^{+3} ferric $\qquad$ Cu^{+2} cupric $\qquad$ Sn^{+4} stannic

The only polyatomic cations to be considered here are:

NH_4^+ ammonium $\qquad$ Hg_2^{+2} mercury(I) or mercurous

625

Negative Ions

Monatomic negative ions are named by adding the suffix -*ide* to the stem of the name of the nonmetal from which they are derived:

N^{-3}	nitride	O^{-2}	oxide	F^-	fluoride	H^-	hydride
		S^{-2}	sulfide	Cl^-	chloride		
		Se^{-2}	selenide	Br^-	bromide		
		Te^{-2}	telluride	I^-	iodide		

The nomenclature of polyatomic anions is more complex. The names of some of the more common oxyanions are:

OH^- hydroxide

ClO_4^- per-chlorate

MnO_4^- per-manganate

O_2^{-2} peroxide NO_3^- nitrate SO_4^{-2} sulfate ClO_3^- chlorate CrO_4^{-2} chromate

CO_3^{-2} carbonate NO_2^- nitrite SO_3^{-2} sulfite ClO_2^- chlorite $Cr_2O_7^{-2}$ dichromate

PO_4^{-3} phosphate

ClO^- hypochlorite

It will be noted (columns 2, 3) that when a nonmetal such as nitrogen or sulfur forms two oxyanions in different oxidation states, the suffixes -*ate* and -*ite* are used to distinguish between the higher and lower states respectively. With elements such as chlorine which form more than two oxyanions, the prefixes *per*- (highest oxidation state) and *hypo*- (lowest oxidation state) are used as well.

Oxyanions that contain hydrogen as well as nonmetal and oxygen atoms are properly named as illustrated in the following examples:

HCO_3^- hydrogen carbonate HPO_4^{-2} hydrogen phosphate

HSO_4^- hydrogen sulfate $H_2PO_4^-$ dihydrogen phosphate

Compounds

The name of the positive ion is given first, followed by the name of the negative ion. Examples:

$CaCl_2$	calcium chloride
$FeBr_2$	iron(II) bromide
$(NH_4)_2SO_4$	ammonium sulfate
$Fe(ClO_4)_3$	iron(III) perchlorate
$NaHCO_3$	sodium hydrogen carbonate

In practice, compounds containing metal atoms, regardless of the type of bonding involved, are ordinarily named as if they were ionic. For example, the compounds $AlCl_3$ and $SnCl_4$, in both of which the bonding is primarily covalent, are named as follows:

$AlCl_3$ aluminum chloride $SnCl_4$ tin(IV) chloride

BINARY COMPOUNDS OF THE NONMETALS

When a pair of nonmetals form only one compound, that compound may be named quite simply. The name of the element whose symbol appears first in the formula is written first. The second portion of the name is formed by adding the suffix *-ide* to the stem of the name of the second nonmetal. Examples include.

$$HCl \quad \text{hydrogen chloride}$$
$$H_2S \quad \text{hydrogen sulfide}$$
$$NF_3 \quad \text{nitrogen fluoride}$$

If more than one binary compound is formed by a pair of nonmetals, as is most often the case, the Greek prefixes, *di* = two, *tri* = three, *tetra* = four, *penta* = five, *hexa* = six, and so on, are used to designate the number of atoms of each element. Thus, for the oxides of nitrogen we have:

$$* \; N_2O_5 \quad \text{dinitrogen pentoxide}$$
$$* \; N_2O_4 \quad \text{dinitrogen tetroxide}$$
$$NO_2 \quad \text{nitrogen dioxide}$$
$$N_2O_3 \quad \text{dinitrogen trioxide}$$
$$NO \quad \text{nitrogen oxide}$$
$$N_2O \quad \text{dinitrogen oxide}$$

A great many of the best-known binary compounds of the nonmetals have acquired common names which are widely and, in some cases, exclusively used. These include:

H_2O	water	PH_3	phosphine
H_2O_2	hydrogen peroxide	AsH_3	arsine
NH_3	ammonia	NO	nitric oxide
N_2H_4	hydrazine	N_2O	nitrous oxide

OXYACIDS

The names of some of the more common oxygen acids are listed as follows:

			$HClO_4$ perchloric acid
H_2CO_3 carbonic acid	HNO_3 nitric acid	H_2SO_4 sulfuric acid	$HClO_3$ chloric acid
H_3BO_3 boric acid	HNO_2 nitrous acid	H_2SO_3 sulfurous acid	$HClO_2$ chlorous acid
			$HClO$ hypochlorous acid

It is of interest to compare the names of these oxyacids to those of the corresponding oxyanions listed previously. Note that oxyanions whose names end in

---

* Note that in this case the a is dropped from the prefixes penta and tetra in the interests of euphony.

-*ate* are derived from acids whose names end in -*ic*. Compare, for example, CO_3^{-2} (carbon*ate*) and H_2CO_3 (carbon*ic* acid); NO_3^- (nit*rate*) and HNO_3 (nit*ric* acid); ClO_4^- (perchlor*ate*) and $HClO_4$ (perchlor*ic* acid). Oxyanions whose names end in -*ite* are derived from acids whose names end in -*ous*. Thus we have NO_2^- (nit*rite*) and HNO_2 (nit*rous* acid); ClO^- (hypochlor*ite*) and $HClO$ (hypochlor*ous* acid).

COORDINATION COMPOUNDS

The nomenclature of compounds containing complex ions in which a metal atom is held by coordinate covalent bonds to two or more ligands is perhaps more involved than that of any other type of inorganic compound. Several rules are required, the more pertinent of which are as follows:

1. As in simple ionic compounds, the cation is named first, followed by the anion.

2. If there is more than one ligand of a particular type attached to the central atom, Greek prefixes are used to indicate the number of these ligands. Where the name of the ligand itself is complex (e.g., ethylenediamine), the number of such ligands is indicated by the prefixes *bis*- or *tris*- instead of *di*- or *tri*- and the name of the ligand is enclosed in parentheses.

3. In naming a complex ion, the names of anionic ligands are written first, followed by those of neutral ligands, and finally by that of the central metal atom. This is exactly the reverse of the order in which the groups are listed in the formula of the complex ion; the symbol of the central atom is written first, followed by the formulas of neutral ligands and then those of negatively charged ligands. In writing the formula of a coordination compound, the formula of the complex ion is often set off by brackets.

4. The names of anionic ligands are modified by substituting the suffix -*o* for the usual ending. Thus we have:

Cl^- chloro	CO_3^{-2} carbonato
OH^- hydroxo	CN^- cyano

The names of neutral ligands are ordinarily not changed. Two important exceptions are:

H_2O aquo	NH_3 ammine

5. The oxidation number of the central metal atom is indicated by a Roman numeral following the name of the metal. If the complex is an anion, the suffix -*ate* is added, often to the Latin stem of the name of the metal. Examples are:

$[Co(NH_3)_6]Cl_3$	hexamminecobalt(III) chloride
$[Co(en)_3](NO_3)_3$	tris(ethylenediamine)cobalt(III) nitrate
$[Cr(NH_3)_4Cl_2]Cl$	dichlorotetramminechromium(III) chloride
$[Pt(H_2O)_3Cl]Br$	chlorotriaquoplatinum(II) bromide
$K_3[Fe(CN)_6]$	potassium hexacyanoferrate(III)
$K_4[Fe(CN)_6]$	potassium hexacyanoferrate(II)

The last two compounds are often referred to as potassium ferricyanide and potassium ferrocyanide respectively.

3 | ATOMIC AND IONIC RADII

Element	Atomic Number	Atomic Radius in Å	Ionic Radius in Å	Element	Atomic Number	Atomic Radius in Å	Ionic Radius in Å
H	1	0.37	(−1) 2.08	Ag	47	1.44	(+1) 1.26
He	2	0.93		Cd	48	1.49	(+2) 0.97
Li	3	1.52	(+1) 0.60	In	49	1.62	(+3) 0.81
Be	4	1.11	(+2) 0.31	Sn	50	1.40	
B	5	0.88		Sb	51	1.41	
C	6	0.77		Te	52	1.37	(−2) 2.21
N	7	0.70		I	53	1.33	(−1) 2.16
O	8	0.66	(−2) 1.40	Xe	54	1.90	
F	9	0.64	(−1) 1.36	Cs	55	2.62	(+1) 1.69
Ne	10	1.12		Ba	56	2.17	(+2) 1.35
Na	11	1.86	(+1) 0.95	La	57	1.87	(+3) 1.15
Mg	12	1.60	(+2) 0.65	Ce	58	1.82	(+3) 1.01
Al	13	1.43	(+3) 0.50	Pr	59	1.82	(+3) 1.00
Si	14	1.17		Nd	60	1.82	(+3) 0.99
P	15	1.10		Pm	61		
S	16	1.04	(−2) 1.84	Sm	62		
Cl	17	0.99	(−1) 1.81	Eu	63	2.04	(+2) 0.97
Ar	18	1.54		Gd	64	1.79	(+3) 0.96
K	19	2.31	(+1) 1.33	Tb	65	1.77	(+3) 0.95
Ca	20	1.97	(+2) 0.99	Dy	66	1.77	(+3) 0.94
Sc	21	1.60	(+3) 0.81	Ho	67	1.76	(+3) 0.93
Ti	22	1.46		Er	68	1.75	(+3) 0.92
V	23	1.31		Tm	69	1.74	(+3) 0.91
Cr	24	1.25	(+3) 0.64	Yb	70	1.93	(+3) 0.89
Mn	25	1.29	(+2) 0.80	Lu	71	1.74	(+3) 0.89
Fe	26	1.26	(+2) 0.75	Hf	72	1.57	
Co	27	1.25	(+2) 0.72	Ta	73	1.43	
Ni	28	1.24	(+2) 0.69	W	74	1.37	
Cu	29	1.28	(+1) 0.96	Re	75	1.37	
Zn	30	1.33	(+2) 0.74	Os	76	1.34	
Ga	31	1.22	(+3) 0.62	Ir	77	1.35	
Ge	32	1.22		Pt	78	1.38	
As	33	1.21		Au	79	1.44	(+1) 1.37
Se	34	1.17	(−2) 1.98	Hg	80	1.55	(+2) 1.10
Br	35	1.14	(−1) 1.95	Tl	81	1.71	(+3) 0.95
Kr	36	1.69		Pb	82	1.75	
Rb	37	2.44	(+1) 1.48	Bi	83	1.46	
Sr	38	2.15	(+2) 1.13	Po	84	1.65	
Y	39	1.80	(+3) 0.93	At	85		
Zr	40	1.57		Rn	86	2.2	
Nb	41	1.43		Fr	87		
Mo	42	1.36		Ra	88	2.20	
Tc	43			Ac	89	2.0	
Ru	44	1.33		Th	90	1.80	
Rh	45	1.34		Pa	91		
Pd	46	1.38		U	92	1.4	

4 | CONVERSION FACTORS AND CONSTANTS

Acceleration of gravity	$g = 980.67$ cm./sec.^{2}
Ampere	1 amp. = 1 coulomb/sec.
Angstrom	1 Å $= 1 \times 10^{-8}$ cm.
	1 Å $= 1 \times 10^{-1}$ mμ
Atmosphere	1 atm. = 760 mm. Hg = 33.9 ft. water
	1 atm. = 14.70 lb./in.^{2}
	1 atm. $= 1.013 \times 10^6$ dynes/cm.^{2}
	1 atm. = 1033 g./cm.^{2}
Atomic mass unit	1 a.m.u. = 931 mev.
Avogadro's number	$N = 6.023 \times 10^{23}$
Boltzmann's constant	$k = 1.3805 \times 10^{-16}$ ergs/°K
British thermal unit	1 B.T.U. = 252 cal.
Calorie	1 cal. = 4.184 joules
	1 cal. = 0.04129 l. atm. (liter atmosphere)
Centimeter	1 cm. $= 1 \times 10^8$ Å
	1 cm. = 0.3937 in.
Centimeter/second	1 cm./sec. = 0.02237 mi./hr.
Cubic centimeter	1 cm.^{3} = 0.06102 in.^{3}
Cubic inch	1 in.^{3} = 16.387 cm.^{3}
Density	D water(1) = 1.000 g./cm.^{3} at 4°C
	D mercury = 13.6 g./cm.^{3} at 0°C
Electronic charge	$e^- = 4.80 \times 10^{-10}$ e.s.u.
	$e^- = 1.60 \times 10^{-19}$ coulomb
Electron volts per atom	1 ev./atom = 23.05 kcal./mole
Erg	1 erg $= 2.389 \times 10^{-8}$ cal.
	1 erg $= 1 \times 10^{-7}$ joule
Faraday	1 faraday = 96500 coulombs = 23070 cal./v.
	1 faraday $= 6.023 \times 10^{23}$ e$^-$
Gas constant	$R = 0.08205$ l. atm./(mole $\times$ °K)
	$R = 1.987$ cal./(mole $\times$ °K)
	$R = 8.314 \times 10^7$ ergs/(mole $\times$ °K)
Gram	1 g. mass $= 2.15 \times 10^{10}$ kcal.
Grams per cubic centimeter	1 g./cm.^{3} = 62.43 lb./ft.^{3}
Gram molecular volume	$V_0 = 22.413$ l./mole at 0°C, and 1 atm.
Ice point	$T_0 = 273.15$°K
Inch	1 in. = 2.540 cm.
Joule	1 j. = 0.2390 cal.
Kilogram	1 kg. = 2.205 lb.
Liter	1 l. = 1000.028 cm.^{3}
	1 l. = 1.0567 quarts
Liter-atmosphere	1 l. atm. = 24.22 cal.
Natural logarithms	$\ln x = 2.3026 \log_{10} x$
Pi	$\pi = 3.1416$
Planck's constant	$h = 6.626 \times 10^{-27}$ erg sec.
Pound	1 lb. = 453.6 g.
Quart	1 qt. = 0.9463 l.
Speed of light	$c = 2.998 \times 10^{10}$ cm./sec.

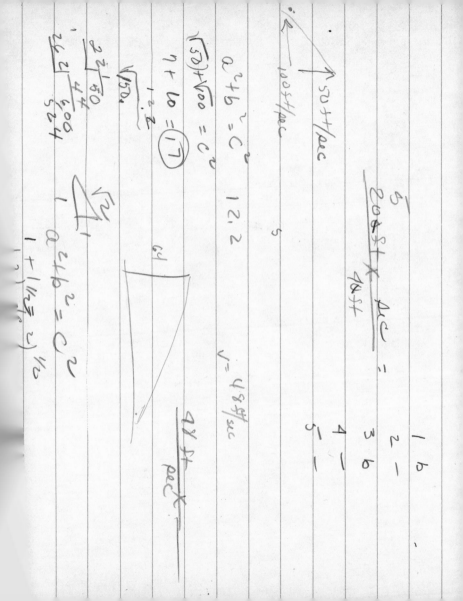

$$\frac{5}{20 \text{ ft} \times \text{sec}} = \frac{\text{sec}}{48 \text{ ft}}$$

1	b
2	—
3	6
4	—
5	—

$a^2 + b^2 = c^2$ 12.2

$\sqrt{50} + \sqrt{100} = c^2$

$7 + 60 = \boxed{17}$

$\sqrt{50}$ 12.2

100 ft/sec

5

50 ft/sec

$v = 48 \text{ ft/sec}$

$\frac{48 \text{ ft}}{\text{sec}} =$

$a^2 + b^2 = c^2$

$1 + 144 = c^2$

$\sqrt{2}$

64

note

$$NH_3 + H_2O \rightleftharpoons OH^- + NH_4^+$$

a)

	NH_3		OH		NH_4
	1	—	γ	—	1-x
OH	—	γ	—	x	
NH_4	—	γ	—	x	

$$K_b = \frac{(x)(x)}{1-x}$$

$$1.8 \times 10^{-5} = \frac{x^2}{1-x}$$

$$1.8 \times 10^{-6} = x^2$$

$$\sqrt{1.8 \times 10^{-4}}$$

b)

$$[H^+][OH^-] = 10^{-14}$$

$$[H^+][1.3 \times 10^{-3}] = 10^{-14}$$

$$[H^+] = \frac{1 \times 10^{-14}}{4.3 \times 10^{-3}}$$

$$= .77 \times 10^{-11}$$

$$= 7.7 \times 10^{-12}$$

$$4.2 \times 10^{-3} = [OH^-]$$

$$[OH^-] = x = 1.3 \times 10^{-3}$$

c)

$$\frac{4.3 \times 10^{-3}}{1 \times 10^{-1}} = (4.3 \times 10^{-2})(1 \times 10^{2}) = 4.3$$

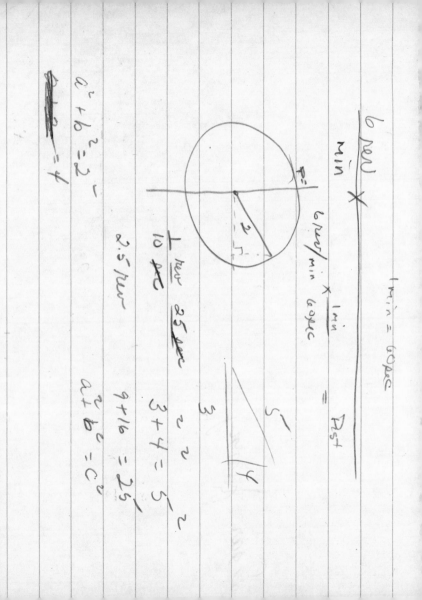

6 rev / min

1 min = 60 sec

6 rev/min × 1 min/60 sec = Dist

$\frac{1 \text{ rev}}{10 \text{ sec}}$ 25 sec   2.5 rev

3² 4² 5²

3 + 4 = 5

9 + 16 = 25

$a^2 + b^2 = c^2$

$a^2 + b^2 = 2$

$a^2 + b^2 = 4$

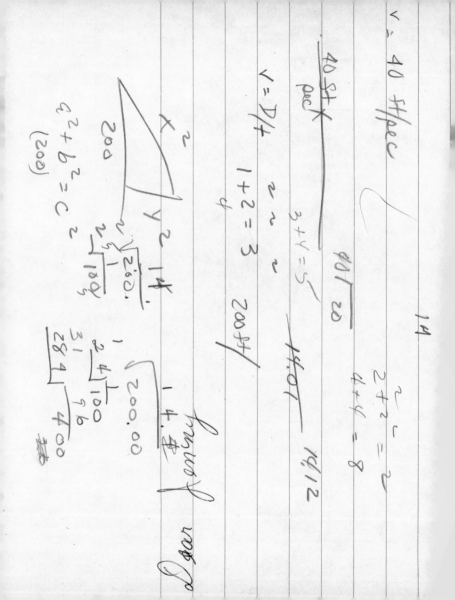

V = 40 ft/sec

1A

2+2 = 2
4+4 = 8

40 ft
sec

20 √40

3+4 = 5
V = D/t
1+2 = 3
4

200 ft

14.0T   14.12

$c^2 + b^2 = c^2$
(200)

200 √2.62
25 √105
5

x²   √2 1.4

2 √200.00
24 √100
31   96
284
400

Dear Jenny

5 | ANSWERS TO SELECTED PROBLEMS

CHAPTER 1

1.8   79°F ; 299°K
1.16 0.8310 g./ml.
1.25 127°B

1.13 55 lb.
1.23 0.0545 cal./g.°C
1.26 28° in a bath at 50°C

CHAPTER 2

2.9   a. 51.1 g.   b. 42.55%
2.13 69.72 g.
2.19 a. 1.99×10^{-23} g.

2.10 29 g.
2.18 76%, 24%
2.22 207 g.

CHAPTER 3

3.1   a. 1.60% H, 22.23% N, 76.17% O
3.5 Fe_2O_3, 0.176 g. H_2O
3.11 C_7H_8
3.16 67%

3.2   a. 7.12 g. Sr
3.8 $CoCO_3$, Co_3O_4
3.14 c. $Tl_4V_2O_7$
3.17 0.050 mole/l.

CHAPTER 4

4.1   a. $Fe_3O_4(s) + 4 H_2(g) \rightarrow 3 Fe(s) + 4 H_2O(g)$
4.3   a. 11.0   c. 8.46×10^{18}
4.8   a. 15.8 g.   b. 51.6%
4.12 a. 0.605 g. SO_2

4.4   a. 11.0 g.   d. 123 g.
4.10 22 g. of ?
4.13 1.65

CHAPTER 5

5.1   a. 38.8 kcal.
5.7   a. 172.4 kcal. evolved   b. 347.4 kcal. evolved
5.10 a. 230 cal./°C
5.17 a. Q′ = 17.7 kcal., ΔG = 1.8 kcal., ΔS = 59.4 cal./°K
5.21 a. −34.4 kcal.   b. −25.8 kcal.   c. −8.6 kcal., −29 cal./°K   d. 9.1 kcal.
      e. ~1200°K
5.24 a. +0.0204 kcal./°K, +0.0250 kcal./°K

5.2   a. 0.720 kcal.

5.13 a. 7900 Å

CHAPTER 6

6.2 1.6×10^{-5} atm.

6.6   22.4 l.

6.14 $40.1 = $ at. wt. X

6.24   327°C

6.5 3.0×10^2 l.

6.7   About 0.70 g./l.

6.19   About 79 mole % H_2 initially

6.26 $MW_{CO_2} = 44.010$

6.28   V.D.W.b: $CCl_4 > CO_2 > O_2 > H_2O > H_2$ (order of molecular or molar volumes of solid or liquid)   V.D.W.a: $H_2O > CCl_4 > CO_2 > O_2 > H_2$ (order of boiling points; actually, $a_{CCl_4} > a_{H_2O}$, probably due to unusually high intermolecular forces in H_2O as compared to other molecules of similar size and mass)

6.29 $E_{molar} = (3/2)RT$ $E_{Ar} = E_{SO_2} = 888$ cal./mole

6.31   492°A , based on Fahrenheit scale

6.32   a.1. no effect   2. increased by factor of $(2)^{1/2}$
         3. no effect   4. increased by factor of $(14)^{1/2}$

CHAPTER 7

7.10   b.p. $AsH_3 = -52°C_{predicted}$
                  $= -55°C_{observed}$

7.12 H_2S $BaCO_3$ ... ... K_3PO_4 ... ... Na_3SbS_4

CHAPTER 8

8.4 $_{19}K^{39}$: 19 electrons; 19 protons; 20 neutrons; $+19$ Cl^-: 18 electrons; 17 protons; calculation of no. neutrons requires knowledge of mass no.; $+17$.

8.8   Some possible sets of quantum numbers for a C atom: 1, 0, 0, $\frac{1}{2}$; 1, 0, 0, $-\frac{1}{2}$; 2, 0, 0, $\frac{1}{2}$; 2, 1, 0, $\frac{1}{2}$; 2, 1, 1, $\frac{1}{2}$; 2, 1, 1, $-\frac{1}{2}$; four other possible sets.

8.9 Cl^-: $1s^2 2s^2 2p^6 3s^2 3p^6$

8.10   N: $1s^2 2s^2 2p^2 3s$ Ar: $1s^2 2s^2 2p^6 3s^2 3p^5 4s$

8.14   Assume I.E. $= C(Z - D)^2$, in which C and D are parameters; fit function to data. I.E. $N^{+3} = 80$ ev.

8.19 $\lambda = 1215$ Å for first line in Lyman series.

8.20 $r = 0.53$ Å; $v = 2.19 \times 10^8$ cm./sec.

8.22   Assume $1/\lambda = C(Z + D)^2$; fit function to data. $Z = 42$

8.23 $\lambda = \dfrac{3645}{4(Z - 1)^2} \times \dfrac{4}{3}$ for strong x-ray lines
         $\lambda = 1.55$ Å for Cu; $\lambda_{obs} = 1.54$ Å

8.24   a. 3 electrons in an s subshell; 9 electrons in a p subshell.

CHAPTER 9

9.1   a. MgH_2 b. Sc_2S_3

9.5   a. NH_4Br b. $(NH_4)_2SO_4$ c. $MgCO_3$

9.8   a. NaCl (Cl^- smaller than Br^-). a. CaO ($+2, -2$ vs. $+1, -1$ ions).

9.10   a. 98.6 cc. b. 4×10^{24} of each c. 279 g.

9.14 $\sqrt{2} - 1$

9.4   a. $2 Na(s) + S(s) \rightarrow Na_2S(s)$

CHAPTER 10

10.1   a. O

10.7   c. d.

10.3   a. 60%

10.9   a. 16 b. 14

10.10   a.
$$:\ddot{C}l-\ddot{A}s-\ddot{C}l:$$
$$\overset{|}{\underset{:\ddot{C}l:}{\,}}$$

10.11   a.
$$:\ddot{O}-\ddot{N}-\ddot{O}:$$
$$\overset{\|}{\underset{:\ddot{O}:}{\,}}$$

10.15   a. sp^3 c. sp^3d^2

10.16   a. $:\ddot{O}-C\equiv O:\leftrightarrow:\ddot{O}=C=\ddot{O}:\leftrightarrow:O\equiv C-\ddot{O}:$

10.22   a. LiCl   b. AsH_3 c. SiO_2 d. HCl   e. $SiCl_4$ f. HCN

10.25 $H_2N-(CH_2)_4-NH_2$, $(CH_3)_2-N-N-(CH_3)_2$, etc.

10.27   M.W. = 57

CHAPTER 11

11.4   a. $\sim$256   c. >256   d. <256

11.6   b. p   c. n

11.13   a. 2   b. 3

11.16   a. 6

11.17 $\sim$10^{16} g.

CHAPTER 12

12.2   a. 42.9 ml.   b. 13,500 ml.   c. 17.3 ml.

12.5   a. 43.3 mm. Hg   b. 17.5 mm. Hg (condensation)

12.7   a. 0.0131 mole   b. 7.62 l.   12.11   40°C

12.21   3° 16′ for n = 1

12.23   a. 2.21×10^{-22} cc.   b. 2   c. 66.6 cc.

12.24   a. CA   b. CA_3 12.25   0.476, 0.320, 0.260

12.27   Energy to create 1 cm.^{2} of surface = 1.74×10^{-9} kcal.
Energy to bring 1 molecule to surface = 7.56×10^{-24} kcal.
Area occupied by 1 molecule = 4.3×10^{-15} cm.^{2}

12.28   a. 290 mm. Hg

CHAPTER 13

13.5 $X_{C_2H_5OH} = 0.143$, m = 9.25

13.15   91.4 mm. Hg

13.20   114

13.28   557

13.11   0.36 mole/l.

13.18   b. 100.046°C, −0.17°C

13.27 $\sim$65 ft. (at 20°C)

CHAPTER 14

14.3   a. $K_c = \dfrac{[CO_2]^2}{[CO]^2[O_2]}$ e. $K_c = \dfrac{[H]^2}{[H_2]}$

14.8   c. $K_c = 0.051$ e. About 22% dissociated

14.12   a. $K_c = [O_2]^{1/2}$ c. $K_c = \dfrac{[PtCl_2]}{[Cl_2]}$

14.13   b. $H_2O(l) \rightleftharpoons H_2O(g)$ $K_c = [H_2O]$ d. $H_2O(l) \rightleftharpoons H^+ + OH^-$ $K_c = [H^+][OH^-]$

14.17   a. 1.2×10^{-4} mole/l.-sec.   c. $k = 6.2 \times 10^{-4}$ sec.$^{-1}$

14.19   Rate = $k(Br_2)[H]$ 14.24   a. 0.12 mm. Hg   b. 190°C

14.25   a. 0.7×10^{26} e. 2×10^{-41} 14.31   126 minutes for 90% to decompose

14.32   c. 3 hr. for 75% decomposition

CHAPTER 15

15.1   a. $+3$, -2 b. $+1$, $+4$, -2

15.2 $W(s) + 3 Cl_2(g) \rightarrow WCl_6(s)$ Tungsten is oxidized, chlorine is reduced; Cl_2 is the oxidizing agent, W the reducing agent.

15.4   a. 6 kcal. evolved

15.7   a. $0.52 NH_3$, $0.12 N_2$, $0.36 H_2$ b. 0.4701.

15.11   a. React CO with O_2 under pressure at a relatively low temperature.

15.13   a. $2 Li(s) + H_2(g) \rightarrow 2 LiH(s)$
           $2 Li(s) + Cl_2(g) \rightarrow 2 LiCl(s)$
           $4 Li(s) + O_2(g) \rightarrow 2 Li_2O(s)$

15.23   Fe   15.24   18

CHAPTER 16

16.1   a. $Ag^+ + Cl^- \rightarrow AgCl(s)$ b. $Pb^{+2} + SO_4^{-2} \rightarrow PbSO_4(s)$

16.2   a. 1.6 moles Na^+, 1.6 moles I^-

16.3   0.345 mole $Fe(OH)_2$; 0.111 mole Fe^{+2}, 0.912 mole Cl^-, 0.690 mole Na^+

16.7   a. 9×10^{-10}

16.9   a. Conc. $Ag^+ \times$ conc. $Cl^- = 1 \times 10^{-6} >$ Ksp. Precipitate forms.

16.15   41.5%

16.20   a. Dissolve RbCl in water, titrate to end point with $AgNO_3$, filter and evaporate.

16.23   a. 1.0×10^{-3} moles $Ca(OH)_2$ 16.24   6.6 ft.

16.25   a. 3 ml.   b. 3.6 ml.

CHAPTER 17

17.2   a. 7   d. 5.6   17.3   a. 10^{-6} c. 3×10^{-2}

17.4   a. $[H^+] = 1.0 \times 10^{-2}$, $[OH^-] = 1.0 \times 10^{-12}$, pH = 2.0

17.6   a. Cl_2O_7, $HClO_4$, ClO_4^-

17.7   a. $HBr(g) + H_2O \rightarrow H_3O^+ + Br^-$

17.8   a. $Ca(OH)_2(s) \rightarrow Ca^{+2} + 2 OH^-$ 17.10 1.6×10^{-5}

17.13   a. pH = 2.8, 1.2% ionized, $[H^+] = 1.5 \times 10^{-3}$, $[OH^-] = 6.7 \times 10^{-12}$

17.17   a. $HF + H_2O \rightarrow H_3O^+ + F^-$
         c. $HCO_3^- + H_2O \rightarrow H_2CO_3 + OH^-$

17.22 $[H_2O] = 55$, $[H_2S] = 10^{-1}$, $[H^+] = 10^{-4}$, $[HS^-] = 10^{-4}$, $[OH^-] = 10^{-10}$, $[S^{-2}] = 10^{-15}$

17.24   HZ < HY < HX   Ka for HY $= 10^{-5}$, HZ $= 10^{-9}$

17.25   0.2 M

CHAPTER 18

18.2   a. $H^+ + OH^- \rightarrow H_2O$ b. $HC_2H_3O_2 + OH^- \rightarrow H_2O + C_2H_3O_2^-$

18.4

	No. moles	Conc.
Ca^{+2}	0.0600	0.150 M
OH^-	0.0450	0.113 M
Cl^-	0.0750	0.188 M

18.8   81.2 g.   18.9   a. N = M   b. N = 3M

18.11   a. 3.0   b. 4.0   c. 5.0   d. 7.0

18.14   a. Titrate sample of $Ca(OH)_2$ to equivalence point with HBr; evaporate.

18.15   c. Dissolve $CoCl_2$ in water; precipitate with OH^-. Titrate $Co(OH)_2$ with HBr; evaporate.

18.18   a. 0.03 M   b. 10 M   18.23   a. 9.3   b. 9.1
18.24   a. 10^{14} b. 4.0×10^4 c. 1.8×10^9 d. 0.7
18.25 10^{-29}, 10^{-43}
18.26   a. 5.3   b. 6.4   c. 9.2   d. 12.0   e. 13.0
18.27   0.052 mole

CHAPTER 19

19.2   a. $+3$ b. 0

19.4   a. $[\text{Cl—Ag—Cl}]^-$ b.

$$\begin{bmatrix} H_3N & & NH_3 \\ & \diagdown \diagup & \\ & Cu & \\ & \diagup \diagdown & \\ H_3N & & NH_3 \end{bmatrix}^{+2}$$

19.8   a. 36   b. 82   19.10   a. d^2sp^3 c. sp
19.16   a. 10^{-9} b. 3×10^{-5} 19.19   a. H^+, EDTA   b. NH_3, $S_2O_3^{-2}$
19.23   a. $Zn^{+2} + 4\,OH^- \rightarrow Zn(OH)_4^{-2}$
19.25 $[Ag^+] = 2.5 \times 10^{-9}$ $[Ag(NH_3)_2^+] = [Cl^-] = 6.3 \times 10^{-2}$ $[H^+] = 2.4 \times 10^{-12}$
          $[OH^-] = 4.2 \times 10^{-3}$
19.27 $[Co(NH_3)_4Cl_2]Cl \cdot H_2O$

CHAPTER 20

20.5   b. $Cu^{+2} + 2\,Br^- \rightarrow Cu(s) + Br_2$
20.6   Electrolyze a water solution of KI; iodine is formed at the anode.
20.9   a. 8.38 g./hr.   20.13   41.4 g.
20.16   a. $Cu(s) + 4\,H^+ + 2\,NO_3^- \rightarrow Cu^{+2} + 2\,NO_2(g) + 2\,H_2O$
20.17   a. $Cr_2O_7^{-2} + 6\,Fe^{+2} + 14\,H^+ \rightarrow 2\,Cr^{+3} + 6\,Fe^{+3} + 7\,H_2O$
20.18   a. $2\,Cr(OH)_3(s) + 3\,ClO^- + 4\,OH^- \rightarrow 2\,CrO_4^{-2} + 3\,Cl^- + 5\,H_2O$
20.24   a. 21.4 g.
20.25 $10\,SO_4^{-2} + 54\,H^+ + 44\,I^- \rightarrow 5\,SO_3^{-2} + 3\,S(s) + 2\,H_2S(g) + 22\,I_2 + 25\,H_2O$
20.26   31.3% $CuCl_2$, 39.2% NaCl, 29.5% $NaNO_3$

CHAPTER 21

21.5   a. 2.12 v.   21.9   1.61 v. (at standard concentrations)
21.12   a. $+0.49$ v.; yes
21.13   a. $2\,Ag^+ + H_2(g) \rightarrow 2\,Ag(s) + 2\,H^+$ $E° = +0.80$ v.
          f. $3\,Fe^{+2} + 4\,H^+ + NO_3^- \rightarrow 3\,Fe^{+3} + NO(g) + 2\,H_2O$ $E° = +0.19$ v.
21.14   a. 10^{25} 21.16 $[Cd^+] = 0.041$
21.19   a. $+1.25$ v.   21.23 $\Delta G° = -35$ kcal. $\Delta G = -27$ kcal.
21.24   a. $[Mn^{+2}] = 0.0026$ $[Cl^-] = 2$ $[H^+] = 2$ b. 63 cc.

21.25 $E = E° - \dfrac{0.059}{2} \log [H^+]^2$

          Setting $E° = 0.00$, $[H^+] = 10^{-14}$, $E = +0.83$

CHAPTER 22

22.1   a. Oxidizing agent ($\rightarrow Cl^-$), reducing agent ($\rightarrow ClO^-$, etc.).
22.4   a. Add zinc to hydrochloric acid; evaporate resulting solution of $ZnCl_2$.
22.6   a. No; Sn^{+4} is incapable of oxidizing Cr^{+3} to $Cr_2O_7^{-2}$.
          b. No; Sn^{+4} would react with Sn(s) to give Sn^{+2}.
          c. Cr^{+2} would reduce Sn^{+2} to Sn(s)

22.11   a. $\frac{1}{2} O_2(g) + 2 H^+ + 2 e^- \rightarrow H_2O$
        b. $H_2S(g) + \frac{1}{2} O_2(g) \rightarrow S(s) + H_2O$

22.13   a. Dissolve KCl in water, electrolyze; Cl_2 given off at anode.

$$2 Cl^- + 2 H_2O \longrightarrow Cl_2(g) + 2 OH^- + H_2(g)$$

22.14   a. S.R.P. decreases by 0.059 v.   b. S.R.P. decreases by 0.071 v.

22.15   a. $Ag(s) + 2 H^+ + NO_3^- \rightarrow Ag^+ + NO_2(g) + H_2O$

22.19   22.9%

22.24   a. 0.600 N   b. 0.500 N

22.25 $E° = +1.28$ v. (see Table 21.1, Chapter 21). Note that since $Fe(OH)_2$ is insoluble, one cannot get $E°$ by adding 22.18a and b. $E°$ acidic solution $= +1.67$ v.

CHAPTER 23

23.5   a. $_{88}Ra^{224} \rightarrow {}_2He^4 + {}_{86}Rn^{220}$

23.7 $8\alpha, 5\beta$

23.8   0.050 g.; 0.0125 g.

23.9   0.073 g.; 0.053 g.; 0.015 g.

23.15 $_{29}Cu^{63} + {}_1H^1 \rightarrow {}_0n^1 + {}_{30}Zn^{63}$

23.17   a. β^- b. β^+

23.20   a. -0.959 mev.   b. -9.27×10^{17} ergs   c. -2.00×10^6 kcal.

23.23   4.64 mev.

23.24   approximately 12

CHAPTER 24

24.3   a. Alcohol   d. Ether

24.4   a. Alcohol   b. Ether or alcohol

24.11   2-Butanone:

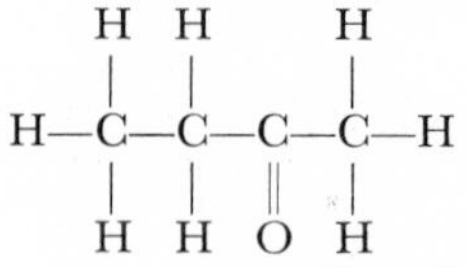

```
        H   H       H
        |   |       |
    H—C—C—C—C—H
        |   |   ‖   |
        H   H   O   H
```

24.17   a. Propane   c. Butyric acid   e. 2-Methyl-2-pentanol

24.27   a. None   c. 1

INDEX

Page numbers in italics refer to illustrations; those followed by (t) refer to table titles.

637

1A　　**2A**

1A	2A	3B	4B	5B	6B	7B		
3 **Li** 6.939 ±0.0005	4 **Be** 9.0122 ±0.00005							
11 **Na** 22.9898 ±0.00005	12 **Mg** 24.312 ±0.0005							
19 **K** 39.102 ±0.0005	20 **Ca** 40.08 ±0.005	21 **Sc** 44.956 ±0.0005	22 **Ti** 47.90 ±0.005	23 **V** 50.942 ±0.0005	24 **Cr** 51.996 ±0.001	25 **Mn** 54.9380 ±0.00005	26 **Fe** 55.847 ±0.003	27 **Co** 58.93 ±0.000
37 **Rb** 85.47 ±0.005	38 **Sr** 87.62 ±0.005	39 **Y** 88.905 ±0.0005	40 **Zr** 91.22 ±0.005	41 **Nb** 92.906 ±0.0005	42 **Mo** 95.94 ±0.005	43 **Tc** (99)	44 **Ru** 101.07 ±0.005	45 **Rh** 102.9(±0.00
55 **Cs** 132.905 ±0.0005	56 **Ba** 137.34 ±0.005	57 ***La** 138.91 ±0.005	72 **Hf** 178.49 ±0.005	73 **Ta** 180.948 ±0.0005	74 **W** 183.85 ±0.005	75 **Re** 186.2 ±0.05	76 **Os** 190.2 ±0.05	77 **Ir** 192. ±0.0
87 **Fr** (223)	88 **Ra** (226)	89 **†Ac** (227)						

*Lanthanum Series

58 **Ce** 140.12 ±0.005	59 **Pr** 140.907 ±0.0005	60 **Nd** 144.24 ±0.005	61 **Pm** (147)	62 **Sr** 150. ±0.0

†Actinium Series

90 **Th** 232.038 ±0.0005	91 **Pa** (231)	92 **U** 238.03 ±0.005	93 **Np** (237)	94 **Pu** (242